Standard Atomic Weights of the Elements 2005, IUPAC

Based on Relative Atomic Mass of ^{12}C in its nuclear and electronic ground state

Name	Symbol	Atomic Number	Atomic Weight
Actinium*	Ac	89	(227)
Aluminum	Al	13	26.9815386(8)
Americium*	Am	95	(243)
Antimony	Sb	51	121.760(1)
Argon	Ar	18	39.948(1)
Arsenic	As	33	74.92160(2)
Astatine*	At	85	(210)
Barium	Ba	56	137.327(7)
Berkelium*	Bk	97	(247)
Beryllium	Be	4	9.012182(3)
Bismuth	Bi	83	208.98040(1)
Bohrium*	Bh	107	(264)
Boron	B	5	10.811(7)
Bromine	Br	35	79.904(1)
Cadmium	Cd	48	112.411(8)
Calcium	Ca	20	40.078(4)
Californium*	Cf	98	(251)
Carbon	C	6	12.0107(8)
Cerium	Ce	58	140.116(1)
Cesium	Cs	55	132.9054519(2)
Chlorine	Cl	17	35.453(2)
Chromium	Cr	24	51.9961(6)
Cobalt	Co	27	58.933195(5)
Copper	Cu	29	63.546(3)
Curium*	Cm	96	(247)
Darmstadtium*	Ds	110	(281)
Dubnium*	Db	105	(262)
Dysprosium	Dy	66	162.500(1)
Einsteinium*	Es	99	(252)
Erbium	Er	68	167.259(3)
Europium	Eu	63	151.964(1)
Fermium*	Fm	100	(257)
Fluorine	F	9	18.9984032(5)
Francium*	Fr	87	(223)
Gadolinium	Gd	64	157.25(3)
Gallium	Ga	31	69.723(1)
Germanium	Ge	32	72.64(1)
Gold	Au	79	196.966569(4)
Hafnium	Hf	72	178.49(2)
Hassium*	Hs	108	(277)
Helium	He	2	4.002602(2)
Holmium	Ho	67	164.93032(2)
Hydrogen	H	1	1.00794(7)
Indium	In	49	114.818(3)
Iodine	I	53	126.90447(3)
Iridium	Ir	77	192.217(3)
Iron	Fe	26	55.845(2)
Krypton	Kr	36	83.798(2)
Lanthanum	La	57	138.90547(7)
Lawrencium*	Lr	103	(262)
Lead	Pb	82	207.2(1)
Lithium	Li	3	[6.941(2)]†
Lutetium	Lu	71	174.967(1)
Magnesium	Mg	12	24.3050(6)
Manganese	Mn	25	54.938045(5)
Meitnerium*	Mt	109	(268)
Mendelevium*	Md	101	(258)
Mercury	Hg	80	200.59(2)
Molybdenum	Mo	[illegible]	[illegible]
Neodymium	Nd	60	144.242(3)
Neon	Ne	10	20.1797(6)
Neptunium*	Np	93	(237)
Nickel	Ni	28	58.6934(2)
Niobium	Nb	41	92.90638(2)
Nitrogen	N	7	14.0067(2)
Nobelium*	No	102	(259)
Osmium	Os	76	190.23(3)
Oxygen	O	8	15.9994(3)
Palladium	Pd	46	106.42(1)
Phosphorus	P	15	30.973762(2)
Platinum	Pt	78	195.084(9)
Plutonium*	Pu	94	(244)
Polonium*	Po	84	(209)
Potassium	K	19	39.0983(1)
Praseodymium	Pr	59	140.90765(2)
Promethium*	Pm	61	(145)
Protactinium*	Pa	91	231.03588(2)
Radium*	Ra	88	(226)
Radon*	Rn	86	(222)
Rhenium	Re	75	186.207(1)
Rhodium	Rh	45	102.90550(2)
Roentgenium*	Rg	111	(272)
Rubidium	Rb	37	85.4678(3)
Ruthenium	Ru	44	101.07(2)
Rutherfordium*	Rf	104	(261)
Samarium	Sm	62	150.36(2)
Scandium	Sc	21	44.955912(6)
Seaborgium*	Sg	106	(266)
Selenium	Se	34	78.96(3)
Silicon	Si	14	28.0855(3)
Silver	Ag	47	107.8682(2)
Sodium	Na	11	22.98976928(2)
Strontium	Sr	38	87.62(1)
Sulfur	S	16	32.065(5)
Tantalum	Ta	73	180.94788(2)
Technetium*	Tc	43	(98)
Tellurium	Te	52	127.60(3)
Terbium	Tb	65	158.92535(2)
Thallium	Tl	81	204.3833(2)
Thorium*	Th	90	232.03806(2)
Thulium	Tm	69	168.93421(2)
Tin	Sn	50	118.710(7)
Titanium	Ti	22	47.867(1)
Tungsten	W	74	183.84(1)
Uranium*	U	92	238.02891(3)
Vanadium	V	23	50.9415(1)
Xenon	Xe	54	131.293(6)
Ytterbium	Yb	70	173.04(3)
Yttrium	Y	39	88.90585(2)
Zinc	Zn	30	65.409(4)
Zirconium	Zr	40	91.224(2)
—‡*		112	(285)
—‡*		113	(284)
—‡*		114	(289)
—‡*		115	(288)

† The atomic weights of many elements vary depending on the origin and treatment of the sample. This is particularly true for Li; commercially available lithium-containing materials have Li atomic weights in the range of 6.939 and 6.996. Uncertainties are given in parentheses following the last significant figure to which they are attributed.

* Elements with no stable nuclide; the value given in parentheses is the atomic mass number of the isotope of longest known half-life. However, three such elements (Th, Pa, and U) have a characteristic terrestrial isotopic composition, and the atomic weight is tabulated for these.

‡ Not yet named.

D1370916

Study smarter—and make every minute count!

ThomsonNOW
Sign in to ThomsonNOW at **www.thomsonedu.com** to work an interactive module based on this material.

$$Mg(s) + 2\,HCl(aq) \longrightarrow MgCl_2(aq) + H_2(g)$$

Calculate the percentage of magnesium in a 1.72-g sample that produced 6.46 g $MgCl_2$ when reacted with excess HCl.

ThomsonNOW
Go to the Chemistry Interactive menu to work modules on **reactions controlled by the supply of one reactant.**

4.5 Reactions with One Reactant in Limited Supply

In the previous section, we assumed that exactly stoichiometric amounts of reactants were present; each reactant was entirely consumed when the reaction was over. However, this is rarely the case when chemists carry out an actual synthesis, whether for small quantities in a laboratory or on a large scale in an industrial process. Usually, one reactant is more expensive or less readily available than others. The cheaper or more available reactants are used in excess to ensure that the more expensive material is completely converted to product.

The industrial production of methanol, CH_3OH, is such a case. Methanol, an important industrial product, is manufactured by the reaction of carbon monoxide and hydrogen.

$$CO(g) + 2\,H_2(g) \longrightarrow CH_3OH(\ell)$$

Succeed in your course with the help of this best-selling text and its powerful diagnostic self-study tool. The Third Edition of ***Chemistry: The Molecular Science*** carefully and thoroughly integrates powerful multimedia learning components with the text, providing a seamless learning system that will improve your understanding of course concepts.

ThomsonNOW™ for *Chemistry: The Molecular Science*

Link to interactive tutorials, simulations, and animations based on your unique level of understanding! **ThomsonNOW** is an online assessment-centered learning tool that gives you a *Personalized Study* plan based on a diagnostic pre-test. Your unique study plan can help you prepare for exams by targeting your study needs and helping you to visualize, practice, and master the material in the text.

How does it work?

Just sign in to **ThomsonNOW** by using the access code packaged with your text.* With a click of the mouse, you can build a complete *Personalized Study* plan for yourself with the program's three powerful components:

What I Know

After you've completed the *Pre-Test,* a detailed *Personalized Study* plan (based on your test results) outlines the concepts you need to review and presents links to specific pages in your textbook that discuss that concept. You find out exactly what you need to study!

What I Need to Know

Working from your *Personalized Study* plan, you are guided to media-enhanced activities including *Interactive Modules, Coached Problems, Active Figures,* tutorials, and exercises. These activities can also be accessed at any time without taking the *Pre-Test.*

What I've Learned

An optional *Post-Test* ensures that you've mastered the concepts in each chapter. As with the *Pre-Test,* your individual results may be e-mailed to your instructor to help you both assess your progress. If you need to improve your score, **ThomsonNOW** will work with you as you continue to build your knowledge.

Sign in at **www.thomsonedu.com** to view chemistry tutorials and simulations, develop problem-solving skills, and test your knowledge with these interactive self-study resources.

* If you purchased a new book, you may already have access to **ThomsonNOW**. Register by following the directions on the card that came with this text. If you did not purchase a new book, you can obtain an access code at **www.thomsonedu.com/thomsonnow/buy**.

Chemistry: The Molecular Science

Volume I

John W. Moore | Conrad L. Stanitski | Peter C. Jurs

CENGAGE Learning™

Australia • Brazil • Japan • Korea • Mexico • Singapore • Spain • United Kingdom • United States

CENGAGE Learning™

Chemistry: The Molecular Science
Volume I

John W. Moore | Conrad L. Stanitski | Peter C. Jurs

Executive Editors:
Maureen Staudt
Michael Stranz
Project Development Manager:
Linda deStefano
Senior Marketing Coordinators:
Sara Mercurio
Lindsay Shapiro
Senior Production / Manufacturing Manager:
Donna M. Brown
PreMedia Services Supervisor:
Joel Brennecke
Rights & Permissions Specialist:
Kalina Hintz
Todd Osborne
Cover Image:
Getty Images*

* Unless otherwise noted, all cover images used by Custom Solutions, a part of Cengage Learning, have been supplied courtesy of Getty Images with the exception of the Earthview cover image, which has been supplied by the National Aeronautics and Space Administration (NASA).

© 2009, 2007 Cengage Learning

ALL RIGHTS RESERVED. No part of this work covered by the copyright herein may be reproduced, transmitted, stored or used in any form or by any means graphic, electronic, or mechanical, including but not limited to photocopying, recording, scanning, digitizing, taping, Web distribution, information networks, or information storage and retrieval systems, except as permitted under Section 107 or 108 of the 1976 United States Copyright Act, without the prior written permission of the publisher.

For product information and technology assistance, contact us at
Cengage Learning Customer & Sales Support, 1-800-354-9706
For permission to use material from this text or product,
submit all requests online at **cengage.com/permissions**
Further permissions questions can be emailed to
permissionrequest@cengage.com

ISBN-13: 978-1-4240-8187-5

ISBN-10: 1-4240-8187-4

Cengage Learning
5191 Natorp Boulevard
Mason, Ohio 45040
USA

Cengage Learning is a leading provider of customized learning solutions with office locations around the globe, including Singapore, the United Kingdom, Australia, Mexico, Brazil, and Japan. Locate your local office at: **international.cengage.com/region**

Cengage Learning products are represented in Canada by Nelson Education, Ltd.

For your lifelong learning solutions, visit **custom.cengage.com**

Visit our corporate website at **cengage.com**

Printed in the United States of America

Custom Contents Overview

Contents Overview

Detailed Contents

© Corbis

© James Hardy/Photo Alto/Getty Images

© Scott Camazine/Photo Researchers, Inc.

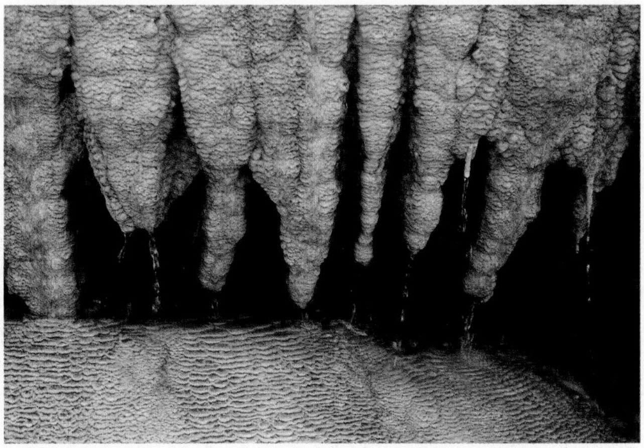
© Carlyn Iverson/Photo Researchers, Inc.

© Thomson Learning/Charles D. Winters

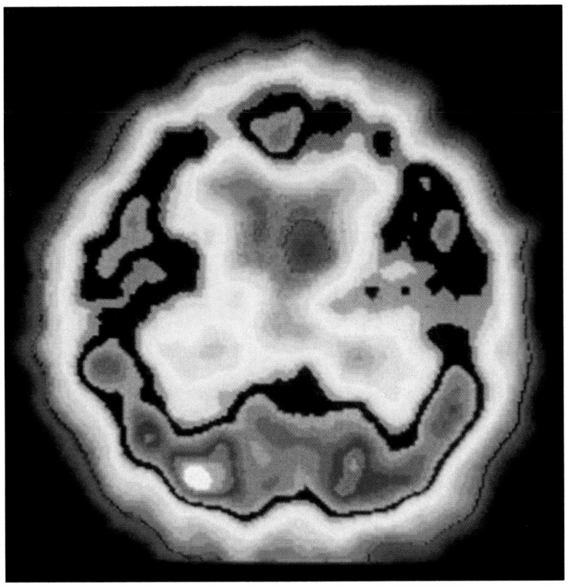

© CEA-ORSAY/CNRI/Science Photo Library/Photo Researchers, Inc.

1 The Nature of Chemistry

Chemistry, in collaboration with many other sciences, can produce spectacular advances in dealing with human suffering and pain. The Pacific yew tree, shown above, harbors in its bark a substance that has been amazingly successful in treating cancer. Chemists first separated the active ingredient from the bark in the late 1960s. A chemical pharmacologist discovered how it works in the body, and other chemists found ways to manufacture it without destroying the trees in which it was discovered. Chemical science involves a unique atomic and molecular perspective that enables us to find useful substances, separate them or synthesize them, and figure out how they work by imagining the behavior of particles that are too small to see.

© Dennis Flaherty/Photo Researchers, Inc./
© Inga Spence/Visuals Unlimited/
© Tom & Pat Leeson/Photo Researchers, Inc.

ThomsonNOW
Throughout the text, this icon indicates an opportunity to test yourself on key concepts and to explore interactive modules by signing in to ThomsonNOW at **www.thomsonedu.com**.

Welcome to the world of chemical science! This chapter describes how modern chemical research is done and how it can be applied to questions and problems that affect our daily lives. It also provides an overview of the methods of science and the fundamental ideas of chemistry. These ideas are extremely important and very powerful. They will be applied over and over throughout your study of chemistry and of many other sciences.

1.1 Why Care About Chemistry?

Why study chemistry? There are many good reasons. **Chemistry** is the science of matter and its transformations from one form to another. **Matter** is anything that has mass and occupies space. Consequently, chemistry has enormous impact on our daily lives, on other sciences, and even on areas as diverse as art, music, cooking, and recreation. Chemical transformations happen all the time, everywhere. Chemistry is intimately involved in the air we breathe and the reasons we need to breathe it; in purifying the water we drink; in growing, cooking, and digesting the food we eat; and in the discovery and production of medicines to help maintain health. Chemists continually provide new ways of transforming matter into different forms with useful properties. Examples include the plastic disks used in CD and DVD players; the microchips and batteries in calculators or computers; and the steel, aluminum, rubber, plastic, and other components of automobiles.

Very human accounts of how fascinating—even romantic—chemistry can be are provided by Primo Levi in his autobiography, *The Periodic Table* (New York: Schocken Books, 1984), and by Oliver Sacks in *Uncle Tungsten: Memories of a Chemical Boyhood* (New York: Knopf, 2001). Levi was sentenced to a death camp during World War II but survived because the Nazis found his chemistry skills useful; those same skills made him a special kind of writer. Sacks describes how his mother and other relatives encouraged his interest in metals, diamonds, magnets, medicines, and other chemicals and how he learned that "science is a territory of freedom and friendship in the midst of tyranny and hatred."

Chemists are people who are fascinated by matter and its transformations—as you are likely to be after seeing and experiencing chemistry in action. Chemists have a unique and spectacularly successful way of thinking about and interpreting the material world around them—an atomic and molecular perspective. Knowledge and understanding of chemistry are crucial in biology, pharmacology, medicine, geology, materials science, many branches of engineering, and other sciences. Modern research is often done by teams of scientists whose members represent several of these different disciplines. In such teams, ability to communicate and collaborate is just as important as knowledge in a single field. Studying chemistry can help you learn how chemists think about the world and solve problems, which in turn can lead to effective collaborations. Such knowledge will be useful in many career paths and will help you become a better-informed citizen in a world that is becoming technologically more and more complex—and interesting.

Atoms are the extremely small particles that are the building blocks of all matter (Section 1.9). In molecules, atoms combine to give the smallest particles with the properties of a particular substance (Section 1.10).

Chemistry, and the chemist's way of thinking, can help answer a broad range of questions—questions that might arise in your mind as you carefully observe the world around you. Here are some that have occurred to us and are answered later in this book:

- How can a disease be caused or cured by a tiny change in a molecule? (Section 12.8)
- Why does rain fall as drops instead of cubes or cylinders? (Section 11.1)
- Why does salt help to clear snow and ice from roads? (Section 15.7)
- Why do droplets of water form on the outside of a cold soft-drink can? (Section 11.3)
- Where does the energy come from to make my muscles work? (Sections 6.12 and 18.9)
- What are the molecules in my eyes doing when I watch a movie? (Section 13.4)
- Why does frost form on top of a parked car in winter, but not on the sides? (Section 10.13)
- Why is the sky blue? (Section 15.9)
- Why can some insects walk on water? (Section 11.1)

- Why is ozone depletion harmful? I thought too much ozone was bad for your lungs. (Section 10.11)
- How does soap help to get clothes clean? (Section 15.9)
- What happens when I hard-boil an egg? (Section 13.9)
- How are plastics made, and why are there so many different kinds? (Section 12.7)
- Why is there a warning on a container of household bleach that says not to mix the bleach with other cleaners, such as toilet-bowl cleaner? (Section 16.10)
- I've heard that most homes in the United States contain small quantities of a radioactive gas. How can I find out whether my home is safe? (Section 20.8)
- Why is iron strongly attracted to a magnet, but most substances are not? (Section 7.8)
- Why do some antacids fizz when added to vinegar? (Section 5.2)

The section number following each question indicates where you can find the answer. There are probably many more questions like these that have occurred to you. We encourage you to add them to the list and think about them as you study chemistry.

1.2 Molecular Medicine

How modern science works, and why the chemist's unique perspective is so valuable, can be seen through an example. (At this point you need not fully understand the science, so don't worry if some words or ideas are unfamiliar.) From many possibilities, we have chosen the anticancer agent paclitaxel. Paclitaxel was brought to market in 1993 by Bristol-Myers Squibb under the trade name Taxol®. It is recognized as an effective drug for treating ovarian cancer, breast cancer, certain forms of lung cancer, and some other cancers. Total sales of this drug reached $10 billion shortly after 2000, and at present it is the all-time best-selling anticancer drug.

"The whole of science is nothing more than a refinement of everyday thinking." —Albert Einstein

The story of paclitaxel began about 50 years ago when Jonathan Hartwell of the National Cancer Institute initiated a program to collect samples of 35,000 kinds of plants from within the United States and examine them as potential sources of anticancer drugs. On August 21, 1962, in a forest near Mount St. Helens in Washington, a group of three graduate students led by U.S. Department of Agriculture botanist Arthur S. Barclay collected three quarters of a pound of bark from *Taxus brevifolia*, commonly called the Pacific yew tree. Preliminary tests at a research center in Wisconsin showed that extracts from the bark were active against cancer, so a larger sample of bark was collected and sent to chemists Monroe Wall and Mansukh Wani at the Research Triangle Institute in North Carolina.

Wall and Wani carried out a painstaking chemical analysis in which they separated and purified several substances found in the bark. By 1967 they had isolated the active ingredient, which they named "taxol." The name was based on the botanic name of the yew (*Taxus*, giving "tax") and the fact that the substance belongs to a class of compounds known as alcohols (giving "ol"). Later the name Taxol® was registered as a trademark by Bristol-Myers Squibb, so paclitaxel is now used to describe the drug generically.

In 1971 Wall and Wani determined the chemical formula of paclitaxel: $C_{47}H_{51}NO_{14}$, a molecule containing 113 atoms. This is small compared with giant biological molecules such as proteins and DNA, but the structure is complicated enough that Wall and Wani had to chemically separate the molecule into two parts, determine the structure of each part using a technique called x-ray crystallography, and then figure out how the two parts were connected. The structure of the smaller of those parts is shown in the figure.

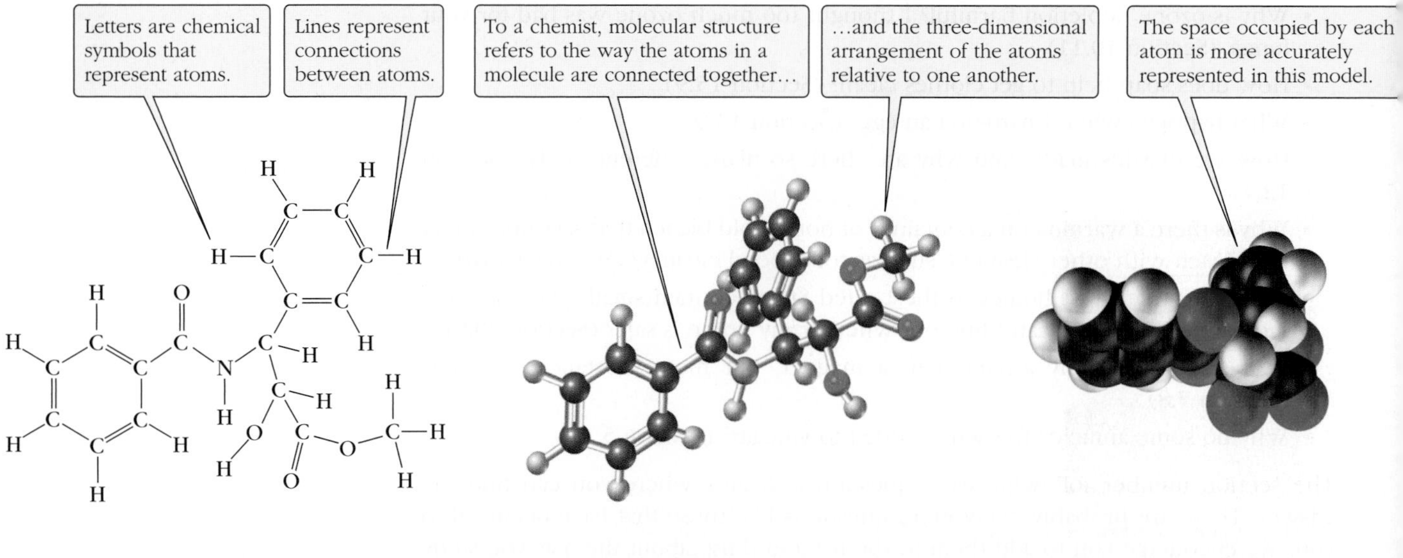

Structural formula | Ball-and-stick model | Space-filling model

The molecular structure of one of the two molecular parts of paclitaxel used by Wall and Wani to determine the structure of the drug.

Throughout this book, computer-generated models of molecular structures will be used to help you visualize chemistry at the atomic and molecular levels.

Even after its structure was known, there was not a great deal of interest in paclitaxel as a drug because the compound was so hard to get. Removing the bark from a Pacific yew kills the tree, the bark from a 40-foot tree yields a very small quantity of the drug (less than half a gram), and it takes more than 100 years for a tree to grow to 40 feet. Had it not been for the discovery that paclitaxel's method for killing cancer cells was unique, which opened new avenues for research, the drug probably would not have been commercialized.

You are probably curious about why this substance can kill cancer cells when thousands of other substances collected by botanists do not. The answer to this question was found in 1979 by Susan Band Horwitz, who was interested in how small molecules, particularly those from natural sources, could be used to treat disease. She obtained a sample of paclitaxel from Wall and Wani and experimented to find out how it worked within biological cells. What she discovered was a unique atomic-scale mechanism of action: Paclitaxel aids the formation of structures known as microtubules and prevents their breakdown once they form. Microtubules help to maintain cell structure and shape. They also serve as conveyor belts, transporting other cell components from place to place. Microtubules form when many molecules of the protein tubulin assemble into long, hollow, cylindrical fibers. Tubulin is an extremely large molecule that consists of two very similar parts, one called alpha and the other beta.

During cell division, microtubules move chromosomes to opposite sides of the cell so that the chromosomes can be incorporated into two new cell nuclei as the cell divides. To carry out this process, the microtubules must grow and shrink by either adding or losing tubulin molecules. Because paclitaxel prevents the microtubules from shrinking, it prevents new cell nuclei from forming. The cells cannot divide and eventually die. An important characteristic of cancer is rapid, uncontrolled division of cells. Because cancer cells divide much faster than most other cells, substances that adversely affect cell division affect cancer cells more than normal cells. This provides an effective treatment, especially for cancers that are particularly virulent.

Horwitz's discovery of a new molecular mode of action, together with dramatic improvement in some patients for whom no other treatment had been successful, generated a great deal of interest in paclitaxel, but the drug faced two additional bar-

Courtesy of Dr. Susan Band Horwitz/Albert Einstein School of Medicine

Susan Band Horwitz
1937–

Susan Band Horwitz is Falkenstein Professor of Cancer Research and co-Chair of the Department of Molecular Pharmacology at the Albert Einstein College of Medicine at Yeshiva University. She is past president of the American Association for Cancer Research and recently won the Warren Alpert Foundation Prize for her work in developing Taxol®. She is currently studying other molecules that are even more effective than Taxol® for treating cancer.

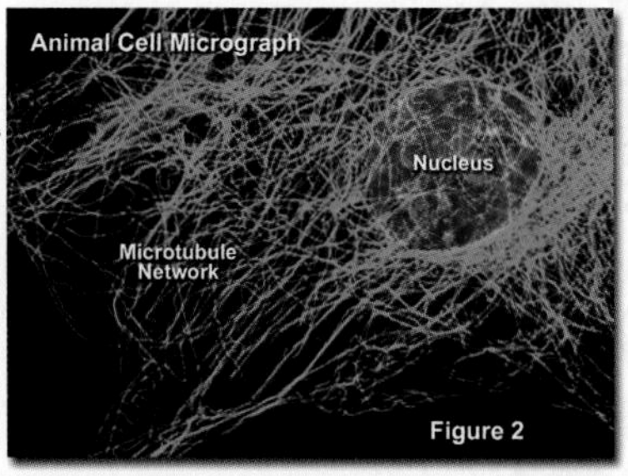

© Michael W. Davidson and The Florida State University

Microtubules as seen through a fluorescence optical microscope. These are from an embryonic mouse cell.

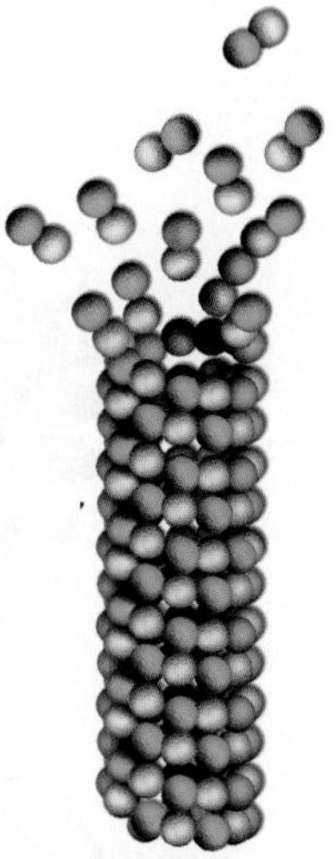

From **http://micro.magnet.fsu.edu/cells/microtubules/microtubules.html**. Reprinted by permission.

Assembly of a microtubule by addition of tubulin molecules. (Each two-part tubulin molecule is shown in yellow and green.)

riers to its widespread use. First, paclitaxel is almost completely insoluble in water, which makes it extremely difficult to deliver into the human body. Researchers at the National Cancer Institute found that castor oil could dissolve the drug, which allowed its use in clinical trials. For patients who were allergic to the castor oil, special medication was developed to alleviate the allergic reaction. These clinical trials showed paclitaxel was extremely effective against ovarian and breast cancers.

But there was another problem. A complete course of treatment for cancer required about two grams of paclitaxel—a mass obtained from six trees that had grown for 100 years. A simple calculation showed that harvesting enough bark to treat all cancer patients would soon cause extinction of the Pacific yew. To find a better way to obtain paclitaxel, chemists tried to synthesize it from simple ingredients. In 1994 they succeeded; paclitaxel was made by two independent groups of chemists without help from *Taxus brevifolia* or any other plant. To date, however, complete chemical synthesis produces only a tiny portion of product from large quantities of starting materials and has not been developed into a cost-effective industrial-scale process. Instead, paclitaxel is produced by the pharmaceutical industry in a four-step synthesis process that begins with the compound 10-deacetylbaccatin, which is isolated from the English yew, *Taxus baccata*. This species is more common than the Pacific yew and grows much faster. Thus, plenty of the drug can be obtained without concerns about extinction of the plant that produces its precursor.

The success of paclitaxel as an anticancer agent led to many attempts to discover even more about how it works. In 1998 Eva Nogales, Sharon Wolf, and Kenneth Downing at the Lawrence Berkeley National Laboratory created the first picture showing how all of the atoms are arranged in three-dimensional space when paclitaxel interacts with tubulin. This provided further insight into how paclitaxel prevents tubulin molecules from leaving a microtubule, thereby causing cell death. In 2001 Nogales, Downing, and coworkers confirmed experimentally a proposal by James P. Snyder of Emory University that the paclitaxel molecule assumes a T-shape when attached to tubulin. Figure 1.1 shows the huge tubulin molecule with a paclitaxel molecule neatly fitting into a "pocket" at the lower right. By attaching to tubulin in this way, paclitaxel makes the tubulin less flexible and prevents tubulin molecules from leaving microtubules. In 2004, James P. Snyder, David G. I. Kingston (Virginia Tech University), Susan Bane (SUNY Binghamton), and five coworkers synthesized a new molecule, similar to paclitaxel but held by chemical bonds in the T-shape

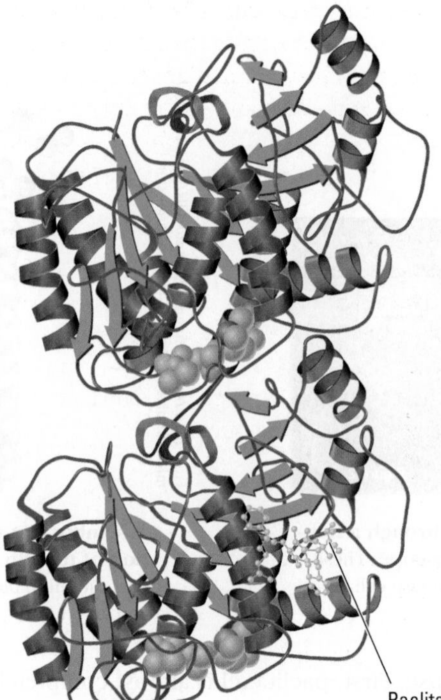

From: http://www.lbl.gov./Science-Articles/Archive/3D-tubulin.html.

Figure 1.1 **Tubulin with paclitaxel attached.** The blue and green ribbon-like structures and the string-like structures represent the "backbone" of tubulin, giving a rough indication of where its atoms are located. Paclitaxel is the light tan group of atoms at the lower right.

required for binding to tubulin. The new compound, designated "**13a**" because it was the 13th mentioned in their article, showed increased activity against cancer of up to 20 times that of paclitaxel. Now that the required structure is known, it will be easier for chemists to devise other molecular structures that are even more effective.

1.3 How Science Is Done

How science is done is dealt with in *Oxygen*, a play written by chemists Carl Djerassi and Roald Hoffmann that premiered in 2001. By revisiting the discovery of oxygen, the play provides many insights regarding the process of science and the people who make science their life's work.

The story of paclitaxel illustrates many aspects of how people do science and how scientific knowledge changes and improves over time. In antiquity it was known that extracts of many plants had medicinal properties. For example, Native Americans in the Pacific Northwest made tonics from the bark of the Pacific yew. Probably this involved a chance observation that led to the hypothesis that yew bark was beneficial. A **hypothesis** is an idea that is tentatively proposed as an explanation for some observation and provides a basis for experimentation. The hypothesis that extracts of some plants might be effective against cancer led Jonathan Hartwell to initiate his program of collecting plant material. Tests of the extract from Pacific yew bark verified that this hypothesis was correct.

Testing a hypothesis may involve collecting qualitative or quantitative data. The observation that extracts from the bark of the Pacific yew killed cancer cells was **qualitative:** It did not involve numeric data. It was clear that there was an effect, but further studies were needed to find out how significant the effect was. **Quantitative** information is obtained from measurements that produce numeric data. Studies of the paclitaxel analog "**13a**" discovered in 2004 showed that it was 20 times more active than paclitaxel against ovarian cancer cells. These quantitative data were important in confirming that a T-shaped molecular structure was important.

A scientific **law** is a statement that summarizes and explains a wide range of experimental results and has not been contradicted by experiments. *A law can predict unknown results and also can be disproved or falsified by new experiments.* When the results of a new experiment contradict a law, that's exciting to a scientist. If several scientists repeat a contradictory experiment and get the same result, then the law must be modified to account for the new results—or even discarded altogether.

A successful hypothesis is often designated as a **theory**—a unifying principle that explains a body of facts and the laws based on them. A theory usually suggests new hypotheses and experiments, and, like a law, it may have to be modified or even discarded if contradicted by new experimental results. A **model** makes a theory more concrete, often in a physical or a mathematical form. Models of molecules, for example, were important in determining how paclitaxel binds to tubulin and kills cells. Molecular models can be constructed by using spheres to represent atoms and sticks to represent the connections between the atoms. Or a computer can be used to calculate the locations of the atoms and display model molecular structures on a screen (as was done to create Figure 1.1). The theories that matter is made of atoms and molecules, that atoms are arranged in specific molecular structures, and that the properties of matter depend on those structures are fundamental to chemists' unique atomic/molecular perspective on the world and to nearly everything modern chemists do. Clearly it is important that you become as familiar as you can with these theories and with models based on them.

Another important aspect of the way science is done involves communication. Science is based on experiments and on hypotheses, laws, and theories that can be contradicted by experiments. Therefore, it is essential that experimental results be communicated to all scientists working in any specific area of research as quickly and accurately as possible. Scientific communication allows contributions to be made by scientists in different parts of the world and greatly enhances the rapidity with which science can develop. In addition, communication among members of scientific research teams is crucial to their success. Examples are the groups of from five to twenty chemists who synthesized paclitaxel from scratch, or the group of eight scientists from three universities that made and tested the new substance "**13a**" with even greater anticancer activity. The importance of scientific communication is emphasized by the fact that the Internet was created not by commercial interests, but by scientists who saw its great potential for communicating scientific information.

In the remainder of this chapter we discuss fundamental concepts of chemistry that have been revealed by applying the processes of science to the study of matter. We begin by considering how matter can be classified according to characteristic properties.

1.4 Identifying Matter: Physical Properties

One type of matter can be distinguished from another by observing the properties of samples of matter and classifying the matter according to those properties. A **substance** is a type of matter that has the same properties and the same composition throughout a sample. Each substance has characteristic properties that are different from the properties of any other substance (Figure 1.2). In addition, one sample of a substance has the same composition as every other sample of that substance—it consists of the same stuff in the same proportions.

You can distinguish sugar from water because you know that sugar consists of small white particles of solid, while water is a colorless liquid. Metals can be

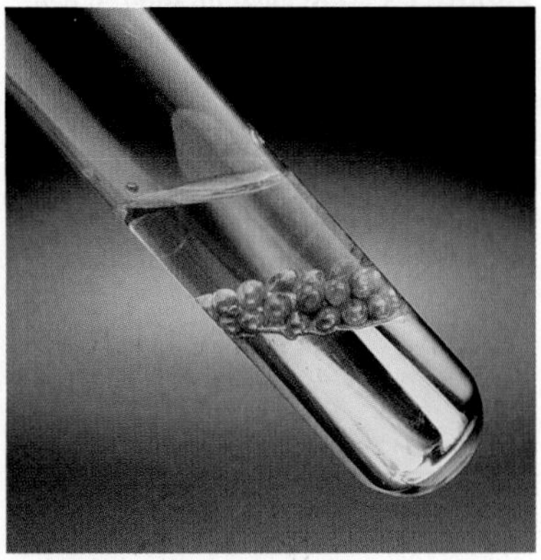

© Thomson Learning/Charles D. Winters

Figure 1.2 Substances have characteristic physical properties. The test tube contains silvery liquid mercury in the bottom, small spheres of solid orange copper in the middle, and colorless liquid water above the copper. Each of these substances has characteristic properties that differentiate it from the others.

Some Physical Properties

Temperature
Pressure
Mass
Volume
State (solid, liquid, gas)
Melting point
Boiling point
Density
Color
Shape of solid crystals
Hardness, brittleness
Heat capacity
Thermal conductivity
Electrical conductivity

© Thomson Learning/Charles D. Winters

Figure 1.3 Physical change. When ice melts it changes—physically—from a solid to a liquid, but it is still water.

If you need to convert from the Fahrenheit to the Celsius scale or from Celsius to Fahrenheit, an explanation of how to do so is in Appendix B.2.

recognized as a class of substances because they usually are solids, have high densities, feel cold to the touch, and have shiny surfaces. These properties can be observed and measured without changing the composition of a substance. They are called **physical properties.**

Physical Change

As a substance's temperature or pressure changes, or if it is mechanically manipulated, some of its physical properties may change. Changes in the physical properties of a substance are called **physical changes.** The same substance is present before and after a physical change, but the substance's physical state or the gross size and shape of its pieces may have changed. Examples are melting a solid (Figure 1.3), boiling a liquid, hammering a copper wire into a flat shape, and grinding sugar into a fine powder.

Melting and Boiling Point

An important way to help identify a substance is to measure the temperature at which the solid melts (the substance's **melting point**) and at which the liquid boils (its **boiling point**). If two or more substances are in a mixture, the melting point depends on how much of each is present, but for a single substance the melting point is always the same. This is also true of the boiling point (as long as the pressure on the boiling liquid is the same). In addition, the melting point of a pure crystalline sample of a substance is sharp—there is almost no change in temperature as the sample melts. When a mixture of two or more substances melts, the temperature when liquid first appears can be quite different from the temperature when the last of the solid is gone.

Temperature is the property of matter that determines whether there can be heat energy transfer from one object to another. It is represented by the symbol T. Energy transfers of its own accord from an object at a higher temperature to a cooler object. In the United States, everyday temperatures are reported using the Fahrenheit temperature scale. On this scale the freezing point of water is by definition 32 °F and the boiling point is 212 °F. The **Celsius temperature scale** is used in most countries of the world and in science. On this scale 0 °C is the freezing point and 100 °C is the boiling point of pure water at a pressure of one atmosphere. The number of units between the freezing and boiling points of water is 180 Fahrenheit degrees and 100 Celsius degrees. This means that the Celsius degree is almost twice as large as the Fahrenheit degree. It takes only 5 Celsius degrees to cover the same temperature range as 9 Fahrenheit degrees, and this relationship can be used to calculate a temperature on one scale from a temperature on the other (see Appendix B.2).

Because temperatures in scientific studies are usually measured in Celsius units, there is little need to make conversions to and from the Fahrenheit scale, but it is quite useful to be familiar with how large various Celsius temperatures are. For example, it is useful to know that water freezes at 0 °C and boils at 100 °C, a comfortable room temperature is about 22 °C, your body temperature is 37 °C, and the hottest water you could put your hand into without serious burns is about 60 °C.

Exercises that are labeled conceptual are designed to test your understanding of a concept.

Answers to exercises are provided near the end of the book in a section with color on the edges of the pages.

CONCEPTUAL EXERCISE 1.1 Temperature

(a) Which is the higher temperature, 110 °C or 180 °F?
(b) Which is the lower temperature, 36 °C or 100 °F?
(c) The melting point of gallium is 29.8 °C. If you hold a sample of gallium in your hand, will it melt?

Density

Another property that is often used to help identify a substance is **density,** the ratio of the mass of a sample to its volume. If you have ten pounds of sugar, it takes up ten times the volume that one pound of sugar does. In mathematical terms, a substance's volume is directly proportional to its mass. This means that a substance's density has the same value regardless of how big the sample is.

$$\text{Density} = \frac{\text{mass}}{\text{volume}} \qquad d = \frac{m}{V}$$

ThomsonNOW™
Go to the Coached Problems menu for tutorials on:

- **evaluating density**
- **using density**

Even if they look similar, you can tell a sample of aluminum from a sample of lead by picking each up. Your brain will automatically estimate which sample has greater mass for the same volume, telling you which is the lead. Aluminum has a density of 2.70 g/mL, placing it among the least dense metals. Lead's density is 11.34 g/mL, so a sample of lead is much heavier than a sample of aluminum of the same size.

The density of a substance varies depending on the temperature and the pressure. Densities of liquids and solids change very little as pressure changes, and they change less with temperature than do densities of gases. Because the volume of a gas varies significantly with temperature and pressure, the density of a gas can help identify the gas only if the temperature and pressure are specified.

Suppose that you are trying to identify a liquid that you think might be ethanol (ethyl alcohol), and you want to determine its density. You could weigh a clean, dry graduated cylinder and then add some of the liquid to it. Suppose that, from the markings on the cylinder, you read the volume of liquid to be 8.30 mL (at 20 °C). You could then weigh the cylinder with the liquid and subtract the mass of the empty cylinder to obtain the mass of liquid. Suppose the liquid mass is 6.544 g. The density can then be calculated as

$$d = \frac{m}{V} = \frac{6.544\ \text{g}}{8.30\ \text{mL}} = 0.788\ \text{g/mL}$$

If you divide 6.544 by 8.30 on a scientific calculator, the answer might come up as 0.788433735. This displays more digits than are meaningful, and we have rounded the result to only three significant digits. Rules for deciding how many digits should be reported in the result of a calculation and procedures for rounding numbers are introduced in Section 2.4 and Appendix A.3.

From a table of physical properties of various substances you find that the density of ethanol is 0.789 g/mL, which helps confirm your suspicion that the substance is ethanol.

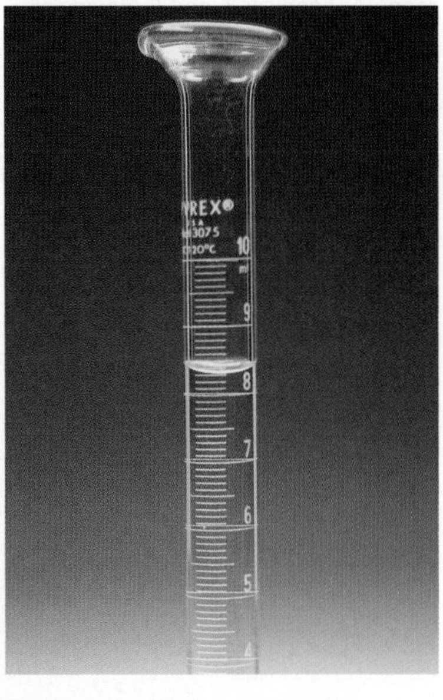
© Thomson Learning/Charles D. Winters

Graduated cylinder containing 8.30 mL of liquid.

CONCEPTUAL EXERCISE 1.2 Density of Liquids

When 5.0 mL each of vegetable oil, water, and kerosene are put into a large test tube, they form three layers, as shown in the photo on the next page.

(a) List the three liquids in order of increasing density (smallest density first, largest density last).

(b) If an additional 5.0 mL of vegetable oil is poured into the test tube, what will happen? Describe the appearance of the tube.

(c) If 5.0 mL of kerosene is added to the test tube with the 5.0 mL of vegetable oil in part (b), will there be a permanent change in the order of liquids from top to bottom of the tube? Why or why not?

EXERCISE 1.3 Physical Properties and Changes

Identify each physical property and physical change mentioned in each of these statements. Also identify the qualitative and the quantitative information given in each statement.

(a) The blue chemical compound azulene melts at 99 °C.

(b) The white crystals of table salt are cubic.

(c) A sample of lead has a mass of 0.123 g and melts at 327 °C.

(d) Ethanol is a colorless liquid that vaporizes easily; it boils at 78 °C and its density is 0.789 g/mL.

© Thomson Learning/Charles D. Winters

Liquid densities. Kerosene *(top layer)*, vegetable oil *(middle layer)*, and water *(bottom layer)* have different densities.

A useful source of data on densities and other physical properties of substances is the *CRC Handbook of Chemistry and Physics*, published by the CRC Press. Information is also available via the Internet—for example, the National Institute for Standards and Technology's Webbook at **http://webbook.nist.gov**.

In this book, units and dimensional analysis techniques are introduced at the first point where you need to know them. Appendices A and B provide all of this information in one place.

Because mercury and mercury vapor are poisonous, carrying a gallon of it around is not a good idea unless it is in a sealed container.

ThomsonNOW
Go to the Coached Problems menu for a tutorial on **unit conversion.**

Measurements and Calculations: Dimensional Analysis

Determining a property such as density requires scientific measurements and calculations. The result of a measurement, such as 6.544 g or 8.30 mL, usually consists of a number and a unit. Both the number and the unit should be included in calculations. For example, the densities in Table 1.1 have units of grams per milliliter (g/mL), because density is defined as the mass of a sample divided by its volume. When a mass is divided by a volume, the units (g for the mass and mL for the volume) are also divided. The result is grams divided by milliliters (g/mL). That is, both numbers *and units* follow the rules of algebra. This is an example of **dimensional analysis,** a method of using units in calculations to check for correctness. More detailed descriptions of dimensional analysis are given in Section 2.3 and Appendix A.2. We will use this technique for problem solving throughout the book.

Suppose that you want to know whether you could lift a gallon (3784 mL) of the liquid metal mercury. To answer the question, calculate the mass of the mercury using the density, 13.55 g/mL, obtained from Table 1.1. One way to do this is to use the equation that defines density, $d = m/V$. Then solve algebraically for m, and calculate the result:

$$m = V \times d = 3784\ \cancel{\text{mL}} \times \frac{13.55\ \text{g}}{1\ \cancel{\text{mL}}} = 51{,}270\ \text{g} \qquad (1.1)$$

This equation emphasizes the fact that mass is proportional to volume, because the volume is multiplied by a proportionality constant, the density. Notice also that the units of volume (mL) appeared once in the denominator of a fraction and once in the numerator, thereby dividing out (canceling) and leaving only mass units (g). (The result, 51,270 g, is more than 100 pounds, so you could probably lift the mercury, but not easily.)

In Equation 1.1, a known quantity (the volume) was multiplied by a proportionality factor (the density), and the units canceled, giving an answer (the mass) with appropriate units. A general approach to this kind of problem is to recognize that the quantity you want to calculate (the mass) is proportional to a quantity whose value you know (the volume). Then use a proportionality factor that relates the two quantities, setting things up so that the units cancel.

$$\cancel{\text{known quantity units}} \times \frac{\text{desired quantity units}}{\cancel{\text{known quantity units}}} = \text{desired quantity units}$$

proportionality (conversion) factor

$$3784\ \cancel{\text{mL}} \times \frac{13.55\ \text{g}}{1\ \cancel{\text{mL}}} = 51{,}270\ \text{g}$$

A **proportionality factor** is a ratio (fraction) whose numerator and denominator have different units but refer to the same thing. In the preceding example, the proportionality factor is the density, which relates the mass and volume of the same sample of mercury. A proportionality factor is often called a **conversion factor** because it enables us to convert from one kind of unit to a different kind of unit.

Because a conversion factor is a fraction, every conversion factor can be expressed in two ways. The conversion factor in the example just given could be expressed either as the density or as its reciprocal:

$$\frac{13.55\ \text{g}}{1\ \text{mL}} \quad \text{or} \quad \frac{1\ \text{mL}}{13.55\ \text{g}}$$

TABLE 1.1 Densities of Some Substances at 20 °C

Substance	Density (g/mL)	Substance	Density (g/mL)
Butane	0.579	Titanium	4.50
Ethanol	0.789	Zinc	7.14
Benzene	0.880	Iron	7.86
Water	0.998	Nickel	8.90
Bromobenzene	1.49	Copper	8.93
Magnesium	1.74	Lead	11.34
Sodium chloride	2.16	Mercury	13.55
Aluminum	2.70	Gold	19.32

The first fraction enables conversion from volume units (mL) to mass units (g). The second allows mass units to be converted to volume units. Which conversion factor to use depends on which units are in the known quantity and which units are in the quantity that we want to calculate. Setting up the calculation so that the units cancel ensures that we are using the appropriate conversion factor. (See Appendix A.2 for more examples.)

PROBLEM-SOLVING EXAMPLE 1.1 Density

In an old movie thieves are shown running off with pieces of gold bullion that are about a foot long and have a square cross section of about six inches. The volume of each piece of gold is 7000 mL. Calculate the mass of gold and express the result in pounds (lb). Based on your result, is what the movie shows physically possible? (1 lb = 454 g)

Answer 1.4×10^5 g; 300 lb

Strategy and Explanation A good approach to problem solving is to (1) define the problem, (2) develop a plan, (3) execute the plan, and (4) check your result to see whether it is reasonable. (These four steps are described in more detail in Appendix A.1).

Step 1: *Define the problem.* You are asked to calculate the mass of the gold, and you know the volume.

Step 2: *Develop a plan.* Density relates mass and volume and is the appropriate proportionality factor, so look up the density in a table. Mass is proportional to volume, so the volume either has to be multiplied by the density or divided by the density. Use the units to decide which.

Step 3: *Execute the plan.* According to Table 1.1, the density of gold is 19.32 g/mL. Setting up the calculation so that the unit (milliliter) cancels gives

$$7000\ \cancel{\text{mL}} \times \frac{19.32\ \text{g}}{1\ \cancel{\text{mL}}} = 1.35 \times 10^5\ \text{g}$$

This can be converted to pounds

$$1.35 \times 10^5\ \cancel{\text{g}} \times \frac{1\ \text{lb}}{454\ \cancel{\text{g}}} = 300\ \text{lb}$$

Notice that the result is expressed to one significant figure, because the volume was given to only one significant figure and only multiplications and divisions were done.

✓ **Reasonable Answer Check** Gold is nearly 20 times denser than water. A liter (1000 mL) of water is about a quart and a quart of water (2 pints) weighs about two pounds. Seven liters (7000 mL) of water should weigh 14 lb, and 20 times 14 gives 280 lb, so the answer is reasonable. The movie is not—few people could run while carrying a 300-lb object!

Rules for assigning the appropriate number of significant figures to a result are given in Appendix A.3.

The checkmark symbol accompanied by the words "Reasonable Answer Check" will be used throughout this book to indicate how to check the answer to a problem to make certain a reasonable result has been obtained.

Answers to Problem-Solving Practice problems are given near the end of the book in a section with color on the edges of the pages.

PROBLEM-SOLVING PRACTICE 1.1

Find the volume occupied by a 4.33-g sample of benzene.

This book includes many examples, like Problem-Solving Example 1.1, that illustrate general problem-solving techniques and ways to approach specific types of problems. Usually, each of these examples states a problem; gives the answer; explains one way to analyze the problem, plan a solution, and execute the plan; and describes a way to check that the result is reasonable. We urge you to first try to solve the problem on your own. Then check to see whether your answer matches the one given. If it does not match, try again before reading the explanation. After you have tried twice, read the explanation to find out why your reasoning differs from that given. If your answer is correct, but your reasoning differs from the explanation, you may have discovered an alternative solution to the problem. Finally, work out the Problem-Solving Practice that accompanies the example. It relates to the same concept and allows you to improve your problem-solving skills.

1.5 Chemical Changes and Chemical Properties

Another way to identify a substance is to observe how it reacts chemically. For example, if you heat a white, granular solid carefully and it caramelizes (turns brown and becomes a syrupy liquid—see Figure 1.4), it is a good bet that the white solid is ordinary table sugar (sucrose). When heated gently, sucrose decomposes to give water and other new substances. If you heat sucrose very hot, it will char, leaving behind a black residue that is mainly carbon (and is hard to clean up). If you drip some water onto a sample of sodium metal, the sodium will react violently with the water, producing a solution of lye (sodium hydroxide) and a flammable gas, hydrogen (Figure 1.5). These are examples of **chemical changes** or **chemical reactions.** In a chemical reaction, one or more substances (the **reactants**) are transformed into one or more different substances (the **products**). Reactant substances

Sucrose (Reactant) $\xrightarrow{\text{changes to}}$ Carbon + Water (Products)

© Thomson Learning/Charles D. Winters

Figure 1.4 Chemical change. Heat can caramelize or char sugar.

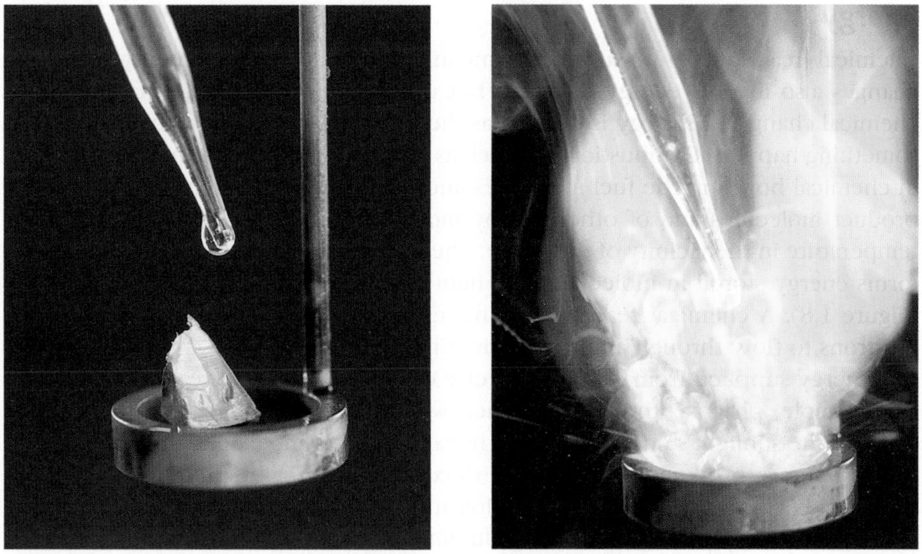

© Thomson Learning/Charles D. Winters

(a) (b)

Figure 1.5 Chemical change. When a drop of water (a) hits a piece of sodium, the resulting violent reaction (b) produces flammable hydrogen gas and a solution of sodium hydroxide (lye). Production of motion, heat, and light when substances are mixed is evidence that a chemical reaction is occurring.

© Thomson Learning/Charles D. Winters

Figure 1.6 Chemical change. Vinegar, which is an acid, has been added to an egg, causing colorless carbon dioxide gas to bubble away from the eggshell, which consists mainly of calcium carbonate. Production of gas bubbles when substances come into contact is one kind of evidence that a chemical reaction is occurring.

are replaced by product substances as the reaction occurs. This process is indicated by writing the reactants, an arrow, and then the products:

Sucrose	$\longrightarrow$	carbon	+	water
Reactant	changes to	Products		

Chemical reactions make chemistry interesting, exciting, and valuable. If you know how, you can make a medicine from the bark of a tree, clothing from crude petroleum, or even a silk purse from a sow's ear (it has been done). This is a very empowering idea, and human society has gained a great deal from it. Our way of life is greatly enhanced by our ability to use and control chemical reactions. And life itself is based on chemical reactions. Biological cells are filled with water-based solutions in which thousands of chemical reactions are happening all the time.

Chemical Properties

A substance's **chemical properties** describe the kinds of chemical reactions the substance can undergo. One chemical property of metallic sodium is that it reacts rapidly with water to produce hydrogen and a solution of sodium hydroxide (Figure 1.5). Because it also reacts rapidly with air and a number of other substances, sodium is also said to have a more general chemical property: It is highly reactive. A chemical property of substances known as metal carbonates is that they produce carbon dioxide when treated with an acid (Figure 1.6). Fuels are substances that have the chemical property of reacting with oxygen or air and at the same time transferring large quantities of energy to their surroundings. An example is natural gas (mainly methane), which is shown reacting with oxygen from the air in a gas stove in Figure 1.7. A substance's chemical properties tell us how it will behave when it contacts air or water, when it is heated or cooled, when it is exposed to sunlight, or when it is mixed with another substance. Such knowledge is very useful to chemists, biochemists, geologists, chemical engineers, and many other kinds of scientists.

George Semple

Figure 1.7 Combustion of natural gas. Natural gas, which in the U.S. consists mostly of methane, burns in air, transferring energy that raises the temperature of its surroundings.

© Thomson Learning/Charles D. Winters

Figure 1.8 Transforming energy. In each of these light sticks a chemical reaction transforms energy stored in molecules into light. Unlike an electric light bulb, the light sticks do not get hot.

Energy

Chemical reactions are usually accompanied by transfers of energy. (Physical changes also involve energy transfers, but usually they are smaller than those for chemical changes.) **Energy** is defined as the capacity to do work—that is, to make something happen. Combustion of a fuel, as in Figure 1.7, transforms energy stored in chemical bonds in the fuel molecules and oxygen molecules into motion of the product molecules and of other nearby molecules. This corresponds to a higher temperature in the vicinity of the flame. The chemical reaction in a light stick transforms energy stored in molecules into light energy, with only a little heat transfer (Figure 1.8). A chemical reaction in a battery makes a calculator work by forcing electrons to flow through an electric circuit.

Energy supplied from somewhere else can cause chemical reactions to occur. For example, photosynthesis takes place when sunlight illuminates green plants. Some of the sunlight's energy is stored in carbohydrate molecules and oxygen molecules that are produced from carbon dioxide and water by photosynthesis. Aluminum, which you may have used as foil to wrap and store food, is produced by passing electricity through a molten, aluminum-containing ore (Section 21.4). You consume and metabolize food, using the energy stored in food molecules to cause chemical reactions to occur in the cells of your body. The relation between chemical changes and energy is an important theme of chemistry.

CONCEPTUAL EXERCISE 1.4 Chemical and Physical Changes

Identify the chemical and physical changes that are described in this statement: Propane gas burns, and the heat of the combustion reaction is used to hard-boil an egg.

1.6 Classifying Matter: Substances and Mixtures

Once its chemical and physical properties are known, a sample of matter can be classified on the basis of those properties. Most of the matter we encounter every day is like the bark of a yew tree, concrete, or the carbon fiber composite frame of a high-tech bicycle—not uniform throughout. There are variations in color, hardness, and other properties from one part of a sample to another. This makes these materials complicated, but also interesting. A major advance in chemistry occurred when it was realized that it was possible to separate several component substances from such nonuniform samples. For example, in 1967 appropriate treatment of yew bark produced a substance, paclitaxel, that was shown to be active against cancer.

Often, as in the case of the bark of a tree, we can easily see that one part of a sample is different from another part. In other cases a sample may appear completely uniform to the unaided eye, but a microscope can reveal that it is not. For example, blood appears smooth in texture, but magnification reveals red and white cells within the liquid (Figure 1.9). The same is true of milk. A mixture in which the uneven texture of the material can be seen with the naked eye or with a microscope is classified as a **heterogeneous mixture.** Properties in one region are different from the properties in another region.

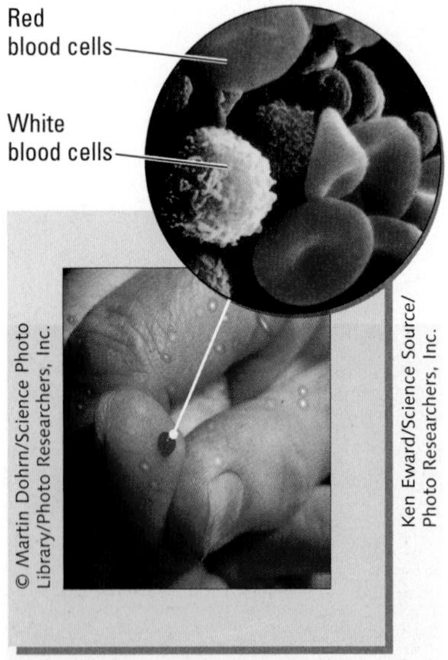

© Martin Dohrn/Science Photo Library/Photo Researchers, Inc.
Ken Eward/Science Source/Photo Researchers, Inc.

Figure 1.9 A heterogeneous mixture. Blood appears to be uniform to the unaided eye, but a microscope reveals that it is not homogeneous. The properties of red blood cells differ from the properties of the surrounding blood plasma, for example.

A **homogeneous mixture,** or **solution,** is completely uniform and consists of two or more substances in the same phase—solid, liquid, or gas (Figure 1.10). No amount of optical magnification will reveal different properties in one region of a solution compared with those in another. Heterogeneity exists in a solution only at the scale of atoms and molecules, which are too small to be seen with visible light. Examples of solutions are clear air (mostly a mixture of nitrogen and oxygen gases), sugar water, and some brass alloys (which are homogeneous mixtures of copper and zinc). The properties of a homogeneous mixture are the same everywhere in any particular sample, but they can vary from one sample to another depending on how much of one component is present relative to another component.

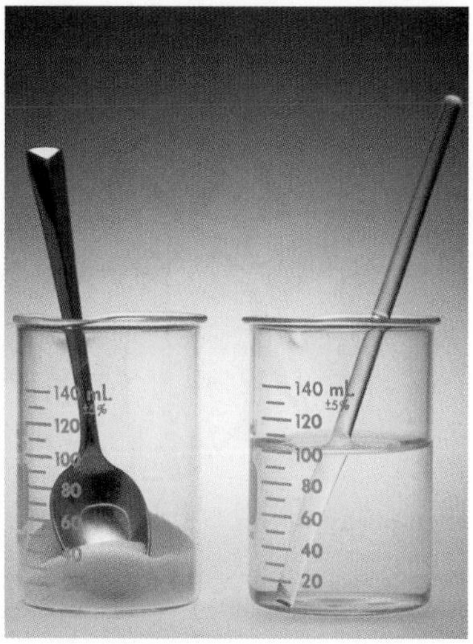

© Thomson Learning/Charles D. Winters

Figure 1.10 **A solution.** When solid salt (sodium chloride) is stirred into liquid water, it dissolves to form a homogeneous liquid mixture. Each portion of the solution has exactly the same saltiness as every other portion, and other properties are also the same throughout the solution.

Separation and Purification

Earlier in this chapter we stated that a substance has characteristic properties that distinguish it from all other substances. However, for those characteristic properties to be observed, the substance must be separated from all other substances; that is, it must be purified. The melting point of an impure substance is different from that of the purified substance. The color and appearance of a mixture may also differ from those of a pure substance. Therefore, when we talk about the properties of a substance, it is assumed that we are referring to a pure substance—one from which all other substances have been separated.

Purification usually has to be done in several repeated steps and monitored by observing some property of the substance being purified. For example, iron can be separated from a heterogeneous mixture of iron and sulfur with a magnet, as shown in Figure 1.11. In this example, color, which depends on the relative quantities of iron and sulfur, indicates purity. The bright yellow color of sulfur is assumed to indicate that all the iron has been removed.

Concluding that a substance is pure on the basis of a single property of the mixture could be misleading because other methods of purification might change some other properties of the sample. It is safe to call sulfur pure when a variety of methods of purification fail to change its physical and chemical properties. Purification is important because it allows us to attribute properties (such as activity against cancer) to specific substances and then to study systematically which kinds of substances have properties that we find useful. In some cases, insufficient purification of a substance has led scientists to attribute to that substance properties that were actually due to a tiny trace of another substance.

Only a few substances occur in nature in pure form. Gold, diamonds, and silicon dioxide (quartz) are examples. We live in a world of mixtures; all living things, the air and food on which we depend, and many products of technology are mixtures. Much of what we know about chemistry, however, is based on separating and purifying the components of those mixtures and then determining their properties. To date, more than 27 million substances have been reported, and many more are being

ThomsonNOW™
Go to the Chemistry Interactive menu to work a module on **separation of mixtures.**

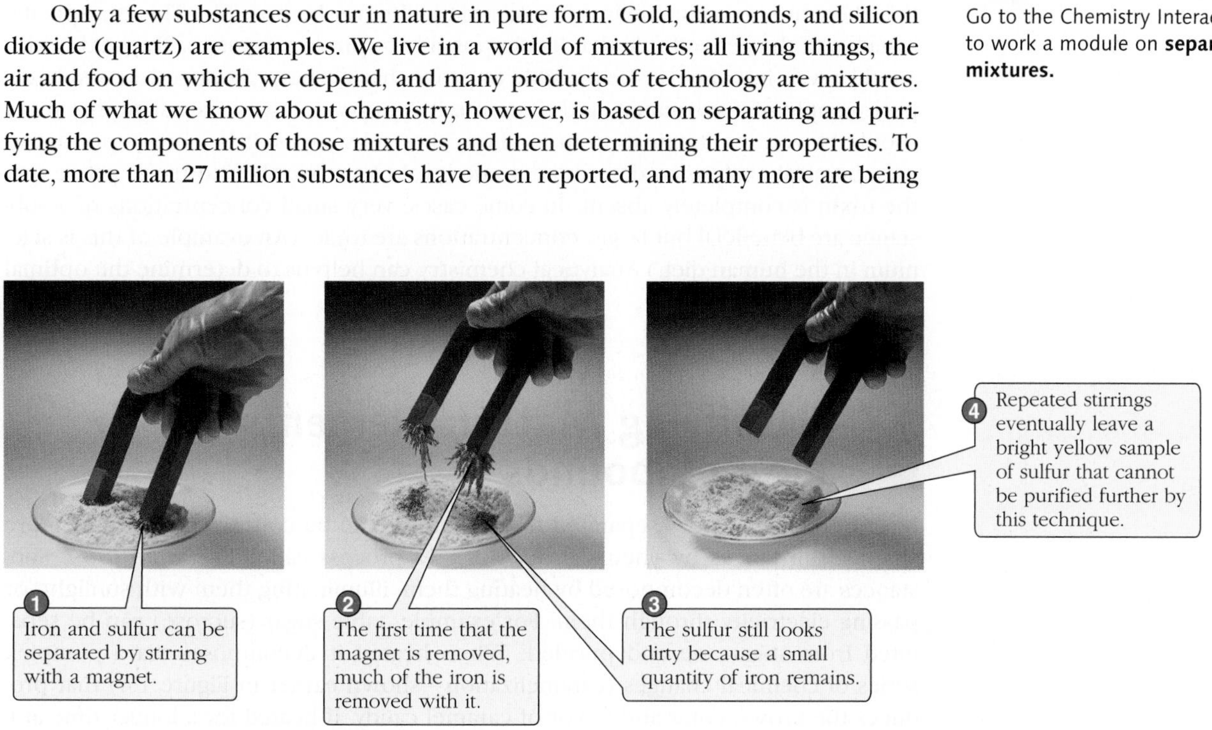

© Thomson Learning/Charles D. Winters

Figure 1.11 **Separating a mixture:** iron and sulfur.

© Thomson Learning/Charles D. Winters

High-purity silicon.

One part per million (ppm) means we can find one gram of a substance in one million grams of total sample. That corresponds to one-tenth of a drop of water in a bucket of water. One part per billion corresponds to a drop in a swimming pool, and one part per trillion corresponds to a drop in a large supermarket.

Absence of evidence is not evidence of absence.

discovered or synthesized by chemists every year. When pure, each of these substances has its own particular composition and its own characteristic properties.

A good example of the importance of purification is the high-purity silicon needed to produce transistors and computer chips. In one billion grams (about 1000 tons) of highly pure silicon there has to be less than one gram of impurity. Once the silicon has been purified, small but accurately known quantities of specific substances, such as boron or arsenic, can be introduced to give the electronic chip the desired properties. (See Sections 11.8 and 11.9.)

Detection and Analysis

Once we know that a given substance (such as an anticancer drug) is either valuable or harmful, it becomes important to know whether that substance is present in a sample and to be able to find out how much of it is there. Does an ore contain enough of a valuable metal to make it worthwhile to mine the ore? Is there enough mercury in a sample of fish to make it unsafe for humans to eat the fish?

Answering questions like these is the job of *analytical chemists,* and they improve their methods every year. For example, in 1960 mercury could be detected at a concentration of one part per million, in 1970 the detection limit was one part per billion, and by 1980 the limit had dropped to one part per trillion. Thus, in 20 years the ability to detect small concentrations of mercury had increased by a factor of one million. This improvement has an important effect. Because we can detect smaller and smaller concentrations of contaminants, such contaminants can be found in many more samples. A few decades ago, toxic substances were usually not found when food, air, or water was tested, but that did not mean they were not there. It just meant that our analytical methods were unable to detect them. Today, with much better methods, toxic substances can be detected in most samples, which prompts demands that concentrations of such substances should be reduced to zero.

Although we expect that chemistry will push detection limits lower and lower, there will always be a limit below which an impurity will be undetectable. Proving that there are no contaminants in a sample will never be possible. This is a specific instance of the general rule that it is impossible to prove a negative. To put this idea another way, it will never be possible to prove that we have produced a completely pure sample of a substance, and therefore it is unproductive to legislate that there should be zero contamination in food or other substances. It is more important to use chemical analysis to determine a safe level of a toxin than to try to prove that the toxin is completely absent. In some cases, very small concentrations of a substance are beneficial but larger concentrations are toxic. (An example of this is selenium in the human diet.) Analytical chemistry can help us to determine the optimal ranges of concentration.

1.7 Classifying Matter: Elements and Compounds

Most of the substances separated from mixtures can be converted to two or more simpler substances by chemical reactions—a process called *decomposition.* Substances are often decomposed by heating them, illuminating them with sunlight, or passing electricity through them. For example, table sugar (sucrose) can be separated from sugarcane and purified. When heated it decomposes via a complex series of chemical changes (caramelization—shown earlier in Figure 1.4) that produces the brown color and flavor of caramel candy. If heated for a longer time at a high enough temperature, sucrose is converted completely to two other substances, carbon and water. Furthermore, if the water is collected, it can be decomposed still further to pure hydrogen and oxygen by passing an electric current through it. However, nobody has found a way to decompose carbon, hydrogen, or oxygen.

Substances like carbon, hydrogen, and oxygen that cannot be changed by chemical reactions into two or more new substances are called **chemical elements** (or just elements). Substances that can be decomposed, like sucrose and water, are **chemical compounds** (or just compounds). When elements are chemically combined in a compound, their original characteristic properties—such as color, hardness, and melting point—are replaced by the characteristic properties of the compound. For example, sucrose is composed of these three elements:

In 1661 Robert Boyle was the first to propose that elements could be defined by the fact that they could not be decomposed into two or more simpler substances.

- Carbon, which is usually a black powder, but is also commonly seen in the form of diamonds
- Hydrogen, a colorless, flammable gas with the lowest density known
- Oxygen, a colorless gas necessary for human respiration

As you know from experience, sucrose is a white, crystalline powder that is completely unlike any of these three elements (Figure 1.12).

If a compound consists of two or more different elements, how is it different from a mixture? There are two ways: (1) A compound has specific composition and (2) a compound has specific properties. Both the composition and the properties of a mixture can vary. A solution of sugar in water can be very sweet or only a little sweet, depending on how much sugar has been dissolved. There is no particular composition of a sugar solution that is favored over any other, and each different composition has its own set of properties. On the other hand, 100.0 g pure water always contains 11.2 g hydrogen and 88.8 g oxygen. Pure water always melts at 0.0 °C and boils at 100 °C (at one atmosphere pressure), and it is always a colorless liquid at room temperature.

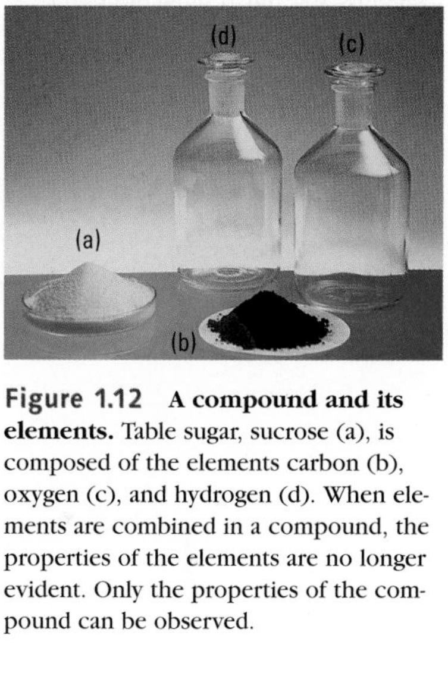

© Thomson Learning/Charles D. Winters

Figure 1.12 A compound and its elements. Table sugar, sucrose (a), is composed of the elements carbon (b), oxygen (c), and hydrogen (d). When elements are combined in a compound, the properties of the elements are no longer evident. Only the properties of the compound can be observed.

PROBLEM-SOLVING EXAMPLE 1.2 Elements and Compounds

A shiny, hard solid (substance A) is heated in the presence of carbon dioxide gas. After a few minutes, a white solid (substance B) and a black solid (substance C) are formed. No other substances are found. When the black solid is heated in the presence of pure oxygen, carbon dioxide is formed. Decide whether each substance (A, B, and C) is an element or a compound, and give a reason for your choice in each case. If there is insufficient evidence to decide, say so.

Answer A, insufficient evidence; B, compound; C, element

Explanation Substance C must be an element, because it combines with oxygen to form a compound, carbon dioxide, that contains only two elements; in fact, substance C must be carbon. Substance B must be a compound, because it must contain oxygen (from the carbon dioxide) and at least one other element (from substance A). There is not enough evidence to decide whether substance A is an element or a compound. If substance A is an element, then substance B must be an oxide of that element. However, there could be two or more elements in substance A (that is, it could be a compound), and the compound could still combine with oxygen from carbon dioxide to form a new compound.

✓ **Reasonable Answer Check** Substance C is black, and carbon (graphite) is black. You could test experimentally to see whether substance A could be decomposed by heating it in a vacuum; if two or more new substances were formed, then substance A would have to be a compound. If there was no change, substance A could be assumed to be an element.

PROBLEM-SOLVING PRACTICE 1.2

A student grinds an unknown sample (A) to a fine powder and attempts to dissolve the sample in 100 mL pure water. Some solid (B) remains undissolved. When the water is separated from the solid and allowed to evaporate, a white powder (C) forms. The dry white powder (C) is found to weigh 0.034 g. All of sample C can be dissolved in 25 mL of pure water. Can you say whether each sample A, B, and C is an element, a compound, or a mixture? Explain briefly.

Types of Matter

Desalinization of water (removing salt) could provide drinking water for large numbers of people who live in dry climates near the ocean. However, distillation requires a lot of energy resources and, therefore, is expensive. When solar energy can be used to evaporate the water, desalinization is less costly.

What we have just said about separating mixtures to obtain elements or compounds and decomposing compounds to obtain elements leads to a useful way to classify matter (Figure 1.13). Heterogeneous mixtures such as iron with sulfur can be separated using simple manipulation—such as a magnet. Homogeneous mixtures are somewhat more difficult to separate, but physical processes will serve. For example, salt water can be purified for drinking by distilling: heating to evaporate the water, and cooling to condense the water vapor back to liquid. When enough water has evaporated, salt crystals will form and they can be separated from the solution. Most difficult of all is separation of the elements that are combined in a compound. Such a separation requires a chemical change, which may involve reactions with other substances or sizable inputs of energy.

EXERCISE 1.5 Classifying Matter

Classify each of these with regard to the type of matter described:

(a) Sugar dissolved in water
(b) The soda pop in a can of carbonated beverage
(c) Used motor oil freshly drained from a car
(d) The diamond in a piece of jewelry
(e) A 25-cent coin
(f) A single crystal of sugar

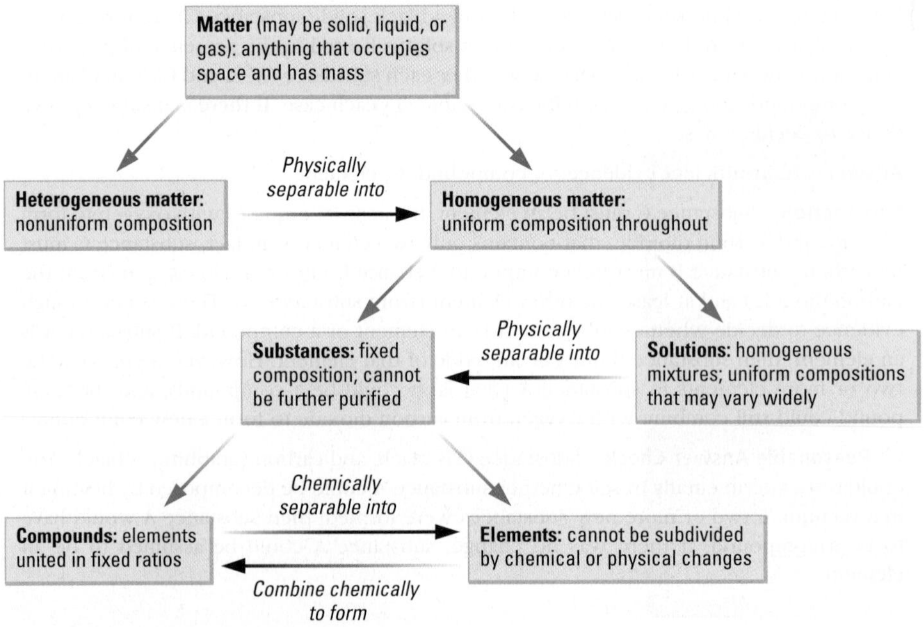

Figure 1.13 **A scheme for classifying matter.**

1.8 Nanoscale Theories and Models

To further illustrate how the methods of science are applied to matter, we now consider how a theory based on atoms and molecules can account for the physical properties, chemical properties, and classification scheme that we have just described. Physical and chemical properties can be observed by the unaided human senses and refer to samples of matter large enough to be seen, measured, and handled. Such samples are macroscopic; their size places them at the **macroscale.** By contrast, samples of matter so small that they have to be viewed with a microscope are **microscale** samples. Blood cells and bacteria, for example, are matter at the microscale. The matter that really interests chemists, however, is at the **nanoscale.** The term is based on the prefix "nano," which comes from the International System of Units (SI units) and indicates something one billion times smaller than something else. (See Table 1.2 for some important SI prefixes and length units.) For example, a line that is one billion (10^9) times shorter than 1 meter is 1 *nano*meter (1×10^{-9} m) long. The sizes of atoms and molecules are at the nanoscale. An average-sized atom such as a sulfur atom has a diameter of two tenths of a nanometer (0.2 nm = 2×10^{-10} m), a water molecule is about the same size, and an aspirin molecule is about three quarters of a nanometer (0.75 nm = 7.5×10^{-10} m) across. Figure 1.14 indicates the relative sizes of various objects at the macroscale, microscale, and nanoscale.

The International System of Units is the modern version of the metric system. It is described in more detail in Appendix B.

Using 10^9 to represent 1,000,000,000 or 1 billion is called scientific notation. It is reviewed in Appendix A.5.

Table 1.2 Some SI (Metric) Prefixes and Units for Length

Prefix	Abbreviation	Meaning	Example
kilo	k	10^3	1 kilometer (km) = 1×10^3 meter (m)
deci	d	10^{-1}	1 decimeter (dm) = 1×10^{-1} m = 0.1 m
centi	c	10^{-2}	1 centimeter (cm) = 1×10^{-2} m = 0.01 m
milli	m	10^{-3}	1 millimeter (mm) = 1×10^{-3} m = 0.001 m
micro	μ	10^{-6}	1 micrometer (μm) = 1×10^{-6} m
nano	n	10^{-9}	1 nanometer (nm) = 1×10^{-9} m
pico	p	10^{-12}	1 picometer (pm) = 1×10^{-12} m

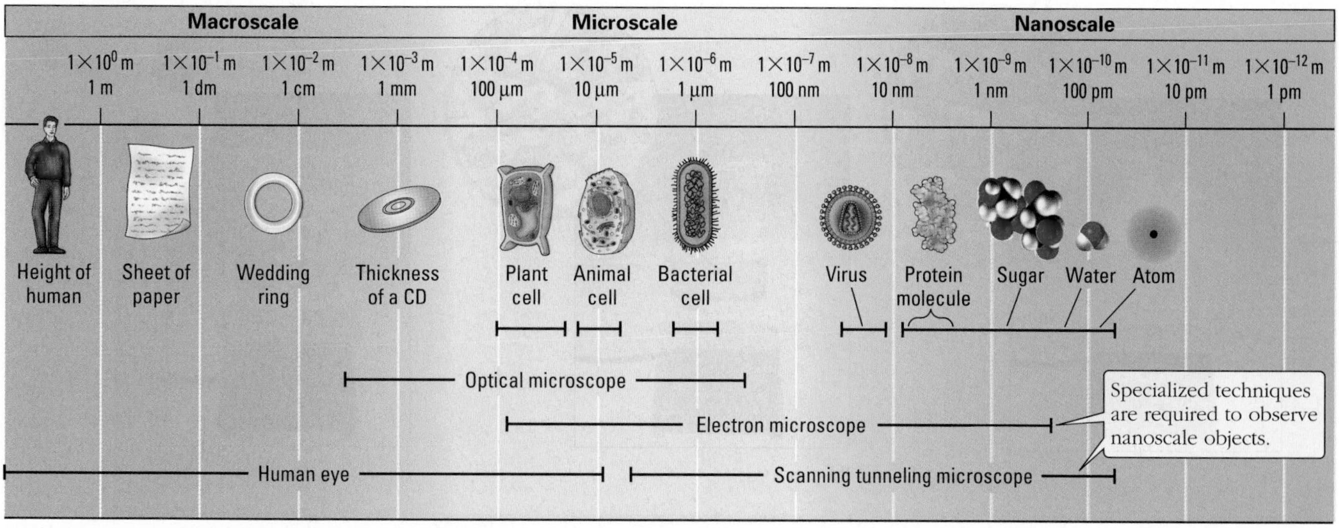

Figure 1.14 Macroscale, microscale, and nanoscale.

Jacob Bronowski, in a television series and book titled *The Ascent of Man,* had this to say about the importance of imagination: "There are many gifts that are unique in man; but at the center of them all, the root from which all knowledge grows, lies the ability to draw conclusions from what we see to what we do not see."

Earlier, we described the chemist's unique atomic and molecular perspective. It is a fundamental idea of chemistry that matter is the way it is because of the nature of its constituent atoms and molecules. Those atoms and molecules are very, very tiny. Therefore, we need to use imagination creatively to discover useful theories that connect the behavior of tiny nanoscale constituents to the observed behavior of chemical substances at the macroscale. Learning chemistry enables you to "see" in the things all around you nanoscale structure that cannot be seen with your eyes.

States of Matter: Solids, Liquids, and Gases

© Thomson Learning/Charles D. Winters

Figure 1.15 Quartz crystal. Quartz, like any solid, has a rigid shape. Its volume changes very little with changes in temperature or pressure.

An easily observed and very useful property of matter is its physical state. Is it a solid, liquid, or gas? A **solid** can be recognized because it has a rigid shape and a fixed volume that changes very little as temperature and pressure change (Figure 1.15). Like a solid, a **liquid** has a fixed volume, but a liquid is fluid—it takes on the shape of its container and has no definite form of its own. **Gases** are also fluid, but gases expand to fill whatever containers they occupy and their volumes vary considerably with temperature and pressure. For most substances, when compared at the same conditions, the volume of the solid is slightly less than the volume of the same mass of liquid, but the volume of the same mass of gas is much, much larger. As the temperature is raised, most solids melt to form liquids; eventually, if the temperature is raised enough, most liquids boil to form gases.

A theory that deals with matter at the nanoscale is the **kinetic-molecular theory.** It states that all matter consists of extremely tiny particles (atoms or molecules) that are in constant motion. In a solid these particles are packed closely together in a regular array, as shown in Figure 1.16a. The particles vibrate back and forth about their average positions, but seldom does a particle in a solid squeeze past its immediate neighbors to come into contact with a new set of particles. Because the particles are packed so tightly and in such a regular arrangement, a solid is rigid, its volume is fixed, and the volume of a given mass is small. The external shape of a solid

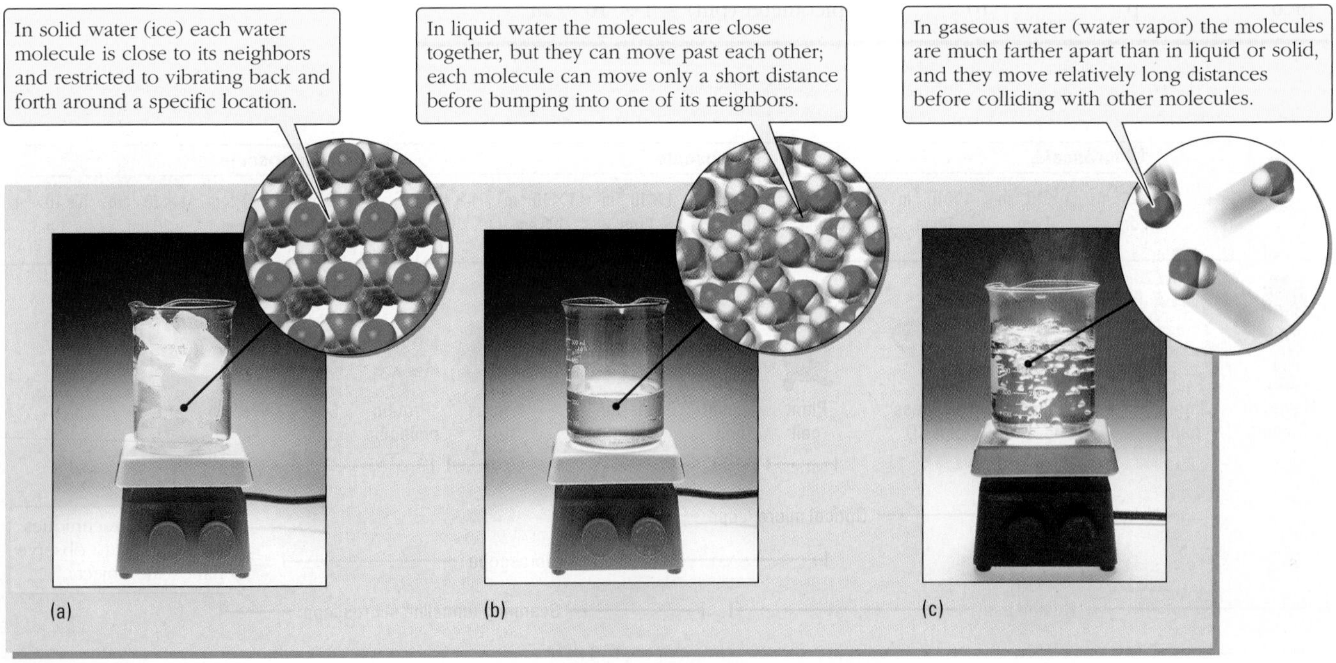

Photos © Thomson Learning/Charles D. Winters

Figure 1.16 Nanoscale representation of three states of matter.

often reflects the internal arrangement of its particles. This relation between the observable structure of the solid and the arrangement of the particles from which it is made is one reason that scientists have long been fascinated by the shapes of crystals and minerals (Figure 1.17).

The kinetic-molecular theory of matter can also be used to interpret the properties of liquids, as shown in Figure 1.16b. Liquids are fluid because the atoms or molecules are arranged more haphazardly than in solids. Particles are not confined to specific locations but rather can move past one another. No particle goes very far without bumping into another—the particles in a liquid interact with their neighbors continually. Because the particles are usually a little farther apart in a liquid than in the corresponding solid, the volume is usually a little bigger. (Ice and liquid water, which are shown in Figure 1.16, are an important exception to this last generality. As you can see from the figure, the water molecules in ice are arranged so that there are empty hexagonal channels. When ice melts, these channels become partially filled by water molecules, accounting for the slightly smaller volume of the same mass of liquid water.)

Like liquids, gases are fluid because their nanoscale particles can easily move past one another. As shown in Figure 1.16c, the particles fly about to fill any container they are in; hence, a gas has no fixed shape or volume. In a gas the particles are much farther apart than in a solid or a liquid. They move significant distances before hitting other particles or the walls of the container. The particles also move quite rapidly. In air at room temperature, for example, the average molecule is going faster than 1000 miles per hour. A particle hits another particle every so often, but most of the time each is quite far away from all the others. Consequently, the nature of the particles is much less important in determining the properties of a gas.

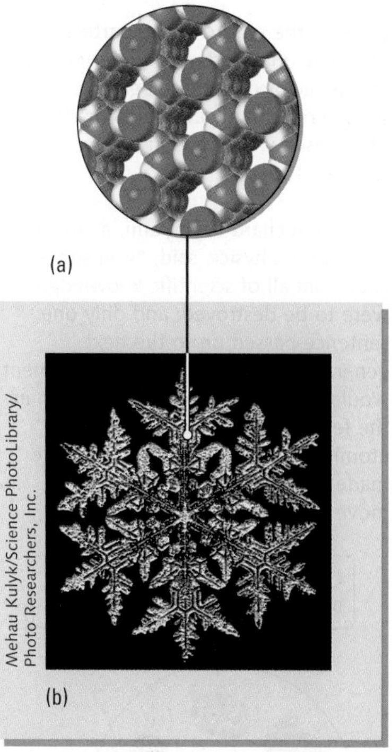

Figure 1.17 Structure and form. (a) In the nanoscale structure of ice, each water molecule occupies a position in a regular array or lattice. (b) The form of a snowflake reflects the hexagonal symmetry of the nanoscale structure of ice.

CHEMISTRY IN THE NEWS

Nanoscale Transistors

The great information-processing capabilities of modern computers, personal digital assistants, calculators, and cellular telephones have been made possible because the number of transistors that can be squeezed into a single electronic chip has increased steadily for at least 30 years. However, decreasing the size of components of electronic circuits cannot go on forever. It has to stop at the level of atoms and molecules, because those are what the transistors must ultimately be made of. Consequently, there has been a lot of scientific competition to produce nanoscale transistors—molecular electronics. In the summer of 2002 the ultimate was reached by several groups of scientists. Transistors have been created whose switching elements are single atoms.

The atomic transistor switches consist of one or two metal atoms embedded in a molecule that connects the metal atom to two microscopic electrodes (conductors of electricity, which is a flow of electrons). One group of researchers used a cobalt atom. Another group used two vanadium atoms. To get from one electrode to another, the electrons need to pass through each metal atom. When a single extra electron is on the atom, it blocks the passage of other electrons. If a positive electric field is applied, it attracts additional electrons to the metal atom. When an average of 1.5 electrons occupy the atom, electrons flow onto the atom from one side and off the atom on the other. That is, the transistor is turned on and an electric current flows. The current can be controlled by the electric field, making the transistor an atomic-scale electrical switch. Currently such transistors can operate only at very low temperatures, but in the not too distant future you may be using a computer whose switches are so tiny that they consist of single atoms.

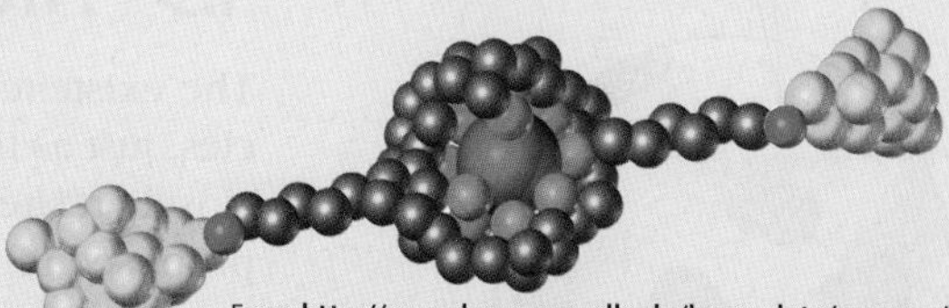

From **http://www.lassp.cornell.edu/lassp_data/mceuen/homepage/welcome.html.** Reprinted by permission.

Nanoscale transistor. A single cobalt atom (purple) embedded in a molecule that connects to two gold electrodes (yellow) serves as a switch that can turn on an electric current from one electrode to the other. The cobalt atom is surrounded by nitrogen atoms (blue) that are bonded to carbon atoms (blue-gray).

SOURCE: *New York Times,* October 1, 2002, p. D1.

Because the nature of the particles is relatively unimportant in determining the behavior of gases, all gases can be described fairly accurately by the ideal gas law, which is introduced in Chapter 10.

The late Richard Feynmann, a Nobel laureate in physics, said, "If in some cataclysm all of scientific knowledge were to be destroyed, and only one sentence passed on to the next generation of creatures, what statement would contain the most information in the fewest words? I believe it is the atomic hypothesis, that all things are made of atoms, little particles that move around in perpetual motion."

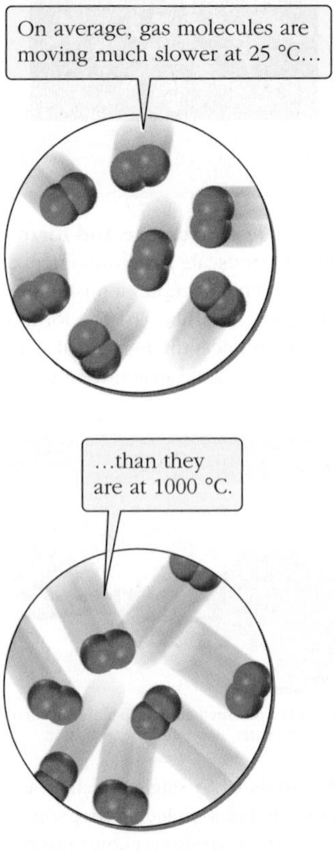

Figure 1.18 Molecular speed and temperature.

Temperature can also be interpreted using the kinetic-molecular theory. The higher the temperature is, the more active the nanoscale particles are. A solid melts when its temperature is raised to the point where the particles vibrate fast enough and far enough to push each other out of the way and move out of their regularly spaced positions. The substance becomes a liquid because the particles are now behaving as they do in a liquid, bumping into one another and pushing past their neighbors. As the temperature goes higher, the particles move even faster, until finally they can escape the clutches of their comrades and become independent; the substance becomes a gas. Increasing temperature corresponds to faster and faster motions of atoms and molecules. This is a general rule that you will find useful in many future discussions of chemistry (Figure 1.18).

Using the kinetic-molecular theory to interpret the properties of solids, liquids, and gases and the effect of changing temperature provides a very simple example of how chemists use nanoscale theories and models to interpret and explain macroscale observations. In the remainder of this chapter and throughout your study of chemistry, you should try to imagine how the atoms and molecules are arranged and what they are doing whenever you consider a macroscale sample of matter. That is, you should try to develop the chemist's special perspective on the relation of nanoscale structure to macroscale behavior.

CONCEPTUAL EXERCISE 1.6 Kinetic-Molecular Theory

Use the idea that matter consists of tiny particles in motion to interpret each observation.

(a) An ice cube sitting in the sun slowly melts, and the liquid water eventually evaporates.
(b) Wet clothes hung on a line eventually dry.
(c) Moisture appears on the outside of a glass of ice water.
(d) Evaporation of a solution of sugar in water forms crystals.

1.9 The Atomic Theory

The existence of elements can be explained by a nanoscale model involving particles, just as the properties of solids, liquids, and gases can be. This model, which is closely related to the kinetic-molecular theory, is called the **atomic theory.** It was proposed in 1803 by John Dalton. According to Dalton's theory, an element cannot be decomposed into two or more new substances because at the nanoscale it consists of one and only one kind of atom and because atoms are indivisible under the conditions of chemical reactions. An **atom** is the smallest particle of an element that embodies the chemical properties of that element. An element, such as the sample of copper in Figure 1.19, is made up entirely of atoms of the same kind.

The fact that a compound can be decomposed into two or more different substances can be explained by saying that each compound must contain two or more different kinds of atoms. The process of decomposition involves separating at least one type of atom from atoms of the other kind(s). For example, charring of sugar corresponds to separating atoms of carbon from atoms of oxygen and atoms of hydrogen.

Dalton also said that each kind of atom must have its own properties—in particular, a characteristic mass. This idea allowed his theory to account for the masses of different elements that combine in chemical reactions to form compounds. An important success of Dalton's ideas was that they could be used to interpret known chemical facts quantitatively.

Two laws known in Dalton's time could be explained by the atomic theory. One was based on experiments in which the reactants were carefully weighed before a

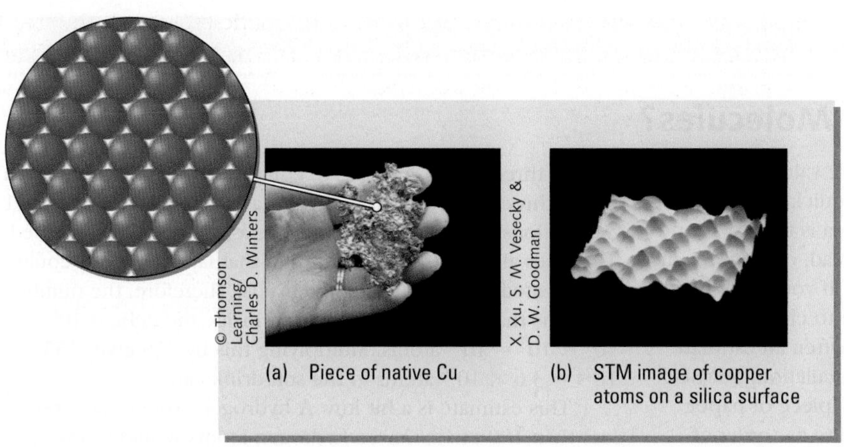

Figure 1.19 Elements, atoms, and the nanoscale world of chemistry. (a) A macroscopic sample of naturally occurring copper metal with a nanoscale, magnified representation of a tiny portion of its surface. It is clear that all the atoms in the sample of copper are the same kind of atoms. (b) A scanning tunneling microscopy (STM) image, enhanced by a computer, of a layer of copper atoms on the surface of silica (a compound of silicon and oxygen). The section of the layer shown is 1.7 nm square and the rows of atoms are separated by about 0.44 nm.

chemical reaction, and the reaction products were carefully collected and weighed afterward. The results led to the **law of conservation of mass** (also called the law of conservation of matter): *There is no detectable change in mass during an ordinary chemical reaction.* The atomic theory says that mass is conserved because the same number of atoms of each kind is present before and after a reaction, and each of those kinds of atoms has its same characteristic mass before and after the reaction.

The other law was based on the observation that in a chemical compound the proportions of the elements by mass are always the same. Water always contains 1 g hydrogen for every 8 g oxygen, and carbon monoxide always contains 4 g oxygen for every 3 g carbon. The **law of constant composition** summarizes such observations: *A chemical compound always contains the same elements in the same proportions by mass.* The atomic theory explains this observation by saying that atoms of different elements always combine in the same ratio in a compound. For example, in carbon monoxide there is always one carbon atom for each oxygen atom. If the mass of an oxygen atom is $\frac{4}{3}$ times the mass of a carbon atom, then the ratio of mass of oxygen to mass of carbon in carbon monoxide will always be 4:3.

Our bodies are made up of atoms from the distant past—atoms from other people and other things. Some of the carbon, hydrogen, and oxygen atoms in our carbohydrates have come from the breaths (first and last) of both famous and ordinary persons of the past.

Dalton's theory has been modified to account for discoveries since his time. The *modern* atomic theory is based on these assumptions:

All matter is composed of atoms, which are extremely tiny. Interactions among atoms account for the properties of matter.

All atoms of a given element have the same chemical properties. Atoms of different elements have different chemical properties.

According to the modern theory, atoms of the same element have the same chemical properties but are not necessarily identical in all respects. The discussion of isotopes in Chapter 2 shows how atoms of the same element can differ in mass.

Compounds are formed by the chemical combination of two or more different kinds of atoms. Atoms usually combine in the ratio of small whole numbers. For example, in a carbon monoxide molecule there is one carbon atom and one oxygen atom; a carbon dioxide molecule consists of one carbon atom and two oxygen atoms.

A chemical reaction involves joining, separating, or rearranging atoms. Atoms in the reactant substances form new combinations in the product substances. Atoms are not created, destroyed, or converted into other kinds of atoms during a chemical reaction.

ESTIMATION

How Tiny Are Atoms and Molecules?

It is often useful to estimate an approximate value for something. Usually this estimation can be done quickly, and often it can be done without a calculator. The idea is to pick round numbers that you can work with in your head, or to use some other method that allows a quick estimate. If you really need an accurate value, an estimate is still useful to check whether the accurate value is in the right ballpark. Often an estimate is referred to as a "back-of-the-envelope" calculation, because estimates might be done over lunch on any piece of paper that is at hand. Some estimates are referred to as "order-of-magnitude calculations" because only the power of ten (the order of magnitude) in the answer is obtained. To help you develop estimation skills, most chapters in this book will provide you with an example of estimating something.

To get a more intuitive feeling for how small atoms and molecules are, estimate how many hydrogen atoms could fit inside a 12-oz (355-mL) soft-drink can. Make the same estimate for protein molecules. Use the approximate sizes given in Figure 1.14.

Because 1 mL is the same volume as a cube 1 cm on each side (1 cm^3), the volume of the can is the same as the volume of 355 cubes 1 cm on each side. Therefore we can first estimate how many atoms would fit into a 1-cm cube and then multiply that number by 355.

According to Figure 1.14, a typical atom has a diameter slightly less than 100 pm. Because this is an estimate, and to make the numbers easy to handle, assume that we are dealing with an atom that is 100 pm in diameter. Then the atom's diameter is 100×10^{-12} m = 1×10^{-10} m, and it will require 10^{10} of these atoms lined up in a row to make a length of 1 m. Since 1 cm is $\frac{1}{100}$ (10^{-2}) of a meter, only $10^{-2} \times 10^{10} = 10^8$ atoms would fit in 1 cm.

In three dimensions, there could be 10^8 atoms along each of the three perpendicular edges of a 1-cm cube (the *x*, *y*, and *z* directions). The one row along the *x*-axis could be repeated 10^8 times along the *y*-axis, and then that layer of atoms could be repeated 10^8 times along the *z*-axis. Therefore, the number of atoms that we estimate would fit inside the cube is $10^8 \times 10^8 \times 10^8 = 10^{24}$ atoms. Multiplying this by 355 gives $355 \times 10^{24} = 3.6 \times 10^{26}$ atoms in the soft-drink can.

This estimate is a bit low. A hydrogen atom's diameter is less than 100 pm, so more hydrogen atoms would fit inside the can. Also, atoms are usually thought of as spheres, so they could pack together more closely than they would if just lined up in rows. Therefore, an even larger number of atoms than 3.6×10^{26} could fit inside the can.

For a typical protein molecule, Figure 1.14 indicates a diameter on the order of 5 nm = 5000 pm. That is 50 times bigger than the 100-pm diameter we used for the hydrogen atom. Thus, there would be 50 times fewer protein molecules in the *x* direction, 50 times fewer in the *y* direction, and 50 times fewer in the *z* direction. Therefore, the number of protein molecules would be fewer by $50 \times 50 \times 50 = 125{,}000$. The number of protein molecules can thus be estimated as $(3.6 \times 10^{26}) / (1.25 \times 10^5)$. Because 3.6 is roughly three times 1.25, and because we are estimating, not calculating accurately, we can take the result to be 3×10^{21} protein molecules. That's still a whole lot of molecules!

ThomsonNOW™

Sign in to ThomsonNOW at **www.thomsonedu.com** to work an interactive module based on this material.

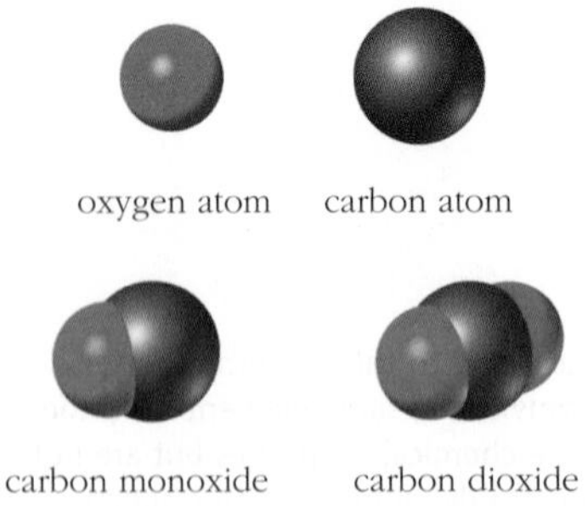

The hallmark of a good theory is that it suggests new experiments, and this was true of the atomic theory. Dalton realized that it predicted a law that had not yet been discovered. If compounds are formed by combining atoms of different elements on the nanoscale, then in some cases there might be more than a single combination. An example is carbon monoxide and carbon dioxide. In carbon monoxide there is one oxygen atom for each carbon atom, while in carbon dioxide there are two oxygen atoms per carbon atom. Therefore, in carbon dioxide the mass of oxygen per gram of carbon ought to be twice as great as it is in carbon monoxide (because twice as many oxygen atoms will weigh twice as much). Dalton called this the **law of multiple proportions,** and he carried out quantitative experiments seeking data to confirm or deny it. Dalton and others obtained data consistent with the law of multiple proportions, thereby enhancing acceptance of the atomic theory.

1.10 The Chemical Elements

Every element has been given a unique *name* and a *symbol* derived from the name. These names and symbols are listed in the periodic table inside the front cover of the book. The first letter of each symbol is capitalized; the second letter, if there is one, is lowercase, as in He, the symbol for helium. Elements discovered a long time ago have names and symbols with Latin or other origins, such as Au for gold (from *aurum,* meaning "bright dawn") and Fe for iron (from *ferrum*). The names of more recently discovered elements are derived from their place of discovery or from a person or place of significance (Table 1.3).

Ancient people knew of nine elements—gold (Au), silver (Ag), copper (Cu), tin (Sn), lead (Pb), mercury (Hg), iron (Fe), sulfur (S), and carbon (C). Most of the other naturally occurring elements were discovered during the 1800s, as one by one they were separated from minerals in the earth's crust or from the earth's oceans or atmosphere. Currently, more than 110 elements are known, but only 90 occur in nature. Elements such as technetium (Tc), neptunium (Np), mendelevium (Md), seaborgium (Sg), and meitnerium (Mt) have been made using nuclear reactions (see Chapter 20), beginning in the 1930s.

Elements are being synthesized even now. Element 115 was made in 2004, but only a few atoms were observed.

Types of Elements

The vast majority of the elements are **metals**—only 24 are not. You are probably familiar with many properties of metals. At room temperature they are solids (except for mercury, which is a liquid), they conduct electricity (and conduct better as the temperature decreases), they are ductile (can be drawn into wires), they are malleable (can be rolled into sheets), and they can form alloys (solutions of one or more metals in another metal). In a solid metal, individual metal atoms are packed close to each other, so metals usually have fairly high densities. Figure 1.20 shows some common metals. Iron (Fe) and aluminum (Al) are used in automobile parts because of their ductility, malleability, and relatively low cost. Copper (Cu) is used in electrical wiring because it conducts electricity better than most metals. Gold (Au) is used for the vital electrical contacts in automobile air bags and in some computers because it does not corrode and is an excellent electrical conductor.

In contrast, **nonmetals** do not conduct electricity (with a few exceptions, such as graphite, one form of carbon). Nonmetals are more diverse in their physical properties than are metals (Figure 1.21). At room temperature some nonmetals are solids

© Thomson Learning/Charles D. Winters

Figure 1.20 **Some metallic elements**—iron, aluminum, copper, and gold. The steel ball bearing is principally iron. The rod is made of aluminum. The inner coil is gold and the other one is copper. Metals are malleable, ductile, and conduct electricity.

Table 1.3 The Names of Some Chemical Elements

Element	Symbol	Date Discovered	Discoverer	Derivation of Name/Symbol
Carbon	C	Ancient	Ancient	Latin, *carbo* (charcoal)
Curium	Cm	1944	G. Seaborg, et al.	Honoring Marie and Pierre Curie, Nobel Prize winners for discovery of radioactive elements
Hydrogen	H	1766	H. Cavendish	Greek, *hydro* (water) and *genes* (generator)
Meitnerium	Mt	1982	P. Armbruster, et al.	Honoring Lise Meitner, codiscoverer of nuclear fission
Mendelevium	Md	1955	G. Seaborg, et al.	Honoring Dmitri Mendeleev, who devised the periodic table
Mercury	Hg	Ancient	Ancient	For Mercury, messenger of the gods, because it flows quickly; symbol from Greek *hydrargyrum,* liquid silver
Polonium	Po	1898	M. Curie and P. Curie	In honor of Poland, Marie Curie's native country
Seaborgium	Sg	1974	G. Seaborg, et al.	Honoring Glenn Seaborg, Nobel Prize winner for synthesis of new elements
Sodium	Na	1807	H. Davy	Latin, *soda* (sodium carbonate); symbol from Latin *natrium*
Tin	Sn	Ancient	Ancient	German, *Zinn;* symbol from Latin, *stannum*

© Thomson Learning/Charles D. Winters
© Thomson Learning/Charles D. Winters
© Thomson Learning/Larry Cameron

(a) (b) (c) (d)

Figure 1.21 **Some nonmetallic elements**—(a) chlorine, (b) sulfur, (c) bromine, (d) iodine. Nonmetals occur as solids, liquids, and gases and have very low electrical conductivities. Bromine is the only nonmetal that is a liquid at room temperature.

(such as phosphorus, sulfur, and iodine), bromine is a liquid, and others are gases (such as hydrogen, nitrogen, and chlorine). The nonmetals helium (He), neon (Ne), argon (Ar), krypton (Kr), xenon (Xe), and radon (Rn) are gases that consist of individual atoms.

A few elements—boron, silicon, germanium, arsenic, antimony, and tellurium—are classified as **metalloids.** Some properties of metalloids are typical of metals and other properties are characteristic of nonmetals. For example, some metalloids are shiny like metals, but they do not conduct electricity as well as metals. Many of them are semiconductors and are essential for the electronics industry. (See Sections 11.8 and 11.9.)

On the periodic table inside the front cover of this book, the metals, nonmetals, and metalloids are color-coded: gray and blue for metals, lavender for nonmetals, and orange for metalloids.

EXERCISE 1.7 Elements

Use Table 1.3, the periodic table inside the front cover, and/or the list of elements inside the front cover to answer these questions.

(a) Four elements are named for planets in our solar system (including the ex-planet Pluto). Give their names and symbols.
(b) One element is named for a state in the United States. Name the element and give its symbol.
(c) Two elements are named in honor of women. What are their names and symbols?
(d) Several elements are named for countries or regions of the world. Find at least four of these and give names and symbols.
(e) List the symbols of all elements that are nonmetals.

Chemical bonds are strong attractions that hold atoms together. Bonding is discussed in detail in Chapter 8.

Space-filling model of Cl_2

Elements that consist of diatomic molecules are H_2, N_2, O_2, F_2, Cl_2, Br_2, and I_2. You need to remember that these elements consist of diatomic molecules, because they will be encountered frequently. Most of these elements are close together in the periodic table, which makes it easier to remember them.

Elements That Consist of Molecules

Most elements that are nonmetals consist of molecules on the nanoscale. A **molecule** is a unit of matter in which two or more atoms are chemically bonded together. For example, a chlorine molecule contains two chlorine atoms and can be represented by the chemical formula Cl_2. A **chemical formula** uses the symbols for the elements to represent the atomic composition of a substance. In gaseous chlorine, Cl_2 molecules are the particles that fly about and collide with each other and the container walls. Molecules, like Cl_2, that consist of two atoms are called **diatomic molecules.** Oxygen (O_2) and nitrogen (N_2) also exist as diatomic molecules, as do hydrogen (H_2), fluorine (F_2), bromine (Br_2), and iodine (I_2).

You have already seen (in Figure 1.1) that really big molecules, such as tubulin, may be represented by ribbons or sticks, without showing individual atoms at all.

Often such representations are drawn by computers, which help chemists to visualize, manipulate, and understand the molecular structures.

EXERCISE 1.8 Elements That Consist of Diatomic Molecules or Are Metalloids

On a copy of the periodic table, circle the symbols of the elements that
(a) Consist of diatomic molecules;
(b) Are metalloids.
Devise rules related to the periodic table that will help you to remember which elements these are.

Allotropes

Oxygen and carbon are among the elements that exist as **allotropes,** different forms of the same element in the same physical state at the same temperature and pressure. Allotropes are possible because the same kind of atoms can be connected in different ways when they form molecules. For example, the allotropes of oxygen are O_2, sometimes called dioxygen, and O_3, ozone. Dioxygen, a major component of earth's atmosphere, is by far the more common allotropic form. Ozone is a highly reactive, pale blue gas first detected by its characteristic pungent odor. Its name comes from *ozein,* a Greek word meaning "to smell."

oxygen molecule (O_2)

ozone molecule (O_3)

Diamond and graphite, known for centuries, have quite different properties. Diamond is a hard, colorless solid and graphite is a soft, black solid, but both consist entirely of carbon atoms. This makes them allotropes of carbon, and for a long time they were thought to be the only allotropes of carbon with well-defined structures. Therefore, it was a surprise in the 1980s when another carbon allotrope was discovered in soot produced when carbon-containing materials are burned with very little oxygen. The new allotrope consists of 60-carbon atom cages and represents a new class of molecules. The C_{60} molecule resembles a soccer ball with a carbon atom at each corner of each of the black pentagons in Figure 1.22b. Each five-membered ring of carbon atoms is surrounded by five six-membered rings. This

A C_{60} molecule's size compared with a soccer ball is almost the same as a soccer ball's size compared with planet Earth.

Grant Heilman

© Thomson Learning/Charles D. Winters

© Thomson Learning/Charles D. Winters

(a) (b) (c)

Figure 1.22 Models for fullerenes. (a) Geodesic domes at Elmira College, Elmira, New York. Geodesic domes, such as those designed originally by R. Buckminster Fuller, contain linked hexagons and pentagons. (b) A soccer ball is a model for the C_{60} structure. (c) The C_{60} fullerene molecule, which is made up of five-membered rings (black rings on the soccer ball) and six-membered rings (white rings on the ball).

molecular structure of carbon pentagons and hexagons reminded its discoverers of a geodesic dome (Figure 1.22a), a structure popularized years ago by the innovative American philosopher and engineer R. Buckminster Fuller. Therefore, the official name of the C_{60} allotrope is buckminsterfullerene. Chemists often call it simply a "buckyball." C_{60} buckyballs belong to a larger molecular family of even-numbered carbon cages that is collectively called fullerenes.

For an up-to-date description of research on nanotubes, see "The Nanotube Site," **http://www.pa.msu.edu/cmp/csc/nanotube.html**.

Carbon atoms can also form concentric tubes that resemble rolled-up chicken wire. These single- and multi-walled *nanotubes* of only carbon atoms are excellent electrical conductors and extremely strong. Imagine the exciting applications for such properties, including making buckyfibers that could substitute for the metal wires now used to transmit electrical power. Dozens of uses have been proposed for fullerenes, buckytubes, and buckyfibers, among them microscopic ball bearings, lightweight batteries, new lubricants, nanoscale electric switches, new plastics, and antitumor therapy for cancer patients (by enclosing a radioactive atom within the cage). All these applications await an inexpensive way of making buckyballs and other fullerenes. Currently buckyballs, the cheapest fullerene, are more expensive than gold.

© M. Slates/J.C.P.A./Corbis Sygma

Sir Harold Kroto
1939–

Along with the late Richard E. Smalley and Robert Curl, Harold Kroto received the Nobel Prize in chemistry in 1996 for discovering fullerenes. In the same year Kroto, who is British, received a knighthood for his work. At the time of the discovery, Smalley assembled paper hexagons and pentagons to make a model of the C_{60} molecule. He asked Kroto, "Who was the architect who worked with big domes?" When Kroto replied, "Buckminster Fuller," the two shouted with glee, "It's Buckminster Fuller—ene!" The structure's name had been coined.

EXERCISE 1.9 Allotropes

A student says that tin and lead are allotropes because they are both dull gray metals. Why is the statement wrong?

1.11 Communicating Chemistry: Symbolism

Chemical symbols—such as Na, I, or Mt—are a shorthand way of indicating what kind of atoms we are talking about. Chemical formulas tell us how many atoms of an element are combined in a molecule and in what ratios atoms are combined in compounds. For example, the formula Cl_2 tells us that there are two chlorine atoms in a chlorine molecule. The formulas CO and CO_2 tell us that carbon and oxygen form two different compounds—one that has equal numbers of C and O atoms and one that has twice as many O atoms as C atoms. In other words, chemical symbols and formulas symbolize the nanoscale composition of each substance.

Chemical symbols and formulas also represent the macroscale properties of elements and compounds. That is, the symbol Na brings to mind a highly reactive metal, and the formula H_2O represents a colorless liquid that freezes at 0 °C, boils at 100 °C, and reacts violently with Na. Because chemists are familiar with both the nanoscale and macroscale characteristics of substances, they usually use symbols to abbreviate their representations of both. Symbols are also useful for representing chemical reactions. For example, the charring of sucrose mentioned earlier is represented by

Sucrose	$\longrightarrow$	carbon	+	water
$C_{12}H_{22}O_{11}$	$\longrightarrow$	12 C	+	11 H_2O
reactant	changes to		products	

The symbolic aspect of chemistry is the third part of the chemist's special view of the world. It is important that you become familiar and comfortable with using chemical symbols and formulas to represent chemical substances and their reactions. Figure 1.23 shows how chemical symbolism can be applied to the process of decomposing water with electricity (electrolysis of water).

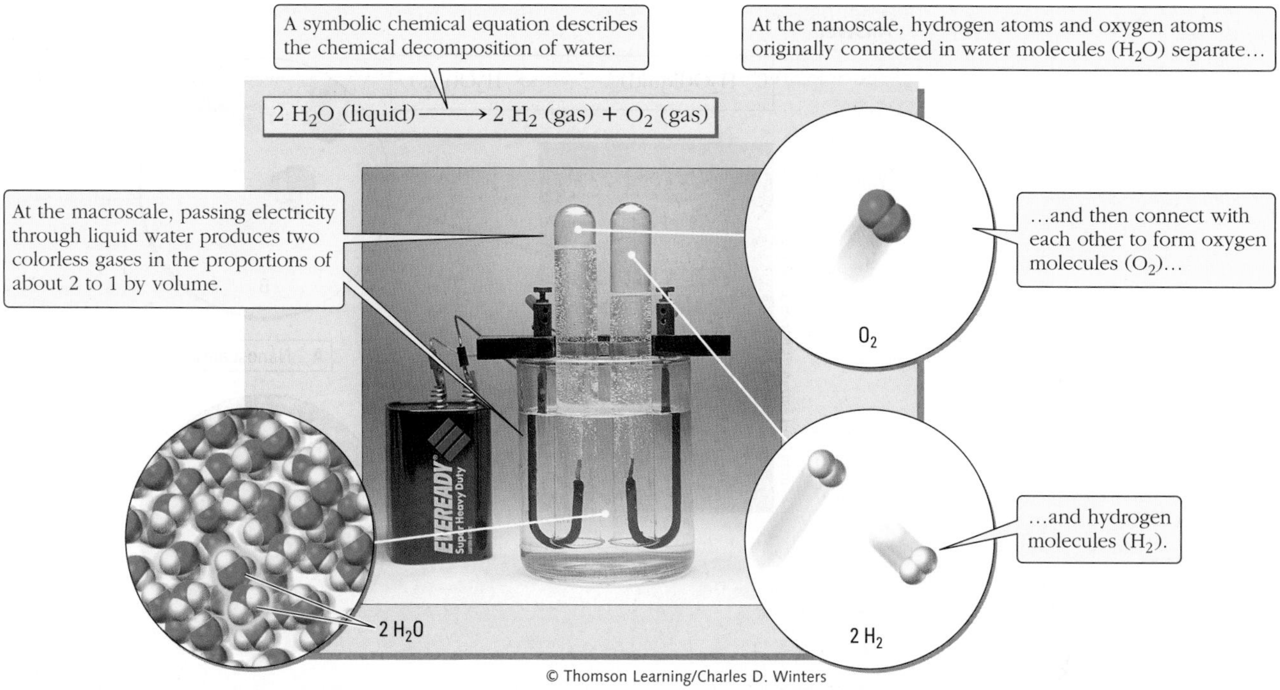

© Thomson Learning/Charles D. Winters

Active Figure 1.23 **Symbolic, macroscale, and nanoscale representations of a chemical reaction. Go to the Active Figures menu at ThomsonNOW to test your understanding of the concepts in this figure.**

PROBLEM-SOLVING EXAMPLE 1.3 Macroscale, Nanoscale, and Symbolic Representations

The figure shows a sample of water boiling. In spaces labeled A, indicate whether the macroscale or the nanoscale is represented. In spaces labeled B, draw the molecules that would be present with appropriate distances between them. One of the circles represents a bubble of gas within the liquid. The other represents the liquid. In space C, write a symbolic representation of the boiling process.

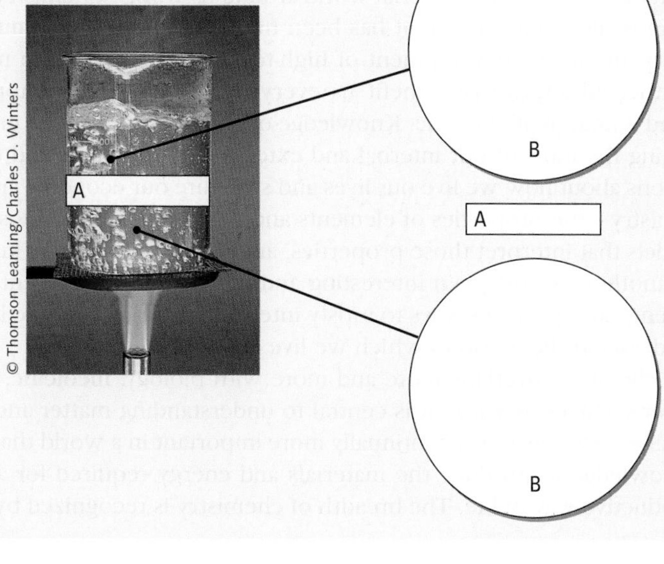

© Thomson Learning/Charles D. Winters

Answer

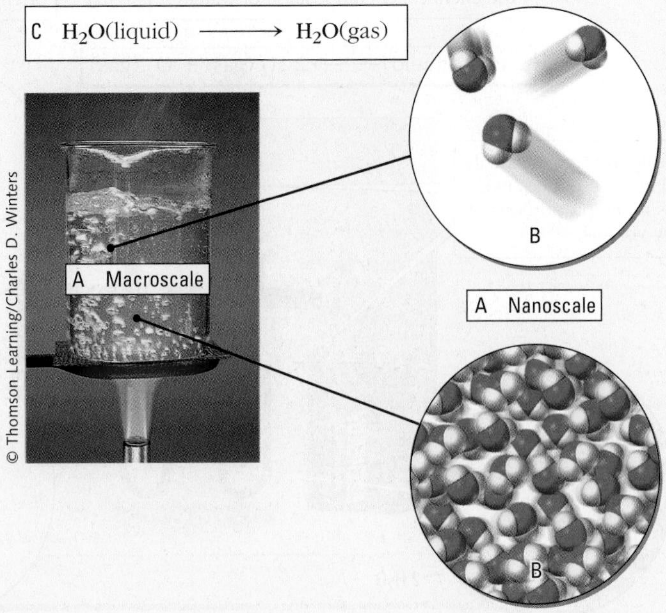

Explanation Each water molecule consists of two hydrogen atoms and one oxygen atom. In liquid water the molecules are close together and oriented in various directions. In a bubble of gaseous water the molecules are much farther apart—there are fewer of them per unit volume. The symbolic representation is the equation

$$H_2O(\text{liquid}) \longrightarrow H_2O(\text{gas})$$

PROBLEM-SOLVING PRACTICE 1.3

Draw a nanoscale representation and a symbolic representation for both allotropes of oxygen. Describe the properties of each allotrope at the macroscale.

1.12 Modern Chemical Sciences

Our goal in this chapter has been to make clear many of the reasons you should care about chemistry. Chemistry is fundamental to understanding many other sciences and to understanding how the material world around us works. Chemistry provides a unique, nanoscale perspective that has been highly successful in stimulating scientific inquiry and in the development of high-tech materials, modern medicines, and many other advances that benefit us every day. Chemistry is happening all around us and within us all the time. Knowledge of chemistry is a key to understanding and making the most of our internal and external environments and to making better decisions about how we live our lives and structure our economy and society. Finally, chemistry—the properties of elements and compounds, the nanoscale theories and models that interpret those properties, and the changes of one kind of substance into another—is just plain interesting and fun. Chemistry presents an intellectual challenge and provides ways to satisfy intellectual curiosity while helping us to better understand the world in which we live.

Modern chemistry overlaps more and more with biology, medicine, engineering, and other sciences. Because it is central to understanding matter and its transformations, chemistry becomes continually more important in a world that relies on chemical knowledge to produce the materials and energy required for a comfortable and productive way of life. The breadth of chemistry is recognized by the term *chemical sciences*, which includes chemistry, chemical engineering, chemical biology, materials chemistry, industrial chemistry, environmental chemistry, medicinal chemistry, and many other fields. Practitioners of the chemical sciences produce new plastics, medicines, superconductors, composite materials, and electronic devices. The chemical sciences enable better understanding of the mechanisms of biological processes, how proteins function, and how to imitate the action of organisms that carry out important functions. The chemical sciences enable us to measure tiny concentrations of substances, separate one substance from another, and determine whether a given substance is helpful or harmful to humans. Practitioners of the chemical sciences create new industrial processes and products that are less hazardous, produce less pollution, and generate smaller quantities of wastes. The enthusiasm of chemists for research in all of these areas and the many discoveries that are made every day offer ample evidence that chemistry is an energetic and exciting science. We hope that this excitement is evident in this chapter and in the rest of the book.

Near the beginning of this chapter we listed questions you may have wondered about that will be answered in this book. More important by far, however, are questions that chemists or other scientists cannot yet answer. Here are some big challenges for chemists of the future, as envisioned by a blue-ribbon panel of experts convened by the U.S. National Academies of Science, Engineering, and Medicine.

The report "Beyond the Molecular Frontier: Challenges for Chemistry and Chemical Engineering" was published in 2003. It is available from the National Academies Press, **http://www.nap.edu/catalog/10633.html**.

- How can chemists design and synthesize new substances with well-defined properties that can be predicted ahead of time? Example substances are medicines, electronic devices, composite materials, and polymeric plastics.
- How can chemists learn from nature to produce new substances efficiently and use biological processes as models for industrial production? An example is extracting a compound from the English yew and then processing it chemically to produce paclitaxel.
- How can chemists design mixtures of molecules that will assemble themselves into useful, more complex structures? Such self-assembly processes, in which each different molecule falls of its own accord into the right place, could be used to create a variety of new nanostructures.
- How can chemists learn to measure more accurately how much of a substance is there, determine the substance's properties, and predict how long it will last? Sensors are now being invented that combine chemical and biological processes to allow rapid, accurate determination of composition and structure.
- How can chemists devise better theories that will predict more accurately the behavior of molecules and of large collections of molecules?
- How can chemists devise new ways of making large quantities of materials without significant negative consequences for Earth's environment and the many species that inhabit our planet?
- How can chemists use improved knowledge of the molecular structures of genes and proteins to create new medicines and therapies to deal with viral diseases such as AIDS; major killers such as cancer, stroke, and heart disease; and psychological problems?
- How can chemists find alternatives to fossil fuels, avoid global warming, enable mobility for all without polluting the planet, and make use of the huge quantities of solar energy that are available?
- How can chemists contribute to national and global security?
- How can chemists improve the effectiveness of education, conveying chemical knowledge to the many students and others who can make use of it in their chosen fields?

A major goal of the authors of this book is to help you along the pathway to becoming a scientist. We encourage you to choose one of the preceding problems and devote your life's work to finding new approaches and useful solutions to it. The future of our society depends on it!

ThomsonNOW
Sign in to ThomsonNOW at **www.thomsonedu.com** to check your readiness for an exam by taking the Pre-Test and exploring the modules recommended in your Personalized Learning Plan.

IN CLOSING

Having studied this chapter, you should be able to . . .

- Appreciate the power of chemistry to answer intriguing questions (Section 1.1).
- Describe the approach used by scientists in solving problems (Sections 1.2, 1.3).
- Understand the differences among a hypothesis, a theory, and a law (Section 1.3).
- Define quantitative and qualitative observations (Section 1.3). ThomsonNOW homework: Study Question 13
- Identify the physical properties of matter or physical changes occurring in a sample of matter (Section 1.4). ThomsonNOW homework: Study Questions 21, 24
- Estimate Celsius temperatures for commonly encountered situations (Section 1.4).
- Calculate mass, volume, or density, given any two of the three (Section 1.4).
- Identify the chemical properties of matter or chemical changes occurring in a sample of matter (Section 1.5). ThomsonNOW homework: Study Question 29
- Explain the difference between homogeneous and heterogeneous mixtures (Section 1.6). ThomsonNOW homework: Study Question 41
- Describe the importance of separation, purification, and analysis (Section 1.6).
- Understand the difference between a chemical element and a chemical compound (Sections 1.7, 1.9). ThomsonNOW homework: Study Questions 37, 39
- Classify matter (Section 1.7, Figure 1.13). ThomsonNOW homework: Study Question 41
- Describe characteristic properties of the three states of matter—gases, liquids, and solids (Section 1.8).
- Identify relative sizes at the macroscale, microscale, and nanoscale levels (Section 1.8).
- Describe the kinetic-molecular theory at the nanoscale level (Section 1.8).
- Use the postulates of modern atomic theory to explain macroscopic observations about elements, compounds, conservation of mass, constant composition, and multiple proportions (Section 1.9). ThomsonNOW homework: Study Questions 52, 58, 63, 71
- Distinguish metals, nonmetals, and metalloids according to their properties (Section 1.10). ThomsonNOW homework: Study Questions 61, 63, 87
- Identify elements that consist of molecules, and define allotropes (Section 1.10).
- Distinguish among macroscale, nanoscale, and symbolic representations of substances and chemical processes (Section 1.11).

KEY TERMS

The following terms were defined and given in boldface type in this chapter. Be sure to understand each of these terms and the concepts with which they are associated. (The number of the section where each term is introduced is given in parentheses.)

allotrope *(1.10)*
atom *(1.9)*
atomic theory *(1.9)*
boiling point *(1.4)*
Celsius temperature scale *(1.4)*
chemical change *(1.5)*
chemical compound *(1.7)*
chemical element *(1.7)*
chemical formula *(1.10)*
chemical property *(1.5)*
chemical reaction *(1.5)*
chemistry *(1.1)*

conservation of mass, law of *(1.9)*
constant composition, law of *(1.9)*
conversion factor *(1.4)*
density *(1.4)*
diatomic molecule *(1.10)*
dimensional analysis *(1.4)*
energy *(1.5)*
gas *(1.8)*
heterogeneous mixture *(1.6)*
homogeneous mixture *(1.6)*
hypothesis *(1.3)*
kinetic-molecular theory *(1.8)*
law *(1.3)*
liquid *(1.8)*
macroscale *(1.8)*
matter *(1.1)*
melting point *(1.4)*
metal *(1.10)*
metalloid *(1.10)*
microscale *(1.8)*
model *(1.3)*
molecule *(1.10)*
multiple proportions, law of *(1.9)*
nanoscale *(1.8)*
nonmetal *(1.10)*
physical changes *(1.4)*
physical properties *(1.4)*
product *(1.5)*
proportionality factor *(1.4)*
qualitative *(1.3)*
quantitative *(1.3)*
reactant *(1.5)*
solid *(1.8)*
solution *(1.6)*
substance *(1.4)*
temperature *(1.4)*
theory *(1.3)*

QUESTIONS FOR REVIEW AND THOUGHT

■ denotes questions available in ThomsonNOW and assignable in OWL.

Blue-numbered questions have short answers at the back of this book and fully worked solutions in the *Student Solutions Manual.*

ThomsonNOW™
Assess your understanding of this chaper's topics with sample tests and other resources found by signing in to ThomsonNOW at **www.thomsonedu.com**.

Review Questions

These questions test vocabulary and simple concepts.

1. What is meant by the structure of a molecule? Why are molecular structures important?
2. Why is it often important to know the structure of an enzyme? How can knowledge of enzyme structures be useful in medicine?
3. Choose an object in your room, such as a CD player or television set. Write down five qualitative observations and five quantitative observations regarding the object you chose.
4. What are three important characteristics of a scientific law? Name two laws that were mentioned in this chapter. State each of the laws that you named.
5. How does a scientific theory differ from a law? How are theories and models related?
6. When James Snyder proposed on the basis of molecular models that paclitaxel assumes the shape of a letter T when attached to tubulin, was this a theory or a hypothesis?
7. What is the unique perspective that chemists use to make sense out of the material world? Give at least one example of how that perspective can be applied to a significant problem.
8. Give two examples of situations in which purity of a chemical substance is important.

Topical Questions

These questions are keyed to the major topics in the chapter. Usually a question that is answered at the end of this book is paired with a similar one that is not.

Why Care About Chemistry?

9. Make a list of at least four issues faced by our society that require scientific studies and scientific data before a democratic society can make informed, rational decisions. Exchange lists with another student and evaluate the quality of each other's choices.
10. Make a list of at least four questions you have wondered about that may involve chemistry. Compare your list with a list from another student taking the same chemistry course. Evaluate the quality of each other's questions and decide how "chemical" they are.

How Science Is Done

11. Identify the information in each sentence as qualitative or quantitative.
    (a) The element gallium melts at 29.8 °C.
    (b) A chemical compound containing cobalt and chlorine is blue.
    (c) Aluminum metal is a conductor of electricity.
    (d) The chemical compound ethanol boils at 79 °C.
    (e) A chemical compound containing lead and sulfur forms shiny, plate-like, yellow crystals.
12. Make as many qualitative and quantitative observations as you can regarding what is shown in the photograph.

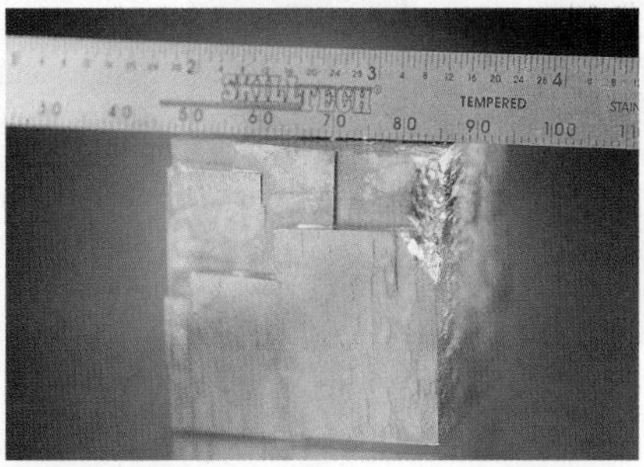

© Thomson Learning/Charles D. Winters

13. ■ Which of these statements are qualitative? Which are quantitative? Explain your choice in each case.
    (a) Sodium is a silvery-white metal.
    (b) Aluminum melts at 660 °C.
    (c) Carbon makes up about 23% of the human body by mass.
    (d) Pure carbon occurs in different forms: graphite, diamond, and fullerenes.
14. Which of the these statements are qualitative? Which are quantitative? Explain your choice in each case.
    (a) The atomic mass of carbon is 12.011 amu (atomic mass units).
    (b) Pure aluminum is a silvery-white metal that is nonmagnetic, has a low density, and does not produce sparks when struck.
    (c) Sodium has a density of 0.968 g/mL.
    (d) In animals the sodium cation is the main extracellular cation and is important for nerve function.

Identifying Matter: Physical Properties

15. The elements sulfur and bromine are shown in the photograph. Based on the photograph, describe as many properties of each sample as you can. Are any properties the same? Which properties are different?

© Thomson Learning/Charles D. Winters

Sulfur and bromine. The sulfur is on the flat dish; the bromine is in a closed flask supported on a cork ring.

16. In the accompanying photo, you see a crystal of the mineral calcite surrounded by piles of calcium and carbon, two of the elements that combine to make the mineral. (The other element combined in calcite is oxygen.) Based on the photo, describe some of the physical properties of the elements and the mineral. Are any properties the same? Are any properties different?

© Thomson Learning/Charles D. Winters

Calcite (the transparent, cube-like crystal) and two of its constituent elements, calcium (chips) and carbon (black grains). The calcium chips are covered with a thin film of calcium oxide.

17. The boiling point of a liquid is 20 °C. If you hold a sample of the substance in your hand, will it boil? Explain briefly.
18. Dry Ice (solid carbon dioxide) sublimes (changes from solid to gas without forming liquid) at −78.6 °C. Suppose you had a sample of gaseous carbon dioxide and the temperature was 30 degrees Fahrenheit below zero (a very cold day). Would solid carbon dioxide form? Explain briefly how you answered the question.
19. ■ Which temperature is higher?
    (a) 20 °C or 20 °F
    (b) 100 °C or 180 °F
    (c) 60 °C or 100 °F
    (d) −12 °C or 20 °F
20. These temperatures are measured at various locations during the same day in the winter in North America: −10 °C at Montreal, 28 °F at Chicago, 20 °C at Charlotte, and 40 °F at Philadelphia. Which city is the warmest? Which city is the coldest?
21. ■ A 105.5-g sample of a metal was placed into water in a graduated cylinder, and it completely submerged. The water level rose from 25.4 mL to 37.2 mL. Use data in Table 1.1 to identify the metal.
22. An irregularly shaped piece of lead weighs 10.0 g. It is carefully lowered into a graduated cylinder containing 30.0 mL of ethanol, and it sinks to the bottom of the cylinder. To what volume reading does the ethanol rise?
23. An unknown sample of a metal is 1.0 cm thick, 2.0 cm wide, and 10.0 cm long. Its mass is 54.0 g. Use data in Table 1.1 to identify the metal. (Remember that 1 cm^3 = 1 mL.)
24. ■ Calculate the volume of a 23.4-g sample of bromobenzene.
25. Calculate the mass of the sodium chloride crystal in the photo that accompanies Question 45 if the dimensions of the crystal are 10 cm thick by 12 cm long by 15 cm wide. (Remember that 1 cm^3 = 1 mL.)
26. Find the volume occupied by a 4.33-g sample of benzene.

Chemical Changes and Chemical Properties

27. In each case, identify the underlined property as a physical or chemical property. Give a reason for your choice.
    (a) The normal color of the element bromine is red-orange.
    (b) Iron is transformed into rust in the presence of air and water.
    (c) Dynamite can explode.
    (d) Aluminum metal, the shiny "foil" you use in the kitchen, melts at 660 °C.
28. In each case, identify the underlined property as a physical or a chemical property. Give a reason for your choice.
    (a) Dry Ice sublimes (changes directly from a solid to a gas) at −78.6 °C.
    (b) Methanol (methyl alcohol) burns in air with a colorless flame.
    (c) Sugar is soluble in water.
    (d) Hydrogen peroxide, H_2O_2, decomposes to form oxygen, O_2, and water, H_2O.
29. ■ In each case, describe the change as a chemical or physical change. Give a reason for your choice.
    (a) A cup of household bleach changes the color of your favorite T-shirt from purple to pink.

(b) The fuels in the space shuttle (hydrogen and oxygen) combine to give water and provide the energy to lift the shuttle into space.
(c) An ice cube in your glass of lemonade melts.

30. In each case, describe the change as a chemical or physical change. Give a reason for your choice.
(a) Salt dissolves when you add it to water.
(b) Food is digested and metabolized in your body.
(c) Crystalline sugar is ground into a fine powder.
(d) When potassium is added to water there is a purplish-pink flame and the water becomes basic (alkaline).

31. In each situation, decide whether a chemical reaction is releasing energy and causing work to be done, or whether an outside source of energy is forcing a chemical reaction to occur.
(a) Your body converts excess intake of food into fat molecules.
(b) Sodium reacts with water as shown in Figure 1.5.
(c) Sodium azide in an automobile air bag decomposes, causing the bag to inflate.
(d) An egg is hard-boiled in a pan on your kitchen stove.

32. While camping in the mountains you build a small fire out of tree limbs you find on the ground near your campsite. The dry wood crackles and burns brightly and warms you. Before slipping into your sleeping bag for the night, you put the fire out by dousing it with cold water from a nearby stream. Steam rises when the water hits the hot coals. Describe the physical and chemical changes in this scene.

Classifying Matter: Substances and Mixtures

33. Small chips of iron are mixed with sand (see photo). Is this a homogeneous or heterogeneous mixture? Suggest a way to separate the iron and sand from each other.

© Thomson Learning/Charles D. Winters

Layers of sand, iron, and sand.

34. Suppose that you have a solution of sugar in water. Is this a homogeneous or heterogeneous mixture? Describe an experimental procedure by which you can separate the two substances.

35. Identify each of these as a homogeneous or a heterogeneous mixture.
(a) Vodka
(b) Blood
(c) Cowhide
(d) Bread

36. Identify each of these as a homogeneous or a heterogeneous mixture.
(a) An asphalt (blacktop) road
(b) Clear ocean water
(c) Iced tea with ice cubes
(d) Filtered apple cider

Classifying Matter: Elements and Compounds

37. ■ For each of the changes described, decide whether two or more elements formed a compound or if a compound decomposed (to form elements or other compounds). Explain your reasoning in each case.
(a) Upon heating, a blue powder turned white and lost mass.
(b) A white solid forms three different gases when heated. The total mass of the gases is the same as that of the solid.

38. For each of the changes described, decide whether two or more elements formed a compound or if a compound decomposed (to form elements or other compounds). Explain your reasoning in each case.
(a) After a reddish-colored metal is placed in a flame, it turns black and has a higher mass.
(b) A white solid is heated in oxygen and forms two gases. The mass of the gases is the same as the masses of the solid and the oxygen.

39. Classify each of these with regard to the type of matter (element, compound, heterogeneous mixture, or homogeneous mixture). Explain your choice in each case.
(a) A piece of newspaper
(b) Solid, granulated sugar
(c) Freshly squeezed orange juice
(d) Gold jewelry

40. Classify each of these with regard to the type of matter (element, compound, heterogeneous mixture, or homogeneous mixture). Explain your choice in each case.
(a) A cup of coffee
(b) A soft drink such as a Coke or Pepsi
(c) A piece of Dry Ice (a solid form of carbon dioxide)

41. ■ Classify each of these as an element, a compound, a heterogeneous mixture, or a homogeneous mixture. Explain your choice in each case.
(a) Chunky peanut butter
(b) Distilled water
(c) Platinum
(d) Air

42. Classify each of these as an element, a compound, a heterogeneous mixture, or a homogeneous mixture. Explain your choice in each case.
(a) Table salt (sodium chloride)
(b) Methane (which burns in pure oxygen to form only carbon dioxide and water)
(c) Chocolate chip cookie
(d) Silicon

43. A black powder is placed in a long glass tube. Hydrogen gas is passed into the tube so that the hydrogen sweeps out all other gases. The powder is then heated with a Bunsen burner. The powder turns red-orange, and water vapor can be seen condensing at the unheated far end of the tube. The red-orange color remains after the tube cools.
(a) Was the original black substance an element? Explain briefly.
(b) Is the new red-orange substance an element? Explain briefly.

44. A finely divided black substance is placed in a glass tube filled with air. When the tube is heated with a Bunsen burner, the black substance turns red-orange. The total mass of the red-orange substance is greater than that of the black substance.
   (a) Can you conclude that the black substance is an element? Explain briefly.
   (b) Can you conclude that the red-orange substance is a compound? Explain briefly.

Nanoscale Theories and Models

45. ■ The accompanying photo shows a crystal of the mineral halite, a form of ordinary salt. Are these crystals at the macroscale, microscale, or nanoscale? How would you describe the shape of these crystals? What might this tell you about the arrangement of the atoms deep inside the crystal?

© Thomson Learning/Charles D. Winters

A halite (sodium chloride) crystal.

46. Galena, shown in the photo, is a black mineral that contains lead and sulfur. It shares its name with a number of towns in the United States; they are located in Alaska, Illinois, Kansas, Maryland, Missouri, and Ohio. How would you describe the shape of the galena crystals? What might this tell you about the arrangement of the atoms deep inside the crystal?

© Thomson Learning/Charles D. Winters

Black crystals of galena (lead sulfide).

47. The photograph shows the four-celled alga *Scenedesmus.* This image has been enlarged by a factor of 400. Are algae such as *Scenedesmus* at the macroscale, microscale, or nanoscale?

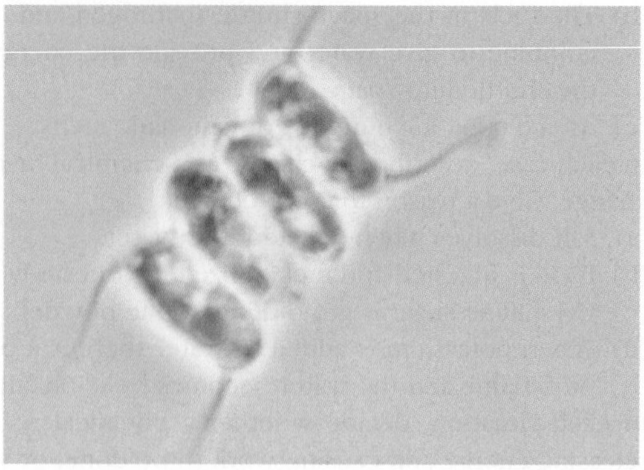
Pietro Pavone **pavone@dipbot.unict.it**

Scenedesmus.

48. The photograph shows an end-on view of tiny wires made from nickel metal by special processing. The scale bar is 1 μm long. Are these wires at the macroscale, microscale, or nanoscale?

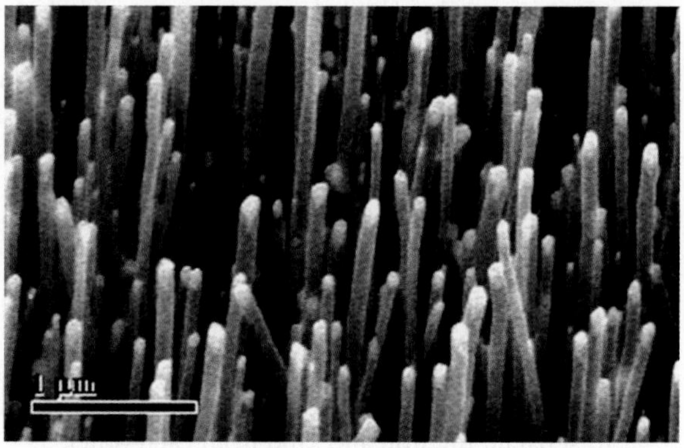
© Science VU/NASA/ARC/Visuals Unlimited

Nickel wires. (The scale bar is 1 μm long.)

49. When you open a can of soft drink, the carbon dioxide gas inside expands rapidly as it rushes from the can. Describe this process in terms of the kinetic-molecular theory.
50. After you wash your clothes, you hang them on a line in the sun to dry. Describe the change or changes that occur in terms of the kinetic-molecular theory. Are the changes that occur physical or chemical changes?
51. Sucrose has to be heated to a high temperature before it caramelizes. Use the kinetic-molecular theory to explain why sugar caramelizes only at high temperatures.
52. ■ Give a nanoscale interpretation of the fact that at the melting point the density of solid mercury is greater than the density of liquid mercury, and at the boiling point the density of liquid mercury is greater than the density of gaseous mercury.
53. ■ Make these unit conversions, using the prefixes in Table 1.2.
   (a) 32.75 km to meters
   (b) 0.0342 mm to nanometers
   (c) 1.21×10^{-12} km to micrometers
54. Make these unit conversions, using the prefixes in Table 1.2.
   (a) 0.00572 kg to grams
   (b) 8.347×10^{7} nL to liters
   (c) 423.7 g to kilograms

The Atomic Theory

55. Explain in your own words, by writing a short paragraph, how the atomic theory explains conservation of mass during a chemical reaction and during a physical change.
56. Explain in your own words, by writing a short paragraph, how the atomic theory explains constant composition of chemical compounds.
57. Explain in your own words, by writing a short paragraph, how the atomic theory predicts the law of multiple proportions.
58. ■ State the four postulates of the modern atomic theory.
59. State the law of multiple proportions in your own words.
60. The element chromium forms three different oxides (that contain only chromium and oxygen). The percentage of chromium (number of grams of chromium in 100 g of oxide) in these compounds is 52.0%, 68.4%, and 76.5%. Do these data conform to the law of multiple proportions? Explain why or why not.

The Chemical Elements

61. ■ Name and give the symbols for two elements that
    (a) Are metals
    (b) Are nonmetals
    (c) Are metalloids
    (d) Consist of diatomic molecules
62. ■ Name and give the symbols for two elements that
    (a) Are gases at room temperature
    (b) Are solids at room temperature
    (c) Do not consist of molecules
    (d) Have different allotropic forms

Communicating Chemistry: Symbolism

63. ■ Write a chemical formula for each substance, and draw a nanoscale picture of how the molecules are arranged at room temperature.
    (a) Water, a liquid whose molecules contain two hydrogen atoms and one oxygen atom each
    (b) Nitrogen, a gas that consists of diatomic molecules
    (c) Neon
    (d) Chlorine
64. Write a chemical formula for each substance and draw a nanoscale picture of how the molecules are arranged at room temperature.
    (a) Iodine, a solid that consists of diatomic molecules
    (b) Ozone
    (c) Helium
    (d) Carbon dioxide
65. Write a nanoscale representation and a symbolic representation and describe what happens at the macroscale when hydrogen reacts chemically with oxygen to form water vapor.
66. Write a nanoscale representation and a symbolic representation and describe what happens at the macroscale when carbon monoxide reacts with oxygen to form carbon dioxide.
67. Write a nanoscale representation and a symbolic representation and describe what happens at the macroscale when iodine sublimes (passes directly from solid to gas with no liquid formation) to form iodine vapor.
68. Write a nanoscale representation and a symbolic representation and describe what happens at the macroscale when bromine evaporates to form bromine vapor.

General Questions

These questions are not explicitly keyed to chapter topics; many require integration of several concepts.

69. Classify the information in each of these statements as quantitative or qualitative and as relating to a physical or chemical property.
    (a) A white chemical compound has a mass of 1.456 g. When placed in water containing a dye, it causes the red color of the dye to fade to colorless.
    (b) A sample of lithium metal, with a mass of 0.6 g, was placed in water. The metal reacted with the water to produce the compound lithium hydroxide and the element hydrogen.
70. Classify the information in each of these statements as quantitative or qualitative and as relating to a physical or chemical property.
    (a) A liter of water, colored with a purple dye, was passed through a charcoal filter. The charcoal adsorbed the dye, and colorless water came through. Later, the purple dye was removed from the charcoal and retained its color.
    (b) When a white powder dissolved in a test tube of water, the test tube felt cold. Hydrochloric acid was then added, and a white solid formed.
71. ■ The density of solid potassium is 0.86 g/mL. The density of solid calcium is 1.55 g/mL, almost twice as great. However, the mass of a potassium atom is only slightly less than the mass of a calcium atom. Provide a nanoscale explanation of these facts.
72. The density of gaseous helium at 25 °C and normal atmospheric pressure is 1.64×10^{-4} g/mL. At the same temperature and pressure the density of argon gas is 1.63×10^{-3} g/mL. The mass of an atom of argon is almost exactly ten times the mass of an atom of helium. Provide a nanoscale explanation of why the densities differ as they do.
73. Describe in your own words how different allotropic forms of an element are different at the nanoscale.
74. Most pure samples of metals are malleable, which means that if you try to grind up a sample of a metal by pounding on it with a hard object, the pieces of metal change shape but do not break apart. Solid samples of nonmetallic elements, such as sulfur or graphite, are often brittle and break into smaller particles when hit by a hard object. Devise a nanoscale theory about the structures of metals and nonmetals that can account for this difference in macroscale properties.

Applying Concepts

These questions test conceptual learning.

75. ■ Using Table 1.1, but without using your calculator, decide which has the larger mass:
    (a) 20. mL of butane or 20. mL of bromobenzene
    (b) 10. mL of benzene or 1.0 mL of gold
    (c) 0.732 mL of copper or 0.732 mL of lead

76. Using Table 1.1, but without using your calculator, decide which has the larger volume:
   (a) 1.0 g of ethanol or 1.0 g of bromobenzene
   (b) 10. g of aluminum or 12. g of water
   (c) 20 g of gold or 40 g of magnesium

77. ■ At 25 °C the density of water is 0.997 g/mL, whereas the density of ice at −10 °C is 0.917 g/mL.
   (a) If a plastic soft-drink bottle (volume = 250 mL) is completely filled with pure water, capped, and then frozen at −10 °C, what volume will the solid occupy?
   (b) What will the bottle look like when you take it out of the freezer?

78. When water alone (instead of engine coolant, which contains water and other substances) was used in automobile radiators to cool cast-iron engine blocks, it sometimes happened in winter that the engine block would crack, ruining the engine. Cast iron is not pure iron and is relatively hard and brittle. Explain in your own words how the engine block in a car might crack in cold weather.

79. Of the substances listed in Table 1.1, which would not float on liquid mercury? (Assume that none of the substances would dissolve in the mercury.)

80. Which of the substances in Figure 1.2 has the greatest density? Which has the lowest density?

81. Water does not dissolve in bromobenzene.
   (a) If you pour 2 mL of water into a test tube that contains 2 mL of bromobenzene, which liquid will be on top?
   (b) If you pour 2 mL of ethanol carefully into the test tube with bromobenzene and water described in part (a) without shaking or mixing the liquids, what will happen?
   (c) What will happen if you thoroughly stir the mixture in part (b)?

82. Water does not mix with either benzene or bromobenzene when it is stirred together with either of them, but benzene and bromobenzene do mix.
   (a) If you pour 2 mL of bromobenzene into a test tube, then add 2 mL of water and stir, what would the test tube look like a few minutes later?
   (b) Suppose you add 2 mL of benzene to the test tube in part (a), pouring the benzene carefully down the side of the tube so that the liquids do not mix together. Describe the appearance of the test tube now.
   (c) If the test tube containing all three liquids is thoroughly shaken and then allowed to stand for five minutes, what will the tube look like?

83. The figure shows a nanoscale view of the atoms of mercury in a thermometer registering 10 °C.

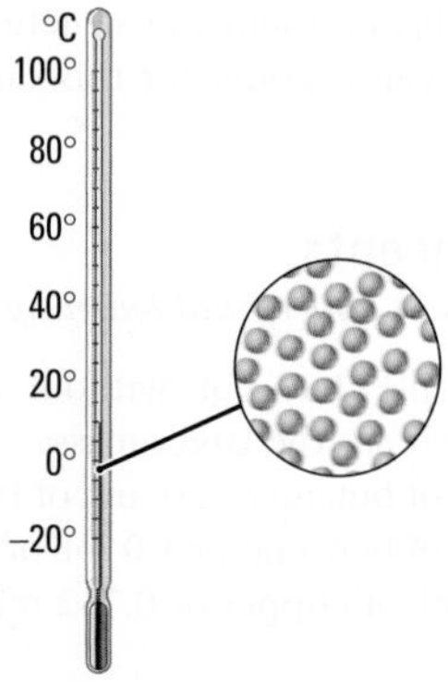

Which nanoscale drawing best represents the atoms in the liquid in this same thermometer at 90 °C? (Assume that the same volume of liquid is shown in each nanoscale drawing.)

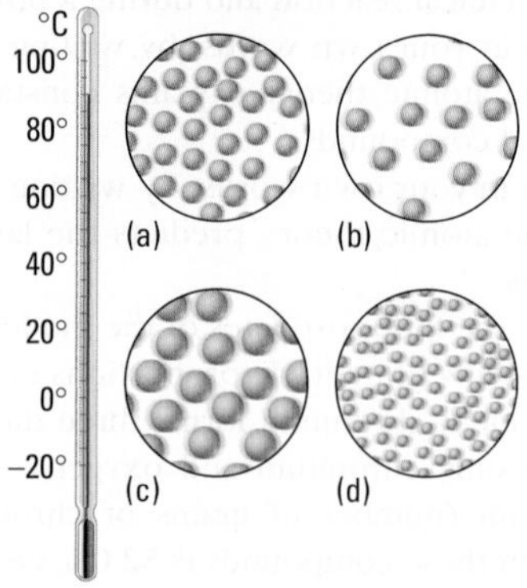

84. Answer these questions using figures (a) through (i). (Each question may have more than one answer.)

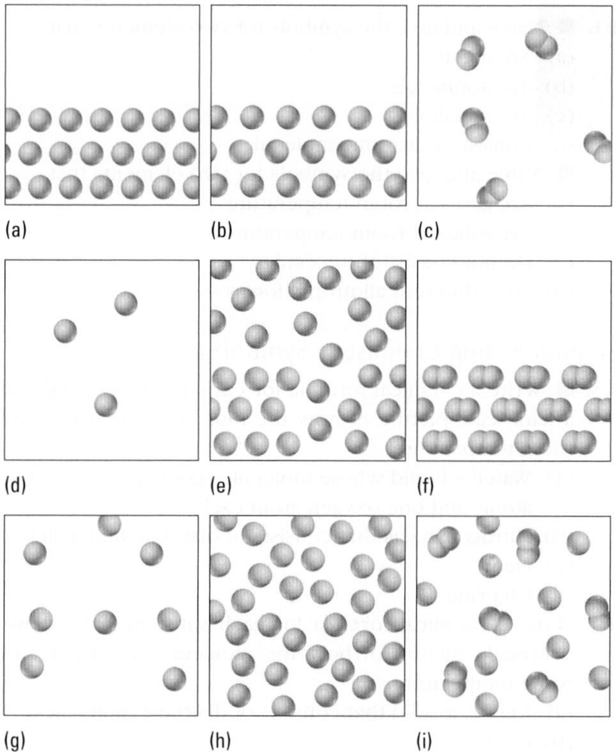

   (a) Which represents nanoscale particles in a sample of solid?
   (b) Which represents nanoscale particles in a sample of liquid?
   (c) Which represents nanoscale particles in a sample of gas?
   (d) Which represents nanoscale particles in a sample of an element?
   (e) Which represents nanoscale particles in a sample of a compound?
   (f) Which represents nanoscale particles in a sample of a pure substance?
   (g) Which represents nanoscale particles in a sample of a mixture?

More Challenging Questions

These questions require more thought and integrate several concepts.

85. ■ The element platinum has a solid-state structure in which platinum atoms are arranged in a cubic shape that repeats throughout the solid. If the length of an edge of the cube is 392 pm (1 pm = 1×10^{-12} m), what is the volume of the cube in cubic meters?

86. The compound sodium chloride has a solid-state structure in which there is a repeating cubic arrangement of sodium ions and chloride ions. If the volume of the cube is 1.81×10^{-22} cm^3, what is the length of an edge of the cube in pm (1 pm = 1×10^{-12} m)?

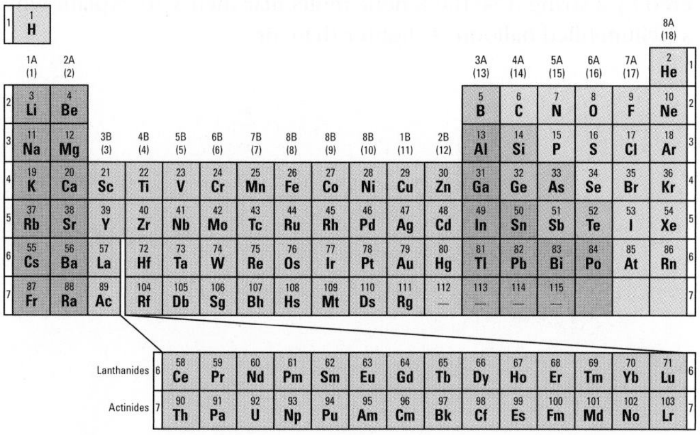

87. ■ The periodic table shown here is color coded gray, blue, orange, and lavender. Identify the color of the area (or colors of the areas) in which you would expect to find each type of element.
    (a) A metal
    (b) A nonmetal
    (c) A metalloid

88. The periodic table shown here is color coded gray, blue, orange, and lavender. Identify the color of the area (or colors of the areas) in which you would expect to find each type of element.
    (a) A shiny solid that conducts electricity
    (b) A gas whose molecules consist of single atoms
    (c) An element that is a semiconductor
    (d) A yellow solid that has very low electrical conductivity

89. ■ When someone discovers a new substance, it is relatively easy to show that the substance is not an element, but it is quite difficult to prove that the substance is an element. Explain why this is so, and relate your explanation to the discussion of scientific laws and theories in Section 1.3.

90. Soap can be made by mixing animal or vegetable fat with a concentrated solution of lye and heating it in a large vat. Suppose that 3.24 kg vegetable fat is placed in a large iron vat and then 50.0 L of water and 5.0 kg of lye (sodium hydroxide, NaOH) are added. The vat is placed over a fire and heated for two hours, and soap forms.
    (a) Classify each of the materials identified in the soap-making process as a substance or a mixture. For each substance, indicate whether it is an element or a compound. For each mixture, indicate whether it is homogeneous or heterogeneous.
    (b) Assuming that the fat and lye are completely converted into soap, what mass of soap is produced?
    (c) What physical and chemical processes occur as the soap is made?

91. The densities of several elements are given in Table 1.1.
    (a) Of the elements nickel, gold, lead, and magnesium, which will float on liquid mercury at 20 °C?
    (b) Of the elements titanium, copper, iron, and gold, which will float highest on the mercury? That is, which element will have the smallest fraction of its volume below the surface of the liquid?

92. You have some metal shot (small spheres like BBs), and you want to identify the metal. You have a flask that is known to contain exactly 100.0 mL when filled with liquid to a mark in the flask's neck. When the flask is filled with water at 20 °C, the mass of flask and water is 122.3 g. The water is emptied from the flask and 20 of the small spheres of metal are carefully placed in the flask. The 20 small spheres had a mass of 42.3 g. The flask is again filled to the mark with water at 20 °C and weighed. This time the mass is 159.9 g.
    (a) What metal is in the spheres? (Assume that the spheres are all the same and consist of pure metal.)
    (b) What volume would 500 spheres occupy?

93. Suppose you are trying to get lemon juice and you have no juicer. Some people say that you can get more juice from a lemon if you roll it on a hard surface, applying pressure with the palm of your hand before you cut it and squeeze out the juice. Others claim that you will get more juice if you first heat the lemon in a microwave and then cut and squeeze it. Apply the methods of science to arrive at a technique that will give the most juice from a lemon. Carry out experiments and draw conclusions based on them. Try to generate a hypothesis to explain your results.

94. If you drink orange juice soon after you brush your teeth, the orange juice tastes quite different. Apply the methods of science to find what causes this effect. Carry out experiments and draw conclusions based on them.

Media Questions

95. Find four articles, advertisements, or cartoons in a newspaper or magazine that are directly related to chemistry.

96. Find four Internet sites that are directly related to chemistry.

97. Search the Internet for sites related to nanoscale or nanotechnology. How many sites are available? Based on your search, is this a hot business area?

Conceptual Challenge Problems

These rigorous, thought-provoking problems integrate conceptual learning with problem solving and are suitable for group work.

CP1.A (Section 1.3) Some people use expressions such as "a rolling stone gathers no moss" and "where there is no light there is no life." Why do you believe these are "laws of nature"?

CP1.B (Section 1.3) Parents teach their children to wash their hands before eating. (a) Do all parents accept the germ theory of disease? (b) Are all diseases caused by germs?

CP1.C (Section 1.8) In Section 1.8 you read that, on an atomic scale, all matter is in constant motion. (For example, the average speed of a molecule of nitrogen or oxygen in the air is greater than 1000 miles per hour at room temperature.) (a) What evidence can you put forward that supports the kinetic-molecular theory? (b) Suppose you accept the notion that molecules of air are moving at speeds near 1000 miles per hour. What can you then reason about the paths that these molecules take when moving at this speed?

CP1.D (Section 1.8) Some scientists think there are living things smaller than bacteria (*New York Times,* January 18, 2000, p. D1). Called "nanobes," they are roughly cylindrical and range from 20 to 150 nm long and about 10 nm in diameter. One approach to determining whether nanobes are living is to estimate how many atoms and molecules could make up a nanobe. If the number is too small, then there would not be enough DNA, protein, and other biological molecules to carry out life processes. To test this method, estimate an upper limit for the number of atoms that could be in a nanobe. (Use a small atom, such as hydrogen.) Also estimate how many protein molecules could fit inside a nanobe. Do your estimates rule out the possibility that a nanobe could be living? Explain why or why not.

CP1.E (Section 1.12) The life expectancy of U.S. citizens in 1992 was 76 years. In 1916 the life expectancy was only 52 years. This is an increase of 46% in a lifetime. (a) Could this astonishing increase occur again? (b) To what single source would you attribute this noteworthy increase in life expectancy? Why did you identify this one source as being most influential?

CP1.F Helium-filled balloons rise and will fly away unless tethered by a string. Use the kinetic-molecular theory to explain why a helium-filled balloon is "lighter than air."

2 Atoms and Elements

The blue bumps making up the letters in the photograph are images of 112 individual CO molecules on a copper surface. Each letter is 4 nm high and 3 nm wide. The overall image was generated by a scanning tunneling microscope (STM), which can detect individual atoms or molecules, allowing us to make images of nanoscale atomic arrangements.

IBM Almaden Labs

ThomsonNOW
Throughout the text, this icon indicates an opportunity to test yourself on key concepts and to explore interactive modules by signing in to ThomsonNOW at **www.thomsonedu.com**.

To study chemistry, we need to start with atoms—the basic building blocks of matter. Early theories of the atom considered atoms to be indivisible, but we know now that this idea is wrong. Elements differ from one another because of differences in the internal structure of their atoms. Under the right conditions, smaller particles within atoms—known as *subatomic particles*—can be removed or rearranged. The term **atomic structure** refers to the identity and arrangement of these subatomic particles in the atom. An understanding of the details of atomic structure aids in the understanding of how atoms combine to form compounds and are rearranged in chemical reactions. Atomic structure also accounts for the properties of materials. The next few sections describe how experiments support the idea that atoms are composed of smaller (subatomic) particles.

2.1 Atomic Structure and Subatomic Particles

Electrical charges played an important role in many of the experiments from which the theory of atomic structure was derived. Two types of electrical charge exist: positive and negative. ***Electrical charges of the same type repel one another, and charges of the opposite type attract one another.*** A positively charged particle repels another positively charged particle. Likewise, two negatively charged particles repel each other. In contrast, two particles with opposite signs attract each other.

CONCEPTUAL EXERCISE 2.1 Electrical Charge

When you comb your hair on a dry day, your hair sticks to the comb. How could you explain this behavior in terms of a nanoscale model in which atoms contain positive and negative charges?

Radioactivity

In 1896, Henri Becquerel discovered that a sample of a uranium ore emitted rays that darkened a photographic plate, even though the plate was covered by a protective black paper. In 1898, Marie and Pierre Curie isolated the new elements polonium and radium, which emitted the same kind of rays. Marie suggested that atoms of such elements spontaneously emit these rays and named the phenomenon **radioactivity.**

Atoms of radioactive elements can emit three types of radiation: alpha (α), beta (β), and gamma (γ) rays. These radiations behave differently when passed between electrically charged plates (Figure 2.1). Alpha and beta rays are deflected, but gamma rays are not. These events occur because alpha rays and beta rays are composed of charged particles that come from within the radioactive atom. Alpha rays have a 2+ charge, and beta rays have a 1− charge. Alpha rays and beta rays are particles because they have mass—they are matter. In the experiment shown in Figure 2.1, alpha particles are deflected less and so must be heavier than beta particles. Gamma rays have no detectable charge or mass; they behave like light rays. If radioactive atoms can break apart to produce subatomic alpha and beta particles, then there must be something smaller inside the atoms.

Electrons

Further evidence that atoms are composed of subatomic particles came from experiments with specially constructed glass tubes called cathode-ray tubes. Most of the

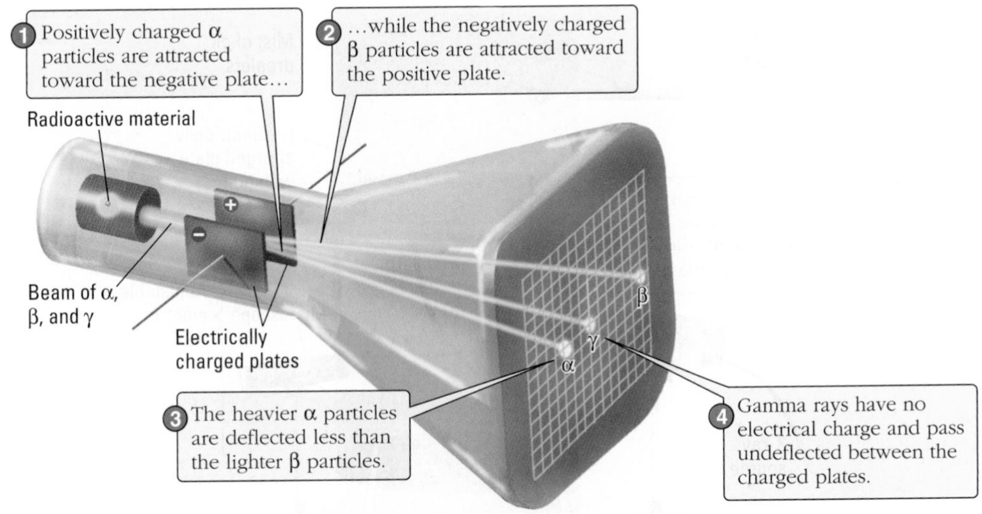

Figure 2.1 **The α, β, and γ rays from a radioactive sample are separated by an electrical field.**

air has been removed from these tubes and a metal electrode sealed into each end. When a sufficiently high voltage is applied to the electrodes, a beam of rays flows from the negatively charged electrode (the *cathode*) to the positively charged electrode (the *anode*). These rays, known as cathode rays, come directly from the metal atoms of the cathode. The cathode rays travel in straight lines, are attracted toward positively charged plates, can be deflected by a magnetic field, can cast sharp shadows, can heat metal objects red hot, and can cause gases and fluorescent materials to glow. When cathode rays strike a fluorescent screen, the energy transferred causes light to be given off as tiny flashes. Thus, the properties of a cathode ray are those of a beam of negatively charged particles, each of which produces a light flash when it hits a fluorescent screen. Sir Joseph John Thomson suggested that cathode rays consist of the same particles that had earlier been named **electrons** and had been suggested to be the carriers of electricity. He also observed that cathode rays were produced from electrodes made of different metals. This implied that electrons are constituents of the atoms of those elements.

ThomsonNOW™
Go to the Coached Problems menu for exercises on:

- **electric charge**
- **cathode rays**
- **Millikan's oil-drop experiment**

The deflection of cathode rays by charged plates is used to create the picture on a television screen or a computer monitor.

In 1897, Thomson used a specially designed cathode-ray tube to simultaneously apply electric and magnetic fields to a beam of cathode rays. By balancing the electric field against the magnetic field and using the basic laws of electricity and magnetism, Thomson calculated the *ratio* of mass to charge for the electrons in the cathode-ray beam: 5.60×10^{-9} grams per coulomb (g/C). (The coulomb, C, is a fundamental unit of electrical charge.)

Fourteen years later, Robert Millikan used a cleverly devised experiment to measure the charge of an electron (Figure 2.2). Tiny oil droplets were sprayed into a chamber. As they settled slowly through the air, the droplets were exposed to x-rays, which caused electrons to be transferred from gas molecules in the air to the droplets. Using a small microscope to observe individual droplets, Millikan adjusted the electrical charge of plates above and below the droplets so that the electrostatic attraction just balanced the gravitational attraction. In this way he could suspend a single droplet motionless. From equations describing these forces, Millikan calculated the charge on the suspended droplets. Different droplets had different charges, but Millikan found that each was an integer multiple of the smallest charge. The smallest charge was 1.60×10^{-19} C. Millikan assumed this to be the fundamental quantity of charge, the charge on an electron. Given this value and the mass-to-charge ratio determined by Thomson, the mass of an electron could be computed: $(1.60 \times 10^{-19}\ \text{C})(5.60 \times 10^{-9}\ \text{g/C}) = 8.96 \times 10^{-28}$ g. The currently accepted most

See Appendix A.2 for a review of scientific notation, which is used to represent very small or very large numbers as powers of 10. For example, 0.000001 is 1×10^{-6} (the decimal point moves six places to the left to give the −6 exponent) and 2,000,000 is 2×10^{6} (the decimal point moves six places to the right to give the +6 exponent).

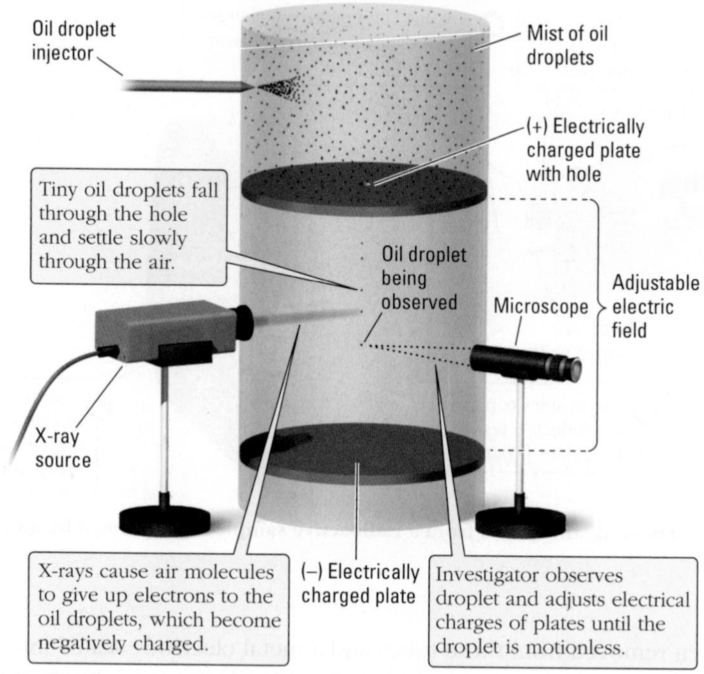

Figure 2.2 Millikan oil-drop experiment. From the known mass of the droplets and the applied voltage at which the charged droplets were held stationary, Millikan could calculate the charges on the droplets.

Electron
Charge = 1−
Mass = 9.1094×10^{-28} g

accurate value for the electron's mass is $9.1093826 \times 10^{-28}$ g, and the currently accepted most accurate value for the electron's charge in coulombs is $-1.60217653 \times 10^{-19}$ C. This quantity is called the *electronic charge.* For convenience, the charges on subatomic particles are given in multiples of electronic charge rather than in coulombs. So the charge on an electron is 1−.

Other experiments provided further evidence that the electron is a *fundamental* particle of matter; that is, it is present in *all* matter. The beta particles emitted by radioactive elements were found to have the same properties as cathode rays, which are streams of electrons.

Protons

When atoms lose electrons, the atoms become positively charged. When atoms gain electrons, the atoms become negatively charged. Such charged atoms, or similarly charged groups of atoms, are known as **ions.** From experiments with positive ions, formed by knocking electrons out of atoms, the existence of a positively charged, fundamental particle was deduced. Positively charged particles with different mass-to-charge ratios were formed by atoms of different elements. The variation in masses showed that atoms of different elements must contain different numbers of positive particles. Those from hydrogen atoms had the smallest mass-to-charge ratio, indicating that they are the fundamental positively charged particles of atomic structure. Such particles are called **protons.** The mass of a proton is known from experiment to be $1.67262129 \times 10^{-24}$ g, which is about 1800 times the mass of an electron. The charge on a proton is $1.602176462 \times 10^{-19}$ C, equal in size, but opposite in sign, to the charge on an electron. The proton's charge is represented by 1+. Thus, an atom that has lost two electrons has a charge of 2+.

As mass increases, mass-to-charge ratio increases for a given amount of charge. For a fixed charge, doubling the mass will double the mass-to-charge ratio. For a fixed mass, doubling the charge will halve the mass-to-charge ratio.

Proton
Charge = 1+
Mass = 1.6726×10^{-24} g

2.2 The Nuclear Atom

The Nucleus

Once it was known that there were subatomic particles, the next question scientists wanted to answer was, How are these particles arranged in an atom? During 1910 and 1911 Ernest Rutherford reported experiments (Figure 2.3) that led to a better understanding of atomic structure. Alpha particles (which have the same mass as helium atoms and a 2+ charge) were allowed to hit a very thin sheet of gold foil. Almost all of the alpha particles passed through undeflected. However, a very few alpha particles were deflected through large angles, and some came almost straight back toward the source. Rutherford described this unexpected result by saying, "It was about as credible as if you had fired a 15-inch [artillery] shell at a piece of paper and it came back and hit you."

ThomsonNOW
Go to the Coached Problems menu for an exercise on the **Rutherford experiment.**

The only way to account for the observations was to conclude that all of the positive charge and most of the mass of the atom are concentrated in a very small region (Figure 2.3). Rutherford called this tiny atomic core the **nucleus.** Only such a region could be sufficiently dense and highly charged to repel an alpha particle. From their results, Rutherford and his associates calculated values for the charge and radius of the gold nucleus. The currently accepted values are a charge of 79+ and a radius of approximately 1×10^{-13} cm. This makes the nucleus about 10,000 times *smaller* than the atom. Most of the volume of the atom is occupied by the electrons. Somehow the space outside the nucleus is occupied by the negatively charged electrons, but their arrangement was unknown to Rutherford and other scientists of the time. The arrangement of electrons in atoms is now well understood and is the subject of Chapter 7.

Alpha particles are four times heavier than the lightest atoms, which are hydrogen atoms.

In 1920 Ernest Rutherford proposed that the nucleus might contain an uncharged particle whose mass approximated that of a proton.

Neutrons

Atoms are electrically neutral (no net charge), so they must contain equal numbers of protons and electrons. However, most neutral atoms have masses greater than the sum of the masses of their protons and electrons. The additional mass indicates that

Neutron
Charge = 0
Mass = 1.6749×10^{-24} g

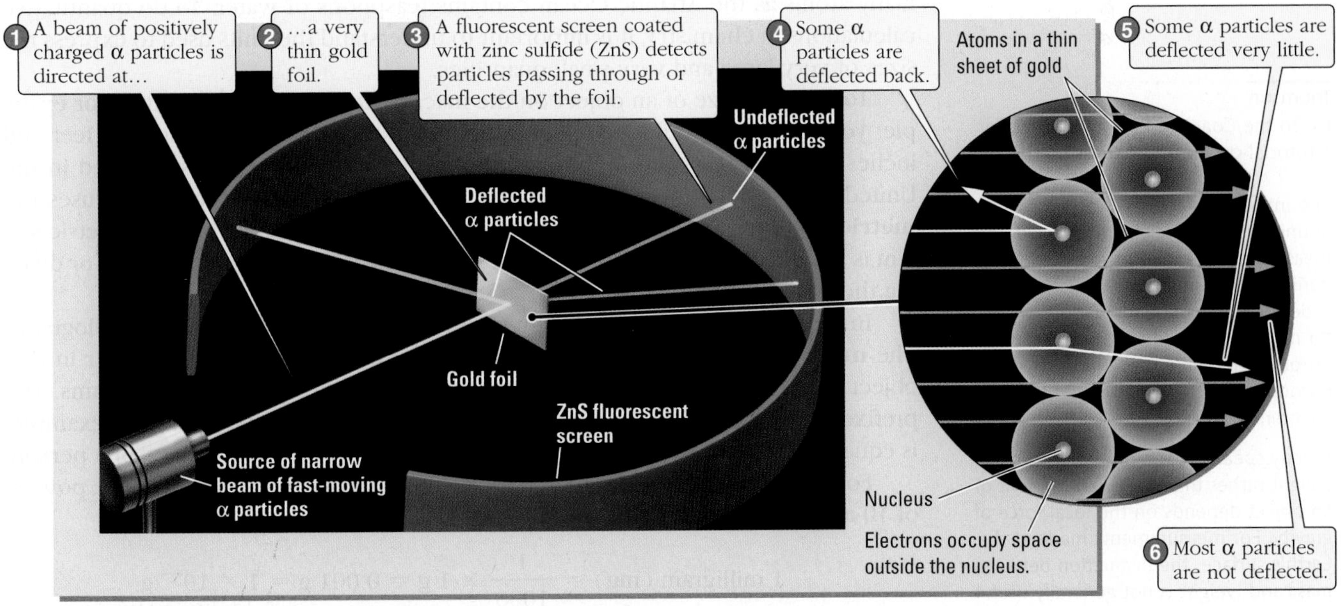

Figure 2.3 The Rutherford experiment and its interpretation.

Ernest Rutherford
1871–1937

Born on a farm in New Zealand, Rutherford earned his Ph.D. in physics from Cambridge University in 1895. He discovered alpha and beta radiation and coined the term "half-life." For proving that alpha radiation is composed of helium nuclei and that beta radiation consists of electrons, Rutherford received the Nobel Prize in chemistry in 1908. As a professor at Cambridge University, he guided the work of no fewer than ten future Nobel Prize recipients. Element 104 is named in Rutherford's honor.

subatomic particles with mass but no charge must also be present. Because they have no charge, these particles are more difficult to detect experimentally. In 1932 James Chadwick devised a clever experiment that detected the neutral particles by having them knock protons out of atoms and then detecting the protons. The neutral subatomic particles are called **neutrons.** They have no electrical charge and a mass of $1.67492728 \times 10^{-24}$ g, nearly the same as the mass of a proton.

In summary, there are three primary subatomic particles: protons, neutrons, and electrons.

- Protons and neutrons make up the nucleus, providing most of the atom's mass; the protons provide all of its positive charge.
- The nuclear radius is approximately 10,000 times smaller than the radius of the entire atom.
- Negatively charged electrons outside the nucleus occupy most of the volume of the atom, but contribute very little mass.
- A neutral atom has no net electrical charge because the number of electrons outside the nucleus equals the number of protons inside the nucleus.

To chemists, the electrons are the most important subatomic particles because they are the first part of the atom to contact another atom. The electrons in atoms largely determine how elements combine to form chemical compounds.

CONCEPTUAL EXERCISE 2.2 Describing Atoms

If an atom had a radius of 100 m, it would approximately fill a football stadium.
(a) What would the approximate radius of the nucleus of such an atom be?
(b) What common object is about that size?

2.3 The Sizes of Atoms and the Units Used to Represent Them

Atoms are extremely small. One teaspoon of water contains about three times as many atoms as the Atlantic Ocean contains teaspoons of water. To do quantitative calculations in chemistry, it is important to understand the units used to express the sizes of very large and very small quantities.

ThomsonNOW
Go to the Coached Problems menu for a tutorial on **metric system prefixes.**

The International System of units (or SI units) is the officially recognized measurement system of science. It is derived from the metric system and is described in Appendix B. The units for mass, length, and volume are introduced here. Other units are introduced as they are needed in later chapters.

Strictly speaking, the pound is a unit of weight rather than mass. The weight of an object depends on the local force of gravity. For measurements made at the Earth's surface, the distinction between mass and weight is not generally useful.

To state the size of an object on the macroscale in the United States (for example, yourself), we would give your weight in pounds and your height in feet and inches. Pounds, feet, and inches are part of the measurement system used in the United States, but almost nowhere else in the world. Most of the world uses the **metric system** of units for recording and reporting measurements. The metric system is a decimal system that adjusts the size of its basic units by multiplying or dividing them by multiples of 10.

In the metric system, your weight (really, your mass) would be given in kilograms. The **mass** of an object is a fundamental measure of the quantity of matter in that object. The metric units for mass are *grams* or multiples or fractions of grams. The prefixes listed in Table 2.1 are used with all metric units. A *kilo*gram, for example, is equal to 1000 grams and is a convenient size for measuring the mass of a person.

For objects much smaller than people, prefixes that represent negative powers of 10 are used. For example, 1 *milli*gram equals 1×10^{-3} g.

$$1 \text{ milligram (mg)} = \frac{1}{1000} \times 1 \text{ g} = 0.001 \text{ g} = 1 \times 10^{-3} \text{ g}$$

Table 2.1 Some Prefixes Used in the SI and Metric Systems

Prefix	Abbreviation	Meaning	Example
mega	M	10^6	1 megaton = 1×10^6 tons
kilo	k	10^3	1 kilometer (km) = 1×10^3 meter (m) 1 kilogram (kg) = 1×10^3 gram (g)
deci	d	10^{-1}	1 decimeter (dm) = 1×10^{-1} m 1 deciliter (dL) = 1×10^{-1} liter (L)
centi	c	10^{-2}	1 centimeter (cm) = 1×10^{-2} m
milli	m	10^{-3}	1 milligram (mg) = 1×10^{-3} g
micro	μ	10^{-6}	1 micrometer (μm) = 1×10^{-6} m
nano	n	10^{-9}	1 nanometer (nm) = 1×10^{-9} m 1 nanogram (ng) = 1×10^{-9} g
pico	p	10^{-12}	1 picometer (pm) = 1×10^{-12} m
femto	f	10^{-15}	1 femtogram (fg) = 1×10^{-15} g

Individual atoms are too small to be weighed directly; their masses can be measured only by indirect experiments. An atom's mass is on the order of 1×10^{-22} g. For example, a sample of copper that weighs one *nano*gram (1 ng = 1×10^{-9} g) contains about 9×10^{12} copper atoms. The most sensitive laboratory balances can weigh samples of about 0.0000001 g (1×10^{-7} g = 0.1 microgram, μg).

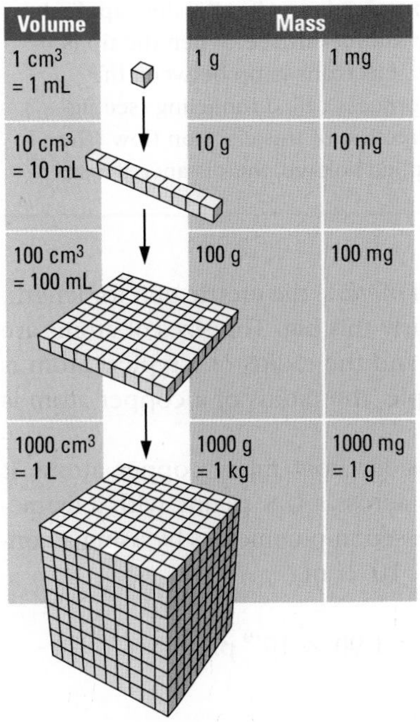

Relative sizes of mass and volume units.

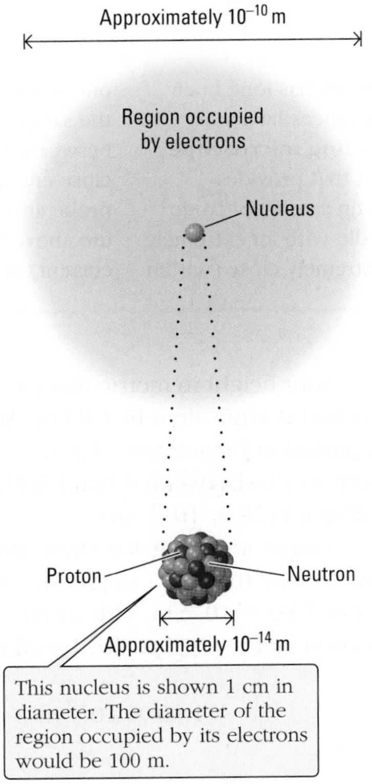

Relative sizes of the atomic nucleus and an atom (not to scale).

TOOLS OF CHEMISTRY

Scanning Tunneling Microscopy

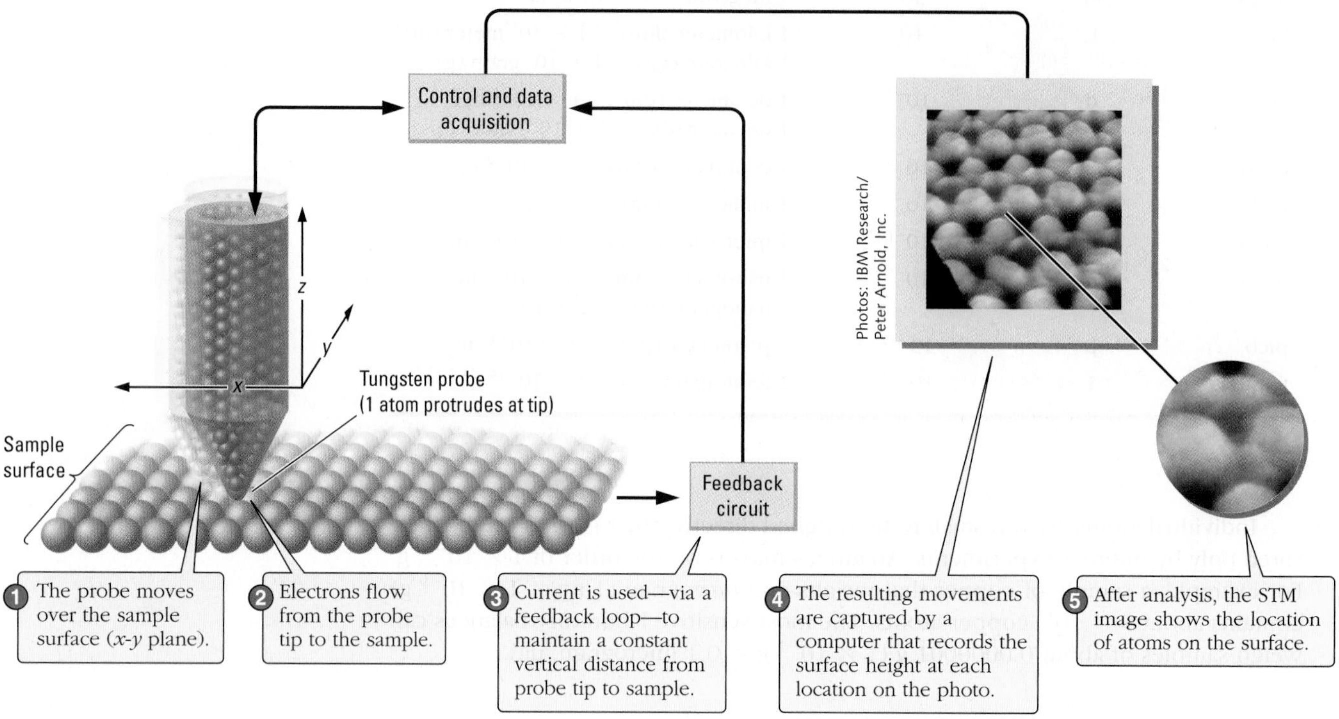

Schematic diagram of scanning tunneling microscopy.

The ability to image individual atoms directly has long been a dream of chemists, and instrumental advances have now fulfilled this dream. The **scanning tunneling microscope** (STM) is an exciting analytical instrument that provides images of individual atoms or molecules on a surface. To do this, a metal probe in the shape of a needle with an extremely fine point (a nanoscale tip) is brought extremely close (within one or two atomic diameters, a few tenths of a nanometer) to the sample surface being examined. A voltage is then applied between the probe and the sample surface. When the tip is close enough to the sample, electrons jump between the probe and the sample in a process called tunneling (see figure above). The size and direction of this electron flow (the current) depend on the applied voltage, the distance between

Your height in metric units would be given in *meters,* the metric unit for length. Six feet is equivalent to 1.83 m. Atoms aren't nearly this big. The sizes of atoms are reported in *pico*meters (1 pm = 1×10^{-12} m), and the radius of a typical atom is very small—between 30 and 300 pm. For example, the radius of a copper atom is 128 pm (128×10^{-12} m).

To get a feeling for these dimensions, consider how many copper atoms it would take to form a single file of copper atoms across a U.S. penny with a diameter of 1.90×10^{-2} m. This distance can be expressed in picometers by using a conversion factor (**p. 10**) based on 1 pm = 1×10^{-12} m.

Conversion factors are the basis for dimensional analysis, a commonly used problem-solving technique. It is described in detail in Appendix A.2.

$$1.90 \times 10^{-2}\ \cancel{\text{m}} \times \underbrace{\frac{1\ \text{pm}}{1 \times 10^{-12}\ \cancel{\text{m}}}}_{\text{conversion factor}} = 1.90 \times 10^{10}\ \text{pm}$$

Note that the units m (for meters) cancel, leaving the answer in pm, the units we want. A penny is 1.90×10^{10} pm in diameter.

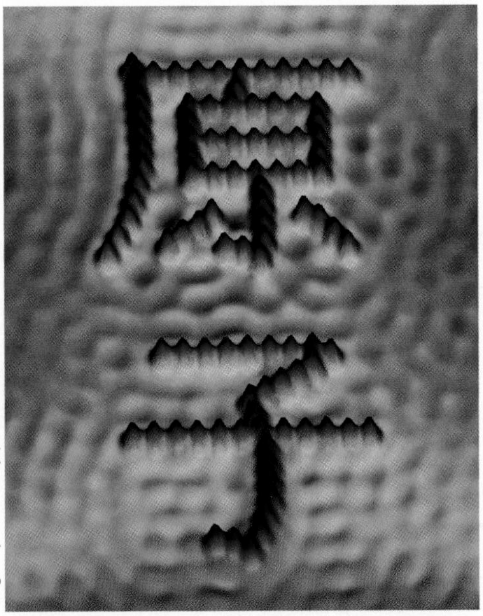
Image reproduced by permission of IBM Research, Almaden Research

An STM image of individual iron atoms arranged on a copper surface. The iron atoms form the Chinese characters for "atom."

probe tip and sample, and the identity and location of the nearest sample atom on the surface and its closest neighboring atoms.

The probe tip is attached to a control mechanism that maintains a constant distance between the tip and the sample at atomic-scale resolution by keeping the current constant. The current decreases exponentially as the distance between the probe tip and the sample increases, so the current provides an extremely sensitive measure of the interatomic separation between probe tip and sample. The probe tip is scanned laterally across the sample surface, and as necessary it moves toward or away from the sample to maintain the constant current. These movements toward or away from the sample are recorded to capture the surface height on an atomic scale.

The probe tip is moved systematically across the surface to form a complete topographic map of that part of the surface. The computer controlling the STM probe records the surface height at each location on the surface. The resulting topographic data are processed by software to form the final images that depict the surface contours. The STM image, which appears much like a photographic image, shows the locations of atoms on the surface being investigated. (The image is actually of the electrons on the atoms.) The height of each point on the surface is represented by the brightness of the image at that point. The figure on this page shows an STM image of a copper surface with a well-ordered array of iron atoms on it.

The STM has been applied to a wide variety of problems throughout science and engineering. The greatest number of studies have focused on the properties of clean surfaces that have been modified. Very high vacuums in the range of 1×10^{-10} mm Hg are necessary to allow study over a period of hours if contamination of the surface is to be avoided. The STM can also be used to study electrode surfaces in a liquid. Applications of STM and closely related techniques to biological molecules on surfaces represent another growing scientific area of research. The STM can be used to move atoms on a surface, and researchers have taken advantage of this capability to generate spectacular images such as the characters in the figure.

The scanning tunneling microscope was invented by Gerd Binnig and Heinrich Rohrer at IBM, Zurich, in 1981, and they shared a Nobel Prize in physics in 1986 for this work.

Every conversion factor can be used in two ways. We just converted meters to picometers by using

$$\frac{1 \text{ pm}}{1 \times 10^{-12} \text{ m}}$$

Picometers can be converted to meters by inverting this conversion factor:

$$8.70 \times 10^{10} \cancel{\text{pm}} \times \frac{1 \times 10^{-12} \text{ m}}{1 \cancel{\text{pm}}} = 8.70 \times 10^{-2} \text{ m} = 0.0870 \text{ m}$$

The number of copper atoms needed to stretch across a penny can be calculated by using a conversion factor linking the penny's diameter in picometers with the diameter of a single copper atom. The diameter of a Cu atom is twice the radius, 2×128 pm = 256 pm. Therefore, the conversion factor is 1 Cu atom per 256 pm, and

$$1.90 \times 10^{10} \cancel{\text{pm}} \times \frac{1 \text{ Cu atom}}{256 \cancel{\text{pm}}} = 7.42 \times 10^{7} \text{ Cu atoms, or } 74{,}200{,}000 \text{ Cu atoms}$$

Notice how "Cu atom" is included in the conversion to keep track of what kind of atom we are interested in.

Table 2.2 Some Common Unit Equalities*

Length	
1 kilometer	= 0.62137 mile
1 meter	= 100 centimeters
1 centimeter	= 10 millimeters
1 nanometer	= 1×10^{-9} meter
1 picometer	= 1×10^{-12} meter
1 inch	= 2.54 centimeters (exactly†)
1 angstrom (Å)	= 1×10^{-10} meter
Volume	
1 liter (L)	= 1×10^{-3} m^3 = 1000 cm^3
	= 1000 mL
	= 1.056710 quarts
1 gallon	= 4 quarts
1 quart	= 2 pints
1 cubic meter (m^3)	= 1×10^3 liter (L)
Mass	
1 kilogram	= 1000 grams
1 gram	= 1000 milligrams
1 amu	= 1.66054×10^{-24} grams
1 pound	= 453.59237 grams = 16 ounces
1 tonne (metric ton)	= 1000 kilograms
1 short ton (American)	= 2000 pounds

*See Appendix B for other unit equalities.
†This exact equality is important for length conversions.

Thus, it takes more than 74 million copper atoms to reach across the penny's diameter. Atoms are indeed tiny.

In chemistry, the most commonly used length units are the centimeter, the millimeter, the nanometer, and the picometer. The most commonly used mass units are the kilogram, gram, and milligram. The relationships among these units and some other units are given in Table 2.2.

Problem-Solving Examples 2.1 and 2.2 illustrate the use of dimensional analysis in unit conversion problems. Notice that in these examples, and throughout the book, the answers are given before the strategy and explanation of how the answers are found. We urge you to first try to answer the problem on your own. Then check to see if your answer is correct. If it does not match, try again. Finally, read the explanation, which generally also includes the strategy for solving the problem. If your answer is correct, but your reasoning differs from the explanation, you might have discovered an alternative way to solve the problem.

PROBLEM-SOLVING EXAMPLE 2.1 Conversion of Units

A medium-sized paperback book has a mass of 530 g. What is the book's mass in kilograms and in pounds?

Answer 0.530 kg and 1.17 lb

Strategy and Explanation Our strategy is to use conversion factors that relate what we know to what we are trying to calculate. For this problem, we use conversion factors derived from Table 2.2 and metric prefixes from Table 2.1 to calculate the answer, being sure to set up the calculation so that only the desired unit remains. The relationship between grams and kilograms is 1 kg = 10^3 g, so 530 g is

$$530 \text{ g} \times \frac{1 \text{ kg}}{10^3 \text{ g}} = 530 \times 10^{-3} \text{ kg} = 0.530 \text{ kg}$$

One pound equals 453.6 g, so we convert grams to pounds as follows:

$$530 \text{ g} \times \frac{1 \text{ lb}}{453.6 \text{ g}} = 1.17 \text{ lb}$$

✓ **Reasonable Answer Check** There are about 2.2 lb per kg, and the book's mass is about ½ kg. Thus its mass in pounds should be about 2.2/2 = 1.1, which is close to our more accurate answer.

On September 23, 1999, the NASA Mars Climate Orbiter spacecraft approached too close and burned up in Mars's atmosphere because of a navigational error due to a failed translation of English units into metric units by the spacecraft's software program.

PROBLEM-SOLVING PRACTICE 2.1

(a) If a car requires 10 gallons to fill its gas tank, how many liters would this be?
(b) An American football field is 100 yards long. How many meters is this?

PROBLEM-SOLVING EXAMPLE 2.2 Nanoscale Distances

The individual letters in the STM image shown as the Chapter Opener photograph are 4.0 nm high and 3.0 nm wide. How many letters could be fit in a distance of 1.00 mm (about the width of the head of a pin)?

Answer 3.3×10^5 letters

Strategy and Explanation Our strategy uses conversion factors to relate what we know to what we want to calculate. A nanometer is 1×10^{-9} m and a millimeter is 1×10^{-3} m. The width of a letter in meters is

$$3.0 \text{ nm} \times \frac{1 \times 10^{-9} \text{ m}}{1 \text{ nm}} = 3.0 \times 10^{-9} \text{ m}$$

Therefore, the number of 3.0-nm-wide letters that could fit into 1.00 mm is

$$1.0 \times 10^{-3} \text{ m} \times \frac{1 \text{ letter}}{3.0 \times 10^{-9} \text{ m}} = 3.3 \times 10^5 \text{ letters}$$

✓ **Reasonable Answer Check** If the letters are 3.0 nm wide, then about one third of 10^9 could fit into 1 m. One mm is 1/1000 of a meter, and multiplying these two estimates gives $(0.33 \times 10^9)(1/1000) = 0.33 \times 10^6$, which is another way of writing the answer we calculated.

PROBLEM-SOLVING PRACTICE 2.2

Do the following conversions using factors based on the equalities in Table 2.2.

(a) How many grams of sugar are in a 5-lb bag of sugar?
(b) Over a period of time, a donor gives 3 pints of blood. How many milliliters (mL) has the donor given?
(c) The same donor's 160-lb body contains approximately 5 L of blood. Considering that 1 L is nearly equal to 1 quart, estimate the percentage of the donor's blood that has been donated in all.

Table 2.2 also lists the liter (L) and milliliter (mL), which are the most common volume units of chemistry. There are 1000 mL in 1 L. One liter is a bit larger than a quart, and a teaspoon of water has a volume of about 5 mL. Chemists often use the terms *milliliter* and *cubic centimeter* (cc) interchangeably because they are equivalent (1 mL = 1 cm^3).

As illustrated in Problem-Solving Example 2.3, two or more steps of a calculation using dimensional analysis are best written in a single setup and entered into a calculator as a single calculation.

PROBLEM-SOLVING EXAMPLE 2.3 Volume Units

A chemist uses 50. μL (microliters) of a sample for her analysis. What is the volume in mL? In cm^3? In L?

Answer 5.0×10^{-2} mL; 5.0×10^{-2} cm^3; 5.0×10^{-5} L

Strategy and Explanation Use the conversion factors in Table 2.1 that involve micro and milli: 1 μL = 1×10^{-6} L and 1 L = 1000 mL. Multiply the conversion factors to cancel μL and L, leaving only mL.

$$50.\ \cancel{\mu L} \times \frac{1 \times 10^{-6}\ \cancel{L}}{1\ \cancel{\mu L}} \times \frac{10^3\ mL}{1\ \cancel{L}} = 5.0 \times 10^{-2}\ mL$$

Because 1 mL and 1 cm^3 are equivalent, the sample size can also be expressed as 5.0×10^{-2} cm^3. Since there are 1000 mL in 1 L, the sample size expressed in liters is 5.0×10^{-5} L.

✓ **Reasonable Answer Check** There is a conversion factor of 1000 between μL and mL, and the final answer is a factor of 1000 larger than the original volume, so the answer is reasonable.

PROBLEM-SOLVING PRACTICE 2.3

A patient's blood cholesterol level measures 165 mg/dL. Express this value in g/L.

© Thomson Learning/Charles D. Winters

Glassware for measuring the volume of liquids.

2.4 Uncertainty and Significant Figures

Measurements always include some degree of uncertainty, because we can never measure quantities exactly or know the value of a quantity with absolute certainty. Scientists have adopted standardized ways of expressing uncertainty in numerical results of measurements.

When the result of a measurement is expressed numerically, the final digit reported is uncertain. The digits we write down from a measurement—both the certain ones and the final, uncertain one—are called **significant figures.** For example, the number 5.025 has four significant figures and the number 4.0 has two significant figures.

To determine the number of significant figures in a measurement, read the number from left to right and count all digits, starting with the first digit that is not zero. All the digits in the number are significant except any zeros that are used only to position the decimal point.

In Section 2.5, we discuss the masses of atoms and begin calculating with numbers that involve uncertainty. Significant figures provide a simple means for keeping track of these uncertainties.

Example	Number of Significant Figures
1.23 g	3
0.00123 g	3; the zeros to the left of the 1 simply locate the decimal point. The number of significant figures is more obvious if you write numbers in scientific notation. Thus, 0.00123 = 1.23×10^{-3}.
2.0 g and 0.020 g	2; both have two significant figures. When a number is greater than 1, *all zeros to the right of the decimal point are significant.* For a number less than 1, only zeros to the right of the first significant figure are significant.
100 g	1; in numbers that do not contain a decimal point, trailing zeros may or may not be significant. To eliminate possible confusion, the practice followed in this book is to include a decimal point if the zeros are significant. Thus, 100. has three significant figures, while 100 has only one. Alternatively, we can write in scientific notation 1.00×10^2 (three significant figures) or 1×10^2 (one significant figure). For a number written in scientific notation, all digits are significant.

(continued on next page)

Example	Number of Significant Figures *(continued)*
100 cm/m	Infinite number of significant figures, because this is a defined quantity. There are *exactly* 100 centimeters in one meter.
$\pi = 3.1415926\ldots$	The value of π is known to a greater number of significant figures than any data you will ever use in a calculation.

PROBLEM-SOLVING EXAMPLE 2.4 Significant Figures

How many significant figures are present in each of these numbers?

(a) 0.0001171 m (b) 26.94 mL (c) 207 cm
(d) 0.7011 g (e) 0.0010 L (f) 12,400. s

Answer

(a) Four (b) Four (c) Three
(d) Four (e) Two (f) Five

Strategy and Explanation Apply the principles of significant figures given in the preceding examples.

(a) The leading zeros do not count, so there are four significant figures.
(b) All four of the digits are significant.
(c) All three digits are significant figures.
(d) Four digits follow the decimal, and all are significant figures.
(e) The leading zeros do not count, so there are two significant figures.
(f) Since there is a decimal point, all five of the digits are significant.

PROBLEM-SOLVING PRACTICE 2.4

Determine the number of significant figures in these numbers: (a) 0.00602 g; (b) 22.871 mg; (c) 344. °C; (d) 100.0 mL; (e) 0.00042 m; (f) 0.002001 L.

Significant Figures in Calculations

When numbers are combined in a calculation, the number of significant figures in the result is determined by the number of significant figures in the starting numbers and the nature of the arithmetic operation being performed.

Addition and Subtraction: *In addition or subtraction, the number of decimal places in the answer equals the number of decimal places in the number with the fewest decimal places.* Suppose you add these three numbers:

0.12	2 significant figures	2 decimal places
1.6	2 significant figures	1 decimal place
10.976	5 significant figures	3 decimal places
12.696 rounds to 12.7		

This sum should be reported as 12.7, a number with one decimal place, because 1.6 has only one decimal place.

Multiplication and Division: *In multiplication or division, the number of significant figures in the answer is the same as that in the quantity with the fewest significant figures.*

$$\frac{0.7608}{0.0546} = 13.9 \quad \text{or, in scientific notation, } 1.39 \times 10^1$$

The numerator, 0.7608, has four significant figures, but the denominator has only three, so the result must be reported with three significant figures.

Full Number	Number Rounded to Three Significant Digits
12.696	12.7
16.249	16.2
18.35	18.4
24.752	24.7
18.351	18.4

Rules for Rounding

The numerical result obtained in many calculations must be rounded to retain the proper number of significant figures. When you round a number to reduce the number of digits, follow these rules:

- The last digit retained is increased by 1 if the following digit is 5 or greater.
- The last digit retained is left unchanged if the following digit is less than 5.
- If the digit to be removed is 5, then the last digit retained is increased by 1 if the following digit is odd, and the last digit retained is left unchanged if the following digit is even.

One last word regarding significant figures, rounding, and calculations. In working problems on a calculator, you should do the calculation using all the digits allowed by the calculator and round only at the end of the problem. Rounding in the middle of a calculation sequence can introduce small errors that can accumulate later in the calculation. If your answers do not quite agree with those in the appendices of this book, this practice may be the source of the disagreement.

PROBLEM-SOLVING EXAMPLE 2.5 Rounding Significant Figures

Do these calculations and round the result to the proper number of significant figures.

(a) $15.80 + 0.0060 - 2.0 + 0.081$ (b) $\dfrac{55.0}{12.34}$

(c) $\dfrac{12.7732 - 2.3317}{5.007}$ (d) $2.16 \times 10^3 + 4.01 \times 10^2$

Answer

(a) 13.9 (b) 4.46 (c) 2.085 (d) 2.56×10^3

Strategy and Explanation In each case, the calculation is done with no rounding. Then the rules for rounding are applied to the answer.

(a) 13.887 is rounded to 13.9 with one decimal place because 2.0 has one decimal place.

(b) 4.457 is rounded to 4.46 with three significant figures just as in 55.0, which also has three significant figures.

(c) The number of significant figures in the result is governed by the least number of significant figures in the quotient. The denominator, 5.007, has four significant figures, so the calculator result, 2.08538 . . . , is properly expressed with four significant figures as 2.085.

(d) We change 4.01×10^2 to 0.401×10^3 and then sum 2.16×10^3 plus 0.401×10^3 and round to three significant figures to get 2.56×10^3.

PROBLEM-SOLVING PRACTICE 2.5

Do these calculations and round the result to the proper number of significant figures.

(a) $244.2 + 0.1732$ (b) 6.19×5.2222 (c) $\dfrac{7.2234 - 11.3851}{4.22}$

2.5 Atomic Numbers and Mass Numbers

Experiments done early in the 20th century found that *atoms of the same element have the same numbers of protons in their nuclei.* This number is called the **atomic number** and is given the symbol Z. In the periodic table on the inside front cover of this book, the atomic number for each element is written above the element's symbol. For example, a copper atom has a nucleus containing 29 protons, so its atomic number is 29 ($Z = 29$). A lead atom (Pb) has 82 protons in its nucleus, so the atomic number for lead is 82.

The periodic table is organized by atomic number; it is discussed in Section 2.9.

Each element has a unique atomic number.

The scale of atomic masses is defined relative to a standard, the mass of a carbon atom that has 6 protons and 6 neutrons in its nucleus. The masses of atoms of every other element are established relative to the mass of this carbon atom, which is defined as having a mass of exactly 12 atomic mass units. In terms of macroscale mass units, 1 **atomic mass unit (amu)** = 1.66054×10^{-24} g. For example, when an experiment shows that a gold atom, on average, is 16.4 times as massive as the standard carbon atom, we then know mass of the gold atom in amu and grams.

$$16.4 \times 12 \text{ amu} = 197 \text{ amu}$$

$$197 \cancel{\text{amu}} \times \frac{1.66054 \times 10^{-24} \text{ g}}{1 \cancel{\text{amu}}} = 3.27 \times 10^{-22} \text{ g}$$

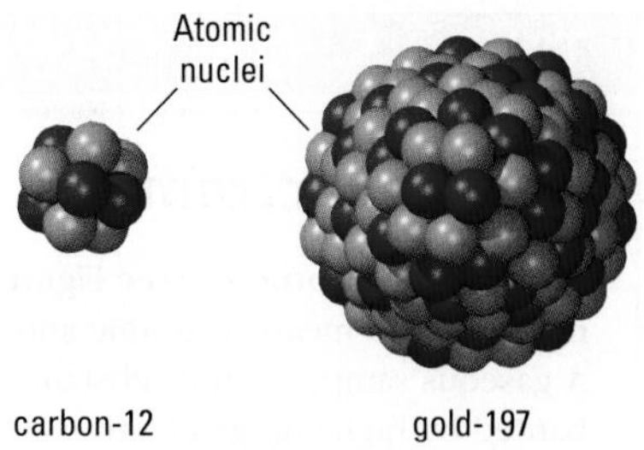

1 atomic mass unit (amu) = $\frac{1}{12}$ the mass of a carbon atom having 6 protons and 6 neutrons in the nucleus.

The masses of the fundamental subatomic particles in atomic mass units have been determined experimentally. The proton and the neutron have masses very close to 1 amu, whereas the electron's mass is approximately 1800 times smaller.

Particle	Mass (grams)	Mass (atomic mass units)	Charge
Electron	$9.1093826 \times 10^{-28}$	0.000548579	1−
Proton	$1.67262129 \times 10^{-24}$	1.00728	1+
Neutron	$1.67492728 \times 10^{-24}$	1.00866	0

Once a relative scale of atomic masses has been established, we can estimate the mass of any atom whose nuclear composition is known. The proton and neutron have masses so close to 1 amu that the difference can be ignored in an estimate. Electrons have much less mass than protons or neutrons. Even though the number of electrons in an atom must equal the number of protons, there are never enough electrons in a neutral atom to significantly contribute to its mass, so their mass need not be considered. To estimate an atom's mass, we add up its number of protons and neutrons. This sum, called the **mass number** of that particular atom, is given the symbol A. For example, a copper atom that has 29 protons and 34 neutrons in its nucleus has a mass number, A, of 63. A lead atom that has 82 protons and 126 neutrons has A = 208.

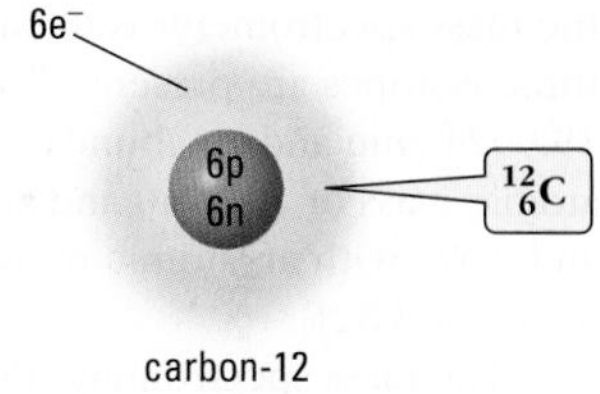

With this information, an atom of known composition, such as a lead-208 atom, can be represented as follows:

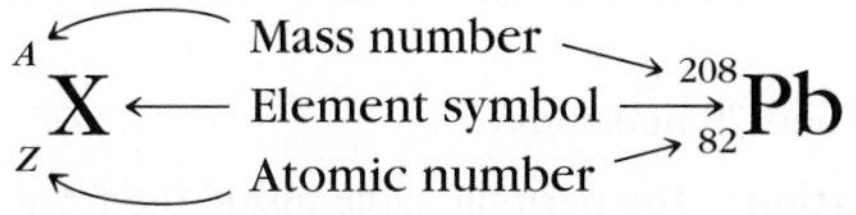

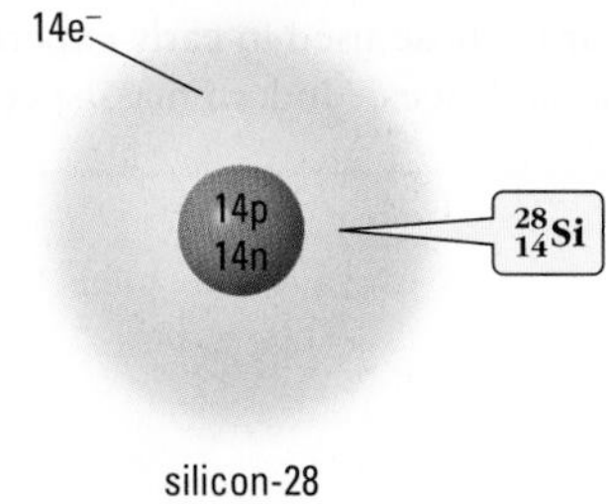

Each element has its own unique one- or two-letter symbol. Because each element is defined by the number of protons its atoms contain, knowing which element you are dealing with means you automatically know the number of protons its atoms have. Thus, the Z part of the notation is redundant. For example, the lead atom might be represented by the symbol ^{208}Pb because the Pb tells us the element is lead, and lead by definition always contains 82 protons. Whether we use the symbol or the alternative notation lead-208, we simply say "lead-208."

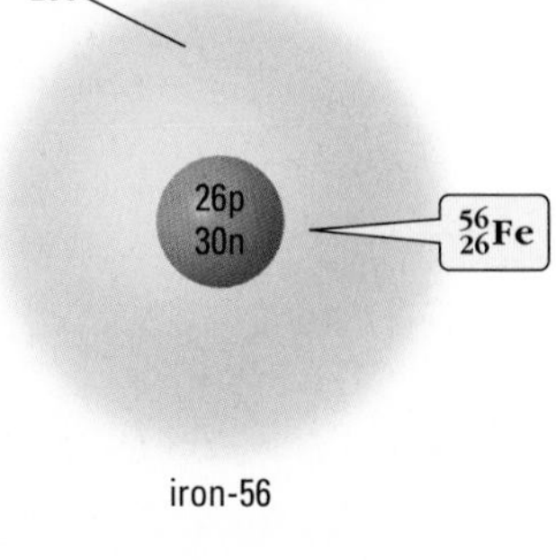

PROBLEM-SOLVING EXAMPLE 2.6 Atomic Nuclei

Iodine-131 is used in medicine to assess thyroid gland function. How many protons and neutrons are present in an iodine-131 atom?

TOOLS OF CHEMISTRY

Mass Spectrometer

A **mass spectrometer** (see Figure 2.4) is an analytical instrument used to measure atomic and molecular masses directly. A gaseous sample of the substance being analyzed is bombarded by high-energy electrons. Collisions between the electrons and the sample's atoms (or molecules) produce positive ions, mostly with 1+ charge, which are attracted to a negatively charged grid. The beam of ions is narrowed and passed through a magnetic field, which deflects the ions; the extent of deflection depends on their mass and charge. Ions with larger mass are deflected less; ions with smaller mass are deflected more. This deflection essentially sorts the ions by mass because most of them have the same 1+ charge. The deflected ions pass through to a detector, which measures the ions as a current that is directly proportional to the number of ions. This allows the determination of the relative abundance of the various ions in the sample.

In practice, the mass spectrometer settings are varied to focus ions of different masses on the stationary detector at different times. The mass spectrometer records the current of ions (the ion abundance) as the magnetic field is varied systematically. After processing by software, the data are plotted as a graph of the ion abundance versus the mass number of the ions, which is a **mass spectrum.**

The means of measuring the mass spectrum of neon is shown in Figure 2.4 and the resulting spectrum is shown in the figure here. The beam of Ne^+ ions passing through the mass spectrometer is divided into three segments because three isotopes are present: ^{20}Ne, with an atomic mass of 19.9924 amu and an abundance of 90.92%; ^{21}Ne, with an atomic mass of 20.9940 and an abundance of only 0.26%; and ^{22}Ne, with an atomic mass of 21.9914 amu and an abundance of 8.82%.

The mass spectrometer described here is a simple one based on magnetic field deflection of the ions, and it is similar to those used in early experiments to determine isotopic abundances. Modern mass spectrometers operate on quite different principles, although they generate similar mass spectra. These instruments are used to measure the masses of molecules as well as atoms. In addition, mass spectrometers are used to investigate details of molecular structure of compounds ranging in complexity from simple organic and inorganic compounds to biomolecules such as proteins. Mass spectrometry is an important and rapidly developing field of chemistry.

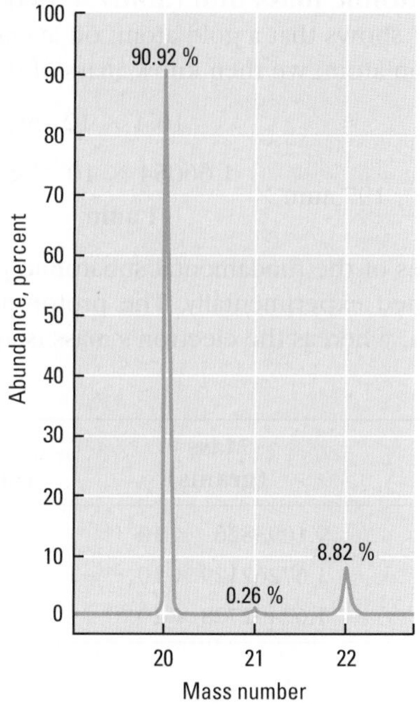

Mass spectrum of neon. The principal peak corresponds to the most abundant isotope, neon-20. The height of each peak indicates the percent relative abundance of each isotope.

Answer 53 protons and 78 neutrons

Strategy and Explanation The periodic table inside the front cover of this book shows that the atomic number of iodine (I) is 53. Therefore, the atom has 53 protons in its nucleus. Because the mass number of the atom is the sum of the number of protons and neutrons in the nucleus,

$$\text{Mass number} = \text{number of protons} + \text{number of neutrons}$$

$$131 = 53 + \text{number of neutrons}$$

$$\text{Number of neutrons} = 131 - 53 = 78$$

PROBLEM-SOLVING PRACTICE 2.6

(a) What is the mass number of a phosphorus atom with 16 neutrons?

(b) How many protons, neutrons, and electrons are there in a neon-22 atom?

(c) Write the symbol for the atom with 82 protons and 125 neutrons.

Although an atom's mass approximately equals its mass number, the actual mass is not an integral number. For example, the actual mass of a gold-196 atom is 195.9231 amu, slightly less than the mass number 196. The masses of atoms are determined experimentally using mass spectrometers. The *Tools of Chemistry* discussion illustrates the use of a mass spectrometer (see Figure 2.4) to determine the atomic masses of neon atoms.

Mass spectrometric analysis of most naturally occurring elements reveals that not all atoms of an element have the same mass. For example, all silicon atoms have 14 protons, but some silicon nuclei have 14 neutrons, others have 15, and others have 16. Thus, naturally occurring silicon (atomic number 14) is always a mixture of silicon-28, silicon-29, and silicon-30 atoms. Such different atoms of the *same* element are called isotopes. **Isotopes** are atoms with the *same* atomic number (Z) but different mass numbers (A). All the silicon atoms have 14 protons; that is what makes them silicon atoms. But these isotopes differ in their mass numbers because they have different numbers of neutrons.

The actual mass of an atom is slightly less than the sum of the masses of its protons, neutrons, and electrons. The difference, known as the mass defect, is related to the energy that binds nuclear particles together, a topic discussed in Chapter 20.

Two elements can't have the same atomic number. If two atoms differ in their number of protons, they are atoms of different elements. If only their number of neutrons differs, they are isotopes of a single element, such as neon-20, neon-21, and neon-22.

PROBLEM-SOLVING EXAMPLE 2.7 Isotopes

Boron has two isotopes, one with five neutrons and the other with six neutrons. What are the mass numbers and symbols of these isotopes?

Answer The mass numbers are 10 and 11. The symbols are $^{10}_{5}B$ and $^{11}_{5}B$.

Strategy and Explanation We use the entry for boron in the periodic table to find the answer. Boron has an atomic number of 5, so it has five protons in its nucleus. Therefore, the mass numbers of the two isotopes are given by the sum of their numbers of protons and neutrons:

Isotope 1: B = 5 protons + 5 neutrons = 10 (boron-10)

Isotope 2: B = 5 protons + 6 neutrons = 11 (boron-11)

Placing the atomic number at the bottom left and the mass number at the top left gives the symbols $^{10}_{5}B$ and $^{11}_{5}B$.

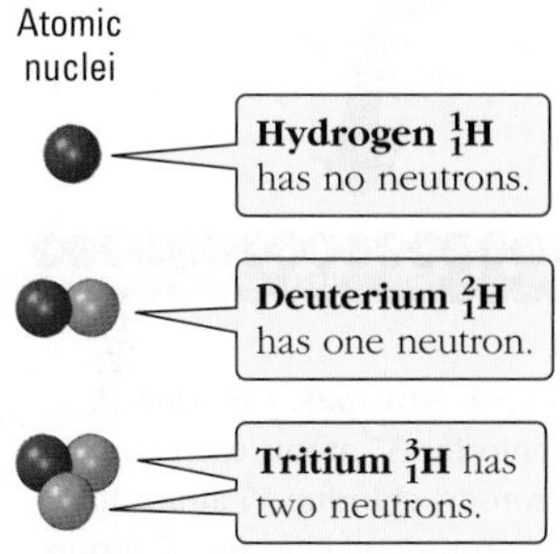

Hydrogen isotopes. Hydrogen, deuterium, and tritium each contain one proton. Hydrogen has no neutrons; deuterium and tritium have one and two neutrons, respectively.

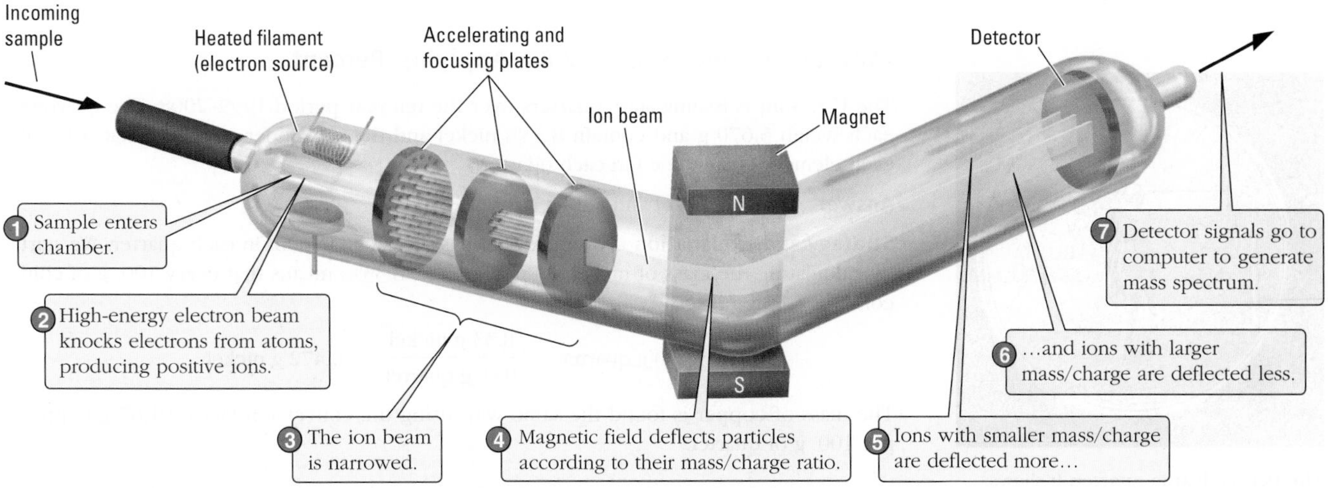

Active Figure 2.4 **Schematic diagram of a mass spectrometer.** This analytical instrument uses a magnetic field to measure atomic and molecular masses directly. **Go to the Active Figures menu at ThomsonNOW to test your understanding of the concepts in this figure.**

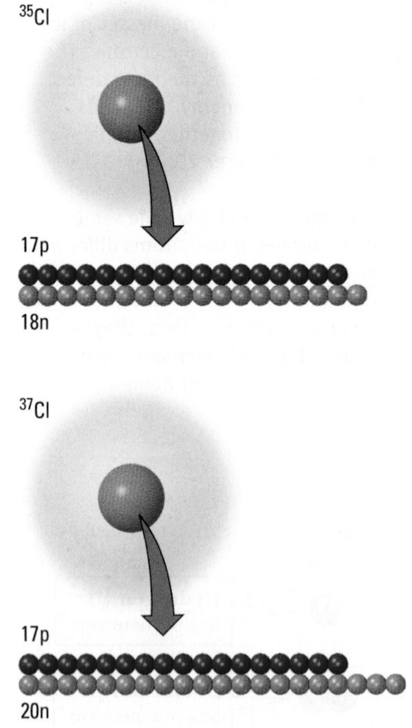

Chlorine isotopes. Chlorine-35 and chlorine-37 atoms each contain 17 protons; chlorine-35 atoms have 18 neutrons, and chlorine-37 atoms contain 20 neutrons.

PROBLEM-SOLVING PRACTICE 2.7

Naturally occurring magnesium has three isotopes with 12, 13, and 14 neutrons. What are the mass numbers and symbols of these three isotopes?

We usually refer to a particular isotope by giving its mass number. For example, $^{238}_{92}U$ is referred to as uranium-238. But a few isotopes have distinctive names and symbols because of their importance, such as the isotopes of hydrogen. All hydrogen isotopes have just one proton. When the single proton is the only nuclear particle, the element is simply called hydrogen. With one neutron as well as one proton present, the isotope $^{2}_{1}H$ is called either deuterium or heavy hydrogen (symbol D). When two neutrons are present, the isotope $^{3}_{1}H$ is called tritium (symbol T).

CONCEPTUAL EXERCISE **2.3 Isotopes**

A student in your chemistry class tells you that nitrogen-14 and nitrogen-15 are not isotopes because they have the same number of protons. How would you refute this statement?

2.6 Isotopes and Atomic Weight

Copper has two naturally occurring isotopes, copper-63 and copper-65, with atomic masses of 62.9296 amu and 64.9278 amu, respectively. In a macroscopic collection of naturally occurring copper atoms, the average mass of the atoms is neither 63 (all copper-63) nor 65 (all copper-65). Rather, the average atomic mass will fall between 63 and 65, with its exact value depending on the proportion of each isotope in the mixture. The proportion of atoms of each isotope in a natural sample of an element is called the **percent abundance,** the percentage of atoms of a *particular* isotope.

The concept of percent is widely used in chemistry, and it is worth briefly reviewing here. For example, earth's atmosphere contains approximately 78% nitrogen, 21% oxygen, and 1% argon. U.S. pennies minted after 1982 contain 2.4% copper; the remainder is zinc.

© Thomson Learning/Charles D. Winters

The Pennsylvania quarter. It shows the statue "Commonwealth," an outline of the state, the state motto, and a keystone.

PROBLEM-SOLVING EXAMPLE 2.8 **Applying Percent**

The U.S. Mint is issuing state quarters over the ten-year period 1999–2008. The quarters each weigh 5.670 g and contain 8.33% nickel and the remainder copper. What mass of each element is contained in each quarter?

Answer 0.472 g nickel and 5.20 g copper

Strategy and Explanation We need the mass of each element in each quarter. We start by calculating the mass of nickel. Its percentage, 8.33%, means that every 100. g of coin contains 8.33 g nickel.

$$5.670\ \cancel{\text{g quarter}} \times \frac{8.33\ \text{g nickel}}{100.\ \cancel{\text{g quarter}}} = 0.472\ \text{g nickel}$$

The mass of copper is found the same way, using the conversion factor 91.67 g copper per 100. g of quarter.

$$5.670\ \cancel{\text{g quarter}} \times \frac{91.67\ \text{g copper}}{100.\ \cancel{\text{g quarter}}} = 5.198\ \text{g copper}$$

We could have obtained this value directly by recognizing that the masses of nickel and copper must sum to the mass of the quarter. Therefore,

$$5.670 \text{ g quarter} = 0.472 \text{ g nickel} + x \text{ g copper}$$

Solving for x, the mass of copper, gives

$$5.670 \text{ g} - 0.472 \text{ g} = 5.198 \text{ g copper}$$

✓ Reasonable Answer Check The ratio of nickel to copper is about 11:1 (91.67/8.33 = 11), and the ratio of the masses calculated is also about 11:1 (5.198/0.472 = 11), so the answer is reasonable.

The sum of the percentages for the composition of a sample must be 100.

PROBLEM-SOLVING PRACTICE 2.8

Many heating devices such as hair dryers contain nichrome wire, an alloy containing 80.% nickel and 20.% chromium, which gets hot when an electric current passes through it. If a heating device contains 75 g of nichrome wire, how many grams of nickel and how many grams of chromium does the wire contain?

The percent abundance of each isotope in a sample of an element is given as follows:

$$\text{Percent abundance} = \frac{\text{number of atoms of a given isotope}}{\text{total number of atoms of all isotopes of that element}} \times 100\%$$

Table 2.3 gives information about the percent abundance for naturally occurring isotopes of hydrogen, boron, and bromine. The percent abundance and isotopic mass of each isotope can be used to find the average mass of atoms of that element, and this average mass is called the atomic weight of the element. The **atomic weight** of an element is the average mass of a representative sample of atoms of the element, expressed in atomic mass units.

Boron, for example, is a relatively rare element present in compounds used in laundry detergents, mild antiseptics, and Pyrex cookware. It has two naturally occurring isotopes: boron-10, with a mass of 10.0129 amu and 19.91% abundance, and boron-11, with a mass of 11.0093 amu and 80.09% abundance. Since the abundances are approximately 20% and 80%, respectively, you can estimate the atomic weight of boron: 20 atoms out of every 100, or 2 atoms out of every 10, are boron-10. If you then add up the masses of 10 atoms, you have 2 atoms with a mass of about 10 amu and 8 atoms with a mass of about 11 amu, so the sum is 108 amu, and

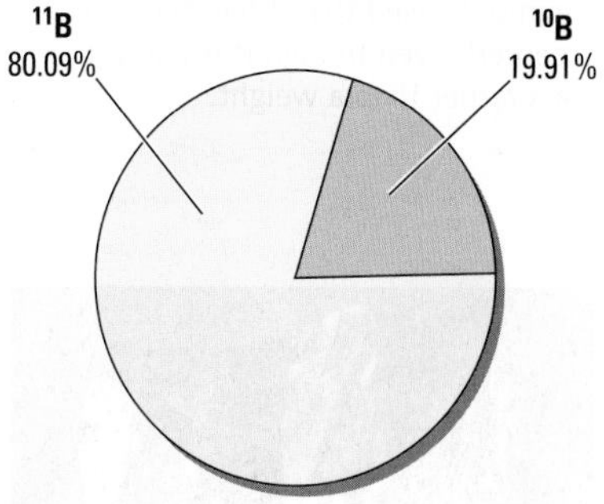

Percent abundance of boron-10 and boron-11.

Table 2.3 Isotopic Masses of the Stable Isotopes of Hydrogen, Boron, and Bromine

Element	Symbol	Atomic Weight (amu)	Mass Number	Isotopic Mass (amu)	Percent Abundance
Hydrogen	H	1.00794	1	1.007825	99.9855
	D		2	2.0141022	0.0145
Boron	B	10.811	10	10.012939	19.91
			11	11.009305	80.09
Bromine	Br	79.904	79	78.918336	50.69
			81	80.916289	49.31

ESTIMATION

The Size of Avogadro's Number

Chemists and other scientists often use estimates in place of exact calculations when they want to know the approximate value of a quantity. Analogies to help us understand the extremely large value of Avogadro's number are an example.

If 1 mol of green peas were spread evenly over the continental United States, how deep would the layer of peas be? The surface area of the continental United States is about 3.0×10^6 square miles (mi²). There are 5280 feet per mile.

Let's start with an estimate of a green pea's size: $\frac{1}{4}$-inch diameter. Then 4 peas would fit along a 1-inch line, and 48 would fit along a 1-foot line, and $48^3 = 110{,}592$ would fit into 1 cubic foot (ft³). Since we are estimating, we will approximate by saying 1×10^5 peas per cubic foot.

Now, let's estimate how many cubic feet of peas are in 1 mol of peas:

$$\frac{6.022 \times 10^{23} \text{ peas}}{1 \text{ mol peas}} \times \frac{1 \text{ ft}^3}{1 \times 10^5 \text{ peas}} \cong \frac{6.0 \times 10^{18} \text{ ft}^3}{1 \text{ mol peas}}$$

(The "approximately equal" sign, ≅, is an indicator of these approximations.) The surface area of the continental United States is 3.0×10^6 square miles (mi²), which is about

$$3.0 \times 10^6 \text{ mi}^2 \times \left(\frac{5280 \text{ ft}}{1 \text{ mi}}\right)^2 \cong 8.4 \times 10^{13} \text{ ft}^2$$

so 1 mol of peas spread evenly over this area will have a depth of

$$\frac{6.0 \times 10^{18} \text{ ft}^3}{1 \text{ mol peas}} \times \frac{1}{8.4 \times 10^{13} \text{ ft}^2} \cong \frac{7.1 \times 10^4 \text{ ft}}{1 \text{ mol peas}}$$

or

$$\frac{7.1 \times 10^4 \text{ ft}}{1 \text{ mol peas}} \times \frac{1 \text{ mi}}{5280 \text{ ft}} \cong \frac{14 \text{ mi}}{1 \text{ mol peas}}$$

Note that in many parts of the estimate, we rounded or used fewer significant figures than we could have used. Our purpose was to *estimate* the final answer, not to compute it exactly. The final answer, 14 miles, is not particularly accurate, but it is a valid estimate. The depth would be more than 10 miles but less than 20 miles. It would not be 6 inches or even 6 feet. Estimating served the overall purpose of developing the analogy for understanding the size of Avogadro's number.

ThomsonNOW™

Sign in to ThomsonNOW at **www.thomsonedu.com** to work an interactive module based on this material.

Each molar mass of copper or aluminum contains Avogadro's number of atoms. *Molar mass differs from one element to the next because the atoms of different elements have different masses.* Think of a mole as analogous to a dozen. We could have a dozen golf balls, a dozen baseballs, or a dozen bowling balls, 12 items in each case. The dozen items do not weigh the same, however, because the individual items do not weigh the same: 45 g per golf ball, 134 g per baseball, and 7200 g per bowling ball. In a similar way, the mass of Avogadro's number of atoms of one element is different from the mass of Avogadro's number of atoms of another element because the atoms of different elements differ in mass.

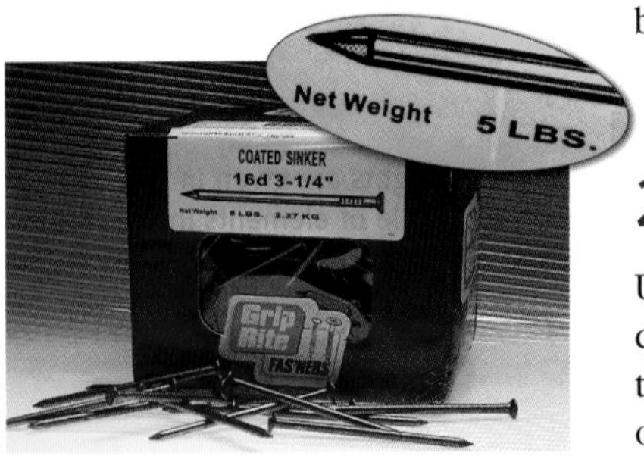

© Thomson Learning/
Charles D. Winters

Items can be counted by weighing. Knowing the mass of one nail, we can estimate the number of nails in this 5-lb box.

2.8 Molar Mass and Problem Solving

Understanding the idea of a mole and applying it properly are *essential* to doing quantitative chemistry. In particular, it is *absolutely necessary* to be able to make two basic conversions: *moles* → *mass* and *mass* → *moles*. To do these and many other calculations in chemistry, it is most helpful to use dimensional analysis in the same way it is used in unit conversions. Along with calculating the final answer, write the units with all quantities in a calculation and cancel the units. If the problem is set up properly, the answer will have the desired units.

Let's see how these concepts apply to converting mass to moles or moles to mass. *In either case, the conversion factor is provided by the molar mass of the substance, the number of grams in one mole, that is, grams per mole (g/mol).*

Mass $\rightleftarrows$ Moles conversions for substance A

Mass A ⟶ moles A

$$\text{Grams A} \times \frac{1\ \text{mol A}}{\text{grams A}} = \text{moles A}$$

$\frac{1}{\text{molar mass}}$

Moles A ⟶ mass A

$$\text{Moles A} \times \frac{\text{grams A}}{1\ \text{mol A}} = \text{grams A}$$

molar mass

ThomsonNOW™

Go to the Coached Problems menu for tutorials on:

- **converting between numbers of atoms and moles**
- **using molar mass to convert between mass and moles.**

Suppose you need 0.250 mol of Cu for an experiment. How many grams of Cu should you use? The atomic weight of Cu is 63.546 amu, so the molar mass of Cu is 63.546 g/mol. To calculate the mass of 0.250 mol of Cu, you need the conversion factor 63.546 g Cu/1 mol Cu.

$$0.250\ \text{mol Cu} \times \frac{63.55\ \text{g Cu}}{1\ \text{mol Cu}} = 15.9\ \text{g Cu}$$

In this book we will, when possible, *use one more significant figure in the molar mass than in any of the other data in the problem.* In the problem just completed, note that we used four significant figures in the molar mass of Cu when three were given in the number of moles. Using one more significant figure in the molar mass guarantees that its precision is greater than that of the other numbers and does not limit the precision of the result of the computation.

EXERCISE 2.7 Grams, Moles, and Avogadro's Number

You have a 10.00-g sample of lithium and a 10.00-g sample of iridium. How many atoms are in each sample, and how many more atoms are in the lithium sample than in the iridium sample?

Frequently, a problem requires converting a mass to the equivalent number of moles, such as calculating the number of moles of bromine in 10.00 g of bromine. Because bromine is a diatomic element, it consists of Br_2 molecules. Therefore, there are 2 mol Br atoms in 1 mol Br_2 molecules. The molar mass of Br_2 is twice its atomic mass, 2×79.904 g/mol = 159.81 g/mol. To calculate the moles of bromine in 10.00 g of Br_2, use the molar mass of Br_2 as the conversion factor, 1 mol Br_2/159.81 g Br_2.

$$10.00\ \text{g Br}_2 \times \frac{1\ \text{mol Br}_2}{159.81\ \text{g Br}_2} = 6.257 \times 10^{-2}\ \text{mol Br}_2$$

Boeing

Titanium and aluminum are metals used in modern airplane manufacturing.

PROBLEM-SOLVING EXAMPLE 2.9 Mass and Moles

(a) Titanium (Ti) is a metal used to build airplanes. How many moles of Ti are in a 100-g sample of the pure metal?

(b) Aluminum is also used in airplane manufacturing. A piece of Al contains 2.16 mol Al. Is the mass of Al greater or less than the mass of Ti in part (a)?

Answer (a) 2.09 mol Ti (b) 58.3 g Al, which is less than the mass of Ti

Strategy and Explanation

(a) This is a mass-to-moles conversion that is solved using the molar mass of Ti as the conversion factor 1 mol Ti/47.87 g Ti.

$$100\ \text{g Ti} \times \frac{1\ \text{mol Ti}}{47.87\ \text{g Ti}} = 2.09\ \text{mol Ti}$$

(b) This is a moles-to-mass conversion that requires the conversion factor 26.98 g Al/1 mol Al.

$$2.16\ \cancel{\text{mol Al}} \times \frac{26.98\text{ g Al}}{1\ \cancel{\text{mol Al}}} = 58.3\text{ g Al}$$

This mass is less than the 100-g mass of titanium.

PROBLEM-SOLVING PRACTICE 2.9

Calculate (a) the number of moles in 1.00 mg molybdenum (Mo) and (b) the number of grams in 5.00×10^{-3} mol gold (Au).

University of Pennsylvania

Dmitri Mendeleev
1834–1907

Originally from Siberia, Mendeleev spent most of his life in St. Petersburg. He taught at the University of St. Petersburg, where he wrote books and published his concept of chemical periodicity, which helped systematize inorganic chemistry. Later in life he moved on to other interests, including studying the natural resources of Russia and their commercial applications.

2.9 The Periodic Table

You have already used the periodic table inside the front cover of this book to obtain atomic numbers and atomic weights of elements. But it is much more valuable than this. The periodic table is an exceptionally useful tool in chemistry. It allows us to organize and interrelate the chemical and physical properties of the elements. For example, the periodic table can be used to classify elements as metals, nonmetals, or metalloids by their positions in the table. You should become familiar with its main features and terminology.

Dmitri Mendeleev (1834–1907), while a professor at the University of St. Petersburg, realized that by ordering the elements by increasing atomic weight, there appeared to be a periodicity to the properties of the elements. He summarized his findings in the table that has come to be called the periodic table. By lining up the elements in horizontal rows in order of increasing atomic weight and starting a new row when he came to an element with properties similar to one already in the previous row, he saw that the resulting columns contained elements with similar properties. In generating his periodic table, Mendeleev found that some positions in his table were not filled, and he predicted that new elements would be found that filled the gaps. Two of the missing elements—gallium (Ga) and germanium (Ge)—were soon discovered, with properties very close to those Mendeleev had predicted.

It gives a useful perspective to realize that Mendeleev developed the periodic table nearly a half-century before electrons, protons, and neutrons were known.

Periodicity of the elements means a recurrence of similar properties at regular intervals when the elements are arranged in the correct order.

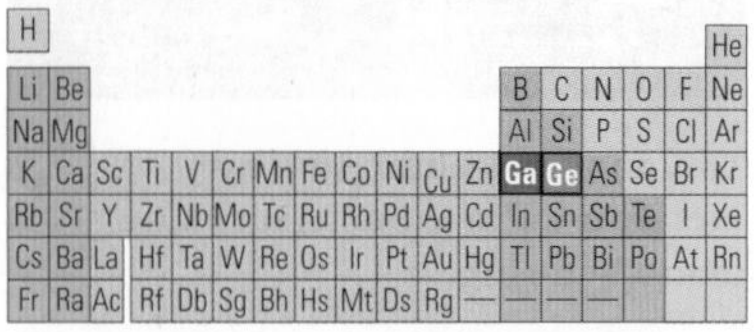

© Thomson Learning/George Semple

Periodicity of piano keys.

- Main group metals
- Transition metals
- Metalloids
- Nonmetals, noble gases

A label of A denotes main group elements…

…and a label of B denotes transition elements, the system used most commonly at present in the United States.

The new international system is to number the groups from 1 to 18.

Period	1A (1)	2A (2)	3B (3)	4B (4)	5B (5)	6B (6)	7B (7)	8B (8)	8B (9)	8B (10)	1B (11)	2B (12)	3A (13)	4A (14)	5A (15)	6A (16)	7A (17)	8A (18)
1	1 H																	2 He
2	3 Li	4 Be											5 B	6 C	7 N	8 O	9 F	10 Ne
3	11 Na	12 Mg											13 Al	14 Si	15 P	16 S	17 Cl	18 Ar
4	19 K	20 Ca	21 Sc	22 Ti	23 V	24 Cr	25 Mn	26 Fe	27 Co	28 Ni	29 Cu	30 Zn	31 Ga	32 Ge	33 As	34 Se	35 Br	36 Kr
5	37 Rb	38 Sr	39 Y	40 Zr	41 Nb	42 Mo	43 Tc	44 Ru	45 Rh	46 Pd	47 Ag	48 Cd	49 In	50 Sn	51 Sb	52 Te	53 I	54 Xe
6	55 Cs	56 Ba	57 La	72 Hf	73 Ta	74 W	75 Re	76 Os	77 Ir	78 Pt	79 Au	80 Hg	81 Tl	82 Pb	83 Bi	84 Po	85 At	86 Rn
7	87 Fr	88 Ra	89 Ac	104 Rf	105 Db	106 Sg	107 Bh	108 Hs	109 Mt	110 Ds	111 Rg	112 —	113 —	114 —	115 —			

	Period														
Lanthanides	6	58 Ce	59 Pr	60 Nd	61 Pm	62 Sm	63 Eu	64 Gd	65 Tb	66 Dy	67 Ho	68 Er	69 Tm	70 Yb	71 Lu
Actinides	7	90 Th	91 Pa	92 U	93 Np	94 Pu	95 Am	96 Cm	97 Bk	98 Cf	99 Es	100 Fm	101 Md	102 No	103 Lr

Periods are horizontal rows of elements.

Groups are vertical columns of elements. Some groups have common names: Group 1A = alkali metals, Group 2A = alkaline earth metals, Group 7A = halogens, Group 8A = noble gases.

Figure 2.6 Modern periodic table of the elements. Elements are listed across the periods in ascending order of atomic number.

Later experiments by H. G. J. Moseley demonstrated that elements in the periodic table should be ordered by atomic numbers rather than atomic weights. Arranging the elements in order of increasing atomic number gives the **law of chemical periodicity: *The properties of the elements are periodic functions of their atomic numbers (numbers of protons).***

ThomsonNOW™
Go to the Coached Problems menu for a guided exploration of the **periodic table.**

Periodic Table Features

Elements in the **periodic table** are arranged according to atomic number so that *elements with similar chemical properties occur in vertical columns* called **groups.** The table commonly used in the United States has groups numbered 1 through 8 (Figure 2.6), with each number followed by either an A or a B. The A groups (Groups 1A and 2A on the left of the table and Groups 3A through 8A at the right) are collectively known as **main group elements.** The B groups (in the middle of the table) are called **transition elements.**

An alternative convention for numbering the groups in the periodic table uses the numbers 1 through 18, with no letters.

The horizontal rows of the table are called **periods,** and they are numbered beginning with 1 for the period containing only H and He. Sodium (Na) is, for example, in Group 1A and is the first element in the third period. Silver (Ag) is in Group 1B and is in the fifth period.

The table in Figure 2.6 and inside the front cover helps us to recognize that most elements are metals (gray and blue), far fewer elements are nonmetals (lavender), and even fewer are metalloids (orange). Elements generally become less metallic from left to right across a period, and eventually one or more nonmetals are found in each period. The six metalloids (B, Si, Ge, As, Sb, Te) fall along a zigzag line passing between Al and Si, Ge and As, and Sb and Te.

The Alkali Metals (Group 1A) and Alkaline Earth Metals (Group 2A)

"Alkali" comes from the Arabic language. Ancient Arabian chemists discovered that ashes of certain plants, which they called *al-qali,* produced water solutions that felt slippery and burned the skin.

The chemistry of Groups 1A and 2A as well as other elements is discussed in Chapters 21 and 22.

Elements found uncombined with any other element in nature are sometimes called "free" elements.

Gold and silver as free metals in nature triggered the great gold and silver rushes of the 1800s in the United States.

Elements in the leftmost column (Group 1A) are called **alkali metals** (except hydrogen) because their aqueous solutions are alkaline (basic). Elements in Group 2A, known as **alkaline earth metals,** are extracted from minerals (earths) and also produce alkaline aqueous solutions (except beryllium).

Alkali metals and alkaline earth metals are very reactive and are found in nature only combined with other elements in compounds, never as the free metallic elements. Their compounds are plentiful, and many are significant to human and plant life. Sodium (Na) in sodium chloride (table salt) is a fundamental part of human and animal diets, and throughout history civilizations have sought salt as a dietary necessity and a commercial commodity. Today, sodium chloride is commercially important as a source of two of the most important industrial chemicals: sodium hydroxide and chlorine. Magnesium (Mg) and calcium (Ca), the sixth and fifth most abundant elements in the earth's crust, respectively, are present in a vast array of chemical compounds.

Fritz W. Goro/Estate of F. W. Goro

Sample of manmade transuranium elements coating the tip of a microscopic spatula. The sample was produced by neutron irradiation of uranium in a breeder nuclear reactor in the 1940s.

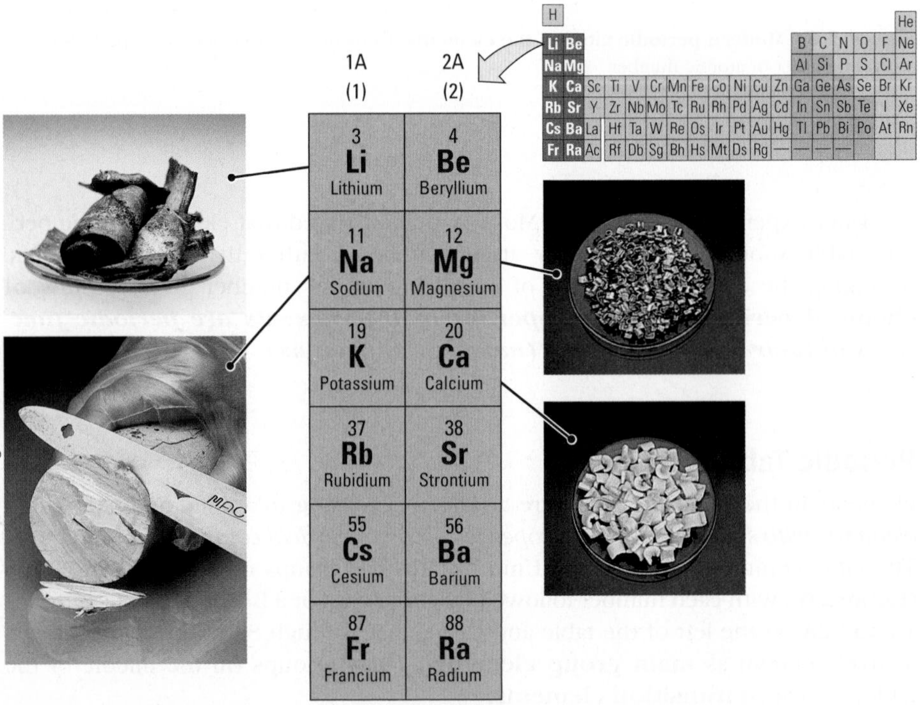

Photos: © Thomson Learning/Charles D. Winters

The Transition Elements, Lanthanides, and Actinides

The transition elements (also known as the *transition metals*) fill the middle of the periodic table in Periods 4 through 7, and most are found in nature only in compounds. The notable exceptions are gold, silver, platinum, copper, and liquid mercury, which can be found in elemental form. Iron, zinc, copper, and chromium are among the most important commercial metals. Because of their vivid colors, transition metal compounds are used for pigments (Section 22.6).

The **lanthanides** and **actinides** are listed separately in two rows at the bottom of the periodic table. Using the extra, separate rows keeps the periodic table from becoming too wide and too cumbersome. These elements are relatively rare and not as commercially important as the transition elements. The elements beyond uranium are synthesized.

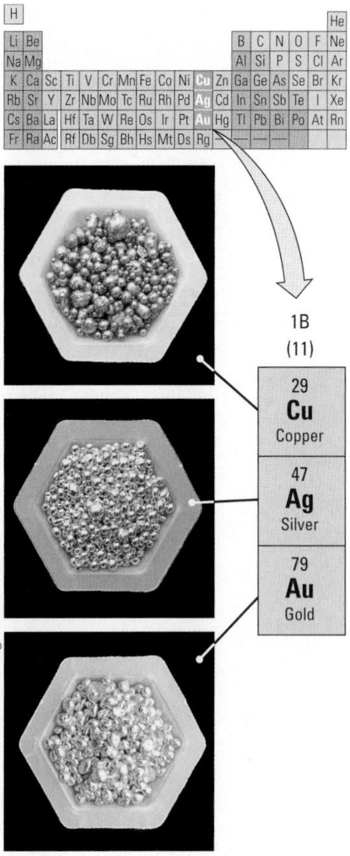

Photos: © Thomson Learning/Charles D. Winters

Groups 3A to 6A

These four groups contain the most abundant elements in the earth's crust and atmosphere (Table 2.4). They also contain the elements present in most of the important molecules in our bodies: carbon (C), nitrogen (N), and oxygen (O). Because of the ability of carbon atoms to bond extensively with each other, huge numbers of carbon compounds exist. Organic chemistry is the branch of chemistry devoted to the study of carbon compounds. Carbon atoms also provide the framework for the molecules essential to living things, which are the subject of the branch of chemistry known as biochemistry.

Groups 4A to 6A each begin with one or more nonmetals, include one or more metalloids, and end with a metal. Group 4A, for example, contains carbon, a nonmetal, includes two metalloids (Si and Ge), and finishes with two metals (Sn and Pb). Group 3A starts with boron (B), a metalloid (Section 21.6).

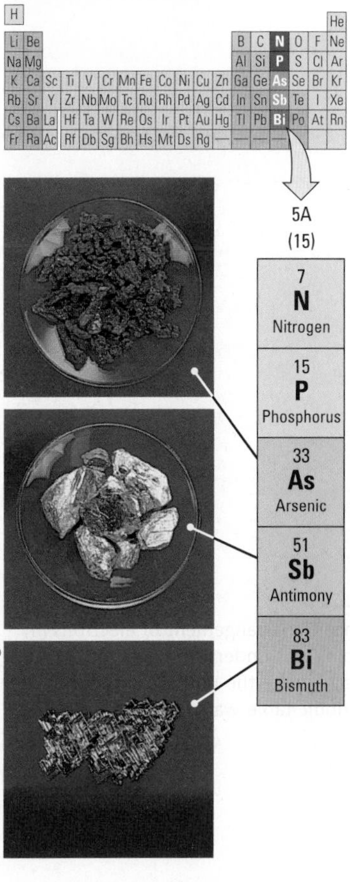

Photos: © Thomson Learning/Charles D. Winters

Table 2.4 Selected Group 3A–6A Elements

Group 3A
Aluminum: Most abundant *metal* in the earth's crust (7%). In nature, always found in compounds, especially with silicon and oxygen in clay minerals.
Group 4A
Carbon: Second most abundant element in living things. Provides the framework for organic and biochemical molecules.
Silicon: Second most abundant element in the earth's crust (25%). Always found combined naturally, usually with oxygen in quartz and silicate minerals.
Group 5A
Nitrogen: Most abundant element in the earth's atmosphere (78%) but not abundant in the earth's crust because of the relatively low chemical reactivity of N_2.
Group 6A
Oxygen: Most abundant element in the earth's crust (47%) because of its high chemical reactivity. Second most abundant element in the earth's atmosphere (21%).

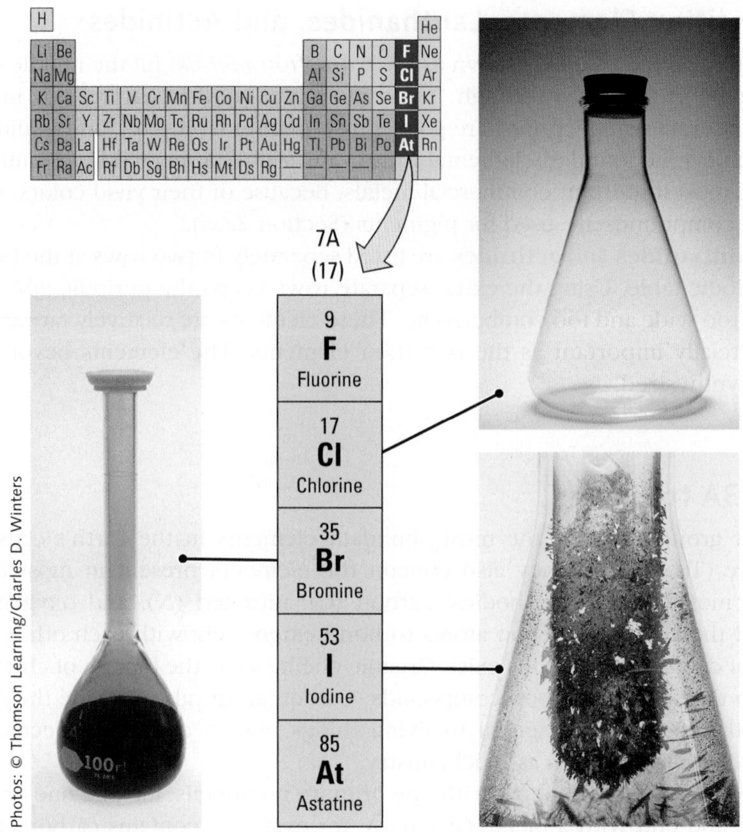

The Halogens (Group 7A)

The elements in this group consist of diatomic molecules and are highly reactive. The group name, **halogens,** comes from the Greek words *hals,* meaning "salt," and *genes,* meaning "forming." The halogens all form salts—compounds similar to sodium chloride (NaCl)—by reacting vigorously with alkali metals and with other metals as well. Halogens also react with most nonmetals. Small carbon compounds containing chlorine and fluorine are relatively unreactive but are involved in seasonal ozone depletion in the upper atmosphere (Section 10.11).

The Noble Gases (Group 8A)

Once the arrangement of electrons in atoms was understood (Section 7.6), the place where the noble gases fit into the periodic table was obvious.

The **noble gases** at the far right of the periodic table are the least reactive elements. Their lack of chemical reactivity, as well as their rarity, prevented them from being discovered until about a century ago. Thus, they were not known when Mendeleev developed his periodic table. Until 1962 they were called the *inert* gases, because they were thought not to combine with any element. In 1962 this basic canon of chemistry was overturned when compounds of xenon with fluorine and with oxygen were synthesized. Since then other xenon compounds have been made, as well as compounds of fluorine with krypton and with radon.

CHEMISTRY IN THE NEWS

Running Out of an Element?

Even though helium is the second most abundant element in the universe, we are about to run out of it. How is this possible? How could we possibly run out of an element? Helium is isolated from its naturally occurring mixture with natural gas, so it is not renewable, just like petroleum or gold or diamonds. And the helium from natural gas wells is now being used up.

Most of us are familiar with helium's use in party balloons, but many other applications of this element are more important. Helium's extremely low boiling point makes it the required coolant for superconducting magnets such as those in magnetic resonance imaging (MRI) scanners. Other uses include high-tech welding where air must be excluded and helium-filled balloons that are used for lifting weather instruments high in the atmosphere.

Helium on earth comes from radioactive decay processes deep within the earth. The gas is trapped in rock formations, where it can mix with natural gas. Concentrations of He in natural gas greater than about 3000 ppm (parts per million) are required for economical recovery to be feasible. Most of the gas wells producing such natural gas with enough He are near Amarillo, Texas. Some gas there contains as much as 80,000 ppm He. In all, in the United States 20 private plants produce 150 million cubic meters of He per year. The rest of the world produces about 10% of that amount.

When helium reaches the atmosphere, it eventually works its way to the edge of the atmosphere and is lost into space. He atoms have too little mass to be retained by the earth's gravitational field. Although much pure helium is recycled for scientific or medical applications, most helium is lost after use.

Experts agree that helium will be in short supply in the coming decades, although estimates vary according to what assumptions about usage levels are made. Increasing uses for MRI scanners and other high-tech industries are making the problem more acute. We could run out of He as early as 2012 or as late as 2060. No matter what assumptions you make, it is clear that the price of helium will go way up and its availability will go way down. No more helium-filled party balloons or advertising blimps.

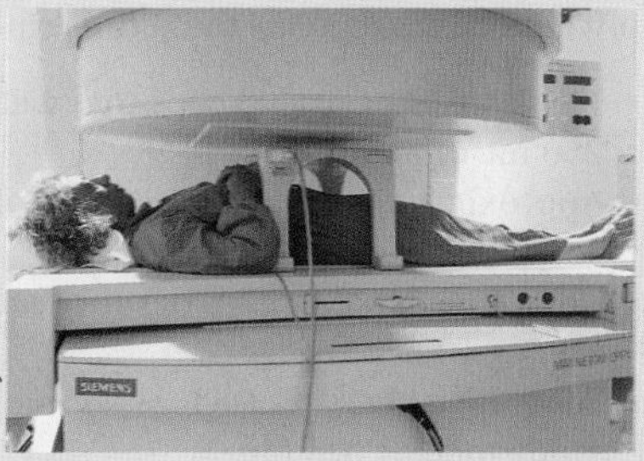

Mauro Fermariello/Science Photo Library/Photo Researchers, Inc.

A patient having an MRI scan. MRI instruments depend on superconducting magnets, which in turn depend on liquid helium to keep them at the necessary extremely low temperature.

SOURCE: Jones, Nicola. "Under Pressure." *New Scientist,* Dec. 21, 2002; p. 48.

EXERCISE 2.8 The Periodic Table

1. How many (a) metals, (b) nonmetals, and (c) metalloids are in the fourth period of the periodic table? Give the name and symbol for each element.
2. Which groups of the periodic table contain (a) only metals, (b) only nonmetals, (c) only metalloids?
3. Which period of the periodic table contains the most metals?

EXERCISE 2.9 Element Names

On June 14, 2000, a major daily American newspaper published this paragraph:

> ABC's *Who Wants to Be a Millionaire* crowned its fourth million-dollar winner Tuesday night. Bob House . . . [answered] the final question: Which of these men does not have a chemical compound named after him? (a) Enrico Fermi, (b) Albert Einstein, (c) Niels Bohr, (d) Isaac Newton

What is wrong with the question? What is the correct answer to the question after it is properly posed? (The question was properly posed and correctly answered on the TV show.)

CHEMISTRY YOU CAN DO

Preparing a Pure Sample of an Element

You will need these items to do this experiment:

- Two glasses or plastic cups that will each hold about 250 mL of liquid
- Approximately 100 mL (about 3.5 oz) of vinegar
- Soap
- An iron nail, paper clip, or other similar-sized piece of iron
- Something abrasive, such as a piece of steel wool, Brillo, sandpaper, or nail file
- About 40 to 50 cm of thin string or thread
- Some table salt
- A magnifying glass (optional)
- 15 to 20 dull pennies (shiny pennies will not work)

Wash the piece of iron with soap, dry it, and clean the surface further with the steel wool or other abrasive until it is shiny. Tie one end of the string around one end of the piece of iron.

Place the pennies in one cup (labeled A) and pour in enough vinegar to cover them. Sprinkle on a little salt, swirl the liquid around so it contacts all the pennies, and observe what happens. When nothing more seems to be happening, pour the liquid into the second cup (labeled B), leaving the pennies in cup A (that is, pour off the liquid). Suspend the piece of iron from the thread so that it is half-submerged in the liquid in cup B.

Observe the piece of iron over a period of 10 minutes or so, and then use the thread to pull it out of the liquid. Observe it carefully, using a magnifying glass if you have one. Compare the part that was submerged with the part that remained above the surface of the liquid.

1. What did you observe happening to the pennies?
2. How could you account for what happened to the pennies in terms of a nanoscale model? Cite observations that support your conclusion.
3. What did you observe happening to the piece of iron?
4. Interpret the experiment in terms of a nanoscale model, citing observations that support your conclusions.
5. Would this method be of use in purifying copper? If so, can you suggest ways that it could be used effectively to obtain copper from ores?

SUMMARY PROBLEM

The atoms of one of the elements contain 47 protons and 62 neutrons.

(a) Identify the element and give its symbol.

(b) What is this atom's atomic number? Mass number?

(c) This element has two naturally occurring isotopes. Calculate the atomic weight of the element.

Isotope	Mass Number	Percent Abundance	Isotopic Mass (amu)
1	107	51.84	106.905
2	109	48.16	108.905

(d) This element is a member of which group in the periodic table? Is this element a metal, nonmetal, or metalloid? Explain your answer.

(e) Consider a piece of jewelry that contains 1.00 g of the element. (i) How many moles of the element are in this mass? (ii) How many atoms of the element are in this mass? (iii) Atoms of this element have an atomic diameter of 304 pm. If all the atoms of this element in the sample were put into a row, how many meters long would the chain of atoms be?

IN CLOSING

Having studied this chapter, you should be able to . . .

- Describe radioactivity, electrons, protons, and neutrons and the general structure of the atom (Sections 2.1–2.2).
- Use conversion factors for the units for mass, volume, and length common in chemistry (Section 2.3). ThomsonNOW homework: Study Questions 16, 111
- Identify the correct number of significant figures in a number and carry significant figures through calculations (Section 2.4). ThomsonNOW homework: Study Questions 22, 26
- Define isotope and give the mass number and number of neutrons for a specific isotope (Section 2.5). ThomsonNOW homework: Study Questions 45, 47
- Calculate the atomic weight of an element from isotopic abundances (Section 2.6). ThomsonNOW homework: Study Questions 57, 59, 104
- Explain the difference between the atomic number and the atomic weight of an element and find this information for any element (Sections 2.5–2.6).
- Relate masses of elements to the mole, Avogadro's number, and molar mass (Section 2.7). ThomsonNOW homework: Study Questions 76, 116
- Do gram-mole and mole-gram conversions for elements (Section 2.8). ThomsonNOW homework: Study Questions 66, 67
- Identify the periodic table location of groups, periods, alkali metals, alkaline earth metals, halogens, noble gases, transition elements, lanthanides, and actinides (Section 2.9). ThomsonNOW homework: Study Questions 85, 87

ThomsonNOW

Sign in to ThomsonNOW at **www.thomsonedu.com** to check your readiness for an exam by taking the Pre-Test and exploring the modules recommended in your Personalized Learning Plan.

KEY TERMS

actinides *(2.9)*
alkali metals *(2.9)*
alkaline earth metals *(2.9)*
atomic mass unit (amu) *(2.5)*
atomic number *(2.5)*
atomic structure *(Introduction)*
atomic weight *(2.6)*
Avogadro's number *(2.7)*
chemical periodicity, law of *(2.9)*
electron *(2.1)*
group *(2.9)*
halogens *(2.9)*
ion *(2.1)*
isotope *(2.5)*
lanthanides *(2.9)*
main group elements *(2.9)*
mass *(2.3)*
mass number *(2.5)*
mass spectrometer *(p. 56)*
mass spectrum *(p. 56)*
metric system *(2.3)*
molar mass *(2.7)*
mole (mol) *(2.7)*
neutron *(2.2)*
noble gases *(2.9)*
nucleus *(2.2)*
percent abundance *(2.6)*
period *(2.9)*
periodic table *(2.9)*
proton *(2.1)*
radioactivity *(2.1)*
scanning tunneling microscope *(p. 48)*
significant figures *(2.4)*
transition elements *(2.9)*

QUESTIONS FOR REVIEW AND THOUGHT

■ denotes questions available in ThomsonNOW and assignable in OWL.

Blue-numbered questions have short answers at the end of this book and fully worked solutions in the *Student Solutions Manual.*

ThomsonNOW™
Assess your understanding of this chaper's topics with sample tests and other resources found by signing in to ThomsonNOW at **www.thomsonedu.com**.

Review Questions

1. What is the fundamental unit of electrical charge?
2. Millikan was able to determine the charge on an electron using his famous oil-drop experiment. Describe the experiment and explain how Millikan was able to calculate the mass of an electron using his results and the ratio discovered earlier by Thomson.
3. The positively charged particle in an atom is called the proton.
   (a) How much heavier is a proton than an electron?
   (b) What is the difference in the charge on a proton and an electron?
4. Ernest Rutherford's famous gold-foil experiment examined the structure of atoms.
   (a) What surprising result was observed?
   (b) The results of the gold-foil experiment enabled Rutherford to calculate that the nucleus is much smaller than the atom. How much smaller?
5. In any given *neutral* atom, how many protons are there compared with the number of electrons?
6. Atoms of elements can have varying numbers of neutrons in their nuclei.
   (a) What are species called that have varying numbers of neutrons for the same element?
   (b) How do the mass numbers vary for these species?
   (c) What are two common elements that exemplify this property?

Topical Questions

Units and Unit Conversions

7. If the nucleus of an atom were the size of a golf ball (4 cm diameter), what would be the diameter of the atom?
8. If a sheet of business paper is exactly 11 inches high, what is its height in centimeters? Millimeters? Meters?
9. The pole vault world record is 6.14 m. What is this in centimeters? In feet and inches?
10. The maximum speed limit in many states is 65 miles per hour. What is this speed in kilometers per hour?
11. A student weighs 168 lb. What is the student's weight in kilograms?
12. Basketball hoops are exactly 10 ft off the floor. How far is this in meters? Centimeters?
13. A Volkswagen engine has a displacement of 120. in.^{3}. What is this volume in cubic centimeters? In liters?
14. An automobile engine has a displacement of 250. in.^{3}. What is this volume in cubic centimeters? In liters?
15. Calculate how many square inches there are in one square meter.
16. ■ One square mile contains exactly 640 acres. How many square meters are in one acre?
17. On May 18, 1980, Mt. St. Helens in Washington erupted. The 9677 ft high summit was lowered by 1314 ft by the eruption. Approximately 0.67 cubic miles of debris was released into the atmosphere. How many cubic meters of debris was released?
18. Suppose a room is 18 ft long, 15 ft wide, and the distance from floor to ceiling is 8 ft, 6 in. You need to know the volume of the room in metric units for some scientific calculations. What is the room's volume in cubic meters? In liters?
19. A crystal of fluorite (a mineral that contains calcium and fluorine) has a mass of 2.83 g. What is this mass in kilograms? In pounds? Give the symbols for the elements in this crystal.

Scanning Tunneling Microscopy

20. Comment on this statement: The scanning tunneling microscope enables scientists to image individual atoms on surfaces directly.
21. The scanning tunneling microscope is based on the flow of electrons from the instrument to the sample surface being investigated. How is this flow converted into an image of the surface?

Significant Figures

22. ■ How many significant figures are present in these measured quantities?
    (a) 1374 kg
    (b) 0.00348 s
    (c) 5.619 mm
    (d) 2.475×10^{-3} cm
    (e) 33.1 mL
23. How many significant figures are present in these measured quantities?
    (a) 1.022×10^2 km
    (b) 34 m^2
    (c) 0.042 L
    (d) 28.2 °C
    (e) 323. mg
24. For each of these numbers, round to three significant digits and write the result in scientific notation.
    (a) 0.0004332
    (b) 44.7337
    (c) 22.4555
    (d) 0.0088418
25. For each of these numbers, round to four significant digits and write the result in scientific notation.
    (a) 247.583
    (b) 100,578
    (c) 0.0000348719
    (d) 0.004003881

26. ■ Perform these calculations and express the result with the proper number of significant figures.
(a) $\dfrac{4.850\text{ g} - 2.34\text{ g}}{1.3\text{ mL}}$
(b) $V = \pi r^3$ where $r = 4.112$ cm
(c) $(4.66 \times 10^{-3}) \times 4.666$
(d) $\dfrac{0.003400}{65.2}$

27. Perform these calculations and express the result with the proper number of significant figures.
(a) $2221.05 - \dfrac{3256.5}{3.20}$
(b) $343.2 \times (2.01 \times 10^{-3})$
(c) $S = 4\pi r^2$ where $r = 2.55$ cm
(d) $\dfrac{2802}{15} - (0.0025 \times 10{,}000.)$

Percent

28. Silver jewelry is actually a mixture of silver and copper. If a bracelet with a mass of 17.6 g contains 14.1 g of silver, what is the percentage of silver? Of copper?
29. The solder once used by plumbers to fasten copper pipes together consists of 67% lead and 33% tin. What is the mass of lead (in grams) in a 1.00-lb block of solder? What is the mass of tin?
30. Automobile batteries are filled with sulfuric acid. What is the mass of the acid (in grams) in 500. mL of the battery acid solution if the density of the solution is 1.285 g/cm^3 and the solution is 38.08% sulfuric acid by mass?
31. When popcorn pops, it loses water explosively. If a kernel of corn weighing 0.125 g before popping weighs 0.106 g afterward, what percentage of its mass did it lose on popping?
32. ■ A well-known breakfast cereal contains 280 mg of sodium per 30-g serving. What percentage of the cereal is sodium?
33. If a 6.0-oz cup of regular coffee contains 100 mg caffeine, what is the percentage of caffeine in the coffee?

Isotopes

34. Are these statements true or false? Explain why in each case.
(a) Atoms of the same element always have the same mass number.
(b) Atoms of the same element can have different atomic numbers.
35. What is the definition of the atomic mass unit?
36. What is the difference between the mass number and the atomic number of an atom?
37. Uranium-235 and uranium-238 differ in terms of the number of which subatomic particle?
38. When you subtract the atomic number from the mass number for an atom, what do you obtain?
39. How many electrons, protons, and neutrons are present in an atom of cobalt-60?
40. The artificial radioactive element technetium is used in many medical studies. Give the number of electrons, protons, and neutrons in an atom of technetium-99.
41. The atomic weight of bromine is 79.904. The natural abundance of ^{81}Br is 49.31%. What is the atomic weight of the only other natural isotope of bromine?
42. The atomic weight of boron is 10.811. The natural abundance of ^{10}B is 19.91%. What is the atomic weight of the only other natural isotope of boron?
43. Give the mass number of each of these atoms: (a) beryllium with 5 neutrons, (b) titanium with 26 neutrons, and (c) gallium with 39 neutrons.
44. Give the mass number of (a) an iron atom with 30 neutrons, (b) an americium atom with 148 neutrons, and (c) a tungsten atom with 110 neutrons.
45. ■ Give the complete symbol $^{A}_{Z}X$ for each of these atoms: (a) sodium with 12 neutrons, (b) argon with 21 neutrons, and (c) gallium with 38 neutrons.
46. Give the complete symbol $^{A}_{Z}X$ for each of these atoms: (a) nitrogen with 8 neutrons, (b) zinc with 34 neutrons, and (c) xenon with 75 neutrons.
47. ■ How many electrons, protons, and neutrons are there in an atom of (a) calcium-40, $^{40}_{20}$Ca, (b) tin-119, $^{119}_{50}$Sn, and (c) plutonium-244, $^{244}_{94}$Pu?
48. How many electrons, protons, and neutrons are there in an atom of (a) carbon-13, $^{13}_{6}$C, (b) chromium-50, $^{50}_{24}$Cr, and (c) bismuth-205, $^{205}_{83}$Bi?
49. Fill in this table:

Z	*A*	**Number of Neutrons**	**Element**
35	81	______	______
______	______	62	Pd
77	______	115	______
______	151	______	Eu

50. Fill in this table:

Z	*A*	**Number of Neutrons**	**Element**
60	144	______	______
______	______	12	Mg
64	______	94	______
______	37	______	Cl

51. Which of these are isotopes of element X, whose atomic number is 9: $^{18}_{9}$X, $^{20}_{9}$X, $^{9}_{4}$X, $^{15}_{9}$X?
52. Which of these species are isotopes of the same element: $^{20}_{10}$X, $^{20}_{11}$X, $^{21}_{10}$X, $^{20}_{12}$X? Explain.

Mass Spectrometry

53. ■ What nanoscale species are moving through a mass spectrometer during its operation?
54. What is plotted on the *x*-axis and on the *y*-axis in a mass spectrum? What information does a mass spectrum convey?
55. How are the ions in the mass spectrometer separated from one another?
56. How can a mass spectrometer be used to measure the masses of individual isotopes of an element?

to water as it comes from a reservoir. Assume you live in a medium-sized city of 150,000 people and that each person uses 175 gal of water per day. How many tons of sodium fluoride must you add to the water supply each year (365 days) to have the required fluoride concentration of 1 part per million (that is, 1 ton of fluoride per million tons of water)? (Sodium fluoride is 45.0% fluoride, and one U.S. gallon of water has a mass of 8.34 lb.)

103. Name three elements that you have encountered today. (Name only those that you have seen as elements, not those combined into compounds.) Give the location of each of these elements in the periodic table by specifying the group and period in which it is found.

104. ■ Potassium has three stable isotopes, ^{39}K, ^{40}K, and ^{41}K, but ^{40}K has a very low natural abundance. Which of the other two is the more abundant?

105. Which one of these symbols conveys more information about the atom: ^{37}Cl or $_{17}Cl$? Explain.

106. The figure in the *Tools* box on p. 56 shows the mass spectrum of neon isotopes. What are the symbols of the isotopes? Which is the most abundant isotope? How many protons, neutrons, and electrons does this isotope have? Without looking at a periodic table, give the approximate atomic weight of neon.

107. When an athlete tears ligaments and tendons, they can be surgically attached to bone to keep them in place until they reattach themselves. A problem with current techniques, though, is that the screws and washers used are often too big to be positioned accurately or properly. Therefore, a titanium-containing device is used.
   (a) What are the symbol, atomic number, and atomic weight of titanium?
   (b) In what group and period is it found? Name the other elements of its group.
   (c) What chemical properties do you suppose make titanium an excellent choice for this and other surgical applications?
   (d) Use a dictionary, a book such as *The Handbook of Chemistry and Physics,* or the Internet to make a list of the properties of the element and its uses.

108. Draw a picture showing the approximate positions of all protons, electrons, and neutrons in an atom of helium-4. Make certain that your diagram indicates both the number and position of each type of particle.

109. Gems and precious stones are measured in carats, a weight unit equivalent to 200 mg. If you have a 2.3-carat diamond in a ring, how many moles of carbon do you have?

110. The international markets in precious metals operate in the weight unit "troy ounce" (where 1 troy ounce is equivalent to 31.1 g). Platinum sells for $1100 per troy ounce.
   (a) How many moles of Pt are there in 1 troy ounce?
   (b) If you have $5000 to spend, how many grams and how many moles of platinum can you purchase?

111. ■ Gold prices fluctuate, depending on the international situation. If gold currently sells for $600 per troy ounce, how much must you spend to purchase 1.00 mol gold (1 troy ounce is equivalent to 31.1 g)?

112. The Statue of Liberty in New York harbor is made of 2.00×10^5 lb of copper sheets bolted to an iron framework. How many grams and how many moles of copper does this represent (1 lb = 454 g)?

113. A piece of copper wire is 25 ft long and has a diameter of 2.0 mm. Copper has a density of 8.92 g/cm^3. How many moles of copper and how many atoms of copper are there in the piece of wire?

Applying Concepts

114. Which sets of values are possible? Why are the others not possible?

	Mass Number	Atomic Number	Number of Protons	Number of Neutrons
(a)	19	42	19	23
(b)	235	92	92	143
(c)	53	131	131	79
(d)	32	15	15	15
(e)	14	7	7	7
(f)	40	18	18	40

115. Which sets of values are possible? Why are the others not possible?

	Mass Number	Atomic Number	Number of Protons	Number of Neutrons
(a)	53	25	25	29
(b)	195	78	195	117
(c)	33	16	16	16
(d)	52	24	24	28
(e)	35	17	18	17

116. ■ Which member of each pair has the greater number of atoms? Explain why.
   (a) 1 mol Cl or 1 mol Cl_2
   (b) 1 molecule of O_2 or 1 mol O_2
   (c) 1 nitrogen atom or 1 nitrogen molecule
   (d) 6.022×10^{23} fluorine molecules or 1 mol fluorine molecules
   (e) 20.2 g Ne or 1 mol Ne
   (f) 1 molecule of Br_2 or 159.8 g Br_2
   (g) 107.9 g Ag or 6.9 g Li
   (h) 58.9 g Co or 58.9 g Cu
   (i) 1 g calcium or 6.022×10^{23} calcium atoms
   (j) 1 g chlorine atoms or 1 g chlorine molecules

117. Which member of each pair has the greater mass? Explain why.
   (a) 1 mol iron or 1 mol aluminum
   (b) 6.022×10^{23} lead atoms or 1 mol lead
   (c) 1 copper atom or 1 mol copper
   (d) 1 mol Cl or 1 mol Cl_2
   (e) 1 g oxygen atoms or 1 g oxygen molecules

(f) 24.3 g Mg or 1 mol Mg
(g) 1 mol Na or 1 g Na
(h) 4.0 g He or 6.022×10^{23} He atoms
(i) 1 molecule of I_2 or 1 mol I_2
(j) 1 oxygen molecule or 1 oxygen atom

More Challenging Questions

118. At 25 °C, the density of water is 0.997 g/cm^3, whereas the density of ice at −10 °C is 0.917 g/cm^3.
   (a) If a plastic soft-drink bottle (volume = 250 mL) is filled with pure water, capped, and then frozen at −10 °C, what volume will the solid occupy?
   (b) Could the ice be contained within the bottle?

119. A high-quality analytical balance can weigh accurately to the nearest 1.0×10^{-4} g. How many carbon atoms are present in 1.000 mg carbon, that could be weighed by such a balance? Given the precision of the balance, what are the high and low limits on the number of atoms present in the 1.000-mg sample?

120. A group of astronauts in a spaceship accidentally encounters a space warp that traps them in an alternative universe where the chemical elements are quite different from the ones they are used to. The astronauts find these properties for the elements that they have discovered:

Atomic Symbol	Atomic Weight	State	Color	Electrical Conductivity	Electrical Reactivity
A	3.2	Solid	Silvery	High	Medium
D	13.5	Gas	Colorless	Very low	Very high
E	5.31	Solid	Golden	Very high	Medium
G	15.43	Solid	Silvery	High	Medium
J	27.89	Solid	Silvery	High	Medium
L	21.57	Liquid	Colorless	Very low	Medium
M	11.23	Gas	Colorless	Very low	Very low
Q	8.97	Liquid	Colorless	Very low	Medium
R	1.02	Gas	Colorless	Very low	Very high
T	33.85	Solid	Colorless	Very low	Medium
X	23.68	Gas	Colorless	Very low	Very low
Z	36.2	Gas	Colorless	Very low	Medium
Ab	29.85	Solid	Golden	Very high	Medium

   (a) Arrange these elements into a periodic table.
   (b) If a new element, X, with atomic weight 25.84 is discovered, what would its properties be? Where would it fit in the periodic table you constructed?
   (c) Are there any elements that have not yet been discovered? If so, what would their properties be?

121. The element bromine is Br_2, so the mass of a Br_2 molecule is the sum of the mass of its two atoms. Bromine has two different isotopes. The mass spectrum of Br_2 produces three peaks with masses of 157.836, 159.834, and 161.832 amu, and relative heights of 25.54%, 49.99%, and 24.46%, respectively.
   (a) What isotopes of bromine are present in each of the three peaks?
   (b) What is the mass of each bromine isotope?
   (c) What is the average atomic mass of bromine?
   (d) What is the abundance of each of the two bromine isotopes?

122. Eleven of the elements in the periodic table are found in nature as gases at room temperature. List them. Where are they located in the periodic table?

123. Ten of the elements are O, H, Ar, Al, Ca, Br, Ge, K, Cu, and P. Pick the one that best fits each description: (a) an alkali metal; (b) a noble gas; (c) a transition metal; (d) a metalloid; (e) a Group 1 nonmetal; (f) a metal that forms a 3+ ion; (g) a nonmetal that forms a 2− ion; (h) an alkaline earth metal; (i) a halogen; (j) a nonmetal that is a solid.

124. Air mostly consists of diatomic molecules of nitrogen (about 80%) and oxygen (about 20%). Draw a nanoscale picture of a sample of air that contains a total of 10 molecules.

125. Identify the element that satisfies each of these descriptions:
   (a) A member of the same group as oxygen whose atoms contain 34 electrons
   (b) A member of the alkali metal group whose atoms contain 20 neutrons
   (c) A halogen whose atoms contain 35 protons and 44 neutrons
   (d) A noble gas whose atoms contain 10 protons and 10 neutrons

Conceptual Challenge Problems

CP2.A (Section 2.1) Suppose you are faced with a problem similar to the one faced by Robert Millikan when he analyzed data from his oil-drop experiment. Below are the masses of three stacks of dimes. What do you conclude to be the mass of a dime, and what is your argument?

Stack 1 = 9.12 g

Stack 2 = 15.96 g

Stack 3 = 27.36 g

CP2.B (Section 2.3) The age of the universe is unknown, but some conclude from measuring Hubble's constant that it is about 18 billion years old, which is about four times the age of the Earth. If so, what is the age of the universe in seconds? If you had a sample of carbon with the same number of carbon atoms as there have been seconds since the universe began, could you measure this sample on a laboratory balance that can detect masses as small as 0.1 mg?

3 Chemical Compounds

Stalactites are natural stone formations hanging from the ceilings of underground caves. They are formed by the interaction of water and limestone (calcite), which is largely $CaCO_3$. The water is weakly acidic due to dissolved carbon dioxide and dissolves $CaCO_3$. When the solution is exposed once again to air, the CO_2 escapes, and solid calcite is deposited. Over long time periods, fantastic shapes of solid stone are formed.

© David Muench/CORBIS

One of the most important things chemists do is synthesize new chemical compounds, substances that on the nanoscale consist of new, unique combinations of atoms. These compounds may have properties similar to those of existing compounds, or they may be very different. Often chemists can custom-design a new compound to have desirable properties. All compounds contain at least two elements, and most compounds contain more than two elements. This chapter deals with two major, general types of chemical compounds—those consisting of individual molecules, and those made of the positively and negatively charged atoms or groups of atoms called ions. We will now examine how compounds are represented by symbols, formulas, and names and how formulas represent the macroscale masses and compositions of compounds.

ThomsonNOW
Throughout the text, this icon indicates an opportunity to test yourself on key concepts and to explore interactive modules by signing in to ThomsonNOW at **www.thomsonedu.com**.

3.1 Molecular Compounds

In a **molecular compound** at the nanoscale level, atoms of two or more different elements are combined into the independent units known as molecules ***(← p. 26)***. Every day we inhale, exhale, metabolize, and in other ways use thousands of molecular compounds. Water, carbon dioxide, sucrose (table sugar), and caffeine, as well as carbohydrates, proteins, and fats, are among the many common molecular compounds in our bodies.

Metabolism is a general term for all of the chemical reactions that act to keep a living thing functioning. We *metabolize* food molecules to extract energy and produce other molecules needed by our bodies. Our *metabolic* reactions are controlled by enzymes (discussed in Section 13.9) and other kinds of molecules.

Molecular Formulas

The composition of a molecular compound is represented in writing by its **molecular formula,** in which the number and kinds of atoms combined to make one molecule of the compound are indicated by subscripts and elemental symbols. For example, the molecular formula for water, H_2O, shows that there are three atoms per molecule—two hydrogen atoms and one oxygen atom. The subscript to the right of each element's symbol indicates the number of atoms of that element present in the molecule. If the subscript is omitted, it is understood to be 1, as for the O in H_2O. These same principles apply to the molecular formulas of all molecules.

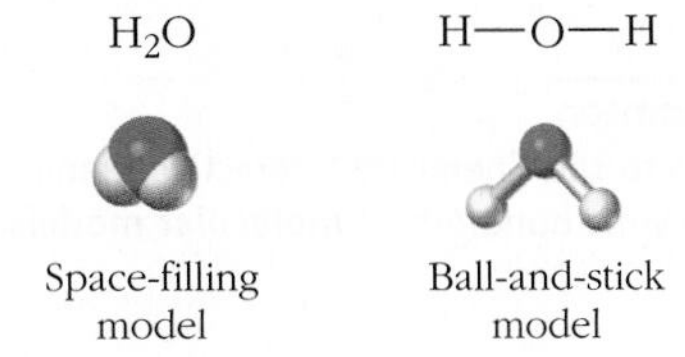

Some molecules are classified as **inorganic compounds** because they do not contain carbon—for example, sulfur dioxide, SO_2, an air pollutant, or ammonia, NH_3, which, dissolved in water, is used as a household cleaning agent. (Many inorganic compounds are ionic compounds, which are described in Section 3.5 of this chapter.) The majority of **organic compounds** are composed of molecules. Organic compounds invariably contain carbon, usually contain hydrogen, and may also contain oxygen, nitrogen, sulfur, phosphorus, or halogens. Such compounds are of great interest because they are the basis for the clothes we wear, the food we eat, the fuels we burn, and the living organisms in our environment. For example, ethanol (C_2H_6O) is the organic compound familiar as a component of "alcoholic" beverages, and methane (CH_4) is the organic compound that is the major component of natural gas.

Some elements are also composed of molecules. In oxygen, for example, two oxygen atoms are joined in an O_2 molecule ***(← p. 27)***.

The formula of a molecular compound, especially an organic compound, can be written in several different ways. The molecular formula given previously for ethanol, C_2H_6O, is one example. For an organic compound, the symbols of the elements other than carbon are frequently written in alphabetical order, and each has a subscript indicating the total number of atoms of that type in the molecule, as illustrated by C_2H_6O. Because of the huge number of organic compounds, this formula may not give sufficient information to indicate what compound is represented. Such identification requires more information about how the atoms are connected to each other. A **structural formula** shows exactly how atoms are connected. In ethanol, for example, the first carbon atom is connected to three hydrogen atoms, and the second carbon atom is connected to two hydrogen atoms and an —OH group.

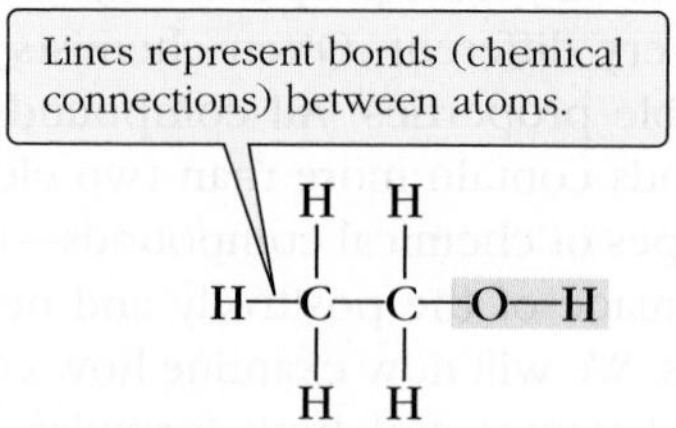

The formula can also be written in a modified form to show how the atoms are grouped together in the molecule. Such formulas, called **condensed formulas,** emphasize the atoms or groups of atoms connected to each carbon atom. For ethanol, the condensed formula is CH_3CH_2OH. If you compare this to the structural formula for ethanol, you can easily see that they represent the same structure. The —OH attached to the C atom is a distinctive grouping of atoms that characterizes the group of organic compounds known as alcohols. Such groups distinctive to the various classes of organic compounds are known as **functional groups.**

To summarize, three different ways of writing formulas are shown here for ethanol:

Structural formula	Condensed formula	Molecular formula
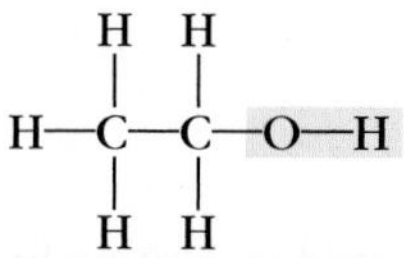	CH_3CH_2OH	C_2H_6O

ThomsonNOW
Go to the Chemistry Interactive menu to view hundreds of **molecular models.**

Atom colors in molecular models: H, light gray; C, dark gray; N, blue; O, red; S, yellow.

As illustrated earlier for molecular elements (p. 27), molecular compounds can also be represented by ball-and-stick and space-filling models.

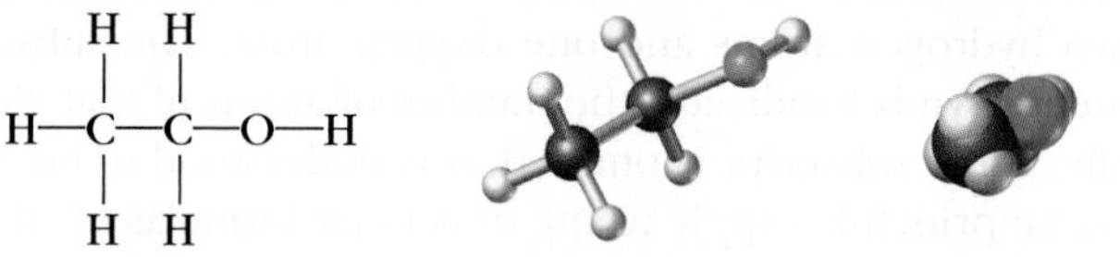
Structural formula — Ball-and-stick model — Space-filling model

Some additional examples of ball-and-stick molecular models are given on page 82 in Table 3.1.

PROBLEM-SOLVING EXAMPLE 3.1 Condensed and Molecular Formulas

(a) Write the molecular formulas for these molecules:

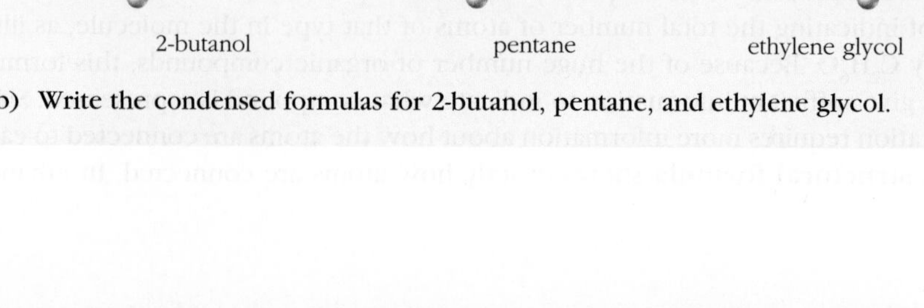

(b) Write the condensed formulas for 2-butanol, pentane, and ethylene glycol.

(c) Write the molecular formula for this molecule:

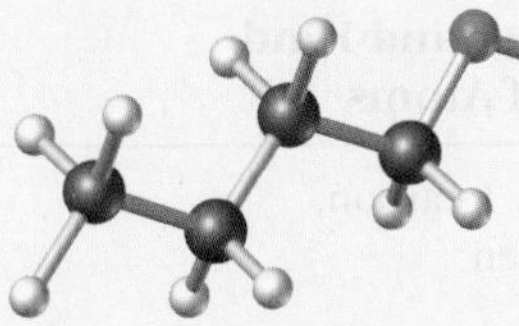

butanol

Answer

(a) 2-butanol, $C_4H_{10}O$; pentane, C_5H_{12}; ethylene glycol, $C_2H_6O_2$

(b)

```
              OH
              |
CH3—CH2—CH—CH3        CH3CH2CH2CH2CH3        HOCH2CH2OH
   2-butanol              pentane             ethylene glycol
```

(c) $C_4H_{10}O$

Strategy and Explanation

(a) Simply count the atoms of each type in each molecule to obtain the molecular formulas. Then write the symbols with their subscripts, putting C first and the others in alphabetical order.

(b) In condensed formulas, each carbon atom and its hydrogen atoms are written without connecting lines (CH_3, CH_2, or CH). Other groups are usually written on the same line with the carbon and hydrogen atoms if the groups are at the beginning or end of the molecule. Otherwise, they are connected above or below the line by straight lines to the respective carbon atoms. Condensed formulas emphasize important groups in molecules, such as the —OH groups in 2-butanol and ethylene glycol.

(c) Count the atoms of each type in the molecule to obtain the molecular formula.

ThomsonNOW™

Go to the Coached Problems menu for a tutorial on **representing compounds.**

PROBLEM-SOLVING PRACTICE 3.1

Write the molecular formulas for these compounds.

(a) Adenosine triphosphate (ATP), an energy source in biochemical reactions, which has 10 carbon, 11 hydrogen, 13 oxygen, 5 nitrogen, and 3 phosphorus atoms per molecule

(b) Capsaicin, the active ingredient in chili peppers, which has 18 carbon, 27 hydrogen, 3 oxygen, and 1 nitrogen atoms per molecule

(c) Oxalic acid, which has the condensed formula HOOCCOOH and is found in rhubarb.

EXERCISE 3.1 Structural, Condensed, and Molecular Formulas

A molecular model of propylene glycol, used in some "environmentally friendly" antifreezes, looks like this:

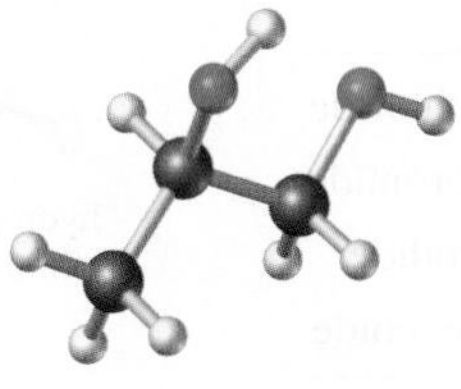

propylene glycol

Write the structural formula, the condensed formula, and the molecular formula for propylene glycol.

© Thomson Learning/George Semple

An automotive antifreeze that contains propylene glycol.

Table 3.1 Examples of Simple Molecular Compounds

Name	Molecular Formula	Number and Kind of Atoms	Molecular Model
Carbon dioxide	CO_2	3 total: 1 carbon, 2 oxygen	
Ammonia	NH_3	4 total: 1 nitrogen, 3 hydrogen	
Nitrogen dioxide	NO_2	3 total: 1 nitrogen, 2 oxygen	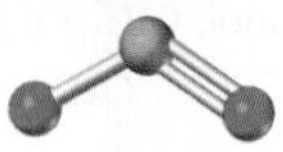
Carbon tetrachloride	CCl_4	5 total: 1 carbon, 4 chlorine	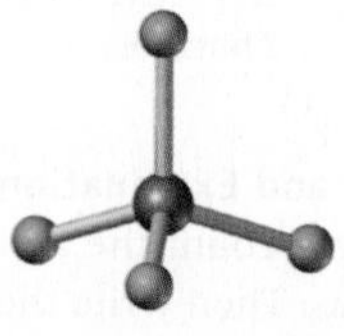
Octane	C_8H_{18}	26 total: 8 carbon, 18 hydrogen	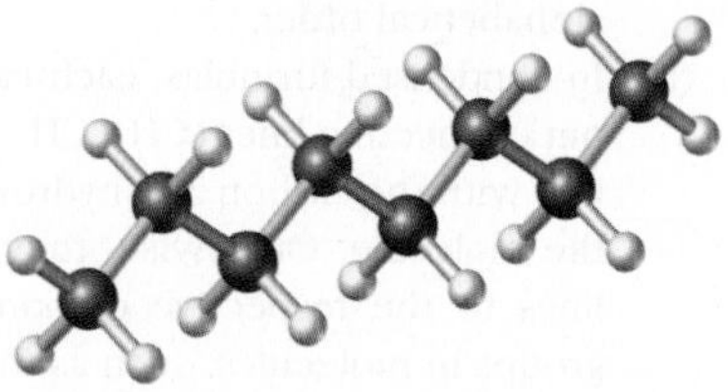

3.2 Naming Binary Inorganic Compounds

Hydrogen compounds with carbon are discussed in the next section.

Each element has a unique name, as does each chemical compound. The names of compounds are assigned in a systematic way based on well-established rules. We will begin by applying the rules used to name simple binary molecular compounds. We will introduce other naming rules as we need them in later chapters.

Binary molecular compounds consist of molecules that contain atoms of only two elements. There is a binary compound of hydrogen with every nonmetal except the noble gases. For hydrogen compounds containing oxygen, sulfur, and the halogens, the hydrogen is written first in the formula and named first. The other nonmetal is then named, with the nonmetal's name changed to end in *-ide.* For example, HCl is named hydrogen chloride.

Table 3.2 Prefixes Used in Naming Chemical Compounds

Prefix	Number
Mono-	1
Di-	2
Tri-	3
Tetra-	4
Penta-	5
Hexa-	6
Hepta-	7
Octa-	8
Nona-	9
Deca-	10

Formula	Name
HCl	Hydrogen chloride
HBr	Hydrogen bromide
HI	Hydrogen iodide
H_2Se	Hydrogen selenide

hydrogen chloride hydrogen bromide hydrogen iodide

Many binary molecular compounds contain nonmetallic elements from Groups 4A, 5A, 6A, and 7A of the periodic table. In these compounds the elements are listed in formulas and names in the order of the group numbers, and prefixes are used to designate the number of a particular kind of atom. The prefixes are listed in Table 3.2. Table 3.3 illustrates how these prefixes are applied.

Table 3.3 Examples of Binary Compounds

Molecular Formula	Name	Use
CO	Carbon monoxide	Steel manufacturing
NO_2	Nitrogen dioxide	Preparation of nitric acid
N_2O	Dinitrogen oxide	Anesthetic; spray can propellant
N_2O_5	Dinitrogen pentoxide	Forms nitric acid
PBr_3	Phosphorus tribromide	Forms phosphorous acid
PBr_5	Phosphorus pentabromide	Forms phosphoric acid
SF_6	Sulfur hexafluoride	Transformer insulator
P_4O_{10}	Tetraphosphorus decoxide	Drying agent

In dinitrogen pentoxide, the "a" is dropped from "penta" because "oxide" begins with a vowel.

A number of binary nonmetal compounds were discovered and named years ago, before systematic naming rules were developed. Such *common names* are still used today and must simply be learned.

Formula	Common Name	Formula	Common Name
H_2O	Water	NO	Nitric oxide
NH_3	Ammonia	N_2O	Nitrous oxide ("laughing gas")
N_2H_4	Hydrazine	PH_3	Phosphine

H_2O is written with H before O, as are the hydrogen compounds of Groups 6A and 7A: H_2S, H_2Se, and HF, HCl, HBr, and HI. Other H-containing compounds are usually written with the H atom after the other atom.

PROBLEM-SOLVING EXAMPLE 3.2 Naming Binary Inorganic Compounds

Name these compounds: (a) CO_2, (b) SiO_2, (c) SO_3, (d) N_2O_4, (e) PCl_5.

Answer

(a) Carbon dioxide (b) Silicon dioxide (c) Sulfur trioxide
(d) Dinitrogen tetroxide (e) Phosphorus pentachloride

Strategy and Explanation These compounds consist entirely of nonmetals, so they are all molecular compounds. The prefixes in Table 3.2 are used as necessary.

(a) Use *di-* to represent the two oxygen atoms.
(b) Use *di-* for the two oxygen atoms.
(c) Use *tri-* for the three oxygen atoms.
(d) Use *di-* for the two nitrogen atoms and *tetra-* for the four oxygen atoms. Drop the "a" because "oxide" begins with a vowel.
(e) Use *penta-* for the five chlorine atoms.

PROBLEM-SOLVING PRACTICE 3.2

Name these compounds: (a) SO_2, (b) BF_3, (c) CCl_4.

ThomsonNOW™
Go to the Coached Problems menu to work modules on **compounds of the nonmetals.**

EXERCISE 3.2 Names and Formulas of Compounds

Give the formula for each of these binary nonmetal compounds:

(a) Carbon disulfide
(b) Phosphorus trichloride
(c) Sulfur dibromide
(d) Selenium dioxide
(e) Oxygen difluoride
(f) Xenon trioxide

3.3 Hydrocarbons

Hydrocarbons are organic compounds composed of only carbon and hydrogen; they are the simplest class of organic compounds. Millions of organic compounds, including hydrocarbons, are known. They vary enormously in structure and function, ranging from the simple molecule methane (CH_4, the major constituent of natural gas) to large, complex biochemical molecules such as proteins, which often contain hundreds or thousands of atoms. Organic compounds are the main constituents of living matter. In organic compounds the carbon atoms are nearly always bonded to other carbon atoms and to hydrogen atoms. Among the reasons for the enormous variety of organic compounds is the characteristic property of carbon atoms to form strong, stable bonds with up to four other carbon atoms. A **chemical bond** is an attractive force between two atoms holding them together. Through their carbon-carbon bonds, carbon atoms can form chains, branched chains, rings, and other more complicated structures. With such a large number of compounds, dividing them into classes is necessary to make organic chemistry manageable.

The simplest major class of hydrocarbons is the **alkanes,** which are economically important fuels and lubricants. The simplest alkane is methane, CH_4, which has a central carbon atom with four bonds joining it to four H atoms (p. 85). The general formula for alkanes is C_nH_{2n+2}, where n is an integer. Table 3.4 provides some information about the first ten alkanes. The first four (methane, ethane, propane, butane) have common names that must be memorized. For $n = 5$ or greater, the names are systematic. The prefixes of Table 3.2 indicate the number of carbon atoms in the molecule, and the ending *-ane* indicates that the compound is an alk*ane*. For example, the five-carbon alkane is *pentane.*

Methane, the simplest alkane, makes up about 85% of natural gas in the U.S. Methane is also known to be one of the greenhouse gases (Section 10.13), meaning that it is one of the chemicals implicated in the problem of global warming. Ethane, propane, and butane are used as heating fuel for homes and in industry. In these simple alkanes, the carbon atoms are connected in unbranched chains, and each carbon atom is connected to either two or three hydrogen atoms.

© Thomson Learning/Charles D. Winters

Pentane is an alkane used as a solvent.

Table 3.4 The First Ten Alkane Hydrocarbons, C_nH_{2n+2}

Molecular Formula	Name	Boiling Point (°C)	Physical State at Room Temperature
CH_4	Methane	−161.6	Gas
C_2H_6	Ethane	−88.6	Gas
C_3H_8	Propane	−42.1	Gas
C_4H_{10}	Butane	−0.5	Gas
C_5H_{12}	Pentane	36.1	Liquid
C_6H_{14}	Hexane	68.7	Liquid
C_7H_{16}	Heptane	98.4	Liquid
C_8H_{18}	Octane	125.7	Liquid
C_9H_{20}	Nonane	150.8	Liquid
$C_{10}H_{22}$	Decane	174.0	Liquid

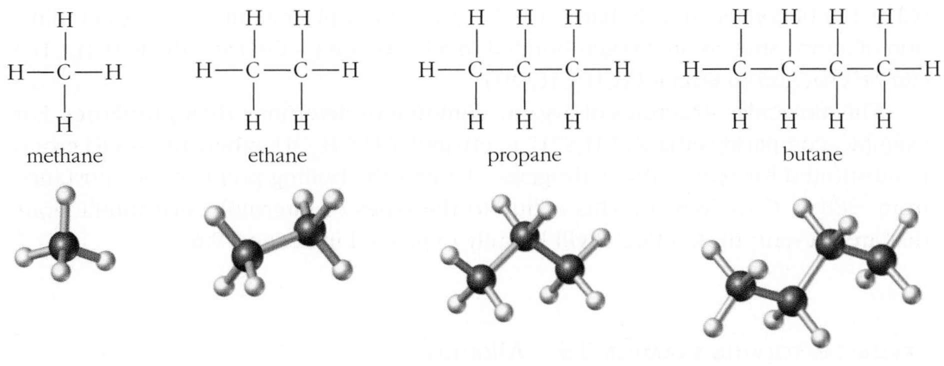

Larger alkanes have longer chains of carbon atoms with hydrogens attached to each carbon. For example, heptane (C_7H_{16}) is found in gasoline, and eicosane ($C_{20}H_{42}$) is found in paraffin wax.

$CH_3(CH_2)_5CH_3$
heptane

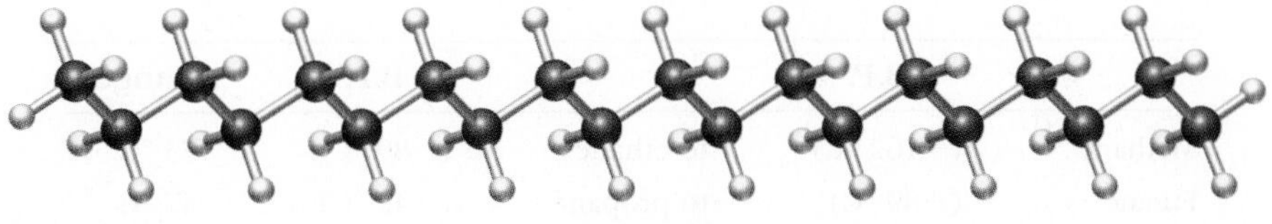

$CH_3(CH_2)_{18}CH_3$
eicosane

There are also cyclic hydrocarbons in which the carbon atoms are connected in rings, for example,

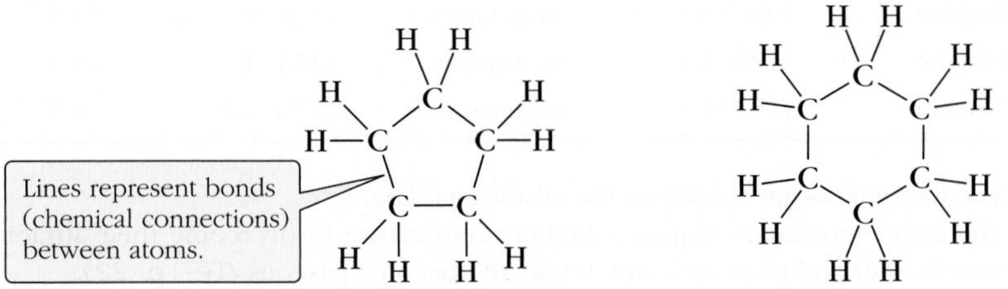

cyclopentane cyclohexane

EXERCISE 3.3 Alkane Molecular Formulas

(a) Using the general formula for alkanes, C_nH_{2n+2}, write the molecular formulas for the alkanes containing 16 and 28 carbon atoms.

(b) How many hydrogen atoms are present in tetradecane, which has 14 carbon atoms?

The molecular structures of hydrocarbons provide the framework for the discussion of the structures of all other organic compounds. If a different atom or combination of atoms replaces one of the hydrogens in the molecular structure of an alkane, a compound with different properties results. A hydrogen atom in an alkane can be replaced by a single atom such as a halogen, for example. In this way ethane

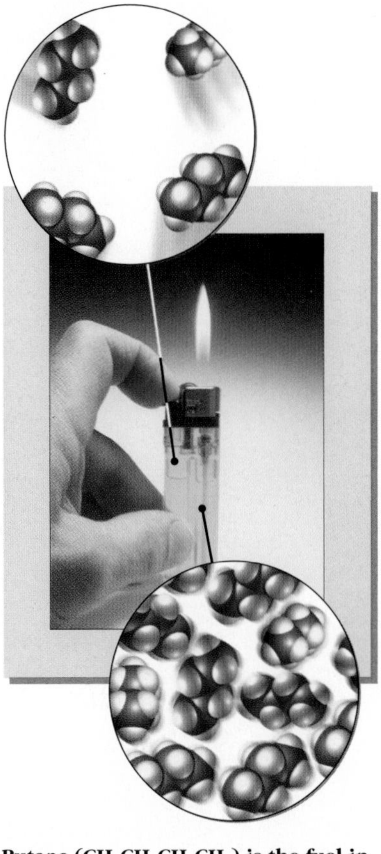

© Thomson Learning/Charles D. Winters

Butane ($CH_3CH_2CH_2CH_3$) is the fuel in this lighter. Butane molecules are present in the liquid and gaseous states in the lighter.

ThomsonNOW™

Go to the Coached Problems menu to work a simulation on **naming alkanes.**

(CH_3CH_3) becomes chloroethane (CH_3CH_2Cl). The replacement can be a combination of atoms such as an oxygen bonded to a hydrogen (—OH) so ethane (CH_3CH_3) can be changed to ethanol (CH_3CH_2OH).

The molecular structures of organic compounds determine their properties. For example, comparing ethane, CH_3CH_3, to ethanol, CH_3CH_2OH, where the —OH group is substituted for one of the hydrogens, changes the boiling point of the substance from −88.6 °C to 78.5 °C. This is due to the types of intermolecular interactions that are present; these effects will be fully explained in Section 9.6.

PROBLEM-SOLVING EXAMPLE 3.3 Alkanes

Table 3.4 gives the boiling points for the first ten alkane hydrocarbons.

(a) Is the change in boiling point constant from one alkane to the next in the series?

(b) What do you propose as the explanation for the manner in which the boiling point changes from one alkane to the next?

Answer

(a) No. The increment is large between methane and ethane and gets progressively smaller as the compounds get larger. It is only 23 °C between nonane and decane.

(b) Larger molecules must interact more strongly and therefore require a higher temperature to move apart and to become gaseous.

Strategy and Explanation We analyze the data given in Table 3.4.

(a) The boiling point differences between successive alkanes are

	B.P.		B.P.	Change
Methane	(−162 °C)	to ethane	(−89 °C):	73 °C
Ethane	(−89 °C)	to propane	(−42 °C):	47 °C
Propane	(−42 °C)	to butane	(0 °C):	42 °C
Butane	(0 °C)	to pentane	(36 °C):	36 °C
Pentane	(36 °C)	to hexane	(69 °C):	33 °C
Hexane	(69 °C)	to heptane	(98 °C):	29 °C
Heptane	(98 °C)	to octane	(126 °C):	28 °C
Octane	(126 °C)	to nonane	(151 °C):	25 °C
Nonane	(151 °C)	to decane	(174 °C):	23 °C

The increments get smaller as the alkanes get larger.

(b) The larger molecules require a higher temperature to overcome their attraction to one another and to cease being liquid and become gaseous (⇐ *p. 22*).

PROBLEM-SOLVING PRACTICE 3.3

Consider a series of molecules formed from the alkanes by substituting one of the hydrogen atoms with a chlorine atom. Would you expect a similar trend in changes in boiling points among this set of compounds as you observed with the alkanes themselves?

3.4 Alkanes and Their Isomers

Two or more compounds that have the same molecular formula but different arrangements of atoms are called **isomers.** Isomers differ from one another in one or more physical properties, such as boiling point, color, and solubility; chemical reactivity differs as well. Several types of isomerism are possible, particularly in organic compounds. **Constitutional isomers** (also called structural isomers) are compounds with the same molecular formula that differ in the order in which their atoms are bonded.

Straight-Chain and Branched-Chain Isomers of Alkanes

The first three alkanes—methane, ethane, and propane—have only one possible structural arrangement. When we come to the alkane with four carbon atoms, C_4H_{10}, there are two possible arrangements—a *straight* chain of four carbons (butane) or a *branched* chain of three carbons with the fourth carbon attached to the central atom of the chain of three (methylpropane), as shown in the table.

Butane and methylpropane are constitutional isomers because they have the same molecular formula, but they are different compounds with different properties. Two constitutional isomers are different from each other in the same sense that two different structures built with identical Lego blocks are different from each other.

Methylpropane, the branched isomer of butane, has a *methyl* group ($—CH_3$) bonded to the central carbon atom. A methyl group is the simplest example of an **alkyl group,** the fragment of the molecule that remains when a hydrogen atom is removed from an alkane. Addition of one hydrogen to a methyl group gives methane:

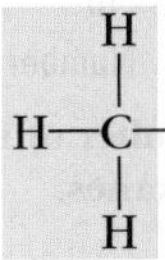

$CH_3—$ methyl group

Addition of one hydrogen to an ethyl group gives ethane:

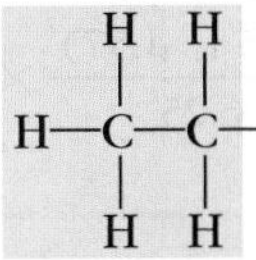

$CH_3CH_2—$ ethyl group

In this context, "straight chain" means a chain of carbon atoms with no branches to other carbon atoms; the carbon atoms are in an unbranched sequence. As you can see from the molecular model of butane, the chain is not actually straight, but rather a zigzag.

Historically, straight-chain hydrocarbons were referred to as *normal* hydrocarbons, and *n*- was used as a prefix in their names. The current practice is not to use *n*-. If a hydrocarbon's name is given without indication that it is a branched-chain compound, assume it is a straight-chain hydrocarbon.

ThomsonNOW
Go to the Coached Problems menu for an exercise on **representing isomers.**

Molecular Formula	Condensed Formula	Structural Formula	Molecular Model
Butane C_4H_{10}	$CH_3CH_2CH_2CH_3$ Melting point −138 °C Boiling point −0.5 °C	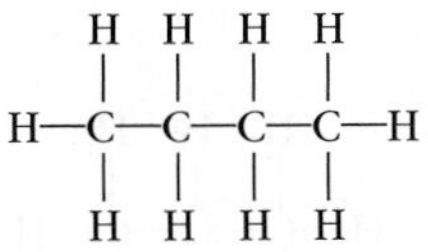	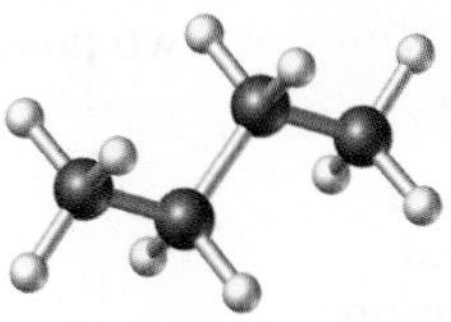
Methylpropane C_4H_{10}	$CH_3—CH(CH_3)—CH_3$ Melting point −145 °C Boiling point −11.6 °C	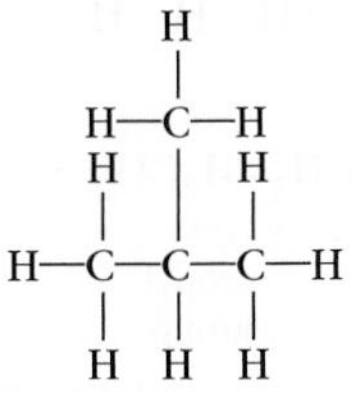	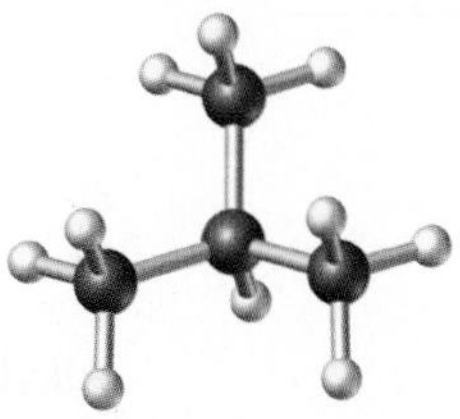

ESTIMATION

Number of Alkane Isomers

The number of possible carbon compounds is truly enormous. Table 3.6 (p. 89) shows how the number of isomers of the simplest hydrocarbon compounds, alkanes, increases as the number of carbon atoms increases. How could we use these data to estimate the number of alkane isomers for a much larger number of carbon atoms? More specifically, let's estimate the number of alkane isomers for C_{40} and check the result against the last entry in the table.

To picture the growth rate, we could plot the number of alkane isomers versus the number of carbon atoms. If we made such a linear plot—that is, with the *x*-axis as the number of carbon atoms and the *y*-axis as the number of alkane isomers—we would see very little, because the plot would be rising so fast. To keep the final point on the plot, the *y*-axis would be so expanded that all the other points would be squashed toward the bottom of the plot. Therefore, to make these data easier to view, we plot the logarithm of the number of isomers, $\log(N_i)$, versus the number of carbon atoms (see the figure). The points lie on a slightly concave-upward curve, but a line fitted through them would be reasonably close to a straight line.

Now we are ready to make our estimate. To estimate how many isomers there are for C_{40}, we will extrapolate from the C_{20} and C_{30} points. The $\log(N_i)$ for C_{20} is 5.56, and the $\log(N_i)$ for C_{30} is 9.61; the difference is $9.61 - 5.56 = 4.05$. Our estimate of the $\log(N_i)$ at C_{40} will be this increment added to the value of the $\log(N_i)$ for C_{30}:

$$\log(N_i) \text{ for } C_{40} = [\log(N_i) \text{ for } C_{30}] + \text{increment}$$
$$= 9.61 + 4.05 = 13.66$$

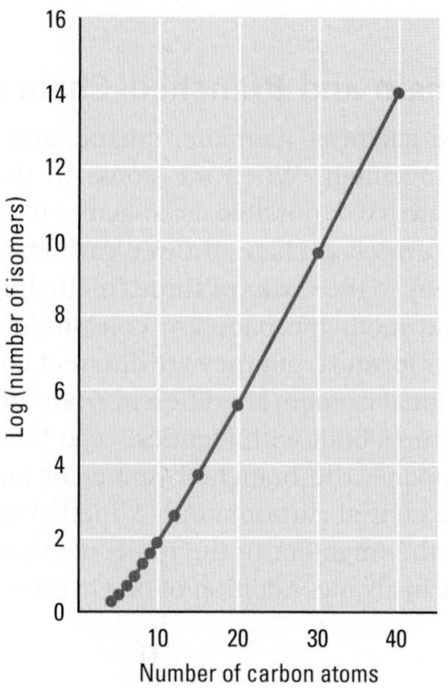

Semilog plot of the number of isomers versus the number of carbon atoms for alkanes.

To calculate the number of isomers at C_{40} we take the antilog$(13.66) = 4.57 \times 10^{13}$. Since the curve on the plot is concave upward, we know that our estimate will be a little too low, but it is still reasonable. The actual number of alkane isomers for C_{40} is 6.25×10^{13}. Our estimate is only 27% off.

$$\frac{(6.25 - 4.57)}{6.25} \times 100\% = 27\%$$

Table 3.5 Some Common Alkyl Groups

Name	Condensed Structural Representation
Methyl	CH_3—
Ethyl	CH_3CH_2—
Propyl	$CH_3CH_2CH_2$—
Isopropyl	CH_3CH— with CH_3 below or $(CH_3)_2CH$—

When we consider the alkyl group with three carbons, the propyl group, there are two possibilities:

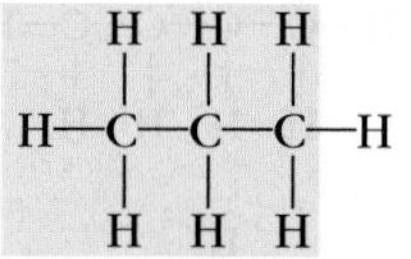

$CH_3CH_2CH_2$—

propyl group

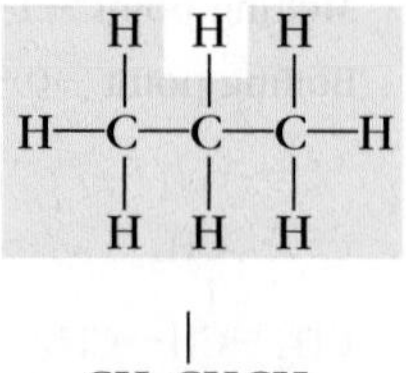

CH_3CHCH_3

isopropyl group

Alkyl groups are named by dropping *-ane* from the parent alkane name and adding *-yl*. Theoretically, an alkyl group can be derived from any alkane. Some of the more common examples of alkyl groups are given in Table 3.5.

Table 3.6 Alkane Isomers

Molecular Formula	Number of Isomers	Molecular Formula	Number of Isomers
CH_4	1	C_9H_{20}	35
C_2H_6	1	$C_{10}H_{22}$	75
C_3H_8	1	$C_{12}H_{26}$	355
C_4H_{10}	2	$C_{15}H_{32}$	4347
C_5H_{12}	3	$C_{20}H_{42}$	366,319
C_6H_{14}	5	$C_{30}H_{62}$	4,111,846,763
C_7H_{16}	9	$C_{40}H_{82}$	62,491,178,805,831
C_8H_{18}	18		

The number of alkane constitutional isomers grows rapidly as the number of carbon atoms increases because of the possibility of chain branching. Table 3.6 shows the number of isomers for some alkanes. Chain branching is another reason for the extraordinary number of possible organic compounds.

CONCEPTUAL EXERCISE **3.4 Straight-Chain and Branched-Chain Isomers**

Three constitutional isomers are possible for pentane. Write structural and condensed formulas for these isomers.

3.5 Ions and Ionic Compounds

Not all compounds are molecular. A compound whose nanoscale composition consists of positive and negative ions is classified as an **ionic compound.** Many common substances, such as table salt (NaCl), lime (CaO), lye (NaOH), and baking soda ($NaHCO_3$), are ionic compounds.

When metals react with nonmetals, the ***metal atoms typically lose electrons to form positive ions.*** Any positive ion is referred to as a **cation** (pronounced CAT-ion). Cations always have *fewer* electrons than protons. For example, Figure 3.1 shows that an electrically neutral sodium atom, which has 11 protons [11+] and 11 electrons [11−], can lose one electron to become a sodium cation, which, with 11 protons but only 10 electrons, has a net 1+ charge and is symbolized as Na^+. ***The quantity of positive charge on a cation equals the number of electrons lost by the neutral metal atom.*** For example, when a neutral magnesium atom loses two electrons, it forms a 2+ magnesium ion, Mg^{2+}.

The terms "cation" and "anion" are derived from the Greek words *ion* (traveling), *cat* (down), and *an* (up).

© Thomson Learning/Charles D. Winters

Ionic compounds. Red iron(III) oxide, black copper(II) bromide, CaF_2 (front crystal), and NaCl (rear crystal).

Conversely, when nonmetals react with metals, the ***nonmetal atoms typically gain electrons to form negatively charged ions.*** Any negative ion is an **anion** (pronounced ANN-ion). Anions always have *more* electrons than protons. Figure 3.1 shows that a neutral chlorine atom (17 protons, 17 electrons) can gain an electron to form a chlor*ide* ion, Cl^-. With 17 protons and 18 electrons, the chloride ion has a *net* 1− charge. ***The quantity of negative charge on a nonmetal anion equals the number of electrons gained by the neutral nonmetal atom.*** For example, a neutral sulfur atom that gains two electrons forms a sulf*ide* ion, S^{2-}.

Monatomic Ions

A **monatomic ion** is a single atom that has lost or gained electrons. The charges of the common monatomic ions are given in Figure 3.2. Notice that metals of

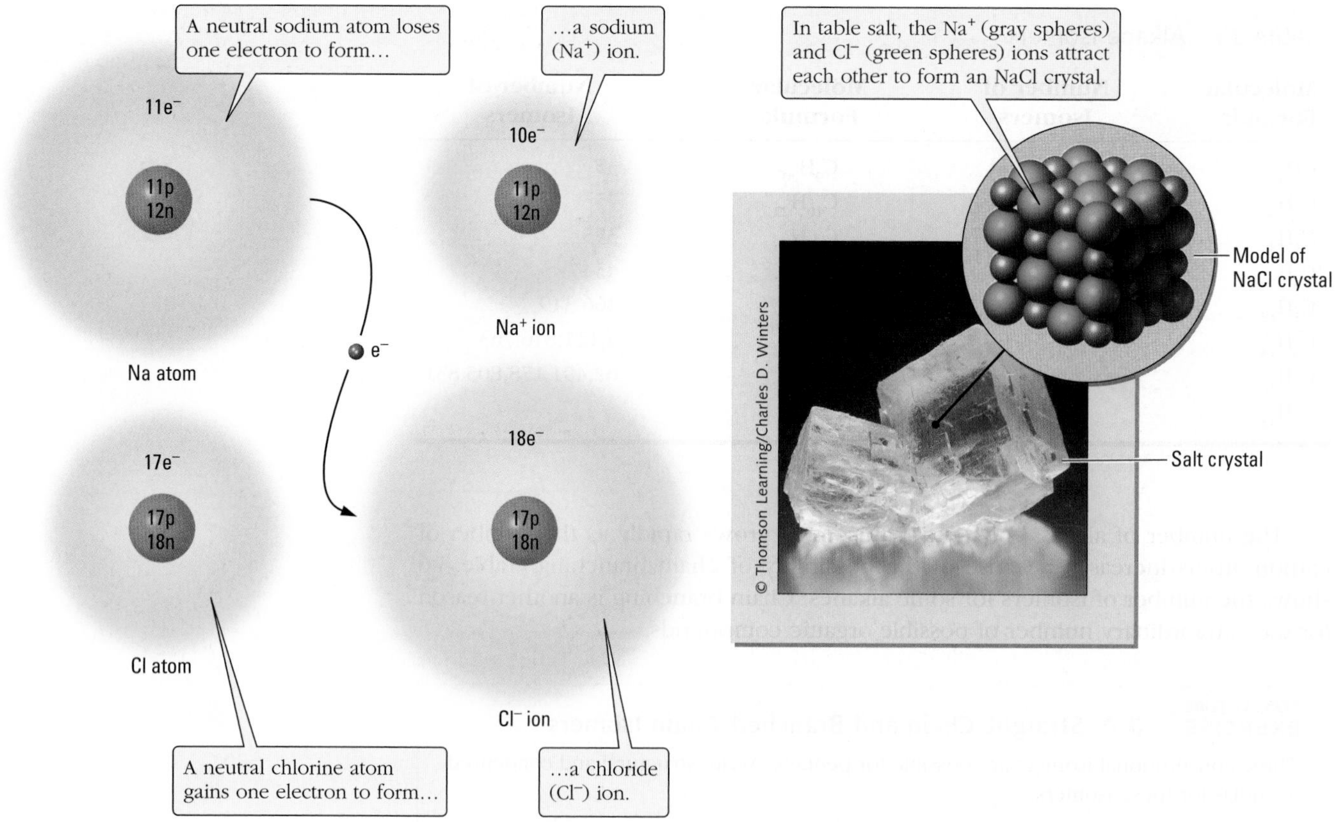

Active Figure 3.1 **Formation of the ionic compound NaCl. Go to the Active Figures menu at ThomsonNOW to test your understanding of the concepts in this figure.**

Groups 1A, 2A, and 3A form monatomic ions with charges *equal to the A group number.* For example,

Group	Neutral Metal Atom	Electrons Lost = A Group Number	Metal Ion
1A	K (19 protons, 19 electrons)	1	K^+ (19 protons, 18 electrons)
2A	Mg (12 protons, 12 electrons)	2	Mg^{2+} (12 protons, 10 electrons)
3A	Al (13 protons, 13 electrons)	3	Al^{3+} (13 protons, 10 electrons)

In Section 8.2 we explain the basis for the (8 − group number) relationship for nonmetals.

Nonmetals of Groups 5A, 6A, and 7A form monatomic ions that have a negative charge *usually equal to 8 minus the A group number.* For example,

Group	Neutral Nonmetal Atom	Electrons Gained = 8 − A Group Number	Nonmetal Ion
5A	N (7 protons, 7 electrons)	3 = (8 − 5)	N^{3-} (7 protons, 10 electrons)
6A	S (16 protons, 16 electrons)	2 = (8 − 6)	S^{2-} (16 protons, 18 electrons)
7A	F (9 protons, 9 electrons)	1 = (8 − 7)	F^- (9 protons, 10 electrons)

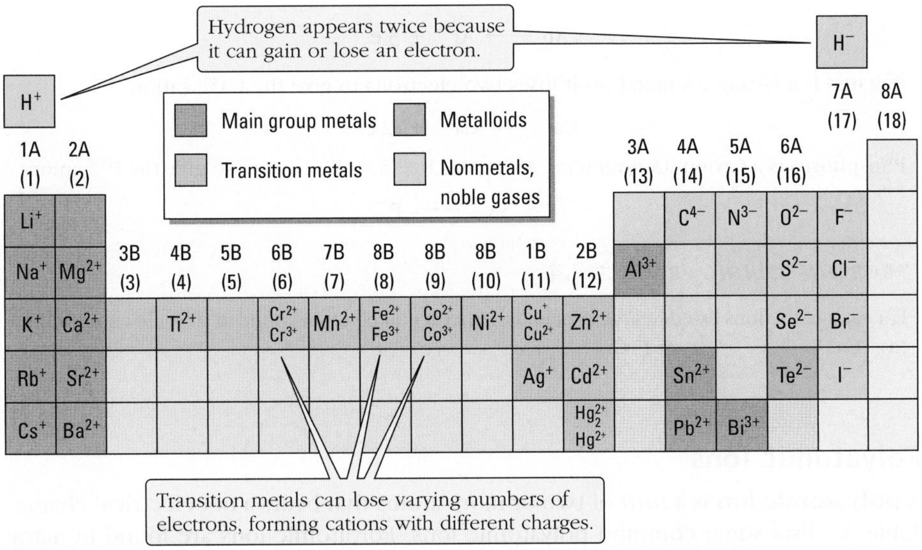

Figure 3.2 **Charges on some common monatomic cations and anions.** Note that metals generally form cations. The cation charge is given by the group number in the case of the main group elements of Groups 1A, 2A, and 3A *(gray)*. For transition elements *(blue)*, the positive charge is variable, and other ions in addition to those illustrated are possible. Nonmetals *(lavender)* generally form anions that have a charge equal to 8 minus the A group number.

It is extremely important that you know the ions commonly formed by the elements shown in Figure 3.2 so that you can recognize ionic compounds and their formulas and write their formulas as reaction products (Section 5.1).

ThomsonNOW™
Go to the Chemistry Interactive menu to view animations on:

- **ion formation**
- **formation of ionic compounds and the reaction of sodium and chlorine**

You might have noticed in Figure 3.2 that hydrogen appears at two locations in the periodic table. This is because a hydrogen atom can either gain or lose an electron. When it loses an electron, it forms a hydrogen ion, H^+ (1 proton, 0 electrons). When it gains an electron, it forms a hydride ion, H^- (1 proton, 2 electrons).

Noble gas atoms do not easily lose or gain electrons and have no common ions to list in Figure 3.2.

Transition metals form cations but can lose varying numbers of electrons, thus forming ions of different charges (Figure 3.2). Therefore, the group number is not an accurate guide to charges in these cases. It is important to learn which ions are formed most frequently by these metals. Many transition metals form 2+ and 3+ ions. For example, iron atoms can lose two or three electrons to form Fe^{2+} (26 protons, 24 electrons) or Fe^{3+} (26 protons, 23 electrons), respectively.

An older naming system for distinguishing between metal ions of different charges uses the ending *-ic* for the ion of higher charge and *-ous* for the ion of lower charge. These endings are combined with the element's name—for example, Fe^{2+} (ferrous) and Fe^{3+} (ferric) or Cu^+ (cuprous) and Cu^{2+} (cupric). We will not use these names in this book, but you might encounter them elsewhere.

PROBLEM-SOLVING EXAMPLE 3.4 Predicting Ion Charges

Predict the charges on ions of aluminum, calcium, and phosphorus, and write symbols for these ions.

Answer Al^{3+}, Ca^{2+}, P^{3-}

Strategy and Explanation We find each element in the periodic table and use its position to answer the questions. Aluminum is a Group 3A metal, so it loses three electrons to give the Al^{3+} cation.

ThomsonNOW™
Go to the Coached Problems menu for a tutorial on **predicting ion charges.**

$$Al \longrightarrow Al^{3+} + 3\ e^-$$

Calcium is a Group 2A metal, so it loses two electrons to give the Ca^{2+} cation.

$$Ca \longrightarrow Ca^{2+} + 2\ e^-$$

Phosphorus is a Group 5A nonmetal, so it gains $8 - 5 = 3$ electrons to give the P^{3-} anion.

$$P + 3\ e^- \longrightarrow P^{3-}$$

PROBLEM-SOLVING PRACTICE 3.4

For each of the ions listed below, explain whether it is likely to be found in an ionic compound.
(a) Ca^{4+} (b) Cr^{2+} (c) Sr^-

Polyatomic Ions

A **polyatomic ion** is a *unit* of two or more atoms that bears a net electrical charge. Table 3.7 lists some common polyatomic ions. Polyatomic ions are found in many places—oceans, minerals, living cells, and foods. For example, hydrogen carbonate (bicarbonate) ion, HCO_3^-, is present in rain water, sea water, blood, and baking soda. It consists of one carbon atom, three oxygen atoms, and one hydrogen atom, with one unit of negative charge spread over the group of five atoms. The polyatomic sulfate ion, SO_4^{2-}, consists of one sulfur atom and four oxygen atoms and has an overall charge of 2−. One of the most common polyatomic cations is NH_4^+, the ammonium ion. In this case, four hydrogen atoms are connected to a nitrogen atom, and the group bears a net 1+ charge. (We discuss the naming of polyatomic ions containing oxygen atoms in Section 3.6.)

In many chemical reactions the polyatomic ion unit remains intact. *It is important to know the names, formulas, and charges of the common polyatomic ions listed in Table 3.7.*

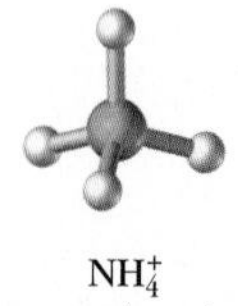
NH_4^+
ammonium ion

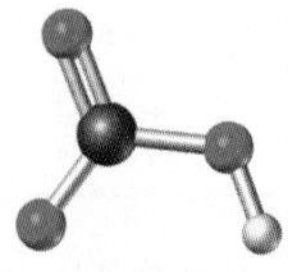
HCO_3^-
hydrogen carbonate ion

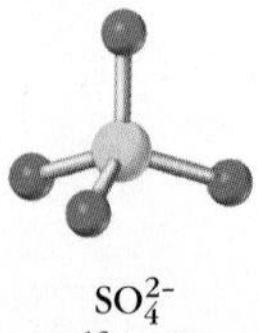
SO_4^{2-}
sulfate ion

Table 3.7 Common Polyatomic Ions

Cation (1+)			
NH_4^+	Ammonium		
Anions (1−)			
OH^-	Hydroxide	NO_2^-	Nitrite
HSO_4^-	Hydrogen sulfate	NO_3^-	Nitrate
CH_3COO^-	Acetate	MnO_4^-	Permanganate
ClO^-	Hypochlorite	$H_2PO_4^-$	Dihydrogen phosphate
ClO_2^-	Chlorite	CN^-	Cyanide
ClO_3^-	Chlorate	HCO_3^-	Hydrogen carbonate (bicarbonate)
ClO_4^-	Perchlorate		
Anions (2−)			
CO_3^{2-}	Carbonate	SO_3^{2-}	Sulfite
HPO_4^{2-}	Monohydrogen phosphate	SO_4^{2-}	Sulfate
$Cr_2O_7^{2-}$	Dichromate	$C_2O_4^{2-}$	Oxalate
$S_2O_3^{2-}$	Thiosulfate		
Anion (3−)			
PO_4^{3-}	Phosphate		

Ionic Compounds

In ionic compounds, cations and anions are attracted to each other by electrostatic forces, the forces of attraction between positive and negative charges. The strength of the electrostatic force dictates many of the properties of ionic compounds.

The attraction between oppositely charged ions increases with charge and decreases with the distance between the ions. The force between two charged particles is given quantitatively by **Coulomb's law:**

$$F = k\frac{Q_1Q_2}{d^2}$$

where Q_1 and Q_2 are the magnitudes of the charges on the two interacting particles, d is the distance between the two particles, and k is a constant. For ions separated by the same distance, the attractive force between 2+ and 2− ions is four times greater than that between 1+ and 1− ions. The attractive force also increases as the distance between the centers of the ions decreases. Thus, a small cation and a small anion will attract each other more strongly than will larger ions. (We discuss the sizes of ions in Section 7.10.)

Classifying compounds as ionic or molecular is very useful because these two types of compounds have quite different properties and thus different uses. The following generalizations will help you to predict whether a compound is ionic.

1. When a compound is composed of a metal cation (the elements in the gray and blue areas in Figure 3.2) and a nonmetal anion (the elements in the lavender area of Figure 3.2), it is an ionic compound, especially if the metal atom is combined with just one or two nonmetal atoms. Examples of such compounds include NaCl, $CaCl_2$, and KI.
2. When a compound is composed of two or more nonmetals, it is likely to be a molecular compound. Examples of such compounds include H_2O, NH_3, and CCl_4. Organic compounds, which contain carbon and hydrogen and possibly also oxygen, nitrogen, or halogens, are molecular compounds. Examples include acetic acid, $HC_2H_3O_2$, and urea, CH_4N_2O.
3. If several nonmetal atoms are combined into a polyatomic anion, such as SO_4^{2-}, and this anion is combined with a metal ion, such as Ca^{2+}, the compound will be ionic. Examples include $CaSO_4$, $NaNO_3$, and KOH. If several nonmetal atoms are combined into a polyatomic cation, such as NH_4^+, this cation can be combined with an anion to form an ionic compound. Examples include NH_4Cl and $(NH_4)_2SO_4$.
4. Metal atoms can be part of polyatomic anions (MnO_4^- or $Cr_2O_7^{2-}$). When such polyatomic anions are combined with a metal ion, an ionic compound results—for example, $K_2Cr_2O_7$.
5. Metalloids (the elements in the orange area of Figure 3.2) can be incorporated into either ionic or molecular compounds. For example, the metalloid boron can combine with the nonmetal chlorine to form the molecular compound BCl_3. The metalloid arsenic is found in the arsenate ion in the ionic compound K_3AsO_4.

ThomsonNOW™
Go to the Coached Problems menu for tutorials on:
- **identifying polyatomic ions**
- **Coulomb's law**

Don't confuse NH_4^+, ammonium ion, with NH_3, which is a molecular compound.

© Thomson Learning/Marna G. Clarke

Potassium dichromate, $K_2Cr_2O_7$. This beautiful orange-red compound contains potassium ions (K^+) and dichromate ions ($Cr_2O_7^{2-}$).

PROBLEM-SOLVING EXAMPLE 3.5 Ionic and Molecular Compounds

Predict whether each compound is likely to be ionic or molecular:

(a) Li_2CO_3	(b) C_3H_8	(c) $Fe_2(SO_4)_3$
(d) N_2H_4	(e) Na_2S	(f) CO_2

Answer

(a) Ionic	(b) Molecular	(c) Ionic
(d) Molecular	(e) Ionic	(f) Molecular

Strategy and Explanation For each compound we use the location of its elements in the periodic table and our knowledge of polyatomic ions to answer the question.

(a) Lithium is a metal, so the lithium ion, Li^+, and the polyatomic carbonate CO_3^{2-} ion form an ionic compound.
(b) This compound is propane, an alkane hydrocarbon, composed entirely of nonmetal atoms, so it is molecular.
(c) Iron is a metal, so the Fe^{3+} ion and the polyatomic SO_4^{2-} sulfate ion form an ionic compound.
(d) This compound is hydrazine, and since it is composed entirely of nonmetal atoms, it is molecular.
(e) Sodium is a metal and sulfur is a nonmetal, so they form an ionic compound of Na^+ and S^{2-} ions.
(f) This compound is carbon dioxide, and since it is composed entirely of nonmetal atoms, it is molecular.

PROBLEM-SOLVING PRACTICE 3.5

Predict whether each of these compounds is likely to be ionic or molecular:
(a) CH_4 (b) $CaBr_2$ (c) $MgCl_2$ (d) PCl_3 (e) KCl

Writing Formulas for Ionic Compounds

All compounds are electrically neutral. Therefore, when cations and anions combine to form an ionic compound, there must be zero net charge. The *total* positive charge of all the cations must equal the *total* negative charge of all the anions. For example, consider the ionic compound formed when potassium reacts with sulfur. Potassium is a Group 1A metal, so a potassium atom loses one electron to become a K^+ ion. Sulfur is a Group 6A nonmetal, so a sulfur atom gains two electrons to become an S^{2-} ion. To make the compound electrically neutral, two K^+ ions (total charge 2+) are needed for each S^{2-} ion. Consequently, the compound has the formula K_2S. The subscripts in an ionic compound formula show the numbers of ions included in the simplest formula unit. In this case, the subscript 2 indicates two K^+ ions for every S^{2-} ion.

As with the formulas for molecular compounds, a subscript of 1 in formulas of ionic compounds is understood to be there and is not written.

Similarly, aluminum oxide, a combination of Al^{3+} and O^{2-} ions, has the formula Al_2O_3: 2 Al^{3+} gives 6+ charge; 3 O^{2-} gives 6− charge; total charge = 0.

Al_2O_3

Two 3+ aluminum ions | Three 2− oxide ions

Notice that in writing the formulas for ionic compounds, *the cation symbol is written first, followed by the anion symbol.* The charges of the ions are *not* included in the formulas of ionic compounds.

Let's now consider several ionic compounds of magnesium, a Group 2A metal that forms Mg^{2+} ions.

ThomsonNOW™
Go to the Coached Problems menu for a tutorial on **ionic compound formulas.**

Combining Ions	Overall Charge	Formula
Mg^{2+} and Br^-	(2+) + 2(1−) = 0	$MgBr_2$
Mg^{2+} and SO_4^{2-}	(2+) + (2−) = 0	$MgSO_4$
Mg^{2+} and OH^-	(2+) + 2(1−) = 0	$Mg(OH)_2$
Mg^{2+} and PO_4^{3-}	3(2+) + 2(3−) = 0	$Mg_3(PO_4)_2$

Notice in the latter two cases that when a polyatomic ion occurs more than once in a formula, the polyatomic ion's formula is put in parentheses followed by the necessary subscript.

$Mg_3(PO_4)_2$

Three 2+ magnesium ions | Two 3− phosphate ions

PROBLEM-SOLVING EXAMPLE 3.6 Ions in Ionic Compounds

For each compound, give the symbol or formula of each ion present and indicate how many of each ion are represented in the formula:

(a) Li_2S (b) Na_2SO_3 (c) $Ca(CH_3COO)_2$ (d) $Al_2(SO_4)_3$

Answer

(a) Two Li^+, one S^{2-} (b) Two Na^+, one SO_3^{2-}

(c) One Ca^{2+}, two CH_3COO^- (d) Two Al^{3+}, three SO_4^{2-}

Strategy and Explanation

(a) Lithium is a Group 1A element and *always* forms 1+ ions. The S^{2-} ion is formed from sulfur, a Group 6A element, by gaining two electrons (8 − 6 = 2). To maintain electrical neutrality, there must be two Li^+ ions for each S^{2-} ion.

(b) Sodium is a Group 1A element and therefore forms Na^+. Two Na^+ ions offset the 2− charge of the single polyatomic sulfite ion, SO_3^{2-} (see Table 3.7).

(c) Calcium is a Group 2A element that always forms 2+ ions. To have electrical neutrality, the two acetate ions with their 1− charge are needed to offset the 2+ charge on the Ca^{2+}.

(d) Aluminum, a Group 3A element, forms Al^{3+} ions. A 2 : 3 combination of two Al^{3+} ions (2 × 3+ = 6+) with three 2− sulfate ions, SO_4^{2-} (3 × 2− = 6−), gives electrical neutrality.

PROBLEM-SOLVING PRACTICE 3.6

Determine how many ions and how many atoms there are in each of these formulas.

(a) $In_2(SO_3)_3$ (b) $(NH_4)_3PO_4$

PROBLEM-SOLVING EXAMPLE 3.7 Formulas of Ionic Compounds

Write the correct formulas for ionic compounds composed of (a) calcium and fluoride ions, (b) barium and phosphate ions, (c) Fe^{3+} and nitrate ions, and (d) sodium and carbonate ions.

Answer

(a) CaF_2 (b) $Ba_3(PO_4)_2$ (c) $Fe(NO_3)_3$ (d) Na_2CO_3

Strategy and Explanation We use the location of each element in the periodic table and the charges on polyatomic anions to answer the questions.

(a) Calcium is a Group 2A metal, so it forms 2+ ions. Fluorine is a Group 7A nonmetal that forms 1− ions. Therefore, we need two 1− F^- ions for every Ca^{2+} ion to make CaF_2.

(b) Barium is a Group 2A metal, so it forms 2+ ions. Phosphate is a 3− polyatomic ion. Therefore, we need two Ba^{2+} ions and three PO_4^{3-} ions to form $Ba_3(PO_4)_2$. The polyatomic phosphate ion is enclosed in parentheses followed by the proper subscript.

(c) Iron is in its Fe^{3+} state. Nitrate is a 1− polyatomic ion. Therefore, we need three nitrate ions for each Fe^{3+} ion to form $Fe(NO_3)_3$. The polyatomic nitrate ion is enclosed in parentheses followed by the proper subscript.

(d) Carbonate is a 2− polyatomic ion that combines with two Na^+ ions to form Na_2CO_3. The polyatomic carbonate ion is not enclosed in parentheses since the formula contains only one carbonate.

PROBLEM-SOLVING PRACTICE 3.7

For each of these ionic compounds, write a list of which ions and how many of each are present.

(a) $MgBr_2$ (b) Li_2CO_3 (c) NH_4Cl (d) $Fe_2(SO_4)_3$

(e) Copper is a transition element that can form two compounds with bromine containing either Cu^+ or Cu^{2+}. Write the formulas for these compounds.

3.6 Naming Ions and Ionic Compounds

Ionic compounds can be named unambiguously by using the rules given in this section. You should learn these rules thoroughly.

Naming Positive Ions

Virtually all cations used in this book are metal ions that can be named by the rules given below. The ammonium ion (NH_4^+) is the major exception; it is a polyatomic ion composed of nonmetal atoms.

An unusual cation that you will see on occasion is Hg_2^{2+}, the mercury(I) ion. The Roman numeral (I) is used to show that the ion is composed of two Hg^+ ions bonded together, giving an overall 2+ charge.

1a. ***For metals that form only one kind of cation, the name is simply the name of the metal plus the word "ion."*** For example, Mg^{2+} is the magnesium ion.

1b. ***For metals that can form more than one kind of cation, the name of each ion must indicate its charge. To do so, a Roman numeral in parentheses is given immediately following the ion's name (the Stock system).*** For example, Cu^{2+} is the copper(II) ion and Cu^+ is the copper(I) ion.

The Stock system is named after Alfred Stock (1876–1946), a German chemist famous for his work on the hydrogen compounds of boron and silicon.

© Thomson Learning/Charles D. Winters

Copper(I) oxide (*left*) and copper(II) oxide. The different copper ion charges result in different colors.

Naming Negative Ions

These rules apply to naming anions.

2a. ***A monatomic anion is named by adding* -ide *to the stem of the name of the nonmetal element from which the ion is derived.*** For example, a *phosphorus* atom gives a *phosphide* ion, and a *chlorine* atom forms a *chloride* ion. Anions of Group 7A elements, the halogens, are collectively called **halide ions.**

2b. ***The names of the most common polyatomic ions are given in Table 3.7 (p. 92).*** Most must simply be memorized. However, some guidelines can help, especially for **oxoanions,** which are polyatomic ions containing oxygen.

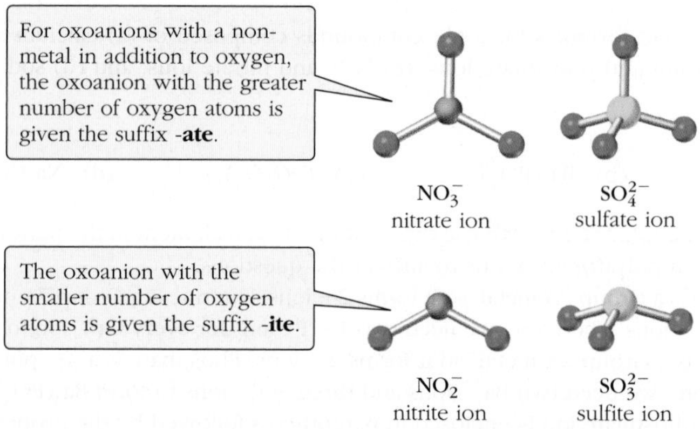

Note that *-ate* and *-ite* suffixes do not relate to the ion's charge, but to the relative number of oxygen atoms.

When more than two different oxoanions of a given nonmetal exist, a more extended naming scheme must be used. When there are four oxoanions involved, the two middle ones are named according to the *-ate* and *-ite* endings; then the ion containing the largest number of oxygen atoms is given the prefix *per-* and the suffix *-ate,* and the one containing the smallest number is given the prefix *hypo-* and the suffix *-ite.* The oxoanions of chlorine are good examples:

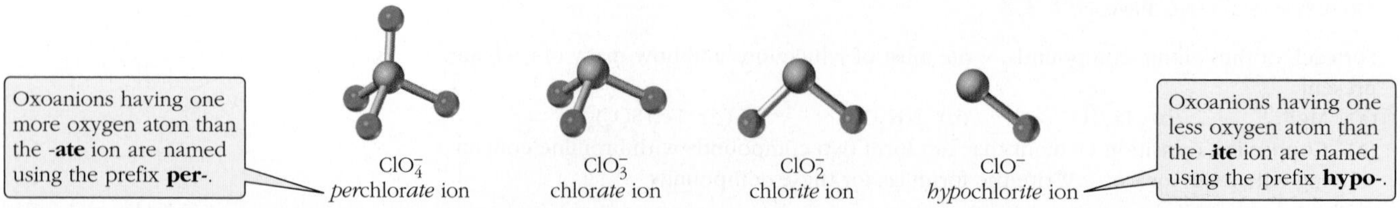

The same naming rules also apply to the oxoanions of bromine and iodine.

Oxoanions containing hydrogen are named simply by adding the word "hydrogen" before the name of the oxoanion, for example, hydrogen sulfate ion, HSO_4^-. When an oxoanion of a given nonmetal can combine with different numbers of hydrogen atoms, we must use prefixes to indicate which ion we are talking about: *di*hydrogen phosphate for $H_2PO_4^-$ and *mono*hydrogen phosphate for HPO_4^{2-}. Because many hydrogen-containing oxoanions have common names that are used often, you should know them. For example, the hydrogen carbonate ion, HCO_3^-, is often called the bicarbonate ion.

Naming Ionic Compounds

Table 3.8 lists a number of common ionic compounds. We will use these compounds to demonstrate the rules for systematically naming ionic compounds. One basic naming rule is by now probably apparent—***the name of the cation comes first, then the name of the anion.*** Also, in naming a compound, the word "ion" is not used with the metal name.

ThomsonNOW™
Go to the Coached Problems menu for a tutorial on **naming ionic compounds.**

Notice the following from Table 3.8:

- Calcium oxide, CaO, is named from calcium for Ca^{2+} (Rule 1a) and oxide for O^{2-} (Rule 2a). Likewise, sodium chloride is derived from sodium (Na^+, Rule 1a) and chloride (Cl^-, Rule 2a).
- Ammonium carbonate, $(NH_4)_2CO_3$, contains two polyatomic ions that are named in Table 3.7 (p. 92).
- In the name copper(II) sulfate, the (II) indicates that Cu^{2+} is present, not Cu^+, the other possibility.

PROBLEM-SOLVING EXAMPLE 3.8 Using Formulas to Name Ionic Compounds

Write the name for each of these ionic compounds.

(a) KCl (b) $Ca(OH)_2$ (c) $Fe_3(PO_4)_2$
(d) $Al(NO_3)_3$ (e) $(NH_4)_2SO_4$

Answer

(a) Potassium chloride (b) Calcium hydroxide (c) Iron(II) phosphate
(d) Aluminum nitrate (e) Ammonium sulfate

Strategy and Explanation

(a) The potassium ion, K^+, and the chloride ion, Cl^-, combine to form potassium chloride.

Table 3.8 Names of Some Common Ionic Compounds

Common Name	Systematic Name	Formula
Baking soda	Sodium hydrogen carbonate	$NaHCO_3$
Lime	Calcium oxide	CaO
Milk of magnesia	Magnesium hydroxide	$Mg(OH)_2$
Table salt	Sodium chloride	NaCl
Smelling salts	Ammonium carbonate	$(NH_4)_2CO_3$
Lye	Sodium hydroxide	NaOH
Blue vitriol	Copper(II) sulfate pentahydrate	$CuSO_4 \cdot 5\ H_2O$

© Thomson Learning/Charles D. Winters

Sodium chloride, NaCl. This common ionic compound contains sodium ions (Na^+) and chloride ions (Cl^-).

(b) The calcium ion, Ca^{2+}, and the hydroxide ion, OH^-, combine to form calcium hydroxide.
(c) The iron(II) ion, Fe^{2+}, and the phosphate ion, PO_4^{3-}, combine to give iron(II) phosphate.
(d) The aluminum ion, Al^{3+}, combines with the nitrate ion, NO_3^-, to form aluminum nitrate.
(e) The ammonium ion, NH_4^+, and the sulfate ion, SO_4^{2-}, combine to form ammonium sulfate.

PROBLEM-SOLVING PRACTICE 3.8

Name these ionic compounds:

(a) KNO_2 (b) $NaHSO_3$ (c) $Mn(OH)_2$
(d) $Mn_2(SO_4)_3$ (e) Ba_3N_2 (f) LiH

PROBLEM-SOLVING EXAMPLE 3.9 Using Names to Write Formulas of Ionic Compounds

Write the formulas for these ionic compounds:

(a) Ammonium sulfide (b) Potassium sulfate
(c) Copper(II) nitrate (d) Iron(II) chloride

Answer

(a) $(NH_4)_2S$ (b) K_2SO_4 (c) $Cu(NO_3)_2$ (d) $FeCl_2$

Strategy and Explanation We use our knowledge of ion charges and the given charges for the metals to write the formulas.

(a) The ammonium cation is NH_4^+ and the sulfide ion is S^{2-}, so two ammonium ions are needed for one sulfide ion to make the neutral compound.
(b) The potassium cation is K^+ and the sulfate anion is SO_4^{2-}, so two potassium ions are needed.
(c) The copper(II) cation is Cu^{2+} and the anion is NO_3^-, so two nitrate ions are needed.
(d) The iron(II) ion is Fe^{2+} and the chloride ion is Cl^-, so two chloride ions are needed.

PROBLEM-SOLVING PRACTICE 3.9

Write the correct formula for each of these ionic compounds:

(a) Potassium dihydrogen phosphate (b) Copper(I) hydroxide
(c) Sodium hypochlorite (d) Ammonium perchlorate
(e) Chromium(III) chloride (f) Iron(II) sulfite

3.7 Properties of Ionic Compounds

The book *Salt: A World History*, by Mark Kurlansky, is a compelling account of salt's importance through the ages.

As is true for all compounds, the properties of an ionic compound differ significantly from those of its component elements. Consider the familiar ionic compound, table salt (sodium chloride, NaCl), composed of Na^+ and Cl^- ions. Sodium chloride is a white, crystalline, water-soluble solid, very different from its component elements, metallic sodium and gaseous chlorine. Sodium is an extremely reactive metal that reacts violently with water. Chlorine is a diatomic, toxic gas that reacts with water. Sodium *ions* and chloride *ions* do not undergo such reactions, and NaCl dissolves uneventfully in water.

ThomsonNOW™
Go to the Chemistry Interactive menu to view animations on:
- **properties of ionic compounds**
- **conduction of molten salt**

In ionic solids, cations and anions are held in an orderly array called a **crystal lattice,** in which each cation is surrounded by anions and each anion is surrounded by cations. This arrangement maximizes the attraction between cations and anions and minimizes the repulsion between ions of like charge. In sodium chloride, as shown in Figure 3.3, six chloride ions surround each sodium ion, and six sodium ions surround each chloride ion. As indicated in the formula, there is one sodium ion for each chloride ion.

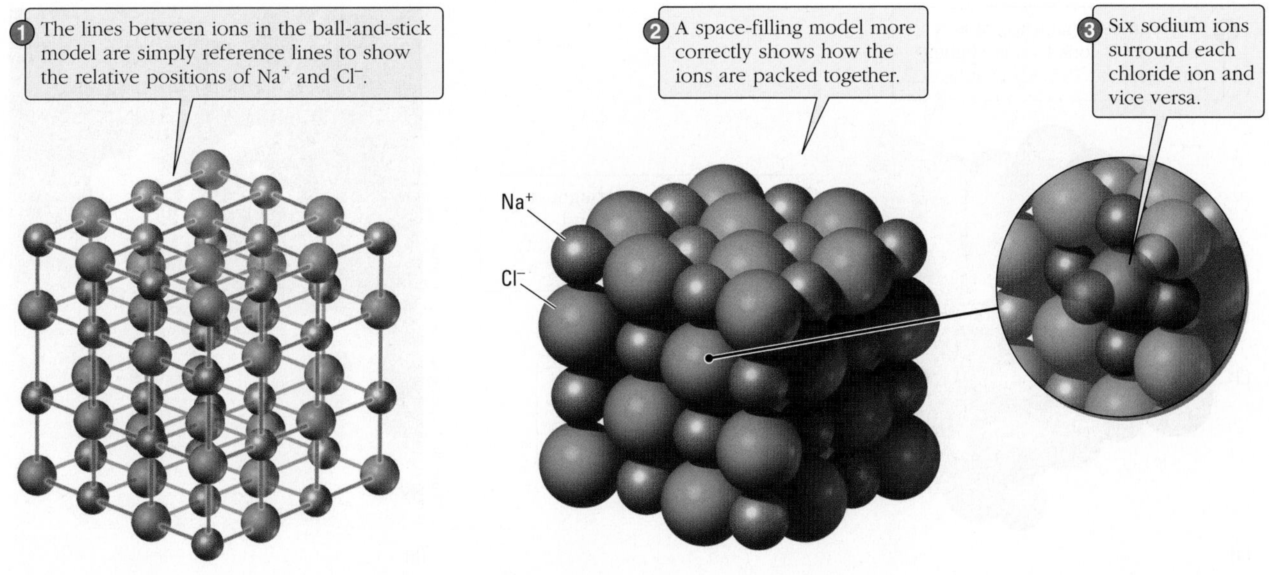

(a) (b)

Figure 3.3 Two models of a sodium chloride crystal lattice. (a) This ball-and-stick model illustrates clearly how the ions are arranged, although it shows the ions too far apart. (b) Although a space-filling model shows how the ions are packed, it is difficult to see the locations of ions other than those on the faces of the crystal lattice.

The formula of an ionic compound indicates only the smallest whole-number ratio of the number of cations to the number of anions in the compound. In NaCl that ratio is 1:1. An Na^+Cl^- pair is referred to as a **formula unit** of sodium chloride. Note that the formula unit of an ionic compound has no independent existence outside of the crystal, which is different from the individual molecules of a molecular compound such as H_2O.

The regular array of ions in a crystal lattice gives ionic compounds two of their characteristic properties—high melting points and distinctive crystalline shapes. The melting points are related to the charges and sizes of the ions. For ions of similar size, such as O^{2-} and F^-, *the larger the charges, the higher the melting point,* because of the greater attraction between ions of higher charge ***(⟵ p. 89).*** For example, CaO (composed of doubly charged Ca^{2+} and O^{2-} ions) melts at 2572 °C, whereas NaF (composed of singly charged Na^+ and F^- ions) melts at 993 °C.

The crystals of ionic solids have characteristic shapes because the ions are held rather rigidly in position by strong attractive forces. Such alignment creates planes of ions within the crystals. Ionic crystals can be cleaved by an outside force that causes the planes of ions to shift slightly, bringing ions of like charge closer together (Figure 3.4). The resulting repulsion causes the layers on opposite sides of the cleavage plane to separate, and the crystal splits apart.

Because the ions in a crystal can only vibrate about fixed positions, ionic solids do not conduct electricity. However, when an ionic solid melts, as shown in Figure 3.5, the ions are free to move and conduct an electric current. Cations move toward the negative electrode and anions move toward the positive electrode, which results in an electric current.

An electric current is the movement of charged particles from one place to another. In a metal wire, the electric current is due to the movement of electrons through the wire.

The general properties of molecular and ionic compounds are summarized in Table 3.9 (on p. 101). In particular, note the differences in physical state, electrical conductivity, melting point, and water solubility.

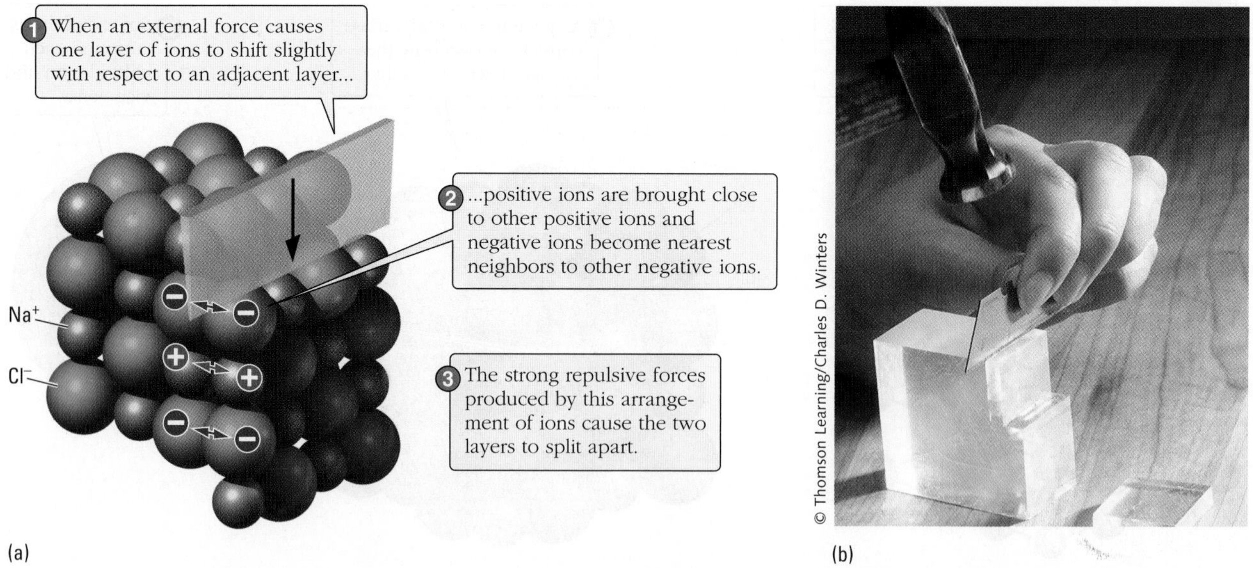

Figure 3.4 **Cleavage of an ionic crystal.** (a) Diagram of the forces involved in cleaving an ionic crystal. (b) A sharp blow on a knife edge lying along a plane of a salt crystal causes the crystal to split.

Figure 3.5 **A molten ionic compound conducts an electric current.** When an ionic compound is melted, ions are freed from the crystal lattice and migrate to the electrodes dipping into the melt. An electric current flows, and the light bulb illuminates, showing a complete circuit.

We use the term "dissociate" for ionic compounds that separate into their constituent ions in water. The term "ionize" is used for molecular compounds whose molecules react with water to form ions.

CONCEPTUAL EXERCISE **3.5 Properties of Molecular and Ionic Compounds**

Is a compound that is solid at room temperature and soluble in water likely to be a molecular or ionic compound? Why?

Ionic Compounds in Aqueous Solution: Electrolytes

Many ionic compounds are soluble in water. As a result, the oceans, rivers, lakes, and even the tap water in our residences contain many kinds of ions in solution. This makes the solubilities of ionic compounds and the properties of ions in solution of great practical interest.

When an ionic compound dissolves in water, it *dissociates*—the oppositely charged ions separate from one another. For example, when solid NaCl dissolves in water, it dissociates into Na^+ and Cl^- ions that become uniformly mixed with water molecules and dispersed throughout the solution.

Aqueous solutions of ionic compounds conduct electricity because the ions are free to move about (Figure 3.6). (This is the same mechanism of conductivity as for molten ionic compounds.) Substances that conduct electricity when dissolved in water are called **electrolytes.**

Most molecular compounds that are water-soluble continue to exist as molecules in solution; table sugar (chemical name, sucrose) is an example. Substances such as sucrose whose solutions do not conduct electricity are called **nonelectrolytes.** Be sure you understand the difference between these two important properties of a compound: its solubility and its ability to release ions in solution. In Section 5.1 we will provide a much more detailed discussion of solubility and the dissociation of ions from electrolytes in solution.

Table 3.9 Properties of Molecular and Ionic Compounds

Molecular Compounds	Ionic Compounds
Many are formed by combination of nonmetals with other nonmetals or with some metals	Formed by combination of reactive metals with reactive nonmetals
Gases, liquids, solids	Crystalline solids
Brittle and weak or soft and waxy solids	Hard and brittle solids
Low melting points	High melting points
Low boiling points (−250 to 600 °C)	High boiling points (700 to 3500 °C)
Poor conductors of electricity	Good conductors of electricity when molten; poor conductors of electricity when solid
Poor conductors of heat	Poor conductors of heat
Many insoluble in water but soluble in organic solvents	Many soluble in water
Examples: hydrocarbons, H_2O, CO_2	Examples: NaCl, CaF_2, NH_4NO_3

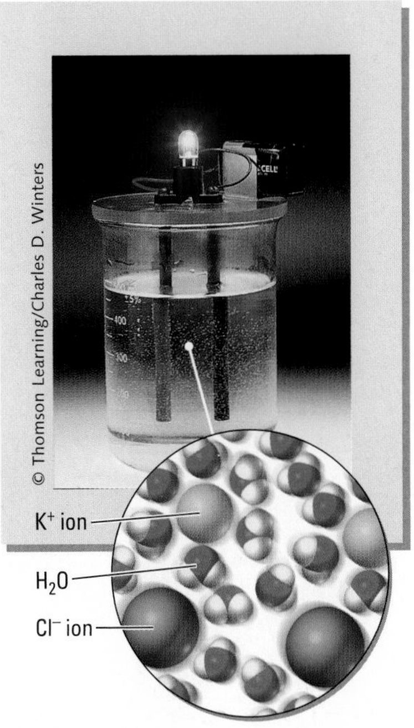

Figure 3.6 Electrical conductivity of an ionic compound solution. When an electrolyte, such as KCl, is dissolved in water and provides ions that move about, the electrical circuit is completed and the light bulb in the circuit glows. The ions of every KCl unit have dissociated: K^+ and Cl^-. The Cl^- ions move toward the positive electrode, and the K^+ ions move toward the negative electrode, transporting electrical charge through the solution.

3.8 Moles of Compounds

In talking about compounds in quantities large enough to manipulate conveniently, we deal with moles of these compounds.

Molar Mass of Molecular Compounds

The most recognizable molecular formula, H_2O, shows us that there are two H atoms for every O atom in a water molecule. In two water molecules, therefore, there are four H atoms and two O atoms; in a dozen water molecules, there are two dozen H atoms and one dozen O atoms. We can extend this until we have one mole of water molecules (Avogadro's number of molecules, 6.022×10^{23}), each containing two moles of hydrogen atoms and one mole of oxygen atoms (⇐ *p. 61*). We can also say that in 1.000 mol water there are 2.000 mol H atoms and 1.000 mol O atoms:

One mole of a molecular compound means 6.022×10^{23} molecules, not one molecule.

H_2O	H	O
6.022×10^{23} water molecules	$2(6.022 \times 10^{23}$ H atoms)	6.022×10^{23} O atoms
1.000 mol H_2O molecules	2.000 mol H atoms	1.000 mol O atoms
18.0153 g H_2O	2(1.0079 g H) = 2.0158 g H	15.9994 g O

The mass of one mole of water molecules—the *molar mass*—is the sum of the masses of two moles of H atoms and one mole of O atoms: 2.0158 g H + 15.9994 g O = 18.0152 g water in a mole of water. For chemical compounds, the *molar mass,* in grams per mole, is *numerically the same* as the **molecular weight,** the sum of the atomic weights (in amu) of *all* the atoms in the compound's formula. The molar masses of several molecular compounds are shown in the following table.

Compound	Structural Formula	Molecular Weight	Molar Mass
Ammonia NH_3	H—N—H | H	14.01 amu, N + 3(1.01 amu, H) = 17.04 amu	17.04 g/mol
Trifluoromethane CHF_3	F | F—C—F | H	12.01 amu, C + 1.01 amu, H + 3(19.00 amu, F) = 70.02 amu	70.02 g/mol
Sulfur dioxide SO_2	O═S—O	32.07 amu, S + 2(16.00 amu, O) = 64.07 amu	64.07 g/mol
Glycerol $C_3H_8O_3$	CH_2OH | CHOH | CH_2OH	3(12.01 amu, C) + 8(1.01 amu, H) + 3(16.00 amu, O) = 92.11 amu	92.11 g/mol

Molar Mass of Ionic Compounds

Because ionic compounds do not contain individual molecules, the term "formula weight" is sometimes used for ionic compounds instead of "molecular weight." As with molecular weight, an ionic compound's **formula weight** is the sum of the atomic weights of all the atoms in the compound's formula. The molar mass of an ionic compound, expressed in grams per mole (g/mol), is numerically equivalent to its formula weight. The term "molar mass" is used for both molecular and ionic compounds.

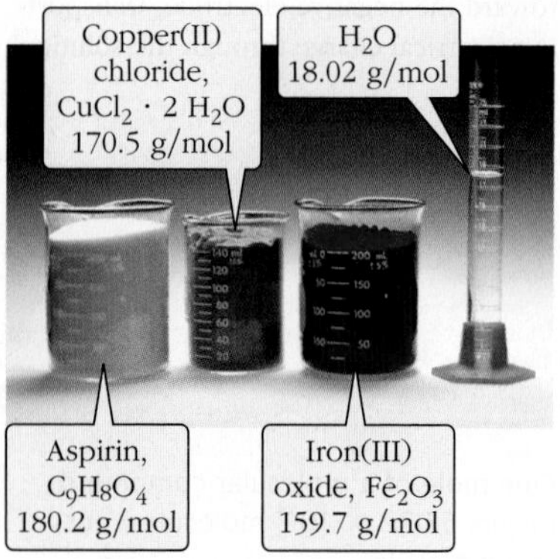

© Thomson Learning/Charles D. Winters

One-mole quantities of four compounds.

Compound	Formula Weight	Molar Mass
Sodium chloride NaCl	22.99 amu, Na + 35.45 amu, Cl = 58.44 amu	58.44 g/mol
Magnesium oxide MgO	24.31 amu, Mg + 16.00 amu, O = 40.31 amu	40.31 g/mol
Potassium sulfide K_2S	2(39.10 amu, K) + 32.07 amu, S = 110.27 amu	110.27 g/mol
Calcium nitrate $Ca(NO_3)_2$	40.08 amu, Ca + 2(14.01 amu, N) + 6(16.00 amu, O) = 164.10 amu	164.10 g/mol
Magnesium phosphate $Mg_3(PO_4)_2$	3(24.31 amu, Mg) + 2(30.97 amu, P) + 8(16.00 amu, O) = 262.87 amu	262.87 g/mol

Notice that $Mg_3(PO_4)_2$ has 2 P atoms and $2 \times 4 = 8$ O atoms because there are two PO_4^{3-} ions in the formula.

EXERCISE 3.6 Molar Masses

Calculate the molar mass of each of these compounds:

(a) K_2HPO_4
(b) $C_{27}H_{46}O$ (cholesterol)
(c) $Mn_2(SO_4)_3$
(d) $C_8H_{10}N_4O_2$ (caffeine)

Gram–Mole Conversions

As you might expect, it is essential to be able to do gram–mole conversions for compounds, just as we did for elements (⇐ *p. 62*). Here also, the key to such conversions is using molar mass as a conversion factor.

ThomsonNOW™
Go to the Coached Problems menu for exercises on:

- **compounds and moles**
- **determining molar mass**
- **using molar mass to convert between moles and mass**

PROBLEM-SOLVING EXAMPLE 3.10 Grams to Moles

Calcium phosphate, $Ca_3(PO_4)_2$, is an ionic compound that is the main constituent of bone. How many moles of $Ca_3(PO_4)_2$ are in 10.0 g of the compound?

Answer 3.22×10^{-2} mol $Ca_3(PO_4)_2$

Strategy and Explanation To convert from grams to moles, we first find calcium phosphate's molar mass, which is the sum of the molar masses of the atoms in the formula.

$$3 \text{ mol Ca } (40.08 \text{ g Ca/mol Ca}) + 2 \text{ mol P } (30.97 \text{ g P/mol P}) + 8 \text{ mol O } (16.00 \text{ g O/mol O})$$
$$= 310.18 \text{ g/mol } Ca_3(PO_4)_2$$

This molar mass is used to convert mass to moles:

$$10.0 \text{ g } \cancel{Ca_3(PO_4)_2} \times \frac{1 \text{ mol } Ca_3(PO_4)_2}{310.18 \text{ g } \cancel{Ca_3(PO_4)_2}} = 3.22 \times 10^{-2} \text{ mol } Ca_3(PO_4)_2$$

✓ **Reasonable Answer Check** We started with 10.0 g calcium phosphate, which has a molar mass of about 300 g/mol, so 10/300 is about 1/30, which is close to the more accurate answer we calculated.

PROBLEM-SOLVING PRACTICE 3.10

Calculate the number of moles in 12.5 g of each of these ionic compounds:
(a) $K_2Cr_2O_7$ (b) $KMnO_4$ (c) $(NH_4)_2CO_3$

PROBLEM-SOLVING EXAMPLE 3.11 Moles to Grams

Cortisone, $C_{21}H_{28}O_5$, is an anti-inflammatory steroid. How many grams of cortisone are in 5.0 mmol cortisone? (1 mmol = 10^{-3} mol)

Answer 1.8 g

Strategy and Explanation First, calculate the molar mass of cortisone, which is 360.46 g/mol. Then use the molar mass to convert from moles to grams:

$$5.0 \times 10^{-3} \text{ } \cancel{\text{mol cortisone}} \times \frac{360.46 \text{ g cortisone}}{1 \text{ } \cancel{\text{mol cortisone}}} = 1.8 \text{ g cortisone}$$

PROBLEM-SOLVING PRACTICE 3.11

(a) How many grams are in 5.0 mmol sucrose, $C_{12}H_{22}O_{11}$?
(b) How many milligrams are in 3.0 μmol adrenocorticotropic hormone (ACTH), which has a molar mass of approximately 4600 g/mol? (1 μmol = 10^{-6} mol)

PROBLEM-SOLVING EXAMPLE 3.12 Grams and Moles

Aspartame is a widely used artificial sweetener (NutraSweet) that is almost 200 times sweeter than sucrose. One sample of aspartame, $C_{14}H_{18}N_2O_5$, has a mass of 1.80 g; another contains 0.220 mol aspartame. To see which sample is larger, answer these questions:
(a) What is the molar mass of aspartame?
(b) How many moles of aspartame are in the 1.80-g sample?
(c) How many grams of aspartame are in the 0.220-mol sample?

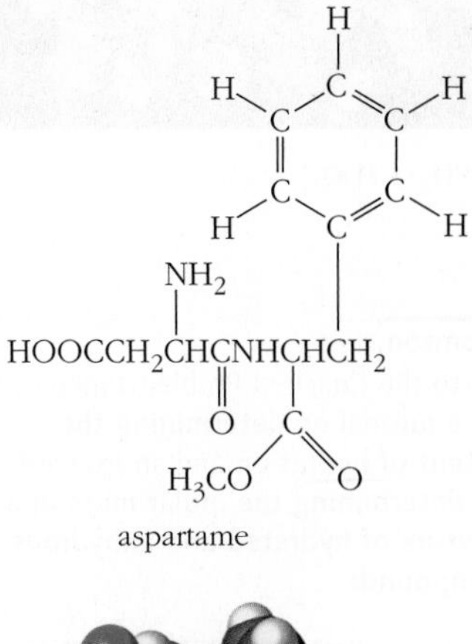

aspartame

Answer
(a) 294.3 g/mol (b) 6.12×10^{-3} mol (c) 64.7 g
The 0.220-mol sample is larger.

Strategy and Explanation
(a) Calculate the molar mass from the molecular formula.

$$[14 \text{ mol C} \times (12.011 \text{ g C/mol C})] + [18 \text{ mol H} \times (1.008 \text{ g H/mol H})]$$
$$+ [2 \text{ mol N} \times (14.007 \text{ g N/mol N})] + [5 \text{ mol O} \times (15.999 \text{ g O/mol O})]$$
$$= 294.3 \text{ g}$$

Thus, the molar mass of aspartame is 294.3 g/mol.

(b) Use the molar mass to calculate moles from grams:

$$1.80 \text{ g aspartame} \times \frac{1 \text{ mol aspartame}}{294.3 \text{ g aspartame}} = 6.12 \times 10^{-3} \text{ mol aspartame}$$

(c) Converting moles to grams is the opposite of part (b):

$$0.220 \text{ mol aspartame} \times \frac{294.3 \text{ g aspartame}}{1 \text{ mol aspartame}} = 64.7 \text{ g aspartame}$$

The 0.220-mol sample of aspartame is the larger one.

PROBLEM-SOLVING PRACTICE 3.12

(a) Calculate the number of moles in 10.0 g $C_{27}H_{46}O$ (cholesterol) and 10.0 g $Mn_2(SO_4)_3$.
(b) Calculate the number of grams in 0.25 mol K_2HPO_4 and 0.25 mol $C_8H_{10}N_4O_2$ (caffeine).

EXERCISE 3.7 Moles and Formulas

Is this statement true? "Two different compounds have the same formula. Therefore, 100 g of each compound contains the same number of moles." Justify your answer.

© Thomson Learning/Charles D. Winters

$CuSO_4 \cdot 5\ H_2O$.

Moles of Ionic Hydrates

Many ionic compounds, known as **ionic hydrates** or hydrated compounds, have water molecules trapped within the crystal lattice. The associated water is called the **water of hydration.** For example, the formula for a beautiful deep-blue compound named copper(II) sulfate pentahydrate is $CuSO_4 \cdot 5\ H_2O$. The $\cdot 5\ H_2O$ and the term "pentahydrate" indicate five moles of water associated with every mole of copper(II) sulfate. The molar mass of a hydrate includes the mass of the water of hydration. Thus, the molar mass of $CuSO_4 \cdot 5\ H_2O$ is 249.7 g: 159.6 g $CuSO_4$ + 90.1 g (for 5 mol H_2O) = 249.7 g. There are many ionic hydrates, including the frequently encountered ones listed in Table 3.10.

One commonly used hydrate may well be in the walls of your room. Plasterboard (sometimes called wallboard or gypsum board) contains hydrated calcium sulfate, or gypsum, $CaSO_4 \cdot 2\ H_2O$, as well as unhydrated $CaSO_4$, sandwiched between two thicknesses of paper. Gypsum is a natural mineral that can be mined, but it is also obtained as a by-product when sulfur dioxide is removed by calcium oxide from exhaust gases in electric power plants.

Heating gypsum to 180 °C drives off some of the water of hydration to form calcium sulfate hemihydrate, $CaSO_4 \cdot \frac{1}{2}\ H_2O$, commonly called plaster of Paris. This compound is widely used in casts for broken limbs. When added to water, it forms a thick slurry that can be poured into a mold or spread out over a part of the body.

ThomsonNOW
Go to the Coached Problems menu for a tutorial on **determining the extent of hydration** and an exercise on **determining the molar mass of a mixture of hydrated and anhydrous compounds.**

Calcium sulfate *hemi*hydrate contains one water molecule per two $CaSO_4$ units. The prefix *hemi-* refers to $\frac{1}{2}$ just as in the familiar word "hemisphere."

Table 3.10 Some Common Hydrated Ionic Compounds

Molecular Formula	Systematic Name	Common Name	Uses
$Na_2CO_3 \cdot 10\ H_2O$	Sodium carbonate decahydrate	Washing soda	Water softener
$Na_2S_2O_3 \cdot 5\ H_2O$	Sodium thiosulfate pentahydrate	Hypo	Photography
$MgSO_4 \cdot 7\ H_2O$	Magnesium sulfate heptahydrate	Epsom salt	Dyeing and tanning
$CaSO_4 \cdot 2\ H_2O$	Calcium sulfate dihydrate	Gypsum	Wallboard
$CaSO_4 \cdot \frac{1}{2}\ H_2O$	Calcium sulfate hemihydrate	Plaster of Paris	Casts, molds
$CuSO_4 \cdot 5\ H_2O$	Copper(II) sulfate pentahydrate	Blue vitriol	Algicide, root killer

© Thomson Learning/Charles D. Winters

Gypsum in its crystalline form. Gypsum is hydrated calcium sulfate, $CaSO_4 \cdot 2\ H_2O$.

As it hardens, it takes on additional water of hydration and its volume increases, forming a rigid protective cast.

EXERCISE 3.8 Moles of an Ionic Hydrate

A home remedy calls for 2 teaspoons (20 g) Epsom salt (see Table 3.10). Calculate the number of moles of the hydrate represented by this mass.

3.9 Percent Composition

You saw in the previous section that the composition of any compound can be expressed as either *(1) the number of atoms of each type per molecule or formula unit* or *(2) the mass of each element in a mole of the compound.* The latter relationship provides the information needed to find the **percent composition by mass** (also called the *mass percent*) of the compound.

It is important to recognize that the percent composition of a compound by mass is independent of the quantity of the compound. The percent composition by mass remains the same whether a sample contains 1 mg, 1 g, or 1 kg of the compound.

PROBLEM-SOLVING EXAMPLE 3.13 Percent Composition by Mass

Propane, C_3H_8, is the fuel used in gas grills. Calculate the percentages of carbon and hydrogen in propane.

Answer 81.7% carbon and 18.3% hydrogen

Strategy and Explanation First, we calculate the molar mass of propane: 3(12.01 g C) + 8(1.0079 g H) = 44.10 g/mol. We can then calculate the percentages of each element from the mass of each element in 1 mol C_3H_8 divided by the molar mass of propane.

$$\% \text{ C} = \frac{\text{mass of C in 1 mol } C_3H_8}{\text{mass of } C_3H_8 \text{ in 1 mol } C_3H_8} \times 100\%$$

$$= \frac{3 \times 12.01 \text{ g C}}{44.10 \text{ g } C_3H_8} \times 100\% = 81.7\% \text{ C}$$

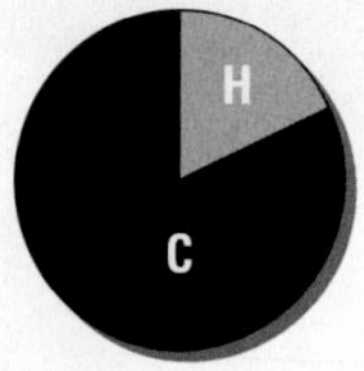

Mass percent carbon and hydrogen in propane, C_3H_8.

$$\% \text{ H} = \frac{\text{mass of H in 1 mol } C_3H_8}{\text{mass of } C_3H_8 \text{ in 1 mol } C_3H_8} \times 100\%$$

$$= \frac{8 \times 1.0079 \text{ g H}}{44.10 \text{ g } C_3H_8} \times 100\% = 18.3\% \text{ H}$$

These answers can also be expressed as 81.7 g C per 100.0 g C_3H_8 and 18.3 g H per 100.0 g C_3H_8.

✓ **Reasonable Answer Check** Each carbon atom has twelve times the mass of a hydrogen atom. Propane has approximately 12 × 3 = 36 amu of carbon and approximately 1 × 8 = 8 amu of hydrogen. So the percentage of carbon should be about 36/8 = 4.5 times as large as the percentage of hydrogen. This agrees with our more carefully calculated answer.

ThomsonNOW™
Go to the Coached Problems menu for a tutorial on **percent composition.**

PROBLEM-SOLVING PRACTICE 3.13

What is the percentage of each element in silicon dioxide, SiO_2?

Note that the percentages calculated in Problem-Solving Example 3.13 add up to 100%. Therefore, once we calculated the percentage of carbon, we also could have determined the percentage of hydrogen simply by subtracting: 100% − 81.7 C = 18.3% H. Calculating all percentages and adding them to confirm that they give 100% is a good way to check for errors.

In many circumstances, we do not need to know the percent composition of a compound with many significant figures, but rather we are interested in having an estimate of the percentage. For example, our objective could be to estimate whether the percentage of oxygen in a compound is about half or closer to two thirds. The labels on garden fertilizers show the approximate percent composition of the product and allow the consumer to compare approximate compositions of products.

© Thomson Learning/Charles D. Winters

Epsom salt.

PROBLEM-SOLVING EXAMPLE 3.14 Percent Composition of Hydrated Salt

Epsom salt has the chemical formula $MgSO_4 \cdot 7\ H_2O$. (a) What is the percent by mass of water in Epsom salt? (b) What are the percentages of each element in Epsom salt?

Answer

(a) 51.2% water (b) 9.86% Mg; 13.0% S; 71.4% O; 5.72% H

Strategy and Explanation

(a) We first find the molar mass of Epsom salt, which is the sum of the molar masses of the atoms in the chemical formula:

$$1 \text{ mol Mg } (24.31 \text{ g/mol}) + 1 \text{ mol S } (32.07 \text{ g/mol}) + 4 \text{ mol O } (16.00 \text{ g/mol})$$
$$+ 14 \text{ mol H } (1.008 \text{ g/mol}) + 7 \text{ mol O } (16.00 \text{ g/mol}) = 246.49 \text{ g/mol Epsom salt}$$

Because 1 mol Epsom salt contains 7 mol H_2O, the mass of water in 1 mol Epsom salt is 7 × (18.015) = 126.11 g

$$\% \text{ } H_2O = \frac{126.11 \text{ g water per mol Epsom salt}}{246.49 \text{ g/mol Epsom salt}} \times 100\% = 51.2\% \text{ } H_2O$$

(b) We calculate the percentage of magnesium from the ratio of the mass of magnesium in 1 mol Epsom salt to the mass of Epsom salt in 1 mol:

$$\% \text{ Mg} = \frac{\text{mass of Mg in 1 mol Epsom salt}}{\text{mass of Epsom salt in 1 mol}} = \frac{24.31 \text{ g Mg}}{246.49 \text{ g/mol Epsom salt}} \times 100\% = 9.86\% \text{ Mg}$$

We calculate the percentages for the remaining elements in the same way:

$$\% \text{ S} = \frac{32.07 \text{ g S}}{246.49 \text{ g/mol Epsom salt}} \times 100\% = 13.0\% \text{ S}$$

$$\% \text{ O} = \frac{(64.00 + 112.00) \text{ g O}}{246.49 \text{ g/mol Epsom salt}} \times 100\% = 71.4\% \text{ O}$$

$$\% \text{ H} = \frac{14.11 \text{ g H}}{246.49 \text{ g/mol Epsom salt}} \times 100\% = 5.72\% \text{ H}$$

✓ **Reasonable Answer Check** In the molecular formula of the hydrated salt, there are 7 waters with a combined mass of $7 \times 18 = 126$ g, and there are 6 other atoms with molar masses ranging between 16 and 32 that total to 120 g. Thus, the hydrated salt should be about 50% water by weight, and it is. There are 11 oxygen atoms in the molecular formula, so oxygen should have the largest percent by weight, and it does. The percentages sum to 99.98% due to rounding.

PROBLEM-SOLVING PRACTICE 3.14

What is the mass percent of each element in hydrated nickel(II) chloride, $NiCl_2 \cdot 6\ H_2O$?

EXERCISE 3.9 Percent Composition

Express the composition of each compound first as the mass of each element in 1.000 mol of the compound, and then as the mass percent of each element:

(a) SF_6 (b) $C_{12}H_{22}O_{11}$
(c) $Al_2(SO_4)_3$ (d) $U(OTeF_5)_6$

3.10 Determining Empirical and Molecular Formulas

A formula can be used to derive the percent composition by mass of a compound, and the reverse process also works—we can determine the formula of a compound from mass percent data. In doing so, keep in mind that the subscripts in a formula indicate the relative numbers of moles of each element in one mole of that compound.

We can apply this method to finding the formula of diborane, a compound consisting of boron and hydrogen. Experiments show that diborane is 78.13% B and 21.87% H. Based on these percentages, a 100.0-g diborane sample contains 78.13 g B and 21.87 g H. From this information we can calculate the number of moles of each element in the sample:

$$78.13 \text{ g B} \times \frac{1 \text{ mol B}}{10.811 \text{ g B}} = 7.227 \text{ mol B}$$

$$21.87 \text{ g H} \times \frac{1 \text{ mol H}}{1.0079 \text{ g H}} = 21.70 \text{ mol H}$$

To determine the formula from these data, we next need to find the number of moles of each element *relative to the other element*—in this case, the ratio of moles of hydrogen to moles of boron. Looking at the numbers reveals that there are about three times as many moles of H atoms as there are moles of B atoms. To calculate the ratio exactly, we divide the larger number of moles by the smaller number of moles. For diborane that ratio is

$$\frac{21.70 \text{ mol H}}{7.227 \text{ mol B}} = \frac{3.003 \text{ mol H}}{1.000 \text{ mol B}}$$

This ratio confirms that there are three moles of H atoms for every one mole of B atoms and that there are three hydrogen atoms for each boron atom. This information gives the formula BH_3, which may or may not be the molecular formula of diborane.

For a molecular compound such as diborane, the molecular formula must also accurately reflect the *total number of atoms in a molecule of the compound.* The calculation we have done gives the *simplest possible ratio of atoms in the molecule,* and BH_3 is the simplest formula for diborane. A formula that reports the simplest possible ratio of atoms in the molecule is called an **empirical formula.** Multiples of the simplest formula are possible, such as B_2H_6, B_3H_9, and so on.

To determine the actual molecular formula from the empirical formula requires that we *experimentally determine* the molar mass of the compound and then compare our result with the molar mass predicted by the empirical formula. If the two molar masses are the same, the empirical and molecular formulas are the same. However, if the experimentally determined molar mass is some multiple of the value predicted by the empirical formula, the molecular formula is that multiple of the empirical formula. In the case of diborane, experiments indicate that the molar mass is 27.67 g/mol. This compares with the molar mass of 13.84 g/mol for BH_3, and so the molecular formula is a multiple of the empirical formula. That multiple is 27.67/13.84 = 2.00. Thus, the molecular formula of diborane is B_2H_6, two times BH_3.

PROBLEM-SOLVING EXAMPLE 3.15 Molecular Formula from Percent Composition by Mass Data

When oxygen reacts with phosphorus, two possible oxides can form. One contains 56.34% P and 43.66% O, and its experimentally determined molar mass is 219.90 g/mol. Determine its molecular formula.

Answer P_4O_6

Strategy and Explanation The first step in finding a molecular formula from percent composition by mass and molar mass is to calculate the relative number of moles of each element and then determine the empirical formula. Considering the percent composition, we know that a 100.0-g sample of this phosphorus oxide contains 56.34 g P and 43.66 g O, so the numbers of moles of each element are

$$56.34\ \cancel{\text{g P}} \times \frac{1\ \text{mol P}}{30.97\ \cancel{\text{g P}}} = 1.819\ \text{mol P}$$

$$43.66\ \cancel{\text{g O}} \times \frac{1\ \text{mol O}}{16.00\ \cancel{\text{g O}}} = 2.729\ \text{mol O}$$

Thus, the mole ratio (and atom ratio) is

$$\frac{2.729\ \text{mol O}}{1.819\ \text{mol P}} = \frac{1.500\ \text{mol O}}{1.000\ \text{mol P}}$$

Because we can't have partial atoms, we double the numbers to convert to whole numbers, which gives us three moles of oxygen atoms for every two moles of phosphorus atoms. This gives an empirical formula of P_2O_3. The molar mass corresponding to this empirical formula is

$$\left(2\ \cancel{\text{mol P}} \times \frac{30.97\ \text{g P}}{1\ \cancel{\text{mol P}}}\right) + \left(3\ \cancel{\text{mol O}} \times \frac{16.00\ \text{g O}}{1\ \cancel{\text{mol O}}}\right) = 109.95\ \text{g P}_2\text{O}_3\ \text{per mole P}_2\text{O}_3$$

compared with a known molar mass of 219.90 g/mol. The known molar mass is $\frac{219.90}{109.95} = 2$ times the molar mass predicted by the empirical formula, so the molecular formula is P_4O_6, twice the empirical formula.

✓ **Reasonable Answer Check** The molar mass of P is about 31 g, so we should have 31 g × 4 = 124 g P in 1 mol P_4O_6. This would give a P percent by mass of 124/220 = 56%, which is just about the right value.

PROBLEM-SOLVING PRACTICE 3.15

The other phosphorus oxide contains 43.64% P and 56.36% O, and its experimentally determined molar mass is 283.89 g/mol. Determine its empirical and molecular formulas.

PROBLEM-SOLVING EXAMPLE 3.16 Molecular Formula from Percent Composition by Mass Data

Aspirin, a commonly used analgesic, has a molar mass of 180.15 g/mol. It contains 60.00% C, 4.4756% H, and the rest is oxygen. What are its empirical and molecular formulas?

Answer Both the empirical and molecular formulas are $C_9H_8O_4$.

Strategy and Explanation First find the number of moles of each element in 100.0 g of the compound:

$$60.00\ \cancel{g\ C} \times \frac{1\ \text{mol C}}{12.01\ \cancel{g\ C}} = 4.996\ \text{mol C}$$

$$4.4756\ \cancel{g\ H} \times \frac{1\ \text{mol H}}{1.0079\ \cancel{g\ H}} = 4.441\ \text{mol H}$$

That leaves moles of oxygen to be calculated. The mass of oxygen in the sample must be

$$100.0\ \text{g sample} - 60.00\ \text{g C} - 4.4756\ \text{g H} = 35.52\ \text{g O}$$

Converting this to moles of oxygen gives

$$35.52\ \cancel{g\ O} \times \frac{1\ \text{mol O}}{15.9994\ \cancel{g\ O}} = 2.220\ \text{mol O}$$

Base the mole ratio on the smallest number of moles present, in this case, moles of oxygen:

$$\frac{4.496\ \text{mol C}}{2.220\ \text{mol O}} = \frac{2.25\ \text{mol O}}{1.00\ \text{mol O}}$$

$$\frac{4.441\ \text{mol H}}{2.220\ \text{mol O}} = \frac{2.00\ \text{mol H}}{1.00\ \text{mol O}}$$

Therefore, the empirical formula has an atom ratio of 2.25 C to 1.00 O and 2.00 H to 1.00 O. To get small whole numbers for empirical formula subscripts, we multiply each molar number by 4, so the empirical formula is $C_9H_8O_4$. The molar mass predicted by this empirical formula is 180.15 g/mol, the same as the experimentally determined molar mass, indicating that the molecular formula is the same as the empirical formula.

✓ **Reasonable Answer Check** The molar mass of C is 12 g, so we should have 12 g × 9 = 108 g C in 1 mol $C_9H_8O_4$. This would give a C percent by mass of 108/180 = 60%, which is just about the right value.

PROBLEM-SOLVING PRACTICE 3.16

Vitamin C (ascorbic acid) contains 40.9% C, 4.58% H, and 54.5% O and has an experimentally determined molar mass of 176.13 g/mol. Determine its empirical and molecular formulas.

3.11 The Biological Periodic Table

Most of the more than 100 known elements are not directly involved with our personal health and well-being. However, more than 30 of the elements, shown in Figure 3.7, are absolutely essential to human life. Among these essential elements are metals, nonmetals, and metalloids from across the periodic table. All are necessary as part of a well-balanced diet.

Table 3.11 lists the building block elements and major minerals in order of their relative abundances per million atoms in the body, showing the preeminence of four

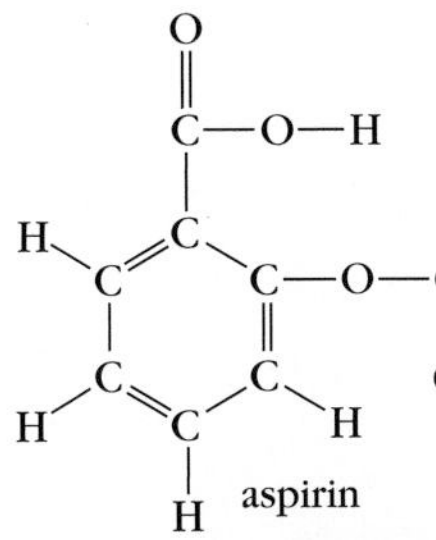

aspirin

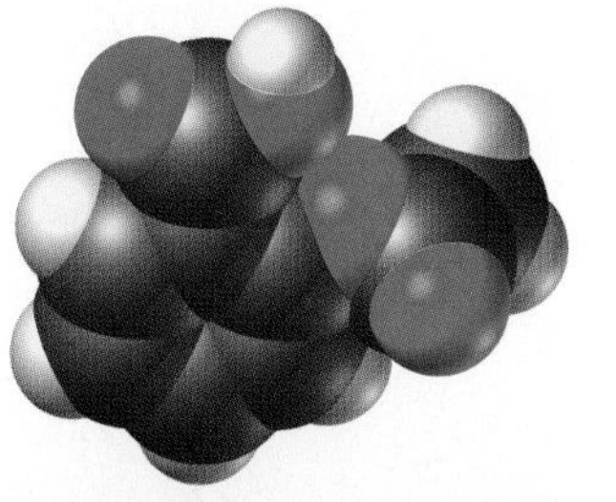

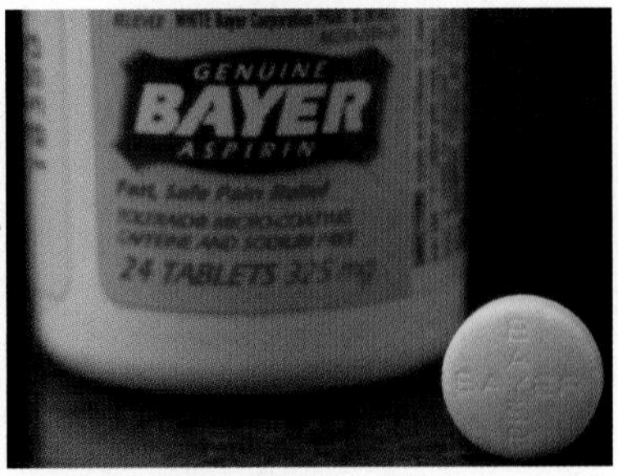

© Thomson Learning/George Semple

Bayer aspirin bottle.

ThomsonNOW™
Go to the Coached Problems menu for a tutorial on **determining empirical and molecular formulas**.

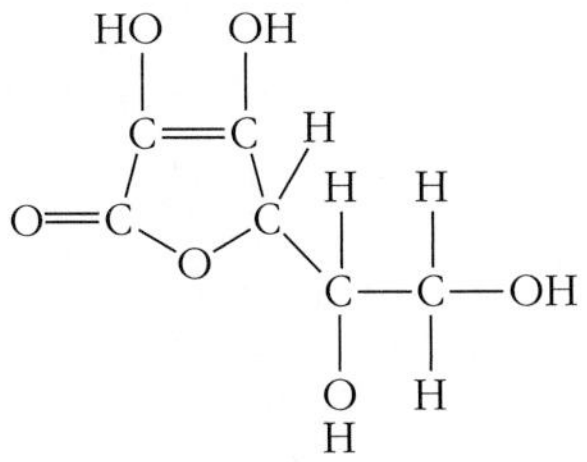

vitamin C

If you weigh 150 lb, about 90 lb (60%) is water, 30 lb is fat, and the remaining 30 lb is a combination of proteins, carbohydrates, and calcium, phosphorus, and other dietary minerals.

Table 3.11 Major Elements of the Human Body

Element	Symbol	Relative Abundance in Atoms/Million Atoms in the Body
Hydrogen	H	630,000
Oxygen	O	255,000
Carbon	C	94,500
Nitrogen	N	13,500
Calcium	Ca	3100
Phosphorus	P	2200
Chlorine	Cl	570
Sulfur	S	490
Sodium	Na	410
Potassium	K	260
Magnesium	Mg	130

of the nonmetals—oxygen, carbon, hydrogen, and nitrogen. These four nonmetals, the building block elements, contribute most of the atoms in the biologically significant chemicals—the biochemicals—composing all plants and animals. With few exceptions, the biochemicals that these nonmetals form are organic compounds.

Nonmetals are also present as anions in body fluids, including chloride ion (Cl^-) phosphorus in three ionic forms (PO_4^{3-}, HPO_4^{2-}, and $H_2PO_4^-$) and H and carbon as bicarbonate ion (HCO_3^-) and carbonate ion (CO_3^{2-}). Metals are present in the body as cations in solution (for example, Na^+, K^+) and in solids (Ca^{2+} in bones and teeth). Metals are also incorporated into large biomolecules (for example, Fe^{2+} in hemoglobin and Co^{3+} in vitamin B-12).

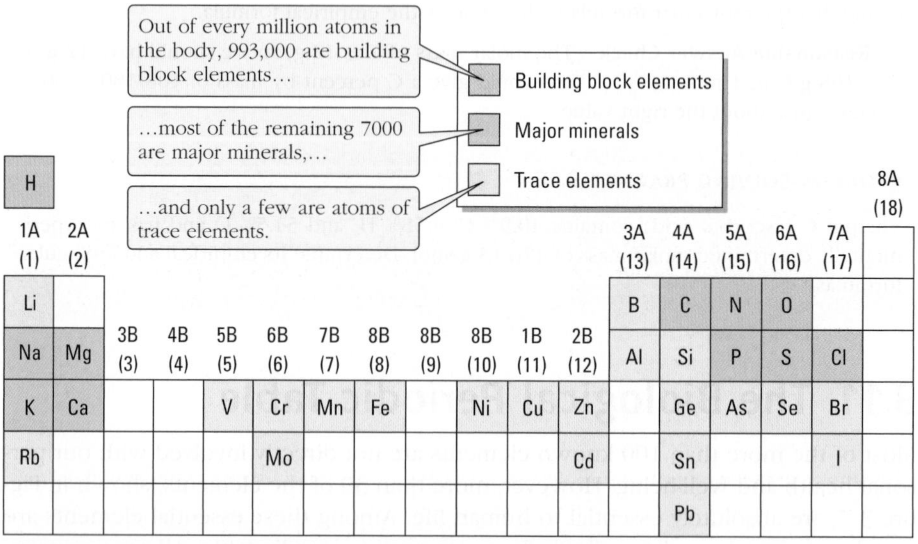

Figure 3.7 **Elements essential to human health.** Four elements—C, H, N, and O—form the many organic compounds that make up living organisms. The major minerals are required in relatively large amounts; trace elements are required in lesser amounts.

EXERCISE 3.10 Essential Elements

Using Figure 3.7, identify (a) the essential nonmetals, (b) the essential alkaline earth metals, (c) the essential halide ions, and (d) four essential transition metals.

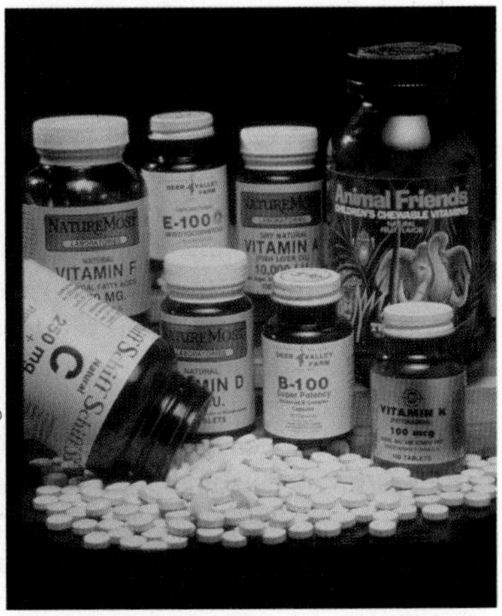

© Thomson Learning/Charles D. Winters

Vitamin and mineral supplements.

The Dietary Minerals

The general term **dietary minerals** refers to the essential elements other than carbon, hydrogen, oxygen, or nitrogen. The dietary necessity and effects of these elements go far beyond that implied by their collective presence as only about 4% of our body weight. They exemplify the old saying, "Good things come in small packages." Because the body uses them efficiently, recycling them through many reactions, dietary minerals are required in only small amounts, but their absence from your diet can cause significant health problems.

The 28 dietary minerals indicated in Figure 3.7 are classified into the relatively more abundant **major minerals** and the less plentiful **trace elements.** Major minerals are those present in quantities greater than 0.01% of body mass (100 mg per kg)—for example, more than 6 g for a 60-kg (132-lb) individual. Trace elements are present in smaller (sometimes far smaller) amounts. For example, the necessary daily total intake of iodine is only 150 μg. In the context of nutrition, major minerals and trace elements usually refer to ions in soluble ionic compounds in the diet.

CHEMISTRY IN THE NEWS

Dietary Selenium

It's easy to become confused by the many claims being made about the value of dietary supplements. A variety of trace minerals is essential to good health, and some of those essential elements are found in our diets in extremely small amounts. Selenium is an example. Selenium supplements are marketed with claims that they will prevent cancer, improve immune function, and protect against environmental pollutants. The media have publicized studies recently showing that people who take supplemental selenium have lower rates for some types of cancers. But other studies show opposite results. Many of the benefits of taking selenium supplements were found for subjects in selenium-poor regions of the world where the people have very low blood levels of selenium. In addition, "though the benefits of selenium supplements have been shown in people who are deficient, nobody is sure that supplemental selenium will do you any good if your diet is supplying adequate selenium."[1] A further complication is the difficulty of finding out how much selenium you are getting from your foods. Finally, excess selenium is toxic. Thus, there is much confusion about the usefulness of selenium supplements.

In the body, selenium functions as part of an antioxidant enzyme system by interacting with vitamin E. As a consequence, the health benefits of selenium and vitamin E are closely linked.

The Institute of Medicine of the National Academy of Sciences issues reports on Dietary Reference Intakes (DRIs). The DRIs have replaced the Recommended Dietary Allowances (RDAs) that the Academy issued for the past 60 years. The DRIs now include the old RDAs, but additionally set upper limits on dietary intake to help people avoid excessive intake of supplements. The latest thinking about selenium is that selenium deficiency is bad, but that large supplementary intake can be harmful, too. Men and women should get 55 μg of selenium per day.[2] This amount is already acquired by most Americans from their food. Where does dietary selenium come from? Food sources include fish, meats, poultry, whole grains, and some kinds of nuts (especially Brazil nuts). The DRI report also sets the upper intake level for selenium at 400 μg per day. More than this amount can cause nausea, hair loss, and tooth loss. Thus, selenium intake has a relatively narrow range (55 to 400 μg per day) that is considered to be healthy. Too little or too much can cause severe chronic conditions.

SOURCES:

[1] *Wellness Letter,* University of California, Berkeley, June 2000.

[2] *Dietary Reference Intakes for Vitamin C, Vitamin E, Selenium, and Carotenoids.* Washington, DC: National Academy of Sciences Press, 2000 (pamphlet).

Thomson, C. D. "Assessment of Requirements for Selenium and Adequacy of Selenium Status: A Review." *Eur. J. Clin. Nutr.* **58,** 2004; pp. 391–402.

http://ods.od.nih.gov/factsheets/selenium.asp

CHEMISTRY YOU CAN DO

Pumping Iron: How Strong Is Your Breakfast Cereal?

Iron is an essential dietary mineral that enters our diets in many ways. To prevent dietary iron deficiency, the U.S. Food and Drug Administration (FDA) allows food manufacturers to "fortify" (add iron to) their products. One way of fortifying a cereal is to add an iron compound, such as iron(III) phosphate, that dissolves in the stomach acid (HCl). Another is the iron in Special K cereal, which consists of particles of pure iron metal baked into the flakes. It is listed on the ingredients label as "reduced iron."

Can you detect metallic iron in a cereal? You can find out with this experiment, for which you will need these items:

- A reasonably strong magnet. You might find a good one holding things to your refrigerator door or in a toy store or hobby shop. Agricultural supply stores have "cow magnets," which will work well.
- A plastic freezer bag (quart size) and a rolling pin (or something else to crush the cereal).
- One serving of Special K (1 cup = about 30 g).

Put the Special K into the plastic bag and crush the cereal into small particles. Place the magnet into the bag and mix it well with the cereal for several minutes. Carefully remove the magnet from the bag and examine it closely. A magnifying glass is helpful. Is anything clinging to the magnet that was not there before?

Think about these questions:

1. Based on this experiment, is there metallic iron in the cereal?
2. What happens to the metallic iron after you swallow it?
3. Does this iron contribute to your daily iron requirement?

CHEMISTRY IN THE NEWS

Removing Arsenic from Drinking Water

Who wants to be a millionaire? In February 2005, the U.S. National Academy of Engineering announced the establishment of a $1 million Grainger Challenge Prize for Sustainable Development for development of technologies to help improve the quality of living throughout the world. Sponsored by the Grainger Foundation, a private philanthropy, the first prize was to be awarded for designing an inexpensive system to reduce arsenic levels in drinking water in developing countries.

Arsenic due to natural sources is found in low levels in the drinking water of tens of millions of people around the world. Arsenic is, of course, a poison when taken in sufficient quantity, and consumption of even small amounts over a long period of time can lead to serious health problems. The current maximum contaminant level (MCL) in the United States is 10 parts per billion (ppb), which is the same as the international standard set by the World Health Organization. All water systems in the United States had to meet this standard by January 2006.

Arsenic in drinking water is a worldwide problem, but it is an acute public health issue in Bangladesh. In the 1980s many shallow wells were dug to supply better quality drinking water than the bacteria-laden groundwater then being used. Recent testing of the well water has shown that tens of millions of people (estimates range from 35 to 77 million people of the total population of 135 million) are now drinking water with levels of arsenic well above the 10 ppb MCL. The situation has been called the largest mass poisoning in history.

In February 2007, the $1 million Gold Award was presented to analytical chemistry professor Abul Hussam of George Mason University. His simple and inexpensive SONO filter for removing arsenic from drinking water uses sand, composite iron matrix made from cast iron pieces, charcoal, and brick chips. Thosands of these filters are now being manufactured and used in Bangladesh to provide drinking water with less than 10 ppb arsenic.

SOURCES:

Wang, J. S. and Wai, C. M. "Arsenic in Drinking Water—A Global Environmental Problem." *Journal of Chemical Education*, 2004; pp. 207–213.

Ritter, S. "Million-Dollar Challenge." *Chem. Engr. News*, Feb. 7, 2005, p. 10.

Ritter, S. "Chemist Wins Arsenic Challenge." *Chem. Engr. News*, Feb. 12, 2007. p. 19.

SUMMARY PROBLEM

Part I

During each launch of the Space Shuttle, the booster rocket uses about 1.5×10^6 lb of ammonium perchlorate as fuel.

1. Write the chemical formulas for (a) ammonium perchlorate, (b) ammonium chlorate, and (c) ammonium chlorite.

2. (a) When ammonium perchlorate dissociates in water, what ions are dispersed in the solution?
   (b) Would this aqueous solution conduct an electric current? Explain your answer.
3. How many moles of ammonium perchlorate are used in Space Shuttle booster rockets during a launch?

Part II

Chemical analysis of ibuprofen (Advil) indicates that it contains 75.69% carbon, 8.80% hydrogen, and the remainder oxygen. The empirical formula is also the molecular formula.

1. Determine the molecular formula of ibuprofen.
2. Two 200-mg ibuprofen tablets were taken by a patient to relieve pain. Calculate the number of moles of ibuprofen contained in the two tablets.

IN CLOSING

Having studied this chapter, you should be able to . . .

- Interpret the meaning of molecular formulas, condensed formulas, and structural formulas (Section 3.1).
- Name binary molecular compounds, including straight-chain alkanes (Sections 3.2 and 3.3). ThomsonNOW homework: Study Question 9
- Write structural formulas for and identify straight- and branched-chain alkane constitutional isomers (Section 3.4). ThomsonNOW homework: Study Question 11
- Predict the charges on monatomic ions of metals and nonmetals (Section 3.5). ThomsonNOW homework: Study Question 20
- Know the names and formulas of polyatomic ions (Section 3.5).
- Describe the properties of ionic compounds and compare them with the properties of molecular compounds (Sections 3.5 and 3.7). ThomsonNOW homework: Study Question 46
- Given their names, write the formulas of ionic compounds (Section 3.5). ThomsonNOW homework: Study Question 34
- Given their formulas, name ionic compounds (Section 3.6). ThomsonNOW homework: Study Question 36
- Describe electrolytes in aqueous solution and summarize the differences between electrolytes and nonelectrolytes (Section 3.7). ThomsonNOW homework: Study Questions 52, 54
- Thoroughly explain the use of the mole concept for chemical compounds (Section 3.8).
- Calculate the molar mass of a compound (Section 3.8). ThomsonNOW homework: Study Question 58
- Calculate the number of moles of a compound given the mass, and vice versa (Section 3.8). ThomsonNOW homework: Study Questions 60, 64, 66
- Explain the formula of a hydrated ionic compound and calculate its molar mass (Section 3.8). ThomsonNOW homework: Study Question 102
- Express molecular composition in terms of percent composition (Section 3.9). ThomsonNOW homework: Study Questions 75, 77
- Use percent composition and molar mass to determine the empirical and molecular formulas of a compound (Section 3.10). ThomsonNOW homework: Study Questions 90, 94, 96
- Identify biologically important elements (Section 3.11).

ThomsonNOW™
Sign in to ThomsonNOW at **www.thomsonedu.com** to check your readiness for an exam by taking the Pre-Test and exploring the modules recommended in your Personalized Learning Plan.

KEY TERMS

alkane *(3.3)*
alkyl group *(3.4)*
anion *(3.5)*
binary molecular compound *(3.2)*
cation *(3.5)*
chemical bond *(3.3)*
condensed formula *(3.1)*
constitutional isomer *(3.4)*
Coulomb's law *(3.5)*
crystal lattice *(3.7)*
dietary mineral *(3.11)*
electrolyte *(3.7)*
empirical formula *(3.10)*
formula unit *(3.7)*
formula weight *(3.8)*
functional groups *(3.1)*
halide ion *(3.6)*
hydrocarbon *(3.3)*
inorganic compound *(3.1)*
ionic compound *(3.5)*
ionic hydrate *(3.8)*
isomer *(3.4)*
major mineral *(3.11)*
molecular compound *(3.1)*
molecular formula *(3.1)*
molecular weight *(3.8)*
monatomic ion *(3.5)*
nonelectrolyte *(3.7)*
organic compound *(3.1)*
oxoanion *(3.6)*
percent composition by mass *(3.9)*
polyatomic ion *(3.5)*
structural formula *(3.1)*
trace element *(3.11)*
water of hydration *(3.8)*

QUESTIONS FOR REVIEW AND THOUGHT

■ denotes questions available in ThomsonNOW and assignable in OWL.

Blue-numbered questions have short answers at the back of this book and fully worked solutions in the *Student Solutions Manual.*

ThomsonNOW™
Assess your understanding of this chapter's topics with sample tests and other resources found by signing in to ThomsonNOW at **www.thomsonedu.com**.

Review Questions

1. A dictionary defines the word "compound" as a "combination of two or more parts." What are the "parts" of a chemical compound? Identify three pure (or nearly pure) compounds you have encountered today. What is the difference between a compound and a mixture?
2. For each of these structural formulas, write the molecular formula and condensed formula.

(a) 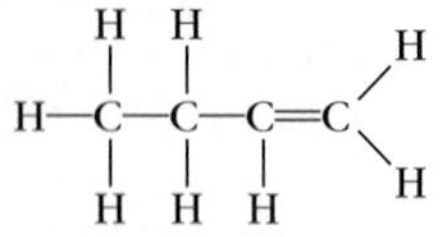

(b) 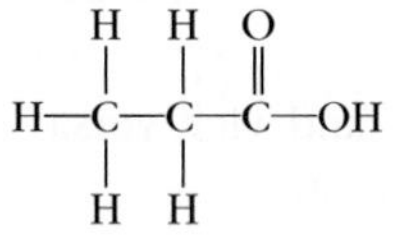

(c) 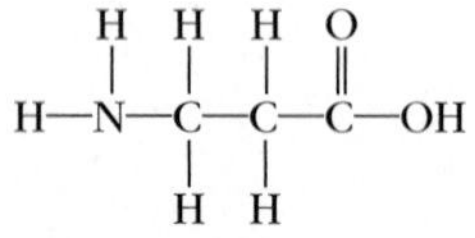

3. Given these condensed formulas, write the structural and molecular formulas.
(a) CH_3OH
(b) $CH_3CH_2NH_2$
(c) $CH_3CH_2SCH_2CH_3$
4. Give a molecular formula for each of these organic acids.

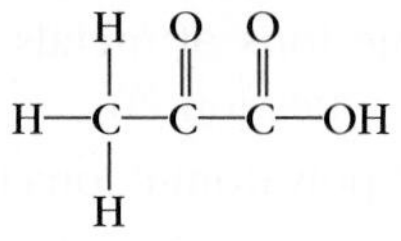

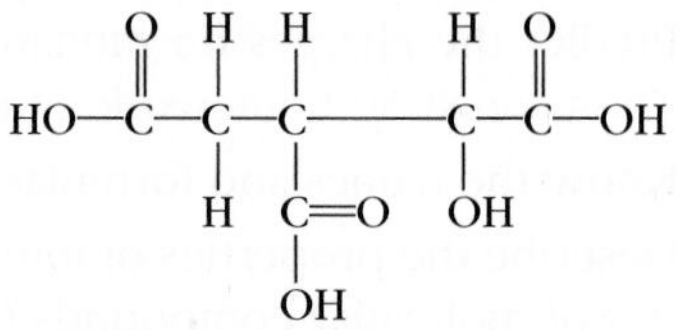

(a) pyruvic acid (b) isocitric acid

5. Give a molecular formula for each of these molecules.

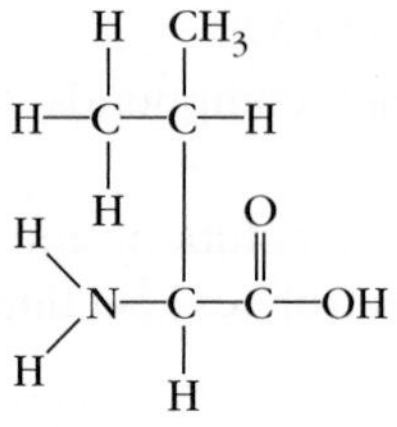

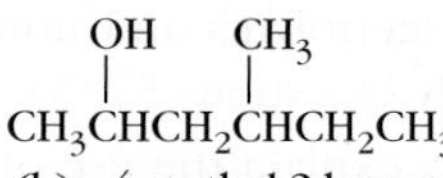

(a) valine (b) 4-methyl-2-hexanol

6. Give the name for each of these binary nonmetal compounds.
(a) NF_3 (b) HI
(c) BBr_3 (d) C_6H_{14}
7. Give the name for each of these binary nonmetal compounds.
(a) C_8H_{18} (b) P_2S_3
(c) OF_2 (d) XeF_4
8. Give the formula for each of these nonmetal compounds.
(a) Sulfur trioxide
(b) Dinitrogen pentoxide
(c) Phosphorous pentachloride
(d) Silicon tetrachloride
(e) Diboron trioxide (commonly called boric oxide)

Topical Questions

Molecular and Structural Formulas

9. ■ Give the formula for each of these nonmetal compounds.
   (a) Bromine trifluoride
   (b) Xenon difluoride
   (c) Diphosphorus tetrafluoride
   (d) Pentadecane
   (e) Hydrazine
10. Write structural formulas for these alkanes.
   (a) Butane (b) Nonane
   (c) Hexane (d) Octane
   (e) Octadecane
11. ■ Write the molecular, condensed, and structural formulas for the simplest alcohols derived from butane and pentane.
12. Octane is an alkane (Table 3.4). For the sake of this problem, we will assume that gasoline, a complex mixture of hydrocarbons, is represented by octane. If you fill the tank of your car with 18 gal of gasoline, how many grams and how many pounds of gasoline have you put into the car? Information you may need is (a) the density of octane, 0.692 g/cm^3, and (b) the volume of 1 gal in milliliters, 3790 mL.
13. Which of these molecules contains more O atoms, and which contains more atoms of all kinds?
   (a) Sucrose, $C_{12}H_{22}O_{11}$
   (b) Glutathione, $C_{10}H_{17}N_3O_6S$ (the major low-molecular-weight sulfur-containing compound in plant or animal cells)
14. Write the molecular formula of each of these compounds.
   (a) Benzene (a liquid hydrocarbon), with 6 carbon atoms and 6 hydrogen atoms per molecule
   (b) Vitamin C, with 6 carbon atoms, 8 hydrogen atoms, and 6 oxygen atoms per molecule
15. Write the formula for each molecule.
   (a) A molecule of the organic compound heptane, which has 7 carbon atoms and 16 hydrogen atoms
   (b) A molecule of acrylonitrile (the basis of Orlon and Acrilan fibers), which has 3 carbon atoms, 3 hydrogen atoms, and 1 nitrogen atom
   (c) A molecule of Fenclorac (an anti-inflammatory drug), which has 14 carbon atoms, 16 hydrogen atoms, 2 chlorine atoms, and 2 oxygen atoms
16. Give the total number of atoms of each element in one formula unit of each of these compounds.
   (a) CaC_2O_4
   (b) $C_6H_5CHCH_2$
   (c) $(NH_4)_2SO_4$
   (d) $Pt(NH_3)_2Cl_2$
   (e) $K_4Fe(CN)_6$
17. Give the total number of atoms of each element in each of these molecules.
   (a) $C_6H_5COOC_2H_5$
   (b) $HOOCCH_2CH_2COOH$
   (c) $NH_2CH_2CH_2COOH$
   (d) $C_{10}H_9NH_2Fe$
   (e) $C_6H_2CH_3(NO_2)_3$

Constitutional Isomers

18. Consider two molecules that are constitutional isomers.
   (a) What is the same on the molecular level between these two molecules?
   (b) What is different on the molecular level between these two molecules?
19. Draw condensed structural formulas for the five constitutional isomers of C_6H_{14}.

Predicting Ion Charges

20. ■ For each of these metals, write the chemical symbol for the corresponding ion (with charge).
   (a) Lithium (b) Strontium
   (c) Aluminum (d) Calcium
   (e) Zinc
21. For each of these nonmetals, write the chemical symbol for the corresponding ion (with charge).
   (a) Nitrogen (b) Sulfur
   (c) Chlorine (d) Iodine
   (e) Phosphorus
22. Predict the charges of the ions in an ionic compound composed of barium and bromine.
23. Predict the charges of the ions in calcium chloride, an ionic compound.
24. Predict the charges for ions of these elements.
   (a) Magnesium (b) Zinc
   (c) Iron (d) Gallium
25. Predict the charges for ions of these elements.
   (a) Selenium (b) Fluorine
   (c) Nickel (d) Nitrogen
26. Cobalt is a transition metal and so can form ions with at least two different charges. Write the formulas for the compounds formed between cobalt ions and the oxide ion.
27. Although not a transition element, lead can form two cations: Pb^{2+} and Pb^{4+}. Write the formulas for the compounds of these ions with the chloride ion.
28. Which of these are the correct formulas of compounds? For those that are not, give the correct formula.
   (a) AlCl (b) NaF_2
   (c) Ga_2O_3 (d) MgS
29. Which of these are the correct formulas of compounds? For those that are not, give the correct formula.
   (a) Ca_2O (b) $SrCl_2$
   (c) Fe_2O_5 (d) K_2O
30. A monatomic ion X^{2+} has 23 electrons and 27 neutrons. Identify element X.
31. A monatomic ion X^{2+} has 22 electrons and 28 neutrons. Identify element X.

Polyatomic Ions

32. For each of these compounds, tell what ions are present and how many there are per formula unit.
   (a) $Pb(NO_3)_2$ (b) $NiCO_3$
   (c) $(NH_4)_3PO_4$ (d) K_2SO_4

33. For each of these compounds, tell what ions are present and how many there are per formula unit.
(a) $Ca(CH_3CO_2)_2$ (b) $Co_2(SO_4)_3$
(c) $Al(OH)_3$ (d) $(NH_4)_2CO_3$

34. ■ Determine the chemical formulas for barium sulfate, magnesium nitrate, and sodium acetate. Each compound contains a monatomic cation and a polyatomic anion. What are the names and electrical charges of these ions?

35. Write the chemical formula for calcium nitrate, potassium chloride, and barium phosphate. What are the names and charges of all the ions in these three compounds?

36. ■ Write the chemical formulas for these compounds.
(a) Nickel(II) nitrate (b) Sodium bicarbonate
(c) Lithium hypochlorite (d) Magnesium chlorate
(e) Calcium sulfite

37. Write the chemical formulas for these compounds.
(a) Iron(III) nitrate (b) Potassium carbonate
(c) Sodium phosphate (d) Calcium chlorite
(e) Sodium sulfate

Ionic Compounds

38. ■ Determine which of these substances are ionic.
(a) CF_4 (b) $SrBr_2$
(c) $Co(NO_3)_3$ (d) SiO_2
(e) KCN (f) SCl_2

39. Which of these substances are ionic? Write the formula for each.
(a) Methane (b) Dinitrogen pentoxide
(c) Ammonium sulfide (d) Hydrogen selenide
(e) Sodium perchlorate

40. Which of these compounds would you expect to be ionic? Explain your answers.
(a) SF_6 (b) CH_4
(c) H_2O_2 (d) NH_3
(e) CaO

41. Which of these compounds would you expect to be ionic? Explain your answers.
(a) NaH (b) HCl
(c) NH_3 (d) CH_4
(e) HI

42. Give the formula for each of these ionic compounds.
(a) Ammonium carbonate (b) Calcium iodide
(c) Copper(II) bromide (d) Aluminum phosphate

43. Give the formula for each of these ionic compounds.
(a) Calcium hydrogen carbonate
(b) Potassium permanganate
(c) Magnesium perchlorate
(d) Ammonium monohydrogen phosphate

44. Name each of these ionic compounds.
(a) K_2S (b) $NiSO_4$
(c) $(NH_4)_3PO_4$ (d) $Al(OH)_3$
(e) $Co_2(SO_4)_3$

45. Name each of these ionic compounds.
(a) KH_2PO_4 (b) $CuSO_4$
(c) $CrCl_3$ (d) $Ca(CH_3COO)_2$
(e) $Fe_2(SO_4)_3$

46. ■ Solid magnesium oxide melts at 2800 °C. This property, combined with the fact that magnesium oxide is not an electrical conductor, makes it an ideal heat insulator for electric wires in cooking ovens and toasters. In contrast, solid NaCl melts at the relatively low temperature of 801 °C. What is the formula of magnesium oxide? Suggest a reason that it has a melting temperature so much higher than that of NaCl.

47. Assume you have an unlabeled bottle containing a white crystalline powder. The powder melts at 310 °C. You are told that it could be NH_3, NO_2, or $NaNO_3$. What do you think it is and why?

Electrolytes

48. What is an electrolyte? How can we differentiate between a strong electrolyte and a nonelectrolyte? Give an example of each.

49. Epsom salt, $MgSO_4 \cdot 7\,H_2O$, is sold for various purposes over the counter in drug stores. Methanol, CH_3OH, is a small organic molecule that is readily soluble in either water or gasoline. Which of these two compounds is an electrolyte and which is a nonelectrolyte?

50. Comment on this statement: "Molecular compounds are generally nonelectrolytes."

51. Comment on this statement: "Ionic compounds are generally electrolytes."

52. ■ For each of these electrolytes, what ions will be present in an aqueous solution?
(a) KOH (b) K_2SO_4
(c) $NaNO_3$ (d) NH_4Cl

53. For each of these electrolytes, what ions will be present in an aqueous solution?
(a) CaI_2 (b) $Mg_3(PO_4)_2$
(c) NiS (d) $MgBr_2$

54. Which of these substances would conduct electricity when dissolved in water?
(a) NaCl (b) $CH_3CH_2CH_3$ (propane)
(c) CH_3OH (ethanol) (d) $Ca(NO_3)_2$

55. Which of these substances would conduct electricity when dissolved in water?
(a) NH_4Cl (b) $CH_3CH_2CH_2CH_3$ (butane)
(c) $C_{12}H_{22}O_{11}$ (table sugar) (d) $Ba(NO_3)_2$

Moles of Compounds

56. Fill in this table for 1 mol methanol, CH_3OH.

	CH_3OH	Carbon	Hydrogen	Oxygen
Number of moles	______	______	______	______
Number of molecules or atoms	______	______	______	______
Molar mass	______	______	______	______

57. Fill in this table for 1 mol glucose, $C_6H_{12}O_6$.

	$C_6H_{12}O_6$	Carbon	Hydrogen	Oxygen
Number of moles	______	______	______	______
Number of molecules or atoms	______	______	______	______
Molar mass	______	______	______	______

58. ■ Calculate the molar mass of each of these compounds.
(a) Fe_2O_3, iron(III) oxide
(b) BF_3, boron trifluoride
(c) N_2O, dinitrogen oxide (laughing gas)
(d) $MnCl_2 \cdot 4\ H_2O$, manganese(II) chloride tetrahydrate
(e) $C_6H_8O_6$, ascorbic acid

59. Calculate the molar mass of each of these compounds.
(a) $B_{10}H_{14}$, a boron hydride once considered as a rocket fuel
(b) $C_6H_2(CH_3)(NO_2)_3$, TNT, an explosive
(c) $PtCl_2(NH_3)_2$, a cancer chemotherapy agent called cisplatin
(d) $CH_3(CH_2)_3SH$, butyl mercaptan, a compound with a skunk-like odor
(e) $C_{20}H_{24}N_2O_2$, quinine, used as an antimalarial drug

60. ■ How many moles are represented by 1.00 g of each of these compounds?
(a) CH_3OH, methanol
(b) Cl_2CO, phosgene, a poisonous gas
(c) NH_4NO_3, ammonium nitrate
(d) $MgSO_4 \cdot 7\ H_2O$, magnesium sulfate heptahydrate (Epsom salt)
(e) $Ag(CH_3COO)$, silver acetate

61. How many moles are present in 0.250 g of each of these compounds?
(a) $C_7H_5NO_3S$, saccharin, an artificial sweetener
(b) $C_{13}H_{20}N_2O_2$, procaine, a painkiller used by dentists
(c) $C_{20}H_{14}O_4$, phenolphthalein, a dye

62. (a) What is the molar mass of iron(II) nitrate, $Fe(NO_3)_2$?
(b) What is the mass, in grams, of 0.200 mol $Fe(NO_3)_2$?
(c) How many moles of $Fe(NO_3)_2$ are present in 4.66 g?

63. Calcium carbonate, found in marine fossils, has the molecular formula $CaCO_3$.
(a) What is the molar mass of $CaCO_3$?
(b) What is the mass, in grams, of 0.400 mol $CaCO_3$?
(c) How many moles of $CaCO_3$ are present in 7.63 g?

64. ■ Acetaminophen, an analgesic, has the molecular formula $C_8H_9O_2N$.
(a) What is the molar mass of acetaminophen?
(b) How many moles are present in 5.32 g acetaminophen?
(c) How many grams are present in 0.166 mol acetaminophen?

65. An Alka-Seltzer tablet contains 324 mg aspirin ($C_9H_8O_4$), 1904 mg $NaHCO_3$, and 1000 mg citric acid ($C_6H_8O_7$). (The last two compounds react with each other to provide the "fizz," bubbles of CO_2, when the tablet is put into water.)
(a) Calculate the number of moles of each substance in the tablet.
(b) If you take one tablet, how many molecules of aspirin are you consuming?

66. ■ How many moles of compound are in
(a) 39.2 g H_2SO_4? (b) 8.00 g O_2?
(c) 10.7 g NH_3?

67. How many moles of compound are in
(a) 46.1 g NH_4Cl? (b) 22.8 g CH_4?
(c) 9.63 g $CaCO_3$?

68. How many oxygen atoms are present in a 14.0-g sample of $Cu(NO_3)_2$?

69. How many sulfur atoms are present in a 21.0-g sample of $Fe_2(SO_4)_3$?

70. The use of CFCs (chlorofluorocarbons) has been curtailed because there is strong evidence that they cause environmental damage. If a spray can contains 250 g of one of these compounds, CCl_2F_2, how many molecules of this CFC are you releasing to the air when you empty the can?

71. Sulfur trioxide, SO_3 is made in enormous quantities by combining oxygen and sulfur dioxide, SO_2. The trioxide is not usually isolated but is converted to sulfuric acid.
(a) If you have 1.00 lb (454 g) sulfur trioxide, how many moles does this represent?
(b) How many molecules?
(c) How many sulfur atoms?
(d) How many oxygen atoms?

72. CFCs (chlorofluorocarbons) are implicated in decreasing the ozone concentration in the stratosphere. A CFC substitute is CF_3CH_2F.
(a) If you have 25.5 g of this compound, how many moles does this represent?
(b) How many atoms of fluorine are contained in 25.5 g of the compound?

73. How many water molecules are in one drop of water? (One drop of water is $\frac{1}{20}$ mL, and the density of water is 1.0 g/mL.)

74. If the water from a well contains 0.10 ppb (parts per billion) chloroform, $CHCl_3$, how many molecules of chloroform are present in one drop of the water? (One drop of water is $\frac{1}{20}$ mL, and the density of water is 1.0 g/mL.)

Percent Composition

75. ■ Calculate the molar mass of each of these compounds and the mass percent of each element.
(a) PbS, lead(II) sulfide, galena
(b) C_2H_6, ethane, a hydrocarbon fuel
(c) CH_3COOH, acetic acid, an important ingredient in vinegar
(d) NH_4NO_3, ammonium nitrate, a fertilizer

76. Calculate the molar mass of each of these compounds and the mass percent of each element.
(a) $MgCO_3$, magnesium carbonate
(b) C_6H_5OH, phenol, an organic compound used in some cleaners
(c) $C_2H_3O_5N$, peroxyacetyl nitrate, an objectionable compound in photochemical smog
(d) $C_4H_{10}O_3NPS$, acephate, an insecticide

77. ■ A certain metal, M, forms two oxides, M_2O and MO. If the percent by mass of M in M_2O is 73.4%, what is its percent by mass in MO?

78. Three oxygen-containing compounds of iron are $FeCO_3$, Fe_2O_3, and Fe_3O_4. What are the percentages of iron in each of these iron compounds?

79. The copper-containing compound $Cu(NH_3)_4SO_4 \cdot H_2O$ is a beautiful blue solid. Calculate the molar mass of the compound and the mass percent of each element.

80. Sucrose, table sugar, is $C_{12}H_{22}O_{11}$. When sucrose is heated, water is driven off. How many grams of pure carbon can be obtained from exactly one pound of sugar?

81. Carbonic anhydrase, an important enzyme in mammalian respiration, is a large zinc-containing protein with a molar

mass of 3.00×10^4 g/mol. The zinc is 0.218% by mass of the protein. How many zinc atoms does each carbonic anhydrase molecule contain?

82. Nitrogen fixation in the root nodules of peas and other legumes occurs with a reaction involving a molybdenum-containing enzyme named *nitrogenase.* This enzyme contains two Mo atoms per molecule and is 0.0872% Mo by mass. What is the molar mass of the enzyme?

83. If you heat Al with an element from Group 6A, an ionic compound is formed that contains 18.55% Al by mass.
    (a) What is the likely charge on the nonmetal in the compound formed?
    (b) Using X to represent the nonmetal, what is the empirical formula for this ionic compound?
    (c) Which element in Group 6A has been combined with Al?

84. Disilane, Si_2H_x, contains 90.28% silicon by mass. What is the value of x in this compound?

85. Chalky, white crystals in mineral collections are often labeled borax, which has the molecular formula $Na_2B_4O_7 \cdot 10\ H_2O$, when actually they are partially dehydrated samples with the molecular formula $Na_2B_4O_7 \cdot 5\ H_2O$, which is more stable under the storage conditions. Real crystals of borax are colorless, transparent crystals.
    (a) What percent of the mass has the mineral lost when it partially dehydrates?
    (b) Will the percent boron by mass be the same in the two compounds?

Empirical and Molecular Formulas

86. What is the difference between an empirical formula and a molecular formula? Use the compound ethane, C_2H_6, to illustrate your answer.

87. The molecular formula of ascorbic acid (vitamin C) is $C_6H_8O_6$. What is its empirical formula?

88. The empirical formula of maleic acid is CHO. Its molar mass is 116.1 g/mol. What is its molecular formula?

89. A well-known reagent in analytical chemistry, dimethylglyoxime, has the empirical formula C_2H_4NO. If its molar mass is 116.1 g/mol, what is the molecular formula of the compound?

90. ■ A compound with a molar mass of 100.0 g/mol has an elemental composition of 24.0% C, 3.0% H, 16.0% O, and 57.0% F. What is the molecular formula of the compound?

91. Acetylene is a colorless gas that is used as a fuel in welding torches, among other things. It is 92.26% C and 7.74% H. Its molar mass is 26.02 g/mol. Calculate the empirical and molecular formulas.

92. A compound contains 38.67% K, 13.85% N, and 47.47% O by mass. What is the empirical formula of the compound?

93. A compound contains 36.76% Fe, 21.11% S, and 42.13% O by mass. What is the empirical formula of the compound?

94. ■ There is a large family of boron-hydrogen compounds called boron hydrides. All have the formula B_xH_y and almost all react with air and burn or explode. One member of this family contains 88.5% B; the remainder is hydrogen. Which of these is its empirical formula: BH_3, B_2H_5, B_5H_7, B_5H_{11}, or BH_2?

95. Nitrogen and oxygen form an extensive series of at least seven oxides of general formula N_xO_y. One of them is a blue solid that comes apart, or "dissociates," reversibly, in the gas phase. It contains 36.84% N. What is the empirical formula of this oxide?

96. ■ Cumene is a hydrocarbon, a compound composed only of C and H. It is 89.94% carbon, and the molar mass is 120.2 g/mol. What are the empirical and molecular formulas of cumene?

97. Acetic acid is the important ingredient in vinegar. It is composed of carbon (40.0%), hydrogen (6.71%), and oxygen (53.29%). Its molar mass is 60.0 g/mol. Determine the empirical and molecular formulas of the acid.

98. An analysis of nicotine, a poisonous compound found in tobacco leaves, shows that it is 74.0% C, 8.65% H, and 17.35% N. Its molar mass is 162 g/mol. What are the empirical and molecular formulas of nicotine?

99. Cacodyl, a compound containing arsenic, was reported in 1842 by the German chemist Bunsen. It has an almost intolerable garlic-like odor. Its molar mass is 210. g/mol, and it is 22.88% C, 5.76% H, and 71.36% As. Determine its empirical and molecular formulas.

100. The action of bacteria on meat and fish produces a poisonous and stinky compound called cadaverine. It is 58.77% C, 13.81% H, and 27.42% N. Its molar mass is 102.2 g/mol. Determine the molecular formula of cadaverine.

101. DDT is an insecticide with this percent composition: 47.5% C, 2.54% H, and the remainder chlorine. What is the empirical formula of DDT?

102. ■ If Epsom salt, $MgSO_4 \cdot x\ H_2O$, is heated to 250 °C, all of the water of hydration is lost. After a 1.687-g sample of the hydrate is heated, 0.824 g $MgSO_4$ remains. How many molecules of water are there per formula unit of $MgSO_4$?

103. The alum used in cooking is potassium aluminum sulfate hydrate, $KAl(SO_4)_2 \cdot x\ H_2O$. To find the value of x, you can heat a sample of the compound to drive off all the water and leave only $KAl(SO_4)_2$. Assume that you heat 4.74 g of the hydrated compound and that it loses 2.16 g water. What is the value of x?

Biological Periodic Table

104. Make a list of the top ten most abundant essential elements needed by the human body.

105. Which types of compounds contain the majority of the oxygen found in the human body?

106. (a) How are metals found in the body, as atoms or as ions?
    (b) What are two uses for metals in the human body?

107. Distinguish between macrominerals and microminerals.

108. Which minerals are essential at smaller concentrations but toxic at higher concentrations?

General Questions

109. (a) Draw a diagram showing the crystal lattice of sodium chloride (NaCl). Show clearly why such a crystal can be cleaved easily by tapping on a knife blade properly aligned along the crystal.
    (b) Describe in words why the cleavage occurs as it does.

110. Give the molecular formula for each of these molecules.

(a)

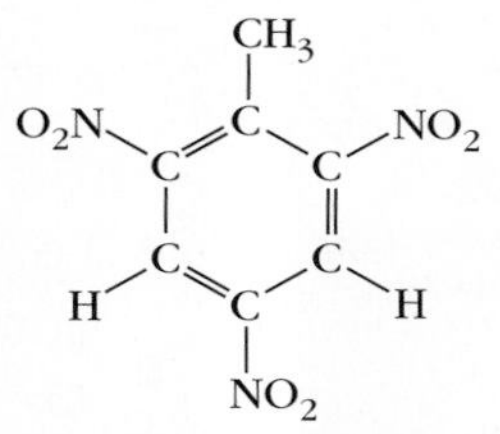

trinitrotoluene, TNT

(b)

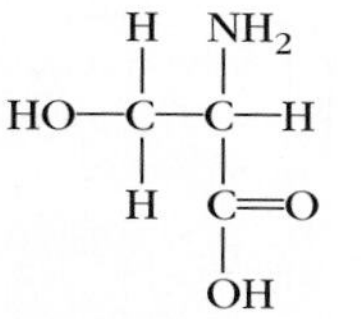

serine, an essential amino acid

111. (a) Calculate the mass of one molecule of nitrogen.
 (b) Calculate the mass of one molecule of oxygen.
 (c) What is the ratio of masses of these two molecules? How does it compare to the ratio of the atomic weights of N and O?

112. (a) Which of these pairs of elements are likely to form ionic compounds?
 (b) Write appropriate formulas for the compounds you expect to form, and name each.
 (i) Chlorine and bromine
 (ii) Lithium and tellurium
 (iii) Sodium and argon
 (iv) Magnesium and fluorine
 (v) Nitrogen and bromine
 (vi) Indium and sulfur
 (vii) Selenium and bromine

113. (a) Name each of these compounds.
 (b) Tell which ones are best described as ionic.
 (i) $ClBr_3$
 (ii) NCl_3
 (iii) $CaSO_4$
 (iv) C_7H_{16}
 (v) XeF_4
 (vi) OF_2
 (vii) NaI
 (viii) Al_2S_3
 (ix) PCl_5
 (x) K_3PO_4

114. (a) Write the formula for each of these compounds.
 (b) Tell which ones are best described as ionic.
 (i) Sodium hypochlorite
 (ii) Aluminum perchlorate
 (iii) Potassium permanganate
 (iv) Potassium dihydrogen phosphate
 (v) Chlorine trifluoride
 (vi) Boron tribromide
 (vii) Calcium acetate
 (viii) Sodium sulfite
 (ix) Disulfur tetrachloride
 (x) Phosphorus trifluoride

115. Precious metals such as gold and platinum are sold in units of "troy ounces," where 1 troy ounce is equivalent to 31.1 g.
 (a) If you have a block of platinum with a mass of 15.0 troy ounces, how many moles of the metal do you have?
 (b) What is the size of the block in cubic centimeters? (The density of platinum is 21.45 g/cm³ at 20 °C.)

116. "Dilithium" is the fuel for the Starship *Enterprise.* However, because its density is quite low, you will need a large space to store a large mass. As an estimate for the volume required, we shall use the element lithium.
 (a) If you want to have 256 mol for an interplanetary trip, what must the volume of a piece of lithium be?
 (b) If the piece of lithium is a cube, what is the dimension of an edge of the cube? (The density of lithium is 0.534 g/cm³ at 20 °C.)

117. Elemental analysis of fluorocarbonyl hypofluorite gave 14.6% C, 39.0% O, and 46.3% F. If the molar mass of the compound is 82.0 g/mol, determine the (a) empirical and (b) molecular formulas of the compound.

118. Azulene, a beautiful blue hydrocarbon, is 93.71% C and has a molar mass of 128.16 g/mol. What are the (a) empirical and (b) molecular formulas of azulene?

119. A major oil company has used an additive called MMT to boost the octane rating of its gasoline. What is the empirical formula of MMT if it is 49.5% C, 3.2% H, 22.0% O, and 25.2% Mn?

120. Direct reaction of iodine (I_2) and chlorine (Cl_2) produces an iodine chloride, I_xCl_y, a bright yellow solid.
 (a) If you completely react 0.678 g iodine to produce 1.246 g I_xCl_y, what is the empirical formula of the compound?
 (b) A later experiment shows that the molar mass of I_xCl_y is 467 g/mol. What is the molecular formula of the compound?

121. Pepto-Bismol, which helps provide relief for an upset stomach, contains 300 mg bismuth subsalicylate, $C_7H_5BiO_4$, per tablet.
 (a) If you take two tablets for your stomach distress, how many moles of the "active ingredient" are you taking?
 (b) How many grams of Bi are you consuming in two tablets?

122. Iron pyrite, often called "fool's gold," has the formula FeS_2. If you could convert 15.8 kg iron pyrite to iron metal and remove the sulfur, how many kilograms of the metal could you obtain?

123. Ilmenite is a mineral that is an oxide of iron and titanium, $FeTiO_3$. If an ore that contains ilmenite is 6.75% titanium, what is the mass (in grams) of ilmenite in 1.00 metric ton (exactly 1000 kg) of the ore?

124. Stibnite, Sb_2S_3, is a dark gray mineral from which antimony metal is obtained. If you have one pound of an ore that contains 10.6% antimony, what mass of Sb_2S_3 (in grams) is there in the ore?

125. Draw a diagram to indicate the arrangement of nanoscale particles of each substance. Consider each drawing to hold a very tiny portion of each substance. Each drawing should contain at least 16 particles, and it need not be three-dimensional.

$Br_2(\ell)$ LiF(s)

126. Draw diagrams of each nanoscale situation below. Represent atoms or monatomic ions as circles; represent molecules or

polyatomic ions by overlapping circles for the atoms that make up the molecule or ion; and distinguish among different kinds of atoms by labeling or shading the circles. In each case draw representations of at least five nanoscale particles. Your diagrams can be two-dimensional.

(a) A crystal of solid sodium chloride
(b) The sodium chloride from part (a) after it has been melted
(c) A sample of molten aluminum oxide, Al_2O_3

127. Draw diagrams of each nanoscale situation below. Represent atoms or monatomic ions as circles; represent molecules or polyatomic ions by overlapping circles for the atoms that make up the molecule or ion; and distinguish among different kinds of atoms by labeling or shading the circles. In each case draw representations of at least five nanoscale particles. Your diagrams can be two-dimensional.
(a) A sample of solid lithium nitrate, $LiNO_3$
(b) A sample of molten lithium nitrate
(c) The same sample of lithium nitrate after electrodes have been placed into it and a direct current applied to the electrodes
(d) A sample of solid lithium nitrate in contact with a solution of lithium nitrate in water

Applying Concepts

128. When asked to draw all the possible constitutional isomers for C_3H_8O, a student drew these structures. The student's instructor said some of the structures were identical.
(a) How many actual isomers are there?
(b) Which structures are identical?

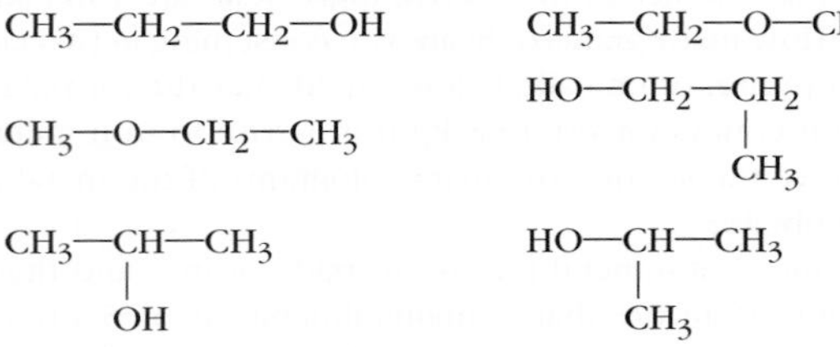

129. The statement that "metals form positive ions by losing electrons" is difficult to grasp for some students because positive signs indicate a gain and negative signs indicate a loss. How would you explain this contradiction to a classmate?

130. The formula for thallium nitrate is $TlNO_3$. Based on this information, what would be the formulas for thallium carbonate and thallium sulfate?

131. The name given with each of these formulas is incorrect. What are the correct names?
(a) CaF_2, calcium difluoride
(b) CuO, copper oxide
(c) $NaNO_3$, sodium nitroxide
(d) NI_3, nitrogen iodide
(e) $FeCl_3$, iron(I) chloride
(f) Li_2SO_4, dilithium sulfate

132. Based on the guidelines for naming oxoanions in a series, how would you name these species?
(a) BrO_4^-, BrO_3^-, BrO_2^-, BrO^-
(b) SeO_4^{2-}, SeO_3^{2-}

133. Which illustration best represents $CaCl_2$ dissolved in water?

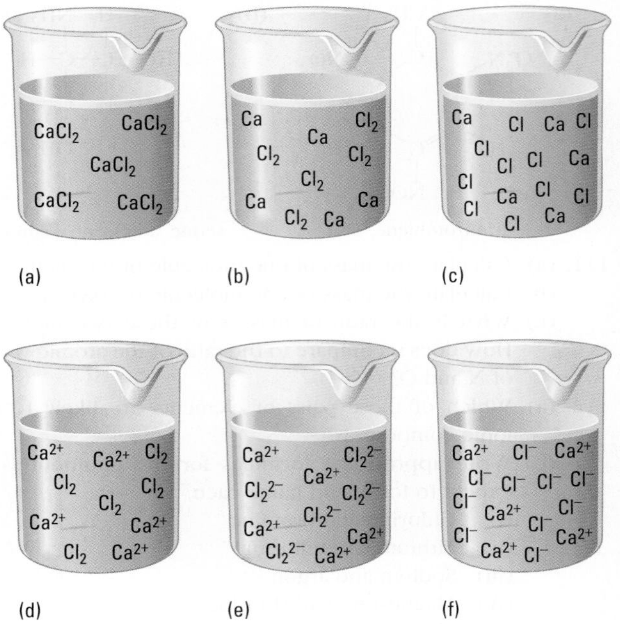

134. Which sample has the largest amount of NH_3?
(a) 6.022×10^{24} molecules of NH_3
(b) 0.1 mol NH_3
(c) 17.03 g NH_3

More Challenging Questions

135. ■ A piece of nickel foil, 0.550 mm thick and 1.25 cm square, was allowed to react with fluorine, F_2, to give a nickel fluoride. (The density of nickel is 8.908 g/cm^3.)
(a) How many moles of nickel foil were used?
(b) If you isolate 1.261 g nickel fluoride, what is its formula?
(c) What is its name?

136. Uranium is used as a fuel, primarily in the form of uranium(IV) oxide, in nuclear power plants. This question considers some uranium chemistry.
(a) A small sample of uranium metal (0.169 g) is heated to 800 to 900 °C in air to give 0.199 g of a dark green oxide, U_xO_y. How many moles of uranium metal were used? What is the empirical formula of the oxide U_xO_y? What is the name of the oxide? How many moles of U_xO_y must have been obtained?
(b) The oxide U_xO_y is obtained if $UO_2NO_3 \cdot n\ H_2O$ is heated to temperatures greater than 800 °C in air. However, if you heat it gently, only the water of hydration is lost. If you have 0.865 g $UO_2NO_3 \cdot n\ H_2O$ and obtain 0.679 g UO_2NO_3 on heating, how many molecules of water of hydration were there in each formula unit of the original compound?

137. One molecule of an unknown compound has a mass of 7.308×10^{-23} g, and 27.3% of that mass is due to carbon; the rest is oxygen. What is the compound?

138. What is the empirical formula of a compound that contains 23.3% Co, 25.3% Mo, and the remainder Cl?

139. What is the empirical formula of a compound that contains 23.3% Mg, 46.0% O, and the remainder S? What is the compound's name?

140. What are the empirical formulas of these compounds?
   (a) A hydrate of Fe(III) thiocyanate, $Fe(SCN)_3$, that contains 19.0% water
   (b) A mineral hydrate of zinc sulfate that contains 43.86% water
   (c) A sodium aluminum silicate hydrate that contains 12.10% Na, 14.19% Al, 22.14% Si, 42.09% O, and 9.48% H_2O

141. The active ingredients in lawn and garden fertilizer are nitrogen, phosphorus, and potassium. Bags of fertilizer usually carry three numbers, as in 5-10-5 fertilizer (a typical fertilizer for flowers). The first number is the mass percent N; the second is the mass percent P_2O_5; the third is the mass percent K_2O. Thus, the active ingredients in a 5-10-5 product are equivalent to 5% N, 10% P_2O_5, and 5% K_2O, by weight. (The reporting of fertilizer ingredients in this way is a convention agreed on by fertilizer manufacturers.) What is the mass in pounds of each of these three elements (N, P, K) in a 100-lb bag of fertilizer?

© Thomson Learning/George Semple

142. Four common ingredients in fertilizers are ammonium nitrate NH_4NO_3, ammonium sulfate $(NH_4)_2SO_4$, urea $(NH_4)_2CO$, and ammonium hydrogen phosphate $(NH_4)_2HPO_4$. On the basis of mass, which of these compounds has the largest mass percent nitrogen? What is the mass percent of nitrogen in this compound?

Conceptual Challenge Problems

CP3.A (Section 3.9) A chemist analyzes three compounds and reports these data for the percent by mass of the elements Ex, Ey, and Ez in each compound.

Compound	% Ex	% Ey	% Ez
A	37.485	12.583	49.931
B	40.002	6.7142	53.284
C	40.685	5.1216	54.193

Assume that you accept the notion that the numbers of atoms of the elements in compounds are in small whole-number ratios and that the number of atoms in a sample of any element is directly proportional to that sample's mass. What is possible for you to know about the empirical formulas for these three compounds?

CP3.B (Section 3.10) The following table displays on each horizontal row an empirical formula for one of the three compounds noted in CP3.A.

Compound A	Compound B	Compound C
______	$ExEy_2Ez$	______
$Ex_6Ey_8Ez_3$	______	______
______	______	Ex_3Ey_2Ez
______	$Ex_9Ey_2Ez_6$	______
______	______	$ExEy_2Ez_3$
$Ex_3Ey_8Ez_3$	______	______

Based only on what was learned in that problem, what is the empirical formula for the other two compounds in that row?

CP3.C (Section 3.10)
(a) Suppose that a chemist now determines that the ratio of the masses of equal numbers of atoms of Ez and Ex atoms is 1.3320 g Ez/1 g Ex. With this added information, what can now be known about the formulas for compounds A, B, and C in Problem CP3.A?
(b) Suppose that this chemist further determines that the ratio of the masses of equal numbers of atoms of Ex and Ey is 11.916 g Ex/1 g Ey. What is the ratio of the masses of equal numbers of Ez and Ey atoms?
(c) If the mass ratios of equal numbers of atoms of Ex, Ey, and Ez are known, what can be known about the formulas of the three compounds A, B, and C?

4 Quantities of Reactants and Products

Launch of a NASA Space Shuttle and its booster rockets. The shuttle engines are powered by the reaction of hydrogen with oxygen. How do the scientists and engineers designing the engine know how much of each reactant to use? Using a balanced chemical equation allows accurate calculations of the masses of reactants needed.

NASA

A major emphasis of chemistry is understanding chemical reactions. To work with chemical reactions requires knowing the correct formula of each reactant and product and the relative molar amounts of each involved in the reaction. This information is contained in balanced chemical equations—equations that are consistent with the law of conservation of mass and the existence of atoms. This chapter begins with a discussion of the nature of chemical equations. It is followed by a brief introduction to some general types of chemical reactions. Many of the very large number of known chemical reactions can be assigned to a few categories: combination, decomposition, displacement, and exchange. Next comes a description of how to write balanced chemical equations. After that, we will look at how the balanced chemical equation can be used to move from an understanding of what the reactants and products are to how much of each is involved under various conditions. Finally, we will introduce methods used to find the formulas of chemical compounds.

While the fundamentals of chemical reactions must be understood at the atomic and molecular levels (the nanoscale), the chemical reactions that we will describe are observable at the macroscale in the everyday world around us. Understanding and applying the quantitative relationships in chemical reactions are essential skills. You should know how to calculate the quantity of product that a reaction will generate from a given quantity of reactants. Facility with these quantitative calculations connects the nanoscale world of the chemical reaction to the macroscale world of laboratory and industrial manipulations of measurable quantities of chemicals.

ThomsonNOW™
Throughout the text, this icon indicates an opportunity to test yourself on key concepts and to explore interactive modules by signing in to ThomsonNOW at **www.thomsonedu.com**.

4.1 Chemical Equations

A candle flame can create a mood as well as provide light. It also is the result of a chemical reaction, a process in which reactants are converted into products (***p. 12***). The reactants and products can be elements, compounds, or both. In equation form we write

$$\text{Reactant(s)} \longrightarrow \text{product(s)}$$

where the arrow means "forms" or "yields" or "changes to."

In a burning candle, the reactants are hydrocarbons from the candle wax and oxygen from the air. Such reactions, in which an element or compound burns in air or oxygen, are called **combustion reactions**. The products of the complete combustion of hydrocarbons (***p. 84***) are always carbon dioxide and water.

$$\underset{\text{a hydrocarbon in candle wax}}{C_{25}H_{52}(s)} + \underset{\text{oxygen}}{38\,O_2(g)} \longrightarrow \underset{\text{carbon dioxide}}{25\,CO_2(g)} + \underset{\text{water}}{26\,H_2O(g)}$$

This **balanced chemical equation** indicates the relative amounts of reactants and products required so that the number of atoms of each element in the reactants equals the number of atoms of the same element in the products. In the next section we discuss how to write balanced equations.

Usually the physical states of the reactants and products are indicated in a chemical equation by placing one of these symbols after each reactant and product: (s) for solid, (ℓ) for liquid, and (g) for gas. The symbol (aq) is used to represent an **aqueous solution**, a substance dissolved in water. This is illustrated by the equation for the reaction of zinc metal with hydrochloric acid, an aqueous solution of

© PhotoLink/PhotoDisc Green/Getty Images

Combustion of hydrocarbons from candle wax produces a candle flame.

Antoine Lavoisier

1743–1794

One of the first to recognize the importance of exact scientific measurements and of carefully planned experiments, Lavoisier introduced principles for naming chemical substances that are still in use today. Further, he wrote a textbook, *Elements of Chemistry* (1789), in which he applied for the first time the principle of conservation of mass to chemistry and used the idea to write early versions of chemical equations. His life was cut short during the Reign of Terror of the French Revolution.

hydrogen chloride. The products are hydrogen gas and an aqueous solution of zinc chloride, a soluble ionic compound ***(⇐ p. 89)***.

$$\underset{\text{Reactants}}{Zn(s) + 2\,HCl(aq)} \longrightarrow \underset{\text{Products}}{H_2(g) + ZnCl_2(aq)}$$

In the 18th century, the great French scientist Antoine Lavoisier introduced the law of conservation of mass, which later became part of Dalton's atomic theory. Lavoisier showed that mass is neither created nor destroyed in chemical reactions. Therefore, if you use 5 g of reactants they will form 5 g of products if the reaction is complete; if you use 500 mg of reactants they will form 500 mg of products; and so on. Combined with Dalton's atomic theory ***(⇐ p. 22)***, this also means that if there are 1000 atoms of a particular element in the reactants, then those 1000 atoms must appear in the products.

There must be an accounting for *all* atoms in a chemical reaction.

Consider, for example, the reaction between gaseous hydrogen and chlorine to produce hydrogen chloride gas:

$$H_2(g) + Cl_2(g) \longrightarrow 2\,HCl(g)$$

When applied to this reaction, the law of conservation of mass means that one diatomic molecule of H_2 (two atoms of hydrogen) and one diatomic molecule of Cl_2 (two atoms of Cl) must produce two molecules of HCl. The numbers in front of the formulas—the **coefficients**—in balanced equations show how matter is conserved. The 2 HCl indicates that two HCl molecules are formed, each containing one hydrogen atom and one chlorine atom. Note how the symbol of an element or the formula of a compound is multiplied through by the coefficient that precedes it. The equality of the number of atoms of each kind in the reactants and in the products is what makes the equation "balanced."

Recall that there are 6.022×10^{23} atoms in a mole of any atomic element ***(⇐ p. 61)*** or 6.022×10^{23} molecules in a mole of any molecular element or compound ***(⇐ p. 63)***.

Multiplying all the coefficients by the same factor gives the relative amounts of reactants and products at any scale. For example, 4 H_2 molecules will react with 4 Cl_2 molecules to produce 8 HCl molecules (Figure 4.1). If we continue to scale up the reaction, we can use Avogadro's number as the common factor. Thus, 1 mol H_2 molecules reacting with 1 mol Cl_2 molecules will produce 2 mol HCl molecules. As demanded by the conservation of mass, the number of atoms of each type in the reactants and the products is the same.

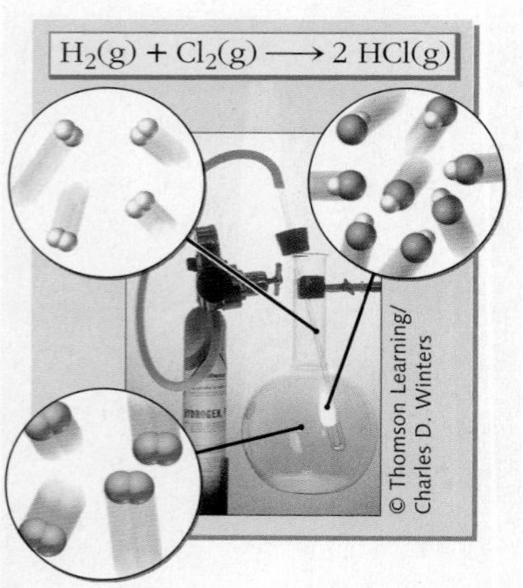

Figure 4.1 Hydrogen (H_2) and chlorine (Cl_2) react to form hydrogen chloride (HCl). Two molecules of HCl are formed when one H_2 molecule reacts with one Cl_2 molecule. This ratio is maintained when the reaction is carried out on a larger scale.

With the numbers of atoms balanced, the masses represented by the equation are also balanced. The molar masses show that 1.000 mol H_2 is equivalent to 2.016 g H_2 and that 1.000 mol Cl_2 is equivalent to 70.90 g Cl_2, so the total mass of reactants must be 2.016 g + 70.90 g = 72.92 g when 1.000 mol each of H_2 and Cl_2 are used. Conservation of mass demands that the same mass, 72.92 g HCl, must result from the reaction, and it does.

$$2.000 \text{ mol HCl} \times \frac{36.45 \text{ g HCl}}{1 \text{ mol HCl}} = 72.90 \text{ g HCl}$$

Relations among the masses of chemical reactants and products are called **stoichiometry** (stoy-key-AHM-uh-tree), and the coefficients (the multiplying numbers) in a balanced equation are called **stoichiometric coefficients** (or just coefficients).

EXERCISE 4.1 Chemical Equations

When methane burns this reaction is occurring:

$$CH_4(g) + 2\,O_2(g) \longrightarrow CO_2(g) + 2\,H_2O(g)$$

Write out in words the meaning of this chemical equation.

EXERCISE 4.2 Stoichiometric Coefficients

Heating iron metal in oxygen forms iron(III) oxide, Fe_2O_3 (Figure 4.2):

$$4\ Fe(s) + 3\ O_2(g) \longrightarrow 2\ Fe_2O_3(s)$$

(a) If 2.50 g Fe_2O_3 is formed by this reaction, what is the maximum *total* mass of iron metal and oxygen that reacted?
(b) Identify the stoichiometric coefficients in this equation.
(c) If 10,000 oxygen atoms reacted, how many Fe atoms were needed to react with this amount of oxygen?

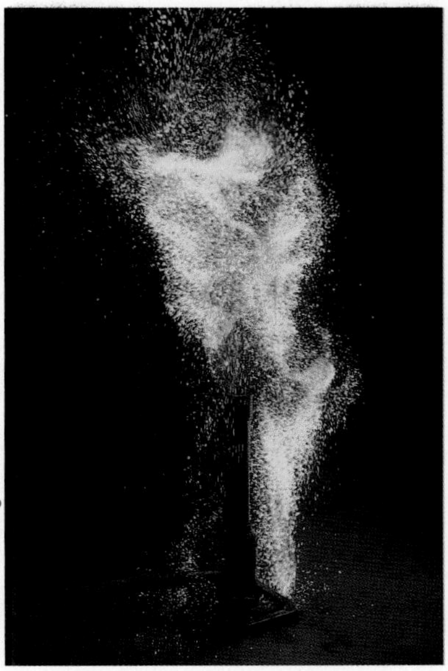

© Thomson Learning/Charles D. Winters

Figure 4.2 Powdered iron burns in air to form the iron oxide Fe_2O_3. The energy released during the reaction heats the particles to incandescence.

4.2 Patterns of Chemical Reactions

Many simple chemical reactions fall into one of the reaction patterns illustrated in Figure 4.3. Learning to recognize these reaction patterns is useful because they serve as a guide to predict what might happen when chemicals are mixed together or heated.

Take a look at the equation below. What does it mean to you at this stage in your study of chemistry?

$$Cl_2(g) + 2\ KBr(aq) \longrightarrow 2\ KCl(aq) + Br_2(\ell)$$

It's easy to let your eye slide by an equation on the printed page, but *don't* do that; ***read the equation.*** In this case it shows you that gaseous diatomic chlorine mixed with an aqueous solution of potassium bromide reacts to produce an aqueous solution of potassium chloride plus liquid diatomic bromine. After you learn to recognize reaction patterns, you will see that this is a *displacement* reaction—chlorine has displaced bromine so that the resulting compound in solution is KCl instead of the KBr originally present. Because chlorine displaces bromine, chlorine is what chemists describe as "more active" than bromine. The occurrence of this reaction implies that when chlorine is mixed with a solution of a different ionic bromide compound, displacement might also take place.

Throughout the rest of this chapter and the rest of this book, you should read and interpret chemical equations as we have just illustrated. Note the physical states of reactants and products. Mentally classify the reactions as described in the next few

ThomsonNOW™
Go to the Chemistry Interactive menu to work a module on **chemical equations.**

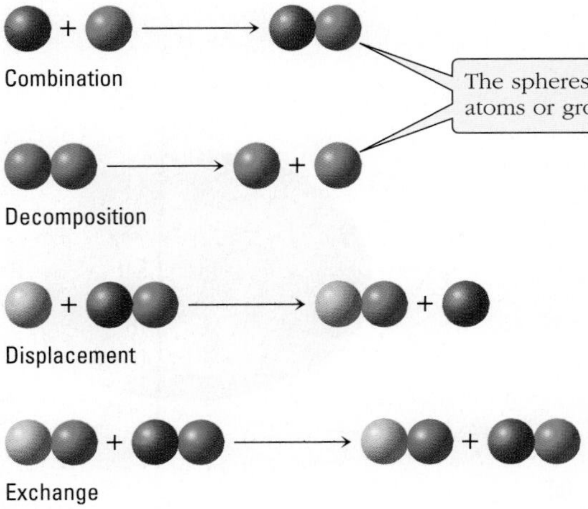

Figure 4.3 Four general types of chemical reactions. This classification of reaction patterns applies mainly to elements and inorganic compounds.

sections and look for what can be learned from each example. Most importantly, *don't* think that the equations must be memorized. There are far too many chemical reactions for that. Instead look for patterns, classes of reactions and the kinds of substances that undergo them, and information that can be applied in other situations. Doing so will give you insight into how chemistry is used every day in a wide variety of applications.

Combination Reactions

In a **combination reaction**, two or more substances react to form a single product.

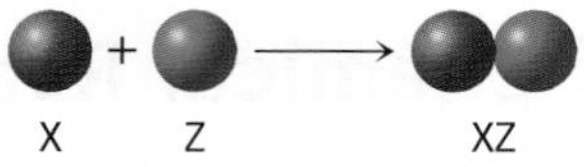

Recall that the halogens are F_2, Cl_2, Br_2, and I_2.

Oxygen and the halogens (Group 7A) are such reactive elements that they undergo combination reactions with most other elements. Thus, if one of two possible reactants is oxygen or a halogen and the other reactant is another element, it is reasonable to expect that a combination reaction will occur.

The combination reaction of a metal with oxygen produces an *ionic compound,* a metal oxide. Like any ionic compound, the metal oxide must be electrically neutral. Because you can predict a reasonable positive charge for the metal ion by knowing its position in the periodic table and by using the guidelines in Section 3.5 ***(⇐ p. 89)*** you can determine the formula of the metal oxide. For example, when aluminum (Al, Group 3A), which forms Al^{3+} ions, reacts with O_2, which forms O^{2-} ions, the product must be aluminum oxide Al_2O_3 (2 Al^{3+} and 3 O^{2-} ions), a compound also known as *alumina,* or *corundum.*

$$4\,Al(s) + 3\,O_2(g) \longrightarrow \underset{\text{aluminum oxide}}{2\,Al_2O_3(s)}$$

The halogens also combine with metals to form ionic compounds with formulas that are predictable based on the charges of the ions formed. The halogens form 1− ions in simple ionic compounds. For example, sodium combines with chlorine, and zinc combines with iodine, to form sodium chloride and zinc iodide, respectively (Figure 4.4).

Photos: © Thomson Learning/Charles D. Winters

(a) (b)

Figure 4.4 Combination of zinc and iodine. (a) The reactants: dark gray iodine crystals *(left)* and gray powdered zinc metal *(right)*. (b) The reaction. In a vigorous combination reaction, zinc atoms react with diatomic iodine molecules to form zinc iodide, an ionic compound, and the heat of the reaction is great enough that excess iodine forms a purple vapor.

$$2\ Na(s) + Cl_2(g) \longrightarrow 2\ NaCl(s)$$

$$Zn(s) + I_2(s) \longrightarrow ZnI_2(s)$$

When nonmetals combine with oxygen or chlorine, the compounds formed are not ionic but are molecular, composed of *molecules.* For example, sulfur, the Group 6A neighbor of oxygen, combines with oxygen to form two oxides, SO_2 and SO_3, in reactions of great environmental and industrial significance.

$$S_8(s) + 8\ O_2(g) \longrightarrow 8\ SO_2(g)$$

sulfur dioxide (colorless; choking odor)

$$2\ SO_2(g) + O_2(g) \longrightarrow 2\ SO_3(g)$$

sulfur trioxide (colorless; even more choking odor)

At room temperature, sulfur is a bright yellow solid. At the nanoscale it consists of molecules with eight-membered rings, S_8.

Sulfur dioxide enters the atmosphere both from natural sources and from human activities. The eruption of Mount St. Helens in May 1980 injected millions of tons of SO_2 into the atmosphere, for example. But about 75% of the sulfur oxides in the atmosphere come from human activities, such as burning coal in power plants. All coal contains sulfur, usually from 1% to 4% by weight.

Yet another example of a combination reaction is that between an organic molecule such as ethylene, C_2H_2, and bromine, Br_2, to form dibromoethane:

$$C_2H_2(g) + Br_2(\ell) \longrightarrow C_2H_2Br_2(g)$$

© Corbis

Mount St. Helens erupting.

The reaction between C_2H_2 and Br_2 is also called an *addition reaction*, as discussed in Section 8.5.

EXERCISE 4.3 Combination Reactions

Indicate whether each equation for a combination reaction is balanced, and if it is not, why not.

(a) $Cu + O_2 \rightarrow CuO$
(b) $Cr + Br_2 \rightarrow CrBr_3$
(c) $S_8 + 3\ F_2 \rightarrow SF_6$

CONCEPTUAL EXERCISE 4.4 Combination Reactions

(a) What information is needed to predict the product of a combination reaction between two elements? (b) What specific information is needed to predict the product of a combination reaction between calcium and fluorine? (c) What is the product formed by this reaction?

Decomposition Reactions

Decomposition reactions can be considered the opposite of combination reactions. In a **decomposition reaction**, one substance decomposes to form two or more products. The general reaction is

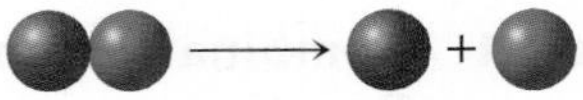

XZ → X + Z

Many compounds that we would describe as "stable" because they exist without change under normal conditions of temperature and pressure undergo decomposition when the temperature is raised, a process known as *thermal decomposition.* For example, a few metal oxides decompose upon heating to give the metal and oxygen gas, the reverse of combination reactions. One of the best-known metal

© Thomson Learning/Charles D. Winters

Decomposition of HgO. When heated, red mercury(II) oxide decomposes into liquid mercury and oxygen gas.

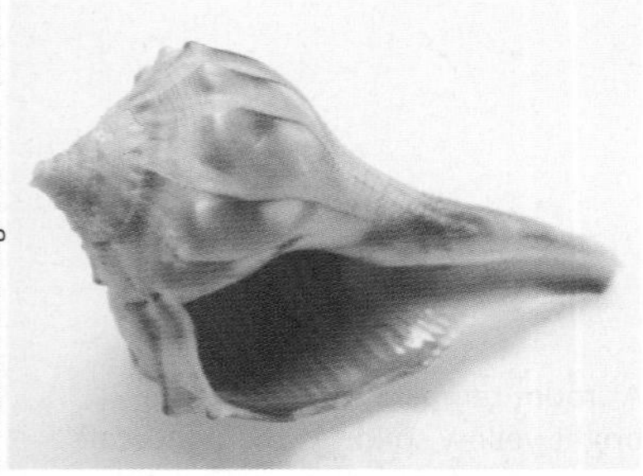
© Thomson Learning/Charles D. Winters

Sea shells are composed largely of calcium carbonate.

© Thomson Learning/Charles D. Winters

Dynamite contains nitroglycerin.

The NO_3 groups in nitroglycerin are not nitrate ions.

The Granger Collection

Alfred Nobel
1833–1896

A Swedish chemist and engineer, Nobel discovered how to mix nitroglycerin (a liquid explosive that is extremely sensitive to light and heat) with diatomaceous earth to make dynamite, which could be handled and shipped safely. Nobel's talent as an entrepreneur combined with his many inventions (he held 355 patents) made him a very rich man. He never married and left his fortune to establish the Nobel Prizes, awarded annually to individuals who "have conferred the greatest benefits on mankind in the fields of physics, chemistry, physiology or medicine, literature and peace."

oxide decomposition reactions is the reaction by which Joseph Priestley discovered oxygen in 1774:

$$2\,HgO(s) \xrightarrow{\text{heat}} 2\,Hg(\ell) + O_2(g)$$

A very common and important type of decomposition reaction is illustrated by the chemistry of *metal carbonates,* and calcium carbonate in particular. Many metal carbonates decompose to give metal oxides plus carbon dioxide:

$$\underset{\text{calcium carbonate}}{CaCO_3(s)} \xrightarrow{800\text{–}1000\ °C} \underset{\text{calcium oxide}}{CaO(s)} + CO_2(g)$$

Calcium is the fifth most abundant element in the earth's crust and the third most abundant metal (after Al and Fe). Naturally occurring calcium is mostly in the form of calcium carbonate from the fossilized remains of early marine life. Limestone, a form of calcium carbonate, is one of the basic raw materials of industry. Lime (calcium oxide), made by the decomposition reaction just discussed, is a raw material used for the manufacture of chemicals, in water treatment, and in the paper industry.

Some compounds are sufficiently unstable that their decomposition reactions are explosive. Nitroglycerin, $C_3H_5(NO_3)_3$, is such a compound. The formula for nitroglycerin contains parentheses around the NO_3 groups; they must be accounted for when balancing chemical equations. Nitroglycerin is a molecular organic compound with the structure shown below.

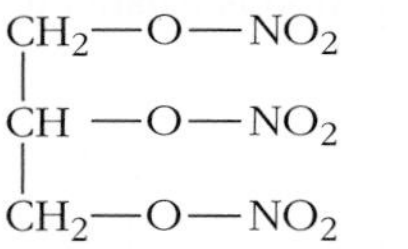
nitroglycerin

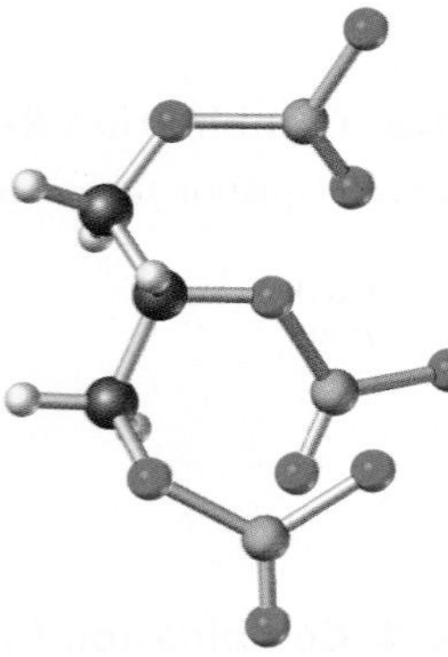

Nitroglycerin is very sensitive to vibrations and bumps. It can decompose violently.

$$4\,C_3H_5(NO_3)_3(\ell) \longrightarrow 12\,CO_2(g) + 10\,H_2O(g) + 6\,N_2(g) + O_2(g)$$

Water, by contrast, is such a stable compound that it can be decomposed to hydrogen and oxygen only at a very high temperature or by using an electric current, a process called electrolysis (Figure 4.5).

$$2\,H_2O(\ell) \xrightarrow{\text{direct current}} 2\,H_2(g) + O_2(g)$$

PROBLEM-SOLVING EXAMPLE 4.1 Combination and Decomposition Reactions

Predict the reaction type and the formula of the missing species for each of these reactions:

(a) $2\,Fe(s) + 3$ ________ $(g) \longrightarrow 2\,FeCl_3(s)$
(b) $Cu(OH)_2(s) \longrightarrow CuO(s) +$ ________ (ℓ)
(c) $P_4(s) + 5\,O_2(g) \longrightarrow$ ________ (s)
(d) $CaSO_3(s) \longrightarrow$ ________ $(s) + SO_2(g)$

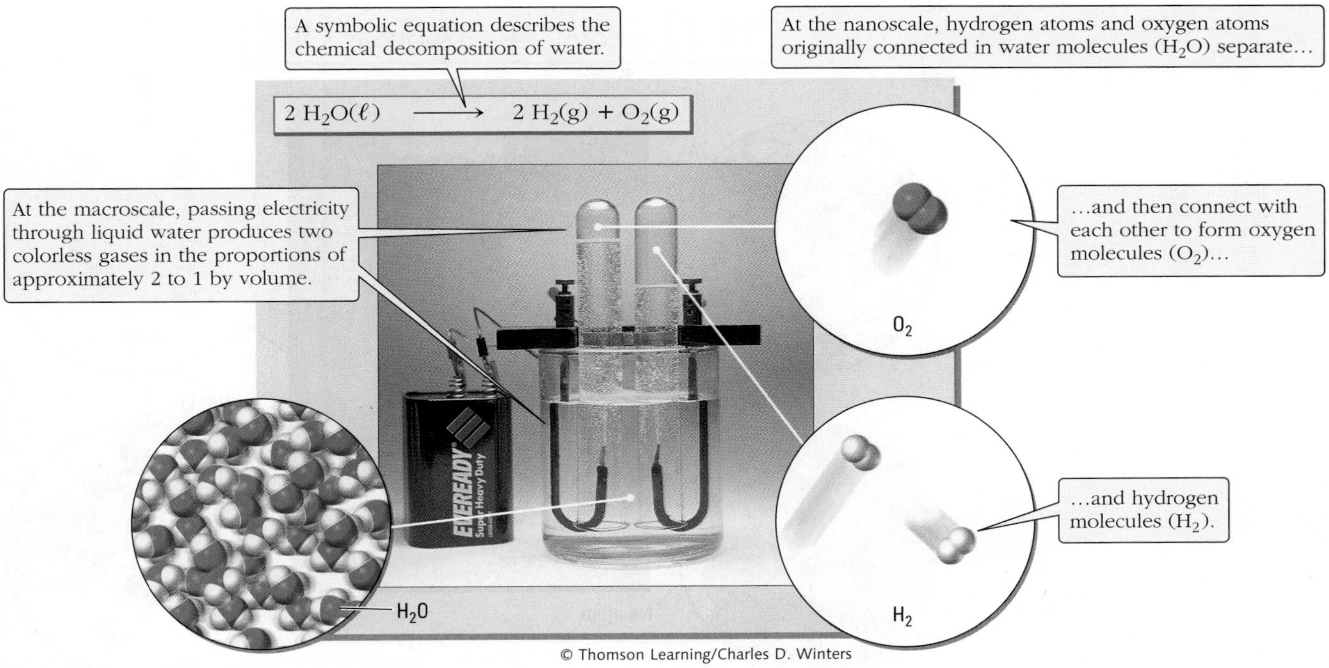

© Thomson Learning/Charles D. Winters

Active Figure 4.5 **Decomposition of water.** A direct electric current decomposes water into gaseous hydrogen (H_2) and oxygen (O_2). **Go to the Active Figures menu at ThomsonNOW to test your understanding of the concepts in this figure.**

Answer

(a) Combination: Cl_2 (b) Decomposition: H_2O

(c) Combination: P_4O_{10} (d) Decomposition: CaO

Strategy and Explanation Use the fact that decomposition reactions have one reactant and combination reactions have one product. (a) Combination of Fe(s) and Cl_2(g) produces $FeCl_3$(s). (b) Decomposition of $Cu(OH)_2$(s) produces CuO(s) and $H_2O(\ell)$. (c) Combination of P_4(s) and O_2(g) produces P_4O_{10}(s). (d) Decomposition of $CaSO_3$(s) produces CaO(s) and SO_2(g).

PROBLEM-SOLVING PRACTICE 4.1

Predict the reaction type and the missing substance for each of these reactions:

(a) ________ (g) + 2 O_2(g) $\longrightarrow$ 2 NO_2(g)

(b) 4 Fe(s) + 3 ________ (g) $\longrightarrow$ 2 Fe_2O_3(s)

(c) 2 NaN_3(s) $\longrightarrow$ 2 Na(s) + 3 ________ (g)

EXERCISE 4.5 Combination and Decomposition Reactions

Predict the products formed by these reactions:

(a) Magnesium with chlorine

(b) The thermal decomposition of magnesium carbonate

Displacement Reactions

Displacement reactions are those in which one element reacts with a compound to form a new compound and release a different element. The element released is said to have been displaced. The general equation for a **displacement reaction** is

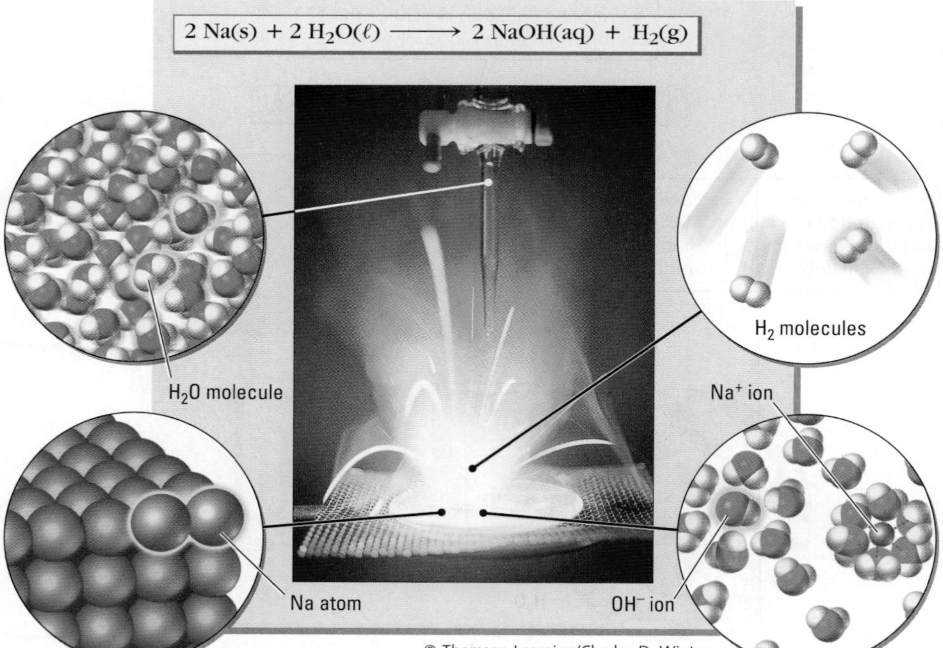

© Thomson Learning/Charles D. Winters

Figure 4.6 **A displacement reaction.** When liquid water drips from a buret onto a sample of solid sodium metal, the sodium displaces hydrogen gas from the water, and an aqueous solution of sodium hydroxide is formed. The hydrogen gas burns, producing the flame shown in the photograph. In the nanoscale pictures, the numbers of atoms, molecules, and ions that appear in the balanced equation are shown with yellow highlights.

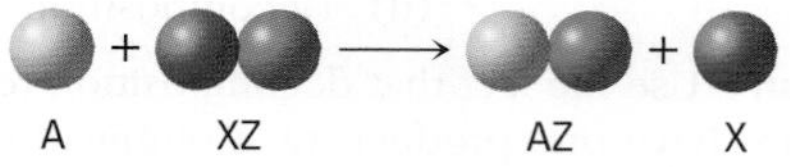

The reaction of metallic sodium with water is such a reaction.

$$2\ Na(s) + 2\ H_2O(\ell) \longrightarrow 2\ NaOH(aq) + H_2(g)$$

Here sodium displaces hydrogen from water (Figure 4.6). All the alkali metals (Group 1A), which are very reactive elements, react in this way when exposed to water.

Another example is the reaction that occurs between metallic copper and a solution of silver nitrate.

$$Cu(s) + 2\ AgNO_3(aq) \longrightarrow Cu(NO_3)_2(aq) + 2\ Ag(s)$$

Here, one metal displaces another. As you will see in Chapter 5, the metals can be arranged in a series from most reactive to least reactive (Section 5.5). This activity series can be used to predict the outcome of displacement reactions.

Exchange Reactions

Exchange reactions are also called metathesis or double-displacement reactions.

In an **exchange reaction,** there is an interchange of partners between two compounds. In general:

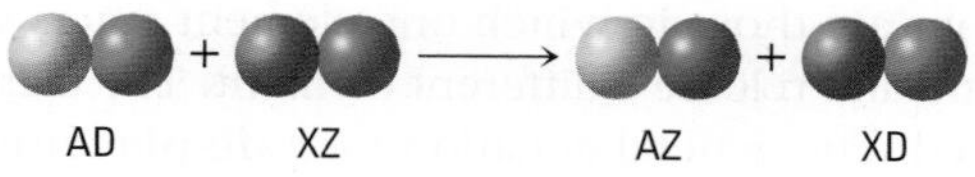

Mixing solutions of lead(II) nitrate and potassium chromate, for example, illustrates an exchange reaction in which an insoluble product is formed. The aqueous Pb^{2+} ions and K^+ ions exchange partners to form insoluble lead chromate and water-soluble potassium nitrate:

$$\underset{\text{lead nitrate}}{Pb(NO_3)_2(aq)} + \underset{\text{potassium chromate}}{K_2CrO_4(aq)} \longrightarrow \underset{\text{lead chromate}}{PbCrO_4(s)} + \underset{\text{potassium nitrate}}{2\ KNO_3(aq)}$$

Such reactions (further discussed in Chapter 5) include several kinds of reactions that take place between reactants that are ionic compounds and are dissolved in water. They occur when reactant ions are removed from solution by the formation of one of three types of product: (1) a solid, (2) a molecular compound, or (3) a gas.

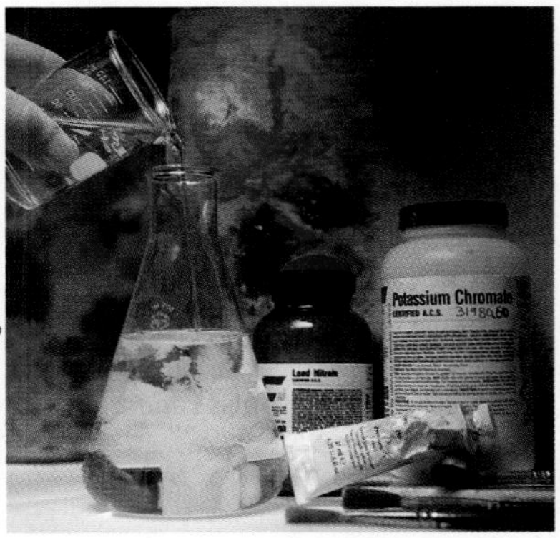

© Thomson Learning/Charles D. Winters

$Pb(NO_3)_2(aq) + K_2CrO_4(aq) \longrightarrow PbCrO_4(s) + 2\ KNO_3(aq)$. When lead nitrate and potassium chromate solutions are mixed, a brilliant yellow precipitate of lead chromate is formed.

PROBLEM-SOLVING EXAMPLE 4.2 Classifying Reactions by Type

Classify each of these reactions as one of the four general types discussed in this section.

(a) $2\ Al(s) + 3\ Br_2(\ell) \longrightarrow Al_2Br_6(s)$
(b) $2\ K(s) + H_2O(\ell) \longrightarrow 2\ KOH(aq) + H_2(g)$
(c) $AgNO_3(aq) + NaCl(aq) \longrightarrow AgCl(s) + NaNO_3(aq)$
(d) $NH_4NO_3(s) \longrightarrow N_2O(g) + 2\ H_2O(g)$

Answer

(a) Combination (b) Displacement (c) Exchange (d) Decomposition

Strategy and Explanation Use the fact that in displacement reactions, one reactant is an element, and in exchange reactions, both reactants are compounds.

(a) With two reactants and a single product, this must be a combination reaction.
(b) The general equation for a displacement reaction, $A + XZ \longrightarrow AZ + X$, matches what occurs in the given reaction. Potassium (A) displaces hydrogen (X) from water (XZ) to form KOH (AZ) plus H_2 (X).
(c) The reactants exchange partners in this exchange reaction. Applying the general equation for an exchange reaction, $AD + XZ \longrightarrow AZ + XD$, to this case, we find A is Ag^+, D is NO_3^-, X is Na^+, and Z is Cl^-.
(d) In this reaction, a single substance, NH_4NO_3, decomposes to form two products, N_2O and H_2O.

PROBLEM-SOLVING PRACTICE 4.2

Classify each of these reactions as one of the four general reaction types described in this section.

(a) $2\ Al(OH)_3(s) \longrightarrow Al_2O_3(s) + 3\ H_2O(g)$
(b) $Na_2O(s) + H_2O(\ell) \longrightarrow 2\ NaOH(aq)$
(c) $S_8(s) + 24\ F_2(g) \longrightarrow 8\ SF_6(g)$
(d) $3\ NaOH(aq) + H_3PO_4(aq) \longrightarrow Na_3PO_4(aq) + 3\ H_2O(\ell)$
(e) $3\ C(s) + Fe_2O_3(s) \longrightarrow 3\ CO(g) + 2\ Fe(\ell)$

4.3 Balancing Chemical Equations

Balancing a chemical equation means using coefficients so that the same number of atoms of each element appears on each side of the equation. We will begin with one of the general classes of reactions, the combination of reactants to produce a single product, to illustrate how to balance chemical equations by a largely trial-and-error process.

We will balance the equation for the formation of ammonia from nitrogen and hydrogen. Millions of tons of ammonia (NH_3) are manufactured worldwide annually by this reaction, using nitrogen extracted from air and hydrogen obtained from natural gas.

ThomsonNOW

Go to the Coached Problems menu for exercises on:

- **law of conservation of matter**
- **balancing chemical equations**

Balancing an equation involves changing the coefficients, but the subscripts in the formulas *cannot* be changed.

Step 1: ***Write an unbalanced equation containing the correct formulas of all reactants and products.***

$$\text{(unbalanced equation)} \qquad N_2 + H_2 \longrightarrow NH_3$$

Clearly, both nitrogen and hydrogen are unbalanced. There are two nitrogen atoms on the left and only one on the right, and two hydrogen atoms on the left and three on the right.

Step 2: ***Balance atoms of one of the elements.*** We start by using a coefficient of 2 on the right to balance the nitrogen atoms: 2 NH_3 indicates two ammonia molecules, each containing a nitrogen atom and three hydrogen atoms. On the right we now have two nitrogen atoms and six hydrogen atoms.

$$\text{(unbalanced equation)} \qquad N_2 + H_2 \longrightarrow 2\ NH_3$$

Step 3: ***Balance atoms of the remaining elements.*** To balance the six hydrogen atoms on the right, we use a coefficient of 3 for the H_2 on the left to furnish six hydrogen atoms.

$$\text{(balanced equation)} \qquad N_2 + 3\ H_2 \longrightarrow 2\ NH_3$$

Step 4: ***Verify that the number of atoms of each element is balanced.*** Do an atom count to check that the numbers of nitrogen and hydrogen atoms are the same on each side of the equation.

$$\begin{array}{lcccc} \text{(balanced equation)} & N_2 + & 3\ H_2 & \longrightarrow & 2\ NH_3 \\ \text{atom count:} & 2\ N + & (3 \times 2)\ H & = & 2\ N + (2 \times 3)\ H \\ & 2\ N + & 6\ H & = & 2\ N + 6\ H \end{array}$$

The physical states of the reactants and products are usually also included in the balanced equation. Thus, the final equation for ammonia formation is

$$N_2(g) + 3\ H_2(g) \longrightarrow 2\ NH_3(g)$$

PROBLEM-SOLVING EXAMPLE 4.3 Balancing a Chemical Equation

Ammonia gas reacts with oxygen gas to form gaseous nitrogen monoxide, NO, and water vapor at 1000 °C. Write the balanced equation for this reaction.

Answer $4\ NH_3(g) + 5\ O_2(g) \longrightarrow 4\ NO(g) + 6\ H_2O(g)$

Strategy and Explanation Use the stepwise approach to balancing chemical equations. Note that oxygen is in both products.

Step 1: *Write an unbalanced equation containing the correct formulas of all reactants and products.* The formula for ammonia is NH_3. The unbalanced equation is

$$\text{(unbalanced equation)} \qquad NH_3(g) + O_2(g) \longrightarrow NO(g) + H_2O(g)$$

Step 2: *Balance atoms of one of the elements.* Hydrogen is unbalanced since there are three hydrogen atoms on the left and two on the right. Whenever three and two atoms must be balanced, use coefficients to give six atoms on both sides of the equation. To do so, use a coefficient of 2 on the left and 3 on the right to have six hydrogens on each side.

$$\text{(unbalanced equation)} \qquad 2\ NH_3(g) + O_2(g) \longrightarrow NO(g) + 3\ H_2O(g)$$

Step 3: *Balance atoms of the remaining elements.* There are now two nitrogen atoms on the left and one on the right, so we balance nitrogen by using the coefficient 2 for the NO molecule.

(unbalanced equation) $2\,NH_3(g) + O_2(g) \longrightarrow 2\,NO(g) + 3\,H_2O(g)$

Now there are two oxygen atoms on the left and five on the right. We use a coefficient of $\frac{5}{2}$ to balance the atoms of O_2.

(balanced equation) $2\,NH_3(g) + \frac{5}{2}O_2(g) \longrightarrow 2\,NO(g) + 3\,H_2O(g)$

The equation is now balanced, but it is customary to use whole-number coefficients. Therefore, we multiply all the coefficients by 2 to get the final balanced equation.

(balanced equation) $4\,NH_3(g) + 5\,O_2(g) \longrightarrow 4\,NO(g) + 6\,H_2O(g)$

Step 4: *Verify that the number of atoms of each element is balanced.*

(balanced equation) $4\,NH_3(g) + 5\,O_2(g) \longrightarrow 4\,NO(g) + 6\,H_2O(g)$

4 N		=	4 N	
12 H		=		12 H
	10 O	=	4 O	6 O

PROBLEM-SOLVING PRACTICE 4.3

Balance these equations:

(a) $Cr(s) + Cl_2(g) \longrightarrow CrCl_3(s)$

(b) $As_2O_3(s) + H_2(g) \longrightarrow As(s) + H_2O(\ell)$

We now turn to the combustion of propane (C_3H_8) to illustrate balancing a somewhat more complex chemical equation. We will assume that complete combustion occurs, meaning that the only products are carbon dioxide and water.

PROBLEM-SOLVING EXAMPLE 4.4 Balancing a Combustion Reaction Equation

Write a balanced equation for the complete combustion of propane, C_3H_8, the fuel used in gas grills.

Answer $C_3H_8(g) + 5\,O_2(g) \longrightarrow 3\,CO_2(g) + 4\,H_2O(\ell)$

Strategy and Explanation

Step 1: *Write an unbalanced equation.* The initial equation is

(unbalanced equation) $C_3H_8 + O_2 \longrightarrow CO_2 + H_2O$

Step 2: *Balance the atoms of one of the elements.* None of the elements are balanced, so we could start with C, H, or O. We will start with C because it appears in only one reactant and one product. The three carbon atoms in C_3H_8 will produce three CO_2 molecules.

It usually works best to first balance the element that appears in the fewest formulas; balance the element that appears in the most formulas last.

(unbalanced equation) $C_3H_8 + O_2 \longrightarrow 3\,CO_2 + H_2O$

Step 3: *Balance atoms of the remaining elements.* We next balance the H atoms. The eight H atoms in the reactants will combine with oxygen to produce 4 water molecules, each containing two H atoms.

(unbalanced equation) $C_3H_8 + O_2 \longrightarrow 3\,CO_2 + 4\,H_2O$

Oxygen is the remaining element to balance. At this point, there are ten oxygen atoms in the products (3×2 in three CO_2 molecules, and 4×1 in four water molecules), but only two in O_2, a reactant. Therefore, O_2 in the reactants needs a coefficient of 5 to have ten oxygen atoms in the reactants.

$$C_3H_8(g) + 5\,O_2(g) \longrightarrow 3\,CO_2(g) + 4\,H_2O(\ell)$$

This combustion equation is now balanced.

Step 4: *Verify that the number of atoms of each element is balanced.*

$$C_3H_8(g) + 5\,O_2(g) \longrightarrow 3\,CO_2(g) + 4\,H_2O(\ell)$$

3 C	=	3 C	
8 H	=		8 H
10 O	=	6 O +	4 O

PROBLEM-SOLVING PRACTICE 4.4

Ethyl alcohol, C_2H_5OH, can be added to gasoline to create a cleaner-burning fuel from a renewable source. Write the balanced equation for:

(a) Complete combustion of ethyl alcohol to produce carbon dioxide and water
(b) Incomplete combustion of ethyl alcohol to produce carbon monoxide and water

When one or more polyatomic ions appear on both sides of a chemical equation, each one is treated as a whole during the balancing steps. When such an ion must have a subscript in the molecular formula, it is enclosed in parentheses. For example, in the equation for the reaction between sodium phosphate and barium nitrate to produce barium phosphate and sodium nitrate,

$$2\,Na_3PO_4(aq) + 3\,Ba(NO_3)_2(aq) \longrightarrow Ba_3(PO_4)_2(s) + 6\,NaNO_3(aq)$$

the nitrate ions, NO_3^-, and phosphate ions, PO_4^{3-}, are kept together as units and are enclosed in parentheses when the polyatomic ion occurs more than once in a chemical formula.

4.4 The Mole and Chemical Reactions: The Macro–Nano Connection

When the molar mass—which links the number of atoms, molecules, or formula units with the mass of the atoms, molecules, or ionic compounds—is combined with a balanced chemical equation, the masses of the reactants and products can be calculated. In this way the nanoscale of chemical reactions is linked with the macroscale, at which we can measure masses of reactants and products by weighing.

We will explore these relationships using the combustion reaction between methane, CH_4, and oxygen, O_2, as an example (Figure 4.7). The balanced equation shows the number of molecules of the reactants, which are methane and oxygen, and of the products, which are carbon dioxide and water. The coefficients on each species can also be interpreted as the numbers of moles of each compound, and we can use the molar mass of each compound to calculate the mass of each reactant and product represented in the balanced equation.

© Thomson Learning/Charles D. Winters

Figure 4.7 Combustion of methane with oxygen. Methane is the main component of natural gas, a primary fuel for industrial economies and the gas commonly used in laboratory Bunsen burners.

$$CH_4\,(g) \;+\; 2\,O_2\,(g) \longrightarrow CO_2\,(g) \;+\; 2\,H_2O\,(g)$$

CH_4	O_2	CO_2	H_2O
1 CH_4 molecule	2 O_2 molecules	1 CO_2 molecule	2 H_2O molecules
1 mol CH_4	2 mol O_2	1 mol CO_2	2 mol H_2O
16.0 g CH_4	64.0 g O_2	44.0 g CO_2	36.0 g H_2O
80.0 g total		80.0 g total	

Notice that the total mass of reactants (16.0 g CH_4 + 64.0 g O_2 = 80.0 g reactants) equals the total mass of products (44.0 g CO_2 + 36.0 g H_2O = 80.0 g products), as must always be the case for a balanced equation.

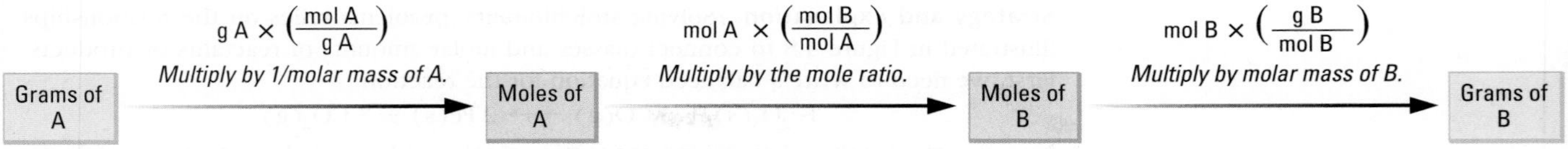

Figure 4.8 **Stoichiometric relationships in a chemical reaction.** The mass or molar amount of one reactant or product (A) is related to the mass or molar amount of another reactant or product (B) by the series of calculations shown.

The mole ratio is also known as the stoichiometric factor.

The stoichiometric coefficients in a balanced chemical equation provide the **mole ratios** that relate the numbers of moles of reactants and products to each other. These mole ratios are used in all quantitative calculations involving chemical reactions. Several of the mole ratios for the example equation are

$$\frac{2 \text{ mol } O_2}{1 \text{ mol } CH_4} \quad \text{or} \quad \frac{1 \text{ mol } CO_2}{1 \text{ mol } CH_4} \quad \text{or} \quad \frac{2 \text{ mol } H_2O}{2 \text{ mol } O_2}$$

These mole ratios tell us that 2 mol O_2 react with every 1 mol CH_4, or 1 mol CO_2 is formed for each 1 mol CH_4 that reacts, or 2 mol H_2O is formed for each 2 mol O_2 that reacts.

We can use the mole ratios in the balanced equation to calculate the molar amount of one reactant or product from the molar amount of another reactant or product. For example, we can calculate the number of moles of H_2O produced when 0.40 mol CH_4 is reacted fully with oxygen.

$$0.40 \text{ mol } CH_4 \times \frac{2 \text{ mol } H_2O}{1 \text{ mol } CH_4} = 0.80 \text{ mol } H_2O$$

CONCEPTUAL EXERCISE **4.6 Mole Ratios**

Write all the possible mole ratios that can be obtained from the balanced equation for the reaction between Al and Br_2 to form Al_2Br_6.

The molar mass and the mole ratio, as illustrated in Figure 4.8, provide the links between masses and molar amounts of reactants and products. When the quantity of a reactant is given in grams, then we use its molar mass to convert to moles of reactant as a first step in using the balanced chemical equation. Then we use the balanced chemical equation to convert from moles of reactant to moles of product. Finally, we convert to grams of product if necessary by using its molar mass. Figure 4.8 illustrates this sequence of calculations.

PROBLEM-SOLVING EXAMPLE 4.5 **Moles and Grams in Chemical Reactions**

An iron ore named hematite, Fe_2O_3, can be reacted with carbon monoxide, CO, to form iron and carbon dioxide. How many moles and grams of iron are produced when 45.0 g hematite are reacted with sufficient CO?

Answer 0.564 mol and 31.5 g Fe

Strategy and Explanation Solving stoichiometry problems relies on the relationships illustrated in Figure 4.8 to connect masses and molar amounts of reactants or products. First, we need to write a balanced equation for the reaction.

$$Fe_2O_3(s) + 3\ CO(g) \longrightarrow 2\ Fe(s) + 3\ CO_2(g)$$

Now we can use the relationships connecting masses and moles of reactants or products, as illustrated in Figure 4.8. We know the mass of hematite, and to proceed we need to know the moles of hematite. The molar mass of hematite is 159.69 g/mol.

$$\text{Grams of hematite} \longrightarrow \text{moles of hematite}$$

$$\text{Amount of hematite reacted: } 45.0 \text{ g hematite} \times \frac{1 \text{ mol hematite}}{159.69 \text{ g hematite}} = 0.282 \text{ mol hematite}$$

We then use the mole ratio (stoichiometric factor) from the balanced reaction to convert moles of hematite reacted to moles of iron produced.

$$\text{Moles of hematite} \longrightarrow \text{moles of iron}$$

$$\text{Amount of iron formed: } 0.282 \text{ mol hematite} \times \frac{2 \text{ mol Fe}}{1 \text{ mol hematite}} = 0.564 \text{ mol Fe}$$

We then multiply the number of moles of iron formed by the molar mass of iron to obtain the mass of iron formed.

$$0.564 \text{ mol Fe} \times \frac{55.845 \text{ g Fe}}{1 \text{ mol Fe}} = 31.5 \text{ g Fe}$$

✓ **Reasonable Answer Check** The balanced equation shows that for every one mole of hematite reacted, two moles of iron are produced. Therefore, approximately 0.3 mol hematite should produce twice that molar amount, or approximately 0.6 mol iron. The answer is reasonable.

PROBLEM-SOLVING PRACTICE 4.5

How many grams of carbon monoxide are required to react completely with 0.433 mol hematite?

We will illustrate the stoichiometric relationships of Figure 4.8 and a stepwise method for solving problems involving mass relations in chemical reactions to answer gram-to-gram conversion questions such as: How many grams of O_2 are needed to react completely with 5.0 g CH_4?

Step 1: ***Write the correct formulas for reactants and products and balance the chemical equation.*** The balanced equation is

$$CH_4(g) + 2\ O_2(g) \longrightarrow CO_2(g) + 2\ H_2O(g)$$

Step 2: ***Decide what information about the problem is known and what is unknown. Map out a strategy for answering the question.*** In this example, you know the mass of CH_4 and you want to calculate the mass of O_2. You also know that you can use molar mass to convert mass of CH_4 to molar amount of CH_4. Then you can use the mole ratio from the balanced equation (2 mol O_2/1 mol CH_4) to calculate the moles of O_2 needed. Finally, you can use the molar mass of O_2 to convert the moles of O_2 to grams of O_2.

Grams of CH_4 → Moles of CH_4 → Moles of O_2 → Grams of O_2

Step 3: ***Calculate moles from grams (if necessary).*** The known mass of CH_4 must be converted to molar amount because the coefficients of the balanced equation express mole relationships.

$$5.0\ g\ CH_4 \times \frac{1\ mol\ CH_4}{16.0\ g\ CH_4} = 0.313\ mol\ CH_4$$

In multistep calculations, remember to carry one additional significant figure in intermediate steps before rounding to the final value.

Step 4: ***Use the mole ratio to calculate the unknown number of moles, and then convert the number of moles to number of grams (if necessary).*** Calculate the number of moles and then grams of O_2.

$$0.313\ mol\ CH_4 \times \frac{2\ mol\ O_2}{1\ mol\ CH_4} = 0.626\ mol\ O_2$$

$$0.626\ mol\ O_2 \times \frac{32.0\ g\ O_2}{1\ mol\ O_2} = 20.\ g\ O_2$$

Step 5: ***Check the answer to see whether it is reasonable.*** The starting mass of CH_4 of 5.0 g is about one third of a mole of CH_4. One third of a mole of CH_4 should react with two thirds of a mole of O_2 because the mole ratio is 1:2. The molar mass of O_2 is 32.0 g/mol, so two thirds of this amount is about 20. Therefore, the answer of 20. g O_2 is reasonable.

ThomsonNOW™

Go to the Coached Problems menu for an exercise on **stoichiometric calculations.**

EXERCISE 4.7 Moles and Grams in Chemical Reactions

Verify that 10.8 g water is produced by the reaction of excess O_2 with 0.300 mol CH_4.

Problem-Solving Examples 4.6 and 4.7 illustrate further the application of the steps for solving problems involving mass relations in chemical reactions.

PROBLEM-SOLVING EXAMPLE 4.6 Moles and Grams in Chemical Reactions

When silicon dioxide, SiO_2, and carbon are reacted at high temperature, silicon carbide, SiC (also known as carborundum, an important industrial abrasive), and carbon monoxide, CO, are produced. Calculate the mass in grams of silicon carbide that will be formed by the complete reaction of 0.400 mol SiO_2 with excess carbon.

Answer 16.0 g SiC

Strategy and Explanation Use the stepwise approach to solve mass relations problems.

Step 1: *Write the correct formulas for reactants and products and balance the chemical equation.* SiO_2 and C are the reactants; SiC and CO are the products.

$$SiO_2(s) + 3\ C(s) \longrightarrow SiC(s) + 2\ CO(g)$$

Step 2: *Decide what information about the problem is known and what is unknown. Map out a strategy for answering the question.* We know how many moles of SiO_2 are available. C is present in excess. If we can calculate how many moles of SiC are formed, then the mass of SiC can be calculated.

Step 3: *Calculate moles from grams (if necessary).* We know there is 0.400 mol SiO_2.

Step 4: *Use the mole ratio to calculate the unknown number of moles, and then convert the number of moles to number of grams (if necessary).* Both steps are needed here to convert moles of SiO_2 to moles of SiC and then to grams of SiC. In a single setup the calculation is

$$0.400\ mol\ SiO_2 \times \frac{1\ mol\ SiC}{1\ mol\ SiO_2} \times \frac{40.10\ g\ SiC}{1\ mol\ SiC} = 16.0\ g\ SiC$$

© Thomson Learning/Charles D. Winters

Silicon carbide, SiC. The grinding wheel *(left)* is coated with SiC. Naturally occurring silicon carbide *(right)* is also known as carborundum. It is one of the hardest substances known, making it valuable as an abrasive.

Step 5: *Check the answer to see whether it is reasonable.* The answer, 16.0 g SiC, is reasonable because 1 mol SiO_2 would produce 1 mol SiC (40.10 g); therefore, four tenths of a mole of SiO_2 would produce four tenths of a mole of SiC (16.0 g).

✓ **Reasonable Answer Check** Step 5 verified that the answer is reasonable.

PROBLEM-SOLVING PRACTICE 4.6

Tin is extracted from its ore cassiterite, SnO_2, by reaction with carbon from coal.

$$SnO_2(s) + 2\,C(s) \rightarrow Sn(\ell) + 2\,CO(g)$$

(a) What mass of tin can be produced from 0.300 mol cassiterite?
(b) How many grams of carbon are required to produce this much tin?

PROBLEM-SOLVING EXAMPLE 4.7 Grams, Moles, and Grams

A popular candy bar contains 21.1 g sucrose (cane sugar), $C_{12}H_{22}O_{11}$. When the candy bar is eaten, the sucrose is metabolized according to the overall equation

$$\text{(unbalanced equation)} \qquad C_{12}H_{22}O_{11}(s) + O_2(g) \longrightarrow CO_2(g) + H_2O(\ell)$$

Balance the chemical equation, and find the mass of O_2 consumed and the masses of CO_2 and H_2O produced by this reaction.

Answer $C_{12}H_{22}O_{11}(s) + 12\,O_2(g) \rightarrow 12\,CO_2(g) + 11\,H_2O(\ell)$

23.7 g O_2 is consumed; 32.6 g CO_2 and 12.2 g H_2O are produced.

Strategy and Explanation First, write the balanced chemical equation. Then use it to calculate the masses required. Coefficients of 12 and 11 for the CO_2 and H_2O products balance the C and H, giving 35 oxygen atoms in the products. In the reactants, these oxygen atoms are balanced by the 12 O_2 molecules plus the 11 oxygen atoms in sucrose.

$$C_{12}H_{22}O_{11}(s) + 12\,O_2(g) \longrightarrow 12\,CO_2(g) + 11\,H_2O(\ell)$$

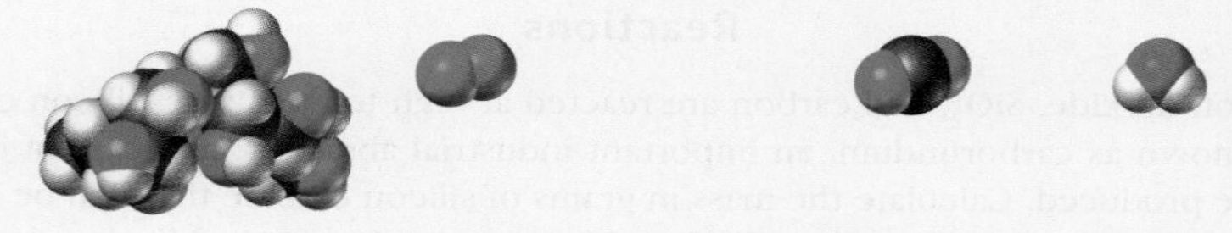

Use sucrose's molar mass (342.3 g/mol) to convert grams of sucrose to moles of sucrose.

$$21.1 \text{ g sucrose} \times \frac{1 \text{ mol sucrose}}{342.3 \text{ g sucrose}} = 0.06164 \text{ mol sucrose}$$

Next, use the mole ratios and molar masses to calculate the masses of O_2, CO_2, and H_2O.

$$0.06164 \text{ mol sucrose} \times \frac{12 \text{ mol } O_2}{1 \text{ mol sucrose}} \times \frac{31.99 \text{ g } O_2}{1 \text{ mol } O_2} = 23.7 \text{ g } O_2$$

$$0.06164 \text{ mol sucrose} \times \frac{12 \text{ mol } CO_2}{1 \text{ mol sucrose}} \times \frac{44.01 \text{ g } CO_2}{1 \text{ mol } CO_2} = 32.6 \text{ g } CO_2$$

$$0.06164 \text{ mol sucrose} \times \frac{11 \text{ mol } H_2O}{1 \text{ mol sucrose}} \times \frac{18.02 \text{ g } H_2O}{1 \text{ mol } H_2O} = 12.2 \text{ g } H_2O$$

The mass of water could have been found by using the conservation of mass.

$$\text{Total mass of reactants} = \text{total mass of products}$$

$$\text{Total mass of reactants} = 21.1 \text{ g sucrose} + 23.7 \text{ g } O_2 = 44.8 \text{ g}$$

$$\text{Total mass of products} = 32.6 \text{ g } CO_2 + ? \text{ g } H_2O = 44.8 \text{ g}$$

$$\text{Mass of } H_2O = 44.8 \text{ g} - 32.6 \text{ g} = 12.2 \text{ g } H_2O$$

✓ **Reasonable Answer Check** These are reasonable answers because approximately 0.05 mol sucrose would require approximately 0.6 mol O_2 and would produce approximately 0.6 mol CO_2 and 0.5 mol H_2O. Therefore, the calculated masses should be somewhat smaller than the molar masses, and they are.

PROBLEM-SOLVING PRACTICE 4.7

A lump of coke (carbon) weighs 57 g.

(a) What mass of oxygen is required to burn it to carbon monoxide?

(b) How many grams of CO are produced?

To this point we have used the methods of stoichiometry to compute the quantity of products given the quantity of reactants. Now we turn to the reverse problem: Given the quantity of products, what quantitative information can we deduce about the reactants? Questions such as these are often confronted by *analytical chemistry,* a field in which chemists creatively identify pure substances and measure the quantities of components of mixtures. Although analytical chemistry is now largely done by instrumental methods, classic chemical reactions and stoichiometry still play a central role. The analysis of mixtures is often challenging. It can take a great deal of imagination to figure out how to use chemistry to determine what, and how much, is there.

PROBLEM-SOLVING EXAMPLE 4.8 Evaluating an Ore

The mass percent of titanium dioxide (TiO_2) in an ore can be evaluated by carrying out the reaction of the ore with bromine trifluoride and measuring the mass of oxygen gas evolved.

$$3\,TiO_2(s) + 4\,BrF_3(\ell) \longrightarrow 3\,TiF_4(s) + 2\,Br_2(\ell) + 3\,O_2(g)$$

If 2.376 g of a TiO_2-containing ore generates 0.143 g O_2, what is the mass percent of TiO_2 in the ore sample?

Answer 15.0% TiO_2

Strategy and Explanation The mass percent of TiO_2 is

$$\text{Mass percent } TiO_2 = \frac{\text{mass of } TiO_2}{\text{mass of ore sample}} \times 100\%$$

The mass of the sample is given, and the mass of TiO_2 can be determined from the known mass of oxygen and the balanced equation.

$$0.143 \text{ g } O_2 \times \frac{1 \text{ mol } O_2}{32.00 \text{ g } O_2} \times \frac{3 \text{ mol } TiO_2}{3 \text{ mol } O_2} \times \frac{79.88 \text{ g } TiO_2}{1 \text{ mol } TiO_2} = 0.3569 \text{ g } TiO_2$$

The mass percent of TiO_2 is

$$\frac{0.3569 \text{ g } TiO_2}{2.376 \text{ g sample}} \times 100\% = 15.0\%$$

Titanium dioxide is a valuable commercial product. It is so widely used in paints and pigments that an ore with only 15% TiO_2 can be mined profitably.

✓ **Reasonable Answer Check** According to the balanced equation, 2.4 g TiO_2 should produce $2.4 \times \frac{(3 \times 32)}{(3 \times 80)} \approx 1$ g of O_2 but this reaction actually produced about 0.14 g, which is close to 15% of the expected amount. The answer is reasonable.

PROBLEM-SOLVING PRACTICE 4.8

The purity of magnesium metal can be determined by reacting the metal with excess hydrochloric acid to form $MgCl_2$, evaporating the water from the resulting solution, and weighing the solid $MgCl_2$ formed.

$$Mg(s) + 2\ HCl(aq) \longrightarrow MgCl_2(aq) + H_2(g)$$

Calculate the percentage of magnesium in a 1.72-g sample that produced 6.46 g $MgCl_2$ when reacted with excess HCl.

4.5 Reactions with One Reactant in Limited Supply

ThomsonNOW
Go to the Chemistry Interactive menu to work modules on **reactions controlled by the supply of one reactant.**

In the previous section, we assumed that exactly stoichiometric amounts of reactants were present; each reactant was entirely consumed when the reaction was over. However, this is rarely the case when chemists carry out an actual synthesis, whether for small quantities in a laboratory or on a large scale in an industrial process. Usually, one reactant is more expensive or less readily available than others. The cheaper or more available reactants are used in excess to ensure that the more expensive material is completely converted to product.

The industrial production of methanol, CH_3OH, is such a case. Methanol, an important industrial product, is manufactured by the reaction of carbon monoxide and hydrogen.

$$CO(g) + 2\ H_2(g) \longrightarrow CH_3OH(\ell)$$

ESTIMATION

How Much CO_2 Is Produced by Your Car?

Your car burns gasoline in a combustion reaction and produces water and carbon dioxide, CO_2, one of the major greenhouse gases, which is involved in global warming (discussed in detail in Section 10.13). For each gallon of gasoline that you burn in your car, how much CO_2 is produced? How much CO_2 is produced by your car per year?

To proceed with the estimation, we need to write a balanced chemical equation with the stoichiometric relationship between the reactant, gasoline, and the product of interest, CO_2. To write the chemical equation we need to make an assumption about the composition of gasoline. We will assume that the gasoline is octane, C_8H_{18}, so the reaction of interest is

$$2\ C_8H_{18} + 25\ O_2 \longrightarrow 16\ CO_2 + 18\ H_2O$$

One gallon equals 4 quarts, which equals

$$4\ \text{qt} \times \frac{1\ \text{L}}{1.057\ \text{qt}} = 3.78\ \text{L}$$

Gasoline floats on water, so its density must be less than that of water. Assume it is 0.80 g/mL, so

$$3.78\ \text{L} \times 0.80\ \text{g/mL} \times 10^3\ \text{mL/L} = 3.02 \times 10^3\ \text{g}$$

We now convert the grams of octane to moles using the molar mass of octane.

$$3020\ \text{g octane} \times \frac{1\ \text{mol}}{114.2\ \text{g}} = 26.4\ \text{mol octane}$$

To convert to moles of CO_2 we use the balanced equation, which shows that for every mole of octane consumed, eight moles of CO_2 are produced; thus, we have $26.4 \times 8 = 211$ mol CO_2. The molar mass of CO_2 is 44 g/mol, so 211 mol $\times$ 44 g/mol = 9280 g CO_2. Thus, for every gallon of gasoline burned, 9.3 kg (20.5 lb) CO_2 is produced.

If you drive your car 10,000 miles per year and get an average of 25 miles per gallon, you use about 400 gallons of gasoline per year. Burning this quantity of gasoline produces 400×9.3 kg = 3720 kg CO_2. That's 3720 kg $\times$ 2.2 lb/kg = 8200 lb, or more than 4 tons CO_2.

How much CO_2 is that? The 3720 kg CO_2 is about 85,000 mol CO_2. At room temperature and atmospheric pressure, that's about 2,080,000 L CO_2 or 2080 m^3 CO_2—enough to fill about 4000 1-m diameter balloons, or 11 such balloons each day of the year. In Section 10.13 we will discuss the effect that CO_2 is having on the earth's atmosphere and its link to global warming.

ThomsonNOW
Sign in to ThomsonNOW at **www.thomsonedu.com** to work an interactive module based on this material.

Carbon monoxide is manufactured cheaply by burning coke (which is mostly carbon) in a limited supply of air so that there is insufficient oxygen to form carbon dioxide. Hydrogen is more expensive to manufacture. Therefore, methanol synthesis uses an excess of carbon monoxide, and the quantity of methanol produced is dictated by the quantity of hydrogen available. In this reaction, hydrogen acts as the limiting reactant.

A **limiting reactant** is the reactant that is completely converted to products during a reaction. Once the limiting reactant has been used up, no more product can form. *The limiting reactant must be used as the basis for calculating the maximum possible amount of product(s)* because the limiting reactant limits the amount of product(s) that can be formed. ***The moles of product(s) formed are always determined by the starting number of moles of the limiting reactant.***

We can make an analogy to a chemistry "limiting reactant" in the assembling of cheese sandwiches. Each sandwich must have 2 slices of bread, 1 slice of cheese, and 1 lettuce leaf. Suppose we have available 40 slices of bread, 25 slices of cheese, and 30 lettuce leaves. How many complete cheese sandwiches can we assemble?

Each sandwich must have the ratio of 2 bread:1 cheese:1 lettuce (analogous to coefficients in a balanced chemical equation):

$$2 \text{ bread slices} + 1 \text{ cheese slice} + 1 \text{ lettuce leaf} = 1 \text{ cheese sandwich}$$

We have enough bread slices to make 20 sandwiches, enough cheese slices to make 25 sandwiches, and enough lettuce leaves to make 30 sandwiches. Thus, using the quantities of ingredients on hand and the 2:1 requirement for bread and cheese, we can assemble only 20 complete sandwiches. At that point, we run out of bread even though there are unused cheese slices and lettuce leaves. Thus, bread slices are the "limiting reactant" because they limit the number of sandwiches that can be made. The overall yield of sandwiches is limited by the bread slices, the "limiting reactant." Overall, the 20 sandwiches contain a total of 40 bread slices, 20 cheese slices, and 20 lettuce leaves. Five cheese slices and 10 lettuce leaves are unused, that is, in excess.

In determining the maximum number of cheese sandwiches that could be assembled, the "limiting reactant" was the bread slices. We ran out of bread slices before using up all the available cheese or lettuce. Similarly, the limiting reactant must be identified in a chemical reaction to determine how much product(s) will be produced if all the limiting reactant is converted to the desired product(s).

If we know which one of a set of reactants is the limiting reactant, we can use that information to solve a quantitative problem directly, as illustrated in Problem-Solving Example 4.9.

PROBLEM-SOLVING EXAMPLE 4.9 Moles of Product from Limiting Reactant

The organic compound urea, $(NH_2)_2CO$, can be prepared with this reaction between ammonia and carbon dioxide:

$$2\,NH_3(g) + CO_2(g) \longrightarrow (NH_2)_2\,CO(aq) + H_2O(\ell)$$

If 2.0 mol ammonia and 2.0 mol carbon dioxide are mixed, how many moles of urea are produced? Ammonia is the limiting reactant.

Answer 1.0 mol $(NH_2)_2CO$

Strategy and Explanation Start with the balanced equation and consider the stoichiometric coefficients. Concentrate on the NH_3 since it is given as the limiting reactant. The coefficients show that for every 2 mol NH_3 reacted, 1 mol $(NH_2)_2CO$ will be produced. Thus, we use this information to answer the question

$$2.0 \text{ mol } NH_3 \times \frac{1 \text{ mol } (NH_2)_2\,CO}{2 \text{ mol } NH_3} = 1.0 \text{ mol } (NH_2)_2\,CO$$

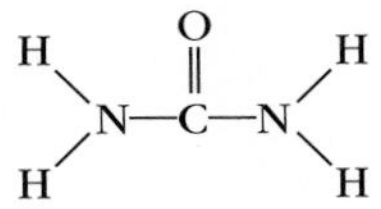

urea

You should be able to explain why NH_3 is the limiting reactant.

✓ **Reasonable Answer Check** The balanced equation shows that the number of moles of $(NH_2)_2CO$ produced must be one half the number of moles of NH_3 that reacted, and it is.

PROBLEM-SOLVING PRACTICE 4.9

If we reacted 2.0 mol NH_3 with 0.75 mol CO_2 (and CO_2 is now the limiting reactant), how many moles of $(NH_2)_2CO$ would be produced?

Next, we consider the case where the quantities of reactants are given, but the limiting reactant is not identified and therefore must be determined. There are two approaches to identifying the limiting reactant—the mole ratio method and the mass method. You can rely on whichever method works better for you.

Mole Ratio Method

In this approach, we start by calculating the number of moles of each reactant available. We then compare their mole ratio with the mole ratio from the stoichiometric coefficients of the balanced equation. From this comparison, we can figure out which reactant is limiting.

Mass Method

ThomsonNOW™
Go to the Coached Problems menu for a simulation on **limiting reactants,** an exercise on **limiting reactants,** and a tutorial on **calculating theoretical yield.**

In this approach, we start by calculating the mass of product that would be produced from the available quantity of each reactant, assuming that an unlimited quantity of the other reactant were available. The limiting reactant is the one that produces the smaller mass of product.

Problem-Solving Example 4.10 illustrates these two methods for identifying a limiting reactant.

PROBLEM-SOLVING EXAMPLE 4.10 Limiting Reactant

Cisplatin is an anticancer drug used for treatment of solid tumors. It can be produced by reacting ammonia with potassium tetrachloroplatinate (ktcp).

$$\underset{\text{potassium tetrachloroplatinate}}{K_2PtCl_4(s)} + \underset{\text{ammonia}}{2\,NH_3(aq)} \longrightarrow \underset{\text{cisplatin}}{Pt(NH_3)_2Cl_2(s)} + 2\,KCl(aq)$$

If the reaction starts with 5.00 g ammonia and 50.0 g ktcp, (a) which is the limiting reactant? (b) How many grams of cisplatin are produced? Assume that all the limiting reactant is converted to cisplatin.

Answer

(a) Potassium tetrachloroplatinate (b) 36.0 g cisplatin

Strategy and Explanation

Method 1 (Mole Ratio Method) We start by finding the number of moles of each reactant that is available. We first calculate the molar mass of ktcp: 2(39.098) + (195.078) + 4(35.453) = 415.3 g/mol.

$$50.0 \text{ g ktcp} \times \frac{1 \text{ mol ktcp}}{415.3 \text{ g ktcp}} = 0.120 \text{ mol ktcp}$$

$$5.00 \text{ g } NH_3 \times \frac{1 \text{ mol } NH_3}{17.0 \text{ g } NH_3} = 0.294 \text{ mol } NH_3$$

From this information we can deduce which reactant is limiting. Looking at the stoichiometric coefficients of the balanced equation, we see that for every two moles of ammonia reacted there is one mole of ktcp reacted.

$$\text{Mole ratio} = \frac{2 \text{ mol ammonia}}{1 \text{ mol ktcp}}$$

There are two possibilities to consider. (a) Ammonia is limiting, which means that 0.294 mol ammonia would require half that number of moles of ktcp, or 0.147 mol ktcp. There is not this much ktcp available, so ktcp must be the limiting reactant. (b) Ktcp is limiting, which means that 0.120 mol ktcp would require twice as many moles of ammonia, or 0.240 mol ammonia. There is 0.294 mol ammonia available, which is more than enough; ammonia is in excess. Therefore, ktcp is the limiting reactant, and the quantity of cisplatin that can be produced by the reaction must be calculated based on the limiting reactant, 0.120 mol ktcp. We first calculate the molar mass of cisplatin: (195.078) + 2(14.0067) + 6(1.0079) + 2(35.453) = 300.1 g/mol. We then use the mole ratio to determine the mass of cisplatin that could be produced.

$$0.120 \text{ mol ktcp} \times \frac{1 \text{ mol cisplatin}}{1 \text{ mol ktcp}} \times \frac{300.1 \text{ g cisplatin}}{1 \text{ mol cisplatin}} = 36.0 \text{ g cisplatin}$$

Method 2 (Mass Method) We first calculate the mass of cisplatin that would be produced from 0.120 mol ktcp and sufficient ammonia. Alternatively, we calculate the mass of cisplatin formed from 0.294 mol ammonia and assume sufficient ktcp.

Mass of cisplatin produced from 0.120 mol ktcp and sufficient ammonia:

$$0.120 \text{ mol ktcp} \times \frac{1 \text{ mol cisplatin}}{1 \text{ mol ktcp}} \times \frac{300.1 \text{ g cisplatin}}{1 \text{ mol cisplatin}} = 36.0 \text{ g cisplatin}$$

The mass method directly gives the maximum mass of product.

Mass of cisplatin produced from 0.294 mol ammonia and sufficient ktcp:

$$0.294 \text{ mol } NH_3 \times \frac{1 \text{ mol cisplatin}}{2 \text{ mol } NH_3} \times \frac{300.1 \text{ g cisplatin}}{1 \text{ mol cisplatin}} = 44.4 \text{ g cisplatin}$$

This comparison shows that the amount of ktcp available would produce less cisplatin than that from the amount of ammonia available, providing proof that ktcp is the limiting reactant.

When cisplatin is produced industrially, ammonia is always provided in excess because it is much cheaper than potassium tetrachloroplatinate.

✓ **Reasonable Answer Check** The ratio of molar masses of cisplatin and ktcp is about three quarters (300/415), so we should have approximately three quarters as much cisplatin product as ktcp reactant (36/50), and we do.

PROBLEM-SOLVING PRACTICE 4.10

Carbon disulfide reacts with oxygen to form carbon dioxide and sulfur dioxide.

$$CS_2(\ell) + O_2(g) \longrightarrow CO_2(g) + SO_2(g)$$

A mixture of 3.5 g CS_2 and 17.5 g O_2 is reacted.

(a) Balance the equation.

(b) What is the limiting reactant?

(c) What is the maximum number of grams of sulfur dioxide that can be formed?

PROBLEM-SOLVING EXAMPLE 4.11 Limiting Reactant

Powdered aluminum can react with iron(III) oxide in the *thermite reaction* to form molten iron and aluminum oxide:

$$2\ Al(s) + Fe_2O_3(s) \longrightarrow 2\ Fe(\ell) + Al_2O_3(s)$$

Liquid iron is produced because the reaction releases so much energy. This liquid iron is used to weld steel railroad rails. (a) What is the limiting reactant when a mixture of

© Thomson Learning/Charles D. Winters

Powdered aluminum reacts with iron(III) oxide extremely vigorously in the thermite reaction to form molten iron and aluminum oxide.

100. g Al and 100. g Fe_2O_3 react? (b) What is the mass of liquid iron formed? (c) How many grams of the excess reactant remain after the reaction is complete?

Answer

(a) Fe_2O_3 (b) 69.9 g Fe (c) 66.4 g Al

Strategy and Explanation

(a) We begin by determining how many moles of each reactant are available.

$$100.\text{ g Al} \times \frac{1\text{ mol Al}}{26.98\text{ g Al}} = 3.71\text{ mol Al}$$

$$100.\text{ g } Fe_2O_3 \times \frac{1\text{ mol } Fe_2O_3}{159.69\text{ g } Fe_2O_3} = 0.626\text{ mol } Fe_2O_3$$

Next, using the mass method for this limiting reactant problem, we find the masses of iron produced, based on the available masses of each reactant.

$$3.71\text{ mol Al} \times \frac{2\text{ mol Fe}}{2\text{ mol Al}} \times \frac{55.845\text{ g Fe}}{1\text{ mol Fe}} = 207.\text{ g Fe}$$

$$0.626\text{ mol } Fe_2O_3 \times \frac{2\text{ mol Fe}}{1\text{ mol } Fe_2O_3} \times \frac{55.845\text{ g Fe}}{1\text{ mol Fe}} = 69.9\text{ g Fe}$$

Clearly, the mass of iron that can be formed using the given masses of aluminum and iron(III) oxide is controlled by the quantity of the iron(III) oxide. The iron(III) oxide is the limiting reactant because it produces less iron. Aluminum is in excess.

(b) The mass of iron formed is 69.9 g Fe.

(c) We can find the number of moles of Al that reacted from the moles of Fe_2O_3 used and the mole ratio of Al to Fe_2O_3.

$$0.626\text{ mol } Fe_2O_3 \times \frac{2\text{ mol Al}}{1\text{ mol } Fe_2O_3} = 1.25\text{ mol Al}$$

By subtracting 1.25 mol Al from the initial amount of Al (3.71 mol − 1.25 mol = 2.46 mol Al), we find that 2.46 mol Al remains unreacted. Therefore, the mass of unreacted Al is

$$2.46\text{ mol Al} \times \frac{26.98\text{ g Al}}{1\text{ mol Al}} = 66.4\text{ g Al}$$

It is useful, although not necessary, to calculate the quantity of excess reactant remaining to verify that the reactant in excess is not the limiting reactant.

✓ **Reasonable Answer Check** The molar masses of Fe_2O_3 (160 g/mol) and Fe (56 g/mol) are in the ratio of approximately 3:1. One mole of Fe_2O_3 produces 2 mol Fe according to the balanced equation. So a given mass of Fe_2O_3 should produce about two thirds as much Fe, and this agrees with our more exact calculation.

PROBLEM-SOLVING PRACTICE 4.11

Preparation of the pure silicon used in silicon chips involves the reaction between purified liquid silicon tetrachloride and magnesium.

$$SiCl_4(\ell) + 2\,Mg(s) \longrightarrow Si(s) + 2\,MgCl_2(s)$$

If the reaction were run with 100. g each of $SiCl_4$ and Mg, which reactant would be limiting, and what mass of Si would be produced?

EXERCISE 4.8 Limiting Reactant

Urea is used as a fertilizer because it can react with water to release ammonia, which provides nitrogen to plants.

$$(NH_2)_2CO(s) + H_2O(\ell) \longrightarrow 2\,NH_3(aq) + CO_2(g)$$

(a) Determine the limiting reactant when 300. g urea and 100. g water are combined.

(b) How many grams of ammonia and how many grams of carbon dioxide form?

(c) What mass of the excess reactant remains after reaction?

CHEMISTRY IN THE NEWS

Smothering Fire—Water That Isn't Wet

Fire is a combustion reaction in which fuel and oxygen, O_2, combine, usually at high temperatures, to form water and carbon dioxide. Three factors are necessary for a fire: combustible fuel, oxygen, and a temperature above the ignition temperature of the fuel. Once the fire has started, it is self-supporting because it supplies the heat necessary to keep the temperature high (if sufficient fuel and oxygen are available). Quenching a fire requires removing the fuel, lowering the oxygen level, cooling the reaction mixture below the ignition temperature or some combination of these.

An effective way to quench a fire is smothering, which reduces the amount of available oxygen below the level needed to support combustion. In other words, smothering decreases the amount of the limiting reactant. Foams, inert gas, and CO_2 are effective substances for smothering.

Developed by 3M, Novec 1230 is a new compound with very desirable fire suppression properties. An organic compound with many carbon-fluorine bonds, it is a colorless liquid at room temperature (B.P. 49.2 °C) that feels like water. When placed on a fire, Novec vaporizes and smothers the fire. Novec 1230 is not an electrical conductor, so it can be used for electrical fires. In fact, in a demonstration on television, a laptop computer was immersed in Novec 1230 and continued to work. The new compound also does not affect the stratospheric ozone layer because its lifetime in the lower atmosphere is short, making it environmentally friendly.

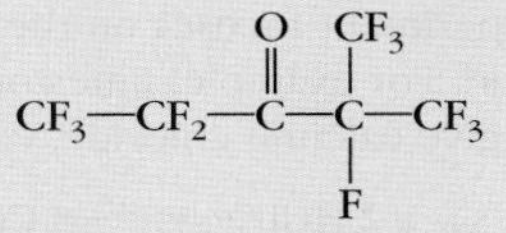

Structural formula for Novec 1230.

SOURCE: *New York Times*, Dec. 12, 2004; p. 103. http://cms.3m.com/cms/US/en/2-68/iclcrFR/view.jhtml

4.6 Evaluating the Success of a Synthesis: Percent Yield

A reaction that forms the maximum possible quantity of product is said to have a 100% yield, which is based on the amount of limiting reactant used. This maximum possible quantity of product is called the **theoretical yield**. Often the **actual yield**, the quantity of desired product actually obtained from a synthesis in a laboratory or industrial chemical plant, is less than the theoretical yield.

The efficiency of a particular synthesis method is evaluated by calculating the **percent yield**, which is defined as

$$\text{Percent yield} = \frac{\text{actual yield}}{\text{theoretical yield}} \times 100\%$$

Percent yield can be applied, for example, to the synthesis of aspirin. Suppose a student carried out the synthesis and obtained 2.2 g aspirin rather than the theoretical yield of 2.6 g. What is the percent yield of this reaction?

$$\text{Percent yield} = \frac{\text{actual yield of product}}{\text{theoretical yield of product}} \times 100\% = \frac{2.2 \text{ g}}{2.6 \text{ g}} \times 100\% = 85\%$$

Although we hope to obtain as close to the theoretical yield as possible when carrying out a reaction, few reactions or experimental manipulations are 100% efficient, despite controlled conditions and careful laboratory techniques. Side reactions can occur that form products other than the desired one, and during the isolation and purification of the desired product, some of it may be lost. When chemists report the synthesis of a new compound or the development of a new synthesis, they also report the percent yield of the reaction or the overall series of reactions. Other chemists who wish to repeat the synthesis then have an idea of how much product can be expected from a certain amount of reactants.

© Thomson Learning/Charles D. Winters

Popcorn yield. We began with 20 popcorn kernels, but only 16 of them popped. The percent yield of popcorn was (16/20) × 100% = 80%.

CHEMISTRY YOU CAN DO

Vinegar and Baking Soda: A Stoichiometry Experiment

This experiment focuses on the reactions of metal carbonates with acid. For example, limestone reacts with hydrochloric acid to give calcium chloride, carbon dioxide, and water:

$$\underset{\text{limestone}}{CaCO_3(s)} + 2\,HCl(aq) \longrightarrow CaCl_2(aq) + CO_2(g) + H_2O(\ell)$$

In a similar way, baking soda (sodium bicarbonate) and vinegar (aqueous acetic acid) react to give sodium acetate, carbon dioxide, and water:

$$\underset{\text{baking soda}}{NaHCO_3(s)} + \underset{\text{acetic acid}}{CH_3COOH(aq)} \longrightarrow \underset{\text{sodium acetate}}{NaCH_3COO(aq)} + CO_2(g) + H_2O(\ell)$$

© Thomson Learning/Charles D. Winters

The setup for the study of the reaction of baking soda with vinegar (acetic acid).

In this experiment we want to explore the relationship between the quantity of acid or bicarbonate used and the quantity of carbon dioxide evolved. To do the experiment you need some baking soda, vinegar, small balloons, and a bottle with a narrow neck and a volume of about 100 mL. The balloon should fit tightly but easily over the top of the bottle. (It may slip on more easily if the bottle and balloon are wet.)

Place 1 level teaspoon of baking soda in the balloon. (You can make a funnel out of a rolled-up piece of paper to help get the baking soda into the balloon.) Add 3 teaspoons of vinegar to the bottle, and then slip the lip of the balloon over the neck of the bottle. Turn the balloon over so that the baking soda runs into the bottle, and then shake the bottle to make sure that the vinegar and baking soda are well mixed. What do you see? Does the balloon inflate? If so, why?

Now repeat the experiment several times using these quantities of vinegar and baking soda:

Baking Soda	Vinegar
1 tsp	1 tsp
1 tsp	4 tsp
1 tsp	7 tsp
1 tsp	10 tsp

Be sure to use a new balloon each time and rinse out the bottle between tests. In each test, record how much the balloon inflates.

Is there a relationship between the quantity of vinegar and baking soda used and the extent to which the balloon inflates? If so, how can you explain this connection? At which point does an increase in the quantity of vinegar not increase the volume of the balloon? Based on what we know about chemical reactions, how could increasing the amount of one reactant not have an effect on the balloon's size?

PROBLEM-SOLVING EXAMPLE 4.12 Calculating Percent Yield

Methanol, CH_3OH, is an excellent fuel, and it can be produced from carbon monoxide and hydrogen.

$$CO(g) + 2\,H_2(g) \longrightarrow CH_3OH(\ell)$$

If 500. g CO reacts with excess H_2 and 485. g CH_3OH are produced, what is the percent yield of the reaction?

Answer 85.0%

Strategy and Explanation To solve the problem we need to calculate the theoretical yield of CH_3OH. We start by calculating the number of moles of CO, the limiting reactant, that react.

$$500.\text{ g CO} \times \frac{1\text{ mol CO}}{28.0\text{ g CO}} = 17.86\text{ mol CO}$$

The coefficients of the balanced equation show that for every 1 mol CO reacted, 1 mol CH_3OH will be produced. Therefore, the maximum number of moles CH_3OH produced will be 17.86 mol CH_3OH. We convert this to the mass of CH_3OH, the theoretical yield:

$$17.86 \text{ mol } CH_3OH \times \frac{32.0 \text{ g } CH_3OH}{1 \text{ mol } CH_3OH} = 571. \text{ g } CH_3OH$$

Thus, the theoretical yield is 571. g CH_3OH. The problem states that 485. g CH_3OH was produced. We calculate the percent yield:

$$\frac{485. \text{ g } CH_3OH \text{ (actual yield)}}{571. \text{ g } CH_3OH \text{ (theoretical yield)}} \times 100\% = 85.0\%$$

✓ **Reasonable Answer Check** The molar mass of CH_3OH is slightly greater than that of CO, and an equal number of moles of CO and CH_3OH are in the balanced equation. So x g CO should produce somewhat more than x g CH_3OH. Slightly less is actually produced, however, so a percent yield slightly less than 100% is about right.

PROBLEM-SOLVING PRACTICE 4.12

If this reaction is run with an 85% yield, and you want to make 1.0 kg CH_3OH, how many grams of H_2 should you use if CO is available in excess?

PROBLEM-SOLVING EXAMPLE 4.13 Percent Yield

Ammonia can be produced from the reaction of a metal oxide such as calcium oxide with ammonium chloride:

$$CaO(s) + 2\,NH_4Cl(s) \rightarrow 2\,NH_3(g) + H_2O(g) + CaCl_2(s)$$

How many grams of calcium oxide would be needed to react with excess ammonium chloride to produce 1.00 g ammonia if the expected percent yield were 25%?

Answer 6.59 g CaO

Strategy and Explanation The expected percent yield expressed as a decimal is 0.25. So the theoretical yield is

$$\text{Theoretical yield} = \frac{\text{actual yield}}{\text{percent yield}} = \frac{1.00 \text{ g } NH_3}{0.25} = 4.00 \text{ g } NH_3$$

Ammonium chloride is in excess, so CaO is the limiting reactant and determines the amount of ammonia that will be produced. The mass of CaO needed can be calculated from the theoretical yield of ammonia and the 1:2 mole ratio for CaO and ammonia as given in the balanced equation.

$$4.00 \text{ g } NH_3 \times \frac{1 \text{ mol } NH_3}{17.03 \text{ g } NH_3} \times \frac{1 \text{ mol CaO}}{2 \text{ mol } NH_3} \times \frac{56.077 \text{ g CaO}}{1 \text{ mol CaO}} = 6.59 \text{ g CaO}$$

✓ **Reasonable Answer Check** To check the answer, we solve the problem a different way. The molar mass of CaO is approximately 56 g/mol, so 6.59 g CaO is approximately 0.12 mol CaO. The coefficients in the balanced equation tell us that this would produce twice as many moles of NH_3 or 0.24 mol NH_3, which is 0.24 × 17 g/mol = 4 g NH_3, if the yield were 100%. The actual yield is 25%, so the amount of ammonia expected is reduced by one fourth to approximately 1 g. This approximate calculation is consistent with our more accurate calculation, and the answer is reasonable.

PROBLEM-SOLVING PRACTICE 4.13

You heat 2.50 g copper with an excess of sulfur and synthesize 2.53 g copper(I) sulfide, Cu_2S:

$$16\,Cu(s) + S_8(s) \longrightarrow 8\,Cu_2S(s)$$

Your laboratory instructor expects students to have at least a 60% yield for this reaction. Did your synthesis meet this standard?

ThomsonNOW™
Go to the Coached Problems menu for a tutorial on **calculating percent yield.**

CONCEPTUAL EXERCISE 4.9 Percent Yield

Percent yield can be reduced by side reactions that produce undesired product(s) and by poor laboratory technique in isolating and purifying the desired product. Identify two other factors that could lead to a low percent yield.

Atom Economy—Another Approach to Tracing Starting Materials

Rather than concentrating simply on percent yield, the concept of **atom economy** focuses on the amounts of starting materials that are incorporated into the desired final product. The greater the fraction of starting atoms incorporated into the desired final product, the fewer waste by-products created. Of course, the objective is to devise syntheses that are as efficient as possible.

Whereas a high percent yield has often been the major goal of chemical synthesis, the concept of atom economy, quantified by the definition of percent atom economy, is becoming important.

$$\text{Percent atom economy} = \frac{\text{sum of atomic weight of atoms in the useful product}}{\text{sum of atomic weight of all atoms in reactants}} \times 100\%$$

Reactions for which all atoms in the reactants are found in the desired product have a percent atom economy of 100%. As an example, consider this combination reaction:

$$CO(g) + 2\,H_2(g) \longrightarrow CH_3OH(\ell)$$

The sum of atomic weights of all atoms in the reactants is $12.011 + 15.9994 + \{2 \times (2 \times 1.0079)\} = 32.042$ amu. The atomic weight of all the atoms in the product is $12.011 + \{3 \times (1.0079)\} + 15.9994 + 1.0079 = 32.042$ amu. The percent atom economy for this reaction is 100%.

Many other reactions in organic synthesis, however, generate other products in addition to the desired product. In such cases, the percent atom economy is far less than 100%. Devising strategies for synthesis of desired compounds with the least waste is a major goal of the current push toward "green chemistry."

Green chemistry aims to eliminate pollution by making chemical products that do not harm health or the environment. It encourages the development of production processes that reduce or eliminate hazardous chemicals. Green chemistry also aims to prevent pollution at its source rather than having to clean up problems after they occur. Each year since 1996 the U.S. Environmental Protection Agency has given Presidential Green Chemistry Challenge Awards for noteworthy green chemistry advances.

ThomsonNOW™

Go to the Coached Problems menu for tutorials on:

- **chemical analysis**
- **determining an empirical formula**

4.7 Percent Composition and Empirical Formulas

In Section 3.10, percent composition data were used to derive empirical and molecular formulas, but nothing was mentioned about how such data are obtained. One way to obtain such data is combustion analysis, which is often employed with organic compounds, most of which contain carbon and hydrogen. In **combustion analysis** a compound is burned in excess oxygen, which converts the carbon to carbon dioxide and the hydrogen to water. These combustion products are collected and weighed, and the masses are used to calculate the quantities of carbon and hydrogen in the original substance using the balanced combustion equation. The apparatus is

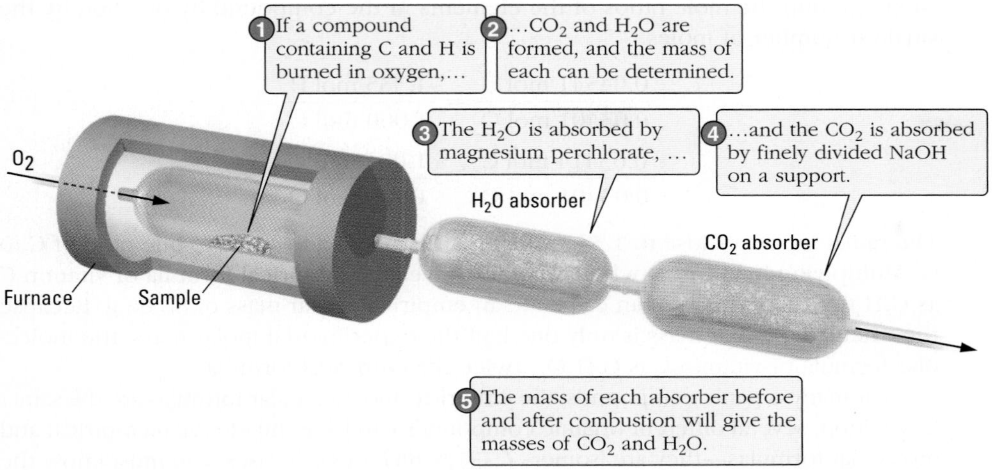

Figure 4.9 Combustion analysis. Schematic diagram of an apparatus for determining the empirical formula of an organic compound. Only a few milligrams of a combustible compound are needed for analysis.

shown in Figure 4.9. Many organic compounds also contain oxygen. In such cases, the mass of oxygen in the sample can be determined simply by difference.

$$\text{Mass of oxygen} = \text{mass of sample} - (\text{mass of C} + \text{mass of H})$$

As an example, consider this problem. An analytical chemist used combustion analysis to determine the empirical formula of vitamin C, an organic compound containing only carbon, hydrogen, and oxygen. Combustion of 1.000 g of pure vitamin C produced 1.502 g CO_2 and 0.409 g H_2O. A different experiment determined that the molar mass of vitamin C is 176.12 g/mol.

The task is to determine the subscripts on C, H, and O in the empirical formula of vitamin C. Recall from Chapter 3 that the subscripts in a chemical formula tell how many moles of atoms of each element are in 1 mol of the compound. *All* of the carbon in the CO_2 and *all* of the hydrogen in the H_2O came from the vitamin C sample that was burned, so we can work backward to assess the composition of vitamin C.

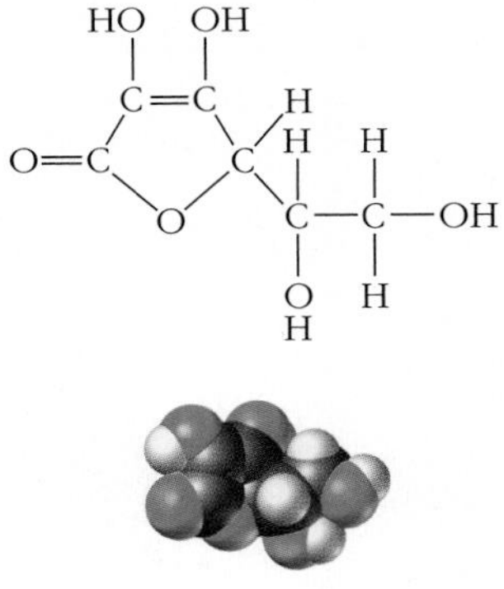

vitamin C

First, we determine the masses of carbon and hydrogen in the original sample.

$$1.502 \text{ g } CO_2 \times \frac{1 \text{ mol } CO_2}{44.009 \text{ g } CO_2} \times \frac{1 \text{ mol C}}{1 \text{ mol } CO_2} \times \frac{12.011 \text{ g C}}{1 \text{ mol C}} = 0.4100 \text{ g C}$$

$$0.409 \text{ g } H_2O \times \frac{1 \text{ mol } H_2O}{18.015 \text{ g } H_2O} \times \frac{2 \text{ mol H}}{1 \text{ mol } H_2O} \times \frac{1.0079 \text{ g H}}{1 \text{ mol H}} = 0.04577 \text{ g H}$$

The mass of oxygen in the original sample can be calculated by difference.

$$1.000 \text{ g sample} - (0.4100 \text{ g C in sample} + 0.04577 \text{ g H in sample}) = 0.5442 \text{ g O in the sample}$$

From the mass data, we can now calculate how many moles of each element were in the sample.

$$0.4100 \text{ g C} \times \frac{1 \text{ mol C}}{12.011 \text{ g C}} = 0.03414 \text{ mol C}$$

$$0.04577 \text{ g H} \times \frac{1 \text{ mol H}}{1.0079 \text{ g H}} = 0.04541 \text{ mol H}$$

$$0.5442 \text{ g O} \times \frac{1 \text{ mol O}}{15.999 \text{ g O}} = 0.03401 \text{ mol O}$$

Carrying an extra digit during the intermediate parts of a multistep problem and rounding at the end is good practice.

Next, we find the mole ratios of the elements in the compound by dividing by the smallest number of moles.

$$\frac{0.04541 \text{ mol H}}{0.03401 \text{ mol O}} = \frac{1.335 \text{ mol H}}{1.000 \text{ mol O}}$$

$$\frac{0.03414 \text{ mol C}}{0.03401 \text{ mol O}} = \frac{1.004 \text{ mol C}}{1.000 \text{ mol O}}$$

If after dividing by the smallest number of moles, the ratios are not whole numbers, multiply each subscript by a number that converts the fractions to whole numbers. For example, multiplying $NO_{2.5}$ by 2 changes it to N_2O_5.

The ratios are very close to 1.33 mol H to 1.00 mol O and a one-to-one ratio of C to O. Multiplying by 3 to get whole numbers gives the empirical formula of vitamin C as $C_3H_4O_3$. From this we can calculate an empirical molar mass of 88.06 g. Because the calculated molar mass is only one half the experimental molar mass, the molecular formula of vitamin C is $C_6H_8O_6$, twice the empirical formula.

For many organic compounds, the empirical and molecular formulas are the same. In addition, several different organic compounds can have the identical empirical and molecular formulas—they are isomers (**p. 86**). In such cases, you must know the structural formula to fully describe the compound. Ethanol (CH_3CH_2OH) and dimethyl ether (CH_3OCH_3), for example, each have the same empirical formula and molecular formula, C_2H_6O, but they are different compounds with different properties.

CH_3CH_2OH — ethanol

CH_3OCH_3 — dimethyl ether

PROBLEM-SOLVING EXAMPLE 4.14 Empirical Formula from Combustion Analysis

Butyric acid, an organic compound with an extremely unpleasant odor, contains only carbon, hydrogen, and oxygen. When 1.20 g butyric acid was burned, 2.41 g CO_2 and 0.982 g H_2O were produced. Calculate the empirical formula of butyric acid. In a separate experiment, the molar mass of butyric acid was determined to be 88.1 g/mol. What is butyric acid's molecular formula?

Answer The empirical formula is C_2H_4O. The molecular formula is $C_4H_8O_2$.

Strategy and Explanation All of the carbon and hydrogen in the butyric acid are burned to form CO_2 and H_2O, respectively. Therefore, we use the masses of CO_2 and H_2O to calculate how many grams of C and H, respectively, were in the original butyric acid sample.

$$2.41 \text{ g } CO_2 \times \frac{1 \text{ mol } CO_2}{44.01 \text{ g } CO_2} \times \frac{1 \text{ mol C}}{1 \text{ mol } CO_2} \times \frac{12.01 \text{ g C}}{\text{mol C}} = 0.658 \text{ g C}$$

$$0.982 \text{ g } H_2O \times \frac{1 \text{ mol } H_2O}{18.02 \text{ g } H_2O} \times \frac{2 \text{ mol H}}{1 \text{ mol } H_2O} \times \frac{1.008 \text{ g H}}{1 \text{ mol H}} = 0.110 \text{ g H}$$

Thus, the original butyric acid sample contained 0.658 g C and 0.110 g H. The remaining mass of the sample, 1.20 g − 0.658 g − 0.110 g = 0.432 g, must be oxygen.

$$0.658 \text{ g C} + 0.110 \text{ g H} + 0.432 \text{ g O} = 1.20 \text{ g sample}$$

We then find the number of moles of each element in the butyric acid sample.

$$0.658 \text{ g C} \times \frac{1 \text{ mol C}}{12.01 \text{ g C}} = 0.0548 \text{ mol C}$$

$$0.110 \text{ g H} \times \frac{1 \text{ mol H}}{1.008 \text{ g H}} = 0.109 \text{ mol H}$$

$$0.432 \text{ g O} \times \frac{1 \text{ mol O}}{16.00 \text{ g O}} = 0.0270 \text{ mol O}$$

To find the mole ratios of the elements, we divide the molar amount of each element by the smallest number of moles.

$$\frac{0.0548 \text{ mol C}}{0.0270 \text{ mol O}} = \frac{2.03 \text{ mol C}}{1.00 \text{ mol O}} \quad \text{and} \quad \frac{0.109 \text{ mol H}}{0.0270 \text{ mol O}} = \frac{4.03 \text{ mol H}}{1.00 \text{ mol O}}$$

The mole ratios show that for every oxygen atom in the molecule, there are two carbon atoms and four hydrogen atoms. Therefore, the empirical formula of butyric acid is C_2H_4O, which has a formula mass of 44.05 g/mol. The experimental molar mass is known to be twice this value, so the molecular formula of butyric acid is $C_4H_8O_2$, twice the empirical formula.

✓ **Reasonable Answer Check** The molar mass of butyric acid is $(4 \times 12.01) + (8 \times 1.008) + (2 \times 15.9994) = 88.10$ g/mol, so the answer is reasonable.

PROBLEM-SOLVING PRACTICE 4.14

Phenol is a compound of carbon, hydrogen, and oxygen that is used commonly as a disinfectant. Combustion analysis of a 175-mg sample of phenol yielded 491. mg CO_2 and 100. mg H_2O.

(a) Calculate the empirical formula of phenol.

(b) What other information is necessary to determine whether the empirical formula is the actual molecular formula?

CONCEPTUAL EXERCISE 4.10 Formula from Combustion Analysis

Nicotine, a compound found in cigarettes, contains C, H, and N. Outline a method by which you could use combustion analysis to determine the empirical formula for nicotine.

Determining Formulas from Experimental Data

One technique to determine the formula of a binary compound formed by direct combination of its two elements is to measure the mass of reactants that is converted to the product compound.

PROBLEM-SOLVING EXAMPLE 4.15 Empirical Formula from Experimental Data

Solid red phosphorus reacts with liquid bromine to produce a phosphorus bromide.

$$P_4(s) + Br_2(\ell) \longrightarrow P_xBr_y(\ell)$$

If 0.347 g P_4 reacts with 0.860 mL Br_2, what is the empirical formula of the product? The density of bromine is 3.12 g/mL.

Answer PBr_3

Strategy and Explanation We start by calculating the moles of P_4 and Br_2 that combined:

$$0.347 \text{ g } P_4 \times \frac{1 \text{ mol } P_4}{123.90 \text{ g } P_4} = 2.801 \times 10^{-3} \text{ mol } P_4$$

To determine the moles of bromine, we first use the density of bromine to convert milliliters of bromine to grams:

$$0.860 \text{ mL } Br_2 \times \frac{3.12 \text{ g } Br_2}{1 \text{ mL } Br_2} = 2.68 \text{ g } Br_2$$

We then convert from grams to moles:

$$2.68 \text{ g } Br_2 \times \frac{1 \text{ mol } Br_2}{159.8 \text{ g } Br_2} = 1.677 \times 10^{-2} \text{ mol } Br_2$$

The mole ratio of bromine atoms to phosphorus atoms in a molecule of the product can be calculated from the moles of atoms of each element.

$$1.677 \times 10^{-2} \text{ mol Br}_2 \text{ molecules} \times \frac{2 \text{ mol Br atoms}}{1 \text{ mol Br}_2 \text{ molecules}} = 3.35 \times 10^{-2} \text{ mol Br atoms}$$

$$2.801 \times 10^{-3} \text{ mol P}_4 \text{ molecules} \times \frac{4 \text{ mol P atoms}}{1 \text{ mol P}_4 \text{ molecules}} = 1.12 \times 10^{-2} \text{ mol P atoms}$$

$$\frac{3.35 \times 10^{-2} \text{ mol Br atoms}}{1.12 \times 10^{-2} \text{ mol P atoms}} = \frac{2.99 \text{ mol Br atoms}}{1.00 \text{ mol P atoms}}$$

The mole ratio in the compound is 3.00 mol bromine atoms for 1.00 mol phosphorus atoms. The empirical formula is PBr_3. By other experimental methods, the known molar mass of this compound is found to be the same as the empirical formula molar mass. Given this additional information, we know that the molecular formula is also PBr_3.

✓ **Reasonable Answer Check** Phosphorus is a Group 5A element, so combining it with three bromines results in a reasonable molecular formula for such a combination of elements.

PROBLEM-SOLVING PRACTICE 4.15

The complete reaction of 0.569 g tin with 2.434 g iodine formed Sn_xI_y. What is the empirical formula of this tin iodide?

SUMMARY PROBLEM

Iron can be smelted from iron(III) oxide in ore via this high-temperature reaction in a blast furnace:

$$Fe_2O_3(s) + 3\,CO(g) \longrightarrow 2\,Fe(\ell) + 3\,CO_2(g)$$

The liquid iron produced is cooled and weighed.

(a) For 19.0 g Fe_2O_3, what mass of CO is required to react completely?

(b) What mass of CO_2 is produced when the reaction runs to completion with 10.0 g Fe_2O_3 as starting material?

When the reaction was run repeatedly with the same mass of iron oxide, 19.0 g Fe_2O_3, but differing masses of carbon monoxide, this graph was obtained.

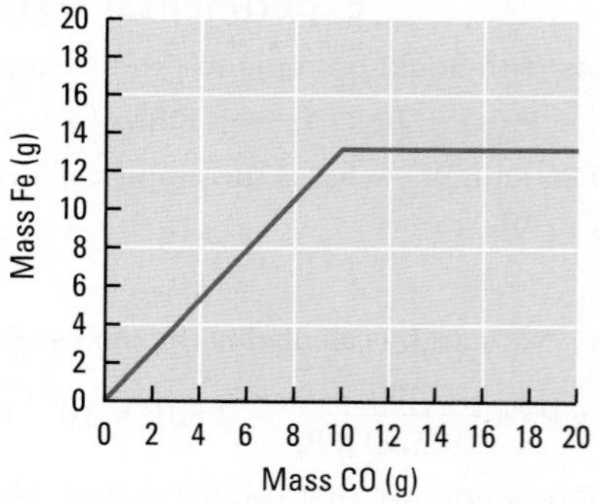

(c) Which reactant is limiting in the part of the graph where there is less than 10.0 g CO available to react with 19.0 g Fe_2O_3?

(d) Which reactant is limiting when more than 10.0 g CO is available to react with 19.0 g Fe_2O_3?

(e) If 24.0 g Fe_2O_3 reacted with 20.0 g CO and 15.9 g Fe was produced, what was the percent yield of the reaction?

IN CLOSING

Having studied this chapter, you should be able to . . .

- Interpret the information conveyed by a balanced chemical equation (Section 4.1).
- Recognize the general reaction types: combination, decomposition, displacement, and exchange (Section 4.2). ThomsonNOW homework: Study Questions 20, 22
- Balance simple chemical equations (Section 4.3). ThomsonNOW homework: Study Questions 30, 32
- Use mole ratios to calculate the number of moles or number of grams of one reactant or product from the number of moles or number of grams of another reactant or product by using the balanced chemical equation (Section 4.4). ThomsonNOW homework: Study Questions 38, 40, 44, 87
- Use principles of stoichiometry in the chemical analysis of a mixture (Section 4.4). ThomsonNOW homework: Study Question 118
- Determine which of two reactants is the limiting reactant (Section 4.5). ThomsonNOW homework: Study Questions 62, 66, 68
- Explain the differences among actual yield, theoretical yield, and percent yield, and calculate theoretical and percent yields (Section 4.6). ThomsonNOW homework: Study Questions 75, 77
- Use principles of stoichiometry to find the empirical formula of an unknown compound using combustion analysis and other mass data (Section 4.7). ThomsonNOW homework: Study Questions 82, 89

ThomsonNOW™
Sign in to ThomsonNOW at **www.thomsonedu.com** to check your readiness for an exam by taking the Pre-Test and exploring the modules recommended in your Personalized Learning Plan.

KEY TERMS

actual yield *(4.6)*
aqueous solution *(4.1)*
atom economy *(4.6)*
balanced chemical equation *(4.1)*
coefficient *(4.1)*
combination reaction *(4.2)*
combustion analysis *(4.7)*
combustion reaction *(4.1)*
decomposition reaction *(4.2)*
displacement reaction *(4.2)*
exchange reaction *(4.2)*
limiting reactant *(4.5)*
mole ratio *(4.4)*
percent yield *(4.6)*
stoichiometric coefficient *(4.1)*
stoichiometry *(4.1)*
theoretical yield *(4.6)*

QUESTIONS FOR REVIEW AND THOUGHT

■ denotes questions available in ThomsonNOW and assignable in OWL.

Blue-numbered questions have short answers at the back of this book and fully worked solutions in the *Student Solutions Manual.*

ThomsonNOW™
Assess your understanding of this chapter's topics with sample tests and other resources found by signing in to ThomsonNOW at **www.thomsonedu.com**.

Review Questions

1. What information is provided by a balanced chemical equation?
2. Complete the table for the reaction

$$3\ H_2(g) + N_2(g) \longrightarrow 2\ NH_3(g)$$

H_2	N_2	NH_3
________ mol	1 mol	________ mol
3 molecules	________ molecules	________ molecules
________ g	________ g	34.08 g

3. What is meant by the statement, "The reactants were present in stoichiometric amounts"?

4. Write all the possible mole ratios for the reaction

$$3\ MgO(s) + 2\ Fe(s) \longrightarrow Fe_2O_3(s) + 3\ Mg(s)$$

5. If a 10.0-g mass of carbon is combined with an exact stoichiometric amount of oxygen (26.6 g) to make carbon dioxide, how many grams of CO_2 can be isolated?
6. Given the reaction

$$2\ Fe(s) + 3\ Cl_2(g) \longrightarrow 2\ FeCl_3(s)$$

fill in the missing conversion factors for the scheme

$$\begin{array}{ccc} g\ Cl_2 & \xrightarrow{?} & g\ FeCl_3 \\ \downarrow ? & & \downarrow ? \\ mol\ Cl_2 & \xrightarrow{?} & mol\ FeCl_3 \end{array}$$

7. When an exam question asks, "What is the limiting reactant?" students may be tempted to guess the reactant with the smallest mass. Why is this not a good strategy?
8. Why can't the product of a reaction ever be the limiting reactant?
9. Does the limiting reactant determine the theoretical yield, actual yield, or both? Explain.

Topical Questions

Stoichiometry

10. For this reaction, fill in the table with the indicated quantities for the balanced equation.

$$4\ NH_3(g) + 5\ O_2(g) \longrightarrow 4\ NO(g) + 6\ H_2O(g)$$

	NH_3	O_2	NO	H_2O
No. of molecules				
No. of atoms				
No. of moles of molecules				
Mass				
Total mass of reactants				
Total mass of products				

11. For this reaction, fill in the table with the indicated quantities for the balanced equation.

$$2\ C_2H_6(g) + 7\ O_2(g) \longrightarrow 4\ CO_2(g) + 6\ H_2O(g)$$

	C_2H_6	O_2	CO_2	H_2O
No. of molecules				
No. of atoms				
No. of moles of molecules				
Mass				
Total mass of reactants				
Total mass of products				

12. Magnesium metal burns brightly in the presence of oxygen to produce a white powdery substance, MgO.

$$Mg(s) + O_2(g) \longrightarrow MgO(s) \qquad \text{(unbalanced)}$$

(a) If 1.00 g MgO(s) is formed by this reaction, what is the *total* mass of magnesium metal and oxygen that reacted?
(b) Identify the stoichiometric coefficients in this equation.
(c) If 50 *atoms* of oxygen reacted, how many magnesium *atoms* were needed to react with this much oxygen?

13. Sucrose (table sugar) reacts with oxygen as follows:

$$C_{12}H_{22}O_{11} + 12\ O_2 \longrightarrow 12\ CO_2 + 11\ H_2O$$

When 1.0 g sucrose is reacted, how many grams of CO_2 are produced? How many grams of O_2 are required to react with 1.0 g sucrose?

14. Balance this *combination reaction* by adding coefficients as needed.

$$Fe(s) + O_2(g) \longrightarrow Fe_2O_3(s)$$

15. Balance this *decomposition reaction* by adding coefficients as needed.

$$KClO_3(s) \longrightarrow KCl(s) + O_2(g)$$

16. The following diagram shows A (blue spheres) reacting with B (tan spheres). Which equation best describes the stoichiometry of the reaction depicted in this diagram?

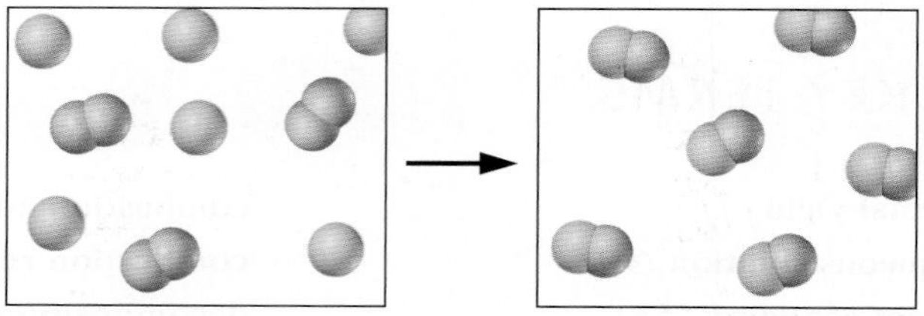

(a) $3\ A_2 + 6\ B \rightarrow 6\ AB$ (b) $A_2 + 2\ B \rightarrow 2\ AB$
(c) $2\ A + B \rightarrow AB$ (d) $3\ A + 6\ B \rightarrow 6\ AB$

17. The following diagram shows A (blue spheres) reacting with B (tan spheres). Write a balanced equation that describes the stoichiometry of the reaction shown in the diagram.

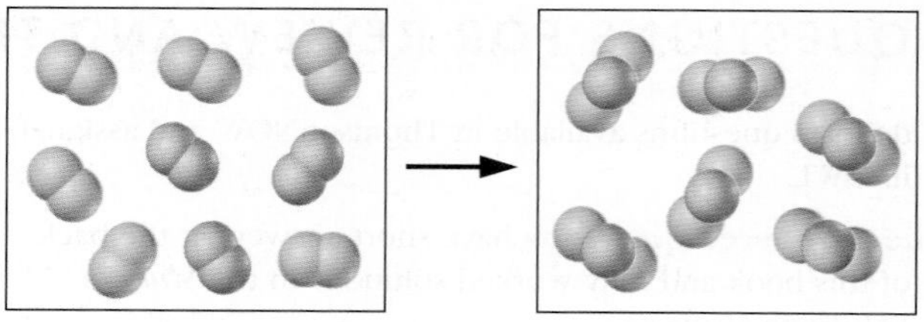

18. Given this equation,

$$4\ A_2 + 3\ B \longrightarrow B_3A_8$$

use a diagram to illustrate the amount of reactant A and product (B_3A_8) that would be needed/produced from the reaction of six atoms of B.

19. Balance this equation and determine which box represents reactants and which box represents products.

$$Sb(g) + Cl_2(g) \longrightarrow SbCl_3(g)$$

■ In ThomsonNOW and OWL **Blue-numbered questions** answered at end of this book

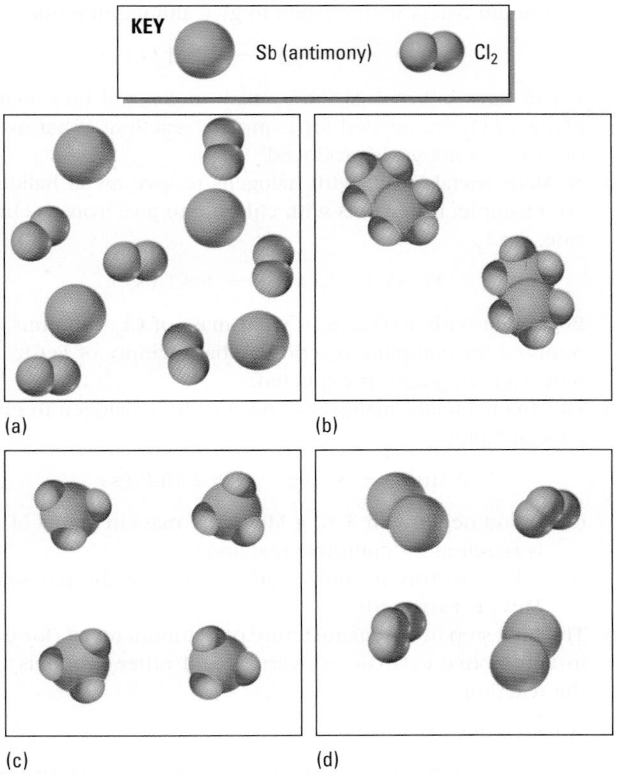

Classification of Chemical Reactions

20. ■ Indicate whether each of these equations represents a combination, decomposition, displacement, or exchange reaction.
    (a) $Cu(s) + O_2(g) \longrightarrow 2\ CuO(s)$
    (b) $NH_4NO_3(s) \longrightarrow N_2O(g) + 2\ H_2O(\ell)$
    (c) $AgNO_3(aq) + KCl(aq) \longrightarrow AgCl(s) + KNO_3(aq)$
    (d) $Mg(s) + 2\ HCl(aq) \longrightarrow MgCl_2(aq) + H_2(g)$
21. Indicate whether each of these equations represents a combination, decomposition, displacement, or exchange reaction.
    (a) $C(s) + O_2(g) \longrightarrow CO_2(g)$
    (b) $2\ KClO_3(s) \longrightarrow 2\ KCl(s) + 3\ O_2(g)$
    (c) $BaCl_2(aq) + K_2SO_4(aq) \longrightarrow BaSO_4(s) + 2\ KCl(aq)$
    (d) $Mg(s) + CoSO_4(aq) \longrightarrow MgSO_4(aq) + Co(s)$
22. ■ Indicate whether each of these equations represents a combination, decomposition, displacement, or exchange reaction.
    (a) $PbCO_3(s) \longrightarrow PbO(s) + CO_2(g)$
    (b) $Cu(s) + 4\ HNO_3(aq) \longrightarrow Cu(NO_3)_2(aq) + 2\ H_2O(\ell) + 2\ NO_2(g)$
    (c) $2\ Zn(s) + O_2(g) \longrightarrow 2\ ZnO(s)$
    (d) $Pb(NO_3)_2(aq) + 2\ KI(aq) \longrightarrow PbI_2(s) + 2\ KNO_3(aq)$
23. Indicate whether each of these equations represents a combination, decomposition, displacement, or exchange reaction.
    (a) $Mg(s) + FeCl_2(aq) \longrightarrow MgCl_2(aq) + Fe(s)$
    (b) $ZnCO_3(s) \longrightarrow ZnO(s) + CO_2(g)$
    (c) $2\ C(s) + O_2(g) \longrightarrow 2\ CO(g)$
    (d) $CaCl_2(aq) + Na_2CO_3(aq) \longrightarrow CaCO_3(s) + 2\ NaCl(aq)$

Balancing Equations

24. Write a balanced equation for each of these combustion reactions.
    (a) $C_4H_{10}(g) + O_2(g) \longrightarrow$
    (b) $C_6H_{12}O_6(s) + O_2(g) \longrightarrow$
    (c) $C_4H_8O(\ell) + O_2(g) \longrightarrow$
25. Write a balanced equation for each of these combustion reactions.
    (a) $C_3H_8O(g) + O_2(g) \longrightarrow$
    (b) $C_5H_{12}(\ell) + O_2(g) \longrightarrow$
    (c) $C_{12}H_{22}O_{11}(s) + O_2(g) \longrightarrow$
26. Complete and balance these equations involving oxygen reacting with an element. Name the product in each case.
    (a) $Mg(s) + O_2(g) \longrightarrow$
    (b) $Ca(s) + O_2(g) \longrightarrow$
    (c) $In(s) + O_2(g) \longrightarrow$
27. Complete and balance these equations involving oxygen reacting with an element.
    (a) $Ti(s) + O_2(g) \longrightarrow$ titanium(IV) oxide
    (b) $S_8(s) + O_2(g) \longrightarrow$ sulfur dioxide
    (c) $Se(s) + O_2(g) \longrightarrow$ selenium dioxide
28. Complete and balance these equations involving the reaction of a halogen with a metal. Name the product in each case.
    (a) $K(s) + Cl_2(g) \longrightarrow$
    (b) $Mg(s) + Br_2(\ell) \longrightarrow$
    (c) $Al(s) + F_2(g) \longrightarrow$
29. Complete and balance these equations involving the reaction of a halogen with a metal.
    (a) $Cr(s) + Cl_2(g) \longrightarrow$ chromium(III) chloride
    (b) $Cu(s) + Br_2(\ell) \longrightarrow$ copper(II) bromide
    (c) $Pt(s) + F_2(g) \longrightarrow$ platinum(IV) fluoride
30. ■ Balance these equations.
    (a) $Al(s) + O_2(g) \longrightarrow Al_2O_3(s)$
    (b) $N_2(g) + H_2(g) \longrightarrow NH_3(g)$
    (c) $C_6H_6(\ell) + O_2(g) \longrightarrow H_2O(\ell) + CO_2(g)$
31. Balance these equations.
    (a) $Fe(s) + Cl_2(g) \longrightarrow FeCl_3(s)$
    (b) $SiO_2(s) + C(s) \longrightarrow Si(s) + CO(g)$
    (c) $Fe(s) + H_2O(g) \longrightarrow Fe_3O_4(s) + H_2(g)$
32. ■ Balance these equations.
    (a) $UO_2(s) + HF(\ell) \longrightarrow UF_4(s) + H_2O(\ell)$
    (b) $B_2O_3(s) + HF(\ell) \longrightarrow BF_3(g) + H_2O(\ell)$
    (c) $BF_3(g) + H_2O(\ell) \longrightarrow HF(\ell) + H_3BO_3(s)$
33. Balance these equations.
    (a) $MgO(s) + Fe(s) \longrightarrow Fe_2O_3(s) + Mg(s)$
    (b) $H_3BO_3(s) \longrightarrow B_2O_3(s) + H_2O(\ell)$
    (c) $NaNO_3(s) + H_2SO_4(aq) \longrightarrow Na_2SO_4(aq) + HNO_3(g)$
34. Balance these equations.
    (a) Reaction to produce hydrazine, N_2H_4:

    $$H_2NCl(aq) + NH_3(g) \longrightarrow NH_4Cl(aq) + N_2H_4(aq)$$

    (b) Reaction of the fuels (dimethylhydrazine and dinitrogen tetroxide) used in the Moon Lander and Space Shuttle:

    $$(CH_3)_2N_2H_2(\ell) + N_2O_4(g) \longrightarrow N_2(g) + H_2O(g) + CO_2(g)$$

(c) Reaction of calcium carbide with water to produce acetylene, C_2H_2:

$$CaC_2(s) + H_2O(\ell) \longrightarrow Ca(OH)_2(s) + C_2H_2(g)$$

35. Balance these equations.
(a) Reaction of calcium cyanamide to produce ammonia:

$$CaNCN(s) + H_2O(\ell) \longrightarrow CaCO_3(s) + NH_3(g)$$

(b) Reaction to produce diborane, B_2H_6:

$$NaBH_4(s) + H_2SO_4(aq) \longrightarrow B_2H_6(g) + H_2(g) + Na_2SO_4(aq)$$

(c) Reaction to rid water of hydrogen sulfide, H_2S, a foul-smelling compound:

$$H_2S(aq) + Cl_2(aq) \longrightarrow S_8(s) + HCl(aq)$$

36. Balance these combustion reactions.
(a) $C_6H_{12}O_6 + O_2 \longrightarrow CO_2 + H_2O$
(b) $C_5H_{12} + O_2 \longrightarrow CO_2 + H_2O$
(c) $C_7H_{14}O_2 + O_2 \longrightarrow CO_2 + H_2O$
(d) $C_2H_4O_2 + O_2 \longrightarrow CO_2 + H_2O$

37. Balance these equations.
(a) $Mg + HNO_3 \longrightarrow H_2 + Mg(NO_3)_2$
(b) $Al + Fe_2O_3 \longrightarrow Al_2O_3 + Fe$
(c) $S_8 + O_2 \longrightarrow SO_3$
(d) $SO_3 + H_2O \longrightarrow H_2SO_4$

The Mole and Chemical Reactions

38. ■ Chlorine can be produced in the laboratory by the reaction of hydrochloric acid with excess manganese(IV) oxide.

$$4\ HCl(aq) + MnO_2(s) \longrightarrow Cl_2(g) + 2\ H_2O(\ell) + MnCl_2(aq)$$

How many moles of HCl are needed to form 12.5 mol Cl_2?

39. Methane, CH_4, is the major component of natural gas. How many moles of oxygen are needed to burn 16.5 mol CH_4?

$$CH_4(g) + 2\ O_2(g) \longrightarrow CO_2(g) + 2\ H_2O(\ell)$$

40. ■ In the laboratory, the salt potassium chlorate, $KClO_3$, can be decomposed thermally to generate small amounts of oxygen gas.

$$2\ KClO_3(s) \longrightarrow 2\ KCl(s) + 3\ O_2(g)$$

How many grams of potassium chlorate must be decomposed to produce 5.00 g O_2?

41. An ingredient in many baking recipes is baking soda, $NaHCO_3$, which decomposes when heated to produce carbon dioxide, causing the baked goods to rise.

$$2\ NaHCO_3(s) \longrightarrow Na_2CO_3(s) + CO_2(g) + H_2O(g)$$

How many grams of carbon dioxide are produced per gram of baking soda?

42. Nitrogen monoxide is oxidized in air to give brown nitrogen dioxide.

$$2\ NO(g) + O_2(g) \longrightarrow 2\ NO_2(g)$$

Starting with 2.2 mol NO, how many moles and how many grams of O_2 are required for complete reaction? What mass of NO_2, in grams, is produced?

43. Aluminum reacts with oxygen to give aluminum oxide.

$$4\ Al(s) + 3\ O_2(g) \longrightarrow 2\ Al_2O_3(s)$$

If you have 6.0 mol Al, how many moles and how many grams of O_2 are needed for complete reaction? What mass of Al_2O_3, in grams, is produced?

44. ■ Many metals react with halogens to give metal halides. For example, iron reacts with chlorine to give iron(II) chloride, $FeCl_2$.

$$Fe(s) + Cl_2(g) \longrightarrow FeCl_2(s)$$

Beginning with 10.0 g iron, what mass of Cl_2, in grams, is required for complete reaction? What quantity of $FeCl_2$, in moles and in grams, is expected?

45. Like many metals, manganese reacts with a halogen to give a metal halide.

$$2\ Mn(s) + 3\ F_2(g) \longrightarrow 2\ MnF_3(s)$$

(a) If you begin with 5.12 g Mn, what mass in grams of F_2 is required for complete reaction?
(b) What quantity in moles and in grams of the red solid MnF_3 is expected?

46. The final step in the manufacture of platinum metal (for use in automotive catalytic converters and other products) is the reaction

$$3\ (NH_4)_2PtCl_6(s) \longrightarrow 3\ Pt(s) + 2\ NH_4Cl(s) + 2\ N_2(g) + 16\ HCl(g)$$

Complete this table of reaction quantities for the reaction of 12.35 g $(NH_4)_2PtCl_6$.

$(NH_4)_2PtCl_6$	Pt	HCl
12.35 g	______ g	______ g
______ mol	______ mol	______ mol

47. Disulfur dichloride, S_2Cl_2, is used to vulcanize rubber. It can be made by treating molten sulfur with gaseous chlorine.

$$S_8(\ell) + 4\ Cl_2(g) \longrightarrow 4\ S_2Cl_2(g)$$

Complete this table of reaction quantities for the production of 103.5 g S_2Cl_2.

S_8	Cl_2	S_2Cl_2
______ g	______ g	103.5 g
______ mol	______ mol	______ mol

48. Many metal halides react with water to produce the metal oxide (or hydroxide) and the appropriate hydrogen halide. For example,

$$TiCl_4(\ell) + 2\ H_2O(g) \longrightarrow TiO_2(s) + 4\ HCl(g)$$

(a) If you begin with 14.0 g $TiCl_4$, how many moles of water are required for complete reaction?
(b) How many grams of each product are expected?

© Thomson Learning/Charles D. Winters

Liquid titanium tetrachloride ($TiCl_4$). When exposed to air it forms a dense fog of titanium(IV) oxide, TiO_2.

49. Gaseous sulfur dioxide, SO_2, can be removed from smokestacks by treatment with limestone and oxygen.

$$2\ SO_2(g) + 2\ CaCO_3(s) + O_2(g) \longrightarrow 2\ CaSO_4(s) + 2\ CO_2(g)$$

(a) How many moles each of $CaCO_3$ and O_2 are required to remove 150. g SO_2?
(b) What mass of $CaSO_4$ is formed when 150. g SO_2 is consumed completely?

50. If 2.5 mol O_2 reacts with propane (C_3H_8) by combustion, how many moles of H_2O will be produced? How many grams of H_2O will be produced?

51. Tungsten(VI) oxide can be reduced to tungsten metal.

$$WO_3(s) + 3\ H_2(g) \longrightarrow W(s) + 3\ H_2O(\ell)$$

How many grams of tungsten are formed from 1.00 kg WO_3?

52. If you want to synthesize 1.45 g of the semiconducting material GaAs, what masses of Ga and of As, in grams, are required?

53. Ammonium nitrate, NH_4NO_3, is a common fertilizer and explosive. When heated, it decomposes into gaseous products.

$$2\ NH_4NO_3(s) \longrightarrow 2\ N_2(g) + 4\ H_2O(g) + O_2(g)$$

How many grams of each product are formed from 1.0 kg NH_4NO_3?

54. Iron reacts with oxygen to give iron(III) oxide, Fe_2O_3.
(a) Write a balanced equation for this reaction.
(b) If an ordinary iron nail (assumed to be pure iron) has a mass of 5.58 g, what mass in grams of Fe_2O_3 would be produced if the nail is converted completely to this oxide?
(c) What mass of O_2 (in grams) is required for the reaction?

55. Nitroglycerin decomposes violently according to the equation

$$4\ C_3H_5(NO_3)_3(\ell) \longrightarrow 12\ CO_2(g) + 10\ H_2O(\ell) + 6\ N_2(g) + O_2(g)$$

How many grams of each gaseous product are produced from 1.00 g nitroglycerin?

56. Chlorinated fluorocarbons, such as CCl_2F_2, have been banned from use in automobile air conditioners because the compounds are destructive to the stratospheric ozone layer. Researchers at MIT have found an environmentally safe way to decompose these compounds by treating them with sodium oxalate, $Na_2C_2O_4$. The products of the reaction are carbon, carbon dioxide, sodium chloride, and sodium fluoride.
(a) Write a balanced equation for this reaction of CCl_2F_2.
(b) What mass of $Na_2C_2O_4$ is needed to remove 76.8 g CCl_2F_2?
(c) What mass of CO_2 is produced?

57. Careful decomposition of ammonium nitrate, NH_4NO_3, gives laughing gas (dinitrogen monoxide, N_2O) and water.
(a) Write a balanced equation for this reaction.
(b) Beginning with 10.0 g NH_4NO_3, what masses of N_2O and water are expected?

58. In making iron from iron ore, this reaction occurs.

$$Fe_2O_3(s) + 3\ CO(g) \longrightarrow 2\ Fe(s) + 3\ CO_2(g)$$

(a) How many grams of iron can be obtained from 1.00 kg iron(III) oxide?
(b) How many grams of CO are required?

59. Cisplatin, $Pt(NH_3)_2Cl_2$, a drug used in the treatment of cancer, can be made by the reaction of K_2PtCl_4 with ammonia, NH_3. Besides cisplatin, the other product is KCl.
(a) Write a balanced equation for this reaction.
(b) To obtain 2.50 g cisplatin, what masses in grams of K_2PtCl_4 and ammonia do you need?

Limiting Reactant

60. The reaction of Na_2SO_4 with $BaCl_2$ is

$$Na_2SO_4(aq) + BaCl_2(aq) \longrightarrow BaSO_4(s) + 2\ NaCl(aq)$$

If solutions containing exactly one gram of each reactant are mixed, which reactant is the limiting reactant, and how many grams of $BaSO_4$ are produced?

61. If a mixture of 100. g Al and 200. g MnO is reacted according to the reaction

$$2\ Al(s) + 3\ MnO(s) \longrightarrow Al_2O_3(s) + 3\ Mn(s)$$

which of the reactants is in excess and how many grams of it remain when the reaction is complete?

62. ■ Aluminum chloride, Al_2Cl_6, is an inexpensive reagent used in many industrial processes. It is made by treating scrap aluminum with chlorine according to the balanced equation

$$2\ Al(s) + 3\ Cl_2(g) \longrightarrow Al_2Cl_6(s)$$

(a) Which reactant is limiting if 2.70 g Al and 4.05 g Cl_2 are mixed?
(b) What mass of Al_2Cl_6 can be produced?
(c) What mass of the excess reactant will remain when the reaction is complete?

63. Hydrogen and oxygen react to form water by combustion.

$$2\ H_2(g) + O_2(g) \longrightarrow 2\ H_2O(\ell)$$

(a) If a mixture containing 100. g of each reactant is ignited, what is the limiting reactant?
(b) How many moles and grams of water are produced?

64. Methanol, CH_3OH, is a clean-burning, easily handled fuel. It can be made by the direct reaction of CO and H_2.

$$CO(g) + 2\,H_2(g) \longrightarrow CH_3OH(\ell)$$

(a) Starting with a mixture of 12.0 g H_2 and 74.5 g CO, which is the limiting reactant?
(b) What mass of the excess reactant, in grams, is left after reaction is complete?
(c) What mass of methanol can be obtained, in theory?

65. The reaction of methane and water is one way to prepare hydrogen.

$$CH_4(g) + 2\,H_2O(g) \longrightarrow CO_2(g) + 4\,H_2(g)$$

If 995 g CH_4 reacts with 2510 g water, how many moles of reactants and products are there when the reaction is complete?

66. ■ Ammonia gas can be prepared by the reaction

$$CaO(s) + 2\,NH_4Cl(s) \longrightarrow 2\,NH_3(g) + H_2O(g) + CaCl_2(s)$$

If 112 g CaO reacts with 224 g NH_4Cl, how many moles of reactants and products are there when the reaction is complete?

67. This reaction between lithium hydroxide and carbon dioxide has been used to scrub CO_2 from spacecraft atmospheres:

$$2\,LiOH + CO_2 \longrightarrow Li_2CO_3 + H_2O$$

(a) If 0.500 kg LiOH were available, how many grams of CO_2 could be consumed?
(b) How many grams of water would be produced?

68. ■ The equation for one of the reactions in the process of turning iron ore into the metal is

$$Fe_2O_3(s) + 3\,CO(g) \longrightarrow 2\,Fe(s) + 3\,CO_2(g)$$

If you start with 2.00 kg of each reactant, what is the maximum mass of iron you can produce?

69. Aspirin is produced by the reaction of salicylic acid and acetic anhydride.

$$2\,C_7H_6O_3(s) + C_4H_6O_3(\ell) \longrightarrow 2\,C_9H_8O_4(s) + H_2O(\ell)$$

salicylic acid — acetic anhydride — aspirin

If you mix 100. g of each of the reactants, what is the maximum mass of aspirin that can be obtained?

70. ■ Consider the chemical reaction $2\,S + 3\,O_2 \longrightarrow 2\,SO_3$. If the reaction is run by adding S indefinitely to a fixed amount of O_2, which of these graphs best represents the formation of SO_3? Explain your choice.

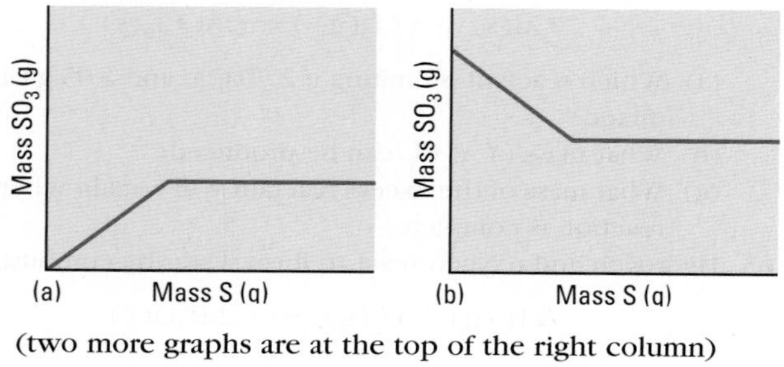

(two more graphs are at the top of the right column)

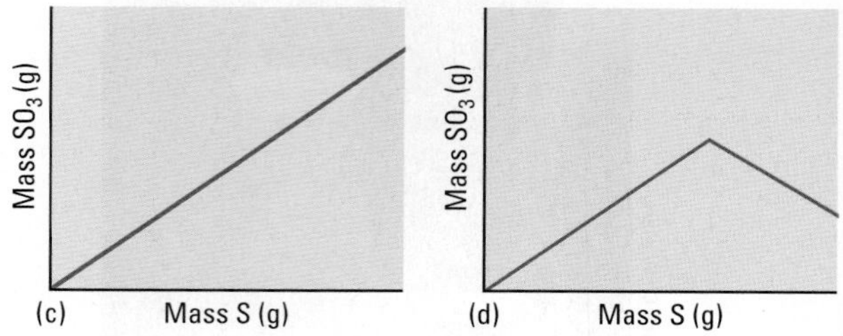

Percent Yield

71. Iron oxide can be reduced to the metal as follows:

$$Fe_2O_3(s) + 3\,CO(g) \longrightarrow 2\,Fe(s) + 3\,CO_2(g)$$

How many grams of iron can be obtained from 1.00 kg of the iron oxide? If 654 g Fe was obtained from the reaction, what was the percent yield?

72. Ammonia gas can be prepared by the reaction of calcium oxide with ammonium chloride.

$$CaO(s) + 2\,NH_4Cl(s) \longrightarrow 2\,NH_3(g) + H_2O(g) + CaCl_2(s)$$

If exactly 100 g ammonia is isolated but the theoretical yield is 136 g, what is the percent yield of this gas?

73. Quicklime, CaO, is formed when calcium hydroxide is heated.

$$Ca(OH)_2(s) \longrightarrow CaO(s) + H_2O(\ell)$$

If the theoretical yield is 65.5 g but only 36.7 g quicklime is produced, what is the percent yield?

74. Diborane, B_2H_6, is valuable for the synthesis of new organic compounds. The boron compound can be made by the reaction

$$2\,NaBH_4(s) + I_2(s) \longrightarrow B_2H_6(g) + 2\,NaI(s) + H_2(g)$$

Suppose you use 1.203 g $NaBH_4$ and excess iodine, and you isolate 0.295 g B_2H_6. What is the percent yield of B_2H_6?

75. ■ Methanol, CH_3OH, is used in racing cars because it is a clean-burning fuel. It can be made by this reaction:

$$CO(g) + 2\,H_2(g) \longrightarrow CH_3OH(\ell)$$

What is the percent yield if 5.0×10^3 g H_2 reacts with excess CO to form 3.5×10^3 g CH_3OH?

76. If 3.7 g sodium metal and 4.3 g chlorine gas react to form NaCl, what is the theoretical yield? If 5.5 g NaCl was formed, what is the percent yield?

77. ■ Disulfur dichloride, which has a revolting smell, can be prepared by directly combining S_8 and Cl_2, but it can also be made by this reaction:

$$3\,SCl_2(\ell) + 4\,NaF(s) \longrightarrow SF_4(g) + S_2Cl_2(\ell) + 4\,NaCl(s)$$

What mass of SCl_2 is needed to react with excess NaF to prepare 1.19 g S_2Cl_2, if the expected yield is 51%?

78. The ceramic silicon nitride, Si_3N_4, is made by heating silicon and nitrogen at an elevated temperature.

$$3\,Si(s) + 2\,N_2(g) \longrightarrow Si_3N_4(s)$$

How many grams of silicon must combine with excess N_2 to produce 1.0 kg Si_3N_4 if this process is 92% efficient?

79. Disulfur dichloride can be prepared by

$$3\ SCl_2 + 4\ NaF \longrightarrow SF_4 + S_2Cl_2 + 4\ NaCl$$

What is the percent yield of the reaction if 5.00 g SCl_2 reacts with excess NaF to produce 1.262 g S_2Cl_2?

Empirical Formulas

80. What is the empirical formula of a compound that contains 60.0% oxygen and 40.0% sulfur by mass?
81. A potassium salt was analyzed to have this percent composition: 26.57% K, 35.36% Cr, and 38.07% O. What is its empirical formula?
82. ■ Styrene, the building block of polystyrene, is a hydrocarbon. If 0.438 g of the compound is burned and produces 1.481 g CO_2 and 0.303 g H_2O, what is the empirical formula of the compound?
83. Mesitylene is a liquid hydrocarbon. If 0.115 g of the compound is burned in pure O_2 to give 0.379 g CO_2 and 0.1035 g H_2O, what is the empirical formula of the compound?
84. Propionic acid, an organic acid, contains only C, H, and O. If 0.236 g of the acid burns completely in O_2 and gives 0.421 g CO_2 and 0.172 g H_2O, what is the empirical formula of the acid?
85. Quinone, which is used in the dye industry and in photography, is an organic compound containing only C, H, and O. What is the empirical formula of the compound if 0.105 g of the compound gives 0.257 g CO_2 and 0.0350 g H_2O when burned completely?
86. Combustion of a 0.2500-g sample of a compound containing only C, H, and O shows that the compound contains 0.1614 g C, 0.02715 g H, and 0.06145 g O. What is the empirical formula of the compound?

General Questions

87. ■ Nitrogen gas can be prepared in the laboratory by the reaction of ammonia with copper(II) oxide according to this unbalanced equation:

$$NH_3(g) + CuO(s) \longrightarrow N_2(g) + Cu(s) + H_2O(g)$$

If 26.3 g of gaseous NH_3 is passed over a bed of solid CuO in stoichiometric excess, what mass, in grams, of N_2 can be isolated?

88. The overall chemical equation for the photosynthesis reaction in green plants is

$$6\ CO_2(g) + 6\ H_2O(\ell) \longrightarrow C_6H_{12}O_6(aq) + 6\ O_2(g)$$

How many grams of oxygen are produced by a plant when 50.0 g CO_2 is consumed?

89. ■ In an experiment, 1.056 g of a metal carbonate containing an unknown metal M was heated to give the metal oxide and 0.376 g CO_2.

$$MCO_3(s) \xrightarrow{\text{heat}} MO(s) + CO_2(g)$$

What is the identity of the metal M?

(a) Ni (b) Cu
(c) Zn (d) Ba

90. Uranium(VI) oxide reacts with bromine trifluoride to give uranium(IV) fluoride, an important step in the purification of uranium ore.

$$6\ UO_3(s) + 8\ BrF_3(\ell) \longrightarrow 6\ UF_4(s) + 4\ Br_2(\ell) + 9\ O_2(g)$$

If you begin with 365 g each of UO_3 and BrF_3, what is the maximum yield, in grams, of UF_4?

91. The cancer chemotherapy agent cisplatin is made by the reaction

$$(NH_4)_2PtCl_4(s) + 2\ NH_3(aq) \longrightarrow 2\ NH_4Cl(aq) + Pt(NH_3)_2Cl_2(s)$$

Assume that 15.5 g $(NH_4)_2PtCl_4$ is combined with 0.15 mol aqueous NH_3 to make cisplatin. What is the theoretical mass, in grams, of cisplatin that can be formed?

92. Diborane, B_2H_6, can be produced by the reaction

$$2\ NaBH_4(aq) + H_2SO_4(aq) \longrightarrow 2\ H_2(g) + Na_2SO_4(aq) + B_2H_6(g)$$

What is the maximum yield, in grams, of B_2H_6 that can be prepared starting with 2.19×10^{-2} mol H_2SO_4 and 1.55 g $NaBH_4$?

93. Silicon and hydrogen form a series of interesting compounds, Si_xH_y. To find the formula of one of them, a 6.22-g sample of the compound is burned in oxygen. All of the Si is converted to 11.64 g SiO_2 and all of the H to 6.980 g H_2O. What is the empirical formula of the silicon compound?
94. Boron forms an extensive series of compounds with hydrogen, all with the general formula B_xH_y. To analyze one of these compounds, you burn it in air and isolate the boron in the form of B_2O_3 and the hydrogen in the form of water. If 0.148 g B_xH_y gives 0.422 g B_2O_3 when burned in excess O_2, what is the empirical formula of B_xH_y?
95. What is the limiting reactant for the reaction

$$4\ KOH + 2\ MnO_2 + O_2 + Cl_2 \longrightarrow 2\ KMnO_4 + 2\ KCl + 2\ H_2O$$

if 5 mol of each reactant is present? What is the limiting reactant when 5 g of each reactant is present?

96. The Hargraves process is an industrial method for making sodium sulfate for use in papermaking.

$$4\ NaCl + 2\ SO_2 + 2\ H_2O + O_2 \longrightarrow 2\ Na_2SO_4 + 4\ HCl$$

(a) If you start with 10 mol of each reactant, which one will determine the amount of Na_2SO_4 produced?
(b) What if you start with 100 g of each reactant?

Applying Concepts

97. Chemical equations can be interpreted on either a nanoscale level (atoms, molecules, ions) or a mole level (moles of reactants and products). Write word statements to describe the combustion of butane on a nanoscale level and a mole level.

$$2\ C_4H_{10}(g) + 13\ O_2(g) \longrightarrow 8\ CO_2(g) + 10\ H_2O(\ell)$$

98. Write word statements to describe this reaction on a nanoscale level and a mole level.

$$P_4(s) + 6\ Cl_2(g) \longrightarrow 4\ PCl_3(\ell)$$

99. What is the single product of this hypothetical reaction?

$$4\ A_2 + AB_3 \longrightarrow 3\_\_\_\_$$

100. What is the single product of this hypothetical reaction?

$$3\ A_2B_3 + B_3 \longrightarrow 6\_\_\_\_$$

101. If 1.5 mol Cu reacts with a solution containing 4.0 mol $AgNO_3$, what ions will be present in the solution at the end of the reaction?

$$Cu(s) + 2\ AgNO_3(aq) \longrightarrow Cu(NO_3)_2(aq) + 2\ Ag(s)$$

102. Ammonia can be formed by a direct reaction of nitrogen and hydrogen.

$$N_2(g) + 3\ H_2(g) \longrightarrow 2\ NH_3(g)$$

A tiny portion of the starting mixture is represented by this diagram, where the blue circles represent N and the white circles represent H.

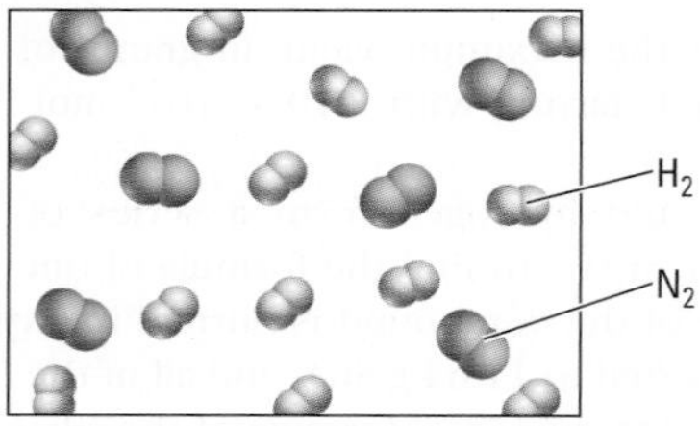

(a)

Which of these represents the product mixture?

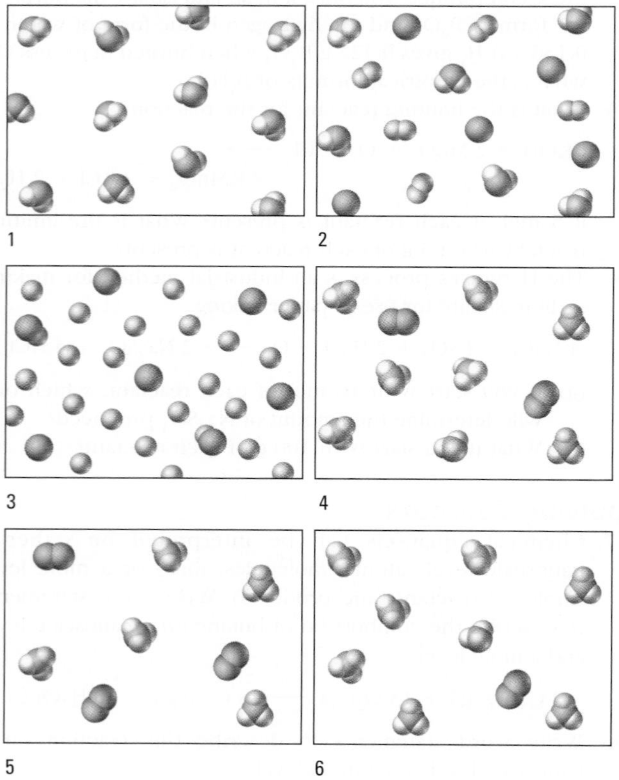

(b)

For the reaction of the given sample, which of these statements is true?

(a) N_2 is the limiting reactant.
(b) H_2 is the limiting reactant.
(c) NH_3 is the limiting reactant.
(d) No reactant is limiting; they are present in the correct stoichiometric ratio.

103. Carbon monoxide burns readily in oxygen to form carbon dioxide.

$$2\ CO(g) + O_2(g) \longrightarrow 2\ CO_2(g)$$

The box on the left represents a tiny portion of a mixture of CO and O_2. If these molecules react to form CO_2, what should the contents of the box on the right look like?

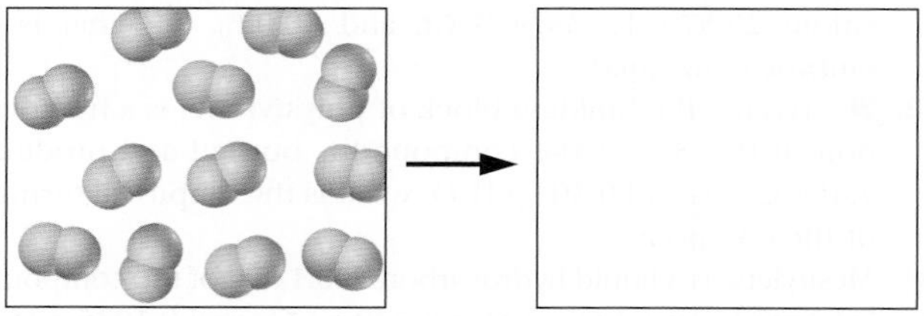

104. Which chemical equation best represents the reaction taking place in this illustration?

(a) $X_2 + Y_2 \longrightarrow n\ XY_3$
(b) $X_2 + 3\ Y_2 \longrightarrow 2\ XY_3$
(c) $6\ X_2 + 6\ Y_2 \longrightarrow 4\ XY_3 + 4\ X_2$
(d) $6\ X_2 + 6\ Y_2 \longrightarrow 4\ X_3Y + 4\ Y_2$

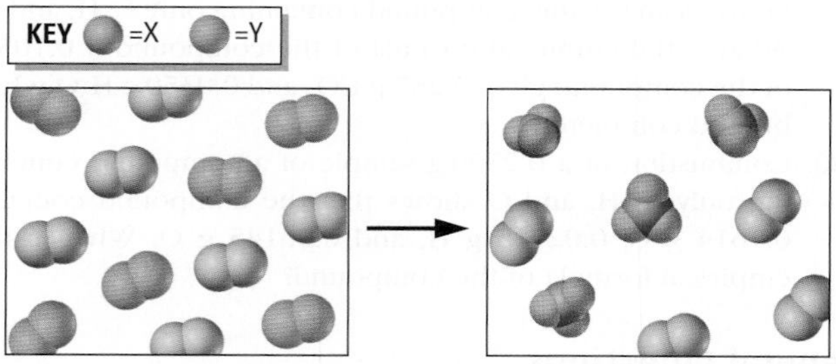

105. A student set up an experiment, like the one described in Chemistry You Can Do on page 146, for six different trials between acetic acid, CH_3COOH, and sodium bicarbonate, $NaHCO_3$.

$$CH_3COOH(aq) + NaHCO_3(s) \longrightarrow NaCH_3CO_2(aq) + CO_2(g) + H_2O(\ell)$$

The volume of acetic acid is kept constant, but the mass of sodium bicarbonate increased with each trial. The results of the tests are shown in the figure.

(a) In which trial(s) is the acetic acid the limiting reactant?
(b) In which trial(s) is sodium bicarbonate the limiting reactant?

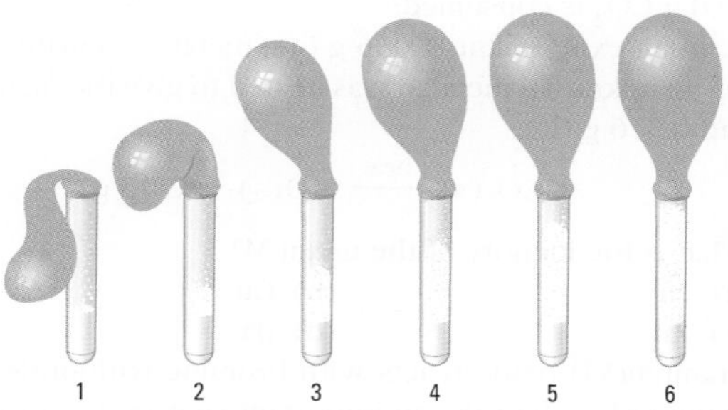

106. ■ A weighed sample of a metal is added to liquid bromine and allowed to react completely. The product substance is then separated from any leftover reactants and weighed. This experiment is repeated with several masses of the metal but with the same volume of bromine. This graph indicates the results. Explain why the graph has the shape that it does.

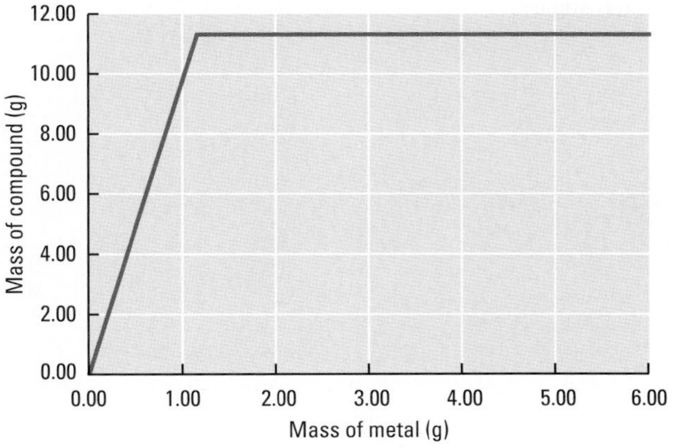

107. A series of experimental measurements like the ones described in Question 106 is carried out for iron reacting with bromine. This graph is obtained. What is the empirical formula of the compound formed by iron and bromine? Write a balanced equation for the reaction between iron and bromine. Name the product.

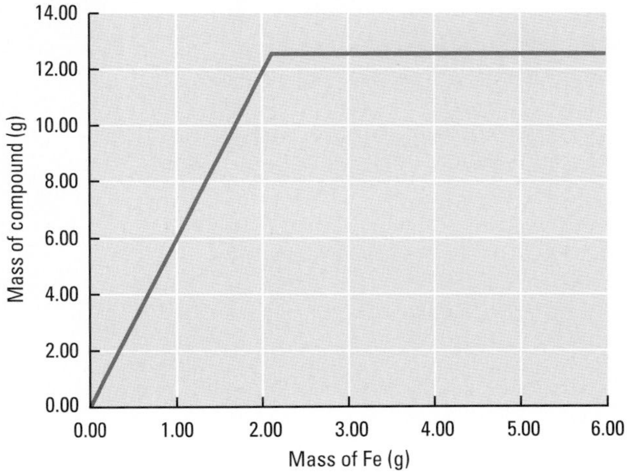

More Challenging Questions

108. ■ Hydrogen gas $H_2(g)$ is reacted with a sample of $Fe_2O_3(s)$ at 400 °C. Two products are formed: water vapor and a black solid compound that is 72.3% Fe and 27.7% O by mass. Write the balanced chemical equation for the reaction.

109. Write the balanced chemical equation for the complete combustion of malonic acid, an organic acid containing 34.62% C, 3.88% H, and the remainder O, by mass.

110. Aluminum bromide is a valuable laboratory chemical. What is the theoretical yield, in grams, of Al_2Br_6 if 25.0 mL liquid bromine (density = 3.1023 g/mL) and excess aluminum metal are reacted?

$$2\ Al(s) + 3\ Br_2(\ell) \longrightarrow Al_2Br_6(s)$$

111. In a reaction, 1.2 g element A reacts with exactly 3.2 g oxygen to form an oxide, AO_x; 2.4 g element A reacts with exactly 3.2 g oxygen to form a second oxide, AO_y.
(a) What is the ratio x/y?
(b) If $x = 2$, what might be the identity of element A?

112. The following reaction can be used to generate hydrogen gas from methane:

$$CH_4(g) + H_2O(g) \longrightarrow CO(g) + 3\ H_2(g)$$

If you use 500. g CH_4 and 1300. g water:
(a) Which reactant is the limiting reactant?
(b) How many grams H_2 can be produced?
(c) How many grams of the excess reactant remain when the reaction is complete?

113. A copper ore contained Cu_2S and CuS plus 10% inert impurities. When 200.0 g of the ore was "roasted," it yielded 150.8 g of 90.0% pure copper and sulfur dioxide gas. What is the percentage of Cu_2S in the ore?

$$Cu_2S + O_2 \longrightarrow 2\ Cu + SO_2 \qquad CuS + O_2 \longrightarrow Cu + SO_2$$

114. A compound with the formula X_2S_3 has a mass of 10.00 g. It is then roasted (reacted with oxygen) to convert it to X_2O_3. After roasting, it weighs 7.410 g. What is the atomic mass of element X?

115. A metal carbonate decomposed to form its metal oxide and CO_2 when it was heated:

$$MCO_3(s) \longrightarrow MO(s) + CO_2(g) \qquad \text{(balanced)}$$

After the reaction, the metal oxide was found to have a mass 56.0% as large as the starting MCO_3. What metal was in the carbonate?

116. When solutions of silver nitrate and sodium carbonate are mixed, solid silver carbonate is formed and sodium nitrate remains in solution. If a solution containing 12.43 g sodium carbonate is mixed with a solution containing 8.37 g silver nitrate, how many grams of the four species are present after the reaction is complete?

117. The following reaction produces sulfuric acid:

$$2\ SO_2 + O_2 + 2\ H_2O \longrightarrow 2\ H_2SO_4$$

If 200. g SO_2, 85. g O_2, and 66. g H_2O are mixed and the reaction proceeds to completion, which reactant is limiting, how many grams of H_2SO_4 are produced, and how many grams of the other two reactants are left over?

118. ■ You have an organic liquid that contains either ethyl alcohol (C_2H_5OH) or methyl alcohol (CH_3OH), or both. You burned a sample of the liquid weighing 0.280 g to form 0.385 g $CO_2(g)$. What was the composition of the sample of liquid?

119. Write the balanced chemical equation for the complete combustion of adipic acid, an organic acid containing 49.31% C, 6.90% H, and the remainder O, by mass.

120. L-dopa is a drug used for the treatment of Parkinson's disease. Elemental analysis shows it to be 54.82% carbon, 7.10% nitrogen, 32.46% oxygen, and the remainder hydrogen.
(a) What is L-dopa's empirical formula?
(b) The molar mass of L-dopa is 197.19 g/mol; what is its molecular formula?

Conceptual Challenge Problems

CP4.A (Section 4.4) In Example 4.7 it was not possible to find the mass of O_2 directly from a knowledge of the mass of sucrose. Are there chemical reactions in which the mass of a product or another reactant can be known directly if you know the mass of a reactant? Cite a couple of these reactions.

CP4.B (Section 4.4) Glucose ($C_6H_{12}O_6$), a monosaccharide, and sucrose ($C_{12}H_{22}O_{11}$), a disaccharide, undergo complete combustion with O_2 (metabolic conversion) to produce H_2O and CO_2.

(a) How many moles of O_2 are needed per mole of each sugar for the reaction to proceed?

(b) How many grams of O_2 are needed per mole of each sugar for the reaction to proceed?

(c) Which combustion reaction produces more H_2O per gram of sugar? How many grams of H_2O are produced per gram of each sugar?

5 Chemical Reactions

5.1 Exchange Reactions: Precipitation and Net Ionic Equations

5.2 Acids, Bases, and Acid-Base Exchange Reactions

5.3 Oxidation-Reduction Reactions

5.4 Oxidation Numbers and Redox Reactions

5.5 Displacement Reactions, Redox, and the Activity Series

5.6 Solution Concentration

5.7 Molarity and Reactions in Aqueous Solutions

5.8 Aqueous Solution Titrations

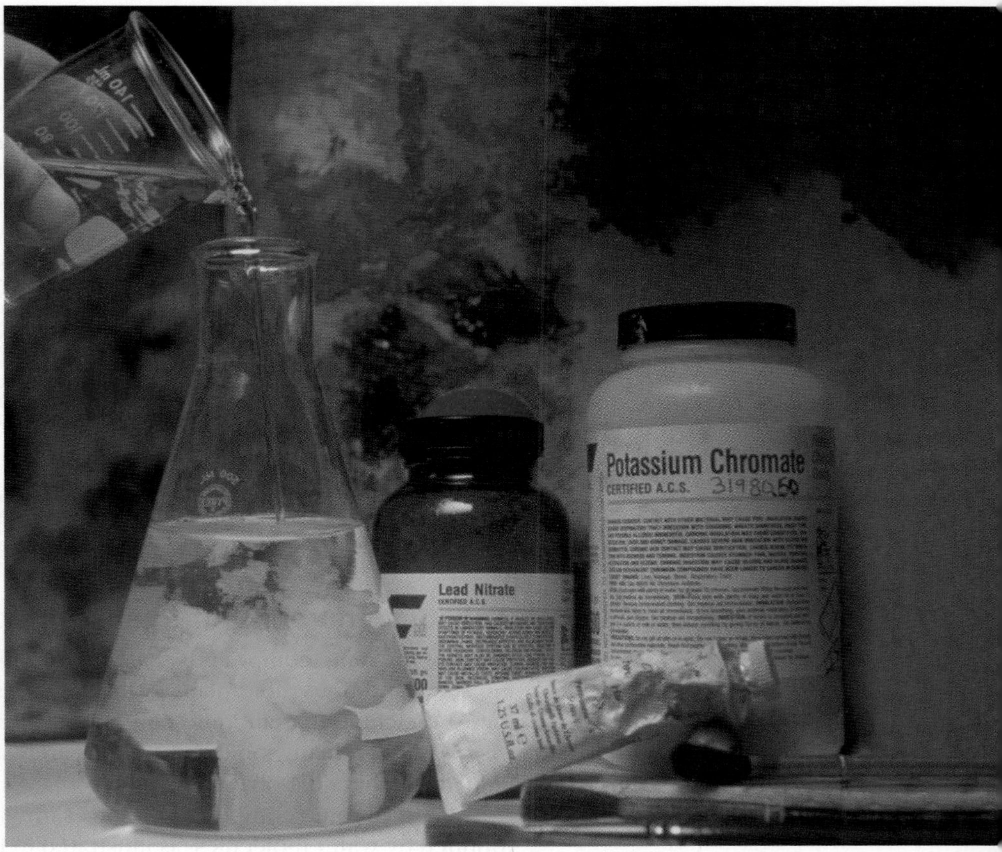

The brilliant yellow precipitate lead chromate, $PbCrO_4$, is formed when lead ions, Pb^{2+}, and chromate ions, CrO_4^{2-}, come together in an aqueous solution. The precipitation reaction occurs because the lead chromate product is insoluble. Although the color of lead chromate is so beautiful that it has been used as a pigment in paint, both lead and chromate are poisons, and the paint must be handled carefully.

© Thomson Learning/Charles D. Winters

ThomsonNOW™
Throughout the text, this icon indicates an opportunity to test yourself on key concepts and to explore interactive modules by signing in to ThomsonNOW at **www.thomsonedu.com**.

Chemistry is concerned with how substances react and what products are formed when they react. A chemical compound can consist of molecules or oppositely charged ions, and often the compound's properties can be deduced from the behavior of these molecules or ions. The *chemical* properties of a compound are the transformations that the molecules or ions can undergo when the substance reacts. A central focus of chemistry is providing answers to questions such as these: When two substances are mixed, will a chemical reaction occur? If a chemical reaction occurs, what will the products be?

As you saw in Chapter 4 (⟵ ***p. 125***), most reactions of simple ionic and molecular compounds can be assigned to a few general categories: combination, decomposition, displacement, and exchange. In this chapter we discuss chemical reactions in more detail, including oxidation-reduction reactions. The ability to recognize which type of reaction occurs for a particular set of reactants will allow you to predict the products.

Chemical reactions involving exchange of ions to form precipitates are discussed first, followed by net ionic equations, which focus on the active participants in such reactions. We then consider acid-base reactions, neutralization reactions, and reactions that form gases as products. Next comes a discussion of oxidation-reduction (redox) reactions, oxidation numbers as a means to organize our understanding of redox reactions, and the activity series of metals.

A great deal of chemistry—perhaps most—occurs in solution, and we introduce the means for quantitatively describing the concentrations of solutes in solutions. This discussion is followed by explorations of solution stoichiometry and finally aqueous titration, an analytical technique that is used to measure solute concentrations.

5.1 Exchange Reactions: Precipitation and Net Ionic Equations

Aqueous Solubility of Ionic Compounds

Many of the ionic compounds that you frequently encounter, such as table salt, baking soda, and household plant fertilizers, are soluble in water. It is therefore tempting to conclude that all ionic compounds are soluble in water, but such is not the case. Although many ionic compounds are water-soluble, some are only slightly soluble, and others dissolve hardly at all.

When an ionic compound dissolves in water, its ions separate and become surrounded by water molecules, as illustrated in Figure 5.1a. The process in which ions separate is called dissociation. Soluble ionic compounds are one type of strong electrolyte. Recall that an electrolyte is a substance whose aqueous solution contains ions and therefore conducts electricity. A **strong electrolyte** is completely converted to ions when it forms an aqueous solution. By contrast, most water-soluble molecular compounds do not ionize when they dissolve. This is shown in Figure 5.1b.

The solubility rules given in Table 5.1 are general guidelines for predicting the water solubilities of ionic compounds based on the ions they contain. *If a compound contains at least one of the ions indicated for soluble compounds in Table 5.1, then the compound is at least moderately soluble.*

Figure 5.2 shows examples illustrating the solubility rules for a few nitrates, hydroxides, and sulfides. Suppose you want to know whether $NiSO_4$ is soluble in water. $NiSO_4$ contains Ni^{2+} and SO_4^{2-} ions. Although Ni^{2+} is not mentioned in Table 5.1, substances containing SO_4^{2-} are described as soluble (except for $SrSO_4$, $BaSO_4$, and $PbSO_4$). Because $NiSO_4$ contains an ion (SO_4^{2-}) that indicates solubility and $NiSO_4$ is not one of the sulfate exceptions, it is predicted to be soluble.

ThomsonNOW™
Go to the Chemistry Interactive menu to work modules on:

- **strong and weak electrolytes and nonelectrolytes**
- **dissolution of $KMnO_4$**

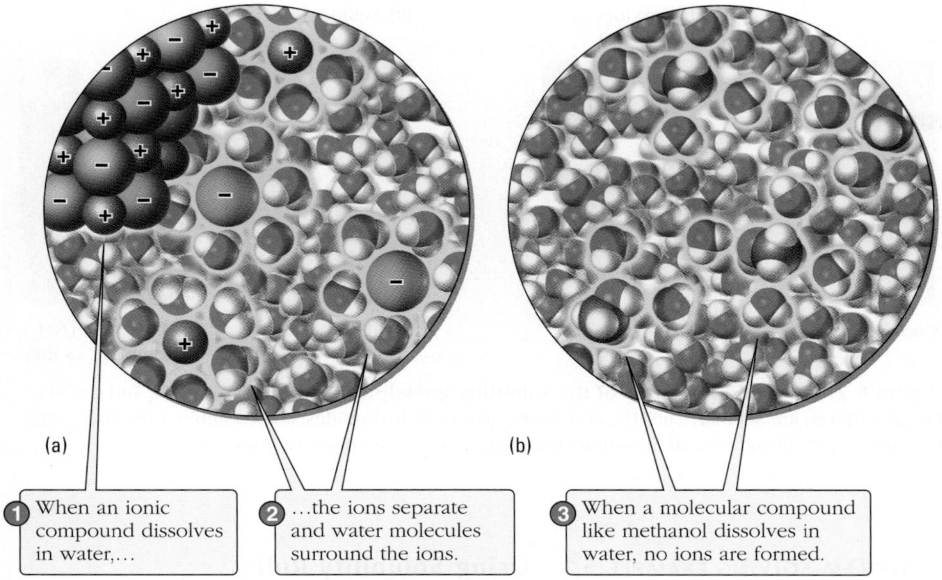

Figure 5.1 **Dissolution of (a) an ionic compound and (b) a molecular compound (methanol, CH_3OH) in water.**

Table 5.1 Solubility Rules for Ionic Compounds

Usually Soluble	
Group 1A, ammonium Li^+, Na^+, K^+, Rb^+, Cs^+, NH_4^+	All Group 1A (alkali metal) and ammonium salts are soluble.
Nitrates, NO_3^-	All nitrates are soluble.
Chlorides, bromides, iodides, Cl^-, Br^-, I^-	All common chlorides, bromides, and iodides are soluble except AgCl, Hg_2Cl_2, $PbCl_2$; AgBr, Hg_2Br_2, $PbBr_2$; AgI, Hg_2I_2; PbI_2.
Sulfates, SO_4^{2-}	Most sulfates are soluble; exceptions include $CaSO_4$, $SrSO_4$, $BaSO_4$, and $PbSO_4$.
Chlorates, ClO_3^-	All chlorates are soluble.
Perchlorates, ClO_4^-	All perchlorates are soluble.
Acetates, CH_3COO^-	All acetates are soluble.
Usually Insoluble	
Phosphates, PO_4^{3-}	All phosphates are insoluble except those of NH_4^+ and Group 1A elements (alkali metal cations).
Carbonates, CO_3^{2-}	All carbonates are insoluble except those of NH_4^+ and Group 1A elements (alkali metal cations).
Hydroxides, OH^-	All hydroxides are insoluble except those of NH_4^+ and Group 1A (alkali metal cations). $Sr(OH)_2$, $Ba(OH)_2$, and $Ca(OH)_2$ are slightly soluble.
Oxalates, $C_2O_4^{2-}$	All oxalates are insoluble except those of NH_4^+ and Group 1A (alkali metal cations).
Sulfides, S^{2-}	All sulfides are insoluble except those of NH_4^+, Group 1A (alkali metal cations) and Group 2A (MgS, CaS, and BaS are sparingly soluble).

ThomsonNOW

Go to the Coached Problems menu for tutorials on:

- **solubility of ionic compounds**
- **predicting precipitation reactions**

(a) nitrates (soluble) (b) hydroxides (insoluble) (c) sulfides

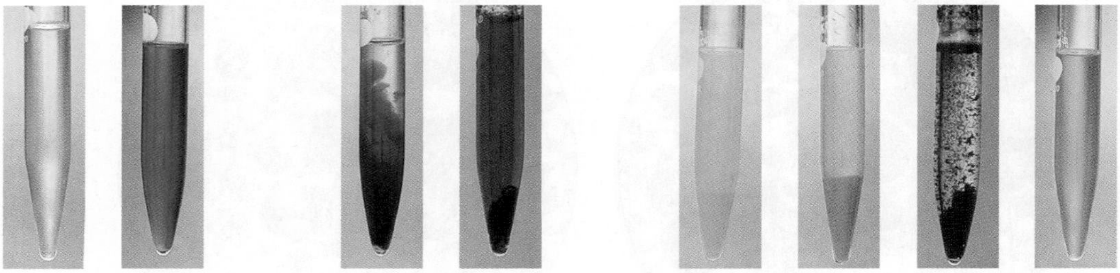

Photos: © Thomson Learning/ Charles D. Winters

Figure 5.2 Illustration of some of the solubility guidelines in Table 5.1. $AgNO_3$ and $Cu(NO_3)_2$, like all nitrates, are soluble. $Cu(OH)_2$ and AgOH, like most hydroxides, are insoluble. CdS, Sb_2S_3, and PbS, like nearly all sulfides, are insoluble, but $(NH_4)_2S$ is an exception (it is soluble).

PROBLEM-SOLVING EXAMPLE 5.1 Using Solubility Rules

Indicate what ions are present in each of these compounds, and then predict whether each compound is water-soluble.

(a) $CaCl_2$ (b) $Fe(OH)_3$ (c) NH_4NO_3
(d) $CuCO_3$ (e) $Ni(ClO_3)_2$

Answer (a) Ca^{2+} and Cl^-, soluble. (b) Fe^{3+} and OH^-, insoluble. (c) NH_4^+ and NO_3^-, soluble. (d) Cu^{2+} and CO_3^{2-}, insoluble. (e) $Ni^{2+}$and ClO_3^-, soluble.

Strategy and Explanation The use of the solubility rules requires identifying the ions present and checking their aqueous solubility (Table 5.1).

(a) $CaCl_2$ contains Ca^{2+} and Cl^- ions. All chlorides are soluble, with a few exceptions for transition metals, so calcium chloride is soluble.
(b) $Fe(OH)_3$ contains Fe^{3+} and OH^- ions. As indicated in Table 5.1, all hydroxides are insoluble except alkali metals and a few other exceptions, so iron(III) hydroxide is insoluble.
(c) NH_4NO_3 contains NH_4^+ and NO_3^- ions. All ammonium salts are soluble, and all nitrates are soluble, so NH_4NO_3 is soluble.
(d) $CuCO_3$ contains Cu^{2+} and CO_3^{2-} ions. All carbonates except those of ammonium and alkali metals are insoluble, and copper is not an alkali metal, so $CuCO_3$ is insoluble.
(e) $Ni(ClO_3)_2$ contains Ni^{2+} and ClO_3^- ions. All chlorates are soluble, so $Ni(ClO_3)_2$ is soluble.

PROBLEM-SOLVING PRACTICE 5.1

Predict whether each of these compounds is likely to be water-soluble.

(a) NaF (b) $Ca(CH_3COO)_2$ (c) $SrCl_2$
(d) MgO (e) $PbCl_2$ (f) HgS

Recall that exchange reactions *(p. 130)* have this reaction pattern:

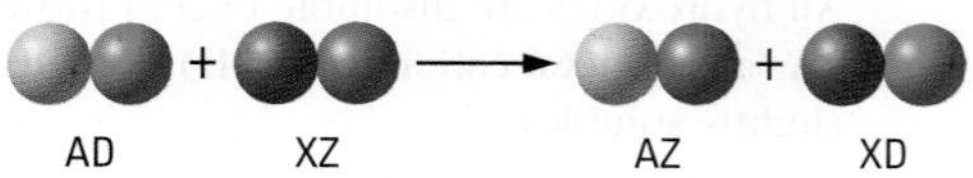

If both the reactants and the products of such a reaction are water-soluble ionic compounds, no overall reaction takes place. In such cases, mixing the solutions of AD and XZ just results in an aqueous solution containing the A, D, X, and Z ions.

What will happen when two aqueous solutions are mixed, one containing dissolved calcium nitrate, $Ca(NO_3)_2$, and the other containing dissolved sodium chloride, NaCl? Both are soluble ionic compounds (Table 5.1), so the resulting solution contains Ca^{2+}, NO_3^-, Na^+, and Cl^- ions. To decide whether a reaction will occur requires determining whether any two of these ions can react with each other to form a *new* compound. For an exchange reaction to occur, the calcium ion and the chloride ion would have to form calcium chloride ($CaCl_2$), and the sodium ion and the nitrate ion would have to form sodium nitrate ($NaNO_3$). Is either a possible chemical reaction? If either product is insoluble the answer is yes. Checking the solubility rules shows that both of these compounds are water-soluble. No reaction to remove the ions from solution is possible; therefore, when these two aqueous solutions are mixed together, no reaction occurs.

If, however, one or both of the potential products of the reaction remove ions from the solution, a reaction will occur. Three different kinds of products can cause an exchange reaction to occur in aqueous solution:

1. Formation of an *insoluble ionic compound:*

$$AgNO_3(aq) + KCl(aq) \longrightarrow KNO_3(aq) + AgCl(s)$$

2. Formation of a *molecular compound* that remains in solution. Most commonly this happens when water is produced in acid-base neutralization reactions:

$$H_2SO_4(aq) + 2\ NaOH(aq) \longrightarrow Na_2SO_4(aq) + 2\ H_2O(\ell)$$

3. Formation of a *gaseous molecular compound* that escapes from the solution:

$$2\ HCl(aq) + Na_2S(aq) \longrightarrow 2\ NaCl(aq) + H_2S(g)$$

© Thomson Learning/Charles D. Winters

Figure 5.3 Precipitation of barium sulfate. Mixing aqueous solutions of barium chloride ($BaCl_2$) and sodium sulfate (Na_2SO_4) forms a precipitate of barium sulfate ($BaSO_4$). Sodium chloride (NaCl), the other product of this exchange reaction, is water soluble, and Na^+ and Cl^- ions remain in solution.

Precipitation Reactions

Consider the possibility of an exchange reaction when aqueous solutions of barium chloride and sodium sulfate are mixed:

$$BaCl_2(aq) + Na_2SO_4(aq) \longrightarrow ? + ?$$

If the barium ions and sodium ions exchange partners to form $BaSO_4$ and NaCl, the equation will be

$$\underset{\text{barium chloride}}{BaCl_2(aq)} + \underset{\text{sodium sulfate}}{Na_2SO_4(aq)} \longrightarrow \underset{\text{barium sulfate}}{BaSO_4} + \underset{\text{sodium chloride}}{2\ NaCl}$$

Will a reaction occur? The answer is yes if an insoluble product—a **precipitate**—can form. Checking Table 5.1, we find that NaCl is soluble, but $BaSO_4$ is not soluble (sulfates of Ca^{2+}, Sr^{2+}, Ba^{2+}, and Pb^{2+} are insoluble). Therefore, an exchange reaction will occur, and solid barium sulfate will precipitate from the solution (Figure 5.3). Precipitate formation is indicated by an (s) next to the precipitate, a solid, in the overall equation. Because it is soluble, NaCl remains dissolved in solution, and we put (aq) next to NaCl in the equation.

$$BaCl_2(aq) + Na_2SO_4(aq) \longrightarrow BaSO_4(s) + 2\ NaCl(aq)$$

Ba^{2+} and Na^+ do not react with each other, and neither do Cl^- and SO_4^{2-}.

PROBLEM-SOLVING EXAMPLE 5.2 **Exchange Reactions**

For each of these pairs of ionic compounds, decide whether an exchange reaction will occur when their aqueous solutions are mixed, and write a balanced equation for those reactions that will occur.

(a) $(NH_4)_2S$ and $Cu(NO_3)_2$ (b) $ZnCl_2$ and Na_2CO_3 (c) $CaCl_2$ and KNO_3

Answer

(a) CuS precipitates. $(NH_4)_2S(aq) + Cu(NO_3)_2(aq) \longrightarrow CuS(s) + 2\ NH_4NO_3(aq)$
(b) $ZnCO_3$ precipitates. $ZnCl_2(aq) + Na_2CO_3(aq) \longrightarrow ZnCO_3(s) + 2\ NaCl(aq)$
(c) No reaction occurs. Both products, $Ca(NO_3)_2$ and KCl, are soluble.

Strategy and Explanation In each case, consider which cation-anion combinations can form, and then decide whether the possible compounds will precipitate. You have to be careful to take into account any polyatomic ions, which must be kept together as a unit during the balancing of the chemical reaction.

(a) An exchange reaction between $(NH_4)_2S$ and $Cu(NO_3)_2$ forms CuS(s) and NH_4NO_3. Table 5.1 shows that all nitrates are soluble, so NH_4NO_3 remains in solution. CuS is not soluble and therefore precipitates.
(b) The exchange reaction between $ZnCl_2$ and Na_2CO_3 forms the insoluble product $ZnCO_3(s)$ and leaves soluble NaCl in solution.
(c) No precipitate forms when $CaCl_2$ and KNO_3 are mixed because each product, $Ca(NO_3)_2$ and KCl, is soluble. All four of the ions (Ca^{2+}, Cl^-, K^+, NO_3^-) remain in solution. No exchange reaction occurs because no product is formed that removes ions from the solution.

PROBLEM-SOLVING PRACTICE 5.2

Predict the products and write a balanced chemical equation for the exchange reaction in aqueous solution between each pair of ionic compounds. Use Table 5.1 to determine solubilities and indicate in the equation whether a precipitate forms.

(a) $NiCl_2$ and NaOH (b) K_2CO_3 and $CaBr_2$

Net Ionic Equations

ThomsonNOW™
Go to the Coached Problems menu for a tutorial on **writing net ionic equations.**

In writing equations for exchange reactions in the preceding section, we used overall equations. There is another way to represent what happens, however. In each case in which a precipitate forms, the product that does not precipitate remains in solution. Therefore, its ions are in solution as reactants and remain there after the reaction. Such ions are commonly called **spectator ions** because, like the spectators at a play or game, they are present but are not involved directly in the real action. Consequently, the spectator ions can be left out of the equation that represents the chemical change that occurs. An equation that includes only the symbols or formulas of ions in solution or compounds that undergo change is called a **net ionic equation.** We will use the reaction of aqueous NaCl with $AgNO_3$ to form AgCl and $NaNO_3$ to illustrate the general steps for writing a net ionic equation.

Step 1:* *Write the overall balanced equation using the correct formulas for the reactants and products.

Overall chemical reaction:

$$\underset{\text{silver nitrate}}{AgNO_3} + \underset{\text{sodium chloride}}{NaCl} \longrightarrow \underset{\text{silver chloride}}{AgCl} + \underset{\text{sodium nitrate}}{NaNO_3}$$

Step 1 actually consists of two parts: first, write the unbalanced equation with the correct formulas for reactants and products; second, balance the equation.

Step 2:* *Use the general guidelines in Table 5.1 to determine the solubilities of reactants and products. In this case, the guidelines indicate that nitrates are soluble, so $AgNO_3$ and $NaNO_3$ are soluble. NaCl is water-soluble because almost all chlorides are soluble. However, AgCl is one of the insoluble chlorides (AgCl, Hg_2Cl_2, and $PbCl_2$). Using this information we can write

$$AgNO_3(aq) + NaCl(aq) \longrightarrow AgCl(s) + NaNO_3(aq)$$

Step 3: ***Recognize that all soluble ionic compounds dissociate into their component ions in aqueous solution.*** Therefore we have

$$AgNO_3(aq) \text{ consists of } Ag^+(aq) + NO_3^-(aq).$$

$$NaCl(aq) \text{ consists of } Na^+(aq) + Cl^-(aq).$$

$$NaNO_3(aq) \text{ consists of } Na^+(aq) + NO_3^-(aq).$$

Step 4: ***Use the ions from Step 3 to write a complete ionic equation with the ions in solution from each soluble compound shown separately.***

Complete ionic equation:

$$Ag^+(aq) + NO_3^-(aq) + Na^+(aq) + Cl^-(aq) \longrightarrow$$
$$AgCl(s) + Na^+(aq) + NO_3^-(aq)$$

Note that the precipitate is represented by its complete formula.

Step 5: ***Cancel out the spectator ions from each side of the complete ionic equation to obtain the net ionic equation.*** Sodium ions and nitrate ions are the spectator ions in this example, and we cancel them from the complete ionic equation to give the net ionic equation (Figure 5.4).

Complete ionic equation:

$$Ag^+(aq) + \cancel{NO_3^-(aq)} + \cancel{Na^+(aq)} + Cl^-(aq) \longrightarrow$$
$$AgCl(s) + \cancel{Na^+(aq)} + \cancel{NO_3^-(aq)}$$

Net ionic equation:

$$Ag^+(aq) + Cl^-(aq) \longrightarrow AgCl(s)$$

Active Figure 5.4 **Precipitation of silver chloride. Go to the Active Figures menu at ThomsonNOW to test your understanding of the concepts in this figure.**

The charge must be the same on both sides of a balanced equation since electrons are neither created nor destroyed.

Step 6: Check that the sum of the charges is the same on each side of the net ionic equation. For the equation in Step 5 the sum of charges is zero on each side: (1+) + (1−) = 0 on the left; AgCl is an ionic compound with zero net charge on the right.

PROBLEM-SOLVING EXAMPLE 5.3 Net Ionic Equations

Write the net ionic equation that occurs when aqueous solutions of lead nitrate, $Pb(NO_3)_2$, and potassium iodide, KI, are mixed.

Answer $Pb^{2+}(aq) + 2\ I^-(aq) \longrightarrow PbI_2(s)$

Strategy and Explanation Use the stepwise procedure presented above.

Step 1: *Write the overall balanced equation using the correct formulas for the reactants and products.* This is an exchange reaction (***p. 130***).

$$Pb(NO_3)_2 + 2\ KI \longrightarrow PbI_2 + 2\ KNO_3$$

Step 2: *Determine the solubilities of reactants and products.* The solubility rules in Table 5.1 predict that all these reactants and products are soluble except PbI_2.

$$Pb(NO_3)_2(aq) + 2\ KI(aq) \longrightarrow PbI_2(s) + 2\ KNO_3(aq)$$

Step 3: *Identify the ions present when the soluble compounds dissociate in solution.*

1 mol $Pb(NO_3)_2$ contains 2 mol NO_3^- ions along with 1 mol Pb^{2+} ions.

$Pb(NO_3)_2(aq)$ consists of $Pb^{2+}(aq)$ and 2 NO_3^-.

$KI(aq)$ consists of $K^+(aq)$ and $I^-(aq)$.

$KNO_3(aq)$ consists of $K^+(aq)$ and $NO_3^-(aq)$.

Step 4: *Write the complete ionic equation.*

$$Pb^{2+}(aq) + 2\ NO_3^-(aq) + 2\ K^+(aq) + 2\ I^-(aq) \longrightarrow PbI_2(s) + 2\ K^+(aq) + 2\ NO_3^-(aq)$$

Step 5 and 6: *Cancel spectator ions* [$K^+(aq)$ and $NO_3^-(aq)$] *to get the net ionic equation; check that charge is balanced.*

Net ionic equation: $Pb^{2+}(aq) + 2\ I^-(aq) \longrightarrow PbI_2(s)$

Net charge $= (2+) + 2 \times (1-) = 0$

PROBLEM-SOLVING PRACTICE 5.3

Write a balanced equation for the reaction (if any) for each of these ionic compound pairs in aqueous solution. Then use the complete ionic equation to write their balanced net ionic equations.

(a) $BaCl_2$ and Na_2SO_4

(b) $(NH_4)_2S$ and $FeCl_2$

CONCEPTUAL EXERCISE 5.1 Net Ionic Equations

It is possible for an exchange reaction in which both products precipitate to occur in aqueous solution. Using Table 5.1, identify the reactants and products of an example of such a reaction.

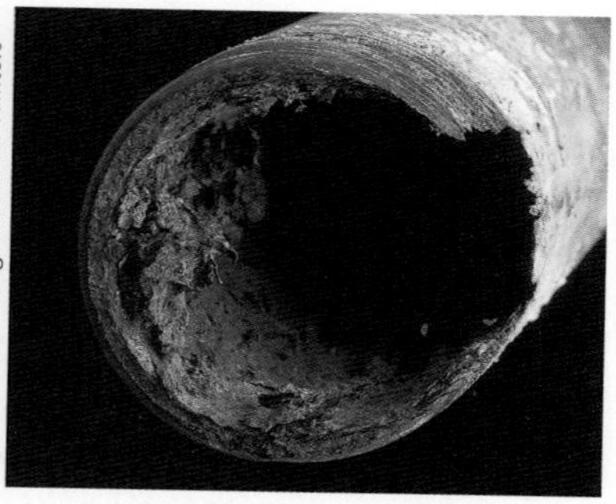

© Thomson Learning/Charles D. Winters

Boiler scale can form inside hot-water pipes.

If you live in an area with "hard water," you have probably noticed the scale that forms inside your teakettle or saucepans when you boil water in them. Hard water is mostly caused by the presence of the cations Ca^{2+}, Mg^{2+}, and also Fe^{2+} or Fe^{3+}. When the water also contains bicarbonate ion (HCO_3^-), this reaction occurs when the water is heated:

$$2\,HCO_3^-(aq) \longrightarrow H_2O(\ell) + CO_2(g) + CO_3^{2-}(aq)$$

The carbon dioxide escapes from the hot water, and the bicarbonate is slowly converted to the carbonate. The carbonate ions can form precipitates with the calcium, magnesium, or iron ions to produce a scale that sticks to metal surfaces. In hot-water heating systems in areas with high calcium ion concentrations, the buildup of such *boiler scale* can plug up the pipes.

$$Ca^{2+}(aq) + 2\,HCO_3^-(aq) \longrightarrow CaCO_3(s) + H_2O(\ell) + CO_2(g)$$

5.2 Acids, Bases, and Acid-Base Exchange Reactions

Acids and bases are two extremely important classes of compounds—so important that this book devotes two chapters to them later (Chapters 16 and 17). Here, we focus on a few general properties and consider how acids and bases react with each other. Acids have a number of properties in common, and so do bases. Some properties of acids are related to properties of bases. Solutions of acids change the colors of pigments in specific ways. For example, acids change the color of litmus from blue to red and cause the dye phenolphthalein to be colorless. In contrast, bases turn red litmus blue and make phenolphthalein pink. If an acid has made litmus red, adding a base will reverse the effect, making the litmus blue again. Thus, acids and bases seem to be opposites. A base can *neutralize* the effect of an acid, and an acid can neutralize the effect of a base.

Litmus is a dye derived from lichens. Phenolphthalein is a synthetic dye.

Acids have other characteristic properties. They taste sour, they produce bubbles of gas when reacting with limestone, and they dissolve many metals while producing a flammable gas. Although you should never taste substances in a chemistry laboratory, you have probably experienced the sour taste of at least one acid—vinegar, which is a dilute solution of acetic acid in water. Bases, in contrast, have a bitter taste. Soap, for example, contains a base. Rather than dissolving metals, bases often cause metal ions to form insoluble compounds that precipitate from solution. Such precipitates can be made to dissolve by adding an acid, another case in which an acid counteracts a property of a base.

Acids

The properties of acids can be explained by a common feature of acid molecules. An **acid** is any substance that increases the concentration of hydrogen ions, H^+, when dissolved in pure water. The H^+ ion is a hydrogen atom that has lost its one electron; the H^+ ion is just a proton. As a "naked" H^+ ion, it cannot exist by itself in water. Because H^+ is a very small, positively charged species, it interacts strongly with oxygen atoms of water molecules. Thus, H^+ combines with H_2O to form H_3O^+, known as the **hydronium ion.** Chapter 16 explores the importance of the hydronium ion to acid-base chemistry. For now, we represent the hydronium ion as $H^+(aq)$. The properties that acids have in common are those of hydrogen ions dissolved in water.

$$H^+ + H_2O \longrightarrow H_3O^+$$

Acids that are entirely converted to ions (completely ionized) when dissolved in water are *strong electrolytes* and are called **strong acids.** One of the most common strong acids is hydrochloric acid, which ionizes completely in aqueous solution to form hydrogen ions and chloride ions (Figure 5.5a).

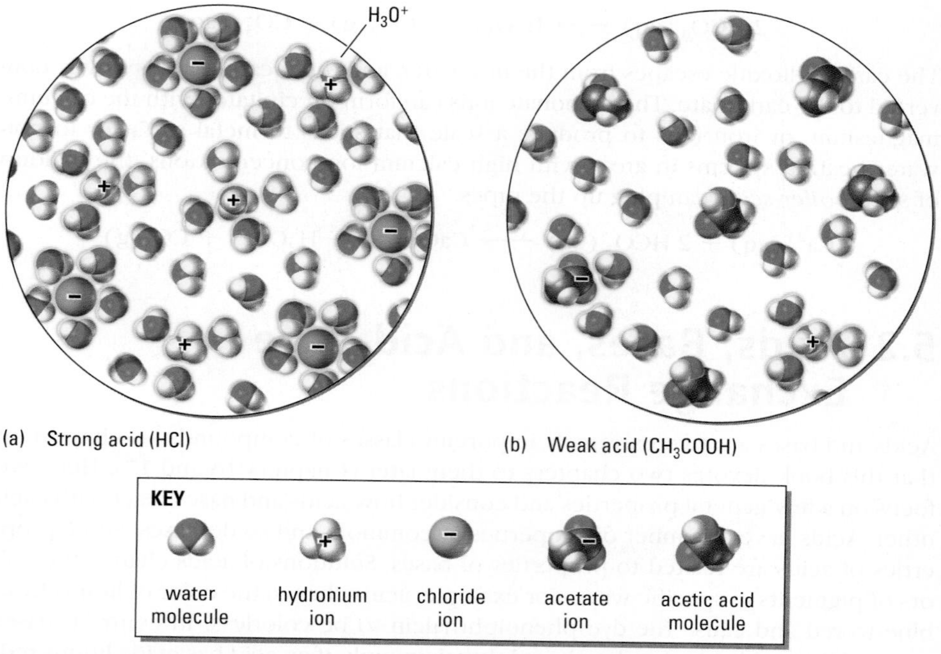

Figure 5.5 The ionization of acids in water. (a) A strong acid such as hydrochloric acid (HCl) is completely ionized in water; all the HCl molecules ionize to form $H_3O^+(aq)$ and $Cl^-(aq)$ ions. (b) Weak acids such as acetic acid (CH_3COOH) are only slightly ionized in water. Nonionized acetic acid molecules far outnumber aqueous H_3O^+ and CH_3COO^- ions formed by the ionization of acetic acid molecules.

ThomsonNOW™
Go to the Coached Problems menu for a simulation of **degree of acid dissociation.**

$$HCl(aq) \longrightarrow H^+(aq) + Cl^-(aq)$$

The more complete, and proper, way to write an equation for the reaction is

$$HCl(aq) + H_2O(\ell) \longrightarrow H_3O^+(aq) + Cl^-(aq)$$

which explicitly shows the hydronium ion, H_3O^+. Table 5.2 lists some other common acids.

In contrast, acids and other substances that ionize only slightly are termed **weak electrolytes.** Acids that are only partially ionized in aqueous solution are termed **weak acids.** For example, when acetic acid dissolves in water, usually fewer than 5% of the molecules are ionized at any time. The remainder of the acetic acid exists as nonionized molecules. Thus, because acetic acid is only slightly ionized in aqueous solution, it is a weak electrolyte and classified as a weak acid (Figure 5.5b).

The organic functional group −COOH is present in all organic carboxylic acids (Section 12.6).

$$CH_3COOH(aq) \rightleftharpoons H^+(aq) + CH_3COO^-(aq)$$

The double arrow in this equation for the ionization of acetic acid signifies a characteristic property of weak electrolytes. They establish a *dynamic equilibrium* in solution between the formation of the ions and their undissociated molecular form. In aqueous acetic acid, hydrogen ions and acetate ions recombine to form CH_3COOH molecules.

Table 5.2 Common Acids and Bases

Strong Acids (Strong Electrolytes)		Strong Bases (Strong Electrolytes)	
HCl	Hydrochloric acid	LiOH	Lithium hydroxide
HNO_3	Nitric acid	NaOH	Sodium hydroxide
H_2SO_4	Sulfuric acid	KOH	Potassium hydroxide
$HClO_4$	Perchloric acid	$Ca(OH)_2$	Calcium hydroxide‡
HBr	Hydrobromic acid	$Ba(OH)_2$	Barium hydroxide‡
HI	Hydroiodic acid	$Sr(OH)_2$	Strontium hydroxide‡
Weak Acids* (Weak Electrolytes)		**Weak Bases† (Weak Electrolytes)**	
H_3PO_4	Phosphoric acid	NH_3	Ammonia
CH_3COOH	Acetic acid	CH_3NH_2	Methylamine
H_2CO_3	Carbonic acid		
HCN	Hydrocyanic acid		
HCOOH	Formic acid		
C_6H_5COOH	Benzoic acid		

*Many organic acids are weak acids.

†Many organic amines (related to ammonia) are weak bases.

‡The hydroxides of calcium, barium, and strontium are only slightly soluble, but all that dissolves is dissociated into ions.

Some common acids, such as sulfuric acid, can provide more than 1 mol H^+ ions per mole of acid:

$$\underset{\text{sulfuric acid}}{H_2SO_4(aq)} \longrightarrow H^+(aq) + \underset{\text{hydrogen sulfate ion}}{HSO_4^-(aq)}$$

$$\underset{\text{hydrogen sulfate ion}}{HSO_4^-(aq)} \rightleftharpoons H^+(aq) + \underset{\text{sulfate ion}}{SO_4^{2-}(aq)}$$

The first ionization reaction is essentially complete, so sulfuric acid is considered a strong electrolyte (and a strong acid as well). However, the hydrogen sulfate ion, like acetic acid, is only partially ionized, so it is a weak electrolyte and also a weak acid.

CONCEPTUAL EXERCISE 5.2 Dissociation of Acids

Phosphoric acid, H_3PO_4, has three protons that can ionize. Write the equations for its three ionization reactions, each of which is a dynamic equilibrium.

Bases

A **base** is a substance that increases the concentration of the **hydroxide ion,** OH^-, when dissolved in pure water. The properties that bases have in common are properties attributable to the aqueous hydroxide ion, $OH^-(aq)$. Compounds that contain hydroxide ions, such as sodium hydroxide or potassium hydroxide, are obvious bases. As ionic compounds they are strong electrolytes and **strong bases.**

$$NaOH(s) \xrightarrow{H_2O} Na^+(aq) + OH^-(aq)$$

Acids and bases that are strong electrolytes are strong acids and bases. Acids and bases that are weak electrolytes are weak acids and bases.

A base that is slightly water-soluble, such as $Ca(OH)_2$, can still be a strong electrolyte if the amount of the compound that dissolves completely dissociates into ions.

Ammonia, NH_3, is another very common base. Although the compound does not have an OH^- ion as part of its formula, it produces the ion by reaction with water.

$$NH_3(aq) + H_2O(\ell) \rightleftharpoons NH_4^+(aq) + OH^-(aq)$$

In the equilibrium between NH_3 and the NH_4^+ and OH^- ions, only a small concentration of the ions is present, so ammonia is a weak electrolyte (<5% ionized), and it is a **weak base.**

To summarize:

- Strong electrolytes are compounds that ionize completely in aqueous solutions. They can be ionic compounds (salts or strong bases) or molecular compounds that are strong acids.
- Weak electrolytes are molecular compounds that are weak acids or bases and establish equilibrium with water.
- Nonelectrolytes are molecular compounds that do not ionize in aqueous solution.

EXERCISE 5.3 Acids and Bases

(a) What ions are produced when perchloric acid, $HClO_4$, dissolves in water?
(b) Calcium hydroxide is only slightly soluble in water. What little does dissolve, however, is dissociated. What ions are produced? Write an equation for the dissociation of calcium hydroxide.

(a)

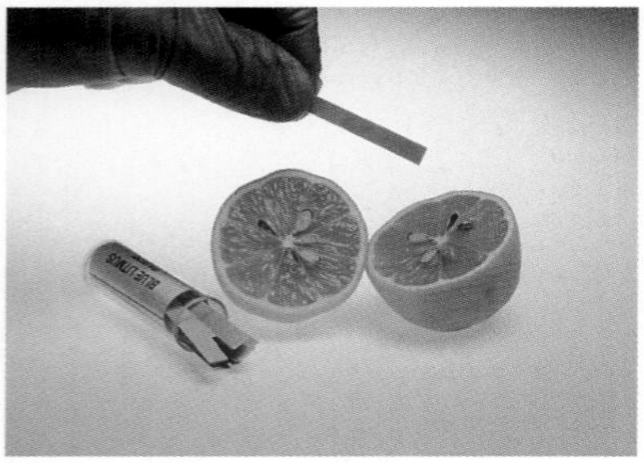

(b)

(c)

© Thomson Learning/Charles D. Winters

Acids and bases. (a) Many common foods and household products are acidic or basic. Citrus fruits contain citric acid, and household ammonia and oven cleaner are basic. (b) The acid in lemon juice turns blue litmus paper red, whereas (c) household ammonia turns red litmus paper blue.

PROBLEM-SOLVING EXAMPLE 5.4 Strong Electrolytes, Weak Electrolytes, and Nonelectrolytes

Identify whether each of these substances in an aqueous solution will be a strong electrolyte, a weak electrolyte, or a nonelectrolyte: HBr (hydrogen bromide); LiOH (lithium hydroxide); HCOOH (formic acid); CH_3CH_2OH (ethanol).

Answer HBr is a strong electrolyte; LiOH is a strong electrolyte; HCOOH is a weak electrolyte; CH_3CH_2OH is a nonelectrolyte.

Strategy and Explanation For the acids and bases we refer to Table 5.2. Hydrogen bromide is a common strong acid and, therefore, is a strong electrolyte. Lithium hydroxide is a common strong base and completely dissociates into ions in aqueous solution, so it is a strong electrolyte. Formic acid is a weak acid because it only partially ionizes in aqueous solution, so it is a weak electrolyte. Ethanol is a molecular compound that does not dissociate into ions in aqueous solution, so it is a nonelectrolye.

PROBLEM-SOLVING PRACTICE 5.4

Look back through the discussion of electrolytes and Table 5.2 and identify at least one additional strong electrolyte, one additional weak electrolyte, and one additional nonelectrolyte beyond those discussed in Problem-Solving Example 5.4.

Neutralization Reactions

When aqueous solutions of a strong acid (such as HCl) and a strong base (such as NaOH) are mixed, the ions in solution are the hydrogen ion and the anion from the acid, the metal cation, and the hydroxide ion from the base:

From hydrochloric acid: $H^+(aq)$, $Cl^-(aq)$
From sodium hydroxide: $Na^+(aq)$, $OH^-(aq)$

As in precipitation reactions, an exchange reaction will occur *if two of these ions can react with each other to form a compound that removes ions from solution*. In an acid-base reaction, that compound is water, formed by the combination of $H^+(aq)$ with $OH^-(aq)$.

When a strong acid and a strong base react, they neutralize each other. This happens because the hydrogen ions from the acid react with hydroxide ions from the base to form water. Water, the product, is a molecular compound. The other ions remain in the solution, which is an aqueous solution of a **salt** (an ionic compound whose cation comes from a base and whose anion comes from an acid). If the water were evaporated, the solid salt would remain. In the case of HCl plus NaOH, the salt is sodium chloride (NaCl).

ThomsonNOW™ Go to the Chemistry Interactive menu for a video of an acid-base reaction in the presence and in the absence of an indicator: **detecting acid-base reactions.**

$$\underset{\text{acid}}{HCl(aq)} + \underset{\text{base}}{NaOH(aq)} \longrightarrow \underset{\text{water}}{H\,OH(\ell)} + \underset{\text{salt}}{Na\,Cl(aq)}$$

The overall neutralization reaction can be written more generally as

$$\underset{\text{acid}}{HX(aq)} + \underset{\text{base}}{MOH(aq)} \longrightarrow \underset{\text{water}}{H\,OH(\ell)} + \underset{\text{salt}}{M\,X(aq)}$$

You should recognize this as an exchange reaction in which the $H^+(aq)$ ions from the aqueous acid and the $M^+(aq)$ ions from the metal hydroxide are exchange partners, as are the X^- and OH^- ions.

The salt that forms depends on the acid and base that react. Magnesium chloride, another salt, is formed when a commercial antacid containing magnesium hydroxide is swallowed to neutralize excess hydrochloric acid in the stomach.

$$\underset{\text{hydrochloric acid}}{2\,HCl(aq)} + \underset{\text{magnesium hydroxide}}{Mg(OH)_2(s)} \longrightarrow 2\,H_2O(\ell) + \underset{\text{magnesium chloride}}{MgCl_2(aq)}$$

Milk of magnesia consists of a suspension of finely divided particles of $Mg(OH)_2(s)$ in water.

Organic acids, such as acetic acid and propionic acid, which contain the acid functional group $-COOH$, also neutralize bases to form salts. The H in the $-COOH$ functional group is the acidic proton. Its removal generates the $-COO^-$ anion. The reaction of propionic acid, CH_3CH_2COOH, and sodium hydroxide produces the salt sodium propionate, $NaCH_3CH_2COO$, containing sodium ions (Na^+) and propionate ions ($CH_3CH_2COO^-$). Sodium propionate is commonly used as a food preservative.

$$\underset{\text{propionic acid}}{CH_3CH_2COOH(aq)} + NaOH(aq) \longrightarrow H_2O(\ell) + \underset{\text{sodium propionate}}{NaCH_3CH_2COO(aq)}$$

Although the propionic acid molecule contains a number of H atoms, it is only the H atom that is part of the acid functional group ($-COOH$) that is involved in this neutralization reaction.

Note that this reaction is analogous to the general reaction shown above on this page.

PROBLEM-SOLVING EXAMPLE 5.5 Balancing Neutralization Equations

Write a balanced chemical equation for the reaction of nitric acid, HNO_3, with calcium hydroxide, $Ca(OH)_2$, in aqueous solution.

Answer $2\,HNO_3(aq) + Ca(OH)_2(aq) \longrightarrow Ca(NO_3)_2(aq) + H_2O\,(\ell)$

Strategy and Explanation This is a neutralization reaction between an acid and a base, so the products are a salt and water. We begin by writing the unbalanced equation with all the substances.

$$\text{(unbalanced equation)}\quad HNO_3(aq) + Ca(OH)_2(aq) \longrightarrow Ca(NO_3)_2(aq) + H_2O\,(\ell)$$

It is generally a good idea to start with the ions and balance the hydrogen and oxygen atoms later. The calcium ions are in balance, but we need to add a coefficient of 2 to the nitric acid since two nitrate ions appear in the products.

(unbalanced equation) $2\ HNO_3(aq) + Ca(OH)_2(aq) \longrightarrow Ca(NO_3)_2(aq) + H_2O(\ell)$

All the coefficients are correct except for water. We count four hydrogen atoms in the reactants (two from nitric acid and two from calcium hydroxide), so we must put a coefficient of 2 in front of the water to balance the equation.

(balanced equation) $2\ HNO_3(aq) + Ca(OH)_2(aq) \longrightarrow Ca(NO_3)_2(aq) + 2\ H_2O(\ell)$

As a check, we note that there are eight oxygen atoms in the reactants (six from nitric acid and two from calcium hydroxide) and there are eight oxygen atoms in the products (six from calcium nitrate and two from water).

PROBLEM-SOLVING PRACTICE 5.5

Write a balanced equation for the reaction of phosphoric acid, H_3PO_4, with sodium hydroxide, NaOH.

PROBLEM-SOLVING EXAMPLE 5.6 Acids, Bases, and Salts

Identify the acid and base used to form each of these salts: (a) $CaSO_4$, (b) $Mg(ClO_4)_2$. Write balanced equations for the formation of these compounds.

Answer (a) Calcium hydroxide, $Ca(OH)_2$, and sulfuric acid, H_2SO_4. (b) Magnesium hydroxide, $Mg(OH)_2$, and perchloric acid, $HClO_4$.

Strategy and Explanation A salt is formed from the cation of a base and the anion of an acid. (a) $CaSO_4$ contains calcium and sulfate ions. Ca^{2+} ions come from $Ca(OH)_2$, calcium hydroxide, and SO_4^{2-} ions come from H_2SO_4, sulfuric acid. The neutralization reaction between $Ca(OH)_2$ and H_2SO_4 produces $CaSO_4$ and water.

$$Ca(OH)_2(aq) + H_2SO_4(aq) \longrightarrow CaSO_4(s) + 2\ H_2O(\ell)$$

(b) Magnesium perchlorate contains magnesium and perchlorate ions, Mg^{2+} and ClO_4^-. Mg^{2+} ions could be derived from $Mg(OH)_2$, magnesium hydroxide, and ClO_4^- ions could be derived from $HClO_4$, perchloric acid. The neutralization reaction between $Mg(OH)_2$ and $HClO_4$ produces $Mg(ClO_4)_2$ and water.

$$Mg(OH)_2(aq) + 2\ HClO_4(aq) \longrightarrow Mg(ClO_4)_2(aq) + 2\ H_2O(\ell)$$

PROBLEM-SOLVING PRACTICE 5.6

Identify the acid and the base that can react to form (a) $MgSO_4$ and (b) $SrCO_3$.

Net Ionic Equations for Acid-Base Reactions

Net ionic equations can be written for acid-base reactions as well as for precipitation reactions. This should not be surprising because precipitation and acid-base neutralization reactions are both exchange reactions.

Consider the reaction given earlier of magnesium hydroxide with hydrochloric acid to relieve excess stomach acid (HCl). The overall balanced equation is

$$2\ HCl(aq) + Mg(OH)_2(s) \longrightarrow 2\ H_2O(\ell) + MgCl_2(aq)$$

The acid and base furnish hydrogen ions and hydroxide ions, respectively.

$$2\ HCl(aq) \longrightarrow 2\ H^+(aq) + 2\ Cl^-(aq)$$

$$Mg(OH)_2(s) \rightleftharpoons Mg^{2+}(aq) + 2\ OH^-(aq)$$

Although magnesium hydroxide is not very soluble, the little that dissolves is completely dissociated.

Note that we retain the coefficients from the balanced overall equation (first step).

We now use this information to write a complete ionic equation. We use Table 5.1 to check the solubility of the product salt, $MgCl_2$. Magnesium chloride is soluble, so the Mg^{2+} and Cl^- ions remain in solution. The complete ionic equation is

$$Mg^{2+}(aq) + 2\,OH^-(aq) + 2\,H^+(aq) + 2\,Cl^-(aq) \longrightarrow Mg^{2+}(aq) + 2\,Cl^-(aq) + 2\,H_2O(\ell)$$

Canceling spectator ions from each side of the complete ionic equation yields the net ionic equation. In this case, magnesium ions and chloride ions are the spectator ions. Canceling them leaves us with this net ionic equation:

$$2\,H^+(aq) + 2\,OH^-(aq) \longrightarrow 2\,H_2O(\ell)$$

or simply

$$H^+(aq) + OH^-(aq) \longrightarrow H_2O(\ell)$$

This is the net ionic equation for the neutralization reaction between a strong acid and a strong base that yields a soluble salt. Note that, as always, there is *conservation of charge* in the net ionic equation. On the left, (1+) + (1−) = 0; on the right, water has zero net charge.

Next, consider a neutralization reaction between a weak acid, HCN, and a strong base, KOH.

$$HCN(aq) + KOH(aq) \longrightarrow KCN(aq) + H_2O(\ell)$$

The weak acid HCN is not completely ionized, so we leave it in the molecular form, but KOH and KCN are strong electrolytes. The complete ionic equation is

$$HCN(aq) + K^+(aq) + OH^-(aq) \longrightarrow K^+(aq) + CN^-(aq) + H_2O(\ell)$$

Canceling spectator ions yields

$$HCN(aq) + OH^-(aq) \longrightarrow CN^-(aq) + H_2O(\ell)$$

The net ionic equation for the neutralization of a weak acid with a calcium base contains the molecular form of the acid and the anion of the salt. The net ionic equation shows that charge is conserved.

PROBLEM-SOLVING EXAMPLE 5.7 Neutralization Reaction with a Weak Acid

Write a balanced equation for the reaction of acetic acid, CH_3COOH, with calcium hydroxide, $Ca(OH)_2$. Then write the net ionic equation for this neutralization reaction.

Answer

Equation: $2\,CH_3COOH(aq) + Ca(OH)_2(aq) \longrightarrow Ca(CH_3COO)_2(aq) + 2\,H_2O\,(\ell)$

Net ionic equation: $CH_3COOH(aq) + OH^-(aq) \longrightarrow CH_3COO^-(aq) + H_2O\,(\ell)$

Strategy and Explanation We have been given the formula of an acid and a base that will react. The two products of the neutralization reaction are water and the salt calcium acetate, $Ca(CH_3COO)_2$, formed from the base's cation, Ca^{2+}, and the acid's anion, CH_3COO^-. Table 5.1 shows that $Ca(CH_3COO)_2$ is soluble.

We start by writing the four species involved in the reaction, not worrying for the moment about balancing the equation.

(unbalanced equation) $CH_3COOH(aq) + Ca(OH)_2(aq) \longrightarrow Ca(CH_3COO)_2(aq) + H_2O\,(\ell)$

To balance the equation, two hydrogen ions (H^+) from the acetic acid react with the two hydroxide ions (OH^-) of the calcium hydroxide. This also means that two water molecules will be produced by the reaction. We must put coefficients of 2 in front of the acetic acid and in front of water to balance the equation.

(balanced equation) $2\,CH_3COOH(aq) + Ca(OH)_2(aq) \longrightarrow Ca(CH_3COO)_2(aq) + 2\,H_2O\,(\ell)$

To write the net ionic equation, we must know whether the four substances involved in the reaction are strong or weak electrolytes. Acetic acid is a weak electrolyte (it is a weak acid). Calcium hydroxide is a strong electrolyte (strong base). Calcium acetate is a strong electrolyte (Table 5.1). Water is a molecular compound and a nonelectrolyte. We now write the complete ionic equation

$$2\ CH_3COOH(aq) + Ca^{2+}(aq) + 2\ OH^-(aq) \longrightarrow Ca^{2+}(aq) + 2\ CH_3COO^-(aq) + 2\ H_2O(\ell)$$

The calcium ions are spectator ions and are canceled to give the net ionic equation:

$$CH_3COOH(aq) + OH^-(aq) \longrightarrow CH_3COO^-(aq) + H_2O(\ell)$$

✓ **Reasonable Answer Check** Note that the spectator ions cancel and each side of the net ionic equation has the same charge (1−) and the same number and types of atoms.

PROBLEM-SOLVING PRACTICE 5.7

Write a balanced equation for the reaction of hydrocyanic acid, HCN, with calcium hydroxide, $Ca(OH)_2$. Then write the balanced complete ionic equation and the net ionic equation for this neutralization reaction.

EXERCISE 5.4 Neutralizations and Net Ionic Equations

Write balanced complete ionic equations and net ionic equations for the neutralization reactions of these acids and bases:

(a) HCl and KOH
(b) H_2SO_4 and $Ba(OH)_2$ (Remember that sulfuric acid can provide 2 mol $H^+(aq)$ per 1 mol sulfuric acid.)
(c) CH_3COOH and NaOH

EXERCISE 5.5 Net Ionic Equations and Antacids

The commercial antacids Maalox, Di-Gel tablets, and Mylanta contain aluminum hydroxide or magnesium hydroxide that reacts with excess hydrochloric acid in the stomach. Write the balanced complete ionic equation and net ionic equation for the soothing neutralization reaction of aluminum hydroxide with HCl. Assume that dissolved aluminum hydroxide is completely dissociated.

© Thomson Learning/Charles D. Winters

Figure 5.6 Reaction of calcium carbonate with an acid. A piece of coral that is largely calcium carbonate, $CaCO_3$, reacts readily with hydrochloric acid to give CO_2 gas and aqueous calcium chloride.

Gas-Forming Exchange Reactions

The formation of a gas is the third way that exchange reactions can occur, since formation of the gas removes the molecular product from the solution. Escape of the gas from the solution removes ions from the solution. Acids are involved in many gas-forming exchange reactions.

The reaction of a metal carbonate with an acid is an excellent example of a gas-forming exchange reaction (Figure 5.6).

$$CaCO_3(s) + 2\ HCl(aq) \longrightarrow CaCl_2(aq) + \cancel{H_2CO_3(aq)}$$

$$\cancel{H_2CO_3(aq)} \longrightarrow H_2O(\ell) + CO_2(g)$$

$$\text{Overall reaction: } CaCO_3(s) + 2\ HCl(aq) \longrightarrow CaCl_2(aq) + H_2O(\ell) + CO_2(g)$$

A salt and H_2CO_3 (carbonic acid) are always the products from an acid reacting with a metal carbonate, and their formation illustrates the exchange reaction pattern. Carbonic acid is unstable, however, and much of it is rapidly converted to water and CO_2 gas. If the reaction is done in an open container, most of the gas will bubble out of the solution.

Carbonates (which contain CO_3^{2-}) and hydrogen carbonates (which contain HCO_3^-) are basic because they react with protons (H^+ ions) in neutralization reactions. Carbon dioxide is always released when acids react with a metal carbonate or a metal hydrogen carbonate. For example, excess hydrochloric acid in the stomach is neutralized by ingesting commercial antacids such as Alka-Seltzer ($NaHCO_3$), Tums ($CaCO_3$), or Di-Gel liquid ($MgCO_3$). Taking an Alka-Seltzer or a Tums to relieve excess stomach acid produces these helpful reactions:

Alka-Seltzer: $NaHCO_3(aq) + HCl(aq) \longrightarrow NaCl(aq) + H_2O(\ell) + CO_2(g)$

Tums: $CaCO_3(aq) + 2\ HCl(aq) \longrightarrow CaCl_2(aq) + H_2O(\ell) + CO_2(g)$

The net ionic equations for these two reactions are

$$HCO_3^-(aq) + H^+(aq) \longrightarrow H_2O(\ell) + CO_2(g)$$

$$CO_3^{2-}(aq) + 2\ H^+(aq) \longrightarrow H_2O(\ell) + CO_2(g)$$

Acids also react by exchange reactions with metal sulfites or sulfides to produce foul-smelling gaseous SO_2 or H_2S, respectively. With sulfites, the initial product is sulfurous acid, which, like carbonic acid, quickly decomposes.

$$CaSO_3(aq) + 2\ HCl(aq) \longrightarrow CaCl_2(aq) + \cancel{H_2SO_3(aq)}$$

$$\cancel{H_2SO_3(aq)} \longrightarrow H_2O(\ell) + SO_2(g)$$

Overall reaction: $CaSO_3(aq) + 2\ HCl(aq) \longrightarrow CaCl_2(aq) + H_2O(\ell) + SO_2(g)$

With sulfides, the gaseous product H_2S is formed directly.

$$Na_2S(aq) + 2\ HCl(aq) \longrightarrow 2\ NaCl(aq) + H_2S(g)$$

This answers the question posed in Chapter 1 (p. 3), "Why do some antacids fizz when added to vinegar?"

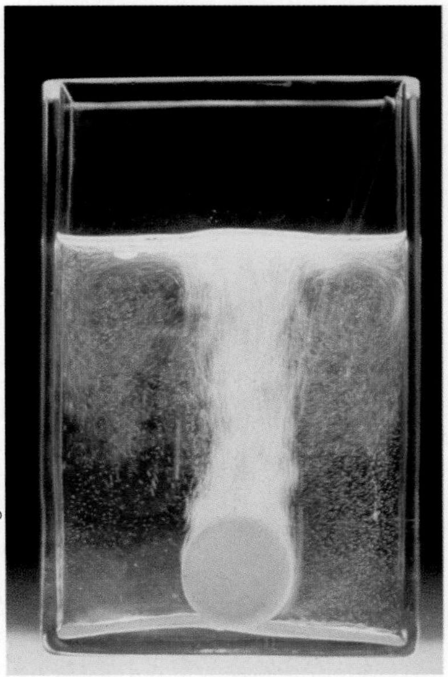

© Thomson Learning/Charles D. Winters

Antacid reacting with HCl.

EXERCISE 5.6 Gas-Forming Reactions

Predict the products and write the balanced overall equation and the net ionic equation for each of these gas-generating reactions.

(a) $Na_2CO_3(aq) + H_2SO_4(aq) \longrightarrow$

(b) $FeS(s) + HCl(aq) \longrightarrow$

(c) $K_2SO_3(aq) + HCl(aq) \longrightarrow$

CONCEPTUAL EXERCISE 5.7 Exchange Reaction Classification

Identify each of these exchange reactions as a precipitation reaction, an acid-base reaction, or a gas-forming reaction. Predict the products of each reaction and write an overall balanced equation and net ionic equation for the reaction.

(a) $NiCO_3(s) + H_2SO_4(aq) \longrightarrow$ (b) $Sr(OH)_2(s) + HNO_3(aq) \longrightarrow$

(c) $BaCl_2(aq) + Na_2C_2O_4(aq) \longrightarrow$ (d) $PbCO_3(s) + H_2SO_4(aq) \longrightarrow$

5.3 Oxidation-Reduction Reactions

Now we turn to oxidation-reduction reactions, which are classified by what happens with electrons at the nanoscale level as a result of the reaction.

The terms "oxidation" and "reduction" come from reactions that have been known for centuries. Ancient civilizations learned how to change metal oxides and sulfides to the metal—that is, how to *reduce* ore to the metal. For example, cassiterite or tin(IV) oxide, SnO_2, is a tin ore discovered in Britain centuries ago. It is very easily reduced to tin by heating with carbon. In this reaction, tin is reduced from tin(IV) in the ore to tin metal.

SnO_2 loses oxygen and is reduced.

$$SnO_2(s) + 2\,C(s) \longrightarrow Sn(s) + 2\,CO(g)$$

When SnO_2 is reduced by carbon, oxygen is removed from the tin and added to the carbon, which is "oxidized" by the addition of oxygen. In fact, any process in which oxygen is added to another substance is an oxidation.

When magnesium burns in air, the magnesium is oxidized to magnesium oxide, MgO.

Mg combines with oxygen and is oxidized.

$$2\,Mg(s) + O_2(g) \longrightarrow 2\,MgO(s)$$

The experimental observations we have just outlined point to several fundamental conclusions:

- If one substance is oxidized, another substance in the same reaction must simultaneously be reduced. For this reason, we refer to such reactions as **oxidation-reduction reactions,** or **redox reactions** for short.
- Oxidation is the reverse of reduction.

For example, the reactions we have just described show that addition of oxygen is oxidation and removal of oxygen is reduction. But oxidation and reduction are more than that, as we see next.

ThomsonNOW™
Go to the Chemistry Interactive menu to work a module on **redox reactions: Mg and HCl.**

Redox Reactions and Electron Transfer

Oxidation and reduction reactions involve transfer of electrons from one reactant to another. When a substance *accepts electrons*, it is said to be **reduced.** The language is descriptive because in a **reduction** there is a decrease (reduction) in the real or apparent electric charge on an atom. For example, in this net ionic equation, Ag^+ ions are reduced to uncharged Ag atoms by accepting electrons from copper atoms (Figure 5.7).

Each Ag^+ accepts an electron and is reduced to Ag. ($+2e^-$)

$$2\,Ag^+(aq) + Cu(s) \longrightarrow 2\,Ag(s) + Cu^{2+}(aq)$$

($-2e^-$) Each Cu donates two electrons and is oxidized to Cu^{2+}.

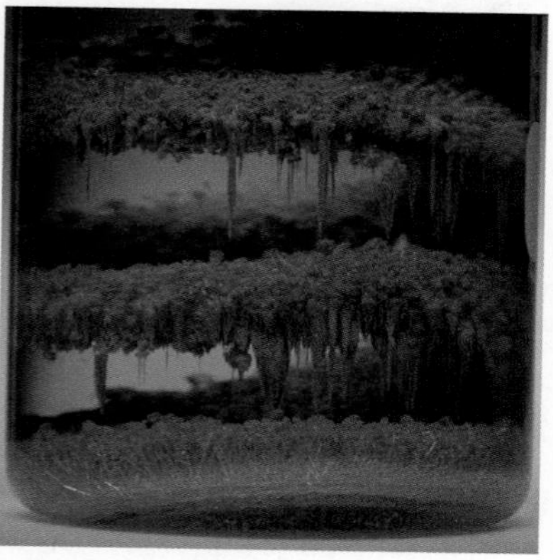

© Thomson Learning/Charles D. Winters

Figure 5.7 Oxidation of copper metal by silver ion. A spiral of copper wire was immersed in an aqueous solution of silver nitrate, $AgNO_3$. With time, the copper reduces Ag^+ ions to silver metal crystals, and the copper metal is oxidized to Cu^{2+} ions. The blue color of the solution is due to the presence of aqueous copper(II) ion.

When a substance *loses electrons*, it is said to be **oxidized.** In **oxidation,** the real or apparent electrical charge on an atom of the substance increases when it gives up electrons. In our example, a copper metal atom releases two electrons forming Cu^{2+}; its electric charge has increased from zero to 2+, and it is said to have been oxidized. For this to happen, something must be available to take the electrons donated by the copper. In this case, Ag^+ is the electron acceptor. ***In every oxidation-reduction reaction, a reactant is reduced and a reactant is oxidized.***

In the reaction of magnesium with oxygen (Figure 5.8), oxygen gains electrons when converted to the oxide ion. The charge of each O atom changes from 0 to 2− as it is reduced.

Mg loses $2e^-$ per atom. Mg is oxidized.

$$2\,Mg(s) + O_2(g) \longrightarrow 2\,[Mg^{2+} + O^{2-}]$$

O_2 gains $4e^-$ per molecule, 2 for each O. O_2 is reduced.

Oxidation is the loss of electrons.

$$X \rightarrow X^+ + e^-$$

X loses one or more electrons and is oxidized.

Reduction is the gain of electrons.

$$Y + e^- \rightarrow Y^-$$

Y gains one or more electrons and is reduced.

Each magnesium atom changes from 0 to 2+ as it is oxidized. All redox reactions can be analyzed in a similar manner.

Common Oxidizing and Reducing Agents

As stated above, in every redox reaction, a reactant is oxidized and a reactant is reduced. The species causing the oxidation (electron loss) is the **oxidizing agent,** and the species causing the reduction (electron gain) is the **reducing agent.** As a redox reaction proceeds, *the oxidizing agent is reduced and the reducing agent is oxidized.* In the reaction just described between Mg and O_2, Mg is oxidized, and it is the reducing agent; O_2 is reduced, and it is the oxidizing agent. Note that the oxidizing agent and the reducing agent are always reactants, not products. Figure 5.9 provides some guidelines to determine which species involved in a redox reaction is the oxidizing agent and which is the reducing agent.

Like oxygen, the halogens (F_2, Cl_2, Br_2, and I_2) are always oxidizing agents in their reactions with metals and most nonmetals. For example, consider the combination reaction of sodium metal with chlorine:

Na loses $1e^-$ per atom.
Na is oxidized and is the reducing agent.

$$2\ Na(s) + Cl_2(g) \longrightarrow 2\ [Na^+ + Cl^-]$$

Cl_2 gains $2e^-$ per molecule.
Cl_2 is reduced and is the oxidizing agent.

Here sodium begins as the metallic element, but it ends up as the Na^+ ion after combining with chlorine. Thus, sodium is oxidized (loses electrons) and is the reducing agent. Chlorine ends up as Cl^-; Cl_2 has been reduced (gains electrons) and therefore is the oxidizing agent. The general reaction for halogen, X_2, reduction is

$$\text{Reduction reaction:} \quad \underset{\text{oxidizing agent}}{X_2} + 2e^- \longrightarrow 2\ X^-$$

That is, a halogen will always oxidize a metal to give a metal halide, and the formula of the product can be predicted from the charge on the metal ion and the charge of the halide. The halogens in decreasing order of oxidizing ability are as follows:

Oxidizing Agent	Usual Reduction Product
F_2 (strongest)	F^-
Cl_2	Cl^-
Br_2	Br^-
I_2 (weakest)	I^-

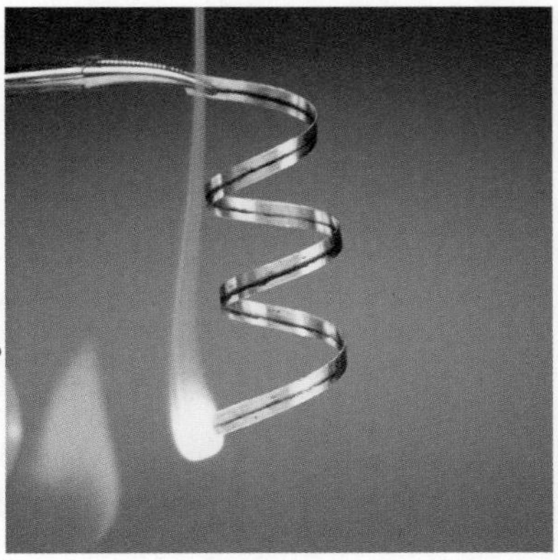

© Thomson Learning/Charles D. Winters

Figure 5.8 **$Mg(s) + O_2(g)$.** A piece of magnesium ribbon burns in air, oxidizing the metal to the white solid magnesium oxide, MgO.

A useful memory aid for keeping the oxidation and reduction definitions straight is **OIL RIG (Oxidation Is Loss; Reduction Is Gain).**

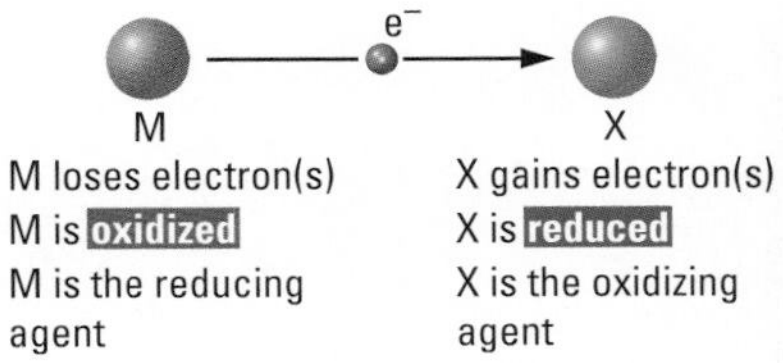

Figure 5.9 **Oxidation-reduction relationships and electron transfer.**

Note that the oxidizing agent is reduced, and the reducing agent is oxidized.

ThomsonNOW™
Go to the Coached Problems menu for an exercise on **redox reactions.**

EXERCISE 5.8 Oxidizing and Reducing Agents

Identify which species is losing electrons and which is gaining electrons, which is oxidized and which is reduced, and which is the oxidizing agent and which is the reducing agent in this reaction:

$$2\ Ca(s) + O_2(g) \longrightarrow 2\ CaO(s)$$

EXERCISE 5.9 Redox Reactions

Write the chemical equation for chlorine gas undergoing a redox reaction with calcium metal. Which species is the oxidizing agent?

Chlorine is widely used as an oxidizing agent in water and sewage treatment. A common contaminant of water is hydrogen sulfide, H_2S, which gives a thoroughly unpleasant "rotten egg" odor to the water and may come from the decay of organic matter or from underground mineral deposits. Chlorine oxidizes H_2S to insoluble elemental sulfur, which is easily removed.

$$8\ Cl_2(g) + 8\ H_2S(aq) \longrightarrow S_8(s) + 16\ HCl(aq)$$

Oxidation and reduction occur readily when a strong oxidizing agent comes into contact with a strong reducing agent. Knowing the easily recognized oxidizing and reducing agents enables you to predict that a reaction will take place when they are combined and in some cases to predict what the products will be. Table 5.3 and the following points provide some guidelines.

- An element that has combined with oxygen has been oxidized. In the process each oxygen atom in oxygen (O_2) gains two electrons and becomes the oxide ion, O^{2-} (as in a metal oxide). Oxygen can also be combined in a molecule such as CO_2 or H_2O (as occurs in the combustion reaction of a hydrocarbon). Therefore, oxygen has been reduced. Since it has accepted electrons, oxygen is the oxidizing agent in such cases.
- An element that has combined with a halogen has been oxidized. In the process the halogen, X_2, is changed to halide ions, X^-, by adding an electron to each halogen atom. Therefore, the halogen atom has been reduced to the halide ion, and the halogen is the oxidizing agent. A halogen can also be combined in a molecule such as HCl. Among the halogens, fluorine and chlorine are particularly strong oxidizing agents.

Table 5.3 Common Oxidizing and Reducing Agents

Oxidizing Agent	Reaction Product	Reducing Agent	Reaction Product
O_2 (oxygen)	O^{2-} (oxide ion) or an oxygen-containing molecular compound	H_2 (hydrogen) or hydrogen-containing molecular compound	H^+ (hydrogen ion) or H combined in H_2O
H_2O_2 (hydrogen peroxide)	$H_2O(\ell)$	C (carbon) used to reduce metal oxides	CO and CO_2
F_2, Cl_2, Br_2, or I_2 (halogens)	F^-, Cl^-, Br^-, or I^- (halide ions)	M, metals such as Na, K, Fe, or Al	M^{n+}, metal ions such as Na^+, K^+, Fe^{3+}, or Al^{3+}
HNO_3 (nitric acid)	Nitrogen oxides such as NO and NO_2		
$Cr_2O_7^{2-}$ (dichromate ion)	Cr^{3+} (chromium(III) ion), in acid solution		
MnO_4^- (permanganate ion)	Mn^{2+} (manganese(II) ion), in acid solution		

- When an elemental metal combines with something to form a compound, the metal has been oxidized. In the process, it has lost electrons, usually to form a positive ion.

$$\text{Oxidation reaction:} \quad \underset{\text{reducing agent}}{M} \longrightarrow M^{n+} + ne^-$$

Therefore, the metal (an electron donor) has been oxidized and has functioned as a reducing agent. Most metals are reasonably good reducing agents, and metals such as sodium, magnesium, and aluminum from Groups 1A, 2A, and 3A are particularly good ones.

- Other common oxidizing and reducing agents are listed in Table 5.3, and some are described below. When one of these agents takes part in a reaction, it is reasonably certain that it is a redox reaction. (Nitric acid can be an exception. In addition to being a good oxidizing agent, it is an acid and functions only as an acid in reactions such as the decomposition of a metal carbonate, a non-redox reaction.)

There are exceptions to the guideline that metals are always positively charged in compounds. However, you probably will not encounter these exceptions in introductory chemistry.

Figure 5.10 illustrates the action of concentrated nitric acid, HNO_3, as an oxidizing agent. Nitric acid oxidizes copper metal to give copper(II) nitrate, and copper metal reduces nitric acid to the brown gas NO_2. The net ionic equation is

$$\underset{\text{reducing agent}}{Cu(s)} + 4\,H^+(aq) + \underset{\text{oxidizing agent}}{2\,NO_3^-(aq)} \longrightarrow Cu^{2+}(aq) + 2\,NO_2(g) + 2\,H_2O(\ell)$$

Figure 5.10 $Cu(s) + HNO_3(aq)$. Copper reacts vigorously with concentrated nitric acid to give brown NO_2 gas.

The metal is the reducing agent, since it is the substance oxidized. In fact, the most common reducing agents are metals. Some metal ions such as Fe^{2+} can also be reducing agents because they can be oxidized to ions of higher charge. Aqueous Fe^{2+} ion reacts readily with the strong oxidizing agent MnO_4^-, the permanganate ion. The Fe^{2+} ion is oxidized to Fe^{3+}, and the MnO_4^- ion is reduced to the Mn^{2+} ion.

$$5\,Fe^{2+}(aq) + MnO_4^-(aq) + 8\,H^+(aq) \longrightarrow 5\,Fe^{3+}(aq) + Mn^{2+}(aq) + 4\,H_2O(\ell)$$

Carbon can reduce many metal oxides to metals, and it is widely used in the metals industry to obtain metals from their compounds in ores. For example, titanium is produced by treating a mineral containing titanium(IV) oxide with carbon and chlorine.

$$TiO_2(s) + C(s) + 2\,Cl_2(g) \longrightarrow TiCl_4(\ell) + CO_2(g)$$

In effect, the carbon reduces the metal oxide to titanium metal, and the chlorine then oxidizes it to titanium(IV) chloride. Because $TiCl_4$ is easily converted to a gas, it can be removed from the reaction mixture and purified. The $TiCl_4$ is then reduced with another metal, such as magnesium, to give titanium metal.

$$TiCl_4(\ell) + 2\,Mg(s) \longrightarrow Ti(s) + 2\,MgCl_2(s)$$

Finally, H_2 gas is a common reducing agent, widely used in the laboratory and in industry. For example, it readily reduces copper(II) oxide to copper metal (Figure 5.11).

$$\underset{\text{reducing agent}}{H_2(g)} + \underset{\text{oxidizing agent}}{CuO(s)} \longrightarrow Cu(s) + H_2O(g)$$

It is important to be aware that it can be dangerous to mix a strong oxidizing agent with a strong reducing agent. A violent reaction, even an explosion, may take place. Chemicals are no longer stored on laboratory shelves in alphabetical order,

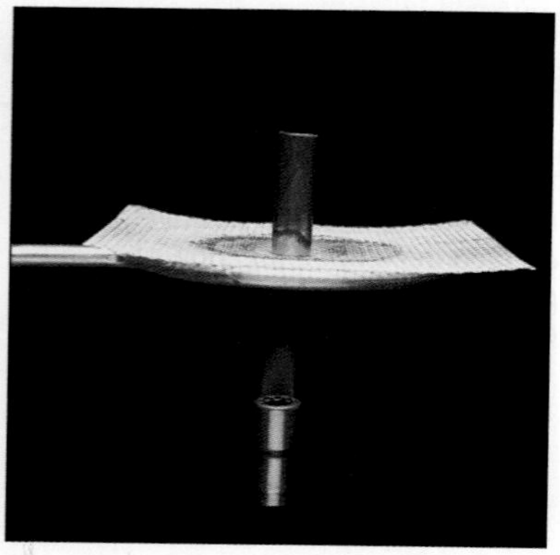

(a)

(b)

© Thomson Learning/Charles D. Winters

Figure 5.11 Reduction of copper oxide with hydrogen. (a) A piece of copper has been heated in air to form a film of black copper(II) oxide on the surface. (b) When the hot copper metal, with its film of CuO, is placed in a stream of hydrogen gas (from the blue and yellow tank at the rear), the oxide is reduced to copper metal, and water forms as the by-product.

How electrons participate in bonding atoms in molecules is the subject of Chapter 8.

because such an ordering may place a strong oxidizing agent next to a strong reducing agent. In particular, swimming pool chemicals that contain chlorine and are strong oxidizing agents should not be stored in the hardware store or the garage next to easily oxidized materials such as ammonia.

EXERCISE 5.10 Oxidation-Reduction Reactions

Decide which of these reactions are oxidation-reduction reactions. In each case explain your choice and identify the oxidizing and reducing agents in the redox reactions.

(a) $NaOH(aq) + HNO_3(aq) \longrightarrow NaNO_3(aq) + H_2O(\ell)$

(b) $4\ Cr(s) + 3\ O_2(g) \longrightarrow 2\ Cr_2O_3(s)$

(c) $NiCO_3(s) + 2\ HCl(aq) \longrightarrow NiCl_2(aq) + H_2O(\ell) + CO_2(g)$

(d) $Cu(s) + Cl_2(g) \longrightarrow CuCl_2(s)$

5.4 Oxidation Numbers and Redox Reactions

An arbitrary bookkeeping system has been devised for keeping track of electrons in redox reactions. It extends the obvious oxidation and reduction case when neutral atoms become ions to reactions in which the changes are less obvious. The system is set up so that ***oxidation numbers always change in redox reactions.*** As a result, oxidation and reduction can be determined in the ways shown in Table 5.4.

An **oxidation number** compares the charge of an uncombined atom with its actual charge or its relative charge in a compound. All neutral atoms have an equal number of protons and electrons and thus have no net charge. When sodium metal atoms (zero net charge) combine with chlorine atoms (zero net charge) to form sodium chloride, each sodium atom loses an electron to form a sodium ion, Na^+, and each chlorine atom gains an electron to form a chloride ion, Cl^-. Therefore, Na^+ has an oxidation number of $+1$ because it has one fewer electron than a sodium atom, and Cl^- has an oxidation number of -1 because it has one more electron than a chlorine atom. Oxidation numbers of atoms in molecular compounds are assigned as though electrons were completely transferred to form ions. In the molecular compound phosphorus trichloride (PCl_3), for example, chlorine is assigned an oxidation number of -1 even though it is not a Cl^- ion; the chlorine is directly bonded to the phosphorus. The chlorine atoms in PCl_3 are thought of as "possessing" more electrons than they have in Cl_2.

Table 5.4 Recognizing Oxidation-Reduction Reactions

	Oxidation	Reduction
In terms of oxygen	Gain of oxygen	Loss of oxygen
In terms of halogen	Gain of halogen	Loss of halogen
In terms of hydrogen	Loss of hydrogen	Gain of hydrogen
In terms of electrons	Loss of electrons	Gain of electrons
In terms of oxidation numbers	Increase of oxidation number	Decrease of oxidation number

You can use this set of rules to determine oxidation numbers.

Oxidation numbers are also called oxidation states.

Rule 1: ***The oxidation number of an atom of a pure element is 0.*** When the atoms are not combined with those of any other element (for example, oxygen in O_2, sulfur in S_8, iron in metallic Fe, or chlorine in Cl_2), the oxidation number is 0.

Rule 2: ***The oxidation number of a monatomic ion equals its charge.*** Thus, the oxidation number of Cu^{2+} is +2; that of S^{2-} is −2.

In this book, oxidation numbers are written as +1, +2, etc., whereas charges on ions are written as 1+, 2+, etc.

Rule 3: ***Some elements have the same oxidation number in almost all their compounds and can be used as references for oxidation numbers of other elements in compounds.***

(a) Hydrogen has an oxidation number of +1 unless it is combined with a metal, in which case its oxidation number is −1.

(b) Fluorine has an oxidation number of −1 in all its compounds. Halogens other than fluorine have an oxidation number of −1 except when combined with a halogen above them in the periodic table or with oxygen.

(c) Oxygen has an oxidation number of −2 except in peroxides, such as hydrogen peroxide, H_2O_2, in which oxygen has an oxidation number of −1 (and hydrogen is +1).

(d) In binary compounds (compounds of two elements), atoms of Group 6A elements (O, S, Se, Te) have an oxidation number of −2 except when combined with oxygen or halogens, in which case the Group 6A elements have positive oxidation numbers.

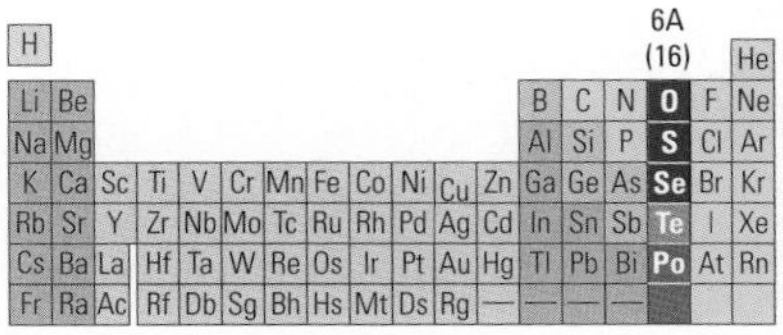

Rule 4: ***The sum of the oxidation numbers in a neutral compound is 0; the sum of the oxidation numbers in a polyatomic ion equals the charge on the ion.*** For example, in SO_2, the oxidation number of oxygen is −2, and with two O atoms, the total for oxygen is −4. Because the sum of the oxidation numbers must equal zero, the oxidation number of sulfur must be +4: $(+4) + 2(-2) = 0$. In the sulfite ion, SO_3^{2-}, the net charge is 2−. Because each oxygen is −2, the oxidation number of sulfur in sulfite must be +4: $(+4) + 3(-2) = 2-$.

ThomsonNOW™
Go to the Coached Problems menu for a tutorial on **assigning oxidation numbers.**

$$\overset{+4}{S}\overset{-2}{O}{}_3^{2-}$$

Now, let's apply these rules to the equations for simple combination and displacement reactions involving sulfur and oxygen.

$$\text{Combination:}\quad \overset{0}{S_8}(s) + 8\,\overset{0}{O_2}(g) \longrightarrow 8\,\overset{+4}{S}\overset{-2}{O_2}(g)$$

$$\text{Combination:}\quad \overset{+2}{Zn}\overset{-2}{S}(s) + 2\,\overset{0}{O_2}(aq) \longrightarrow \overset{+2}{Zn}\overset{+6}{S}\overset{-2}{O_4}(aq)$$

$$\text{Displacement:}\quad \overset{+1}{Cu_2}\overset{-2}{S}(s) + \overset{0}{O_2}(g) \longrightarrow 2\,\overset{0}{Cu}(s) + \overset{+4}{S}\overset{-2}{O_2}(g)$$

These are all oxidation-reduction reactions, as shown by the fact that there has been a change in the oxidation numbers of atoms from reactants to products.

Every reaction in which an element becomes combined in a compound is a redox reaction. The oxidation number of the element must increase or decrease from its original value of zero. Combination reactions and displacement reactions in which one element displaces another are all redox reactions.

Those decomposition reactions in which elemental gases are produced are also redox reactions. Millions of tons of ammonium nitrate, NH_4NO_3, are used as fertilizer to supply nitrogen to crops. Ammonium nitrate is also used as an explosive that is decomposed by heating.

Ammonium nitrate was used in the 1995 bombing of the Federal Building in Oklahoma City, Oklahoma.

$$2\,NH_4NO_3(s) \longrightarrow 2\,N_2(g) + 4\,H_2O(g) + O_2(g)$$

Like a number of other explosives, ammonium nitrate contains an element with two different oxidation numbers, in effect having an oxidizing and reducing agent in the same compound.

$$\overset{-3\ +1}{NH_4^+} \qquad \overset{+5\ -2}{NO_3^-}$$

Note that nitrogen's oxidation number is −3 in the ammonium ion and +5 in the nitrate ion. Therefore, in the decomposition of ammonium nitrate to N_2, the N in the ammonium ion is oxidized from −3 to 0, and the ammonium ion is the reducing agent. The N in the nitrate ion is reduced from +5 to 0, and the nitrate ion is the oxidizing agent.

PROBLEM-SOLVING EXAMPLE 5.8 Applying Oxidation Numbers

Metallic copper and dilute nitric acid react according to this redox equation:

$$3\ Cu(s) + 8\ HNO_3(aq) \longrightarrow 3\ Cu(NO_3)_2(aq) + 2\ NO(g) + 4\ H_2O\ (\ell)$$

Assign oxidation numbers for each atom in the equation. Identify which element has been oxidized and which has been reduced.

Answer

$$3\ \overset{0}{Cu}(s) + 8\ \overset{+1+5-2}{HNO_3}(aq) \longrightarrow 3\ \overset{+2+5-2}{Cu(NO_3)_2}(aq) + 2\ \overset{+2-2}{NO}(g) + 4\ \overset{+1-2}{H_2O}\ (\ell)$$

Copper metal is oxidized. Nitrogen (in HNO_3) is reduced.

Strategy and Explanation Use the four rules introduced earlier and knowledge of the formulas of polyatomic ions to assign oxidation numbers. Copper is in its elemental state as a reactant, so its oxidation number is 0 (Rule 1).

For nitric acid we start by recognizing that it is a compound and has no net charge (Rule 4). Therefore, because the oxidation number of each oxygen is −2 (Rule 3c) for a total of −6 and the oxidation number of the hydrogen is +1 (Rule 3a), the oxidation number of nitrogen must be +5: $0 = 3(-2) + (+1) + (+5)$.

For the product combining copper and nitrate ions, we start by assigning the oxidation number of +2 to copper to balance the charges of the two nitrate ions. The oxidation numbers of the oxygen and nitrogen atoms within the nitrate anion are the same as in the reactant nitrate anions. For the NO molecules, we assign an oxidation number of −2 to oxygen (Rule 3c), so the oxidation number of the nitrogen in NO must be +2. The oxygen in water has oxidation number −2 and the hydrogen is +1.

Copper has changed from an oxidation number of 0 to an oxidation number of +2; it has been oxidized. Nitrogen has changed from an oxidation number of +5 to an oxidation number of +2; it has been reduced.

PROBLEM-SOLVING PRACTICE 5.8

Determine the oxidation number for each atom in this equation:

$$Sb_2S_3(s) + 3\ Fe(s) \longrightarrow 3\ FeS(s) + 2\ Sb(s)$$

Cite the oxidation number rule(s) you used to obtain your answers.

PROBLEM-SOLVING EXAMPLE 5.9 Oxidation-Reduction Reaction

Most metals we use are found in nature as cations in ores. The metal ion must be reduced to its elemental form, which is done with an appropriate oxidation-reduction reaction. The copper ore chalcocite (Cu_2S) is reacted with oxygen in a process called roasting to form metallic copper.

$$Cu_2S(s) + O_2(g) \longrightarrow 2\ Cu(s) + SO_2(g)$$

Identify the atoms that are oxidized and reduced, and name the oxidizing and reducing agents.

Answer Cu^+ ions and O_2 are reduced; S^{2-} ions are oxidized. O_2 is the oxidizing agent; Cu_2S is the reducing agent.

Strategy and Explanation We first assign the oxidation numbers for all the atoms in reaction according to Rules 1 through 4.

$$\overset{+1\,-2}{Cu_2S(s)} + \overset{0}{O_2(g)} \longrightarrow 2\,\overset{0}{Cu(s)} + \overset{+4\,-2}{SO_2(g)}$$

The oxidation number of Cu^+ decreases from +1 to 0, so Cu^+ is reduced. The oxidation number of S increases from −2 to +4, so S^{2-} is oxidized. The oxidation number of oxygen decreases from 0 to −2, so oxygen is reduced. The oxidizing agent is O_2, which accepts electrons. The reducing agent is S^{2-} in Cu_2S, which donates electrons.

PROBLEM-SOLVING PRACTICE 5.9

Which are the oxidizing and reducing agents, and which atoms are oxidized and reduced in this reaction?

$$PbO(s) + CO(g) \longrightarrow Pb(s) + CO_2(g)$$

CONCEPTUAL EXERCISE 5.11 Redox in CFC Disposal

This redox reaction is used for the disposal of chlorofluorocarbons (CFCs) by their reaction with sodium oxalate, $Na_2C_2O_4$:

$$CF_2Cl_2(g) + 2\,Na_2C_2O_4(s) \longrightarrow 2\,NaF(s) + 2\,NaCl(s) + C(s) + 4\,CO_2(g)$$

(a) What is oxidized in this reaction?
(b) What is reduced?

Exchange reactions of ionic compounds in aqueous solutions are not redox reactions because no change of oxidation numbers occurs. Consider, for example, the precipitation of barium sulfate when aqueous solutions of barium chloride and sulfuric acid are mixed.

$$Ba^{2+}(aq) + 2\,Cl^-(aq) + 2\,H^+(aq) + SO_4^{2-}(aq) \longrightarrow BaSO_4(s) + 2\,H^+(aq) + 2\,Cl^-(aq)$$

Net ionic equation: $\quad Ba^{2+}(aq) + SO_4^{2-}(aq) \longrightarrow BaSO_4(s)$

The oxidation numbers of all atoms remain unchanged from the reactants to products, so this is not a redox reaction.

5.5 Displacement Reactions, Redox, and the Activity Series

Recall that displacement reactions (⇐ *p. 130*) have this reaction pattern:

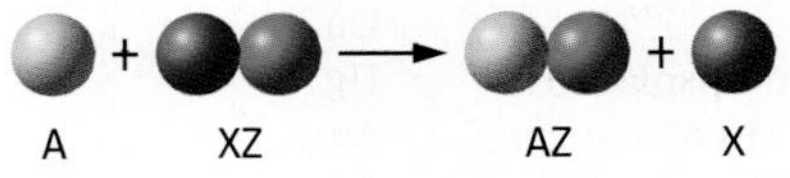

Displacement reactions, like combination reactions, are oxidation-reduction reactions. For example, in the reaction of hydrochloric acid with iron (Figure 5.12),

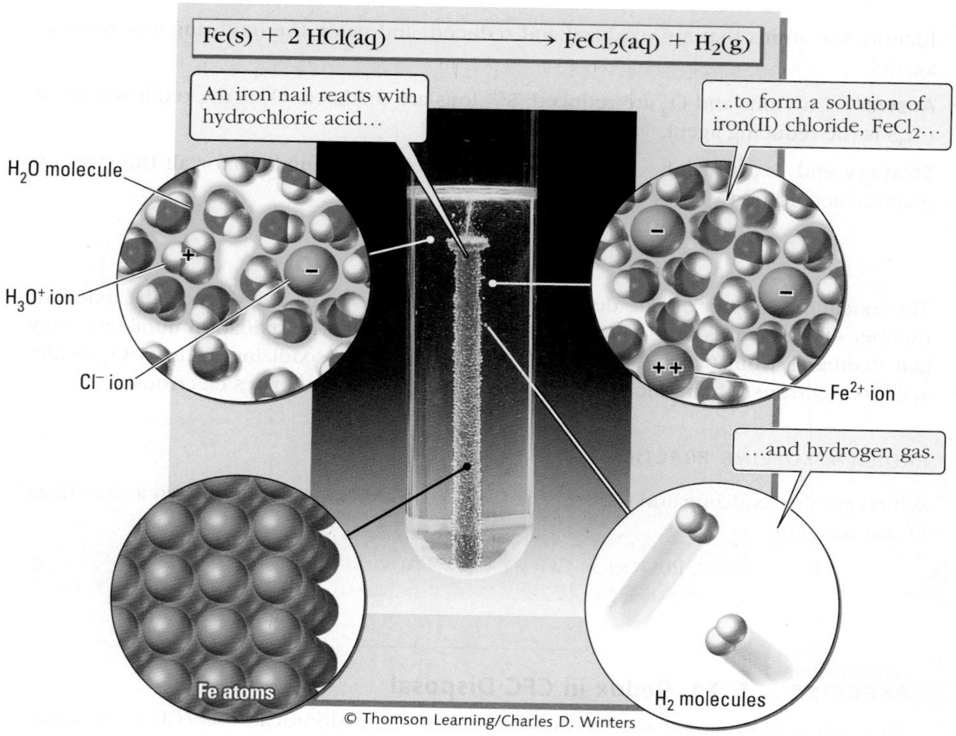

Figure 5.12 **Metal + acid displacement reaction.**

Table 5.5 Activity Series of Metals

Displace H_2 from $H_2O(\ell)$, steam, or acid	Li K Ba Sr Ca Na	↑ Ease of oxidation increases
Displace H_2 from steam, or acid	Mg Al Mn Zn Cr	
Displace H_2 from acid	Fe Ni Sn Pb	
	H_2	
Do not displace H_2 from $H_2O(\ell)$, steam, or acid	Sb Cu Hg Ag Pd Pt Au	

CHEMISTRY IN THE NEWS

The Breathalyzer

Police officers often need to determine whether a driver is DUI (driving under the influence) or DWI (driving while intoxicated) during a traffic stop. One type of breath alcohol testing device that was used involves this oxidation-reduction reaction:

$$3\ CH_3CH_2OH(g) + 2\ K_2Cr_2O_7(aq) + 8\ H_2SO_4(aq) \longrightarrow$$

ethyl alcohol — potassium dichromate — sulfuric acid

$$3\ CH_3COOH(aq) + 2\ Cr_2(SO_4)_3(aq) + 2\ K_2SO_4(aq) + 11\ H_2O(\ell)$$

acetic acid — chromium(III) sulfate

(Chromium is reduced from +6 to +3, and ethyl alcohol is oxidized to acetic acid.) The instrument contains two ampules, each containing potassium dichromate dissolved in sulfuric acid. One ampule is used as a reference and the other for the measurement. The measurement ampule is opened and the breath sample is added. The dichromate ion $Cr_2O_7^{2-}$ is yellow-orange in color, but the product of the reaction, Cr^{3+}, is green. If there is alcohol present in the breath sample, the color of the solution changes. The color of the reference is unchanged. The degree of color change can be measured by a simple visible light monitor, and the reading provides a direct measurement of the amount of alcohol present in the breath sample. This breath reading is converted to blood-alcohol concentration (BAC) using the assumption that 2100 mL of breath sample contains the same amount of alcohol as 1 mL blood. The final result is reported in units of %BAC on a scale from zero to 0.40%. The definition of DUI or DWI has varied from state to state but now is 0.08% BAC. A BAC reading of 0.08% means that the person has a blood-alcohol concentration of 0.080 g alcohol per 100 mL blood.

SOURCE: http://science.howstuffworks.com/breathalyzer.htm.

$$Fe(s) + 2\ HCl(aq) \longrightarrow FeCl_2(aq) + H_2(g)$$

metallic iron is the reducing agent; it is oxidized from an oxidation number of 0 in Fe(s) to +2 in $FeCl_2$. Hydrogen ions, H^+, in hydrochloric acid are reduced to hydrogen gas (H_2), in which hydrogen has an oxidation number of 0.

Extensive studies with many metals have led to the development of a **metal activity series,** a ranking of relative reactivity of metals in displacement and other kinds of reactions (Table 5.5). The most reactive metals appear at the top of the series, and activity decreases going down the series. Metals at the top are powerful reducing agents and readily lose electrons to form cations. The metals at the lower end of the series are poor reducing agents. However, their cations (Au^+, Ag^+) are powerful oxidizing agents that readily gain an electron to form the free metal.

An element higher in the activity series will displace an element below it in the series from its compounds. For example, zinc displaces copper ions from copper(II) sulfate solution, and copper metal displaces silver ions from silver nitrate solution (Figure 5.13).

$$Zn(s) + CuSO_4(aq) \longrightarrow ZnSO_4(aq) + Cu(s)$$

$$Cu(s) + 2\ AgNO_3(aq) \longrightarrow Cu(NO_3)_2(aq) + 2\ Ag(s)$$

In each case, the elemental metal (Zn, Cu) is the reducing agent and is oxidized; Cu^{2+} ions and Ag^+ ions are oxidizing agents and are reduced to Cu(s) and Ag(s), respectively.

Metals above hydrogen in the series react with acids whose anions are not oxidizing agents, such as hydrochloric acid, to form hydrogen (H_2) and the metal salt containing the cation of the metal and the anion of the acid. For example, $FeCl_2$ is formed from iron and hydrochloric acid, and $ZnBr_2$ is formed from zinc and hydrobromic acid.

$$Fe(s) + 2\ HCl(aq) \longrightarrow FeCl_2(aq) + H_2(g)$$

$$Zn(s) + 2\ HBr(aq) \longrightarrow ZnBr_2(aq) + H_2(g)$$

Metals below hydrogen in the activity series do not displace hydrogen from acids in this way.

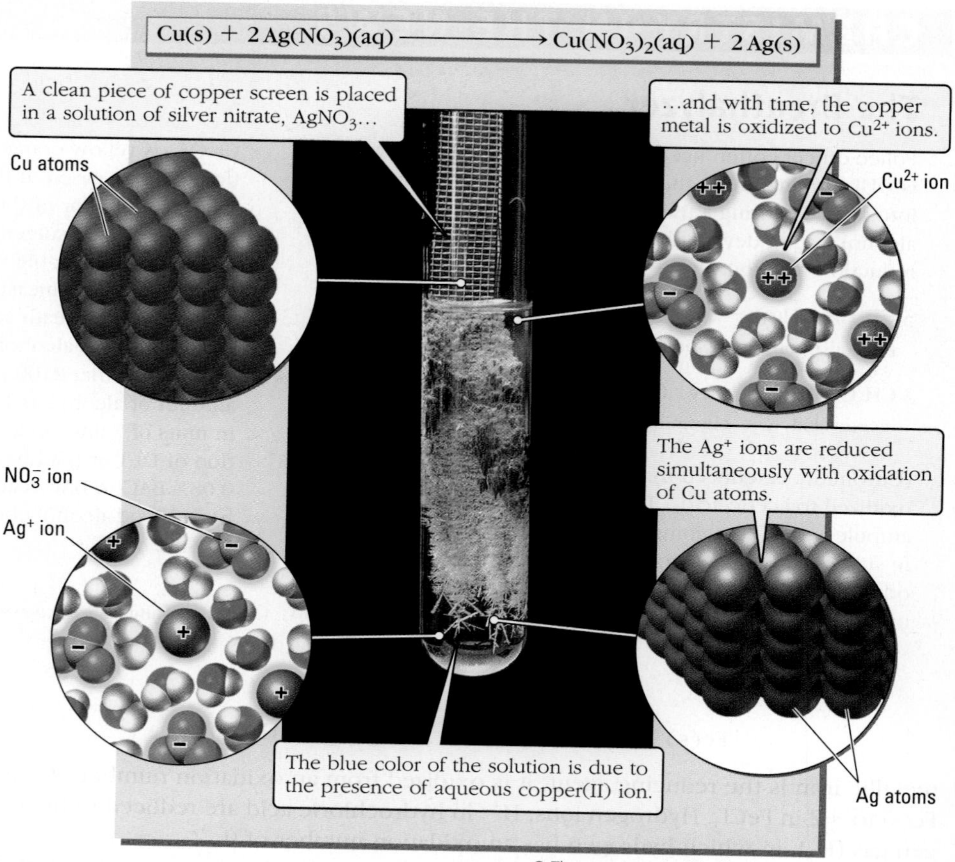

© Thomson Learning/Charles D. Winters

Active Figure 5.13 **Metal + aqueous metal salt displacement reaction.** The oxidation of copper metal by silver ion. (Atoms or ions that take part in the reaction have been highlighted in the nanoscale pictures.) **Go to the Active Figures menu at ThomsonNOW to test your understanding of the concepts in this figure.**

Very reactive metals—those at the top of the activity series, from lithium (Li) through sodium (Na)—can displace hydrogen from water. Some do so violently (Figure 5.14). Metals of intermediate activity (Mg through Cr) displace hydrogen from steam, but not from liquid water at room temperature.

Elements very low in the activity series are unreactive. Sometimes called noble metals (Au, Ag, Pt), they are prized for their nonreactivity. It is no accident that gold and silver have been used extensively for coinage since antiquity. These metals do not react with air, water, or even common acids, thus maintaining their luster (and value) for many years. Their low reactivity explains why they occur naturally as free metals and have been known as elements since antiquity. These metals are discussed in Chapter 22.

© Thomson Learning/Charles D. Winters

Figure 5.14 **Potassium, an active metal.** When a drop of water falls onto a sample of potassium metal, it reacts vigorously to give hydrogen gas and a solution of potassium hydroxide.

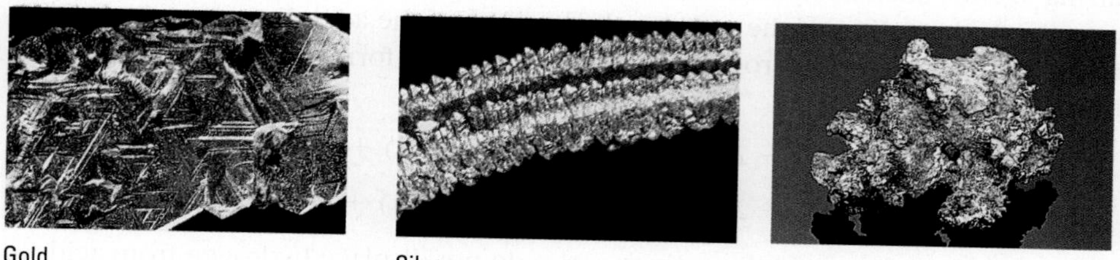

© Thomson Learning/Charles D. Winters

Gold Silver Copper

PROBLEM-SOLVING EXAMPLE 5.10 Activity Series of Metals

Use the activity series found in Table 5.5 to predict which of these reactions will occur. Complete and balance the equations for those reactions that will occur.

(a) $Cr(s) + MgCl_2(aq) \longrightarrow$
(b) $Zn(s) + CuSO_4(aq) \longrightarrow$
(c) Iron + hydrochloric acid $\longrightarrow$

Answer

(a) No reaction
(b) $Zn(s) + CuSO_4(aq) \longrightarrow ZnSO_4(aq) + Cu(s)$
(c) $Fe(s) + 2\ HCl(aq) \longrightarrow FeCl_2(aq) + H_2(g)$

Strategy and Explanation

(a) Chromium is less active than magnesium, so it will not displace magnesium ions from magnesium chloride. Therefore, no reaction occurs.

(b) Zinc is above copper in the activity series, so it will displace copper ions from a solution of copper(II) sulfate to form metallic copper and Zn^{2+} ions.

$$Zn(s) + CuSO_4(aq) \longrightarrow ZnSO_4(aq) + Cu(s)$$

(c) Iron is above hydrogen in the activity series, so it will displace hydrogen ions from HCl to form the metal salt $FeCl_2$ plus hydrogen gas.

$$Fe(s) + 2\ HCl(aq) \longrightarrow FeCl_2(aq) + H_2(g)$$

PROBLEM-SOLVING PRACTICE 5.10

Use Table 5.5 to predict whether each of these reactions will occur. If a reaction occurs, identify what has been oxidized or reduced and what the oxidizing agent and the reducing agent are.

(a) $2\ Al(s) + 3\ CuSO_4(aq) \longrightarrow Al_2(SO_4)_3(aq) + 3\ Cu(s)$
(b) $2\ Al(s) + Cr_2O_3(s) \longrightarrow Al_2O_3(s) + 2\ Cr(s)$
(c) $Pt(s) + 4\ HCl(aq) \longrightarrow PtCl_4(aq) + 2\ H_2(g)$
(d) $Au(s) + 3\ AgNO_3(aq) \longrightarrow Au(NO_3)_3(aq) + 3\ Ag(s)$

CONCEPTUAL EXERCISE 5.12 Reaction Product Prediction

For these pairs of reactants, predict what kind of reaction would occur and what the products might be. Which reactions are redox reactions?

(a) Combustion of ethanol: $CH_3CH_2OH(\ell) + O_2(g) \longrightarrow ?$
(b) $Fe(s) + HNO_3(aq) \longrightarrow ?$
(c) $AgNO_3(aq) + KBr(aq) \longrightarrow ?$

Other elements can also be ranked according to their oxidizing strength. Consider the halogens. As was shown previously (p. 182), the halogens have oxidizing strength in this order: F_2, Cl_2, Br_2, I_2. As an example of the relative reactivity of the halogens, bromine, Br_2, will oxidize iodine ions, I^-, to molecular iodine:

$$Br_2(\ell) + 2\ KI(aq) \longrightarrow 2\ KBr(aq) + I_2(s)$$

5.6 Solution Concentration

Many of the chemicals in your body or in other living systems are dissolved in water—that is, they are in an aqueous solution. Like chemical reactions in living systems, many reactions studied in the chemical laboratory are carried out in solution. Frequently, this chemistry must be done quantitatively. For example, intravenous fluids

ThomsonNOW™
Go to the Coached Problems menu for tutorials on:

- **solution concentration**
- **ion concentration**

CHEMISTRY YOU CAN DO

Pennies, Redox, and the Activity Series of Metals

In this experiment, you will use pennies to test the reactivity of copper and zinc with acid. Post-1982 pennies are a copper and zinc "sandwich" with zinc in the middle covered by a layer of copper. Pre-1982 pennies do not have this composition.

To do this experiment you will need:

- Two glasses or plastic cups that will each hold 50 mL (about 1.5 oz) of liquid
- About 100 mL "pickling" vinegar, such as Heinz Ultrastrength brand (Regular vinegar is only about 4–5% acetic acid.)
- An abrasive such as a piece of sandpaper, steel wool, or a Brillo pad
- A small file such as a nail file
- Four pennies—two pre-1982 and two post-1982

Clean the pennies with the abrasive until all the surfaces (including the edges) are shiny. Use the file to make two cuts into the edge of each penny, one across from the other. If you look carefully, you might observe a shiny metal where you cut into the post-1982 pennies.

Caution: Keep the vinegar away from your skin and clothes and especially your eyes. If vinegar spills on you, rinse it off with flowing water.

Place the two pre-1982 pennies into one of the cups and the post-1982 pennies into the other cup. Add the same volume of vinegar to each cup, making sure that the pennies are completely covered by the liquid. Let the pennies remain in the liquid for several hours (even overnight), and periodically observe any changes in them. After several hours, pour off the vinegar and remove the pennies. Dry them carefully and observe any changes that have occurred.

1. What difference did you observe between the pre-1982 pennies and the post-1982 ones?
2. Which is the more reactive element—copper or zinc?
3. What happened to the zinc in the post-1982 pennies? Interpret the change in redox terms, and write a chemical equation to represent the reaction.
4. How could this experiment be modified to determine the percent zinc and percent copper in post-1982 pennies?

administered to patients contain many compounds (salts, nutrients, drugs, and so on), and the concentration of each must be known accurately. To accomplish this task, we continue to use balanced equations and moles, but we measure volumes of solution rather than masses of solids, liquids, and gases.

A solution is a homogeneous mixture of a **solute,** the substance that has been dissolved, and the **solvent,** the substance in which the solute has been dissolved. To know the quantity of solute in a given volume of a liquid solution requires knowing the **concentration** of the solution—the relative quantities of solute and solvent. Molarity, which relates the amount of solute expressed in moles to the solution volume expressed in liters, is the most useful of the many ways of expressing solution concentration for studying chemical reactions in solution.

Molarity

The **molarity** of a solution is defined as the amount of solute expressed in moles per unit volume of solution, expressed in liters (mol/L).

$$\text{Molarity} = \frac{\text{moles of solute}}{\text{liters of solution}}$$

Note that the volume term in the denominator is liters of *solution,* not liters of solvent.

If, for example, 40.0 g (1.00 mol) NaOH is dissolved in sufficient water to produce a solution with a total volume of 1.00 L, the solution has a concentration of 1.00 mol NaOH/1.00 L of solution, which is a 1.00 molar solution. The molarity of this solution is reported as 1.00 M, where the capital M stands for moles/liter. Molarity is also represented by square brackets around the formula of a compound or ion, such as [NaOH] or $[OH^-]$. The brackets indicate amount (in moles) of the species (compound or ion) per unit volume (in liters) of solution.

molarity of NaOH solution

$$[NaOH] = 2\ M$$

2 moles per liter

A solution of known molarity can be made by adding the required amount of solute to a volumetric flask, adding some solvent to dissolve all the solute, and then adding sufficient solvent with continual mixing to fill the flask to the mark. As shown in Figure 5.15, the etched marking indicates the liquid level equal to the specified volume of the flask.

PROBLEM-SOLVING EXAMPLE 5.11 Molarity

Potassium permanganate, $KMnO_4$, is a strong oxidizing agent whose solutions are often used in laboratory experiments.

(a) If 0.433 g $KMnO_4$ is added to a 500.0-mL volumetric flask and water is added until the solution volume is exactly 500.0 mL, what is the molarity of the resulting solution?

(b) You need to prepare a 0.0250 M solution of $KMnO_4$ for an experiment. How many grams of $KMnO_4$ should be added with sufficient water to a 1.00-L volumetric flask to give the desired solution?

Answer

(a) 0.00548 M (b) 3.95 g

Strategy and Explanation

(a) To calculate the molarity of the solution, we need to calculate the moles of solute and the solution volume in liters. The volume was given as 500.0 mL, which is 0.5000 L. We use the molar mass of $KMnO_4$ (158.03 g/mol) to obtain the moles of solute.

$$0.433\ \text{g KMnO}_4 \times \frac{1\ \text{mol KMnO}_4}{158.03\ \text{g KMnO}_4} = 2.74 \times 10^{-3}\ \text{mol KMnO}_4$$

We can now calculate the molarity.

$$\text{Molarity of KMnO}_4 = \frac{2.74 \times 10^{-3}\ \text{mol KMnO}_4}{0.500\ \text{L solution}} = 5.48 \times 10^{-3}\ \text{mol/L}$$

This can be expressed as 0.00548 M or in the notation $[KMnO_4] = 0.00548$ M.

(b) To make a 0.0250 M solution in a 1.00-L volumetric flask requires 0.0250 mol $KMnO_4$. We convert to grams using the molar mass of $KMnO_4$.

$$0.0250\ \text{mol KMnO}_4 \times \frac{158.03\ \text{g KMnO}_4}{1\ \text{mol KMnO}_4} = 3.95\ \text{g KMnO}_4$$

✓ **Reasonable Answer Check** (a) We have about a half gram of solute with a molar mass of about 160. We will put this solute into a half-liter flask, so it is as if we put about one gram into a one-liter flask. The molarity should be about 1/160 = 0.00625, which is close to our more exact answer. (b) We need a little more than 2/100 of a mole of $KMnO_4$, which has a molar mass of about 160. One one-hundredth of 160 is 1.6, so two one-hundredths is twice that, or 3.2, which is close to our more exact answer.

PROBLEM-SOLVING PRACTICE 5.11

Calculate the molarity of sodium sulfate in a solution that contains 36.0 g Na_2SO_4 in 750. mL solution.

Photos: © Thomson Learning/Charles D. Winters

Figure 5.15 Solution preparation from a solid solute. Making a 0.0100 M aqueous solution of $KMnO_4$.

EXERCISE 5.13 Cholesterol Molarity

A blood serum cholesterol level greater than 240 mg of cholesterol per deciliter (0.100 L) of blood generally indicates the need for medical intervention. Calculate this serum cholesterol level in molarity. Cholesterol's molecular formula is $C_{27}H_{46}O$.

Sometimes the molarity of a particular ion in a solution is required, a value that depends on the formula of the solute. For example, potassium chromate is a soluble ionic compound and a strong electrolyte that completely dissociates in solution to form 2 mol K^+ ions and 1 mol CrO_4^{2-} ions for each mole of K_2CrO_4 that dissolves:

$$\underset{\substack{1\text{ mol}\\100\%\text{ dissociation}}}{K_2CrO_4(aq)} \longrightarrow \underset{2\text{ mol}}{2\,K^+(aq)} + \underset{1\text{ mol}}{CrO_4^{2-}(aq)}$$

The K^+ concentration is twice the K_2CrO_4 concentration because each mole of K_2CrO_4 contains 2 mol K^+. Therefore, a 0.00283 M K_2CrO_4 solution has a K^+ concentration of 2 × 0.00283 M = 0.00566 M and a CrO_4^{2-} concentration of 0.00283 M.

EXERCISE 5.14 Molarity

A student dissolves 6.37 g aluminum nitrate in sufficient water to make 250.0 mL of solution. Calculate (a) the molarity of aluminum nitrate in this solution and (b) the molarity of aluminum ions and of nitrate ions in this solution.

CONCEPTUAL EXERCISE 5.15 Molarity

When solutions are prepared, the final volume of solution can be different from the sum of the volumes of the solute and solvent because some expansion or contraction can occur. Why is it always better to describe solution preparation as "adding enough solvent" to make a certain volume of solution?

Preparing a Solution of Known Molarity by Diluting a More Concentrated One

Frequently, solutions of the same solute need to be available at several different molarities. For example, hydrochloric acid is often used at concentrations of 6.0 M, 1.0 M, and 0.050 M. To make these solutions, chemists often use a concentrated solution of known molarity and dilute samples of it with water to make solutions of lesser molarity. *The number of moles of solute in the sample that is diluted remains constant throughout the dilution operation.* Therefore, the number of moles of solute in the dilute solution must be the same as the number of moles of solute in the sample of the more concentrated solution. Diluting a solution does increase the volume, so the molarity of the solution is lowered by the dilution operation, even though the number of moles of solute remains unchanged.

The number of moles in each case is the same and a simple relationship applies:

$$\textit{Molarity}(\text{conc.}) \times V(\text{conc.}) = \textit{Molarity}(\text{dil}) \times V(\text{dil})$$

where *Molarity*(conc.) and *V*(conc.) represent the molarity and the volume (in liters) of the concentrated solution, and *Molarity*(dil) and *V*(dil) represent the molarity and volume of the dilute solution. *Multiplying a volume in liters by a solution's molarity (moles/liter) yields the number of moles of solute.*

We can calculate, for example, the concentration of a hydrochloric acid solution made by diluting 25.0 mL of 6.0 M HCl to 500. mL. In this case, we want to determine *Molarity*(dil) when *Molarity*(conc.) = 6.0 M, *V*(conc.) = 0.0250 L, and *V*(dil) = 0.500 L. We algebraically rearrange the relationship to get the concentration of the diluted HCl.

$$\textit{Molarity}(\text{dil}) = \frac{\textit{Molarity}(\text{conc.}) \times V(\text{conc.})}{V(\text{dil})}$$

$$= \frac{6.0\ \text{mol/L} \times 0.0250\ \text{L}}{0.500\ \text{L}} = 0.30\ \text{mol/L}$$

A diluted solution will always be less concentrated (lower molarity) than the more concentrated solution (Figure 5.16).

Use caution when diluting a concentrated acid. The more concentrated acid should be added slowly to the solvent (water) so that the heat released during the dilution is rapidly dissipated into a large volume of water. If water is added to the

ThomsonNOW™

Go to the Chemistry Interactive menu to work modules on:

- **preparation of an aqueous solution by dilution**
- **preparation of an aqueous solution by direct addition**

Consider two cases: A teaspoonful of sugar ($C_{12}H_{22}O_{11}$) is dissolved in a glass of water and a teaspoonful of sugar is dissolved in a swimming pool full of water. The swimming pool and the glass contain the same number of moles of sugar, but the concentration of sugar in the swimming pool is far less because the volume of solution in the pool is much greater than that in the glass.

A quick and useful check on a dilution calculation is to make certain that the molarity of the diluted solution is lower than that of the concentrated solution.

Photos: © Thomson Learning/Charles D. Winters

Figure 5.16 **Solution preparation by dilution.**

acid, the heat released by the dissolving could be sufficient to vaporize the solution, spraying the acid over you and anyone nearby.

EXERCISE 5.16 Moles of Solute in Solutions

Consider 100. mL of 6.0 M HCl solution, which is diluted with water to yield 500. mL of 1.20 M HCl. Show that 100. mL of the more concentrated solution contains the same number of moles of HCl as 500. mL of the more dilute solution.

PROBLEM-SOLVING EXAMPLE 5.12 Solution Concentration and Dilution

Describe how to prepare 500.0 mL 1.00 M H_2SO_4 solution from a concentrated sulfuric acid solution that is 18.0 M.

Answer Add 27.7 mL of the concentrated sulfuric acid slowly and carefully to enough water to make up a total volume of 500.0 mL of solution.

Strategy and Explanation In this dilution problem, the concentrations of the concentrated (18.0 M) and less concentrated (1.00 M) solutions are given, as well as the volume of the diluted solution (500.0 mL). The volume of the concentrated sulfuric acid, *V*(conc.), to be diluted is needed, and can be calculated from this relationship:

$$Molarity(\text{conc.}) \times V(\text{conc.}) = Molarity(\text{dil}) \times V(\text{dil})$$

$$V(\text{conc.}) = \frac{Molarity(\text{dil}) \times V(\text{dil})}{Molarity(\text{conc.})}$$

$$= \frac{1.00 \text{ mol/L} \times 0.500 \text{ L}}{18.0 \text{ mol/L}} = 0.0277 \text{ L} = 27.7 \text{ mL}$$

Thus, 27.7 mL of concentrated sulfuric acid is added slowly, with stirring, to about 350 mL of distilled water. When the solution has cooled to room temperature, sufficient water is added to bring the final volume to 500.0 mL, resulting in a 1.00 M sulfuric acid solution.

✓ **Reasonable Answer Check** The ratio of molarities is 18:1, so the ratio of volumes should be the same, and it is.

PROBLEM-SOLVING PRACTICE 5.12

A laboratory procedure calls for 50.0 mL of 0.150 M NaOH. You have available 100. mL 0.500 M NaOH. What volume of the more concentrated solution should be diluted to make the desired solution?

CONCEPTUAL EXERCISE 5.17 Solution Concentration

The molarity of a solution can be decreased by dilution. How could the molarity of a solution be increased without adding additional solute?

Preparing a Solution of Known Molarity from a Pure Solute

In Problem-Solving Example 5.11, we described finding the molarity of a $KMnO_4$ solution that was prepared from known quantities of solute and solution. More frequently, a solid or liquid solute (sometimes even a gas) must be used to make up a solution of known molarity. The problem becomes one of calculating what mass of solute to use to provide the proper number of moles.

Consider a laboratory experiment that requires 2.00 L of 0.750 M NH_4Cl solution. What mass of NH_4Cl must be dissolved in water to make 2.00 L of solution? The number of moles of NH_4Cl required can be calculated from the molarity.

$M \times L = mol/L \times L = mol$

$$0.750 \text{ mol/L } NH_4Cl \text{ solution} \times 2.00 \text{ L solution} = 1.500 \text{ mol } NH_4Cl$$

Then the molar mass can be used to calculate the number of grams of NH_4Cl needed.

$$1.500 \text{ mol } NH_4Cl \times 53.49 \text{ g/mol } NH_4Cl = 80.2 \text{ g } NH_4Cl$$

The solution is prepared by putting 80.2 g NH_4Cl into a beaker, dissolving it in pure water, rinsing all of the solution into a volumetric flask, and adding distilled water until the solution volume is 2.00 L, which results in a 0.750 M NH_4Cl solution.

PROBLEM-SOLVING EXAMPLE 5.13 Solute Mass and Molarity

Describe how to prepare 500.0 mL of 0.0250 M $K_2Cr_2O_7$ solution starting with solid potassium dichromate.

Answer Dissolve 3.68 g $K_2Cr_2O_7$ in water and add enough water to make 500.0 mL of solution.

Strategy and Explanation Use the definition of molarity and the molar mass of potassium dichromate to solve the problem. First, find the number of moles of the solute, $K_2Cr_2O_7$, in 500.0 mL of 0.0250 M $K_2Cr_2O_7$ solution by multiplying the volume in liters times the molarity of the solution.

$$0.500 \text{ L solution} \times \frac{0.0250 \text{ mol } K_2Cr_2O_7}{1 \text{ L solution}} = 1.25 \times 10^{-2} \text{ mol } K_2Cr_2O_7$$

From this calculate the number of grams of $K_2Cr_2O_7$.

$$1.25 \times 10^{-2} \text{ mol } K_2Cr_2O_7 \times \frac{294.2 \text{ g } K_2Cr_2O_7}{1 \text{ mol } K_2Cr_2O_7} = 3.68 \text{ g } K_2Cr_2O_7$$

The solution is prepared by putting 3.68 g $K_2Cr_2O_7$ into a 500-mL volumetric flask and adding enough distilled water to dissolve the solute and then additional water sufficient to bring the solution volume up to the mark of the flask. This results in 500.0 mL of 0.0250 M $K_2Cr_2O_7$ solution.

✓ **Reasonable Answer Check** The molar mass of $K_2Cr_2O_7$ is about 300 g/mol, and we want a 0.025 M solution, so we need about 300 g/mol × 0.0250 mol/L = 7.5 g/L. But only one-half liter is required, so 0.5 L × 7.5 g/L = 3.75 g is needed, which agrees with our more accurate answer.

PROBLEM-SOLVING PRACTICE 5.13

Describe how you would prepare these solutions:

(a) 1.00 L of 0.125 M Na_2CO_3 from solid Na_2CO_3
(b) 100. mL of 0.0500 M Na_2CO_3 from a 0.125 M Na_2CO_3 solution
(c) 500. mL of 0.0215 M $KMnO_4$ from solid $KMnO_4$
(d) 250. mL of 0.00450 M $KMnO_4$ from 0.0215 M $KMnO_4$

5.7 Molarity and Reactions in Aqueous Solutions

Many kinds of reactions—acid-base (p. 175), precipitation (p. 167), and redox (p. 180)—occur in aqueous solutions. In such reactions, molarity is the concentration unit of choice because it quantitatively relates a volume of one reactant and the molar amount of that reactant contained in solution to the volume and corresponding molar amount of another reactant or product in solution. Molarity allows us to make conversions between volumes of solutions and moles of reactants and products as given by the stoichiometric coefficients. Molarity is used to link mass, amount (moles), and volume of solution (Figure 5.17).

PROBLEM-SOLVING EXAMPLE 5.14 Solution Reaction Stoichiometry

A major industrial use of hydrochloric acid is for "pickling," the removal of rust from steel by dipping the steel into very large baths of HCl. The acid reacts in an exchange reaction with rust, which is essentially Fe_2O_3, leaving behind a clean steel surface.

$$Fe_2O_3(s) + 6\,HCl(aq) \longrightarrow 2\,FeCl_3(aq) + 3\,H_2O(\ell)$$

Once the rust is taken off, the steel is removed from the acid bath and rinsed before the acid reacts significantly with the iron in the steel.

How many pounds of rust can be removed when rust-covered steel reacts with 800. L of 12.0 M HCl? Assume that only the rust reacts with the HCl (1.000 lb = 453.6 g).

Answer 563 lb Fe_2O_3

Strategy and Explanation We use the stoichiometric relationships in Figure 5.17. We must calculate the number of moles of HCl, then the number of moles of Fe_2O_3, and finally the mass of Fe_2O_3. First, calculate the number of moles of HCl available in 800. L of the solution.

$$800.\text{ L HCl} \times \frac{12.0\text{ mol HCl}}{1\text{ L solution}} = 9.600 \times 10^3\text{ mol HCl}$$

Then the mass of Fe_2O_3 can be determined.

$$(9.600 \times 10^3\text{ mol HCl}) \times \frac{1\text{ mol }Fe_2O_3}{6\text{ mol HCl}} = 1.600 \times 10^3\text{ mol }Fe_2O_3$$

$$(1.600 \times 10^3\text{ mol }Fe_2O_3) \times \frac{159.7\text{ g }Fe_2O_3}{1\text{ mol }Fe_2O_3} = 2.555 \times 10^5\text{ g }Fe_2O_3$$

$$(2.555 \times 10^5\text{ g }Fe_2O_3) \times \frac{1\text{ lb }Fe_2O_3}{453.6\text{ g }Fe_2O_3} = 563\text{ lb }Fe_2O_3$$

ThomsonNOW™
Go to the Chemistry Interactive menu to work a module on **solution stoichiometry: reaction of Fe^{2+} and MnO_4^-.**

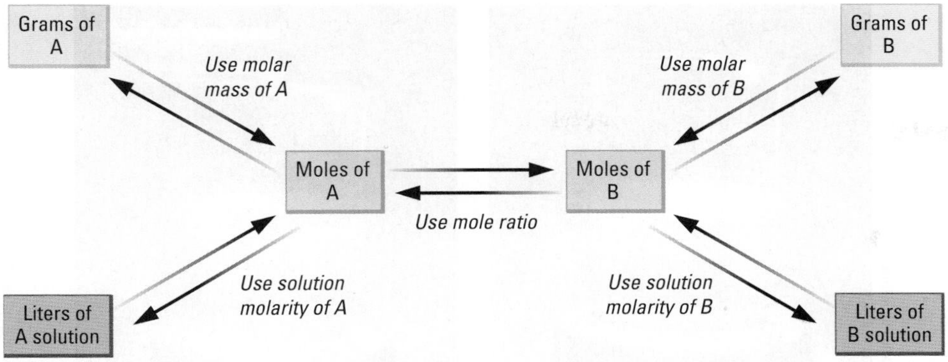

Figure 5.17 Stoichiometric relationships for a chemical reaction in aqueous solution. A mole ratio provides the connection between moles of a reactant or product and moles of another reactant or product.

Placing all the conversion factors in the same mathematical setup gives

$$800.\ \text{L HCl} \times \frac{12.0\ \text{mol HCl}}{1\ \text{L solution}} \times \frac{1\ \text{mol Fe}_2\text{O}_3}{6\ \text{mol HCl}}$$

$$\times \frac{159.7\ \text{g Fe}_2\text{O}_3}{1\ \text{mol Fe}_2\text{O}_3} \times \frac{1\ \text{lb Fe}_2\text{O}_3}{453.6\ \text{g Fe}_2\text{O}_3} = 563\ \text{lb Fe}_2\text{O}_3$$

The solution remaining in the acid bath presents a real disposal challenge because of the metal ions it contains.

✓ **Reasonable Answer Check** We have about 10,000 mol HCl. It will react with one sixth as many moles of rust, or about 1600 mol Fe_2O_3. Converting number of moles of Fe_2O_3 to number of pounds requires multiplying by the molar mass (160 g/mol) and then multiplying by the grams-to-pounds conversion factor (roughly 1 lb/500 g), which is equivalent to dividing by about 3. So $1600/3 \approx 500$, which checks with our more accurate answer.

PROBLEM-SOLVING PRACTICE 5.14

In a recent year, 1.2×10^{10} kg sodium hydroxide (NaOH) was produced in the United States by passing an electric current through brine, an aqueous solution of sodium chloride.

$$2\ \text{NaCl(aq)} + 2\ \text{H}_2\text{O}(\ell) \longrightarrow 2\ \text{NaOH(aq)} + \text{Cl}_2\text{(g)} + \text{H}_2\text{(g)}$$

What volume of brine is needed to produce this mass of NaOH? (*Note*: 1.0 L brine contains 360 g dissolved NaCl.)

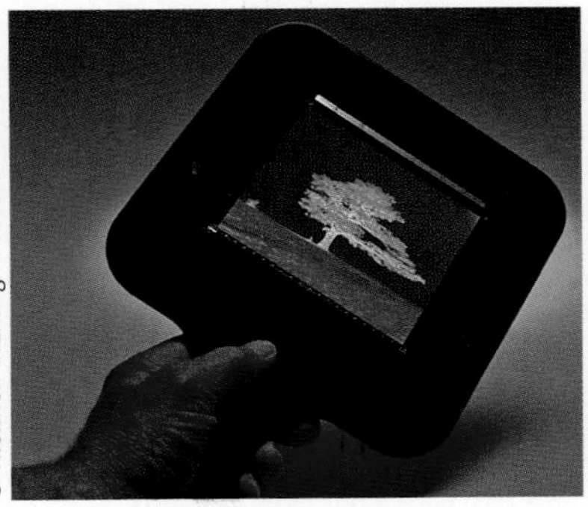

© Thomson Learning/Charles D. Winters

A photographic negative.

The chemistry of photography provides another application of solution stoichiometry. When silver bromide in black-and-white photographic film is exposed to light, silver ions in the silver bromide are reduced to metallic silver. When the photograph is developed, this reaction creates black regions on the negative. If left on the film, the unreacted silver bromide would ruin the picture because it would darken when exposed to light. AgBr(s) is dissolved away from the film with a solution of the "fixer," sodium thiosulfate ($Na_2S_2O_3$). Aqueous thiosulfate ions ($S_2O_3^{2-}$) combine with silver ions from AgBr to form a soluble product (Figure 5.18). The net ionic equation for this exchange reaction is

$$\text{AgBr(s)} + 2\ \text{S}_2\text{O}_3^{2-}\text{(aq)} \longrightarrow \text{Ag(S}_2\text{O}_3)_2^{3-}\text{(aq)} + \text{Br}^-\text{(aq)}$$

The following example is a quantitative look at this chemistry.

Sodium ions are spectator ions in this reaction and are not included in the net ionic equation.

© Thomson Learning/Charles D. Winters

(a) (b)

Figure 5.18 Dissolving silver bromide with thiosulfate. (a) A precipitate of AgBr formed by adding $AgNO_3(aq)$ to $KBr(aq)$. (b) When sodium thiosulfate, $Na_2S_2O_3(aq)$ is added, the solid AgBr dissolves.

One mol $Na_2S_2O_3$ dissociates into 2 mol sodium ions and 1 mol thiosulfate ions. Thus, the 0.0150 mol $Na_2S_2O_3$ in 1 L of 0.0150 M $Na_2S_2O_3$ solution dissociates into 0.0300 mol Na^+ and 0.0150 mol $S_2O_3^{2-}$ ions.

PROBLEM-SOLVING EXAMPLE 5.15 Solution Reaction Stoichiometry

If you need to dissolve 50.0 mg (0.0500 g) AgBr, how many milliliters of 0.0150 M $Na_2S_2O_3$ should you use?

Answer 35.5 mL of 0.0150 M $Na_2S_2O_3$ solution

Strategy and Explanation Use the diagram in Figure 5.17, and follow the appropriate path. We need to find the number of moles of $Na_2S_2O_3$ required, considering that 2 mol $S_2O_3^{2-}$ is required for 1 mol AgBr, and that 1 mol $Na_2S_2O_3$ contains 1 mol $S_2O_3^{2-}$ ions.

$$0.0500 \text{ g AgBr} \times \frac{1 \text{ mol AgBr}}{187.8 \text{ g AgBr}} \times \frac{2 \text{ mol } S_2O_3^{2-}}{1 \text{ mol AgBr}}$$

$$\times \frac{1 \text{ mol } Na_2S_2O_3}{1 \text{ mol } S_2O_3^{2-}} = 5.324 \times 10^{-4} \text{ mol } Na_2S_2O_3$$

The volume of 0.0150 M $Na_2S_2O_3$ required is obtained by using the molarity of the solution.

$$5.324 \times 10^{-4} \text{ mol } Na_2S_2O_3 \times \frac{1 \text{ L solution}}{0.0150 \text{ mol } Na_2S_2O_3}$$

$$= 0.0355 \text{ L of } 0.0150 \text{ M } Na_2S_2O_3 \text{ solution, or } 35.5 \text{ mL}$$

✓ **Reasonable Answer Check** We have 0.050 g/(190 g/mol) ≈ 0.00026 mol AgBr. We have (0.0150 mol/L)(0.0355 L) ≈ 0.00053 mol $S_2O_3^{2-}$. This is about the 2:1 ratio needed according to the balanced equation.

PROBLEM-SOLVING PRACTICE 5.15

If you had 125 mL of a 0.0200 M solution of $Na_2S_2O_3$ on hand, how many milligrams of AgBr could you dissolve?

ThomsonNOW

Go to the Coached Problems menu for tutorials on:

- **stoichiometry**
- **solution stoichiometry**

EXERCISE 5.18 Molarity

Sodium chloride is used in intravenous solutions for medical applications. The NaCl concentration in such solutions must be accurately known and can be assessed by reacting the solution with an experimentally determined volume of $AgNO_3$ solution of known concentration. The net ionic equation is

$$Ag^+(aq) + Cl^-(aq) \longrightarrow AgCl(s)$$

Suppose that a chemical technician uses 19.3 mL of 0.200 M $AgNO_3$ to convert all the NaCl in a 25.0-mL sample of an intravenous solution to AgCl. Calculate the molarity of NaCl in the solution.

5.8 Aqueous Solution Titrations

One important quantitative use of aqueous solution reactions is to determine the unknown concentration of a reactant in a solution, such as the concentration of HCl in a solution of HCl. This is done with a titration using a **standard solution,** a solution whose concentration is known accurately. In a **titration,** a substance in the standard solution reacts with a known stoichiometry with the substance whose concentration is to be determined. When the stoichiometrically equivalent amount of standard solution has been added, the **equivalence point** is reached. At that point, the molar amount of reactant that has been added from the standard solution is exactly what is needed to react completely with the substance whose concentration is to be determined. The progress of the reaction is monitored by an indicator, a dye that changes color at the equivalence point, or through some other means with appropriate instruments. Phenolphthalein, for example, is commonly used as the indicator in strong acid–strong base titrations because it is colorless in acidic solutions and pink in basic solutions. The point at which the indicator is seen to change color is called the end point.

Acid-base titrations are described more extensively in Chapter 17.

A common example of a titration is the determination of the molarity of an acid by titration of the acid with a standard solution of a base. For example, we can use a standard solution of 0.100 M KOH to determine the concentration of an HCl solution. To carry out this titration, we use a carefully measured volume of the HCl solution and slowly add the standardized KOH solution until the equivalence point is reached (Figure 5.19). At that point, the number of moles of OH^- added to the HCl solution exactly matches the number of moles of H^+ that were in the original acid sample.

PROBLEM-SOLVING EXAMPLE 5.16 Acid-Base Titration

A student has an aqueous solution of calcium hydroxide that is approximately 0.10 M. She titrated a 50.0-mL sample of the calcium hydroxide solution with a standardized solution of 0.300 M $HNO_3(aq)$. To reach the end point, 41.4 mL of the HNO_3 solution was needed. What is the molarity of the calcium hydroxide solution?

Answer 0.124 M $Ca(OH)_2$

Strategy and Explanation Start by writing the balanced equation for this acid-base reaction.

$$2\ HNO_3(aq) + Ca(OH)_2(aq) \longrightarrow Ca(NO_3)_2(aq) + 2\ H_2O(\ell)$$

The net ionic equation is

$$H^+(aq) + OH^-(aq) \longrightarrow H_2O(\ell)$$

ThomsonNOW™
Go to the Chemistry Interactive menu to work a module on a **titration.**

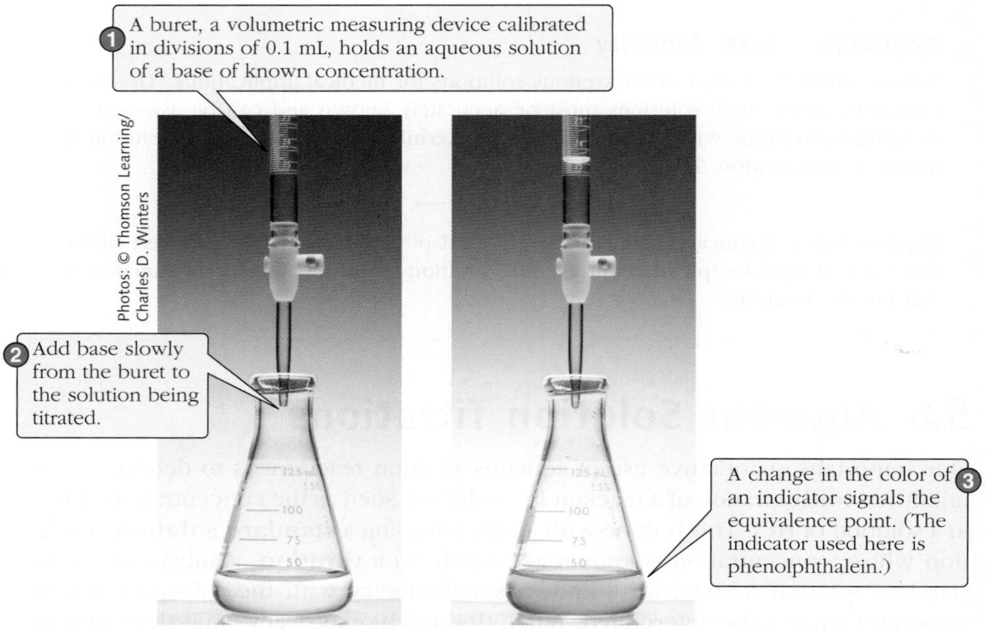

Figure 5.19 **Titration of an acid in aqueous solution with a standard solution of base.**

Then calculate the number of moles of HNO_3 consumed.

$$0.0414 \text{ L } HNO_3 \text{ solution} \times \frac{0.300 \text{ mol } HNO_3}{1.00 \text{ L } HNO_3 \text{ solution}} = 0.0124 \text{ mol } HNO_3$$

The balanced equation shows that for every 2 mol HNO_3 reacted, one mol $Ca(OH)_2$ is consumed. Therefore, if 1.24×10^{-2} mol HNO_3 was reacted, (1.24×10^{-2} mol HNO_3)[(1 mol $Ca(OH)_2$)/(2 mol HNO_3)] = 6.21×10^{-3} mol $Ca(OH)_2$ must have been consumed. From the number of moles of calcium hydroxide and the volume of the calcium hydroxide solution, calculate the molarity of the solution.

$$\frac{6.21 \times 10^{-3} \text{ mol } Ca(OH)_2}{0.0505 \text{ L } Ca(OH)_2 \text{ solution}} = 0.124 \text{ M } Ca(OH)_2$$

✓ **Reasonable Answer Check** At the equivalence point, the number of moles of $H^+(aq)$ added and $OH^-(aq)$ in the initial sample must be equal. The number of moles of each reactant is its volume multiplied by its molarity. For the HNO_3 we have 0.0414 L × 0.300 M = 0.0124 mol HNO_3. For the $Ca(OH)_2$ we have 0.050 L × 0.124 M × 2 = 0.0124 mol $Ca(OH)_2$. The answer is reasonable.

ThomsonNOW™

Go to the Coached Problems menu for a simulation and a tutorial on **acid-base titrations.**

PROBLEM-SOLVING PRACTICE 5.16

In a titration, a 20.0-mL sample of sulfuric acid (H_2SO_4) was titrated to the end point with 41.3 mL of 0.100 M NaOH. What is the molarity of the H_2SO_4 solution?

SUMMARY PROBLEM

Gold in its elemental state can be separated from gold-bearing rock by treating the ore with cyanide, CN^-, in the presence of oxygen via this reaction:

$$4 \text{ Au(s)} + 8 \text{ CN}^-(aq) + O_2(g) + 2 \text{ } H_2O(\ell) \longrightarrow 4 \text{ Au(CN)}_2^-(aq) + 4 \text{ OH}^-(aq)$$

The CN^- is supplied by NaCN, but Na^+ is a spectator ion and is left out of the net ionic equation.

(a) Which reactant is oxidized? What are the oxidation numbers of this species as a reactant and as a product?

(b) Which reactant is reduced? What are the oxidation numbers of this species as a reactant and as a product?

(c) What is the oxidizing agent?

(d) What is the reducing agent?

(e) What mass of NaCN would it take to prepare 1.0 L of 0.075 M NaCN?

(f) If the ore contains 0.019% gold by weight, what mass of gold is found in one metric ton (exactly 1000 kg) of the ore?

(g) How many grams of NaCN would you require to extract the gold in one metric ton of this ore?

(h) How many liters of the 0.075 M NaCN solution would you require to extract the gold in one metric ton of this ore?

IN CLOSING

ThomsonNOW™
Sign in to ThomsonNOW at **www.thomsonedu.com** to check your readiness for an exam by taking the Pre-Test and exploring the modules recommended in your Personalized Learning Plan.

Having studied this chapter, you should be able to . . .

- Predict products of common types of chemical reactions: precipitation, acid-base, and gas-forming (Sections 5.1–5.3). ThomsonNOW homework: Study Question 38
- Write a net ionic equation for a given reaction in aqueous solution (Section 5.1). ThomsonNOW homework: Study Questions 19, 23
- Recognize common acids and bases and predict when neutralization reactions will occur (Section 5.2). ThomsonNOW homework: Study Question 34
- Identify the acid and base used to form a specific salt (Section 5.2). ThomsonNOW homework: Study Question 36
- Recognize oxidation-reduction reactions and common oxidizing and reducing agents (Section 5.3). ThomsonNOW homework: Study Questions 48, 51
- Assign oxidation numbers to reactants and products in a redox reaction, identify what has been oxidized or reduced, and identify oxidizing agents and reducing agents (Section 5.4). ThomsonNOW homework: Study Questions 40, 57
- Use the activity series to predict products of displacement redox reactions (Section 5.5). ThomsonNOW homework: Study Questions 56, 61
- Define molarity and calculate molar concentrations (Section 5.6). ThomsonNOW homework: Study Questions 65, 67, 69, 71
- Determine how to prepare a solution of a given molarity from the solute and water or by dilution of a more concentrated solution (Section 5.6). ThomsonNOW homework: Study Questions 71, 75
- Solve stoichiometry problems by using solution molarities (Section 5.7). ThomsonNOW homework: Study Questions 78, 79
- Understand how aqueous solution titrations can be used to determine the concentration of an unknown solution (Section 5.8). ThomsonNOW homework: Study Questions 81, 87

KEY TERMS

acid *(5.2)*
base *(5.2)*
concentration *(5.6)*
equivalence point *(5.8)*
hydronium ion *(5.2)*
hydroxide ion *(5.2)*
metal activity series *(5.5)*
molarity *(5.6)*
net ionic equation *(5.1)*
oxidation *(5.3)*
oxidation number *(5.4)*
oxidation-reduction reaction *(5.3)*
oxidized *(5.3)*
oxidizing agent *(5.3)*
precipitate *(5.1)*
redox reactions *(5.3)*
reduced *(5.3)*
reducing agent *(5.3)*
reduction *(5.3)*
salt *(5.2)*
solute *(5.6)*
solvent *(5.6)*
spectator ion *(5.1)*
standard solution *(5.8)*
strong acid *(5.2)*
strong base *(5.2)*
strong electrolyte *(5.1)*
titration *(5.8)*
weak acid *(5.2)*
weak base *(5.2)*
weak electrolyte *(5.2)*

QUESTIONS FOR REVIEW AND THOUGHT

■ denotes questions available in ThomsonNOW and assignable in OWL.

Blue-numbered questions have short answers at the back of this book and fully worked solutions in the *Student Solutions Manual.*

ThomsonNOW™
Assess your understanding of this chapter's topics with sample tests and other resources found by signing in to ThomsonNOW at **www.thomsonedu.com**.

Review Questions

1. Find in this chapter one example of each of these reaction types, and write the balanced equation for the reaction: (a) combustion, (b) combination, (c) exchange, (d) decomposition, and (e) oxidation-reduction. Name the products of each reaction.
2. Classify each of these reactions as a combination, decomposition, exchange, acid-base, or oxidation-reduction reaction.
   (a) $MgO(s) + 2\,HCl(aq) \longrightarrow MgCl_2(aq) + H_2O(\ell)$
   (b) $2\,NaHCO_3(s) \xrightarrow{\text{heat}} Na_2CO_3(s) + CO_2(g) + H_2O(g)$
   (c) $CaO(s) + SO_2(g) \longrightarrow CaSO_3(s)$
   (d) $3\,Cu(s) + 8\,HNO_3(aq) \longrightarrow 3\,Cu(NO_3)_2(aq) + 2\,NO(g) + 4\,H_2O(\ell)$
   (e) $2\,NO(g) + O_2(g) \longrightarrow 2\,NO_2(g)$
3. Find two examples in this chapter of the reaction of a metal with a halogen, write a balanced equation for each example, and name the product.
4. Find two examples of acid-base reactions in this chapter. Write balanced equations for these reactions, and name the reactants and products.
5. Find two examples of precipitation reactions in this chapter. Write balanced equations for these reactions, and name the reactants and products.
6. Find an example of a gas-forming reaction in this chapter. Write a balanced equation for the reaction, and name the reactants and products.
7. Explain the difference between oxidation and reduction. Give an example of each.
8. For each of the following, does the oxidation number increase or decrease in the course of a redox reaction?
   (a) An oxidizing agent
   (b) A reducing agent
   (c) A substance undergoing oxidation
   (d) A substance undergoing reduction
9. Explain the difference between an oxidizing agent and a reducing agent. Give an example of each.

Topical Questions

Solubility

10. Tell how solubility rules predict that $Ni(NO_3)_2$ is soluble in water, whereas $NiCO_3$ is not soluble in water.
11. ■ Predict whether each of these compounds is likely to be water-soluble. Indicate which ions are present in solution for the water-soluble compounds.
    (a) $Fe(ClO_4)_2$ (b) Na_2SO_4
    (c) KBr (d) Na_2CO_3
12. Predict whether each of these compounds is likely to be water-soluble. For those compounds which are soluble, indicate which ions are present in solution.
    (a) $Ca(NO_3)_2$ (b) KCl
    (c) $CuSO_4$ (d) $FeCl_3$
13. Predict whether each of these compounds is likely to be water-soluble. Indicate which ions are present in solution for the water-soluble compounds.

(a) Potassium monohydrogen phosphate
(b) Sodium hypochlorite
(c) Magnesium chloride
(d) Calcium hydroxide
(e) Aluminum bromide

14. Predict whether each of these compounds is likely to be water-soluble. Indicate which ions are present in solution for the water-soluble compounds.
(a) Ammonium nitrate (b) Barium sulfate
(c) Potassium acetate (d) Calcium carbonate
(e) Sodium perchlorate

Exchange Reactions

15. Write a balanced equation for the reaction of nitric acid with calcium hydroxide.
16. Write a balanced equation for the reaction of hydrochloric acid with magnesium hydroxide.
17. ■ For each of these pairs of ionic compounds, write a balanced equation reflecting whether precipitation will occur in aqueous solution. For those combinations that do not produce a precipitate, write "NP."
(a) $MnCl_2 + Na_2S$ (b) $HNO_3 + CuSO_4$
(c) $NaOH + HClO_4$ (d) $Hg(NO_3)_2 + Na_2S$
(e) $Pb(NO_3)_2 + HCl$ (f) $BaCl_2 + H_2SO_4$
18. For each of these pairs of ionic compounds, write a balanced equation reflecting whether precipitation will occur in aqueous solution. For those combinations that do not produce a precipitate, write "NP."
(a) $HNO_3 + Na_3PO_4$ (b) $NaCl + Pb(CH_3COO)_2$
(c) $(NH_4)_2S + NiCl_2$ (d) $K_2SO_4 + Cu(NO_3)_2$
(e) $FeCl_3 + NaOH$ (f) $AgNO_3 + KCl$
19. Identify the water-insoluble product in each of these reactions. Write the net ionic equations for these reactions. Identify the spectator ions.
(a) $CuCl_2(aq) + H_2S(aq) \longrightarrow CuS + 2\ HCl$
(b) $CaCl_2(aq) + K_2CO_3(aq) \longrightarrow 2\ KCl + CaCO_3$
(c) $AgNO_3(aq) + NaI(aq) \longrightarrow AgI + NaNO_3$
20. Identify the water-insoluble product in each of these reactions. Write the net ionic equations for these reactions. Identify the spectator ions.
(a) $Pb(NO_3)_2(aq) + Na_2SO_4(aq) \longrightarrow PbSO_4 + NaNO_3$
(b) $K_3PO_4(aq) + Mg(NO_3)_2(aq) \longrightarrow Mg_3(PO_4)_2 + KNO_3$
(c) $(NH_4)_2SO_4(aq) + BaBr_2(aq) \longrightarrow BaSO_4 + NH_4Br$
21. If aqueous solutions of potassium carbonate and copper(II) nitrate are mixed, a precipitate is formed. Write the complete and net ionic equations for this reaction, and name the precipitate.
22. If aqueous solutions of potassium sulfide and iron(III) chloride are mixed, a precipitate is formed. Write the complete and net ionic equations for this reaction, and name the precipitate.
23. ■ Balance each of these equations, and then write the complete ionic and net ionic equations.
(a) $Zn(s) + HCl(aq) \longrightarrow H_2(g) + ZnCl_2(aq)$
(b) $Mg(OH)_2(s) + HCl(aq) \longrightarrow MgCl_2(aq) + H_2O(\ell)$
(c) $HNO_3(aq) + CaCO_3(s) \longrightarrow Ca(NO_3)_2(aq) + H_2O(\ell) + CO_2(g)$
(d) $HCl(aq) + MnO_2(s) \longrightarrow MnCl_2(aq) + Cl_2(g) + H_2O(\ell)$
24. Balance each of these equations, and then write the complete ionic and net ionic equations.
(a) $(NH_4)_2CO_3(aq) + Cu(NO_3)_2(aq) \longrightarrow CuCO_3(s) + NH_4NO_3(aq)$
(b) $Pb(NO_3)_2(aq) + HCl(aq) \longrightarrow PbCl_2(s) + HNO_3(aq)$
(c) $BaCO_3(s) + HCl(aq) \longrightarrow BaCl_2(aq) + H_2O(\ell) + CO_2(g)$
25. Balance each of these equations, and then write the complete ionic and net ionic equations. Refer to Tables 5.1 and 5.2 for information on solubility and on acids and bases. Show states (s, ℓ, g, aq) for all reactants and products.
(a) $Ca(OH)_2 + HNO_3 \longrightarrow Ca(NO_3)_2 + H_2O$
(b) $BaCl_2 + Na_2CO_3 \longrightarrow BaCO_3 + NaCl$
(c) $Na_3PO_4 + Ni(NO_3)_2 \longrightarrow Ni_3(PO_4)_2 + NaNO_3$
26. Balance each of these equations, and then write the complete ionic and net ionic equations. Refer to Tables 5.1 and 5.2 for information on solubility and on acids and bases. Show states (s, ℓ, g, aq) for all reactants and products.
(a) $ZnCl_2 + KOH \longrightarrow KCl + Zn(OH)_2$
(b) $AgNO_3 + KI \longrightarrow AgI + KNO_3$
(c) $NaOH + FeCl_2 \longrightarrow Fe(OH)_2 + NaCl$
27. Barium hydroxide is used in lubricating oils and greases. Write a balanced equation for the reaction of this hydroxide with nitric acid to give barium nitrate, a compound used in pyrotechnics devices such as green flares.
28. Aluminum is obtained from bauxite, which is not a specific mineral but a name applied to a mixture of minerals. One of those minerals, which can dissolve in acids, is gibbsite, $Al(OH)_3$. Write a balanced equation for the reaction of gibbsite with sulfuric acid.
29. Balance the equation for this precipitation reaction, and then write the complete ionic and net ionic equations.

$$CdCl_2 + NaOH \longrightarrow Cd(OH)_2 + NaCl$$

30. Balance the equation for this precipitation reaction, and then write the complete ionic and net ionic equations.

$$Ni(NO_3)_2 + Na_2CO_3 \longrightarrow NiCO_3 + NaNO_3$$

31. Write an overall balanced equation for the precipitation reaction that occurs when aqueous lead(II) nitrate is mixed with an aqueous solution of potassium chloride. Name each reactant and product. Indicate the state of each substance (s, ℓ, g, or aq).
32. Write an overall balanced equation for the precipitation reaction that occurs when aqueous copper(II) nitrate is mixed with an aqueous solution of sodium carbonate. Name each reactant and product. Indicate the state of each substance (s, ℓ, g, or aq).
33. The beautiful mineral rhodochrosite is manganese(II) carbonate. Write an overall balanced equation for the reaction of the mineral with hydrochloric acid. Name each reactant and product.
34. ■ Classify each of these as an acid or a base. Which are strong and which are weak? What ions are produced when each is dissolved in water?
(a) KOH (b) $Mg(OH)_2$
(c) HClO (d) HBr
(e) LiOH (f) H_2SO_3

35. Classify each of these as an acid or a base. Which are strong and which are weak? What ions are produced when each is dissolved in water?
(a) HNO_3 (b) $Ca(OH)_2$
(c) NH_3 (d) H_3PO_4
(e) KOH (f) CH_3COOH

36. ■ Identify the acid and base used to form these salts, and write the overall neutralization reaction in both complete and net ionic form.
(a) $NaNO_2$ (b) $CaSO_4$
(c) NaI (d) $Mg_3(PO_4)_2$

37. Identify the acid and base used to form these salts, and write the overall neutralization reaction in both complete and net ionic form.
(a) $NaCH_3COO$ (b) $CaCl_2$
(c) LiBr (d) $Ba(NO_3)_2$

38. ■ Classify each of these exchange reactions as an acid-base reaction, a precipitation reaction, or a gas-forming reaction. Predict the products of the reaction, and then balance the completed equation.
(a) $MnCl_2(aq) + Na_2S(aq) \longrightarrow$
(b) $Na_2CO_3(aq) + ZnCl_2(aq) \longrightarrow$
(c) $K_2CO_3(aq) + HClO_4(aq) \longrightarrow$

39. Classify each of these exchange reactions as an acid-base reaction, a precipitation reaction, or a gas-forming reaction. Predict the products of the reaction, and then balance the completed equation.
(a) $Fe(OH)_3(s) + HNO_3(aq) \longrightarrow$
(b) $FeCO_3(s) + H_2SO_4(aq) \longrightarrow$
(c) $FeCl_2(aq) + (NH_4)_2S(aq) \longrightarrow$
(d) $Fe(NO_3)_2(aq) + Na_2CO_3(aq) \longrightarrow$

Oxidation-Reduction Reactions

40. ■ Assign oxidation numbers to each atom in these compounds.
(a) SO_3 (b) HNO_3
(c) $KMnO_4$ (d) H_2O
(e) LiOH (f) CH_2Cl_2

41. Assign oxidation numbers to each atom in these compounds.
(a) $Fe(OH)_3$ (b) $HClO_3$
(c) $CuCl_2$ (d) K_2CrO_4
(e) $Ni(OH)_2$ (f) N_2H_4

42. Assign oxidation numbers to each atom in these ions.
(a) SO_4^{2-} (b) NO_3^-
(c) MnO_4^- (d) $Cr(OH)_4^-$
(e) $H_2PO_4^-$ (f) $S_2O_3^{2-}$

43. What is the oxidation number of Mn in each of these species?
(a) $(MnF_6)^{3-}$ (b) Mn_2O_7
(c) MnO_4^- (d) $Mn(CN)_6^-$
(e) MnO_2

44. What is the oxidation number of Cl in each of these species?
(a) HCl (b) HClO
(c) $HClO_2$ (d) $HClO_3$
(e) $HClO_4$

45. What is the oxidation number of S in each of these species?
(a) H_2SO_4 (b) H_2SO_3
(c) SO_2 (d) SO_3
(e) $H_2S_2O_7$ (f) $Na_2S_2O_3$

46. Sulfur can exist in many oxidation states. What is the oxidation state of S in each of these species?
(a) H_2S (b) S_8
(c) SCl_2 (d) SO_3^{2-}
(e) K_2SO_4

47. What is the oxidation state of Cr in each of these species?
(a) $CrCl_3$ (b) Na_2CrO_4
(c) $K_2Cr_2O_7$

48. ■ Which of these reactions are oxidation-reduction reactions? Explain your answer briefly. Classify the remaining reactions.
(a) $CdCl_2(aq) + Na_2S(aq) \longrightarrow CdS(s) + 2\ NaCl(aq)$
(b) $2\ Ca(s) + O_2(g) \longrightarrow 2\ CaO(s)$
(c) $Ca(OH)_2(s) + 2\ HCl(aq) \longrightarrow CaCl_2(aq) + 2\ H_2O(\ell)$

49. Which of these reactions are oxidation-reduction reactions? Explain your answer briefly. Classify the remaining reactions.
(a) $Zn(s) + 2\ NO_3^-(aq) + 4\ H_3O^+(aq) \longrightarrow Zn^{2+}(aq) - 2\ NO_2(g) + 6\ H_2O(\ell)$
(b) $Zn(OH)_2(s) + H_2SO_4(aq) \longrightarrow ZnSO_4(aq) + 2\ H_2O(\ell)$
(c) $Ca(s) + 2\ H_2O(\ell) \longrightarrow Ca(OH)_2(s) + H_2(g)$

50. Which region of the periodic table has the best reducing agents? The best oxidizing agents?

51. ■ Which of these substances are oxidizing agents?
(a) Zn (b) O_2
(c) HNO_3 (d) MnO_4^-
(e) H_2 (f) H^+

52. Which of these substances are reducing agents?
(a) Ca (b) Ca^{2+}
(c) $Cr_2O_7^{2-}$ (d) Al
(e) Br_2 (f) H_2

53. Identify the products of these redox combination reactions.
(a) $C(s) + O_2(g) \longrightarrow$
(b) $P_4(s) + Cl_2(g) \longrightarrow$
(c) $Ti(s) + Cl_2(g) \longrightarrow$
(d) $Mg(s) + N_2(g) \longrightarrow$
(e) $FeO(s) + O_2(g) \longrightarrow$
(f) $NO(g) + O_2(g) \longrightarrow$

54. Complete and balance these equations for redox displacement reactions.
(a) $K(s) + H_2O(\ell) \longrightarrow$
(b) $Mg(s) + HBr(aq) \longrightarrow$
(c) $NaBr(aq) + Cl_2(aq) \longrightarrow$
(d) $WO_3(s) + H_2(g) \longrightarrow$
(e) $H_2S(aq) + Cl_2(aq) \longrightarrow$

55. Which halogen is the strongest oxidizing agent? Which is the strongest reducing agent?

56. ■ Predict the products of these halogen displacement reactions. If no reaction occurs, write "NR."
(a) $I_2(s) + NaBr(aq) \longrightarrow$
(b) $Br_2(\ell) + NaI(aq) \longrightarrow$
(c) $F_2(g) + NaCl(aq) \longrightarrow$
(d) $Cl_2(g) + NaBr(aq) \longrightarrow$
(e) $Br_2(\ell) + NaCl(aq) \longrightarrow$
(f) $Cl_2(g) + NaF(aq) \longrightarrow$

57. ■ For the reactions in Question 56 that occur, identify the species oxidized or reduced as well as the oxidizing and reducing agents.

58. For the reactions in Question 56 that do not occur, rewrite the equation so that a reaction does occur (consider the halogen activity series).

Activity Series

59. Give an example of a displacement reaction that is also a redox reaction and identify which species is (a) oxidized, (b) reduced, (c) the reducing agent, and (d) the oxidizing agent.
60. (a) In what groups of the periodic table are the most reactive metals found? Where do we find the least reactive metals?
    (b) Silver (Ag) does not react with 1 M HCl solution. Will Ag react with a solution of aluminum nitrate, $Al(NO_3)_3$? If so, write a chemical equation for the reaction.
    (c) Lead (Pb) will react very slowly with 1 M HCl solution. Aluminum will react with lead(II) sulfate solution, $PbSO_4$. Will Pb react with an $AgNO_3$ solution? If so, write a chemical equation for the reaction.
    (d) On the basis of the information obtained in answering parts (a), (b), and (c), arrange Ag, Al, and Pb in decreasing order of reactivity.
61. ■ Use the activity series of metals (Table 5.5) to predict the outcome of each of these reactions. If no reaction occurs, write "NR."
    (a) $Na^+(aq) + Zn(s) \longrightarrow$
    (b) $HCl(aq) + Pt(s) \longrightarrow$
    (c) $Ag^+(aq) + Au(s) \longrightarrow$
    (d) $Au^{3+}(aq) + Ag(s) \longrightarrow$
62. Using the activity series of metals (Table 5.5), predict whether these reactions will occur in aqueous solution.
    (a) $Mg(s) + Ca(s) \longrightarrow Mg^{2+}(aq) + Ca^{2+}(aq)$
    (b) $2\ Al^{3+}(aq) + 3\ Pb^{2+}(aq) \longrightarrow 2\ Al(s) + 3\ Pb(s)$
    (c) $H_2(g) + Zn^{2+}(aq) \longrightarrow 2\ H^+(aq) + Zn(s)$
    (d) $Mg(s) + Cu^{2+}(aq) \longrightarrow Mg^{2+}(aq) + Cu(s)$
    (e) $Pb(s) + 2\ H^+(aq) \longrightarrow H_2(g) + Pb^{2+}(aq)$
    (f) $2\ Ag^+(aq) + Cu(s) \longrightarrow 2\ Ag(s) + Cu^{2+}(aq)$
    (g) $2\ Al^{3+}(aq) + 3\ Zn(s) \longrightarrow 3\ Zn^{2+}(aq) + 2\ Al(s)$

Solution Concentrations

63. You have a 0.12 M solution of $BaCl_2$. What ions exist in the solution, and what are their concentrations?
64. A flask contains 0.25 M $(NH_4)_2SO_4$. What ions exist in the solution, and what are their concentrations?
65. ■ Assume that 6.73 g Na_2CO_3 is dissolved in enough water to make 250. mL of solution.
    (a) What is the molarity of the sodium carbonate?
    (b) What are the concentrations of the Na^+ and CO_3^{2-} ions?
66. Some $K_2Cr_2O_7$, with a mass of 2.335 g, is dissolved in enough water to make 500. mL of solution.
    (a) What is the molarity of the potassium dichromate?
    (b) What are the concentrations of the K^+ and $Cr_2O_7^{2-}$ ions?
67. ■ What is the mass, in grams, of solute in 250. mL of a 0.0125 M solution of $KMnO_4$?
68. What is the mass, in grams, of solute in 100. mL of a 1.023×10^{-3} M solution of Na_3PO_4?
69. ■ What volume of 0.123 M NaOH, in milliliters, contains 25.0 g NaOH?
70. What volume of 2.06 M $KMnO_4$, in liters, contains 322 g solute?
71. ■ If 6.00 mL of 0.0250 M $CuSO_4$ is diluted to 10.0 mL with pure water, what is the concentration of copper(II) sulfate in the diluted solution?
72. If you dilute 25.0 mL of 1.50 M HCl to 500. mL, what is the molar concentration of the diluted HCl?
73. If you need 1.00 L of 0.125 M H_2SO_4, which method would you use to prepare this solution?
    (a) Dilute 36.0 mL of 1.25 M H_2SO_4 to a volume of 1.00 L.
    (b) Dilute 20.8 mL of 6.00 M H_2SO_4 to a volume of 1.00 L.
    (c) Add 950. mL water to 50.0 mL of 3.00 M H_2SO_4.
    (d) Add 500. mL water to 500. mL of 0.500 M H_2SO_4.
74. If you need 300. mL of 0.500 M $K_2Cr_2O_7$, which method would you use to prepare this solution?
    (a) Dilute 250. mL of 0.600 M $K_2Cr_2O_7$ to 300. mL.
    (b) Add 50.0 mL of water to 250. mL of 0.250 M $K_2Cr_2O_7$.
    (c) Dilute 125 mL of 1.00 M $K_2Cr_2O_7$ to 300. mL.
    (d) Add 30.0 mL of 1.50 M $K_2Cr_2O_7$ to 270. mL of water.
75. ■ You need to make a 0.300 M solution of $NiSO_4(aq)$. How many grams of $NiSO_4 \cdot 6\ H_2O$ should you put into a 0.500-L volumetric flask?
76. You wish to make a 0.200 M solution of $NiSO_4(aq)$. How many grams of $NiSO_4 \cdot 6\ H_2O$ should you put in a 0.500-L volumetric flask?

Calculations for Reactions in Solution

77. What mass, in grams, of Na_2CO_3 is required for complete reaction with 25.0 mL of 0.155 M HNO_3?

$$Na_2CO_3(aq) + 2\ HNO_3(aq) \longrightarrow 2\ NaNO_3(aq) + CO_2(g) + H_2O(\ell)$$

78. ■ Hydrazine, N_2H_4, a base like ammonia, can react with an acid such as sulfuric acid.

$$2\ N_2H_4(aq) + H_2SO_4(aq) \longrightarrow 2\ N_2H_5^+(aq) + SO_4^{-2}(aq)$$

What mass of hydrazine can react with 250. mL of 0.225 M H_2SO_4?

79. What volume, in milliliters, of 0.125 M HNO_3 is required to react completely with 1.30 g $Ba(OH)_2$?

$$2\ HNO_3(aq) + Ba(OH)_2(s) \longrightarrow Ba(NO_3)_2(aq) + 2\ H_2O(\ell)$$

80. Diborane, B_2H_6, can be produced by this reaction:

$$2\ NaBH_4(s) + H_2SO_4(aq) \longrightarrow 2\ H_2(g) + Na_2SO_4(aq) + B_2H_6(g)$$

What volume, in milliliters, of 0.0875 of M H_2SO_4 should be used to completely react with 1.35 g $NaBH_4$?

81. ■ What volume, in milliliters, of 0.512 M NaOH is required to react completely with 25.0 mL of 0.234 M H_2SO_4?
82. What volume, in milliliters, of 0.812 M HCl would be required to neutralize 15.0 mL of 0.635 M NaOH?
83. What is the maximum mass, in grams, of AgCl that can be precipitated by mixing 50.0 mL of 0.025 M $AgNO_3$ solution with 100.0 mL of 0.025 M NaCl solution? Which reactant is in excess? What is the concentration of the excess reactant remaining in solution after the AgCl has precipitated?

84. Suppose you mix 25.0 mL of 0.234 M $FeCl_3$ solution with 42.5 mL of 0.453 M NaOH.
 (a) What is the maximum mass, in grams, of $Fe(OH)_3$ that will precipitate?
 (b) Which reactant is in excess?
 (c) What is the concentration of the excess reactant remaining in solution after the maximum mass of $Fe(OH)_3$ has precipitated?

85. A soft drink contains an unknown amount of citric acid, $C_3H_5O(COOH)_3$. A volume of 10.0 mL of the soft drink requires 6.42 mL of 9.580×10^{-2} M NaOH to neutralize the citric acid.

$$C_3H_5O(COOH)_3(aq) + 3\ NaOH(aq) \longrightarrow Na_3C_3H_5O(COO)_3(aq) + 3\ H_2O(\ell)$$

 (a) Which step in these calculations for the mass of citric acid in 1 mL of soft drink is not correct?
 (b) What is the correct answer?
  (i) Moles NaOH = $(6.42\ mL)(1L/1000\ mL)(9.580 \times 10^{-2}\ mol/L)$
  (ii) Moles citric acid = $(6.15 \times 10^{-4}\ mol\ NaOH) \times$ (3 mol citric acid/1 mol NaOH)
  (iii) Mass citric acid in sample = $(1.85 \times 10^{-3}$ mol citric acid) $\times$ (192.12 g/mol citric acid)
  (iv) Mass citric acid in 1 mL soft drink = (0.354 g citric acid)/(10 mL soft drink)

86. Vitamin C is the compound $C_6H_8O_6$. Besides being an acid, it is a reducing agent that reacts readily with bromine, Br_2 a good oxidizing agent.

$$C_6H_8O_6(aq) + Br_2(aq) \longrightarrow 2\ HBr(aq) + C_6H_6O_6(aq)$$

Suppose a 1.00-g chewable vitamin C tablet requires 27.85 mL of 0.102 M Br_2 to react completely.
 (a) Which step in these calculations for the mass, in grams, of vitamin C in the tablet is incorrect?
 (b) What is the correct answer?
  (i) Mole Br_2 = (27.85 mL)(0.102 mol/L)
  (ii) Moles $C_6H_8O_6$ = (2.84 mol Br_2)(1 mol $C_6H_8O_6$/1 mol Br_2)
  (iii) Mass $C_6H_8O_6$ = (2.84 mol $C_6H_8O_6$)(176 g/mol $C_6H_8O_6$)
  (iv) Mass $C_6H_8O_6$ = (500 g $C_6H_8O_6$)/(1 g tablet)

87. ■ If a volume of 32.45 mL HCl is used to completely neutralize 2.050 g Na_2CO_3 according to this equation, what is the molarity of the HCl?

$$Na_2CO_3(aq) + 2\ HCl(aq) \longrightarrow 2\ NaCl(aq) + CO_2(g) + H_2O(\ell)$$

88. Potassium acid phthalate, $KHC_8H_4O_4$, is used to standardize solutions of bases. The acidic anion reacts with bases according to this net ionic equation:

$$HC_8H_4O_4^-(aq) + OH^-(aq) \longrightarrow H_2O(\ell) + C_8H_4O_4^{2-}(aq)$$

If a 0.902-g sample of potassium acid phthalate requires 26.45 mL NaOH to react, what is the molarity of the NaOH?

89. Sodium thiosulfate, $Na_2S_2O_3$, is used as a "fixer" in black-and-white photography. Assume you have a bottle of sodium thiosulfate and want to determine its purity. The thiosulfate ion can be oxidized with I_2 according to this equation:

$$I_2(aq) + 2\ S_2O_3^{2-}(aq) \longrightarrow 2\ I^-(aq) + S_4O_6^{2-}(aq)$$

If you use 40.21 mL of 0.246 M I_2 to completely react a 3.232-g sample of impure $Na_2S_2O_3$, what is the percent purity of the $Na_2S_2O_3$?

90. A sample of a mixture of oxalic acid, $H_2C_2O_4$, and sodium chloride, NaCl, has a mass of 4.554 g. If a volume of 29.58 mL of 0.550 M NaOH is required to neutralize all the $H_2C_2O_4$, what is the weight percent of oxalic acid in the mixture? Oxalic acid and NaOH react according to this equation:

$$H_2C_2O_4(aq) + 2\ NaOH(aq) \longrightarrow Na_2C_2O_4(aq) + 2\ H_2O(\ell)$$

General Questions

91. Name the spectator ions in the reaction of calcium carbonate and hydrochloric acid, and write the net ionic equation.

$$CaCO_3(s) + 2\ H^+(aq) + 2\ Cl^-(aq) \longrightarrow CO_2(g) + Ca^{2+}(aq) + 2\ Cl^-(aq) + H_2O(\ell)$$

What type of reaction is this?

92. Magnesium metal reacts readily with HNO_3, as shown in this equation:

$$Mg(s) + HNO_3(aq) \longrightarrow Mg(NO_3)_2(aq) + NO_2(g) + H_2O(\ell)$$

 (a) Balance the equation.
 (b) Name each reactant and product.
 (c) Write the net ionic equation.
 (d) What type of reaction is this?

93. Aqueous solutions of $(NH_4)_2S$ and $Hg(NO_3)_2$ react to give HgS and NH_4NO_3.
 (a) Write the overall balanced equation. Indicate the state (s or aq) for each compound.
 (b) Name each compound.
 (c) Write the net ionic equation.
 (d) What type of reaction does this appear to be?

94. Classify these reactions and predict the products formed.
 (a) $Li(s) + H_2O(\ell) \longrightarrow$
 (b) $Ag_2O(s) \xrightarrow{heat}$
 (c) $Li_2O(s) + H_2O(\ell) \longrightarrow$
 (d) $I_2(s) + Cl^-(aq) \longrightarrow$
 (e) $Cu(s) + HCl(aq) \longrightarrow$
 (f) $BaCO_3(s) \xrightarrow{heat}$

95. Classify these reactions and predict the products formed.
 (a) $SO_3(g) + H_2O(\ell) \longrightarrow$
 (b) $Sr(s) + H_2(g) \longrightarrow$
 (c) $Mg(s) + H_2SO_4$(aq, dilute) $\longrightarrow$
 (d) $Na_3PO_4(aq) + AgNO_3(aq) \longrightarrow$
 (e) $Ca(HCO_3)_2(s) \xrightarrow{heat}$
 (f) $Fe^{3+}(aq) + Sn^{2+}(aq) \longrightarrow$

96. Azurite is a copper-containing mineral that often forms beautiful crystals. Its formula is $Cu_3(CO_3)_2(OH)_2$. Write a balanced equation for the reaction of this mineral with hydrochloric acid.

97. What species (atoms, molecules, ions) are present in an aqueous solution of each of these compounds?
(a) NH_3 (b) CH_3COOH
(c) NaOH (d) HBr

98. Use the activity series to predict whether these reactions will occur.
(a) $Fe(s) + Mg^{2+}(aq) \longrightarrow Mg(s) + Fe^{2+}(aq)$
(b) $Ni(s) + Cu^{2+}(aq) \longrightarrow Ni^{2+}(aq) + Cu(s)$
(c) $Cu(s) + 2\,H^{+}(aq) \longrightarrow Cu^{2+}(aq) + H_2(g)$
(d) $Mg(s) + H_2O(g) \longrightarrow MgO(s) + H_2(g)$

99. Determine which of these are redox reactions. Identify the oxidizing and reducing agents in each of the redox reactions.
(a) $NaOH(aq) + H_3PO_4(aq) \rightarrow NaH_2PO_4(aq) + H_2O(\ell)$
(b) $NH_3(g) + CO_2(g) + H_2O(\ell) \rightarrow NH_4HCO_3(aq)$
(c) $TiCl_4(g) + 2\,Mg(\ell) \longrightarrow Ti(s) + 2\,MgCl_2(\ell)$
(d) $NaCl(s) + NaHSO_4(aq) \longrightarrow HCl(g) + Na_2SO_4(aq)$

100. Identify the substance oxidized, the substance reduced, the reducing agent, and the oxidizing agent in the equations in Question 99. For each oxidized or reduced substance, identify the change in its oxidation number.

Applying Concepts

101. When these pairs of reactants are combined in a beaker, (a) describe in words what the contents of the beaker would look like before and after any reaction occurs, (b) use different circles for atoms, molecules, and ions to draw a nanoscale (particulate-level) diagram of what the contents would look like, and (c) write a chemical equation to represent symbolically what the contents would look like.

$LiCl(aq)$ and $AgNO_3(aq)$

$NaOH(aq)$ and $HCl(aq)$

102. When these pairs of reactants are combined in a beaker, (a) describe in words what the contents of the beaker would look like before and after any reaction occurs, (b) use different circles for atoms, molecules, and ions to draw a particulate-level diagram of what the contents would look like, and (c) write a chemical equation to represent symbolically what the contents would look like.

$CaCO_3(s)$ and $HCl(aq)$

$NH_4NO_3(aq)$ and $KOH(aq)$

103. Explain how you could prepare barium sulfate by (a) an acid-base reaction, (b) a precipitation reaction, and (c) a gas-forming reaction. The materials you have to start with are $BaCO_3$, $Ba(OH)_2$, Na_2SO_4, and H_2SO_4.

104. Students were asked to prepare nickel sulfate by reacting a nickel compound with a sulfate compound in water and then evaporating the water. Three students chose these pairs of reactants:

Student 1	$Ni(OH)_2$ and H_2SO_4
Student 2	$Ni(NO_3)_2$ and Na_2SO_4
Student 3	$NiCO_3$ and H_2SO_4

Comment on each student's choice of reactants and how successful you think each student will be at preparing nickel sulfate by the procedure indicated.

105. An unknown solution contains either lead ions or barium ions, but not both. Which one of these solutions could you use to tell whether the ions present are Pb^{2+} or Ba^{2+}? Explain the reasoning behind your choice.

$HCl(aq)$, $H_2SO_4(aq)$, $H_3PO_4(aq)$

106. An unknown solution contains either calcium ions or strontium ions, but not both. Which one of these solutions could you use to tell whether the ions present are Ca^{2+} or Sr^{2+}? Explain the reasoning behind your choice.

$NaOH(aq)$, $H_2SO_4(aq)$, $H_2S(aq)$

107. When you are given an oxidation-reduction reaction and asked what is oxidized or what is reduced, why should you never choose one of the products for your answer?

108. When you are given an oxidation-reduction reaction and asked what is the oxidizing agent or what is the reducing agent, why should you never choose one of the products for your answer?

109. You prepared a NaCl solution by adding 58.44 g NaCl to a 1-L volumetric flask and then adding water to dissolve it. When you were finished, the final volume in your flask looked like this:

1.00-L flask

The solution you prepared is
(a) Greater than 1 M because you added more solvent than necessary.
(b) Less than 1 M because you added less solvent than necessary.
(c) Greater than 1 M because you added less solvent than necessary.
(d) Less than 1 M because you added more solvent than necessary.
(e) 1 M because the amount of solute, not solvent, determines the concentration.

110. These drawings represent beakers of aqueous solutions. Each orange circle represents a dissolved solute particle.

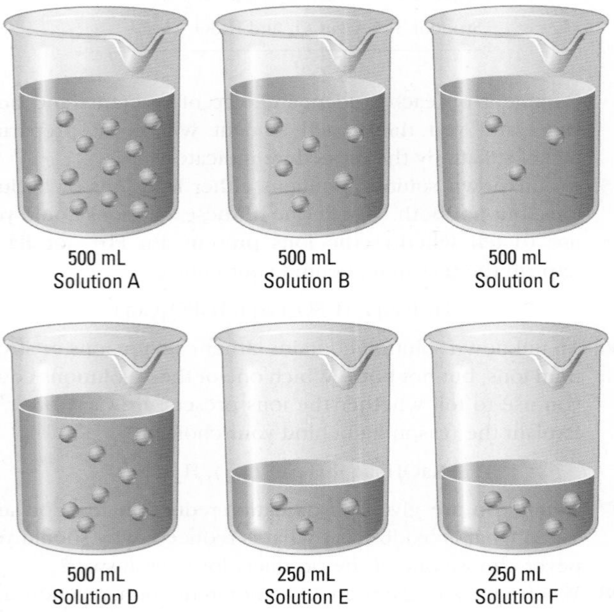

(a) Which solution is most concentrated?
(b) Which solution is least concentrated?
(c) Which two solutions have the same concentration?
(d) When solutions E and F are combined, the resulting solution has the same concentration as solution __________.
(e) When solutions B and E are combined, the resulting solution has the same concentration as solution __________.
(f) If you evaporate half of the water from solution B, the resulting solution will have the same concentration as solution __________.
(g) If you place half of solution A in another beaker and then add 250 mL water, the resulting solution will have the same concentration as solution __________.

111. Ten milliliters of a solution of an acid is mixed with 10 mL of a solution of a base. When the mixture was tested with litmus paper, the blue litmus turned red, and the red litmus remained red. Which of these interpretations is (are) correct?
(a) The mixture contains more hydrogen ions than hydroxide ions.
(b) The mixture contains more hydroxide ions than hydrogen ions.
(c) When an acid and a base react, water is formed, so the mixture cannot be acidic or basic.
(d) If the acid was HCl and the base was NaOH, the concentration of HCl in the initial acidic solution must have been greater than the concentration of NaOH in the initial basic solution.
(e) If the acid was H_2SO_4 and the base was NaOH, the concentration of H_2SO_4 in the initial acidic solution must have been greater than the concentration of NaOH in the initial basic solution.

112. A chemical company was interested in characterizing a competitor's organic acid (it consists of C, H, and O). After determining that it was a diacid, H_2X, a 0.1235-g sample was neutralized with 15.55 mL 0.1087 M NaOH. Next, a 0.3469-g sample was burned completely in pure oxygen, producing 0.6268 g CO_2 and 0.2138 g H_2O.
(a) What is the molar mass of H_2X?
(b) What is the empirical formula for the diacid?
(c) What is the molecular formula for the diacid?

113. Various masses of the three Group 2A elements magnesium, calcium, and strontium were allowed to react with liquid bromine, Br_2. After the reaction was complete, the reaction product was freed of excess reactant(s) and weighed. In each case, the mass of product was plotted against the mass of metal used in the reaction (as shown below).

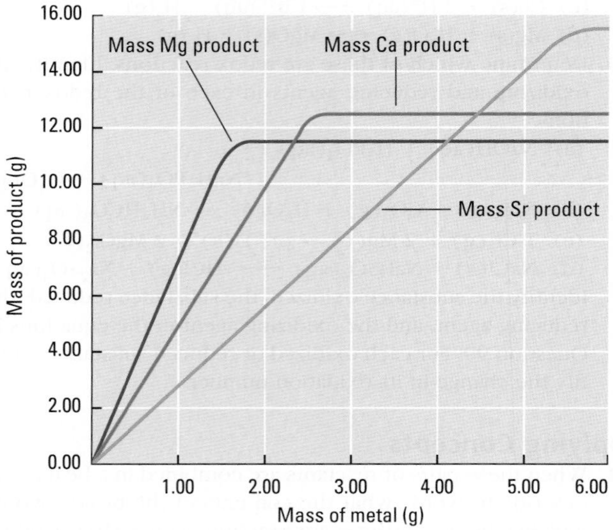

(a) Based on your knowledge of the reactions of metals with halogens, what product is predicted for each reaction? What are the name and formula for the reaction product in each case?
(b) Write a balanced equation for the reaction occurring in each case.
(c) What kind of reaction occurs between the metals and bromine—that is, is the reaction a gas-forming reaction, a precipitation reaction, or an oxidation-reduction reaction?
(d) Each plot shows that the mass of product increases with increasing mass of metal used, but the plot levels out at some point. Use these plots to verify your prediction of the formula of each product, and explain why the plots become level at different masses of metal and different masses of product.

114. Gold can be dissolved from gold-bearing rock by treating the rock with sodium cyanide in the presence of the oxygen in air.

$$4\ Au(s) + 8\ NaCN(aq) + O_2(g) + 2\ H_2O(\ell) \longrightarrow 4\ NaAu(CN)_2(aq) + 4\ NaOH(aq)$$

Once the gold is in solution in the form of the $Au(CN)_2^-$ ion, it can be precipitated as the metal according to the following unbalanced equation:

$$Au(CN)_2^-(aq) + Zn(s) \longrightarrow Zn^{2+}(aq) + Au(s) + CN^-(aq)$$

(a) Are the two reactions above acid-base or oxidation-reduction reactions? Briefly describe your reasoning.
(b) How many liters of 0.075 M NaCN will you need to extract the gold from 1000 kg of rock if the rock is 0.019% gold?
(c) How many kilograms of metallic zinc will you need to recover the gold from the $Au(CN)_2^-$ obtained from the gold in the rock?
(d) If the gold is recovered completely from the rock and the metal is made into a cylindrical rod 15.0 cm long, what is the diameter of the rod? (The density of gold is 19.3 g/cm^3.)

115. Four groups of students from an introductory chemistry laboratory are studying the reactions of solutions of alkali metal halides with aqueous silver nitrate, $AgNO_3$. They use these salts.
Group A: NaCl
Group B: KCl
Group C: NaBr
Group D: KBr
Each of the four groups dissolves 0.004 mol of their salt in some water. Each then adds various masses of silver nitrate, $AgNO_3$, to their solutions. After each group collects the precipitated silver halide, the mass of this product is plotted versus the mass of $AgNO_3$ added. The results are given on this graph.

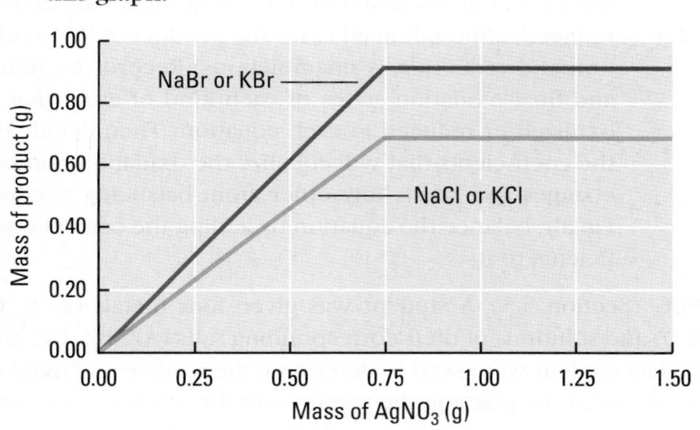

(a) Write the balanced net ionic equation for the reaction observed by each group.
(b) Explain why the data for groups A and B lie on the same line, whereas those for groups C and D lie on a different line.
(c) Explain the shape of the curve observed by each group. Why do they level off at the same mass of added $AgNO_3$ (0.75 g) but give different masses of product?

116. One way to determine the stoichiometric relationships among reactants is continuous variations. In this process, a series of reactions is carried out in which the reactants are varied systematically, while keeping the total volume of each reaction mixture constant. When the reactants combine stoichiometrically, they react completely; none is in excess. These data were collected to determine the stoichiometric relationship for the reaction.

$$mX^{n+} + nY^{m-} \longrightarrow X_mY_n$$

Trial	A	B	C	D	E
0.10 M X^{n+}	7 mL	6 mL	5 mL	4 mL	3 mL
0.20 M Y^{m-}	3 mL	4 mL	5 mL	6 mL	7 mL
Excess X^{n+} present?	Yes	Yes	Yes	No	No
Excess Y^{m-} present?	No	No	No	No	Yes

(a) In which trial are the reactants present in stoichiometric amounts?
(b) How many moles of X^{n+} reacted in that trial?
(c) How many moles of Y^{m-} reacted in that trial?
(d) What is the whole-number mole ratio of X^{n+} to Y^{m-}?
(e) What is the chemical formula for the product X_mY_n in terms of x and y?

More Challenging Questions

117. You are given 0.954 g of an unknown acid, H_2A, which reacts with NaOH according to the balanced equation

$$H_2A(aq) + 2\ NaOH(aq) \longrightarrow Na_2A(aq) + 2\ H_2O(\ell)$$

If a volume of 36.04 mL 0.509 M NaOH is required to react with all of the acid, what is the molar mass of the acid?

118. You are given an acid and told only that it could be citric acid (molar mass = 192.1 g/mol) or tartaric acid (molar mass = 150.1 g/mol). To determine which acid you have, you react it with NaOH. The appropriate reactions are

Citric acid:

$$C_6H_8O_7(aq) + 3\ NaOH(aq) \longrightarrow Na_3C_6H_5O_7(aq) + 3\ H_2O(\ell)$$

Tartaric acid:

$$C_4H_6O_6(aq) + 2\ NaOH(aq) \longrightarrow Na_2C_4H_4O_6(aq) + 2\ H_2O(\ell)$$

You find that a 0.956-g sample requires 29.1 mL 0.513 M NaOH to reach the equivalence point. What is the unknown acid?

119. Much has been written about chlorofluorocarbons and their effects on our environment. Their manufacture begins with the preparation of HF from the mineral fluorspar, CaF_2, according to this unbalanced equation:

$$CaF_2(s) + H_2SO_4(aq) \longrightarrow HF(g) + CaSO_4(s)$$

HF is combined with, for example, CCl_4 in the presence of $SbCl_5$ to make CCl_2F_2, called dichlorodifluoromethane or CFC-12, and other chlorofluorocarbons.

$$2\ HF(g) + CCl_4(\ell) \longrightarrow CCl_2F_2(g) + 2\ HCl(g)$$

(a) Balance the first equation above and name each substance.
(b) Is the first reaction best classified as an acid-base reaction, an oxidation-reduction reaction, or a precipitation reaction?
(c) Give the names of the compounds CCl_4, $SbCl_5$, and HCl.
(d) Another chlorofluorocarbon produced in the reaction is composed of 8.74% C, 77.43% Cl, and 13.83% F. What is the empirical formula of the compound?

120. In the past, devices for testing a driver's breath for alcohol depended on this reaction:

$$\underset{\text{ethanol}}{3\ C_2H_5OH(aq)} + 2\ K_2Cr_2O_7(aq) + 8\ H_2SO_4(aq) \longrightarrow$$

$$\underset{\text{acetic acid}}{3\ CH_3COOH(aq)} + 2\ Cr_2(SO_4)_3(aq) + 2\ K_2SO_4(aq) + 11\ H_2O(\ell)$$

Write the net ionic equation for this reaction. What oxidation numbers are changing in the course of this reaction? Which substances are being oxidized and reduced? Which substance is the oxidizing agent and which is the reducing agent?

121. How much salt is in your chicken soup? A student added excess $AgNO_3(aq)$ to a 1-cup serving of regular chicken soup (240 mL) and got 5.55 g AgCl precipitate. How many grams of NaCl were in the regular chicken soup? Assume that all the chloride ions in the soup were from NaCl. In a second experiment, the same procedure was done with chicken soup advertised to have "less salt," and the student got 3.55 g AgCl precipitate. How many grams of NaCl are in the "less salt" version?

122. The drug methamphetamine, also called "speed," has the molecular formula $C_{10}H_{15}N$. In the body it undergoes a series of metabolic reactions by which it is ultimately oxidized to produce carbon dioxide, nitrogen, and water. Write a balanced equation for this overall reaction.

123. The salt calcium sulfate is sparingly soluble in water with a solubility of 0.209 g/100 mL of water at 30 °C. If you stirred 0.550 g $CaSO_4$ into 100.0 mL water at 30 °C, what would the molarity of the resulting solution be? How many grams of $CaSO_4$ would remain undissolved?

124. What is the molarity of water in pure water?

125. A typical mug (250 mL) of coffee contains 125 mg caffeine ($C_8H_{10}N_4O_2$). What is the molarity of the caffeine?

126. (a) How many mL of 0.050 M HCl should be added to 50.0 mL of 0.40 M HCl to have a final solution with a molarity of 0.30 M?

(b) What volume of 0.154 M NaCl, "physiological saline solution," can you prepare by diluting 100 mL of 6.0 M NaCl solution?

127. The balanced equation for the oxidation of ethanol to acetic acid by potassium dichromate in an acidic aqueous solution is

$$3\,C_2H_5OH(aq) + 2\,K_2Cr_2O_7(aq) + 16\,HCl(aq) \longrightarrow 3\,CH_3COOH(aq) + 4\,CrCl_3(aq) + 4\,KCl(aq) + 11\,H_2O(\ell)$$

What volume of a 0.600 M potassium dichromate solution is needed to generate 0.166 mol acetic acid (CH_3COOH) from a solution containing excess ethanol and HCl?

128. Dolomite, found in soil, is $CaMg(CO_3)_2$. If a 20.0-g sample of soil is titrated with 65.25 mL of 0.2500 M HCl, what is the mass percent of dolomite in the soil sample?

129. Vitamin C is ascorbic acid, $HC_6H_7O_6$, which can be titrated with a strong base.

$$HC_6H_7O_6(aq) + NaOH(aq) \longrightarrow NaC_6H_7O_6(aq) + H_2O(\ell)$$

In a laboratory experiment, a student dissolved a 500.0-mg vitamin C tablet in 200.0 mL water and then titrated it with 0.1250 M NaOH. It required 21.30 mL of the base to reach the equivalence point. What percentage of the mass of the tablet is impurity?

130. In this redox reaction methanol reduces chlorate ion to chlorine dioxide in the presence of acid, and the methanol is oxidized to CO_2:

$$CH_3OH(\ell) + 6\,HClO_3(aq) \longrightarrow 6\,ClO_2(g) + CO_2(g) + 5\,H_2O(\ell)$$

How many mL of methanol would be needed to produce 100.0 kg of chlorine dioxide? The density of methanol is 0.791 g/mL.

Conceptual Challenge Problems

CP5.A (Section 5.3) There is a conservation of the number of electrons exchanged during redox reactions, which is tantamount to stating that electrical charge is conserved during chemical reactions. The assignment of oxidation numbers is an arbitrary yet clever way to do the bookkeeping for these electrons. What makes it possible to assign the same oxidation number to all elements that are not bound to other elements not in chemical compounds?

CP5.B (Section 5.4) Consider these redox reactions:

$$HIO_3 + FeI_2 + HCl \longrightarrow FeCl_3 + ICl + H_2O$$

$$CuSCN + KIO_3 + HCl \longrightarrow CuSO_4 + KCl + HCN + ICl + H_2O$$

(a) Identify the species that have been oxidized or reduced in each of the reactions.

(b) After you have correctly identified the species that have been oxidized or reduced in each equation, you might like to try using oxidation numbers to balance each equation. This will be a challenge because, as you have discovered, more than one kind of atom is oxidized or reduced, although in all cases the product of the oxidation and reduction is unambiguous. Record the initial and final oxidation states of each kind of atom that is oxidized or reduced in each equation. Then decide on the coefficients that will equalize the oxidation number changes and satisfy any other atom balancing needed. Finally, balance the equation by adding the correct coefficients to it.

CP5.C (Section 5.5) A student was given four metals (A, B, C, and D) and solutions of their corresponding salts (AZ, BZ, CZ, and DZ). The student was asked to determine the relative reactivity of the four metals by reacting the metals with the solutions. The student's laboratory observations are indicated in the table. Arrange the four metals in order of decreasing activity.

Metal	AZ(aq)	BZ(aq)	CZ(aq)	DZ(aq)
A	No reaction	No reaction	No reaction	No reaction
B	Reaction	No reaction	Reaction	No reaction
C	Reaction	No reaction	No reaction	No reaction
D	Reaction	Reaction	Reaction	No reaction

CP5.D (Section 5.6) How would you prepare 1 L of 1.00×10^{-6} M NaCl (molar mass = 58.44 g/mol) solution by using a balance that can measure mass only to 0.01 g?

CP5.E (Section 5.8) How could you show that when baking soda reacts with the acetic acid, CH_3COOH, in vinegar, all of the carbon and oxygen atoms in the carbon dioxide produced come from the baking soda alone and none comes from the acetic acid in vinegar?

6

Energy and Chemical Reactions

Combustion of a fuel. Burning propane, C_3H_8, releases a great deal of energy to anything in contact with the reactant and product molecules—in this case glass, boiling water, and soon-to-be-hard-boiled eggs. The energy released when a fuel such as propane burns can be transformed to provide many of the benefits of our technology-intensive society.

© Royalty-Free/CORBIS

ThomsonNOW™
Throughout the text, this icon indicates an opportunity to test yourself on key concepts and to explore interactive modules by signing in to ThomsonNOW at **www.thomsonedu.com**.

"A theory is the more impressive the greater the simplicity of its premises is, the more different kinds of things it relates, and the more extended is its area of applicability. Therefore, the deep impression which classical thermodynamics made upon me. It is the only physical theory of universal content concerning which I am convinced that, within the framework of the applicability of its basic concepts, it will never be overthrown." (Albert Einstein, quoted in Schlipp, P. A. [ed.] "Albert Einstein: Philosopher-Scientist." In *The Library of Living Philosophers*, Vol. VII. Autobiographical notes, 3rd ed. LaSalle, IL: Open Court Publishing, 1969; p. 33.)

Work and *heat* refer to the quantity of energy transferred from one object or sample to another by working or heating *processes*. However, we often talk about work and heat as if they were forms of energy. Working and heating processes transfer energy from one form or one place to another. To emphasize this, we often will use the words *working* and *heating* where many people would use *work* and *heat*.

© Scott McDermott/CORBIS

Figure 6.1 Kinetic energy. As it speeds toward the player, a tennis ball has kinetic energy that depends on its mass and velocity.

In our industrialized, high-technology, appliance-oriented society, the average use of energy per person is at nearly its highest point in history. The United States, with only 5% of the world's population, consumes about 30% of the world's energy resources. In every year since 1958 we have consumed more energy resources than have been produced within our borders. Most of the energy we use comes from chemical reactions: combustion of the fossil fuels coal, petroleum, and natural gas. The rest comes from hydroelectric power plants, nuclear power plants, solar energy and wind collectors, and burning wood and other plant material. Both U.S. and world energy use are growing rapidly.

Chemical reactions involve transfers of energy. When a fuel burns, the energy of the products is less than the energy of the reactants. The leftover energy shows up in anything that is in contact with the reactants and products. For example, when propane burns in air, the carbon, hydrogen, and oxygen atoms in the C_3H_8 and O_2 reactant molecules rearrange to form CO_2 and H_2O product molecules.

$$C_3H_8(g) + 5\,O_2(g) \longrightarrow 3\,CO_2(g) + 4\,H_2O(g)$$

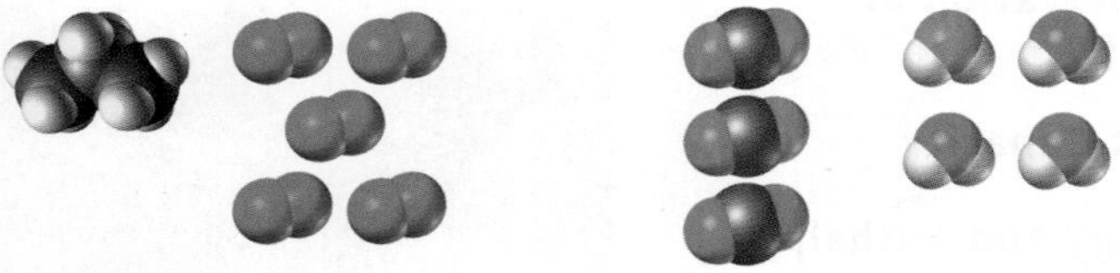

Because of the way their atoms are bonded together, the CO_2 and H_2O molecules have less total energy than the C_3H_8 and O_2 reactant molecules did. After the reaction, some energy that was in the reactants is not contained in the product molecules. That energy heats everything that is close to where the reaction takes place. To describe this effect, we say that the reaction transfers energy to its surroundings.

For the past hundred years or so, most of the energy society has used has come from combustion of fossil fuels, and this will continue to be true well into the future. Consequently, it is very important to understand how energy and chemical reactions are related and how chemistry might be used to alter our dependence on fossil fuels. This requires knowledge of **thermodynamics,** the science of heat, work, and transformations of one to the other. The fastest-growing new industries in the twenty-first century may well be those that capitalize on such knowledge and the new chemistry and chemical industries it spawns.

6.1 The Nature of Energy

What is energy? Where does the energy we use come from? And how can chemical reactions result in the transfer of energy to or from their surroundings? *Energy,* represented by E, was defined in Section 1.5 (**p. 14**) as the capacity to do work. If you climb a mountain or a staircase, you work against the force of gravity as you move upward, and your gravitational energy increases. The energy you use to do this work is released when food you have eaten is metabolized (undergoes chemical reactions) within your body. Energy from food enables you to work against the force of gravity as you climb, and it warms your body (climbing makes you hotter as well as higher). Therefore our study of the relations between energy and chemistry also needs to consider processes that involve work and processes that involve heat.

Energy can be classified as kinetic or potential. **Kinetic energy** is energy that something has because it is moving (Figure 6.1). Examples of kinetic energy are

- Energy of motion of a macroscale object, such as a moving baseball or automobile; this is often called *mechanical energy.*
- Energy of motion of nanoscale objects such as atoms, molecules, or ions; this is often called *thermal energy.*

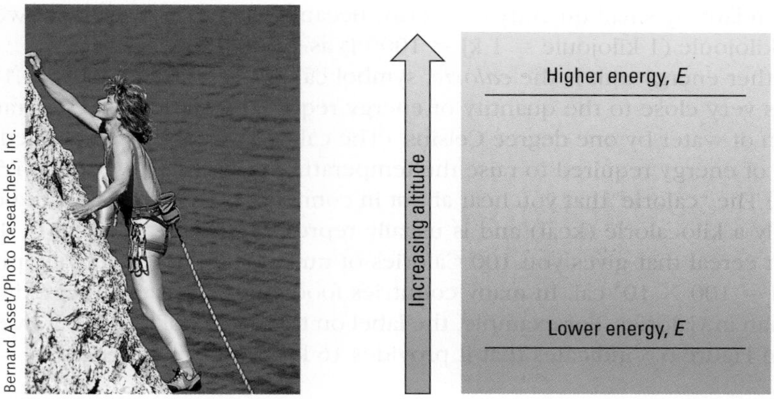

(a) (b)

Rock climbing. (a) Climbing requires energy. (b) The higher the altitude, the greater the climber's gravitational energy.

- Energy of motion of electrons through an electrical conductor; this is often called *electrical energy.*
- Energy of periodic motion of nanoscale particles when a macroscale sample is alternately compressed and expanded (as when a sound wave passes through air).

Kinetic energy, E_k, can be calculated as $E_k = \frac{1}{2}mv^2$, where m represents the mass and v represents the velocity of a moving object.

Potential energy is energy that something has as a result of its position and some force that is capable of changing that position. Examples include

- Energy that a ball held in your hand has because the force of gravity attracts it toward the floor; this is often called *gravitational energy.*
- Energy that charged particles have because they attract or repel each other; this is often called *electrostatic energy.* An example is the potential energy of positive and negative ions close together.
- Energy resulting from attractions and repulsions among electrons and atomic nuclei in molecules; this is often called *chemical potential energy* and is the kind of energy stored in foods and fuels.

Potential energy can be calculated in different ways, depending on the type of force that is involved. For example, near the surface of the earth, gravitational potential energy, E_p, can be calculated as $E_p = mgh$, where m is mass, g is the gravitational constant ($g = 9.8\ m/s^2$), and h is the height above the surface.

Potential energy can be converted to kinetic energy, and vice versa. As droplets of water fall over a waterfall (Figure 6.2), the potential energy they had at the top is converted to kinetic energy—they move faster and faster. Conversely, the kinetic energy of falling water could drive a water wheel to pump water to an elevated reservoir, where its potential energy would be higher.

Figure 6.2 Gravitational potential energy. Water on the brink of a waterfall has potential energy (stored energy that could be used to do work) because of its position relative to the earth; that energy could be used to generate electricity, for example, as in a hydroelectric power plant.

James P. Joule
1818–1889

The energy unit joule is named for James P. Joule. The son of a brewer in Manchester, England, Joule was a student of John Dalton (**p. 22**). Joule established the idea that working and heating are both processes by which energy can be transferred from one sample of matter to another.

Energy Units

The SI unit of energy is the *joule* (rhymes with rule), symbol J. The joule is a derived unit, which means that it can be expressed as a combination of other more fundamental units: $1\ J = 1\ kg\ m^2/s^2$. If a 2.0-kg object (which weighs about $4\frac{1}{2}$ pounds) is moving with a velocity of 1.0 meter per second (roughly 2 miles per hour), its kinetic energy is

$$E_k = \frac{1}{2}mv^2 = \frac{1}{2} \times (2.0\ kg)(1.0\ m/s)^2 = 1.0\ kg\ m^2/s^2 = 1.0\ J$$

The joule is the unit of energy in the International System of units (SI units). SI units are described in Appendix B. A joule is approximately the quantity of energy required for one human heartbeat.

1 cal = 4.184 J exactly

1 Cal = 1 kcal = 1000 cal = 4.184 kJ = 4184 J

The food Calorie measures how much energy is released when a given quantity of food undergoes combustion with oxygen.

This is a relatively small quantity of energy. Because the joule is so small, we often use the kilojoule (1 kilojoule = 1 kJ = 1000 J) as a unit of energy.

Another energy unit is the *calorie*, symbol cal. By definition 1 cal = 4.184 J. A calorie is very close to the quantity of energy required to raise the temperature of one gram of water by one degree Celsius. (The calorie was originally defined as the quantity of energy required to raise the temperature of 1 g $H_2O(\ell)$ from 14.5 °C to 15.5 °C.) The "calorie" that you hear about in connection with nutrition and dieting is actually a kilocalorie (kcal) and is usually represented with a capital C. Thus, a breakfast cereal that gives you 100 Calories of nutritional energy actually provides 100 kcal = 100×10^3 cal. In many countries food energy is reported in kilojoules rather than in Calories. For example, the label on the packet of nonsugar sweetener shown in Figure 6.3 indicates that it provides 16 kJ of nutritional energy.

© Thomson Learning/Charles D. Winters

Figure 6.3 Food energy. A packet of artificial sweetener from Australia. As its label shows, the sweetener in the packet supplies 16 kJ of nutritional energy. It is equivalent in sweetness to 2 level teaspoonfuls of sugar, which would supply 140 kJ of nutritional energy.

PROBLEM-SOLVING EXAMPLE 6.1 Energy Units

A single Fritos snack chip has a food energy of 5.0 Cal. What is this energy in units of joules?

Answer 2.1×10^4 J

Strategy and Explanation To find the energy in joules, we use the fact that 1 Cal = 1 kcal, the definition of the prefix *kilo-* (= 1000), and the definition 1 cal = 4.184 J to generate appropriate proportionality factors (conversion factors).

$$E = 5.0\ \text{Cal} \times \frac{1\ \text{kcal}}{1\ \text{Cal}} \times \frac{1000\ \text{cal}}{1\ \text{kcal}} \times \frac{4.184\ \text{J}}{1\ \text{cal}} = 2.1 \times 10^4\ \text{J}$$

✓ **Reasonable Answer Check** 2.1×10^4 J is 21 kJ. Because 1 Cal = 1 kcal = 4.184 kJ, the result in kJ should be about four times the original 5 Cal (that is, about 20 kJ), which it is.

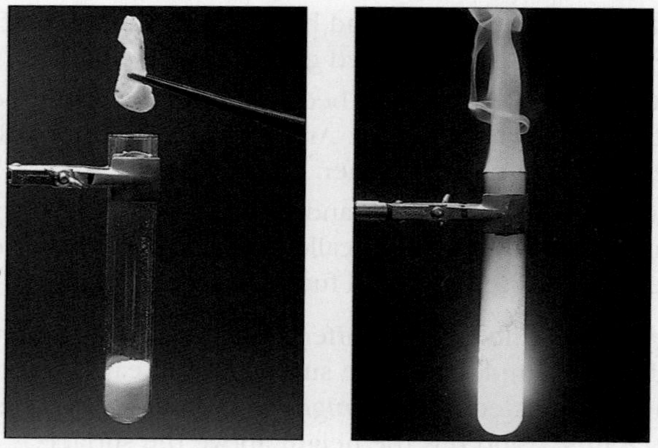

© Thomson Learning/Charles D. Winters

(a) (b)

Food energy. A single Fritos chip burns in oxygen generated by thermal decomposition of potassium chlorate.

PROBLEM-SOLVING PRACTICE 6.1

(a) If you eat a hot dog, it will provide 160 Calories of energy. Express this energy in joules.

(b) A watt (W) is a unit of power that corresponds to the transfer of one joule of energy in one second. The energy used by an x-watt light bulb operating for y seconds is $x \times y$ joules. If you turn on a 75-watt bulb for 3.0 hours, how many joules of electrical energy will be transformed into light and heat?

(c) The packet of nonsugar sweetener in Figure 6.3 provides 16 kJ of nutritional energy. Express this energy in kilocalories.

ThomsonNOW

Go to the Coached Problems menu for an exercise on **energy conversions** and a tutorial on **energy unit conversions.**

ESTIMATION

Earth's Kinetic Energy

Estimate the earth's kinetic energy as it moves through space in orbit around the sun.

From an encyclopedia, a dictionary, or the Internet, you can obtain the facts that the earth's mass is about 3×10^{24} kg and its distance from the sun is about 150,000,000 km. Assume earth's orbit is a circle and calculate the distance traveled in a year as the circumference of this circle, $\pi d = 2\pi r = 2 \times 3.14 \times 1.5 \times 10^8$ km. Since $2 \times 3 = 6$, $1.5 \times 6 = 9$, and 3.14 is a bit more than 3, estimate the distance as 10×10^8 km. Earth's speed, then, is a bit less than 10×10^8 km/yr.

Because $1\ \text{J} = 1\ \text{kg m}^2/\text{s}^2$, convert the time unit from years to seconds. Estimate the number of seconds in one year as 60 s/min × 60 min/h × 24 h/d × 365 d/yr = 60 × 60 × 24 × 365 s/yr. To make the arithmetic easy, round 24 to 20 and 365 to 400, giving 60 × 60 × 20 × 400 s/yr = 6 × 6 × 2 × 4 × 10^5 s/yr. This gives 288 × 10^5 s/yr, or 3×10^7 s/yr rounded to one significant figure. Therefore earth's speed is about $10/3 \times 10^8/10^7 \cong 30$ km/s or 3×10^4 m/s.

Now the equation for kinetic energy can be used.

$$E_k = \frac{1}{2}mv^2$$

$$= \frac{1}{2} \times (3 \times 10^{24}\ \text{kg}) \times (3 \times 10^4\ \text{m/s})^2 \simeq 1 \times 10^{33}\ \text{J}$$

Although the earth's speed is not high, its mass is very large. This results in an extraordinarily large kinetic energy—far more energy than has been involved in all of the hurricanes and typhoons that earth has ever experienced.

ThomsonNOW™
Sign in to ThomsonNOW at **www.thomsonedu.com** to work an interactive module based on this material.

6.2 Conservation of Energy

When you dive from a diving board into a pool of water, several transformations of energy occur (Figure 6.4). Eventually, you float on the surface and the water becomes still. However, on average, the water molecules are moving a little faster in the vicinity of your point of impact; that is, the temperature of the water is now a little higher. Energy has been transformed from potential to kinetic and from macroscale kinetic to nanoscale kinetic (that is, thermal). Nevertheless, the total quantity of energy, kinetic plus potential, is the same before and after the dive. In many, many experiments, the total energy has always been found to be the same before and after an event. These experiments are summarized by the **law of conservation of energy,** which states that *energy can neither be created nor destroyed—the total energy of the universe is constant.* This is also called the **first law of thermodynamics.**

In Section 1.8 (*p. 21*) the kinetic-molecular theory was described qualitatively. A corollary to this theory is that *molecules move faster, on average, as the temperature increases.*

The nature of scientific laws is discussed in Chapter 1 (*p. 6*).

CONCEPTUAL EXERCISE 6.1 Energy Transfers

You toss a rubber ball up into the air. It falls to the floor, bounces for a while, and eventually comes to rest. Several energy transfers are involved. Describe them and the changes they cause.

Energy and Working

When a force acts on an object and moves the object, the change in the object's kinetic energy is equal to the work done on the object. Work has to be done, for example, to accelerate a car from 0 to 60 miles per hour or to hit a baseball out of a stadium. Work is also required to increase the potential energy of an object. Thus, work has to be done to raise an object against the force of gravity (as in an elevator), to separate a sodium ion (Na^+) from a chloride ion (Cl^-), or to move an electron away from an atomic nucleus. The work done on an object corresponds to the quantity of energy transferred to that object; that is, doing **work** (or **working**) on

Work is required to cause some chemical and biochemical processes to occur. Examples are moving ions across a cell membrane and synthesizing adenosine triphosphate (ATP) from adenosine diphosphate (ADP).

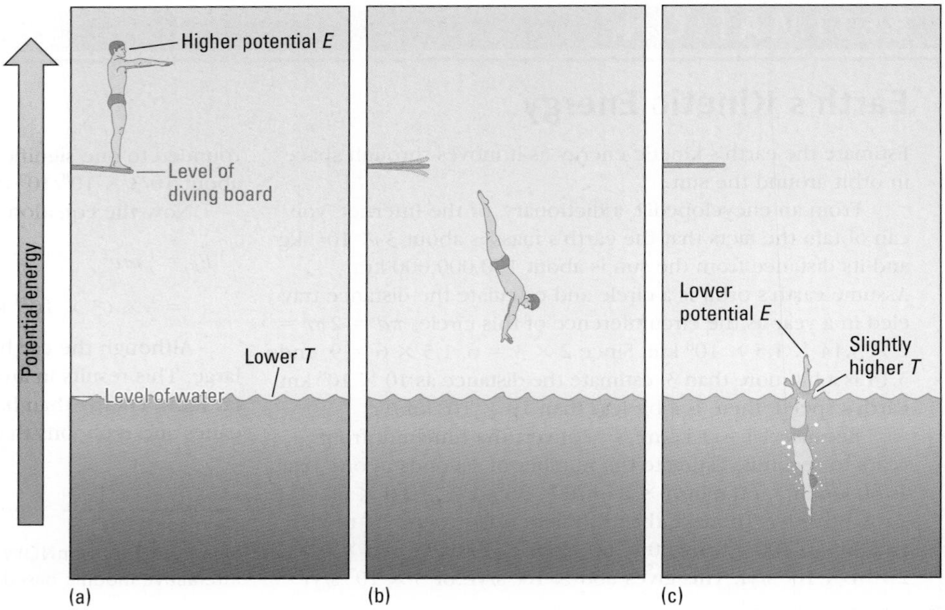

Figure 6.4 Energy transformations. Potential and kinetic energy are interconverted when someone dives into water. These interconversions are governed by the law of conservation of energy. (a) The diver has greater gravitational potential energy on the diving board than at the surface of the water, because the platform is higher above the earth. (b) Some of the potential energy has been converted into kinetic energy as the diver's altitude above the water decreases and velocity increases; maximum kinetic energy occurs just prior to impact with the water. (c) Upon impact, the diver works on the water, splashing it aside; eventually, the initial potential energy difference is converted into motion on the nanoscale—the temperature of the water has become slightly higher.

an object is *a process that transfers energy to an object.* Conversely, if an object does work on something else, the quantity of energy associated with the object must decrease. In the rest of this chapter (and book), we will refer to a transfer of energy by doing work as a "work transfer."

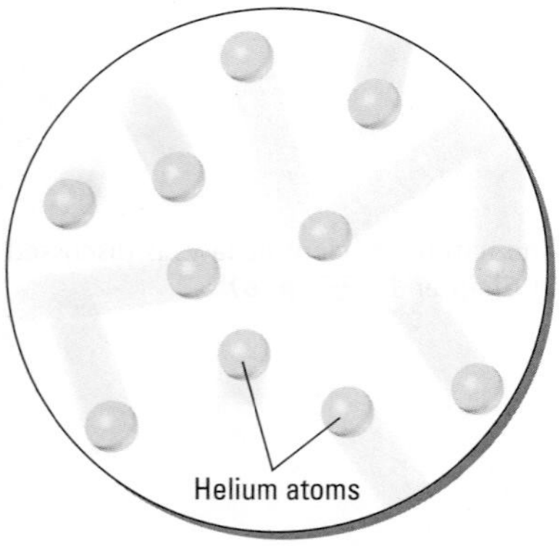

Figure 6.5 Thermal energy. According to the kinetic-molecular theory, nanoscale particles (atoms, molecules, and ions) are in constant motion. Here, atoms of gaseous helium are shown. Each atom has kinetic energy that depends on how fast it is moving (as indicated by the length of the "tail," which shows how far each atom travels per unit time). The thermal energy of the sample is the sum of the kinetic energies of all the helium atoms. The higher the temperature of the helium, the faster the average speed of the molecules, and therefore the greater the thermal energy.

Energy, Temperature, and Heating

According to the kinetic-molecular theory ***(⇐ p. 21)***, all matter consists of nanoscale particles that are in constant motion (Figure 6.5). Therefore, all matter has thermal energy. For a given sample, the quantity of thermal energy is greater the higher the temperature is. Transferring energy to a sample of matter usually results in a temperature increase that can be measured with a thermometer. For example, when a mercury thermometer is placed into warm water (Figure 6.6), energy transfers from the water to the thermometer (the water heats the thermometer). The increased energy of the mercury atoms means that they move about more rapidly, which slightly increases the volume of the spaces between the atoms. Consequently, the mercury expands (as most substances do upon heating), and the column of mercury rises higher in the thermometer tube.

Heat (or **heating**) refers to *the energy transfer process that happens whenever two samples of matter at different temperatures are brought into contact.* ***Energy always transfers from the hotter to the cooler sample until both are at the same temperature.*** For example, a piece of metal at a high temperature in a Bunsen burner flame and a beaker of cold water (Figure 6.7a) are two samples of matter with different temperatures. When the hot metal is plunged into the cold water (Figure 6.7b), energy transfers from the metal to the water until the two samples reach the same temperature. Once that happens, the metal and water are

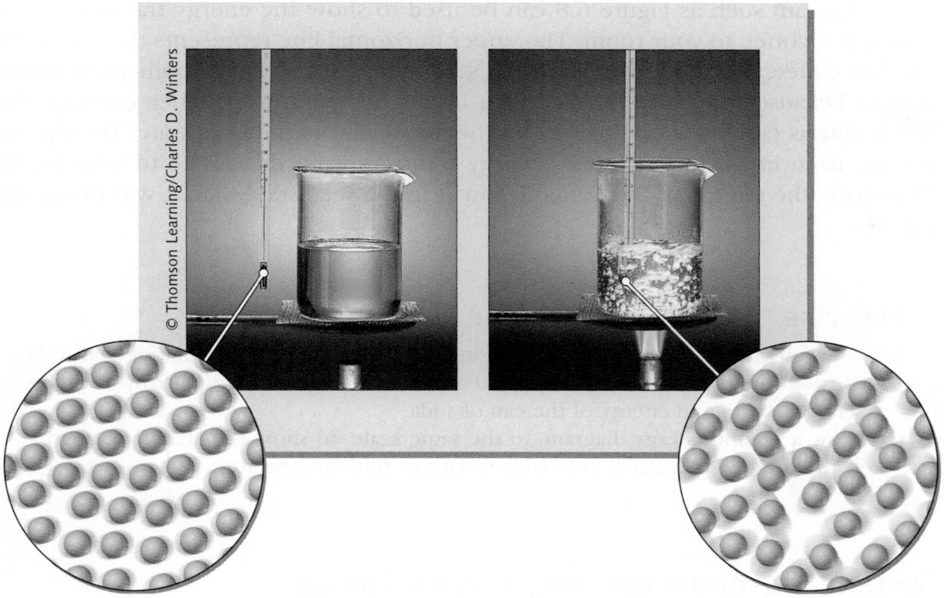

Figure 6.6 **Measuring temperature.** The mercury in a thermometer expands because the mercury atoms are moving faster (have more energy) after the boiling water transfers energy to (heats) the mercury; the temperature and the volume of the mercury have both increased.

said to be in **thermal equilibrium.** When thermal equilibrium is reached, the metal has heated the water (and the water has cooled the metal) to a common temperature. In the rest of this chapter (and book), we will refer to a transfer of energy by heating and cooling as a "heat transfer."

Usually most objects in a given region, such as your room, are at about the same temperature—at thermal equilibrium. A fresh cup of coffee, which is hotter than room temperature, transfers energy by heating the rest of the room until the coffee cools off (and the rest of the room warms up a bit). A can of cold soda, which is much cooler than its surroundings, receives energy from everything else until it warms up (and your room cools off a little). Because the total quantity of material in your room is very much greater than that in a cup of coffee or a can of soda, the room temperature changes only a tiny bit to reach thermal equilibrium, whereas the temperature of the coffee or the soda changes a lot.

Transferring energy by heating is a process, but it is common to talk about that process as if heat were a form of energy. It is often said that one sample transfers heat to another, when what is meant is that one sample transfers energy by heating the other.

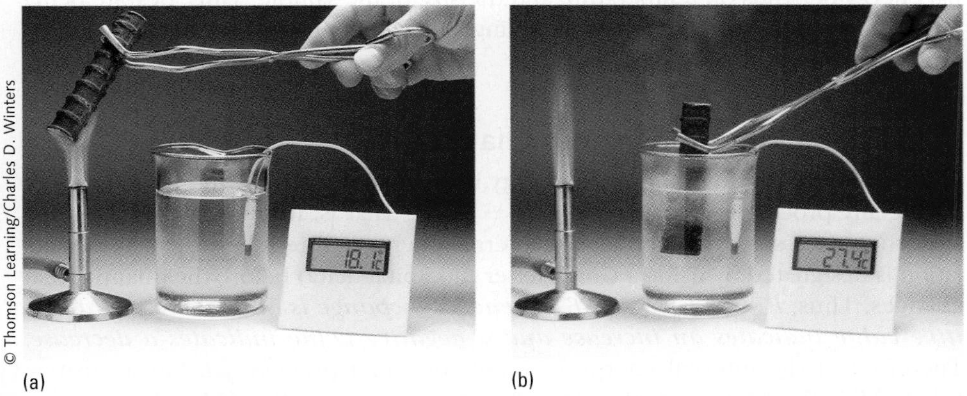

Figure 6.7 **Energy transfer by heating.** Water in a beaker is heated when a hotter sample (a steel bar) is plunged into the water. There is a transfer of energy from the hotter metal bar to the cooler water. Eventually, enough energy is transferred so that the bar and the water reach the same temperature—that is, thermal equilibrium is achieved.

ThomsonNOW™

Go to the Chemistry Interactive menu to work modules on:

- **transfer of thermal energy from heated bar to cool water**
- **transfer of thermal energy to water by drilling**

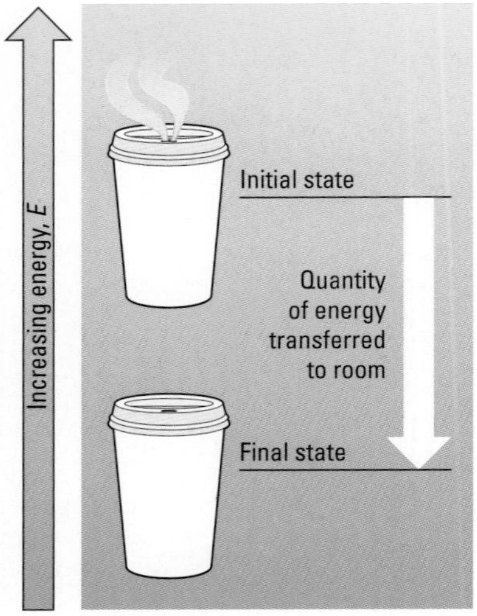

Figure 6.8 Energy diagram for a cup of hot coffee. The diagram compares the energy of a cup of hot coffee with the energy after the coffee has cooled to room temperature. The higher something is in the diagram, the more energy it has. As the coffee and cup cool to room temperature, energy is transferred to the surrounding matter in the room. According to the law of conservation of energy, the energy remaining in the coffee must be less after the change (in the final state) than it was before the change (in the initial state). The quantity of energy transferred is represented by the arrow from the initial to the final state.

A diagram such as Figure 6.8 can be used to show the energy transfer from a cup of hot coffee to your room. The upper horizontal line represents the energy of the hot coffee and the lower line represents the energy of the room-temperature coffee. Because the coffee started at a higher temperature (higher energy), the upper line is labeled the initial state. The lower line is the final state. During the change from initial to final state, energy transfers from the coffee to your room. Therefore, the energy of the coffee is lower in the final state than it was in the initial state.

EXERCISE 6.2 Energy Diagrams

(a) Draw an energy diagram like the one in Figure 6.8 for warming a can of cold soda to room temperature. Label the initial and final states and use an arrow to represent the change in energy of the can of soda.

(b) Draw a second energy diagram, to the same scale, to show the change in energy of the room as the can of cold soda warms to room temperature.

System, Surroundings, and Internal Energy

In thermodynamics it is useful to define a *region of primary concern* as the **system.** Then we can decide whether energy transfers into or out of the system and keep an accounting of how much energy transfers in each direction. *Everything that can exchange energy with the system* is defined as the **surroundings.** A system may be delineated by an actual physical boundary, such as the inside surface of a flask or the membrane of a cell in your body. Or the boundary may be indistinct, as in the case of the solar system within its surroundings, the rest of the galaxy. In the case of a hot cup of coffee in your room, the cup and the coffee might be the system, and your room would be the surroundings. For a chemical reaction, the system is usually defined to be all of the atoms that make up the reactants. These same atoms will be bonded in a different way in the products after the reaction, and it is their energy before and after reaction that interests us most.

The **internal energy** of a system is the *sum of the individual energies (kinetic and potential) of all nanoscale particles (atoms, molecules, or ions)* in that system. Increasing the temperature increases the internal energy because it increases the average speed of motion of nanoscale particles. ***The total internal energy of a sample of matter depends on temperature, the type of particles, and the number of particles in the sample.*** For a given substance, internal energy depends on temperature and the size of the sample. Thus, despite being at a higher temperature, a cupful of boiling water contains less energy than a bathtub full of warm water.

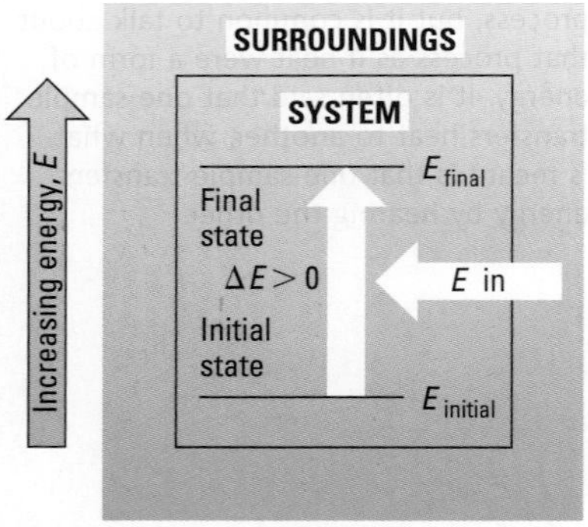

ΔE positive: Internal energy increases.

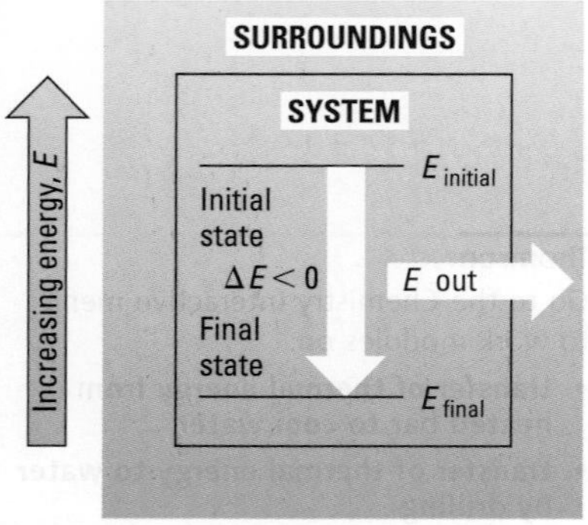

ΔE negative: Internal energy decreases.

Calculating Thermodynamic Changes

If we represent a system's internal energy by E, then the change in internal energy during any process is calculated as $E_{final} - E_{initial}$. That is, from the internal energy after the process is over subtract the internal energy before it began. Such a calculation is designated by using a Greek letter Δ (capital delta) before the quantity that changes. Thus, $E_{final} - E_{initial} = \Delta E$. *Whenever a change is indicated by Δ, a positive value indicates an increase and a negative value indicates a decrease.* Therefore, if the internal energy increases during a process, ΔE has a positive value ($\Delta E > 0$); if the internal energy decreases, ΔE is negative ($\Delta E < 0$).

A good analogy to this thermodynamic calculation is your bank account. Assume that in your account (the system) you have a balance B of \$260 ($B_{initial}$), and you withdraw \$60 in spending money. After the withdrawal the balance is \$200 (B_{final}). The change in your balance is

$$\text{Change in balance} = \Delta B = B_{\text{final}} - B_{\text{initial}} = \$200 - \$260 = -\$60$$

The negative sign on the \$60 indicates that money has been withdrawn from the account (system) and transferred to you (the surroundings). The cash itself is not negative, but during the process of withdrawing your money the balance in the bank went down, so ΔB was negative. Similarly, the *magnitude* of change of a thermodynamic quantity is a number with no sign. To indicate the *direction* of a change, we attach a negative sign (transferred out of the system) or a positive sign (transferred into the system).

CONCEPTUAL EXERCISE 6.3 Direction of Energy Transfer

It takes about 1.5 kJ to raise the temperature of a can of Classic Coke from 25.0 °C to 26.0 °C. You put the can of Coke into a refrigerator to cool it from room temperature (25.0 °C) to 1.0 °C.

(a) What quantity of heat transfer is required? Express your answer in kilojoules.
(b) What is a reasonable choice of system for this situation?
(c) What constitutes the surroundings?
(d) What is the sign of ΔE for this situation? What is the calculated value of ΔE?
(e) Draw an energy diagram showing the system, the surroundings, the change in energy of the system, and the energy transfer between the system and the surroundings.

Conservation of Energy and Chemical Reactions

For many chemical reactions the only energy transfer processes are heating and doing work. If no other energy transfers (such as emitting light) take place, the law of conservation of energy for any system can be written as

$$\Delta E = q + w \qquad [6.1]$$

where q represents the quantity of energy transferred by heating the system, and w represents the quantity of energy transferred by doing work on the system. If energy is transferred into the system from the surroundings by heating, then q is positive; if energy is transferred into the system because the surroundings do work on the system, then w is positive. If energy is transferred out of the system by heating the surroundings, then q has a negative value; if energy is transferred out of the system because work is done on the surroundings, then w has a negative value. The *magnitudes* of q and w indicate the *quantities* of energy transferred, and the *signs* of q and w indicate the *direction* in which the energy is transferred. The relationships among ΔE, q, and w for a system are shown in Figure 6.9.

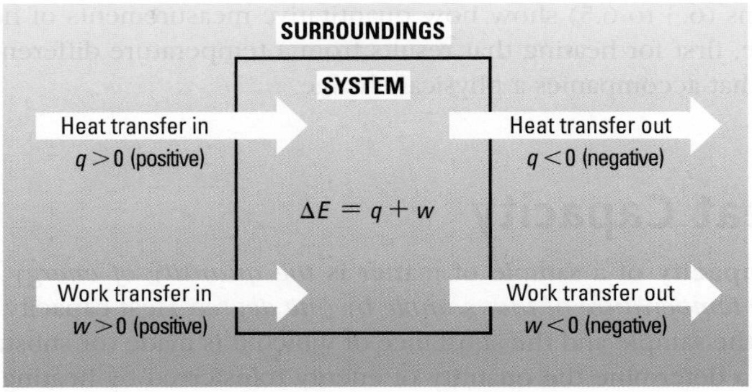

Figure 6.9 Internal energy, heat, and work. Schematic diagram showing energy transfers between a thermodynamic system and its surroundings.

PROBLEM-SOLVING EXAMPLE 6.2 Internal Energy, Heat, and Work

A fuel cell that operates on the reaction of hydrogen with oxygen powers a small automobile by running an electric motor. The motor draws 75 kilowatts (75 kJ/s) and runs for 2 minutes and 20 seconds. During this period, 5.0×10^3 kJ must be carried away from the fuel cell to prevent it from overheating. If the system is defined to be the hydrogen and oxygen that react, what is the change in the system's internal energy?

Answer -15.5×10^3 kJ

Strategy and Explanation Because the system is the reactants and products, the rest of the fuel cell is part of the surroundings. The problem states that the motor powers a car, which means that the system is doing work (to cause electric current to flow, which then makes the car move). Therefore energy is transferred out of the system and w must be negative. The work is

$$w = -75 \frac{\text{kJ}}{\text{s}} \times 140 \text{ s} = -10.5 \times 10^3 \text{ kJ}$$

Energy is also transferred out of the system when the system heats its surroundings, which means that q must be negative, and $q = -5.0 \times 10^3$ kJ. Using Equation 6.1

$$\Delta E = q + w = (-5.0 \times 10^3 \text{ kJ}) + (-10.5 \times 10^3 \text{ kJ}) = -15.5 \times 10^3 \text{ kJ}$$

Thus the internal energy of the reaction product (water) is 15.5×10^3 kJ lower than the internal energy of the reactants (hydrogen and oxygen).

✓ **Reasonable Answer Check** ΔE is negative, which is reasonable. The internal energy of the reaction products should be lower than that of the reactants, because energy transferred from the reactions heats the surroundings and does work on the surroundings.

PROBLEM-SOLVING PRACTICE 6.2

Suppose that the internal energy decreases by 2400 J when a mixture of natural gas (methane) and oxygen is ignited and burns. If the surroundings are heated by 1.89 kJ, how much work was done by this system on the surroundings?

So far we have seen that

- energy transfers can occur either by heating or by working;
- it is convenient to define a system so that energy transfers into a system (positive) and out of a system (negative) can be accounted for; and
- the internal energy of a system can change as a result of heating or doing work on the system.

Our primary interest in this chapter is heat transfers (the "thermo" in thermodynamics). Heat transfers can take place between two objects at different temperatures. Heat transfers also accompany physical changes and chemical changes. The next three sections (6.3 to 6.5) show how quantitative measurements of heat transfers can be made, first for heating that results from a temperature difference and then for heating that accompanies a physical change.

6.3 Heat Capacity

The **heat capacity** of a sample of matter is *the quantity of energy required to increase the temperature of that sample by one degree.* Heat capacity depends on the mass of the sample and the substance of which it is made (or substances, if it is not pure). To determine the quantity of energy transferred by heating, we usually measure the change in temperature of a substance whose heat capacity is known. Often that substance is water.

Specific Heat Capacity

To make useful comparisons among samples of different substances with different masses, the **specific heat capacity** (which is sometimes just called *specific heat*) is defined as the quantity of energy needed to increase the temperature of one gram of a substance by one degree Celsius. For water at 15 °C, the specific heat capacity is 1.00 cal g^{-1} $°C^{-1}$ or 4.184 J g^{-1} $°C^{-1}$; for common window glass, it is only about 0.8 J g^{-1} $°C^{-1}$. That is, it takes about five times as much heat to raise the temperature of a gram of water by 1 °C as it does for a gram of glass. Like density **(⇐ p. 9)**, specific heat capacity is a property that can be used to distinguish one substance from another. It can also be used to distinguish a pure substance from a solution or mixture, because the specific heat capacity of a mixture will vary with the proportions of the mixture's components.

The notation J g^{-1} $°C^{-1}$ means that the units are joules divided by grams and divided by degrees Celsius; that is, $\frac{J}{g\ °C}$. We will use negative exponents to show unambiguously which units are in the denominator whenever the denominator includes two or more units.

The specific heat capacity, c, of a substance can be determined experimentally by measuring the quantity of energy transferred to or from a known mass of the substance as its temperature rises or falls. We assume that there is no work transfer of energy to or from the sample and we treat the sample as a thermodynamic system, so $\Delta E = q$.

$$\text{Specific heat capacity} = \frac{\text{quantity of energy transferred by heating}}{\text{sample mass} \times \text{temperature change}}$$

or

$$c = \frac{q}{m \times \Delta T} \qquad [6.2]$$

ThomsonNOW™

Go to the Coached Problems menu for simulations and tutorials on:

- **temperature changes during heat transfer**
- **specific heat capacity**
- **thermal equilibrium**

Suppose that for a 25.0-g sample of ethylene glycol (a compound used as antifreeze in automobile engines) it takes 90.7 J to change the temperature from 22.4 °C to 23.9 °C. Thus,

$$\Delta T = (23.9\ °C - 22.4\ °C) = 1.5\ °C$$

From Equation 6.2, the specific heat capacity of ethylene glycol is

$$c = \frac{q}{m \times \Delta T} = \frac{90.7\ J}{25.0\ g \times 1.5\ °C} = 2.4\ J\ g^{-1}\ °C^{-1}$$

© Don Mason/Corbis

Moderation of microclimate by water. In cities near bodies of water (such as Seattle, shown here), summertime temperatures are lower within a few hundred meters of the waterfront than they are a few kilometers away from the water. Wintertime temperatures are higher, unless the water freezes, in which the moderating effect is less, because ice on the surface insulates the rest of the water from the air.

The high specific heat capacity of water helps to keep your body temperature relatively constant. Water accounts for a large fraction of your body mass, and warming or cooling that water requires a lot of energy transfer.

The specific heat capacities of many substances have been determined. A few values are listed in Table 6.1. Notice that water has one of the highest values. This is important because a high specific heat capacity means that a great deal of energy must be transferred to a large body of water to raise its temperature by just one degree. Conversely, a lot of energy must be transferred away from the water before its temperature falls by one degree. Thus, a lake or ocean can store an enormous quantity of energy and thereby moderate local temperatures. This has a profound influence on weather near lakes or oceans.

When the specific heat capacity of a substance is known, you can calculate the temperature change that should occur when a given quantity of energy is transferred to or from a sample of known mass. More important, by measuring the temperature change and the mass of a substance, you can calculate q, the quantity of energy transferred to or from it by heating. For these calculations it is convenient to rearrange Equation 6.2 algebraically as

$$\Delta T = \frac{q}{c \times m} \quad \text{or} \quad q = c \times m \times \Delta T \qquad [6.2']$$

PROBLEM-SOLVING EXAMPLE 6.3 Using Specific Heat Capacity

If 100.0 g water is cooled from 25.3 °C to 16.9 °C, what quantity of energy has been transferred away from the water?

Answer 3.5 kJ transferred away from the water

Table 6.1 Specific Heat Capacities for Some Elements, Compounds, and Common Solids

Symbol or Formula	Name	Specific Heat Capacity ($J\ g^{-1}\ °C^{-1}$)
Elements		
Al	Aluminum	0.902
C	Carbon (graphite)	0.720
Fe	Iron	0.451
Cu	Copper	0.385
Au	Gold	0.128
Compounds		
$NH_3(\ell)$	Ammonia	4.70
$H_2O(\ell)$	Water (liquid)	4.184
$C_2H_5OH(\ell)$	Ethanol	2.46
$HOCH_2CH_2OH(\ell)$	Ethylene glycol (antifreeze)	2.42
$H_2O(s)$	Water (ice)	2.06
$CCl_4(\ell)$	Carbon tetrachloride	0.861
$CCl_2F_2(\ell)$	A chlorofluorocarbon (CFC)	0.598
Common solids		
	Wood	1.76
	Concrete	0.88
	Glass	0.84
	Granite	0.79

© Thomson Learning/Charles D. Winters

Samples of substances having different specific heat capacities: glass, water, copper, aluminum, graphite, iron.

Strategy and Explanation Treat the water as a system. The quantity of energy is proportional to the specific heat capacity of water (Table 6.1), the mass of water, and the change in temperature. This is summarized in Equation 6.2′ as

$$\Delta E = q = c \times m \times \Delta T$$
$$= 4.184 \text{ J g}^{-1} \text{ °C}^{-1} \times 100.0 \text{ g} \times (16.9 \text{ °C} - 25.3 \text{ °C}) = -3.5 \times 10^3 \text{ J} = -3.5 \text{ kJ}$$

✓ **Reasonable Answer Check** It requires about 4 J to heat 1 g water by 1 °C. In this case the temperature change is not quite 10 °C and we have 100 g water, so q should be about 4 J g^{-1} °C^{-1} × (−10 °C) × 100 g = −4000 J = −4 kJ, which it is. The sign is negative because energy is transferred out of the water as it cools.

PROBLEM-SOLVING PRACTICE 6.3

A piece of aluminum with a mass of 250. g is at an initial temperature of 5.0 °C. If 24.1 kJ is supplied to warm the Al, what is its final temperature? Obtain the specific heat capacity of Al from Table 6.1.

CONCEPTUAL EXERCISE 6.4 Specific Heat Capacity and Temperature Change

Suppose you put two 50-mL beakers in a refrigerator so energy is transferred out of each sample at the same constant rate. If one beaker contains 10. g pulverized glass and one contains 10. g carbon (graphite), which beaker has the lower temperature after 3 min in the refrigerator?

Molar Heat Capacity

It is often useful to know the heat capacity of a sample in terms of the same number of particles instead of the same mass. For this purpose we use the **molar heat capacity,** symbol c_m. This is *the quantity of energy that must be transferred to increase the temperature of one mole of a substance by 1 °C.* The molar heat capacity is easily calculated from the specific heat capacity by using the molar mass of the substance. For example, the specific heat capacity of liquid ethanol is given in Table 6.1 as 2.46 J g^{-1} °C^{-1}. The molecular formula of ethanol is CH_3CH_2OH, so its molar mass is 46.07 g/mol. The molar heat capacity can be calculated as

$$c_m = \frac{2.46 \text{ J}}{\text{g °C}} \times \frac{46.07 \text{ g}}{\text{mol}} = 113 \text{ J mol}^{-1} \text{ °C}^{-1}$$

CONCEPTUAL EXERCISE 6.5 Molar Heat Capacity

Calculate the molar heat capacities of all the metals listed in Table 6.1. Compare these with the value just calculated for ethanol. Based on your results, suggest a way to predict the molar heat capacity of a metal. Can this same rule be applied to other kinds of substances?

As you should have found in Conceptual Exercise 6.5, molar heat capacities of metals are very similar. This can be explained if we consider what happens on the nanoscale when a metal is heated. The energy transferred by heating a solid makes the atoms vibrate more extensively about their average positions in the solid crystal lattice. Every metal consists of many, many atoms, all of the same kind and packed closely together; that is, the structures of all metals are very similar. As a consequence, the ways that the metal atoms can vibrate (and therefore the ways that their energies can be increased) are very similar. Thus, no matter what the metal, nearly the same quantity of energy must be transferred per metal atom to increase the temperature by one degree. The quantity of energy per mole is therefore very similar for all metals.

ThomsonNOW™
Go to the Chemistry Interactive menu to work a module on **thermal energy transfer on the molecular scale.**

PROBLEM-SOLVING EXAMPLE 6.4 Direction of Energy Transfer

People sometimes drink hot tea to keep warm. Suppose that you drink a 250.-mL cup of tea that is at 65.0 °C. Calculate the quantity of energy transferred to your body and the surrounding air when the temperature of the tea drops to 37.0 °C (normal body temperature). Make reasonable assumptions to obtain the mass and specific heat capacity of the liquid.

Usually the surroundings contain a great deal more matter than the system and hence have a much greater heat capacity. Consequently the change in temperature of the surroundings is often so small that it cannot be measured.

Answer 29.3 kJ transferred out of the tea

Strategy and Explanation Treat the tea as the system. Assume the density of tea, which is mostly water, is 1.00 g/mL, so the tea has a mass of 250. g; also assume the specific heat capacity of tea is the same as that of water, 4.184 J g^{-1} $°C^{-1}$. The initial temperature is 63.0 °C and the final temperature is 37.0 °C. Thus the quantity of energy transferred is

$$\Delta E = q = c \times m \times \Delta T$$

$$= 4.184\ \text{J g}^{-1}\ °\text{C}^{-1} \times 250.\ \text{g} \times (37.0 - 65.0)\ °\text{C} = -29.3 \times 10^3\ \text{J} = -29.3\ \text{kJ}$$

The negative sign of the result indicates that 29.3 kJ is transferred from the tea (system) to the surroundings (you) as the temperature of the tea decreases.

✓ **Reasonable Answer Check** Estimate the heat transfer as a bit more than (4 × 25 × 250) J = (100 × 250) J = 25,000 J = 25 kJ, which it is. The transfer is from the tea so q should be negative, which it is.

PROBLEM-SOLVING PRACTICE 6.4

Assume that the same cup of tea described in Problem-Solving Example 6.4 is warmed from 37 °C to 65 °C and there is no work done by the heating process. What is ΔE for this process?

PROBLEM-SOLVING EXAMPLE 6.5 Transfer of Energy Between Samples by Heating

Suppose that you have 100. mL H_2O at 20.0 °C and you add to the water 55.0 g iron pellets that had been heated to 425 °C. What is the temperature of both the water and the iron when thermal equilibrium is reached? (Assume that there is no energy transfer to the glass beaker or to the air or to anything else but the water. Assume also that no work is done, that no liquid water vaporizes, and that the density of water is 1.00 g/mL.)

Answer T_{final} = 42.7 °C

Strategy and Explanation Thermal equilibrium means that the water and the iron bar will have the same final temperature, which is what we want to calculate. Consider the iron to be the system and the water to be the surroundings. The energy transferred from the iron is the same energy that is transferred to the water. None of this energy goes anywhere other than to the water. Therefore $\Delta E_{water} = -\Delta E_{iron}$ and $q_{water} = -q_{iron}$. The quantity of energy transferred to the water and the quantity transferred from the iron are equal. They are opposite in algebraic sign because energy was transferred *from* the iron as its temperature dropped, and energy was transferred *to* the water to raise its temperature.

The quantities of energy transferred have opposite signs because they take place from the iron (negative) to the water (positive).

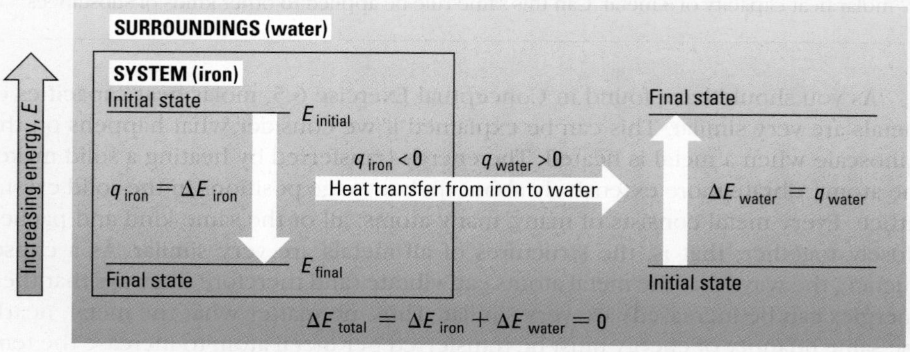

Specific heat capacities for iron and water are listed in Table 6.1. The mass of water is 100. mL × 1.00 g/mL = 100. g. $T_{initial}$ for the iron is 425 °C and $T_{initial}$ for the water is 20 °C.

$$q_{water} = -q_{iron}$$

$$c_{water} \times m_{water} \times \Delta T_{water} = -c_{iron} \times m_{iron} \times \Delta T_{iron}$$

$$(4.184 \text{ J g}^{-1}\,°\text{C}^{-1})(100.\text{ g})(T_{final} - 20\ °\text{C}) = -(0.451 \text{ J g}^{-1}\,°\text{C}^{-1})(55.0 \text{ g})(T_{final} - 425\ °\text{C})$$

$$(418.4 \text{ J }°\text{C}^{-1})T_{final} - (8.368 \times 10^3 \text{ J}) = -(24.80 \text{ J }°\text{C}^{-1})T_{final} + (1.054 \times 10^4 \text{ J})$$

$$(443.2 \text{ J }°\text{C}^{-1})T_{final} = 1.891 \times 10^4 \text{ J}$$

Solving, we find T_{final} = 42.7 °C. The iron has cooled a lot (ΔT_{iron} = −382 °C) and the water has warmed a little (ΔT_{water} = 23 °C).

✓ **Reasonable Answer Check** As a check, note that the final temperature must be between the two initial values, which it is. Also, don't be concerned by the fact that transferring the same quantity of energy resulted in two very different values of ΔT; this difference arises because the specific heat capacities and masses of iron and water are different. There is much less iron and its specific heat capacity is smaller, so its temperature changes much more than the temperature of the water.

PROBLEM-SOLVING PRACTICE 6.5

A 400.-g piece of iron is heated in a flame and then immersed in 1000. g of water in a beaker. The initial temperature of the water was 20.0 °C, and both the iron and the water are at 32.8 °C at the end of the experiment. What was the original temperature of the hot iron bar? (Assume that all energy transfer is between the water and the iron.)

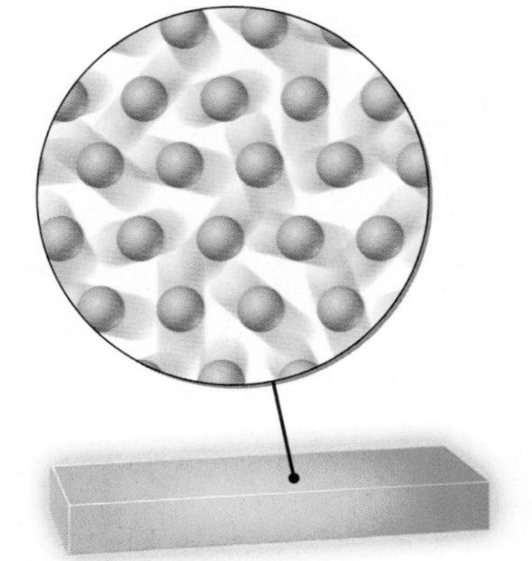

Hot iron bar

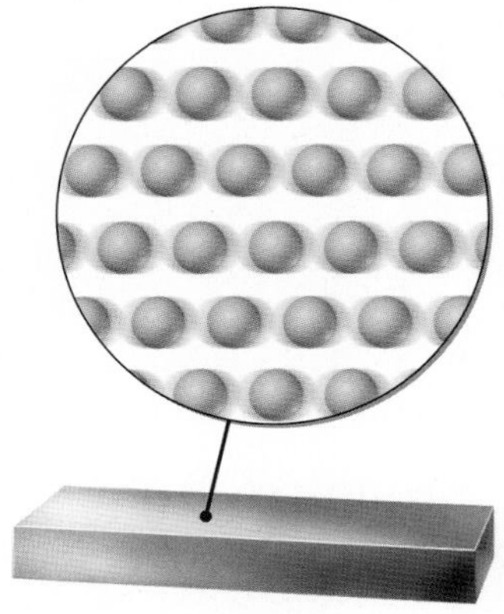

Cold iron bar

Hot and cold iron. On the nanoscale the atoms in the sample of hot iron are vibrating much further from their average positions than those in the sample of room-temperature iron. The greater vibration of atoms in hot iron means harder collisions of iron atoms with water molecules. Such collisions transfer energy to the water molecules, heating the water.

6.4 Energy and Enthalpy

Using heat capacity we can account for transfers of energy between samples of matter as a result of temperature differences. But energy transfers also accompany physical or chemical changes, *even though there may be no change in temperature.* We will first consider the simpler case of physical change and then apply the same ideas to chemical changes.

Conservation of Energy and Changes of State

Consider a system that consists of water at its boiling temperature in a container with a balloon attached (Figure 6.10). The system is under a constant atmospheric pressure. If the water is heated, it will boil, the temperature will remain at 100 °C, and the steam produced by boiling the water will inflate the balloon (Figure 6.10b). If the heating stops, then the water will stop boiling, some of the steam will condense to liquid, and the volume of steam will decrease (Figure 6.10c). There will be heat transfer of energy to the surroundings. However, as long as steam is condensing to liquid water, the temperature will remain at 100 °C. In summary, transferring energy *into* the system produces more steam; transferring energy *out of* the system results in less steam. Both the boiling and condensing processes occur at the same temperature—the boiling point.

The boiling process can be represented by the equation

$$H_2O(\ell) \longrightarrow H_2O(g) \qquad \text{endothermic}$$

We call this process **endothermic** because, as it occurs, energy must be transferred *into* the system to maintain constant temperature. If no energy transfer took place, the liquid water would get cooler. Evaporation of water (perspiration) from your

Changes of state (between solid and liquid, liquid and gas, or solid and gas) are described in more detail in Section 11.3. Because the temperature remains constant during a change of state, melting points and boiling points can be measured relatively easily and used to identify substances (← ***p. 8***).

Thermic or *thermo* comes from the Greek word *thermé,* meaning "heat." *Endo* comes from the Greek word *endon,* meaning "within or inside." *Endothermic* therefore indicates transfer of energy *into* the system.

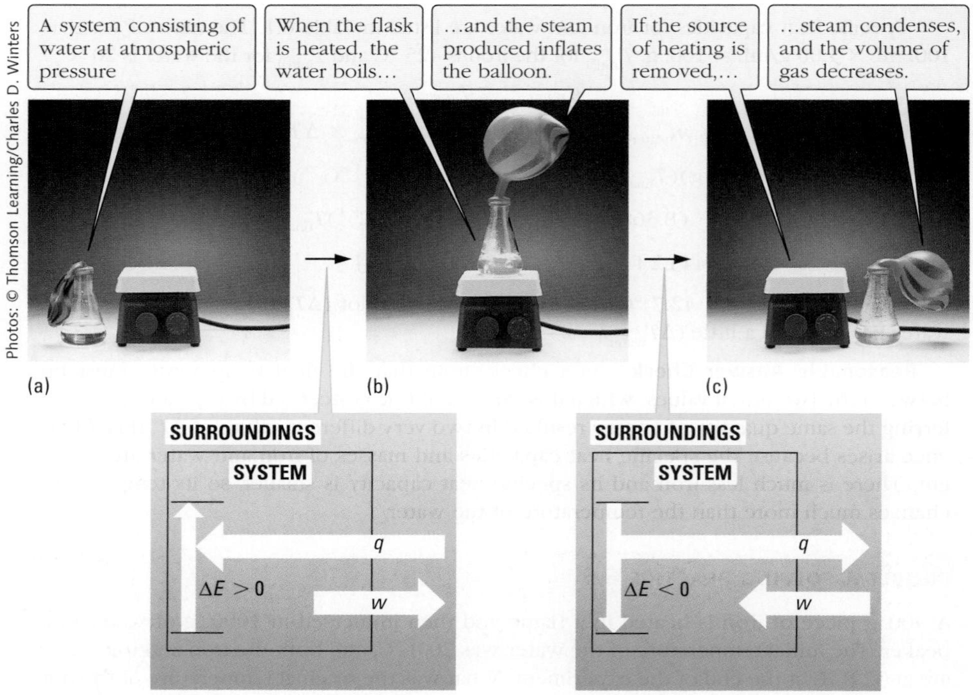

Active Figure 6.10 **Boiling water at constant pressure.** When water boils, the steam pushes against atmospheric pressure and does work on the atmosphere (which is part of the surroundings). The balloon allows the expansion of the steam to be seen; even if the balloon were not there, the steam would push back the surrounding air. In general, for any constant-pressure process, if a change in volume occurs, some work is done, either on the surroundings or on the system. **Go to the Active Figures menu at ThomsonNOW to test your understanding of the concepts in this figure.**

skin, which occurs at a lower temperature than boiling, is an endothermic process that you are certainly familiar with. Energy must be transferred from your skin to the evaporating water, and this energy transfer cools your skin.

The opposite of boiling is condensation. It can be represented by the opposite equation,

$$H_2O(g) \longrightarrow H_2O(\ell) \qquad \text{exothermic}$$

This process is said to be **exothermic** because energy must be transferred *out of* the system to maintain constant temperature. Because condensation of $H_2O(g)$ (steam) is exothermic, a burn from steam at 100 °C is much worse than a burn from liquid water at 100 °C. The steam heats the skin a lot more because there is a heat transfer due to the condensation as well as the difference in temperature between the water and your skin.

Exo comes from the Greek word *exō*, meaning "out of." *Exothermic* indicates transfer of energy *out of* the system.

Phase Change	Direction of Energy Transfer	Sign of q	Type of Change
$H_2O(\ell) \rightarrow H_2O(g)$	Surroundings → system	Positive ($q > 0$)	*Endo*thermic
$H_2O(g) \rightarrow H_2O(\ell)$	System → surroundings	Negative ($q < 0$)	*Exo*thermic

ThomsonNOW
Go to the Chemistry Interactive menu to work a module on **heat and work.**

The system in Figure 6.10 can be analyzed by using the law of conservation of energy, $\Delta E = q + w$. Vaporizing 1.0 g water requires heat transfer of 2260 J, so $q =$ 2260 J (a positive value because the transfer is from the surroundings to the system). At the same time, the expansion of the steam pushes back the atmosphere, doing work. The quantity of work is more difficult to calculate, but it is clear that w must be negative, because the system does work on the surroundings. Therefore, the internal energy of the system is increased by the quantity of heating and decreased by the quantity of work done.

Now suppose that the heating is stopped and the direction of heat transfer is reversed. The water stops boiling and some of the steam condenses to liquid water. The balloon deflates and the atmosphere pushes back the steam. If 1.0 g steam condenses, then $q = -2260$ J. Because the surrounding atmosphere pushes on the system, the surroundings have done work on the system, which makes w positive. As long as steam is condensing to liquid, the temperature remains at 100 °C. The internal energy of the system is increased by the work done on it and decreased by the heat transfer of energy to the surroundings.

The device described here is a crude example of a steam engine. Burning fuel boils water, and the steam does work. In a real steam engine the steam would drive a piston and then be allowed to escape, providing a means for the system to continually do work on its surroundings. Systems that convert heat into work are called heat engines. Another example is the engine in an automobile, which converts heat from the combustion of fuel into work to move the car.

Enthalpy: Heat Transfer at Constant Pressure

In the previous section it was clear that work was done. When the balloon's volume increased, the balloon pushed aside air that had occupied the space the gas in the balloon expanded to fill. Work is done when a force moves something through some distance. If the flask containing the boiling water had been sealed, nothing would have moved and no work would have been done. Therefore, in a closed container where the system's volume is constant, $w = 0$, and

$$\Delta E = q + w = q + 0 = q_V$$

The subscript V indicates constant volume; that is, q_V is the heat transfer into a constant-volume system. This means that ***if a process is carried out in a closed container and the heat transfer is measured, ΔE has been determined***.

In plants, animals, laboratories, and the environment, physical processes and chemical reactions seldom take place in closed containers. Instead they are carried out in contact with the atmosphere. For example, the vaporization of water shown in Figure 6.10 took place under conditions of constant atmospheric pressure, and the expanding steam had to push back the atmosphere. In such a case,

$$\Delta E = q_P + w_{\text{atm}}$$

That is, ΔE differs from the heat transfer at constant pressure, q_P, by the work done to push back the atmosphere, w_{atm}.

To see how much work is required, consider the idealized system shown in the margin, which consists of a cylinder with a weightless piston. (The purpose of the piston is to distinguish the water system from the surrounding air.) When some of the water in the bottom of the cylinder boils, the volume of the system increases. The piston and the atmosphere are forced upward. The system (water and steam) does work to raise the surrounding air. The work can be calculated as $w_{\text{atm}} = -(\text{force} \times \text{distance}) = -(F \times d)$. (The negative sign indicates that the system is doing work on the surroundings.) The distance the piston moves is clear from the diagram. The force can be calculated from the pressure (P), which is defined as force per unit area (A). Since $P = F/A$, the force is $F = P \times A$, and the work is $w_{\text{atm}} = -F \times d = -P \times A \times d = -P\Delta V$. The change in the volume of the system, ΔV, is the volume of the cylinder through which the piston moves. This is calculated as the area of the base times the height, or $\Delta V = A \times d$. Thus the work is $w_{\text{atm}} = -P \times A \times d = -P\Delta V$. This means that the work of pushing back the atmosphere is always equal to the atmospheric pressure times the change in volume of the system.

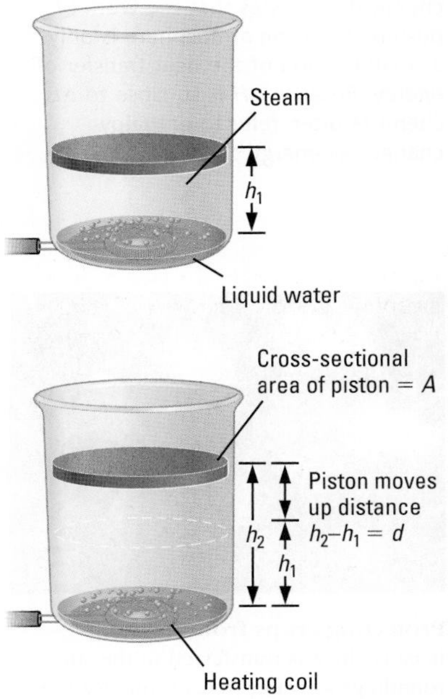

Vaporization of water. When a sample of water boils at constant pressure, energy must be supplied to expand the steam against atmospheric pressure.

The law of conservation of energy for a constant-pressure process can now be written as

$$\Delta E = q_P + w_{\text{atm}} \quad \text{or} \quad q_P = \Delta E - w_{\text{atm}} = \Delta E + P\Delta V$$

Because it is equal to the quantity of thermal energy transferred at constant pressure, and because most chemical reactions are carried out at atmospheric (constant) pressure, the enthalpy change for a process is often called the *heat of that process*. For example, the enthalpy change for melting (fusion) is also called the heat of fusion.

This equation says that when we carry out reactions in beakers or other containers open to the atmosphere, the heat transfer differs from the change in energy by an easily calculated term, $P\Delta V$. Therefore it is convenient to use q_P to characterize energy transfers in typical chemical and physical processes. ***The quantity of thermal energy transferred into a system at constant pressure,*** q_P, is called the **enthalpy change** of the system, symbolized by ΔH. Thus, $\Delta H = q_P$, and

$$\Delta H = \Delta E + P\Delta V$$

ΔH accounts for all the energy transferred except the quantity that does the work of pushing back the atmosphere. For processes that do not involve gases, w_{atm} is very small. Even when gases are involved, w_{atm} is usually much smaller than q_P. That is, ΔH is closely related to the change in the internal energy of the system but is slightly different in magnitude. ***Whenever heat transfer is measured at constant pressure, it is*** ΔH ***that is determined.***

PROBLEM-SOLVING EXAMPLE 6.6 Changes of State, ΔH, and ΔE

Methanol, CH_3OH, boils at 65.0 °C. When 5.0 g methanol boils at 1 atm, the volume of $CH_3OH(g)$ is 4.32 L greater than the volume of the liquid. The heat transfer is 5865 J, and the process is endothermic. Calculate ΔH and ΔE. (The units 1 L × 1 atm = 101.3 J.)

Answer $\Delta H = 5865$ J; $\Delta E = 5427$ J

Strategy and Explanation The process takes place at constant pressure. By definition, $\Delta H = q_P$. Because thermal energy is transferred to the system, the sign of ΔH must be positive. Therefore $\Delta H = 5865$ J. Because the system expands, ΔV is positive. This makes the sign of w_{atm} negative, and

$$w_{atm} = -P\Delta V = -1 \text{ atm} \times 4.32 \text{ L} = -4.32 \text{ L atm} = -4.32 \times 101.3 \text{ J} = -438 \text{ J}$$

To calculate ΔE, add the expansion work to the enthalpy change.

$$\Delta E = q_P + w_{atm} = \Delta H + w_{atm} = 5865 \text{ J} - 438 \text{ J} = 5427 \text{ J}$$

✓ **Reasonable Answer Check** Boiling is an endothermic process, so ΔH must be positive. Because the system did work on the surroundings, the change in internal energy must be less than the enthalpy change, and it is.

The results of this example show that ΔE differs by less than 10% from ΔH—that is, by 440 J out of 5865 J, which is 7.5%. It is true for most physical and chemical processes that the work of pushing back the atmosphere is only a small fraction of the heat transfer of energy. Because ΔH is so close to ΔE, chemists often refer to enthalpy changes as energy changes.

PROBLEM-SOLVING PRACTICE 6.6

When potassium melts at atmospheric pressure, the heat transfer is 14.6 cal/g. The density of liquid potassium at its melting point is 0.82 g/mL, and that of solid potassium is 0.86 g/mL. Given that a volume change of 1.00 mL at atmospheric pressure corresponds to 0.10 J, calculate ΔH and ΔE for melting 1.00 g potassium.

Tony Ranze/AFP/Getty Images

Protecting crops from freezing. Because heat is transferred to the surroundings as water freezes, one way to protect plants from freezing if the temperature drops just below the freezing point is to spray water on them. As the water freezes, energy transfer to the leaves, stems, and fruits keeps the plants themselves from freezing.

Freezing and Melting (Fusion)

Consider what happens when ice is heated at a slow, constant rate from −50 °C to +50 °C. A graph of temperature as a function of quantity of transferred energy is shown in Figure 6.11. When the temperature reaches 0 °C, it remains constant, despite the fact that the sample is still being heated. As long as ice is melting, thermal energy must be continually supplied to overcome forces that hold the water molecules in their regularly spaced positions in the nanoscale structure of solid ice. Overcoming these forces raises the potential energy of the water molecules and therefore requires a transfer of energy into the system.

Melting a solid is an example of a **change of state** or **phase change,** a physical process in which one state of matter is transformed into another. During a phase change, the temperature remains constant, but energy must be continually transferred into (melting, boiling) or out of (condensing, freezing) the system because the nanoscale particles have higher or lower potential energy after the phase

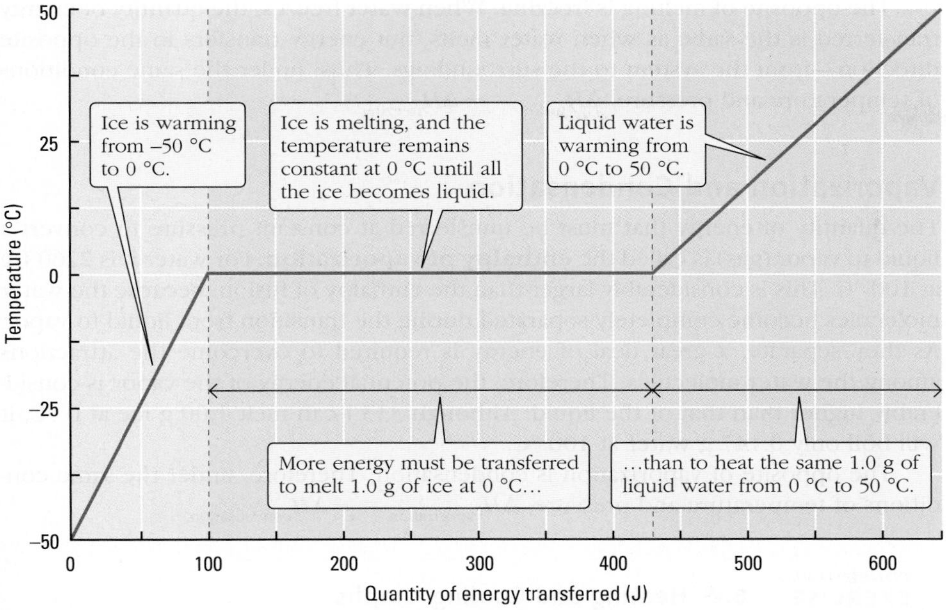

Figure 6.11 **Heating graph.** When a 1.0-g sample of ice is heated at a constant rate, the temperature does not always increase at a constant rate.

change than they did before it. As shown in Figure 6.11, the quantity of energy transferred is significant.

The quantity of thermal energy that must be transferred to a solid as it melts at constant pressure is called the **enthalpy of fusion.** For ice the enthalpy of fusion is 333 J/g at 0 °C. This same quantity of energy could raise the temperature of a 1.00-g block of iron from 0 °C to 738 °C (red hot), or it could melt 0.50 g ice and heat the liquid water from 0 °C to 80 °C. This is illustrated schematically in Figure 6.12.

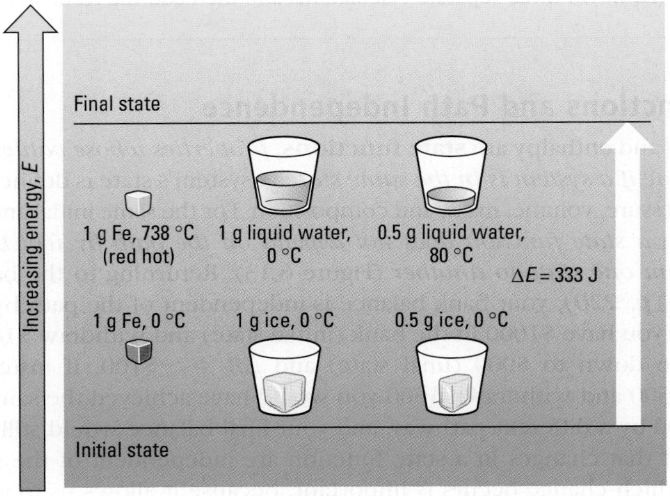

Figure 6.12 **Heating, temperature change, and phase change.** Heating a substance can cause a temperature change, a phase change, or both. Here, 333 J has been transferred to each of three samples: a 1-g block of iron at 0 °C; a 1-g block of ice at 0 °C; and a 0.5-g block of ice at 0 °C. The iron block becomes red hot; its temperature increases to 738 °C. The 1-g block of ice melts, resulting in 1 g of liquid water at 0 °C. The 0.5-g block of ice melts, and there is enough energy to heat the liquid water to 80 °C.

The opposite of melting is freezing. When water freezes, the quantity of energy transferred is the same as when water melts, but energy transfers in the opposite direction—from the system to the surroundings. Thus, under the same conditions of temperature and pressure, $\Delta H_{\text{fusion}} = -\Delta H_{\text{freezing}}$.

ThomsonNOW™
Go to the Coached Problems menu for a tutorial on **heat transfer and phase change.**

Vaporization and Condensation

The quantity of energy that must be transferred at constant pressure to convert a liquid to vapor (gas) is called the **enthalpy of vaporization.** For water it is 2260 J/g at 100 °C. This is considerably larger than the enthalpy of fusion, because the water molecules become completely separated during the transition from liquid to vapor. As they separate, a great deal of energy is required to overcome the attractions among the water molecules. Therefore, the potential energy of the vapor is considerably higher than that of the liquid. Although 333 J can melt 1.00 g ice at 0 °C, it will boil only 0.147 g water at 100 °C.

$$333\ \text{J} \times \frac{1.00\ \text{g water vaporized}}{2260\ \text{J}} = 0.147\ \text{g water vaporized}$$

The opposite of vaporization is condensation. Therefore, under the same conditions of temperature and pressure, $\Delta H_{\text{vaporization}} = -\Delta H_{\text{condensation}}$.

You experience cooling due to evaporation of water when you perspire. If you work up a real sweat, then lots of water evaporates from your skin, producing a much greater cooling effect. People who exercise in cool weather need to carry a sweatshirt or jacket. When they stop exercising they generate less body heat, but lots of perspiration remains on their skin. Its evaporation can cool the body enough to cause a chill.

CONCEPTUAL EXERCISE 6.6 Heating and Cooling Graphs

(a) Assume that a 1.0-g sample of ice at −5 °C is heated at a uniform rate until the temperature is 105 °C. Draw a graph like the one in Figure 6.10 to show how temperature varies with energy transferred. Your graph should be to approximately the correct scale.

(b) Assume that a 0.50-g sample of water is cooled [at the same uniform rate as the heating in part (a)] from 105 °C to −5 °C. Draw a cooling curve to show how temperature varies with energy transferred. Your graph should be to the same scale as in part (a).

EXERCISE 6.7 Changes of State

Assume you have 1 cup of ice (237 g) at 0.0 °C. How much heating is required to melt the ice, warm the resulting water to 100.0 °C, and then boil the water to vapor at 100.0 °C? (*Hint:* Do three separate calculations and then add the results.)

State Functions and Path Independence

Both energy and enthalpy are **state functions,** *properties whose values are invariably the same if a system is in the same state.* A system's state is defined by its temperature, pressure, volume, mass, and composition. For the same initial and final states, *a change in a state function does not depend on the path by which the system changes from one state to another* (Figure 6.13). Returning to the bank account analogy (**p. 220**), your bank balance is independent of the path by which you change it. If you have \$1000 in the bank (initial state) and withdraw \$100, your balance will go down to \$900 (final state) and $\Delta B = -\$100$. If instead you had deposited \$500 and withdrawn \$600 you would have achieved the same change of $\Delta B = -\$100$ by a different pathway, and your final balance would still be \$900.

The fact that changes in a state function are independent of the sequence of events by which change occurs is important, because it allows us to apply laboratory measurements to real-life situations. For example, if you measure in the lab the heat transfer when 1.0 g glucose (dextrose sugar) burns in exactly the amount of oxygen required to convert it to carbon dioxide and water, you will find that $\Delta H = -15.5$ kJ. When you eat something that contains 1.0 g glucose and your body

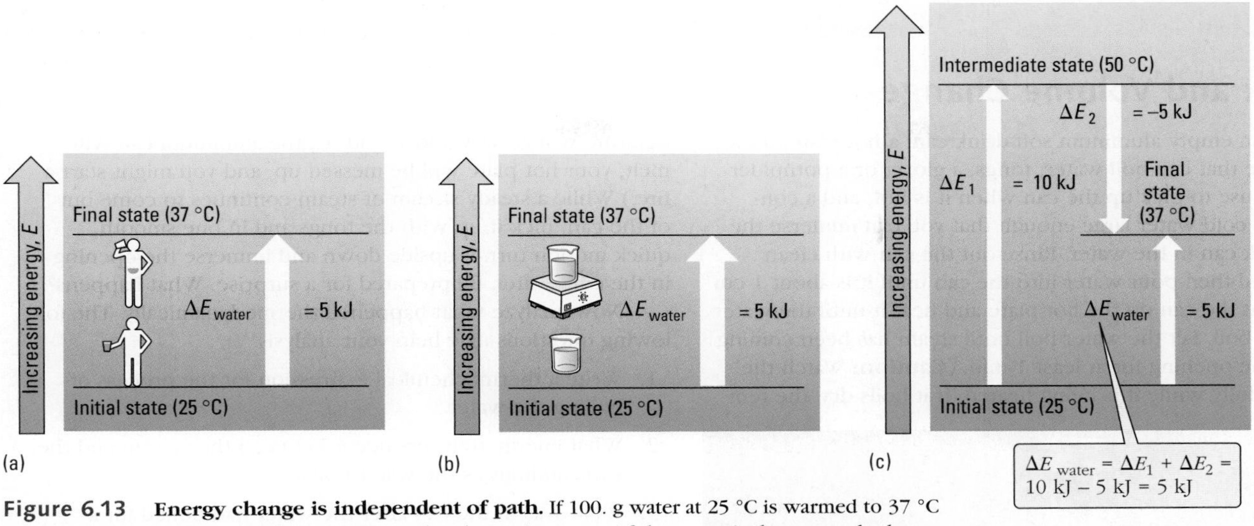

Figure 6.13 **Energy change is independent of path.** If 100. g water at 25 °C is warmed to 37 °C (body temperature) at atmospheric pressure, the change in energy of the water is the same whether (a) you drank the water and your body warmed it to 37 °C, (b) you put the water in a beaker and heated it with a hot plate, or (c) you heated the water to 50 °C and then cooled it to 37 °C.

metabolizes the glucose (producing the same products at the same temperature and pressure), there is the same change in enthalpy. Thus, laboratory measurements can be used to determine how much energy you can get from a given quantity of food, which is the basis for the caloric values listed on labels.

6.5 Thermochemical Expressions

To indicate the heat transfer that occurs when either a physical or chemical process takes place, we write a **thermochemical expression,** *a balanced chemical equation together with the corresponding value of the enthalpy change.* For evaporation of water near room temperature and at typical atmospheric pressure, this thermochemical expression can be written:

$$H_2O(\ell) \longrightarrow H_2O(g) \qquad \Delta H° = +44.0 \text{ kJ} \qquad (25\ °C,\ 1\ \text{bar})$$

The symbol $\Delta H°$ (pronounced "delta-aitch-standard") represents the **standard enthalpy change,** which is defined as the *enthalpy change at the standard pressure of 1 bar and a specified temperature.* Because the value of the enthalpy change depends on the pressure at which the process is carried out, all enthalpy changes are reported at the same standard pressure, 1 bar. (The bar is a unit of pressure that is very close to the pressure of the earth's atmosphere at sea level; you may have heard this unit used in a weather report.) The value of the enthalpy change also varies slightly with temperature. For thermochemical expressions in this book, the temperature can be assumed to be 25 °C, unless some other temperature is specified.

The thermochemical expression given above indicates that when *one mole* of liquid water (at 25 °C and 1 bar) evaporates to form *one mole* of water vapor (at 25 °C and 1 bar), 44.0 kJ of energy must be transferred from the surroundings to the system to maintain the temperature at 25 °C. The size of the enthalpy change depends on how much process (in this case evaporation) takes place. The more water that evaporates, the more the surroundings are cooled. If 2 mol $H_2O(\ell)$ is converted to 2 mol $H_2O(g)$, 88 kJ of energy is transferred; if 0.5 mol $H_2O(\ell)$ is converted to 0.5 mol $H_2O(g)$, only 22 kJ is required. The numerical value of $\Delta H°$ corresponds

In 1982 the International Union of Pure and Applied Chemistry chose a pressure of 1 bar as the standard for tabulating information for thermochemical expressions. This pressure is very close to the standard atmosphere: 1 bar = 0.98692 atm = 1×10^5 kg m^{-1} s^{-2}. (Pressure units are discussed further in Section 10.2.)

Usually the surroundings contain far more matter than the system and hence have a much greater heat capacity. Consequently, the temperature of the surroundings often does not change significantly, even though energy transfer has occurred. For evaporation of water at 25 °C, the temperature of the surroundings would not drop much below 25 °C.

CHEMISTRY YOU CAN DO

Work and Volume Change

Obtain an empty aluminum soft-drink can; a hot plate or electric stove that can boil water; tongs, a glove, or a potholder you can use to pick up the can when it is hot; and a container of cold water large enough that you can immerse the soft-drink can in the water. Rinse out the can with clean water and then pour water into the can until it is about 1 cm deep. Put the can on the hot plate and heat it until the water starts to boil. Let the water boil until steam has been coming out of the opening for at least 1 min. (**Caution:** Watch the can carefully while it is being heated. If it boils dry, the temperature will go way above 100 °C, the aluminum can will melt, your hot plate will be messed up, and you might start a fire.) While a steady stream of steam continues to come out of the can, pick it up with the tongs and in one smooth, quick motion turn it upside down and immerse the opening in the cold water. Be prepared for a surprise. What happens?

© Thomson Learning/George Semple

Now analyze what happened thermodynamically. The following questions may help your analysis.

1. Write a thermochemical expression for the process of boiling the water.
2. What energy transfers occur between the system and the surroundings as the water boils?
3. What was in the can after the water had boiled for a minute or two? What happened to the air that was originally in the can?
4. What happened to the contents of the can as soon as it was immersed in the cold water?
5. Write a thermochemical expression for the process in Question 4.
6. Did the atmosphere do work on the can and its contents after the can was immersed in the water? Cite observations to support your answer.

to the reaction as written, with the coefficients indicating moles of each reactant and moles of each product. For the thermochemical expression

$$2\,H_2O(\ell) \longrightarrow 2\,H_2O(g) \qquad \Delta H^\circ = +88.0\text{ kJ}$$

the process is evaporating 2 mol $H_2O(\ell)$ to form 2 mol $H_2O(g)$, both at 25 °C and 1 bar. For this process the enthalpy change is twice as great as for the case where there is a coefficient of 1 on each side of the equation.

Now consider water vapor condensing to form liquid. If 44.0 kJ of energy is required to do the work of separating the water molecules in 1 mol of the liquid as it vaporizes, the same quantity of energy will be released when the molecules move closer together as the vapor condenses to form liquid.

$$H_2O(g) \longrightarrow H_2O(\ell) \qquad \Delta H^\circ = -44.0\text{ kJ}$$

This thermochemical expression indicates that 44.0 kJ of energy is transferred to the surroundings *from* the system when 1 mol of water vapor condenses to liquid at 25 °C and 1 bar.

The idea here is similar to the example given earlier of water falling from top to bottom of a waterfall. The decrease in potential energy of the water when it falls from the top to the bottom of the waterfall is exactly equal to the increase in potential energy that would be required to take the same quantity of water from the bottom of the fall to the top. The signs are opposite because in one case potential energy is transferred *from* the water and in the other case it is transferred *to* the water.

CONCEPTUAL EXERCISE 6.8 Interpreting Thermochemical Expressions

What part of the thermochemical expression for vaporization of water indicates that energy is transferred from the surroundings to the system when the evaporation process occurs?

CONCEPTUAL EXERCISE 6.9 Thermochemical Expressions

Why is it essential to specify the state (s, ℓ, or g) of each reactant and each product in a thermochemical expression?

PROBLEM-SOLVING EXAMPLE 6.7 Changes of State and $\Delta H°$

Calculate the energy transferred to the surroundings when water vapor in the air condenses at 25 °C to give rain in a thunderstorm. Suppose that one inch of rain falls over one square mile of ground, so that 6.6×10^{10} mL has fallen. (Assume $d_{H_2O(\ell)} = 1.0$ g/mL.)

Answer 1.6×10^{11} kJ

Strategy and Explanation The thermochemical expression for condensation of 1 mol water at 25 °C is

$$H_2O(g) \longrightarrow H_2O(\ell) \qquad \Delta H° = -44.0 \text{ kJ}$$

The standard enthalpy change tells how much heat transfer is required when 1 mol water condenses at constant pressure, so we first calculate how many moles of water condensed.

$$\text{Amount of water condensed} = 6.6 \times 10^{10} \text{ g water} \times \frac{1 \text{ mol}}{18.0 \text{ g}} = 3.66 \times 10^9 \text{ mol water}$$

Next, calculate the quantity of energy transferred from the fact that 44.0 kJ is transferred per mole of water.

$$\text{Quantity of energy transferred} = 3.66 \times 10^9 \text{ mol water} \times \frac{44.0 \text{ kJ}}{1 \text{ mol}} = 1.6 \times 10^{11} \text{ kJ}$$

The negative sign of $\Delta H°$ in the thermochemical expression indicates transfer of the 1.6×10^{11} kJ *from the water* (system) *to the surroundings.*

✓ **Reasonable Answer Check** The quantity of water is about 10^{11} g. The energy transfer is 44 kJ for one mole (18 g) of water. Since 44 is about twice 18, this is about 2 kJ/g. Therefore, the energy transferred in kJ should be about twice the number of grams, or about 2×10^{11} kJ, and it is.

PROBLEM-SOLVING PRACTICE 6.7

The enthalpy change for sublimation of 1 mol solid iodine at 25 °C and 1 bar is 62.4 kJ. (Sublimation means changing directly from solid to gas.)

$$I_2(s) \longrightarrow I_2(g) \qquad \Delta H° = +62.4 \text{ kJ}$$

(a) What quantity of energy must be transferred to vaporize 10.0 g solid iodine?
(b) If 3.42 g iodine vapor changes to solid iodine, what quantity of energy is transferred?
(c) Is the process in part (b) exothermic or endothermic?

Agronomists and meteorologists measure quantities of rainwater in units of acre-feet; an acre-foot is enough water to cover an acre of land to a depth of one foot.

Since the explosion of 1000 tons of dynamite is equivalent to 4.2×10^9 kJ, the energy transferred by our hypothetical thunderstorm is about the same as that released when 38,000 tons of dynamite explodes! A great deal of energy can be stored in water vapor, which is one reason why storms can cause so much damage.

Like all examples in this chapter, this one assumes that the temperature of the system remains constant, so that all the energy transfer associated with the phase change goes to or from the surroundings.

Richard Ramette

Iodine "thermometer." A glass sphere containing a few iodine crystals rests on the ground in desert sunshine. The hotter the flask, the more iodine sublimes, producing the beautiful violet color.

6.6 Enthalpy Changes for Chemical Reactions

Having developed methods for quantitative treatment of energy transfers as a result of temperature differences and as a result of phase changes, we are now ready to apply these ideas to energy transfers that accompany chemical reactions.

Like phase changes, chemical reactions can be exothermic or endothermic, but reactions usually involve much larger energy transfers than do phase changes. Indeed, a temperature change is one piece of evidence that a chemical reaction has taken place. The large energy transfers that occur during chemical reactions result

The relationship of reaction heat transfer and enthalpy change:

Reactant → product with transfer of thermal energy *from* system to surroundings. ΔH is negative; reaction is *exo*thermic.

Reactant → product with transfer of thermal energy *into* system from surroundings. ΔH is positive; reaction is *endo*thermic.

ThomsonNOW™
Go to the Coached Problems menu for a tutorial on **calculating enthalpy change for a reaction.**

(a)

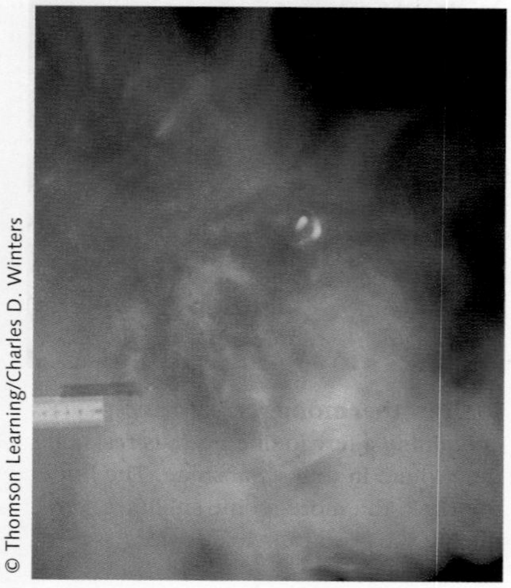

(b)

Combustion of hydrogen gas. The combination reaction of hydrogen and oxygen produces water vapor in a highly exothermic process.

from the breaking and making of chemical bonds as reactants are converted into products. These energy transfers have important applications in living systems, in industrial processes, in heating or cooling your home, and in many other situations.

Hydrogen is an excellent fuel. It produces very little pollution when it burns in air, and its reaction with oxygen to form water is highly exothermic. It is used as a fuel in the Space Shuttle, for example. The thermochemical expression for formation of 1 mol water vapor from hydrogen and oxygen is

$$H_2(g) + \tfrac{1}{2}O_2(g) \longrightarrow H_2O(g) \qquad \Delta H° = -241.8 \text{ kJ} \quad [6.3]$$

Like all thermochemical expressions, this one has four important characteristics:

- The *sign of* $\Delta H°$ indicates the direction of energy transfer.
- The magnitude of $\Delta H°$ depends on the *states of matter* of the reactants and products.
- The *balanced equation represents moles* of reactants and of products.
- The *quantity of energy transferred is proportional to the quantity of reaction* that occurs.

Sign of $\Delta H°$.

Thermochemical Expression 6.3 tells us that this process is exothermic, because $\Delta H°$ is negative. Formation of 1 mol water vapor transfers 241.8 kJ of energy from the reacting chemicals to the surroundings. If 1 mol water vapor is decomposed to hydrogen and oxygen (the reverse process), the magnitude of $\Delta H°$ is the same, but the sign is opposite, indicating transfer of energy from the surroundings to the system:

$$H_2O(g) \longrightarrow H_2(g) + \tfrac{1}{2}O_2(g) \qquad \Delta H° = +241.8 \text{ kJ} \quad [6.4]$$

The reverse of an exothermic process is endothermic. The magnitude of the energy transfer is the same, but the direction of transfer is opposite.

States of Matter.

If liquid water is involved instead of water vapor, the magnitude of $\Delta H°$ is different from that in Equation 6.3:

$$H_2(g) + \tfrac{1}{2}O_2(g) \longrightarrow H_2O(\ell) \qquad \Delta H° = -285.8 \text{ kJ} \quad [6.5]$$

Our discussion of phase changes (⇐ ***p. 227***) showed that an enthalpy change occurs when a substance changes state. Vaporizing 1 mol $H_2O(\ell)$ requires 44.0 kJ. Forming 1 mol $H_2O(\ell)$ from $H_2(g)$ and $O_2(g)$ is 285.8 kJ − 241.8 kJ = 44.0 kJ more exothermic than is forming 1 mol $H_2O(g)$. Figure 6.14 shows the relationships

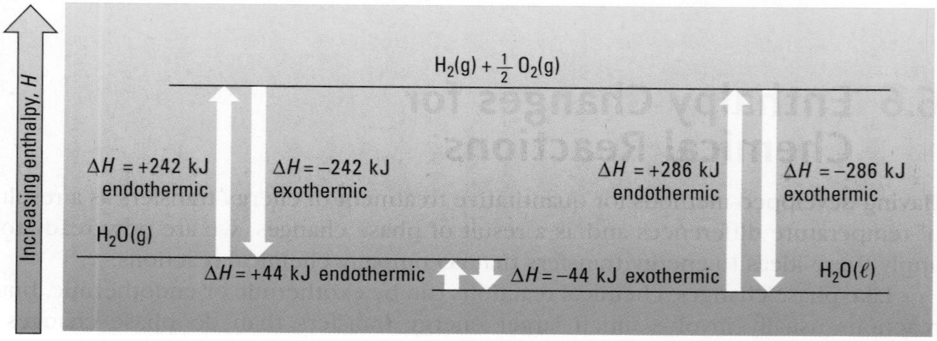

Figure 6.14 Enthalpy diagram. Water vapor [1 mol $H_2O(g)$], liquid water [1 mol $H_2O(\ell)$], and a stoichiometric mixture of hydrogen and oxygen gases [1 mol $H_2(g)$ and $\frac{1}{2}$ mol $O_2(g)$] all have different enthalpy values. The figure shows how these are related, with the highest enthalpy at the top.

among these quantities. The enthalpy of the reactants [$H_2(g)$ and $\frac{1}{2}$ $O_2(g)$] is greater than that of the product [$H_2O(g)$]. Because the system has less enthalpy after the reaction than before, the law of conservation of energy requires that 241.8 kJ must be transferred *to* the surroundings as the reaction takes place. $H_2O(\ell)$ has even less enthalpy than $H_2O(g)$, so when $H_2O(\ell)$ is formed, even more energy, 285.8 kJ, must be transferred to the surroundings.

Balanced Equation Represents Moles.

To write an equation for the formation of 1 mol H_2O it is necessary to use a fractional coefficient for O_2. This is acceptable in a thermochemical expression, because the coefficients mean moles, not molecules, and half a mole of O_2 is a perfectly reasonable quantity.

Quantity of Energy Is Proportional to Quantity of Reaction.

Thermochemical expressions obey the rules of stoichiometry (**⇐ *p. 131***). The more reaction there is, the more energy is transferred. Because the balanced equation represents moles, we can calculate how much heat transfer occurs from the number of moles of a reactant that is consumed or the number of moles of a product that is formed. If the thermochemical expression for combination of gaseous hydrogen and oxygen is written without the fractional coefficient, so that 2 mol $H_2O(g)$ is produced, then the energy transfer is twice as great; that is, $2(-241.8 \text{ kJ}) = -483.6 \text{ kJ}$.

The direct proportionality between quantity of reaction and quantity of heat transfer is in line with your everyday experience. Burning twice as much natural gas produces twice as much heating.

$$2\,H_2(g) + O_2(g) \longrightarrow 2\,H_2O(g) \qquad \Delta H° = -483.6 \text{ kJ} \quad [6.6]$$

EXERCISE 6.10 Enthalpy Change and Stoichiometry

Calculate the change in enthalpy if 0.5000 mol $H_2(g)$ reacts with an excess of $O_2(g)$ to form water vapor at 25 °C.

PROBLEM-SOLVING EXAMPLE 6.8 Thermochemical Expressions

Given the thermochemical expression

$$2\,C_2H_6(g) + 7\,O_2(g) \longrightarrow 4\,CO_2(g) + 6\,H_2O(g) \qquad \Delta H° = -2856 \text{ kJ}$$

write a thermochemical expression for

(a) Formation of 1 mol $CO_2(g)$ by burning $C_2H_6(g)$
(b) Formation of 1 mol $C_2H_6(g)$ by reacting $CO_2(g)$ with $H_2O(g)$
(c) Combination of 1 mol $O_2(g)$ with a stoichiometric quantity of $C_2H_6(g)$

Answer

(a) $\frac{1}{2}\,C_2H_6(g) + \frac{7}{4}\,O_2(g) \rightarrow CO_2(g) + \frac{3}{2}\,H_2(g) \qquad \Delta H° = -714 \text{ kJ}$

(b) $2\,CO_2(g) + 3\,H_2O(g) \rightarrow C_2H_6(g) + \frac{7}{2}\,O_2(g) \qquad \Delta H° = +1428 \text{ kJ}$

(c) $\frac{2}{7}\,C_2H_6(g) + O_2(g) \rightarrow \frac{4}{7}\,CO_2(g) + \frac{6}{7}\,H_2O(g) \qquad \Delta H° = -408 \text{ kJ}$

Strategy and Explanation

(a) Producing 1 mol $CO_2(g)$ requires that one quarter the molar amount of each reactant and product be used and also makes the $\Delta H°$ value one quarter as big.
(b) Forming $C_2H_6(g)$ means that $C_2H_6(g)$ must be a product. This changes the direction of the reaction and the sign of $\Delta H°$; forming 1 mol $C_2H_6(g)$ requires that each coefficient be halved and this halves the size of $\Delta H°$.
(c) If 1 mol $O_2(g)$ reacts, only $\frac{2}{7}$ mol $C_2H_6(g)$ is required; each coefficient is one seventh its original value, and $\Delta H°$ is also one seventh the original value.

✓ **Reasonable Answer Check** In each case examine the coefficients, the direction of the chemical equation, and the sign of $\Delta H°$ to make certain that the appropriate quantity of reactant or product and the appropriate sign have been written.

PROBLEM-SOLVING PRACTICE 6.8

Given the thermochemical expression

$$BaO(s) + CO_2(g) \longrightarrow BaCO_3(s) \qquad \Delta H° = -662.8 \text{ kJ}$$

write the thermochemical expression for the production of 4 mol CO_2 by decomposition of solid barium carbonate.

In Section 4.4 we derived stoichiometric factors (mole ratios) from the coefficients in balanced chemical equations (⟵ ***p. 134***). Stoichiometric factors that relate quantity of energy transferred to quantity of reactant used up or quantity of product produced can be derived from a thermochemical expression. From the equation

$$2\ H_2(g) + O_2(g) \longrightarrow 2\ H_2O(g) \qquad \Delta H° = -483.6 \text{ kJ}$$

these factors (and their reciprocals) can be derived:

$$\frac{-483.6 \text{ kJ}}{2 \text{ mol } H_2 \text{ reacted}} \qquad \frac{-483.6 \text{ kJ}}{1 \text{ mol } O_2 \text{ reacted}} \qquad \frac{-483.6 \text{ kJ}}{2 \text{ mol } H_2O \text{ produced}}$$

The first factor says that 483.6 kJ of energy will transfer from the system to the surroundings whenever 2 mol H_2 is consumed in this reaction. The reciprocal of the second factor says that if the reaction transfers 483.6 kJ to the surroundings, then 1 mol of O_2 must have been used up. We shall refer to stoichiometric factors that include thermochemical information as *thermostoichiometric factors.*

EXERCISE 6.11 Thermostoichiometric Factors from Thermochemical Expressions

Write all of the thermostoichiometric factors (including their reciprocals) that can be derived from this expression:

$$N_2(g) + 3\ H_2(g) \longrightarrow 2\ NH_3(g) \qquad \Delta H° = -92.22 \text{ kJ}$$

© Thomson Learning/Charles D. Winters

Portable hand warmer.

CONCEPTUAL EXERCISE 6.12 Hand Warmer

When the tightly sealed outer package is opened, the portable hand warmer shown in the margin transfers energy to its surroundings. In cold weather it can keep fingers or toes warm for several hours. Suggest a way that such a hand warmer could be designed. What chemicals might be used? Why is the tightly sealed package needed?

Enthalpy changes for reactions have many practical applications. For instance, when enthalpies of combustion are known, the quantity of energy transferred by the combustion of a given mass of fuel can be calculated. Suppose you are designing a heating system, and you want to know how much heating can be provided per pound (454 g) of propane, C_3H_8, burned in a furnace. The reaction that occurs is *exothermic* (which is not surprising, given that it is a combustion reaction).

CHEMISTRY YOU CAN DO

Rusting and Heating

Chemical reactions can heat their surroundings, and a simple experiment demonstrates this fact very well. To perform the experiment you will need a steel wool pad (without soap), $\frac{1}{4}$ cup of vinegar, a cooking or outdoor thermometer, and a large jar with a lid. (The thermometer must fit inside the jar.)

Soak the steel wool pad in vinegar for several minutes. While doing so, place the thermometer in the jar, close the lid, and let it stand for several minutes. Read the temperature.

Squeeze the excess vinegar out of the steel wool pad, wrap the pad around the bulb of the thermometer, and place both in the jar. Close the lid but do not seal it tightly. After about 5 min, read the temperature again. What has happened?

Repeat the experiment with another steel wool pad, but wash it with water instead of vinegar. Try a third pad that is not washed at all. Allow each pad to stand in air for a few hours or for a day and observe the pad carefully. Do you see any change in the metal? Suggest an explanation for your observations of temperature changes and appearance of the steel wool.

© Thomson Learning/Charles D. Winters

$$C_3H_8(g) + 5\,O_2(g) \longrightarrow 3\,CO_2(g) + 4\,H_2O(\ell) \qquad \Delta H° = -2220 \text{ kJ}$$

According to this thermochemical expression, 2220 kJ of energy transfers to the surroundings for every 1 mol $C_3H_8(g)$ burned, for every 5 mol $O_2(g)$ consumed, for every 3 mol $CO_2(g)$ formed, and for every 4 mol $H_2O(\ell)$ produced. We know that 454 g $C_3H_8(g)$ has been burned, so we can calculate how many moles of propane that is.

$$\text{Amount of propane} = 454 \text{ g} \times \frac{1 \text{ mol } C_3H_8}{44.10 \text{ g}} = 10.29 \text{ mol } C_3H_8$$

Then we multiply by the appropriate thermostoichiometric factor to find the total energy transferred.

$$\text{Energy transferred} = 10.29 \text{ mol } C_3H_8 \times \frac{-2220 \text{ kJ}}{1 \text{ mol } C_3H_8} = -22{,}900 \text{ kJ}$$

Burning a pound of fuel such as propane releases a substantial quantity of energy.

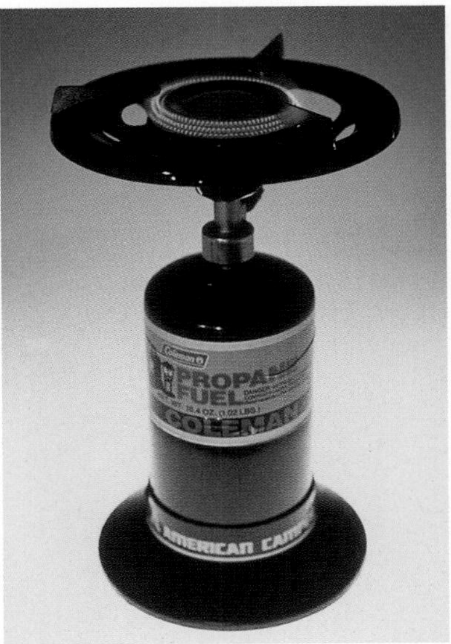

© Thomson Learning/Charles D. Winters

Propane burning. This portable camp stove burns propane fuel. Propane is a major component of liquified petroleum (LP) gas, which is used for heating some houses.

PROBLEM-SOLVING EXAMPLE 6.9 Calculating Energy Transferred

The reaction of iron with oxygen from the air provides the energy transferred by the hot pack described in Conceptual Exercise 6.12. Assuming that the iron is converted to iron(III) oxide, how much heating can be provided by a hot pack that contains a tenth of a pound of iron? The thermochemical expression is

$$2\,Fe(s) + \tfrac{3}{2}\,O_2(g) \longrightarrow Fe_2O_3(s) \qquad \Delta H° = -824.2 \text{ kJ}$$

Answer −335 kJ

Strategy and Explanation Begin by calculating how many moles of iron are present. A pound is 454 g, so

$$\text{Amount of iron} = 0.100 \text{ lb} \times \frac{454 \text{ g}}{1 \text{ lb}} \times \frac{1 \text{ mol Fe}}{55.84 \text{ g}} = 0.8130 \text{ mol Fe}$$

Then use a thermostoichiometric factor to calculate the energy transferred. The appropriate factor is 824.2 kJ transferred to the surroundings per 2 mol Fe, so

$$\text{Energy transferred} = 0.8130 \text{ mol Fe} \times \frac{-824.2 \text{ kJ}}{2 \text{ mol Fe}} = -335 \text{ kJ}$$

Thus, 335 kJ is transferred by the reaction to heat your fingers.

✓ **Reasonable Answer Check** A tenth of a pound is about 45 g, which is a bit less than the molar mass of iron, so we are oxidizing less than a mole of iron. Two moles of iron gives about 800 kJ, so less than a mole should give less than 400 kJ, which makes 335 kJ a reasonable value. The sign should be negative because the enthalpy of the hand warmer (system) should go down when it transfers energy to your hand.

PROBLEM-SOLVING PRACTICE 6.9

How much thermal energy transfer is required to maintain constant temperature during decomposition of 12.6 g liquid water to the elements hydrogen and oxygen at 25.0 °C? In what direction does the energy transfer?

$$H_2O(\ell) \longrightarrow H_2(g) + \tfrac{1}{2}O_2(g) \qquad \Delta H° = 285.8 \text{ kJ}$$

6.7 Where Does the Energy Come From?

During melting or boiling, nanoscale particles (atoms, molecules, or ions) that attract each other are separated, which increases their potential energy. This requires transfer of energy from the surroundings to enable the particles to overcome their mutual attractions. During a chemical reaction, chemical compounds are created or broken down; that is, reactant molecules are converted into product molecules. Atoms in molecules are held together by chemical bonds. When existing chemical bonds are broken and new chemical bonds are formed, atomic nuclei and electrons move farther apart or closer together, and their energy increases or decreases. These energy differences are usually much greater than those for phase changes.

Consider the reaction of hydrogen gas with chlorine gas to form hydrogen chloride gas.

$$H_2(g) + Cl_2(g) \longrightarrow 2\,HCl(g) \qquad [6.7]$$

When this reaction occurs, the two hydrogen atoms in a H_2 molecule separate, as do the two chlorine atoms in a Cl_2 molecule. In the product the atoms are combined in a different way—as two HCl molecules. We can think of this change as involving two steps:

$$H_2(g) + Cl_2(g) \longrightarrow 2\,H(g) + 2\,Cl(g) \longrightarrow 2\,HCl(g)$$

The first step is to break all bonds in the reactant H_2 and Cl_2 molecules. The second step is to form the bonds in the two product HCl molecules. The net effect of these two steps is the same as for Equation 6.7: One hydrogen molecule and one chlorine molecule change into two hydrogen chloride molecules. The enthalpy changes for these two processes are shown in Figure 6.15.

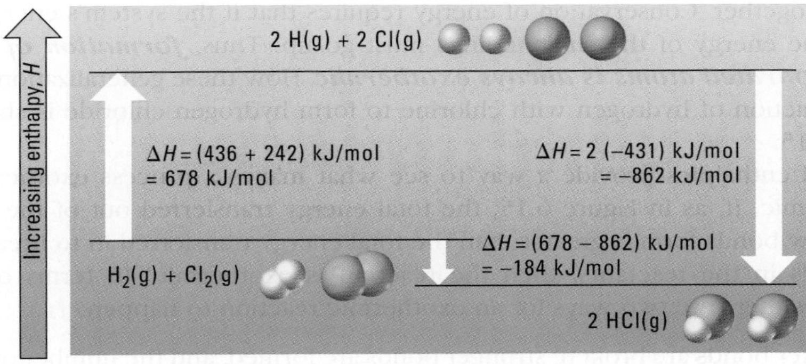

Figure 6.15 Stepwise energy changes in a reaction. Breaking a mole of H_2 molecules into H atoms requires 436 kJ. Breaking a mole of Cl_2 molecules into Cl atoms requires 242 kJ. Putting 2 mol H atoms together with 2 mol Cl atoms to form 2 mol HCl provides $2 \times (-431 \text{ kJ}) = -862$ kJ, so the reaction is exothermic. $\Delta H° = 436 \text{ kJ} + 242 \text{ kJ} - 862 \text{ kJ} = -184$ kJ. The relatively weak Cl—Cl bond in the reactants accounts for the fact that this reaction is exothermic.

The reaction of hydrogen with chlorine actually occurs by a complicated series of steps, but the details of how the atoms rearrange do not matter, because enthalpy is a state function and the initial and final states are the same. This means that we can concentrate on products and reactants and not worry about exactly what happens in between.

Another analogy for the enthalpy change for a reaction is the change in altitude when you climb a mountain. No matter which route you take to the summit (which atoms you separate or combine first), the difference in altitude between the summit and where you started to climb (the enthalpy difference between products and reactants) is the same.

CONCEPTUAL EXERCISE 6.13 Reaction Pathways and Enthalpy Change

Suppose that the enthalpy change differed depending on the pathway a reaction took from reactants to products. For example, suppose that 190 kJ was released when a mole of hydrogen gas and a mole of chlorine gas combined to form two moles of hydrogen chloride (Equation 6.7), but that only 185 kJ was released when the same reactant molecules were broken into atoms and the atoms then recombined to form hydrogen chloride (Equation 6.8). Would this violate the first law of thermodynamics? Explain why or why not.

Bond Enthalpies

Separating two atoms that are bonded together requires a transfer of energy into the system, because work must be done against the force holding the pair of atoms together. *The enthalpy change that occurs when two bonded atoms in a gas-phase molecule are separated completely at constant pressure* is called the **bond enthalpy** (or the **bond energy**—the two terms are often used interchangeably). The bond enthalpy is usually expressed per mole of bonds. For example, the bond enthalpy for a Cl_2 molecule is 243 kJ/mol, so we can write

$$Cl_2(g) \longrightarrow 2\,Cl(g) \qquad \Delta H° = 243 \text{ kJ} \qquad [6.8]$$

Bond enthalpy and bond energy differ because a volume change occurs when one molecule changes to two atoms at constant pressure. Therefore work is done on the surroundings (⇐ ***p. 229***) and $\Delta E \neq \Delta H$. For a more detailed discussion, see Treptow, R. S., *Journal of Chemical Education* 1995, 72, 497.

Bond enthalpies are always positive, and they range in magnitude from about 150 kJ/mol to a little more than 1000 kJ/mol. ***Bond breaking is always endothermic,*** because there is always a transfer of energy into the system (in this case, the mole of Cl_2 molecules) to separate pairs of bonded atoms. Conversely, when atoms come together to form a bond, energy will invariably be transferred to the surroundings because the potential energy of the atoms is lower when they are

Bond ***breaking*** is ***endo***thermic.

Bond ***making*** is ***exo***thermic.

bonded together. Conservation of energy requires that if the system's energy goes down, the energy of the surroundings must go up. Thus, ***formation of bonds from separated atoms is always exothermic.*** How these generalizations apply to the reaction of hydrogen with chlorine to form hydrogen chloride is shown in Figure 6.15.

Bond enthalpies provide a way to see what makes a process exothermic or endothermic. If, as in Figure 6.15, the total energy transferred out of the system when new bonds form is greater than the total energy transferred in to break all of the bonds in the reactants, then the reaction is exothermic. In terms of bond enthalpies there are two ways for an exothermic reaction to happen:

- Weaker bonds are broken, stronger bonds are formed, and the number of bonds is the same.
- Bonds in reactants and products are of about the same strength, but more bonds are formed than are broken.

An endothermic reaction involves breaking stronger bonds than are formed, breaking more bonds than are formed, or both.

CONCEPTUAL EXERCISE 6.14 Enthalpy Change and Bond Enthalpies

Consider the endothermic reactions

(a) $2\ HF(g) \longrightarrow H_2(g) + F_2(g)$

(b) $2\ H_2O(g) \longrightarrow 2\ H_2(g) + O_2(g)$

In which case is formation of weaker bonds the more important factor in making the reaction endothermic? In which case is formation of fewer bonds more important?

6.8 Measuring Enthalpy Changes: Calorimetry

ThomsonNOW
Go to the Coached Problems menu for a tutorial on **calorimetry calculations** and a simulation of a **bomb calorimeter.**

A thermochemical expression tells us how much energy is transferred as a chemical process occurs. This knowledge enables us to calculate the heat obtainable when a fuel is burned, as was done in the preceding section. Also, when reactions are carried out on a larger scale—say, in a chemical plant that manufactures sulfuric acid—the surroundings must have enough cooling capacity to prevent an exothermic reaction from overheating, speeding up, running out of control, and possibly damaging the plant. For these and many other reasons it is useful to know as many $\Delta H°$ values as possible.

For many reactions, direct experimental measurements can be made by using a **calorimeter,** *a device that measures heat transfers.* Calorimetric measurements can be made at constant volume or at constant pressure. Often, in finding heats of combustion or the caloric value of foods, where at least one of the reactants is a gas, the measurement is done at a constant volume in a *bomb calorimeter* (Figure 6.16). The "bomb" is a cylinder about the size of a large fruit juice can with heavy steel walls so that it can contain high pressures. A weighed sample of a combustible solid or liquid is placed in a dish inside the bomb. The bomb is then filled with pure O_2(g) and placed in a water-filled container with well-insulated walls. The sample is ignited, usually by an electrical spark. When the sample burns, it warms the bomb and the water around it to the same temperature.

In this configuration, the oxygen and the compound represent the *system* and the bomb and the water around it are the *surroundings*. For the system, $\Delta E = q + w$. Because there is no change in volume of the sealed, rigid bomb, $w = 0$. Therefore, $\Delta E = q_V$. To calculate q_V and ΔE, we can sum the energy transfers from the reaction to the bomb and to the water. Because each of these is a transfer out of the system, each will be negative. For example, the energy transfer to heat the water can be calculated as $c_{water} \times m_{water} \times \Delta T_{water}$, where c_{water} is the specific heat capacity of water, m_{water} is the mass of water, and ΔT_{water} is the change in temperature of the water. Because this energy transfer is out of the system, the energy transfer from the system to the water is negative, that is, $-(c_{water} \times m_{water} \times \Delta T_{water})$. Problem-Solving Example 6.10 illustrates how this works.

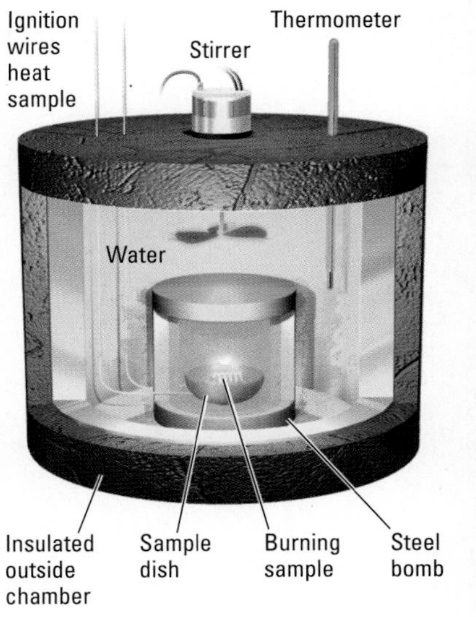

Figure 6.16 **Combustion (bomb) calorimeter.**

PROBLEM-SOLVING EXAMPLE 6.10 **Measuring Energy Change with a Bomb Calorimeter**

A 3.30-g sample of the sugar glucose, $C_6H_{12}O_6$(s), was placed in a bomb calorimeter, ignited, and burned to form carbon dioxide and water. The temperature of the water changed from 22.4 °C to 34.1 °C. If the calorimeter contained 850. g water and had a heat capacity of 847 J/°C, what is ΔE for combustion of 1 mol glucose? (The heat capacity of the bomb is the energy transfer required to raise the bomb's temperature by 1 °C.)

Answer −2810 kJ

Strategy and Explanation When the glucose burns, it heats the calorimeter and the water. Calculate the heat transfer from the reaction to the calorimeter and the water from the temperature change and their heat capacities. (Look up the heat capacity of water in Table 6.1.) Use this result to calculate the heat transfer from the reaction. Then use a proportion to find the heat transfer for 1 mol glucose.

$$\Delta T = (34.1 - 22.4)\text{°C} = 11.7\ \text{°C}$$

$$\text{Energy transferred from system to bomb} = -\text{heat capacity of bomb} \times \Delta T$$

$$= -\frac{847\ \text{J}}{\text{°C}} \times 11.7\ \text{°C} = -9910\ \text{J} = -9.910\ \text{kJ}$$

$$\text{Energy transferred from system to water} = -(c \times m \times \Delta T)$$

$$= -\left(\frac{4.184\ \text{J}}{\text{g °C}} \times 850.\ \text{g} \times 11.7\ \text{°C}\right) = -41{,}610\ \text{J} = -41.61\ \text{kJ}$$

$$\Delta E = q_V = -9.910\ \text{kJ} - 41.61\ \text{kJ} = -51.52\ \text{kJ}$$

This quantity of energy transfer corresponds to burning 3.30 g glucose. To scale to 1 mol glucose, first calculate how many moles of glucose were burned.

$$3.30\ \text{g}\ C_6H_{12}O_6 \times \frac{1\ \text{mol}}{180.16\ \text{g}} = 1.832 \times 10^{-2}\ \text{mol}\ C_6H_{12}O_6$$

Then set up this proportion.

$$\frac{-51.52\ \text{kJ}}{1.832 \times 10^{-2}\ \text{mol}} = \frac{\Delta E}{1\ \text{mol}} \qquad \Delta E = 1\ \text{mol} \times \frac{-51.52\ \text{kJ}}{1.832 \times 10^{-2}\ \text{mol}} = -2.81 \times 10^3\ \text{kJ}$$

✓ **Reasonable Answer Check** The result is negative, which correctly reflects the fact that burning sugar is exothermic. A mole of glucose (180 g) is more than a third of a pound, and a third of a pound of sugar contains quite a bit of energy (many Calories), so it is reasonable that the magnitude of the answer is in the thousands of kilojoules.

PROBLEM-SOLVING PRACTICE 6.10

In Problem-Solving Example 6.1, a single Fritos chip was oxidized by potassium chlorate. Suppose that a single chip weighing 1.0 g is placed in a bomb calorimeter that has a heat capacity of 877 J/°C. The calorimeter contains 832 g water. When the bomb is filled with excess oxygen and the chip is ignited, the temperature rises from 20.64 °C to 25.43 °C. Use these data to verify the statement that the chip provides 5 Cal when metabolized.

CONCEPTUAL EXERCISE 6.15 Comparing Enthalpy Change and Energy Change

Write a balanced equation for the combustion of glucose to form $CO_2(g)$ and $H_2O(\ell)$ Use what you already know about the volume of a mole of any gas at a given temperature and pressure (or look in Section 10.5) to predict whether ΔH would differ significantly from ΔE for the reaction in Problem-Solving Example 6.10.

When reactions take place in solution, it is much easier to use a calorimeter that is open to the atmosphere. An example, often encountered in introductory chemistry courses, is the *coffee cup calorimeter* shown in Figure 6.17. The nested coffee cups (which are made of expanded polystyrene) provide good thermal insulation; reactions can occur when solutions are poured together in the inner cup. Because a coffee cup calorimeter is a constant-pressure device, the measured heat transfer is q_P, which equals ΔH.

(a)

(b)

© Photos: Jerold J. Jacobsen

Figure 6.17 Coffee cup calorimeter. (a) A simple constant-pressure calorimeter can be made from two coffee cups that are good thermal insulators, a cork or other insulating lid, a temperature probe, and a stirrer. (b) Close-up of the nested cups that make up the calorimeter. A reaction carried out in an aqueous solution within the calorimeter will change the temperature of the solution. Because the thermal insulation is extremely good, essentially no energy transfer can occur to or from anything outside the calorimeter. Therefore, the heat capacity of the solution and its change in temperature can be used to calculate q_P and ΔH.

PROBLEM-SOLVING EXAMPLE 6.11 Measuring Enthalpy Change with a Coffee Cup Calorimeter

A coffee cup calorimeter is used to determine ΔH for the reaction

$$NaOH(aq) + HCl(aq) \longrightarrow H_2O(\ell) + NaCl(aq) \qquad \Delta H = ?$$

When 250. mL of 1.00 M NaOH was added to 250. mL of 1.00 M HCl at 1 bar, the temperature of the solution increased from 23.4 °C to 30.4 °C. Use this information to determine ΔH and complete the thermochemical expression. Assume that the heat capacities of the coffee cups, the temperature probe, and the stirrer are negligible, that the solution has the same density and the same specific heat capacity as water, and that there is no change in volume of the solutions upon mixing.

Answer $\Delta H = -58.7$ kJ

Strategy and Explanation Use the definition of specific heat capacity [Equation 6.2′ (p. 224)] to calculate q_P, the heat transfer for the constant-pressure conditions (1 bar). Because the density of the solution is assumed to be the same as for water and the total volume is 500. mL, the mass of solution is 500. g. Because the reaction system heats the solution, q_P is negative and

$$q_P = -c \times m \times \Delta T$$
$$= -(4.184 \text{ J g}^{-1} \text{ °C}^{-1})(500. \text{ g})(30.4 \text{ °C} - 23.4 \text{ °C}) = -1.46 \times 10^4 \text{ J} = -14.6 \text{ kJ}$$

This quantity of heat transfer does not correspond to the equation as written, however; instead it corresponds to consumption of

$$250. \text{ mL} \times \frac{1.00 \text{ mol}}{1000 \text{ mL}} = 0.250 \text{ mol HCl} \quad \text{and} \quad 250. \text{ mL} \times \frac{1.00 \text{ mol}}{1000 \text{ mL}} = 0.250 \text{ mol NaOH}$$

From the balanced equation, 1 mol HCl is required for each 1 mol NaOH. Therefore the reactants are in the stoichiometric ratio and neither reactant is a limiting reactant. Because the chemical equation involves 1 mol HCl, the heat transfer must be scaled in proportion to this quantity of HCl.

$$\frac{\Delta H}{1 \text{ mol HCl}} = \frac{-14.6 \text{ kJ}}{0.250 \text{ mol HCl}}$$

$$\Delta H = 1 \text{ mol HCl} \times \frac{-14.6 \text{ kJ}}{0.250 \text{ mol HCl}} = -58.6 \text{ kJ}$$

(Note that because the reactants were in the stoichiometric ratio, the NaOH could also have been used in the preceding calculation.)

✓ **Reasonable Answer Check** The temperature of the surroundings increased, so the reaction is exothermic and $\Delta H°$ must be negative. The temperature of 500.-g solution

When expanded polystyrene coffee cups are used to make a calorimeter, the masses of substances other than the solvent water are often so small that their heat capacities can be ignored; all of the energy of a reacton can be assumed to be transferred to the water.

CHEMISTRY IN THE NEWS

How Small Can a Calorimeter Be?

With the development of nanotechnology, it has become important to make calorimetric measurements at the nanoscale. For example, when studying how reactions occur in an automobile catalytic converter, it is useful to be able to measure the heat transfer during catalytic dissociation of carbon monoxide molecules on a metal surface. Because the reaction occurs on a two-dimensional surface, a much smaller number of atoms and molecules is involved than would be present in a three-dimensional sample, and so the heat transfer is also much smaller. This calls for a small and highly sensitive calorimeter.

The ultimate in sensitivity and small size at present is a nanoscale calorimeter reported by W. Chung Fon, Keith C. Schwab, John M. Worlock, and Michael L. Roukes. A scanning electron micrograph of their calorimeter is shown in the photograph. The calorimeter was patterned from a 120-nm-thick layer of silicon nitride (SiN) on an area about 25 μm on a side. Four 8-μm-long and 600-nm-wide "beams" of SiN (the X shape in the photograph) suspend a thermometer and heater. The heater is made of gold and the thermometer is AuGe. Four thin films of niobium metal serve as electrical leads to the heater and thermometer. The device was prepared using special nanofabrication techniques.

The tiny volume of the metallic heater and thermometer ensure that their contribution to the heat capacity of the calorimeter is very small. This makes possible measurements of very small energy transfers. (The smaller the heat capacity is, the larger the temperature change is for a given energy transfer.) When a pulse of electric current was applied to the gold heater, delivering 0.125 nW (0.125×10^{-9} J/s) at an initial temperature of 4.5 K, the calorimeter responded as shown in the graph. Unlike experiments involving coffee cup calorimeters that you may have performed, this experiment is over in about 75 μs (75×10^{-6} s)—a very short time. The graph shows an increase in temperature that levels off, which is similar to what would be observed in a coffee cup calorimeter. The 75-μs timescale, however, requires special electronics to measure the temperature change of less than 0.1 K (100 mK).

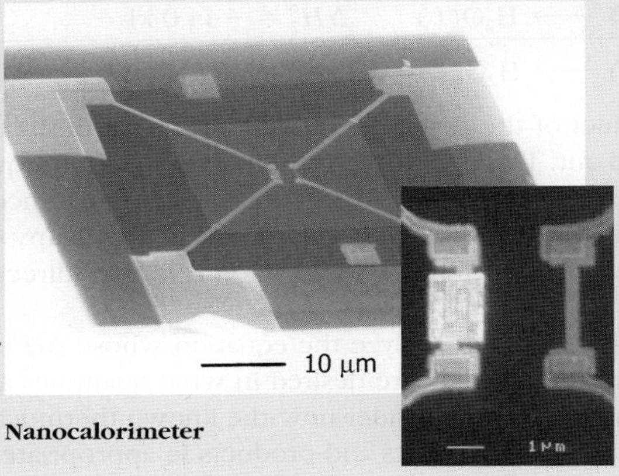

Nanocalorimeter

Photos courtesy of W. Chung Fon. Reprinted with permission from *Nano Letters*, vol. 5 (10), fig. 1, 1968–1971. © 2005 American Chemical Society.

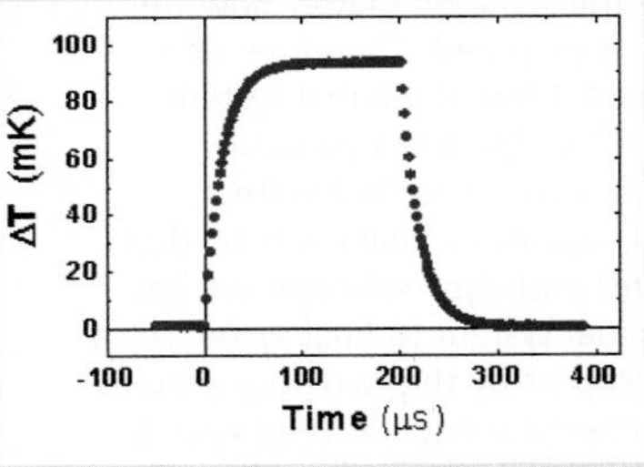

To check that the calorimeter could measure the heat capacity of a real substance, a thin layer of helium atoms was condensed on its surface—about 2 He atoms per square nanometer of surface. The heat capacity of this film was measured to be about 3 fJ/K (3×10^{-15} J/K). This result is similar to observations for thin layers of helium on other surfaces. Based on their experiments, the four scientists conclude that their nanocalorimeter could measure energy transfers as small as about 0.5 aJ/K (5×10^{-19} J/K)—very tiny energy transfers indeed!

SOURCE: *Nano Letters*, Vol. 5, October 2005, pp. 1968–1971.

went up 7.0 °C, so the heat transfer was about (500 × 7 × 4) J = 14,000 J = 14 kJ. This corresponded to one-quarter mole of each reactant, so the heat transfer per mole must be about 4 × 14 kJ = 56 kJ. Therefore ΔH should be about −56 kJ, which it is.

PROBLEM-SOLVING PRACTICE 6.11

Suppose that 100. mL 1.00 M HCl and 100. mL 0.50 M NaOH, both at 20.4 °C, are mixed in a coffee cup calorimeter. Use the result from Problem-Solving Example 6.11 to predict what will be the highest temperature reached in the calorimeter after mixing the solutions. Make similar assumptions to those made in Problem-Solving Example 6.11.

CONCEPTUAL EXERCISE 6.16 Calorimetry

In Problem-Solving Example 6.11 ΔT was observed to be 7.0 °C for mixing 250. mL 1.00 M HCl and 250. mL 1.00 M NaOH in a coffee cup calorimeter. Predict ΔT for mixing

(a) 200. mL 1.0 M HCl and 200. mL 1.0 M NaOH.
(b) 100. mL 1.0 M H_2SO_4 and 100. mL 1.0 M NaOH.

6.9 Hess's Law

Calorimetry works well for some reactions, but for many others it is difficult to use. Besides, it would be very time-consuming to measure values for every conceivable reaction, and it would take a great deal of space to tabulate so many values. Fortunately, there is a better way. It is based on **Hess's law,** which states that, *if the equation for a reaction is the sum of the equations for two or more other reactions, then $\Delta H°$ for the first reaction must be the sum of $\Delta H°$ values of the other reactions.* Hess's law is a corollary of the law of conservation of energy. It works even if the overall reaction does not actually occur by way of the separate equations that are summed.

For example, in Figure 6.14 (**p. 236**) we noted that the formation of liquid water from its elements $H_2(g)$ and $O_2(g)$ could be thought of as two successive changes: (a) formation of water vapor from the elements and (b) condensation of water vapor to liquid water. As shown below, the equation for formation of liquid water can be obtained by adding algebraically the chemical equations for these two steps. Therefore, according to Hess's law, the $\Delta H°$ value can be found by adding the $\Delta H°$ values for the two steps.

Hess's law is based on a fact we mentioned earlier (**p. 232**). A system's enthalpy and internal energy will be the same no matter how the system is prepared. Therefore, at 25 °C and 1 bar, the initial system, $H_2(g) + \frac{1}{2} O_2(g)$, has a particular enthalpy value. The final system, $H_2O(\ell)$, also has a characteristic (but different) enthalpy. Whether we get from initial system to final system by a single step or by the two-step process of the chemical equations (a) and (b), the enthalpy change will be the same.

Note that it takes 1 mol $H_2O(g)$ to cancel 1 mol $H_2O(g)$. If the coefficient of $H_2O(g)$ had been different on one side of the chemical from the coefficient on the other side, $H_2O(g)$ could not have been completely canceled.

$$\text{(a)}\quad H_2(g) + \tfrac{1}{2}O_2(g) \longrightarrow \cancel{H_2O(g)} \qquad \Delta H_1° = -241.8\text{ kJ}$$

$$\text{(b)}\quad \cancel{H_2O(g)} \longrightarrow H_2O(\ell) \qquad \Delta H_2° = -44.0\text{ kJ}$$

$$\text{(a) + (b)}\quad H_2(g) + \tfrac{1}{2}O_2(g) \longrightarrow H_2O(\ell) \qquad \Delta H° = \Delta H_1° + \Delta H_2° = -285.8\text{ kJ}$$

Here, 1 mol $H_2O(g)$ is a product of the first reaction and a reactant in the second. Thus, $H_2O(g)$ can be canceled out. This is similar to adding two algebraic equations: If the same quantity or term appears on both sides of the equation, it cancels. The net result is an equation for the overall reaction and its associated enthalpy change. This overall enthalpy change applies even if the liquid water is formed directly from hydrogen and oxygen.

A useful approach to Hess's law is to analyze the equation whose $\Delta H°$ you are trying to calculate. Identify which reactants are desired in what quantities and also which products in what quantities. Then consider how the known thermochemical expressions could be changed to give reactants and products in appropriate quantities. For example, suppose you want the thermochemical expression for the reaction

$$\tfrac{1}{2}\,CH_4(g) + O_2(g) \longrightarrow \tfrac{1}{2}\,CO_2(g) + H_2O(\ell) \qquad \Delta H^\circ = ?$$

and you already know the thermochemical expressions

$$\text{(a) } CH_4(g) + 2\,O_2(g) \longrightarrow CO_2(g) + 2\,H_2O(g) \qquad \Delta H^\circ_a = -802.34 \text{ kJ}$$

and

$$\text{(b) } H_2O(\ell) \longrightarrow H_2O(g) \qquad \Delta H^\circ_b = 44.01 \text{ kJ}$$

The target equation has only $\frac{1}{2}$ mol $CH_4(g)$ as a reactant; it also has $\frac{1}{2}$ mol $CO_2(g)$ and 1 mol $H_2O(\ell)$ as products. Equation (a) has the same reactants and products, but twice as many moles of each; also, water is in the gaseous state in equation (a). If we change each coefficient and the ΔH° value of expression (a) to one half their original values, we have the thermochemical expression

$$\text{(a}'\text{) } \tfrac{1}{2}\,CH_4(g) + O_2(g) \longrightarrow \tfrac{1}{2}\,CO_2(g) + H_2O(g) \qquad \Delta H^\circ_{a'} = -401.17 \text{ kJ}$$

which differs from the target expression only in the phase of water. Expression (b) has liquid water on the left and gaseous water on the right, but our target expression has liquid water on the right. If the equation in (b) is reversed (which changes the sign of ΔH°), the thermochemical expression becomes

$$\text{(b}'\text{) } H_2O(g) \longrightarrow H_2O(\ell) \qquad \Delta H^\circ_{b'} = -44.01 \text{ kJ}$$

Summing the expressions (a′) and (b′) gives the target expression, from which $H_2O(g)$ has been canceled.

$$\text{(a}' + \text{b}'\text{) } \tfrac{1}{2}\,CH_4(g) + O_2(g) \longrightarrow \tfrac{1}{2}\,CO_2(g) + H_2O(\ell) \qquad \Delta H^\circ = \Delta H^\circ_{a'} + \Delta H^\circ_{b'}$$

$$\Delta H^\circ = (-401.17 \text{ kJ}) + (-44.01 \text{ kJ}) = -445.18 \text{ kJ}$$

PROBLEM-SOLVING EXAMPLE 6.12 Using Hess's Law

In designing a chemical plant for manufacturing the plastic polyethylene, you need to know the enthalpy change for the removal of H_2 from C_2H_6 (ethane) to give C_2H_4 (ethylene), a key step in the process.

$$C_2H_6(g) \longrightarrow C_2H_4(g) + H_2(g) \qquad \Delta H^\circ = ?$$

From experiments you know these thermochemical expressions:

$$\text{(a) } 2\,C_2H_6(g) + 7\,O_2(g) \longrightarrow 4\,CO_2(g) + 6\,H_2O(\ell) \qquad \Delta H^\circ_a = -3119.4 \text{ kJ}$$

$$\text{(b) } C_2H_4(g) + 3\,O_2(g) \longrightarrow 2\,CO_2(g) + 2\,H_2O(\ell) \qquad \Delta H^\circ_b = -1410.9 \text{ kJ}$$

$$\text{(c) } 2\,H_2(g) + O_2(g) \longrightarrow 2\,H_2O(\ell) \qquad \Delta H^\circ_c = -571.66 \text{ kJ}$$

Use this information to find the value of ΔH° for the formation of ethylene from ethane.

Answer $\Delta H^\circ = 137.0$ kJ

Strategy and Explanation Analyze reactions (a), (b), and (c). Reaction (a) involves 2 mol ethane on the reactant side, but only 1 mol ethane is required in the desired reaction. Reaction (b) has C_2H_4 as a reactant, but C_2H_4 is a product in the desired reaction. Reaction (c) has 2 mol H_2 as a reactant, but 1 mol H_2 is a product in the desired reaction.

First, since the desired expression has only 1 mol ethane on the reactant side, we multiply expression (a) by $\frac{1}{2}$ to give an expression (a′) that also has 1 mol ethane on the reactant side. Halving the coefficients in the equation also halves the enthalpy change.

$$\text{(a}'\text{)} = \tfrac{1}{2}\text{(a)} \qquad C_2H_6(g) + \tfrac{7}{2}\,O_2(g) \longrightarrow 2\,CO_2(g) + 3\,H_2O(\ell) \qquad \Delta H^\circ_{a'} = -1559.7 \text{ kJ}$$

Next, we reverse expression (b) so that C_2H_4 is on the product side, giving expression (b′). This also reverses the sign of the enthalpy change.

$$\text{(b}'\text{)} = -\text{(b)} \qquad 2\,CO_2(g) + 2\,H_2O(\ell) \longrightarrow C_2H_4(g) + 3\,O_2(g)$$

$$\Delta H^\circ_{b'} = -\Delta H^\circ_b = +1410.9 \text{ kJ}$$

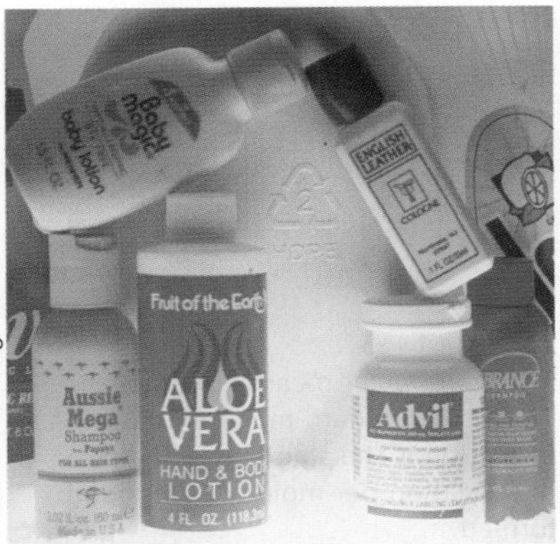

© Thomson Learning/Charles D. Winters

Polyethylene is a common plastic. Many products are packaged in polyethylene bottles.

To get 1 mol $H_2(g)$ on the product side, we reverse expression (c) and multiply all coefficients by $\frac{1}{2}$. This changes the sign and halves the enthalpy change.

$$(c') = -\tfrac{1}{2}(c) \qquad H_2O(\ell) \longrightarrow H_2(g) + \tfrac{1}{2}O_2(g) \qquad \Delta H^\circ_{c'} = -\tfrac{1}{2}\Delta H^\circ_c = +285.83 \text{ kJ}$$

Now it is possible to add expressions (a′), (b′), and (c′) to give the desired expression.

$$(a') \qquad C_2H_6(g) + \cancel{\tfrac{7}{2}O_2(g)} \longrightarrow \cancel{2\,CO_2(g)} + \cancel{3\,H_2O(\ell)} \qquad \Delta H^\circ_{a'} = -1559.7 \text{ kJ}$$

$$(b') \qquad \cancel{2\,CO_2(g)} + \cancel{2\,H_2O(\ell)} \longrightarrow C_2H_4(g) + \cancel{3\,O_2(g)} \qquad \Delta H^\circ_{b'} = +1410.9 \text{ kJ}$$

$$(c') \qquad \cancel{H_2O(\ell)} \longrightarrow H_2(g) + \cancel{\tfrac{1}{2}O_2(g)} \qquad \Delta H^\circ_{c'} = +285.83 \text{ kJ}$$

$$\text{Net equation:} \qquad C_2H_6(g) \longrightarrow C_2H_4(g) + H_2(g) \qquad \Delta H^\circ_{net} = 137.0 \text{ kJ}$$

When the chemical equations are added, there is $\frac{7}{2}$ mol $O_2(g)$ on the reactant side and $(3 + \frac{1}{2}) = \frac{7}{2}$ mol $O_2(g)$ on the product side. There is 3 mol $H_2O(\ell)$ on each side and 2 mol $CO_2(g)$ on each side. Therefore, $O_2(g)$, $CO_2(g)$, and $H_2O(\ell)$ all cancel, and the chemical equation for the conversion of ethane to ethylene and hydrogen remains.

✓ **Reasonable Answer Check** The overall process involves breaking a molecule apart into simpler molecules, which is likely to involve breaking bonds. Therefore it should be endothermic, and ΔH° should be positive.

PROBLEM-SOLVING PRACTICE 6.12

When iron is obtained from iron ore, an important reaction is conversion of $Fe_3O_4(s)$ to $FeO(s)$. Write a balanced equation for this reaction. Then use these thermochemical expressions to calculate ΔH° for the reaction.

$$3\,Fe(s) + 2\,O_2(g) \longrightarrow Fe_3O_4(s) \qquad \Delta H^\circ_1 = -1118.4 \text{ kJ}$$

$$Fe(s) + \tfrac{1}{2}O_2(g) \longrightarrow FeO(s) \qquad \Delta H^\circ_2 = -272.0 \text{ kJ}$$

6.10 Standard Molar Enthalpies of Formation

Hess's law makes it possible to tabulate ΔH° values for a relatively few reactions and, by suitable combinations of these few reactions, to calculate ΔH° values for a great many other reactions. To make such a tabulation we use standard molar enthalpies of formation. The **standard molar enthalpy of formation,** H_f°, is the *standard enthalpy change for formation of one mole of a compound from its elements in their standard states.* The subscript *f* indicates *f*ormation of the compound. The **standard state** of an element or compound is the physical state in which it exists at 1 bar and a specified temperature. At 25 °C the standard state for hydrogen is $H_2(g)$ and for sodium chloride is $NaCl(s)$. For an element that can exist in several different allotropic forms (p. 27) at 1 bar and 25 °C, the most stable form is usually selected as the standard state. For example, graphite, not diamond or buckminsterfullerene, is the standard state for carbon; $O_2(g)$, not $O_3(g)$, is the standard state for oxygen.

The word *molar* means "per mole." Thus, the standard molar enthalpy of formation is the standard enthalpy of formation per mole of compound formed.

It is common to use the term "heat of formation" interchangeably with "enthalpy of formation." It is only the heat of reaction at constant pressure that is equivalent to the enthalpy change. If heat of reaction is measured under other conditions, it may not equal the enthalpy change. For example, when measured at constant volume in a bomb calorimeter, heat of reaction corresponds to the change of internal energy, not enthalpy.

Some examples of thermochemical expressions involving standard molar enthalpies of formation are

$$H_2(g) + \tfrac{1}{2}O_2(g) \longrightarrow H_2O(\ell) \qquad \Delta H^\circ = \Delta H_f^\circ\{H_2O(\ell)\} = -285.8 \text{ kJ/mol}$$

$$2\,C(\text{graphite}) + 2\,H_2(g) \longrightarrow C_2H_4(g) \qquad \Delta H^\circ = \Delta H_f^\circ\{C_2H_4(g)\} = 52.26 \text{ kJ/mol}$$

$$2\,C(\text{graphite}) + 3\,H_2(g) + \tfrac{1}{2}O_2 \longrightarrow C_2H_5OH(\ell)$$

$$\Delta H^\circ = \Delta H_f^\circ\{C_2H_5OH(\ell)\} = -277.69 \text{ kJ/mol}$$

Notice that in each case *1 mol of a compound in its standard state is formed directly from appropriate amounts of elements in their standard states.*

Some examples of thermochemical expressions at 25 °C and 1 bar where $\Delta H°$ is *not* a standard molar enthalpy of formation (and the reason why it is not) are

$$MgO(s) + SO_3(g) \longrightarrow MgSO_4(s) \qquad \Delta H° = -287.5 \text{ kJ} \qquad [6.9]$$

(reactants are not elements)

and

$$P_4(s) + 6\,Cl_2(g) \longrightarrow 4\,PCl_3(\ell) \qquad \Delta H° = -1278.8 \text{ kJ} \qquad [6.10]$$

(4 mol product formed instead of 1 mol)

© Thomson Learning/Charles D. Winters

Burning charcoal. Charcoal is mainly carbon, and it burns to form mainly carbon dioxide gas. The energy transfer from a charcoal grill could be estimated from the mass of charcoal and the standard molar enthalpy of formation of $CO_2(g)$.

PROBLEM-SOLVING EXAMPLE 6.13 **Thermochemical Expressions for Standard Molar Enthalpies of Formation**

Rewrite thermochemical Expressions 6.9 and 6.10 so that they represent standard molar enthalpies of formation of their products. (The standard molar enthalpy of formation value for $MgSO_4(s)$ is -1284.9 kJ/mol at 25 °C.)

Answer

$$Mg(s) + \tfrac{1}{8}\,S_8(s) + 2\,O_2(g) \longrightarrow MgSO_4(s) \qquad \Delta H_f°\{MgSO_4(s)\} = -1284.9 \text{ kJ/mol}$$

and

$$\tfrac{1}{4}\,P_4(s) + \tfrac{3}{2}\,Cl_2(g) \longrightarrow PCl_3(\ell) \qquad \Delta H_f°\{PCl_3(\ell)\} = -319.7 \text{ kJ/mol}$$

Strategy and Explanation Expression 6.9 has 1 mol $MgSO_4(s)$ on the right side, but the reactants are not elements in their standard states. Write a new expression so that the left side contains the elements Mg(s), $S_8(s)$, and $O_2(g)$. For this expression $\Delta H°$ is the standard molar enthalpy of formation, -1284.9 kJ/mol. The new thermochemical expression is given in the Answer section above.

Expression 6.10 has elements in their standard states on the left side, but more than 1 mol of product is formed. Rewrite the expression so the right side involves only 1 mol $PCl_3(\ell)$, and reduce the coefficients of the elements on the left side in proportion—that is, divide all coefficients by 4. Then $\Delta H°$ must also be divided by 4 to obtain the second thermochemical expression in the Answer section.

✓ **Reasonable Answer Check** Check each expression carefully to make certain the substance whose standard enthalpy of formation you want is on the right side and has a coefficient of 1. For $PCl_3(\ell)$, $\Delta H_f°$ should be one fourth of about -1300 kJ, and it is.

PROBLEM-SOLVING PRACTICE 6.13

Write an appropriate thermochemical expression in each case. (You may need to use fractional coefficients.)

(a) The standard molar enthalpy of formation of $NH_3(g)$ at 25 °C is -46.11 kJ/mol.
(b) The standard molar enthalpy of formation of CO(g) at 25 °C is -110.525 kJ/mol.

CONCEPTUAL EXERCISE 6.17 **Standard Molar Enthalpies of Formation of Elements**

Write the thermochemical expression that corresponds to the standard molar enthalpy of formation of $N_2(g)$.

(a) What process, if any, takes place in the chemical equation?
(b) What does this imply about the enthalpy change?

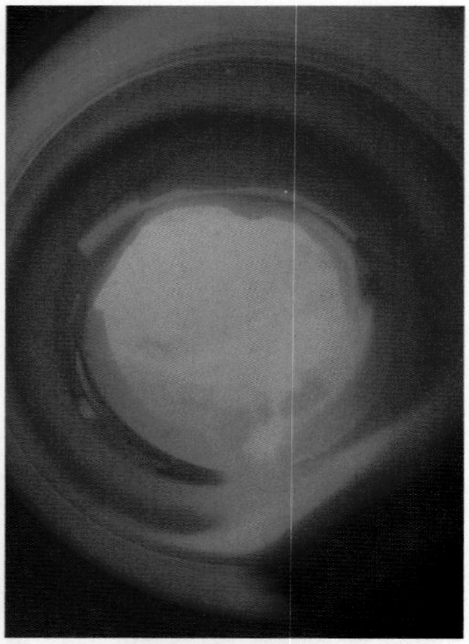

H. David Seawell/Corbis

Lime production. At high temperature in a lime kiln, calcium carbonate (limestone, $CaCO_3$) decomposes to calcium oxide (lime, CaO) and carbon dioxide (CO_2).

Table 6.2 and Appendix J list values of ΔH_f°, obtained from the National Institute for Standards and Technology (NIST), for many compounds. Notice that no values are listed in these tables for elements in their most stable forms, such as C(graphite) or O_2(g). As you probably realized from Conceptual Exercise 6.17, *standard enthalpies of formation for the elements in their standard states are zero,* because forming an element in its standard state from the same element in its standard state involves no chemical or physical change.

Hess's law can be used to find the standard enthalpy change for any reaction if there is a set of reactions whose enthalpy changes are known and whose chemical equations, when added together, will give the equation for the desired reaction. For example, suppose you are a chemical engineer and want to know how much heating is required to decompose limestone (calcium carbonate) to lime (calcium oxide) and carbon dioxide.

$$CaCO_3(s) \longrightarrow CaO(s) + CO_2(g) \qquad \Delta H^\circ = ?$$

As a first approximation you can assume that all substances are in their standard states at 25 °C and look up the standard molar enthalpy of formation of each substance in a table such as Table 6.2 or Appendix J. This gives the thermochemical expressions on the next page.

Table 6.2 Selected Standard Molar Enthalpies of Formation at 25 °C*

Formula	Name	Standard Molar Enthalpy of Formation (kJ/mol)	Formula	Name	Standard Molar Enthalpy of Formation (kJ/mol)
$Al_2O_3(s)$	Aluminum oxide	−1675.7	HI(g)	Hydrogen iodide	26.48
$BaCO_3(s)$	Barium carbonate	−1216.3	KF(s)	Potassium fluoride	−567.27
$CaCO_3(s)$	Calcium carbonate	−1206.92	KCl(s)	Potassium chloride	−436.747
CaO(s)	Calcium oxide	−635.09	KBr(s)	Potassium bromide	−393.8
C(s, diamond)	Diamond	1.895	MgO(s)	Magnesium oxide	−601.70
$CCl_4(\ell)$	Carbon tetrachloride	−135.44	$MgSO_4(s)$	Magnesium sulfate	−1284.9
$CH_4(g)$	Methane	−74.81	$Mg(OH)_2(s)$	Magnesium hydroxide	−924.54
$C_2H_5OH(\ell)$	Ethyl alcohol	−277.69	NaF(s)	Sodium fluoride	−573.647
CO(g)	Carbon monoxide	−110.525	NaCl(s)	Sodium chloride	−411.153
$CO_2(g)$	Carbon dioxide	−393.509	NaBr(s)	Sodium bromide	−361.062
$C_2H_2(g)$	Acetylene (ethyne)	226.73	NaI(s)	Sodium iodide	−287.78
$C_2H_4(g)$	Ethylene (ethene)	52.26	$NH_3(g)$	Ammonia	−46.11
$C_2H_6(g)$	Ethane	−84.68	NO(g)	Nitrogen monoxide	90.25
$C_3H_8(g)$	Propane	−103.8	$NO_2(g)$	Nitrogen dioxide	33.18
$C_4H_{10}(g)$	Butane	−126.148	$O_3(g)$	Ozone	142.7
$C_6H_{12}O_6(s)$	α-D-Glucose	−1274.4	$PCl_3(\ell)$	Phosphorus trichloride	−319.7
$CuSO_4(s)$	Copper(II) sulfate	−771.36	$PCl_5(s)$	Phosphorus pentachloride	−443.5
$H_2O(g)$	Water vapor	−241.818	$SiO_2(s)$	Silicon dioxide (quartz)	−910.94
$H_2O(\ell)$	Liquid water	−285.830	$SnCl_2(s)$	Tin(II) chloride	−325.1
HF(g)	Hydrogen fluoride	−271.1	$SnCl_4(\ell)$	Tin(IV) chloride	−511.3
HCl(g)	Hydrogen chloride	−92.307	$SO_2(g)$	Sulfur dioxide	−296.830
HBr(g)	Hydrogen bromide	−36.40	$SO_3(g)$	Sulfur trioxide	−395.72

*From Wagman, D. D., Evans, W. H., Parker, V. B., Schumm, R. H., Halow, I., Bailey, S. M., Churney, K. L., and Nuttall, R. The NBS Tables of Chemical Thermodynamic Properties. *Journal of Physical and Chemical Reference Data,* Vol. 11, Suppl. 2, 1982. (NBS, the National Bureau of Standards, is now NIST, the National Institute for Standards and Technology.)

$$\text{(a)} \quad \text{Ca(s)} + \text{C(graphite)} + \tfrac{3}{2}\,\text{O}_2\text{(g)} \longrightarrow \text{CaCO}_3\text{(s)} \qquad \Delta H^\circ_{\text{a}} = -1206.9 \text{ kJ}$$

$$\text{(b)} \quad \text{Ca(s)} + \tfrac{1}{2}\,\text{O}_2\text{(g)} \longrightarrow \text{CaO(s)} \qquad \Delta H^\circ_{\text{b}} = -635.1 \text{ kJ}$$

$$\text{(c)} \quad \text{C(graphite)} + \text{O}_2\text{(g)} \longrightarrow \text{CO}_2\text{(g)} \qquad \Delta H^\circ_{\text{c}} = -393.5 \text{ kJ}$$

Now add the three chemical equations in such a way that the resulting equation is the one given above for the decomposition of limestone. In expression (a), $CaCO_3$(s) is a product, but it must appear in the desired expression as a reactant. Therefore, the equation in (a) must be reversed, and the sign of $\Delta H_a°$ must also be reversed. On the other hand, CaO(s) and CO_2(g) are products in the desired expression, so expressions (b) and (c) can be added with the same direction and sign of $\Delta H°$ as they have in the $\Delta H_f°$ equations:

$$\text{(a}'\text{)} = -\text{(a)} \quad \text{CaCO}_3\text{(s)} \longrightarrow \cancel{\text{Ca(s)}} + \cancel{\text{C(graphite)}} + \cancel{\tfrac{3}{2}\,\text{O}_2\text{(g)}}$$

$$\Delta H^\circ_{\text{a}'} = +1206.9 \text{ kJ}$$

$$\text{(b)} \quad \cancel{\text{Ca(s)}} + \cancel{\tfrac{1}{2}\,\text{O}_2\text{(g)}} \longrightarrow \text{CaO(s)} \qquad \Delta H^\circ_{\text{b}} = -635.1 \text{ kJ}$$

$$\text{(c)} \quad \cancel{\text{C(graphite)}} + \cancel{\text{O}_2\text{(g)}} \longrightarrow \text{CO}_2\text{(g)} \qquad \Delta H^\circ_{\text{c}} = -393.5 \text{ kJ}$$

$$\text{CaCO}_3\text{(s)} \longrightarrow \text{CaO(s)} + \text{CO}_2\text{(g)} \qquad \Delta H^\circ = +178.3 \text{ kJ}$$

When the expressions are added in this fashion, 1 mol each of C(graphite) and Ca(s) and $\frac{3}{2}$ mol O_2(g) appear on opposite sides and so are canceled out. Thus, the sum of these chemical equations is the desired one for the decomposition of calcium carbonate, and the sum of the enthalpy changes of the three expressions gives that for the desired expression.

Another very useful conclusion can be drawn from this example. The calculation can be written mathematically as

$$\Delta H^\circ = \Delta H^\circ_f\{\text{CaO(s)}\} + \Delta H^\circ_f\{\text{CO}_2\text{(g)}\} - \Delta H^\circ_f\{\text{CaCO}_3\text{(s)}\}$$
$$= (-635.1 \text{ kJ}) + (-393.5 \text{ kJ}) - (-1206.9 \text{ kJ}) = 178.3 \text{ kJ}$$

which involves adding the $\Delta H_f°$ values for the products of the reaction, CaO(s) and CO_2(g), and subtracting the $\Delta H_f°$ value for the reactant, $CaCO_3$(s). The mathematics of the problem can be summarized by the equation

$$\Delta H^\circ = \sum\{(\text{moles of product}) \times \Delta H^\circ_f(\text{product})\}$$
$$-\sum\{(\text{moles of reactant})\} \times \Delta H^\circ_f(\text{reactant})\} \qquad [6.11]$$

This equation says that to get the standard enthalpy change of the reaction you should (1) multiply the standard molar enthalpy of formation of each product by the number of moles of that product and then sum over all products; (2) multiply the standard molar enthalpy of formation of each reactant by the number of moles of that reactant and then sum over all reactants; and (3) subtract the sum for the reactants from the sum for the products. This is a useful shortcut to writing the thermochemical expressions for all appropriate formation reactions and applying Hess's law, as we did above.

Courtesy Reatha Clark King

Reatha Clark King
1938–

Reatha Clark was born in Georgia and married N. Judge King in 1961. She obtained degrees from Clark Atlanta University and the University of Chicago and began her career with the National Bureau of Standards (now the National Institute for Standards and Technology, NIST), where she determined enthalpies of formation of fluorine compounds that were important to the U.S. space program and NASA. She became a dean at York College, president of Metropolitan State University (Minneapolis), and is currently president of the General Mills Foundation.

ThomsonNOW
Go to the Coached Problems menu for a tutorial on **calculating enthalpy change.**

PROBLEM-SOLVING EXAMPLE 6.14 Using Standard Molar Enthalpies of Formation

Benzene, C_6H_6, is a commercially important hydrocarbon that is present in gasoline, where it enhances the octane rating. Calculate its enthalpy of combustion per mole; that is, find the value of $\Delta H°$ for the reaction

$$\text{C}_6\text{H}_6(\ell) + \tfrac{15}{2}\,\text{O}_2\text{(g)} \longrightarrow 6\,\text{CO}_2\text{(g)} + 3\,\text{H}_2\text{O}(\ell)$$

For benzene, $\Delta H_f°\{C_6H_6(\ell)\} = 49.0$ kJ/mol. Use Table 6.2 for any other values you may need.

Answer $\Delta H° = -3169.5$ kJ

Strategy and Explanation To calculate $\Delta H°$ you need standard molar enthalpies of formation for all compounds (and elements, if they are not in their standard states) involved in the reaction. (Since $O_2(g)$ is in its standard state, it is not included). From Table 6.2,

$$C(graphite) + O_2(g) \longrightarrow CO_2(g) \qquad \Delta H_f° = -393.509 \text{ kJ/mol}$$

$$H_2(g) + \tfrac{1}{2}O_2(g) \longrightarrow H_2O(\ell) \qquad \Delta H_f° = -285.830 \text{ kJ/mol}$$

Using Equation 6.11,

$$\Delta H° = [6 \text{ mol} \times \Delta H_f°\{CO_2(g)\} + 3 \text{ mol} \times \Delta H_f°\{H_2O(\ell)\}] - [1 \text{ mol } C_6H_6(\ell) \times \Delta H_f°\{C_6H_6(\ell)\}$$
$$= [6 \text{ mol} \times (-393.509 \text{ kJ/mol}) + 3 \text{ mol} \times (-285.830 \text{ kJ/mol})]$$
$$-[1 \text{ mol} \times (49.0 \text{ kJ/mol})] = -3267.5 \text{ kJ}$$

✓ **Reasonable Answer Check** As expected, the enthalpy change for combustion of a fuel is negative and large.

PROBLEM-SOLVING PRACTICE 6.14

Nitroglycerin is a powerful explosive because it decomposes exothermically and four different gases are formed.

$$2\ C_3H_5(NO_3)_3(\ell) \longrightarrow 3\ N_2(g) + \tfrac{1}{2}O_2(g) + 6\ CO_2(g) + 5\ H_2O(g)$$

For nitroglycerin, $\Delta H_f°\{C_3\ H_5(NO_3)_3(\ell)\} = -364$ kJ/mol. Using data from Table 6.2, calculate the energy transfer when 10.0 g nitroglycerin explodes.

When the enthalpy change for a reaction is known, it is possible to use that information to calculate $\Delta H_f°$ for one substance in the reaction provided that $\Delta H_f°$ values are known for all of the rest of the substances. Problem-Solving Example 6.15 indicates how to do this.

PROBLEM-SOLVING EXAMPLE 6.15 Standard Molar Enthalpy of Formation from Enthalpy of Combustion

Octane, C_8H_{18}, is a hydrocarbon that is present in gasoline. At 25 °C the enthalpy of combustion per mole for octane is −5116.0 kJ/mol. Use data from Table 6.2 to calculate the standard molar enthalpy of formation of octane. (Assume that water vapor is produced by the combustion reaction.)

Answer $\Delta H_f° = -208.4$ kJ

Strategy and Explanation Write a balanced equation for the target reaction whose $\Delta H°$ you want to calculate. Also write a balanced equation for combustion of octane, for which you know the standard enthalpy change. By studying these two equations, decide what additional information is needed to set up a Hess's law calculation that will yield the standard molar enthalpy of formation of octane.

(target reaction) $8\ C(s) + 9\ H_2(g) \longrightarrow C_8H_{18}(\ell) \qquad \Delta H_f° = ??$ kJ/mol

(a) $C_8H_{18}(\ell) + \tfrac{25}{2}O_2(g) \longrightarrow 8\ CO_2(g) + 9\ H_2O(g) \qquad \Delta H°_{combustion} = -5116.0$ kJ

Notice that the combustion equation involves 1 mol $C_8H_{18}(\ell)$ as a reactant and the target equation (for enthalpy of formation) involves 1 mol $C_8H_{18}(\ell)$ as a product. Therefore, it seems reasonable to reverse the combustion equation and see where that leads.

(a′) $8\ CO_2(g) + 9\ H_2O(g) \longrightarrow C_8H_{18}(\ell) + \tfrac{25}{2}O_2(g) \qquad \Delta H° = +5116.0$ kJ

On the reactant side of the target equation we have 8 C(s) and 9 $H_2(g)$. These elements, combined with $O_2(g)$, are on the left side of equation (a′), so perhaps it would be reasonable to use the equations corresponding to standard molar enthalpies of formation of carbon dioxide and water. From Table 6.2, we have

(b) $C(s) + O_2(g) \longrightarrow CO_2(g)$ $\Delta H_f^\circ = -393.509$ kJ/mol

(c) $H_2(g) + \frac{1}{2}O_2(g) \longrightarrow H_2O(g)$ $\Delta H_f^\circ = -241.818$ kJ/mol

Multiplying equation (b) by 8 and equation (c) by 9 gives the correct number of moles of C(s) and of H_2(g) on the reactant side of the target equation. This gives

(a′) $8\,CO_2(g) + 9\,H_2O(g) \longrightarrow C_8H_{18}(\ell) + \frac{25}{2}O_2(g)$ $\Delta H^\circ = +5116.0$ kJ

(b′) $8\,C(s) + 8\,O_2(g) \longrightarrow 8\,CO_2(g)$ $\Delta H^\circ = -3148.072$ kJ

(c′) $9\,H_2(g) + \frac{9}{2}O_2(g) \longrightarrow 9\,H_2O(g)$ $\Delta H^\circ = -2176.362$ kJ/mol

$8\,C(s) + 9\,H_2(g) \longrightarrow C_8H_{18}(\ell)$ $\Delta H_f^\circ = \Delta H_{a'}^\circ + \Delta H_{b'}^\circ + \Delta H_{c'}^\circ = -208.4$ kJ/mol

PROBLEM-SOLVING PRACTICE 6.15

Use data from Table 6.2 to calculate the molar heat of combustion of sulfur dioxide, SO_2(g), to form sulfur trioxide, SO_3(g).

6.11 Chemical Fuels for Home and Industry

A **chemical fuel** is any substance that will react exothermically with atmospheric oxygen and is available at reasonable cost and in reasonable quantity. It is desirable that when a fuel burns, the products create as little environmental damage as possible. As indicated in Figure 6.18, most of the fuels that supply us with thermal energy are fossil fuels: coal, petroleum, and natural gas. Biomass fuels consisting of

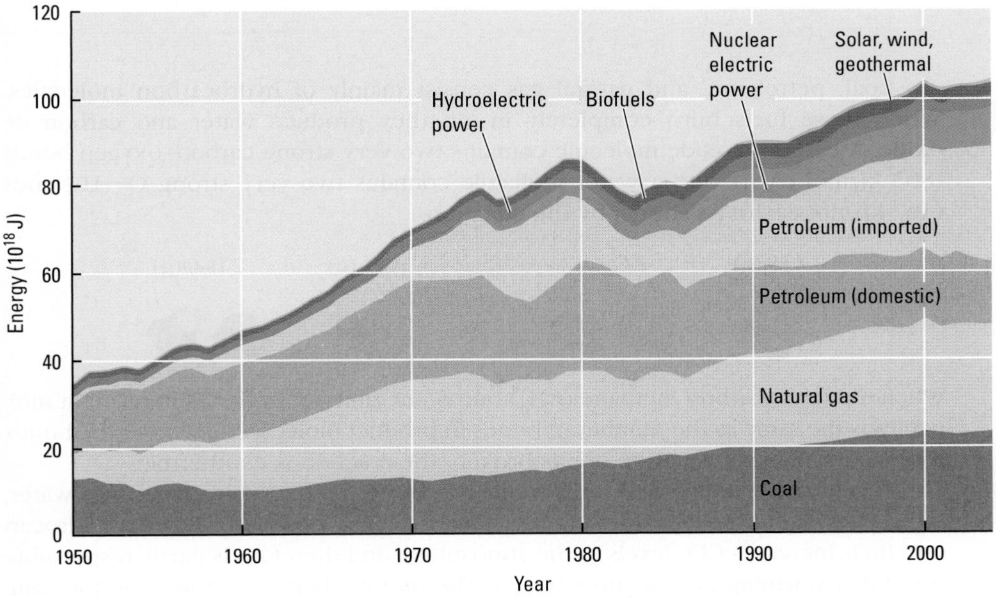

Figure 6.18 Use of energy resources in the United States. Use of energy resources in the United States is plotted from 1950 to 2004. (An energy resource is a naturally occurring fuel, such as petroleum, or a continuous supply, such as sunlight.) At the midpoint of the twentieth century, coal and petroleum were almost equally important, with natural gas coming in third. Today, petroleum and natural gas are used in greater quantities than coal, and more than half of U.S. petroleum is imported. Nuclear electric power did not exist in 1949 but contributes significantly to energy resources today, whereas hydroelectric electricity generation has grown only slightly since 1950.

wood, peat, and other plant matter are a distant second among chemical fuels. A significant quantity of energy comes from nuclear reactors and hydroelectric power plants, and a much smaller quantity from solar, wind, and geothermal (hot springs or other sources of heat within the earth) sources. For specific applications, other fuels are sometimes chosen because of their special properties. For example, hydrogen is used as the fuel for the Space Shuttle, and hydrazine (N_2H_4) is used as a rocket fuel in some applications.

What nanoscale characteristics make for a good fuel? If some or all of the bonds in the molecules of a fuel are weak, or if the bonds in the products of its combustion are strong, then the combustion reaction will be exothermic. An example of a molecule with a weak bond is hydrazine, N_2H_4(g), which burns according to the equation

$$N_2H_4(g) + O_2(g) \longrightarrow N_2(g) + 2\,H_2O(g)$$

In N_2H_4 the N—N bond enthalpy is only 160 kJ/mol, although its four N—H bonds are reasonably strong at 391 kJ/mol. The O_2 bond enthalpy is 498 kJ/mol. The reaction products are N_2, which has a very strong bond at 946 kJ/mol, and H_2O, which also has strong O—H bonds at 467 kJ/mol. In this case there are fewer bonds after the reaction than before, but the bonds are much stronger, so the reaction is exothermic.

EXERCISE 6.18 Using Bond Enthalpies to Evaluate a Fuel

Based on the molecular structures and bond enthalpies given above for combustion of hydrazine:

(a) Calculate $\Delta H°$ when all the bonds in the reactant molecules are broken.
(b) Calculate $\Delta H°$ when all the bonds in the product molecules are formed.
(c) Calculate $\Delta H°$ for the reaction and write the thermochemical expression.

Coal, petroleum, and natural gas consist mainly of hydrocarbon molecules. When these fuels burn completely in air, they produce water and carbon dioxide. A carbon dioxide molecule contains two very strong carbon-oxygen bonds (803 kJ/mol each), and a water molecule contains two very strong O—H bonds (467 kJ/mol each). As shown by the equation,

$$CH_4(g) + 2\,O_2(g) \longrightarrow CO_2(g) + 2\,H_2O(g)$$

when the hydrocarbon methane (CH_4) burns, the number of bonds in reactant molecules is the same as the number of bonds in product molecules. Because the bonds formed are stronger than the bonds broken, the reaction is exothermic.

Another very good fuel is hydrogen. It burns in air to produce only water, which is a big advantage from an environmental point of view. Burning hydrocarbon fuels increases CO_2 levels in the atmosphere and therefore is partly responsible for global warming (see Section 10.13). The thermochemical expression for combustion of hydrogen corresponds to the formation of water from its elements, so the standard enthalpy change is just $\Delta H_f^\circ\{H_2O(g)\}$:

$$H_2(g) + \tfrac{1}{2}\,O_2(g) \longrightarrow H_2O(g) \qquad \Delta H_f^\circ = -241.818 \text{ kJ}$$

On earth, little or no hydrogen is available naturally as the element; it is always combined in compounds. Therefore hydrogen fails to meet the criterion of availability

CHEMISTRY IN THE NEWS

Can Hydrogen Be Stored in Tiny Tanks?

Hydrogen has been proposed as the fuel of the future. It produces almost no pollution when it burns. It does not contribute to global warming, because the product of its combustion, water, is already a major component of the atmosphere and is easily removed as rainfall. As Exercise 6.19 shows, it has a high fuel value.

Unfortunately hydrogen's energy density is low unless it can be liquefied or otherwise stored at much greater density than in the gas phase. Any storage medium used must be able to absorb hydrogen and then release it when the hydrogen is needed to burn in a combustion engine or to power a fuel cell to produce electric current.

One proposal for storing hydrogen calls for the use of single-walled carbon nanotubes. If you took a single layer of graphite, which consists of connected hexagons of carbon atoms, and rolled it up to make a tube, it would have the structure of a nanotube. If the opposite edges of the graphite layer met and matched exactly, you would have a single-walled carbon nanotube. On the macroscale you could make a tube out of a single thickness of chicken wire and its structure would be very similar to the nanotube. Several single-walled carbon nanotubes are shown in the figure, with hydrogen molecules distributed around them. The diameters of such tubes range from 0.5 nm to 2.5 nm.

Researchers have found widely varying results regarding the quantities of hydrogen that can be stored in single-walled carbon nanotubes. Reported experimental values range from 0.4% by weight up to 67% by weight. Scientists who have achieved high uptakes of hydrogen have proposed that the nanotubes would make an ideal storage medium for hydrogen-powered vehicles.

Shigeo Maruyama

Others dispute this, based on their inability to replicate the high-uptake experiments.

At present the issue remains unresolved. Nevertheless, it is possible that in the future the gas tank of your car will be full of a very large number of nanoscale tanks—carbon nanotubes.

SOURCE: *Chemical & Engineering News*, January 14, 2002, p. 25.

in reasonable quantity mentioned at the beginning of this section. It is manufactured as a by-product of petroleum refining at present, which makes it too expensive for most fuel applications. However, considerable research is aimed at finding ways to produce hydrogen either by electrolysis of water or photochemically. For example, electricity supplied by solar cells could be used to electrolyze water and produce hydrogen, which could then be used as fuel. Or solar energy might be used directly to cause a series of chemical reactions to occur in which hydrogen was produced from water. At present none of these ways of producing hydrogen is inexpensive enough to be competitive with fossil fuels. As supplies of fossil fuels become exhausted, however, hydrogen may become much more important.

Before the Industrial Revolution the main fuel was wood. It is now referred to more generically as biomass, because plant matter other than wood can also be burned. Biomass is very important as a fuel in many less developed countries, and it is a renewable resource. Coal, petroleum, and natural gas will eventually be used up, but it is possible to continue growing plants to create biomass. Although biomass is a mixture of materials, it is primarily carbohydrate (cellulose in wood, for example) and can be represented by the empirical formula CH_2O. Combustion of biomass is highly exothermic:

Scientists at the University of California, Berkeley, and the National Renewable Energy Laboratory have found that when sulfur is removed from the growing environment of *Chlamydomonas reinhardtii*, the algae generate hydrogen gas (*Plant Physiology*, Vol. 122, 2000; p. 127). Optimizing hydrogen production from algae might provide an inexpensive source of fuel.

$$CH_2O(s) + O_2(g) \longrightarrow CO_2(g) + H_2O(g) \qquad \Delta H^\circ = -425 \text{ kJ}$$

Two important criteria for a fuel are the **fuel value,** which is the quantity of energy released when 1 g of fuel is burned to form carbon dioxide and water, and the **energy density,** which is the quantity of energy released per unit volume of fuel. For gaseous fuels the fuel value may be high, but the energy density will be low because the density of a gas is low. Fuels with low energy density take a large volume for storage and therefore are not convenient to use unless, as in the case of natural gas, they can be supplied on demand via pipes (mains). Often gaseous fuels, such as propane and butane, are condensed and stored as liquids under pressure. Fuels such as methane and hydrogen cannot be liquefied by pressure alone. If they are to be stored as liquids, the temperature must be kept low and the pressure high. This makes them less convenient than liquid fuels for use in cars and airplanes, for example.

EXERCISE 6.19 Comparing Fuels

Evaluate each of the following fuels on the basis of fuel value and energy density. Assume that water vapor is formed, use thermodynamic data from Table 6.2 or Appendix J, and use density data from the *CRC Handbook of Chemistry and Physics* (CRC Press, **http://crcpress.com/**). Which fuel provides the largest fuel value? Which provides the greatest energy density?

(a) Methane, $CH_4(g)$
(b) Octane, $C_8H_{18}(\ell)$
(c) Ethanol, $C_2H_5OH(\ell)$
(d) Hydrazine, $N_2H_4(\ell)$
(e) Hydrogen, $H_2(g)$
(f) Glucose, $C_6H_{12}O_6(s)$
(g) Biomass (assume that the fuel is entirely carbohydrate and has the same density as glucose)

6.12 Foods: Fuels for Our Bodies

This discussion answers the question "Where does the energy come from to make my muscles work?" that was posed in Chapter 1 (p. 2).

Foods are similar to fuels, in that the **caloric value** of fats and carbohydrates corresponds to the standard enthalpy of combustion per gram of the food. Foods consist mainly of carbohydrate, fat, and protein. **Carbohydrates** have the general formula $C_x(H_2O)_y$. They are converted in the intestines to glucose, $C_6H_{12}O_6$, which is soluble in blood and thereby can be transported throughout the body. Glucose is metabolized in a complicated series of reactions that eventually produce $CO_2(g)$ and $H_2O(\ell)$, with release of energy. The net effect is equivalent to combustion of glucose,

$$C_6H_{12}O_6(s) + 6\,O_2(g) \longrightarrow 6\,CO_2(g) + 6\,H_2O(\ell) \qquad \Delta H^\circ = -2801.6\text{ kJ}$$

Because enthalpy is a state function and the initial and final states are the same, it is appropriate and convenient to measure the caloric values for carbohydrates using a bomb calorimeter (p. 243). A sample of glucose or other carbohydrate is ignited inside the bomb, and the heat transfer to the calorimeter and surrounding water is measured. The average caloric value of carbohydrates in food is 4 Cal/g (17 kJ/g).

EXERCISE 6.20 Caloric Value of Carbohydrate

Use the thermochemical expression given above to verify that the caloric value of glucose corresponds to the average 4 Cal/g for carbohydrates.

Carbohydrates are metabolized quickly and large quantities are not usually stored in the body. The energy released by carbohydrates is used to power muscles, to transmit nerve impulses, and to cause chemical reactions to occur that construct and repair tissues. Energy is also required to maintain body temperature. Energy from carbohydrates that is not needed for these purposes is stored in fats.

Fats also compose a significant portion of most people's diets. Like carbohydrates, fats are metabolized to $CO_2(g)$ and $H_2O(\ell)$. For example, tristearin is oxidized according to the thermochemical expression

$$2\ C_{57}H_{110}O_6(s) + 163\ O_2(g) \longrightarrow 114\ CO_2(g) + 110\ H_2O(\ell) \quad \Delta H° = -75{,}520\ kJ$$

Again, bomb calorimetry simulates the metabolic process quite well. Fat molecules make excellent storehouses for energy. They are insoluble in water and therefore are not excreted easily. When metabolized they release 9 Cal/g (38 kJ/g)—more than twice the energy from the same mass of carbohydrate or protein.

The third dietary component, protein, contains nitrogen in addition to carbon, hydrogen, and oxygen. The nitrogen is metabolized in the body to produce new proteins or urea, $(NH_2)_2CO(aq)$, which is excreted. The carbon, hydrogen, and oxygen are metabolized in pathways that release energy. On average, protein metabolism releases 4 Cal/g (17 kJ/g), the same caloric value as for carbohydrate.

A few substances may be part of your diet that are not protein, carbohydrate, or fat. For example, ethanol in alcoholic beverages contributes calories because ethanol can be oxidized, or metabolized, exothermically. Most food labels provide information about the caloric value of a typical serving and about the percentages of carbohydrate, fat, and protein in the food. An example is shown in Figure 6.19. The caloric value of the food can be estimated from the quantities of protein, carbohydrate, and fat, as long as no other component (such as alcohol) is present. Table 6.3 gives the content of fat, carbohydrate, and protein along with caloric values for some representative foods.

The release of energy upon combustion or metabolism of carbohydrates, fats, proteins, and other substances can be understood in terms of bond enthalpies. For example, fats consist almost entirely of long chains of carbon atoms to which hydrogen atoms are attached. Therefore, fats contain mostly C—H and C—C bonds. When fats burn or are metabolized, each carbon atom becomes bonded to oxygen in CO_2 and each hydrogen becomes bonded to oxygen in H_2O. The bond in each O_2 molecule that reacts with the fat must be broken, as must the C—H and C—C

Caloric Values (approximate)

Carbohydrate	4 Cal/g (17 kJ/g)
Fat	9 Cal/g (38 kJ/g)
Protein	4 Cal/g (17 kJ/g)

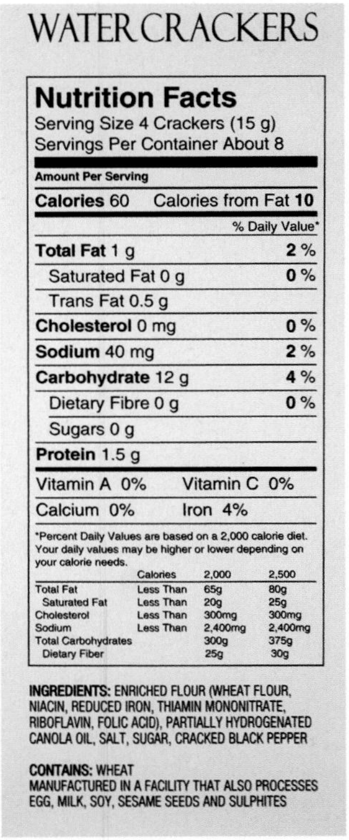

Courtesy Peter McGahey

Figure 6.19 **Nutrition facts from a package of snack crackers.**

Table 6.3 Composition and Caloric Values of Some Foods

Food	Approximate Composition per 100. g			Caloric Value	
	Fat	Carbohydrate	Protein	Cal/g	kJ/g
All-purpose flour	0.0	73.3	13.3	3.33	13.95
Apple	0.5	13.0	0.4	0.59	2.47
Brownie with nuts	16.0	64.0	4.0	4.04	16.9
Cheese pizza	10.2	25.8	11.2	2.41	10.1
Egg	0.7	10.0	13.0	1.40	5.86
Egg noodle substitute	0.9	73.2	14.3	3.75	15.69
Grapes, white	0.6	17.5	0.6	0.7	2.9
Green beans	0.0	7.0	1.9	0.38	0.00
Hamburger	30.0	0.0	22.0	3.60	15.06
Microwave popcorn (popped)	7.1	11.4	2.9	1.00	4.18
Peanuts (unsalted)	50.0	21.4	28.6	5.71	23.91
Prunes (pitted)	0.0	65.0	2.5	2.75	11.51
Rice	1.0	77.6	8.2	3.47	14.52
Salad dressing (vinaigrette)	20.0	40.0	0.0	3.33	13.95
Tomato sauce	0.0	4.8	1.6	0.24	1.01
Wheat crackers	10.7	71.4	14.3	4.29	17.93

bonds in the fat. The respective bond enthalpies are 498 kJ/mol, 416 kJ/mol, and 356 kJ/mol. The strengths of the bonds formed in the products are 803 kJ/mol for carbon–oxygen bonds and 467 kJ/mol for hydrogen–oxygen bonds. Because the number of bonds before and after reaction is nearly the same, and because the bonds formed are stronger than the bonds broken, metabolism of fats transfers energy to the surroundings.

As we implied earlier, there is a balance between the quantity of food energy that is taken into our bodies and the quantity that is used for body functions. If food intake exceeds consumption, the body stores energy in fat molecules. If consumption exceeds intake, some fat is burned to provide the needed energy. The **basal metabolic rate (BMR)** is the minimum energy intake required to maintain a body that is awake and at rest, excluding the energy needed to digest, absorb, and metabolize the food, which is about 10% of the caloric intake. The BMR varies considerably depending on age, gender, and body mass. For a 70-kg (155-lb) human between 18 and 30 years old, the average BMR is 1750 Cal/day for a male and 1525 Cal/day for a female. The basal metabolic rate is approximately 1 Cal kg^{-1} h^{-1}; that is, about 1 Calorie is expended per hour for each kilogram of body mass. Thus, the average 60-kg (132-1b) person has a daily BMR of

$$\frac{1\text{ Cal}}{\text{kg} \times \text{h}} \times 60\text{ kg} \times \frac{24\text{ h}}{\text{day}} = 1440\text{ Cal/day}$$

This value is multiplied by factors of up to 7 depending on the level of muscular activity. For example, walking or other light work requires 2.5 times the BMR. Heavy work, such as playing basketball or soccer, requires 7 times the BMR. Therefore, the appropriate food energy intake varies greatly from one individual to another.

PROBLEM-SOLVING EXAMPLE 6.16 Energy Value of Food

A 70-kg, 22-year-old female eats 50. g of unsalted peanuts and then exercises by playing basketball for 30 min.

(a) What fraction of the food energy of the peanuts comes from fat, carbohydrate, and protein?

(b) Is the exercise sufficient to use up the energy provided by the food?

Answer

(a) 69% from fat, 13% from carbohydrate, and 18% from protein

(b) No

Strategy and Explanation

(a) Data from Table 6.3 show that 100. g of unsalted peanuts contains 50.0 g of fat, 21.4 g of carbohydrate, and 28.6 g of protein. The fat provides 38 kJ/g and the carbohydrate and protein provide 17 kJ/g each. Therefore the energy provided is

$$\text{Energy from fat} = 50.\text{ g peanuts} \times \frac{50.0\text{ g fat}}{100.\text{ g peanuts}} \times \frac{38\text{ kJ}}{1\text{ g fat}} = 950\text{ kJ}$$

$$\text{Energy from carbohydrate} = 50.\text{ g peanuts} \times \frac{21.4\text{ g carbo}}{100.\text{ g peanuts}} \times \frac{17\text{ kJ}}{1\text{ g carbo}} = 182\text{ kJ}$$

$$\text{Energy from protein} = 50.\text{ g peanuts} \times \frac{28.6\text{ g protein}}{100.\text{ g peanuts}} \times \frac{17\text{ kJ}}{1\text{ g protein}} = 243\text{ kJ}$$

The total caloric intake is 1375 kJ, and the fractions are (950/1375) × 100% = 69% from fat, (182/1375) × 100% = 13% from carbohydrate, and (243/1375) × 100% = 18% from protein.

(b) Playing basketball requires seven times the BMR—that is, 7 × 1525 Cal/day.

$$\text{Energy required} = 7 \times \frac{1525\text{ Cal}}{\text{day}} \times \frac{1\text{ day}}{24\text{ h}} \times \frac{1\text{ h}}{60\text{ min}} \times 30\text{ min} \times \frac{4.184\text{ kJ}}{1\text{ Cal}} = 930.\text{ kJ}$$

In addition, 10% of the caloric intake is required to digest, absorb, and metabolize the food. The quantity of energy required is thus

$$930.\ \text{kJ} + (0.10 \times 1375\ \text{kJ}) = 1068\ \text{kJ}$$

which is less than the caloric value of the 50. g of peanuts.

✓ **Reasonable Answer Check** As you might have expected, peanuts contain fat (oil), protein, and some carbohydrate, so the quantities of energy from these sources seem reasonable. However, it takes a lot of exercise to work off what we eat, so you may have been surprised by the answer to part (b). A little less than 2 oz of peanuts corresponds to 50. g, so eating peanuts without exercising can easily increase your weight.

PROBLEM-SOLVING PRACTICE 6.16

Whole milk contains 5.0% carbohydrate, 4.0% fat, and 3.3% protein by mass.

(a) Estimate the caloric value of an 8-oz (227-g) glass of milk.

(b) For how long would this caloric intake support a 70-kg male who was taking a leisurely walk?

EXERCISE 6.21 Power of a Person

Use the average BMR values in the text to calculate the power (energy per unit time) required to sustain a 70-kg male (a) at rest and (b) playing basketball. Express your result in watts. (1 W = 1 J/s.) Compare your results with the power of a typical incandescent light bulb.

SUMMARY PROBLEM

Sulfur dioxide, SO_2, is a major pollutant emitted by coal-fired electric power generating plants. A large power plant can produce 8.64×10^{13} J electrical energy every day by burning 7000. ton coal (1 ton = 9.08×10^5 g).

(a) Assume that the fuel value of coal is approximately the same as for graphite. Calculate the quantity of energy transferred to the surroundings by the coal combustion reaction in a plant that burns 7000. ton coal.

(b) What is the efficiency of this power plant in converting chemical energy to electrical energy—that is, what percentage of the thermal energy transfer shows up as electrical energy?

(c) When SO_2 is given off by a power plant, it can be trapped by reaction with MgO in the smokestack to form $MgSO_4$.

$$\text{MgO(s)} + \text{SO}_2\text{(g)} + \tfrac{1}{2}\,\text{O}_2\text{(g)} \longrightarrow \text{MgSO}_4\text{(s)}$$

If 140. ton SO_2 is given off by a coal-burning power plant each day, how much MgO would you have to supply to remove all of this SO_2? How much $MgSO_4$ would be produced?

(d) How much heat transfer does the reaction in part (c) add or take away from the heat transfer of the coal combustion?

(e) Sulfuric acid comes from the oxidation of sulfur, first to SO_2 and then to SO_3. The SO_3 is then absorbed by water in 98% H_2SO_4 solution to make H_2SO_4.

$$\text{S(s)} + \text{O}_2\text{(g)} \longrightarrow \text{SO}_2\text{(g)}$$

$$\text{SO}_2\text{(g)} + \tfrac{1}{2}\,\text{O}_2\text{(g)} \longrightarrow \text{SO}_3\text{(g)}$$

$$\text{SO}_3\text{(g)} + \text{H}_2\text{O (in 98\% H}_2\text{SO}_4) \longrightarrow \text{H}_2\text{SO}_4(\ell)$$

For which of these reactions can you calculate $\Delta H°$ using data in Table 6.2 or Appendix J? Do the calculation for each case where data are available.

ThomsonNOW
Sign in to ThomsonNOW at **www.thomsonedu.com** to check your readiness for an exam by taking the Pre-Test and exploring the modules recommended in your Personalized Learning Plan.

IN CLOSING

Having studied this chapter, you should be able to . . .

- Understand the difference between kinetic energy and potential energy (Section 6.1).
- Be familiar with typical energy units and be able to convert from one unit to another (Section 6.1).
- Understand conservation of energy and energy transfer by heating and working (Section 6.2). ThomsonNOW homework: Study Questions 23, 25
- Recognize and use thermodynamic terms: system, surroundings, heat, work, temperature, thermal equilibrium, exothermic, endothermic, and state function (Sections 6.2 and 6.4). ThomsonNOW homework: Study Question 19
- Use specific heat capacity and the sign conventions for transfer of energy (Section 6.3). ThomsonNOW homework: Study Questions 32, 35, 37, 41, 47, 53
- Distinguish between the change in internal energy and the change in enthalpy for a system (Section 6.4).
- Use thermochemical expressions and derive thermostoichiometric factors from them (Sections 6.5 and 6.6). ThomsonNOW homework: Study Question 61
- Use the fact that the standard enthalpy change for a reaction, $\Delta H°$, is proportional to the quantity of reactants consumed or products produced when the reaction occurs (Section 6.6). ThomsonNOW homework: Study Questions 63, 69, 73
- Understand the origin of the enthalpy change for a chemical reaction in terms of bond enthalpies (Section 6.7). ThomsonNOW homework: Study Questions 75–77
- Describe how calorimeters can measure the quantity of thermal energy transferred during a reaction (Section 6.8). ThomsonNOW homework: Study Questions 81, 85
- Apply Hess's law to find the enthalpy change for a reaction (Sections 6.9 and 6.10). ThomsonNOW homework: Study Question 89
- Use standard molar enthalpies of formation to calculate the thermal energy transfer when a reaction takes place (Section 6.10). ThomsonNOW homework: Study Questions 95, 101, 115
- Define and give examples of some chemical fuels and evaluate their abilities to provide heating (Section 6.11).
- Describe the main components of food and evaluate their contributions to caloric intake (Section 6.12).

KEY TERMS

basal metabolic rate (BMR) *(6.12)*
bond enthalpy (bond energy) *(6.7)*
caloric value *(6.12)*
calorimeter *(6.8)*
carbohydrate *(6.12)*
change of state *(6.4)*
chemical fuel *(6.11)*
conservation of energy, law of *(6.2)*
endothermic *(6.4)*
energy density *(6.11)*
enthalpy change *(6.4)*
enthalpy of fusion *(6.4)*
enthalpy of vaporization *(6.4)*
exothermic *(6.4)*
first law of thermodynamics *(6.2)*
fuel value *(6.11)*
heat/heating *(6.2)*
heat capacity *(6.3)*
Hess's law *(6.9)*
internal energy *(6.2)*
kinetic energy *(6.1)*

molar heat capacity *(6.3)*
phase change *(6.4)*
potential energy *(6.1)*
specific heat capacity *(6.3)*
standard enthalpy change *(6.5)*
standard molar enthalpy of formation *(6.10)*
standard state *(6.10)*
state function *(6.4)*
surroundings *(6.2)*
system *(6.2)*
thermal equilibrium *(6.2)*
thermochemical expression *(6.5)*
thermodynamics *(Introduction)*
work/working *(6.2)*

QUESTIONS FOR REVIEW AND THOUGHT

■ denotes questions available in ThomsonNOW and assignable in OWL.

Blue-numbered questions have short answers at the back of this book and fully worked solutions in the *Student Solutions Manual.*

ThomsonNOW™
Assess your understanding of this chapter's topics with sample tests and other resources found by signing in to ThomsonNOW at **www.thomsonedu.com**.

Review Questions

1. Name two laws stated in this chapter and explain each in your own words.
2. For each of the following, define a system and its surroundings and give the direction of heat transfer:
   (a) Propane is burning in a Bunsen burner in the laboratory.
   (b) After you have a swim, water droplets on your skin evaporate.
   (c) Water, originally at 25 °C, is placed in the freezing compartment of a refrigerator.
   (d) Two chemicals are mixed in a flask on a laboratory bench. A reaction occurs and heat is evolved.
3. What is the value of the standard enthalpy of formation for any element under standard conditions?
4. Criticize each of these statements:
   (a) Enthalpy of formation refers to a reaction in which 1 mol of one or more reactants produces some quantity of product.
   (b) The standard enthalpy of formation of O_2 as a gas at 25 °C and a pressure of 1 atm is 15.0 kJ/mol.
5. Explain how a coffee cup calorimeter may be used to measure the enthalpy change of (a) a change in state and (b) a chemical reaction.
6. What is required for heat transfer of energy from one sample of matter to another to occur?
7. Name two exothermic processes and two endothermic processes that you encountered recently and that were not associated with your chemistry course.
8. Explain what is meant by (a) energy density of a fuel and (b) caloric value of a food. Why is each of these terms important?
9. Explain in your own words why it is useful in thermodynamics to distinguish a system from its surroundings.
10. In a steelmaking plant, molten metal is poured from ladles into furnaces. Considering the molten iron to be the system, what is the sign of q in the process shown in the photograph?

© James Hardy/Photo Alto/Getty Images

Topical Questions

The Nature of Energy

11. (a) A 2-inch piece of two-layer chocolate cake with frosting provides 1670 kJ of energy. What is this in Cal?
    (b) If you were on a diet that calls for eating no more than 1200 Cal per day, how many joules would you consume per day?
12. Sulfur dioxide, SO_2, is found in wines and in polluted air. If a 32.1-g sample of sulfur is burned in the air to get 64.1 g SO_2, 297 kJ of energy is released. Express this energy in (a) joules, (b) calories, and (c) kilocalories.
13. ■ Melting lead requires 5.91 cal/g. How many joules are required to melt 1.00 lb (454 g) lead?
14. ■ On a sunny day, solar energy reaches the earth at a rate of 4.0 J min^{-1} cm^{-2}. Suppose a house has a square, flat roof of dimensions 12 m by 12 m. How much solar energy reaches this roof in 1 h? (*Note:* This is why roofs painted with light-reflecting paint are better than black, unpainted roofs in warm climates: They reflect most of this energy rather than absorb it.)
15. ■ When an electrical appliance whose power usage is X watts is run for Y seconds, it uses $X \times Y$ J of energy. The energy unit used by electrical utilities in their monthly bills is the *kilowatt hour* (kWh; 1 kilowatt used for 1 hour).

How many joules are there in a kilowatt hour? If electricity costs $.09 per kilowatt hour, how much does it cost per megajoule?

16. A 100-W light bulb is left on for 14 h. How many joules of energy are used? With electricity at $0.09 per kWh, how much does it cost to leave the light on for 14 h?

Conservation of Energy

17. Describe how energy is changed from one form to another in these processes:
    (a) At a July 4th celebration, a match is lit and ignites the fuse of a rocket firecracker, which fires off and explodes at an altitude of 1000 ft.
    (b) A gallon of gasoline is pumped from an underground storage tank into the fuel tank of your car, and you use it up by driving 25 mi.
18. Analyze transfer of energy from one form to another in each situation below.
    (a) In a space shuttle, hydrogen and oxygen combine to form water, boosting the shuttle into orbit above the earth.
    (b) You eat a package of Fritos, go to class and listen to a lecture, walk back to your dorm, and climb the stairs to the fourth floor.
19. ■ Suppose that you are studying the growth of a plant, and you want to apply thermodynamic ideas.
    (a) Make an appropriate choice of system and surroundings and describe it unambiguously.
    (b) Explain why you chose the system and surroundings you did.
    (c) Identify transfers of energy and material into and out of the system that would be important for you to monitor in your study.
20. Suppose that you are studying an ecosystem and want to apply thermodynamic ideas.
    (a) Make an appropriate choice of system and surroundings and describe it unambiguously.
    (b) Explain why you chose the system and surroundings you did.
    (c) Identify transfers of energy and material into and out of the system that would be important for you to monitor in your study.
21. ■ Solid ammonium chloride is added to water in a beaker and dissolves. The beaker becomes cold to the touch.
    (a) Make an appropriate choice of system and surroundings and describe it unambiguously.
    (b) Explain why you chose the system and surroundings you did.
    (c) Identify transfers of energy and material into and out of the system that would be important for you to monitor in your study.
    (d) Is the process of dissolving $NH_4Cl(s)$ in water exothermic or endothermic?
22. A bar of Monel (an alloy of nickel, copper, iron, and manganese) is heated until it melts, poured into a mold, and solidifies.
    (a) Make an appropriate choice of system and surroundings and describe it unambiguously.
    (b) Explain why you chose the system and surroundings you did.
    (c) Identify transfers of energy and material into and out of the system that would be important for you to monitor in your study.
23. ■ If a system does 75.4 J of work on its surroundings and simultaneously there is 25.7 cal of heat transfer from the surroundings to the system, what is ΔE for the system?
24. A 20.0-g sample of water cools from 30 °C to 20.0 °C, which transfers 840 J to the surroundings. No work is done on the water. What is ΔE_{water}?
25. ■ Make a diagram like the one in Figure 6.9 for a system in which 127.6 kJ of work is done on the surroundings and there is 843.2 kJ of heat transfer into the system. Use the diagram to help you determine ΔE_{system}.
26. Make a diagram like the one in Figure 6.9 for a system in which 876.3 J of work is done on the surroundings and there is 37.4 J of heat transfer into the system. Use the diagram to help you determine ΔE_{system}.

Heat Capacity

27. Which requires greater transfer of energy: (a) cooling 10.0 g water from 50 °C to 20 °C or (b) cooling 20.0 g Cu from 37 °C to 25 °C?
28. Which requires more energy: (a) warming 15.0 g water from 25 °C to 37 °C or (b) warming 60.0 g aluminum from 25 °C to 37 °C?
29. You hold a gram of copper in one hand and a gram of aluminum in the other. Each metal was originally at 0 °C. (Both metals are in the shape of a little ball that fits into your hand.) If they both take up heat at the same rate, which will warm to your body temperature first?
30. Ethylene glycol, $(CH_2OH)_2$, is often used as an antifreeze in cars. Which requires greater transfer of thermal energy to warm from 25.0 °C to 100.0 °C, pure water or an equal mass of pure ethylene glycol?
31. How much thermal energy is required to heat all the aluminum in a roll of aluminum foil (500. g) from room temperature (25 °C) to the temperature of a hot oven (250 °C)? Report your result in kilojoules.
32. ■ How much thermal energy is required to heat all of the water in a swimming pool by 1.0 °C if the dimensions are 4.0 ft deep by 20. ft wide by 75 ft long? Report your result in megajoules.
33. If the cooling system in an automobile has a capacity of 5.00 quarts of liquid, compare the quantity of thermal energy transferred to the liquid in the system when its temperature is raised from 25.0 °C to 100.0 °C for water and ethylene glycol. The densities of water and ethylene glycol are 1.00 g/cm^3 and 1.113 g/cm^3, respectively. 1 quart = 0.946 L. Report your results in joules.
34. One way to cool a cup of coffee is to plunge an ice-cold piece of aluminum into it. Suppose a 20.0-g piece of aluminum is stored in the refrigerator at 32 °F (0.0 °C) and then put into a cup of coffee. The coffee's temperature drops from 90.0 °C to 75.0 °C. How much energy (in kilojoules) did the coffee transfer to the piece of aluminum?

35. ■ A piece of iron (400. g) is heated in a flame and then plunged into a beaker containing 1.00 kg water. The original temperature of the water was 20.0 °C, but it is 32.8 °C after the iron bar is put in and thermal equilibrium is reached. What was the original temperature of the hot iron bar?
36. A 192-g piece of copper was heated to 100.0 °C in a boiling water bath and then put into a beaker containing 750. mL water (density = 1.00 g/cm^3) at 4.0 °C. What is the final temperature of the copper and water after they come to thermal equilibrium?
37. ■ A 12.3-g sample of iron requires heat transfer of 41.0 J to raise its temperature from 17.3 °C to 24.7 °C.
    (a) Calculate the specific heat capacity of iron.
    (b) Calculate the molar heat capacity of iron.
38. A diamond weighing 310. mg requires 2.38 J to raise its temperature from 23.4 °C to 38.7 °C.
    (a) Calculate the specific heat capacity of diamond.
    (b) Calculate the molar heat capacity of diamond.
    (c) Is the specific heat capacity of diamond the same as the specific heat capacity of carbon in the form of graphite? Give one reason why you might expect them to be the same and one reason why you might expect them to be different.
39. An unknown metal requires 34.7 J to heat a 23.4-g sample of it from 17.3°C to 28.9 °C. Which of the metals in Table 6.1 is most likely to be the unknown?
40. An unknown metal requires 336.9 J to heat a 46.3-g sample of it from 24.3 °C to 43.2 °C. Which of the metals in Table 6.1 is most likely to be the unknown?
41. ■ A 200.-g sample of Al is heated in a flame and then immersed in 500. mL water in an insulated container. The initial temperature of the water was 22.0 °C. After the Al and water reached thermal equilibrium, the temperature of both was 33.6 °C. What was the temperature of the Al just before it was plunged into the water? (Assume that the density of water is 0.98 g/mL and that there is no heat transfer other than between the water and aluminum.)
42. A 200.-g sample of copper is heated to 500. °C in a flame and then plunged into 1000. g water in an insulated container. If the water's initial temperature was 23.4 °C, what is the temperature of the water and Cu when thermal equilibrium has been reached? (Assume that the only energy transfer is between water and copper.)
43. A chemical reaction occurs, and 20.7 J is transferred from the chemical system to its surroundings. (Assume that no work is done.)
    (a) What is the algebraic sign of $\Delta T_{surroundings}$?
    (b) What is the algebraic sign of ΔE_{system}?
44. A physical process called a phase transition occurs in a sample of an alloy, and 437 kJ transfers from the surroundings to the alloy. (Assume that no work is done.)
    (a) What is the algebraic sign of ΔT_{alloy}?
    (b) What is the algebraic sign of ΔE_{alloy}?

Energy and Enthalpy

45. The thermal energy transfer required to melt 1.00 g ice at 0 °C is 333 J. If one ice cube has a mass of 62.0 g, and a tray contains 20 ice cubes, how much energy is required to melt a tray of ice cubes at 0 °C?
46. Calculate the quantity of heating required to convert the water in four ice cubes (60.1 g each) from $H_2O(s)$ at 0 °C to $H_2O(g)$ at 100. °C. The enthalpy of fusion of ice at 0 °C is 333 J/g and the enthalpy of vaporization of liquid water at 100. °C is 2260 J/g.
47. ■ The hydrocarbon benzene, C_6H_6, boils at 80.1 °C. How much energy is required to heat 1.00 kg of this liquid from 20.0 °C to the boiling point and then change the liquid completely to a vapor at that temperature? The specific heat capacity of liquid C_6H_6 is 1.74 J g^{-1} °C^{-1}, and the enthalpy of vaporization is 395 J/g. Report your result in joules.
48. How much energy (in joules) would be required to raise the temperature of 1.00 lb lead (1.00 lb = 454 g) from room temperature (25 °C) to its melting point (327 °C), and then melt the lead completely at 327 °C? The specific heat capacity of lead is 0.159 J g^{-1} °C^{-1}, and its enthalpy of fusion is 24.7 J/g.
49. Mercury, with a freezing point of −39 °C, is the only metal that is liquid at room temperature. How much thermal energy must be transferred to its surroundings if 1.00 mL of the mercury is cooled from room temperature (23.0 °C) to −39 °C and then frozen to a solid? The density of mercury is 13.6 g/cm^3. Its specific heat capacity is 0.138 J g^{-1} °C^{-1}, and its enthalpy of fusion is 11 J/g.
50. On a cold day in winter, ice can sublime (go directly from solid to gas without melting). The heat of sublimation is approximately equal to the sum of the heat of fusion and the heat of vaporization (see Question 46). How much thermal energy in joules does it take to sublime 0.1 g of frost on a windowpane?
51. Draw a cooling graph for steam-to-water-to-ice.
52. Draw a heating graph for converting Dry Ice to carbon dioxide gas.
53. ■ Based on the heating graph shown in the figure for a substance, X, at constant pressure,
    (a) Which has the largest specific heat capacity, X(s), $X(\ell)$, or X(g)?
    (b) Which is smaller, the heat of fusion or the heat of vaporization?
    (c) What is the algebraic sign of the enthalpy of vaporization at the boiling point?

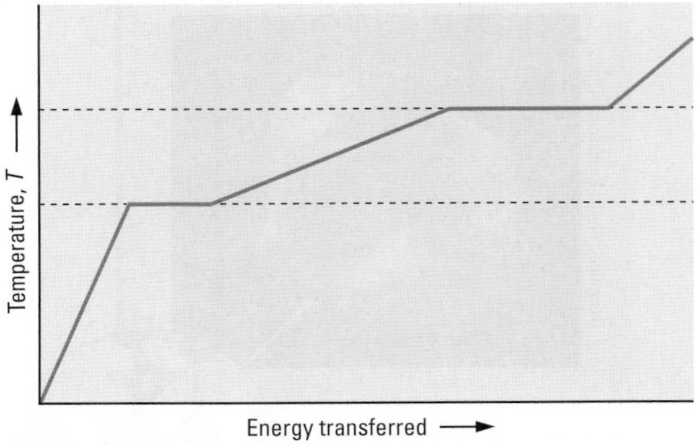

54. Based on the cooling graph shown in the figure for a substance, *Y*, at constant pressure,
    (a) Which has the smallest specific heat capacity, *Y*(s), *Y*(ℓ), or *Y*(g)?
    (b) Which is larger, the heat of fusion or the heat of vaporization?
    (c) What is the algebraic sign of the enthalpy of fusion at the melting point?

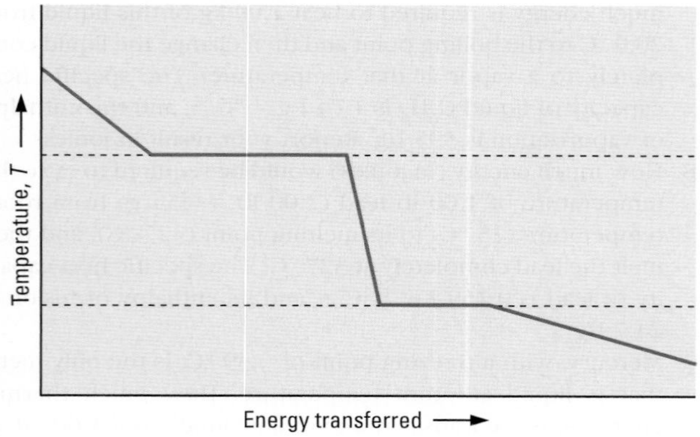

Thermochemical Expressions

55. Energy is stored in the body in adenosine triphosphate, ATP, which is formed by the reaction between adenosine diphosphate, ADP, and dihydrogen phosphate ions.

$$ADP^{3-}(aq) + H_2PO_4^{2-}(aq) \longrightarrow ATP^{4-}(aq) + H_2O(\ell) \qquad \Delta H° = 38 \text{ kJ}$$

    Is the reaction endothermic or exothermic?

56. Calcium carbide, CaC_2, is manufactured by reducing lime with carbon at high temperature. (The carbide is used in turn to make acetylene, an industrially important organic chemical.)

$$CaO(s) + 3\,C(s) \longrightarrow CaC_2(s) + CO(g) \qquad \Delta H° = 464.8 \text{ kJ}$$

    Is the reaction endothermic or exothermic?

57. A diamond can be considered a giant all-carbon supermolecule in which almost every carbon atom is bonded to four other carbons. When a diamond cutter cleaves a diamond, carbon-carbon bonds must be broken. Is the cleavage of a diamond endothermic or exothermic? Explain.

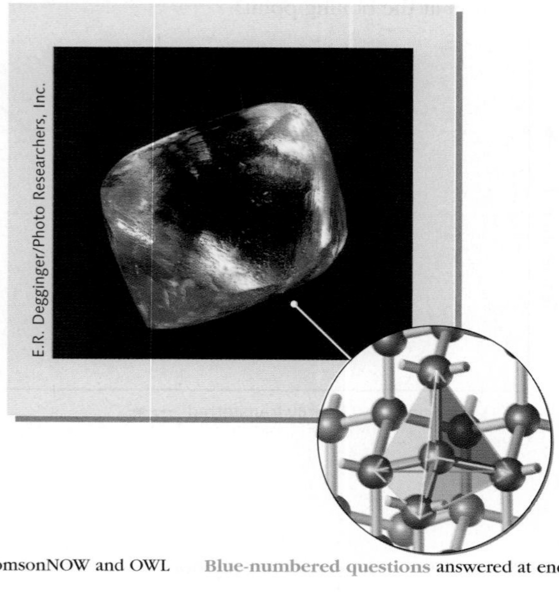

58. When table salt is dissolved in water, the temperature drops slightly. Write a chemical equation for this process, and indicate if it is exothermic or endothermic.

59. Write a word statement for the thermochemical expression

$$H_2O(s) \longrightarrow H_2O(\ell) \qquad \Delta H° = 6.0 \text{ kJ}$$

60. Write a word statement for the thermochemical expression

$$HI(\ell) \longrightarrow HI(s) \qquad \Delta H° = -2.87 \text{ kJ}$$

61. ■ Given the thermochemical expression

$$H_2O(s) \longrightarrow H_2O(\ell) \qquad \Delta H° = 6.0 \text{ kJ}$$

    what quantity of energy is transferred to the surroundings when
    (a) 34.2 mol liquid water freezes?
    (b) 100.0 g liquid water freezes?

62. Given the thermochemical expression

$$CaO(s) + 3\,C(s) \longrightarrow CaC_2(s) + CO(g) \qquad \Delta H° = 464.8 \text{ kJ}$$

    what quantity of energy is transferred when
    (a) 34.8 mol CO(g) is formed by this reaction?
    (b) a metric ton (1000 kg) of CaC_2(s) is manufactured?
    (c) 0.432 mol carbon reacts with CaO(s)?

Enthalpy Changes for Chemical Reactions

63. ■ Given the thermochemical expression for combustion of isooctane (a component of gasoline),

$$2\,C_8H_{18}(\ell) + 25\,O_2(g) \longrightarrow 16\,CO_2(g) + 18\,H_2O(\ell) \qquad \Delta H° = -10{,}992 \text{ kJ}$$

    write a thermochemical expression for
    (a) production of 4.00 mol CO_2(g).
    (b) combustion of 100. mol isooctane.
    (c) combination of 1.00 mol isooctane with a stoichiometric quantity of air.

64. Given the thermochemical expression for combustion of benzene,

$$2\,C_6H_6(\ell) + 15\,O_2(g) \longrightarrow 12\,CO_2(g) + 6\,H_2O(\ell) \qquad \Delta H° = -6534.8 \text{ kJ}$$

    write a thermochemical expression for
    (a) combustion of 0.50 mol benzene.
    (b) consumption of 5 mol O_2(g).
    (c) production of 144 mol CO_2(g).

65. Write all the thermostoichiometric factors that can be derived from the thermochemical expression

$$CaO(s) + 3\,C(s) \longrightarrow CaC_2(s) + CO(g) \qquad \Delta H° = 464.8 \text{ kJ}$$

66. Write all the thermostoichiometric factors that can be derived from the thermochemical expression

$$2\,CH_3OH(\ell) + 3\,O_2(g) \longrightarrow 2\,CO_2(g) + 4\,H_2O(\ell) \qquad \Delta H° = -1530 \text{ kJ}$$

67. Consider the decomposition of methanol into carbon monoxide and hydrogen (a possible method for producing combustible gaseous fuel).

$$CH_3OH(\ell) \longrightarrow CO(g) + 2\,H_2(g) \qquad \Delta H° = 90.7 \text{ kJ}$$

    (a) How much heat transfer into the system is required to decompose 100. kg methanol?

(b) If 400. mol CO(g) is produced, what quantity of energy must be transferred?

(c) Suppose that the reverse reaction were to occur, in which carbon monoxide and hydrogen combine to form methanol. If 43.0 g CO(g) reacts with an excess of hydrogen, what is the heat transfer?

68. When $KClO_3$(s), potassium chlorate, is heated, it melts and decomposes to form oxygen gas. [Molten $KClO_3$ was shown reacting with a Fritos chip earlier in this chapter (⇐ ***p. 216***).] The thermochemical expression for decomposition of potassium chlorate is

$$2\ KClO_3(s) \longrightarrow 2\ KCl(s) + 3\ O_2(g) \qquad \Delta H^\circ = -89.4\ kJ$$

Calculate q at constant pressure for
(a) formation of 97.8 g KCl(s).
(b) production of 24.8 mol O_2(g).
(c) decomposition of 35.2 g $KClO_3$(s).

69. ■ "Gasohol," a mixture of gasoline and ethanol, C_2H_5OH, is used as automobile fuel. The alcohol releases energy in a combustion reaction with O_2.

$$C_2H_5OH(\ell) + 3\ O_2(g) \longrightarrow 2\ CO_2(g) + 3\ H_2O(\ell)$$

If 0.115 g alcohol evolves 3.62 kJ when burned at constant pressure, what is the molar enthalpy of combustion for ethanol?

70. White phosphorus, P_4, ignites in air to produce P_4O_{10}.

$$P_4(s) + 5\ O_2(g) \longrightarrow P_4O_{10}(s)$$

When 3.56 g P_4 is burned, 85.8 kJ of thermal energy is evolved at constant pressure. What is the molar enthalpy of combustion of P_4?

71. A laboratory "volcano" can be made from ammonium dichromate. When ignited, the compound decomposes in a fiery display.

$$(NH_4)_2Cr_2O_7(s) \longrightarrow N_2(g) + 4\ H_2O(g) + Cr_2O_3(s)$$

If the decomposition transfers 315 kJ per mole of ammonium dichromate at constant pressure, how much thermal energy would be transferred by 28.4 g (1.00 oz) of the solid? (The substances involved in this reaction are poisons, so do not carry out the reaction.)

72. The thermite reaction, the reaction between aluminum and iron(III) oxide,

$$2\ Al(s) + Fe_2O_3(s) \longrightarrow Al_2O_3(s) + 2\ Fe(s) \qquad \Delta H^\circ = -851.5\ kJ$$

produces tremendous heat. If you begin with 10.0 g Al and excess Fe_2O_3, how much energy is released at constant pressure?

73. ■ When wood is burned we may assume that the reaction is the combustion of cellulose (empirical formula, CH_2O).

$$CH_2O(s) + O_2(g) \longrightarrow CO_2(g) + H_2O(g) \qquad \Delta H^\circ = -425\ kJ$$

How much energy is released when a 10.0-lb wood log burns completely? (Assume the wood is 100% dry and burns via the reaction above.)

74. A plant takes CO_2 and H_2O from its surroundings and makes cellulose by the reverse of the reaction in the preceding problem. The energy provided for this process comes from the sun via photosynthesis. How much energy does it take for a plant to make 100 g of cellulose?

Where Does the Energy Come From?

Use these bond enthalpy values to answer the questions below.

Bond	**Bond Enthalpy (kJ/mol)**
H—F	566
H—Cl	431
H—Br	366
H—I	299
H—H	436
F—F	158
Cl—Cl	242
Br—Br	193
I—I	151

75. ■ Which of the four molecules HF, HCl, HBr, and HI has the strongest chemical bond?

76. ■ Which of the four molecules F_2, Cl_2, Br_2, and I_2 has the weakest chemical bond?

77. ■ For the reactions of molecular hydrogen with fluorine and with chlorine:
(a) Calculate the enthalpy change for breaking all the bonds in the reactants.
(b) Calculate the enthalpy change for forming all the bonds in the products.
(c) From the results in parts (a) and (b), calculate the enthalpy change for the reaction.
(d) Which reaction is most exothermic?

78. For the reactions of molecular hydrogen with bromine and with iodine:
(a) Calculate the enthalpy change for breaking all the bonds in the reactants.
(b) Calculate the enthalpy change for forming all the bonds in the products.
(c) From the results in parts (a) and (b), calculate the enthalpy change for the reaction.
(d) Which reaction is most exothermic?

Measuring Enthalpy Changes: Calorimetry

79. Suppose you add a small ice cube to room-temperature water in a coffee cup calorimeter. What is the final temperature when all of the ice is melted? Assume that you have 200. mL water at 25 °C and that the ice cube weighs 15.0 g and is at 0 °C before being added to the water.

80. A coffee cup calorimeter can be used to investigate the "cold pack reaction," the process that occurs when solid ammonium nitrate dissolves in water:

$$NH_4NO_3(s) \longrightarrow NH_4^+(aq) + NO_3^-(aq)$$

Suppose 25.0 g solid NH_4NO_3 at 23.0 °C is added to 250. mL H_2O at the same temperature. After the solid is all dissolved, the temperature is measured to be 15.6 °C. Calculate the enthalpy change for the cold pack reaction. (*Hint:* Calculate the energy transferred per mole of NH_4NO_3.) Is the reaction endothermic or exothermic?

81. ■ When a 13.0-g sample of NaOH(s) dissolves in 400.0 mL water in a coffee cup calorimeter, the temperature of the water changes from 22.6 °C to 30.7 °C. Assuming that the specific heat capacity of the solution is the same as for water, calculate
(a) The heat transfer from system to surroundings.
(b) ΔH for the reaction.

$$NaOH(s) \longrightarrow Na^+(aq) + OH^-(aq)$$

82. Suppose that you mix 200.0 mL 0.200 M RbOH(aq) with 100. mL 0.400 M HBr(aq) in a coffee cup calorimeter. If the temperature of each of the two solutions was 24.40 °C before mixing, and the temperature rises to 26.18 °C,
(a) Calculate the heat transfer as a result of the reaction.
(b) Write the thermochemical expression for the reaction.

83. How much thermal energy is evolved by a reaction in a bomb calorimeter (Figure 6.16) in which the temperature of the bomb and water increases from 19.50 °C to 22.83 °C? The bomb has a heat capacity of 650 J/°C; the calorimeter contains 320. g of water. Report your result in kilojoules.

84. Sulfur (2.56 g) was burned in a bomb calorimeter with excess $O_2(g)$. The temperature increased from 21.25 °C to 26.72 °C. The bomb had a heat capacity of 923 J °C^{-1} and the calorimeter contained 815 g water. Calculate the heat transfer, per mole of SO_2 formed, in the course of the reaction

$$S(s) + O_2(g) \longrightarrow SO_2(g)$$

85. ■ You can find the quantity of thermal energy transferred during combustion of carbon by carrying out the reaction in a combustion calorimeter. Suppose you burn 0.300 g C(graphite) in an excess of $O_2(g)$ to give $CO_2(g)$.

$$C(graphite) + O_2(g) \longrightarrow CO_2(g)$$

The temperature of the calorimeter, which contains 775 g water, increases from 25.00 °C to 27.38 °C. The heat capacity of the bomb is 893 J °C^{-1}. What quantity of thermal energy is transferred per mole of graphite?

86. Benzoic acid, $C_7H_6O_2$, occurs naturally in many berries. Suppose you burn 1.500 g of the compound in a combustion calorimeter and find that the temperature of the calorimeter increases from 22.50 °C to 31.69 °C. The calorimeter contains 775 g water, and the bomb has a heat capacity of 893 J °C^{-1}. How much thermal energy is transferred per mole of benzoic acid? What is the change in internal energy, ΔE, of the system?

Hess's Law

87. Calculate the standard enthalpy change, $\Delta H°$, for the formation of 1 mol strontium carbonate (the material that gives the red color in fireworks) from its elements.

$$Sr(s) + C(graphite) + \tfrac{3}{2}O_2(g) \longrightarrow SrCO_3(s)$$

The information available is

$$Sr(s) + \tfrac{1}{2}O_2(g) \longrightarrow SrO(s) \qquad \Delta H° = -592 \text{ kJ}$$
$$SrO(s) + CO_2(g) \longrightarrow SrCO_3(s) \qquad \Delta H° = -234 \text{ kJ}$$
$$C(graphite) + O_2(g) \longrightarrow CO_2(g) \qquad \Delta H° = -394 \text{ kJ}$$

88. What is the standard enthalpy change for the reaction of lead(II) chloride with chlorine to give lead(IV) chloride?

$$PbCl_2(s) + Cl_2(g) \longrightarrow PbCl_4(\ell)$$

It is known that $PbCl_2(s)$ can be formed from the metal and $Cl_2(g)$,

$$Pb(s) + Cl_2(g) \longrightarrow PbCl_2(s) \qquad \Delta H° = -359.4 \text{ kJ}$$

and that $PbCl_4(\ell)$ can be formed directly from the elements.

$$Pb(s) + 2\,Cl_2(g) \longrightarrow PbCl_4(\ell) \qquad \Delta H° = -329.3 \text{ kJ}$$

89. ■ Using these reactions, find the standard enthalpy change for the formation of 1 mol PbO(s) from lead metal and oxygen gas.

$$PbO(s) + C(graphite) \longrightarrow Pb(s) + CO(g) \qquad \Delta H° = 106.8 \text{ kJ}$$

$$2\,C(graphite) + O_2(g) \longrightarrow 2\,CO(g) \qquad \Delta H° = -221.0 \text{ kJ}$$

If 250. g lead reacts with oxygen to form lead(II) oxide, what quantity of thermal energy (in kJ) is absorbed or evolved?

90. Three reactions very important to the semiconductor industry are
(a) the reduction of silicon dioxide to crude silicon,

$$SiO_2(s) + 2\,C(s) \longrightarrow Si(s) + 2\,CO(g) \qquad \Delta H° = 689.9 \text{ kJ}$$

(b) the formation of silicon tetrachloride from crude silicon,

$$Si(s) + 2\,Cl_2(g) \longrightarrow SiCl_4(g) \qquad \Delta H° = -657.0 \text{ kJ}$$

(c) and the reduction of silicon tetrachloride to pure silicon with magnesium,

$$SiCl_4(g) + 2\,Mg(s) \longrightarrow 2\,MgCl_2(s) + Si(s) \qquad \Delta H° = -625.6 \text{ kJ}$$

What is the overall enthalpy change when 1.00 mol sand (SiO_2) changes into very pure silicon by this series of reactions?

Standard Molar Enthalpies of Formation

91. The standard molar enthalpy of formation of AgCl(s) is −127.1 kJ/mol. Write a balanced thermochemical expression for which the enthalpy of reaction is −127.1 kJ.

92. The standard molar enthalpy of formation of methanol, $CH_3OH(\ell)$, is −238.7 kJ/mol. Write a balanced thermochemical expression for which the enthalpy of reaction is −238.7 kJ.

93. For each compound below, write a balanced thermochemical expression depicting the formation of 1 mol of the compound. Standard molar enthalpies of formation are found in Appendix J.
(a) $Al_2O_3(s)$ (b) $TiCl_4(\ell)$
(c) $NH_4NO_3(s)$

94. The standard molar enthalpy of formation of glucose, $C_6H_{12}O_6(s)$, is −1274.4 kJ/mol.
(a) Is the formation of glucose from its elements exothermic or endothermic?
(b) Write a balanced equation depicting the formation of glucose from its elements and for which the enthalpy of reaction is −1274.4 kJ.

95. ■ An important reaction in the production of sulfuric acid is

$$SO_2(g) + \frac{1}{2} O_2(g) \longrightarrow SO_3(g)$$

It is also a key reaction in the formation of acid rain, beginning with the air pollutant SO_2. Using the data in Table 6.2, calculate the enthalpy change for the reaction.

96. The Romans used CaO as mortar in stone structures. The CaO was mixed with water to give $Ca(OH)_2$, which slowly reacted with CO_2 in the air to give limestone.

$$Ca(OH)_2(s) + CO_2(g) \longrightarrow CaCO_3(s) + H_2O(g)$$

Calculate the enthalpy change for this reaction.

97. In photosynthesis, the sun's energy brings about the combination of CO_2 and H_2O to form O_2 and a carbon-containing compound such as a sugar. In its simplest form, the reaction could be written

$$6\ CO_2(g) + 6\ H_2O(\ell) \longrightarrow 6\ O_2(g) + C_6H_{12}O_6(s)$$

Using the enthalpies of formation in Table 6.2, (a) calculate the enthalpy of reaction and (b) decide whether the reaction is exothermic or endothermic.

98. The first step in the production of nitric acid from ammonia involves the oxidation of NH_3.

$$4\ NH_3(g) + 5\ O_2(g) \longrightarrow 4\ NO(g) + 6\ H_2O(g)$$

Use the information in Table 6.2 or Appendix J to calculate the enthalpy change for this reaction. Is the reaction exothermic or endothermic?

99. A key reaction in the processing of uranium for use as fuel in nuclear power plants is

$$UO_2(s) + 4\ HF(g) \longrightarrow UF_4(s) + 2\ H_2O(g)$$

Calculate the enthalpy change, $\Delta H°$, for the reaction using the data in Table 6.2, Appendix J, and the following:

$\Delta H_f°$ for $UO_2(s) = -1085$ kJ/mol;
$\Delta H_f°$ for $UF_4(s) = -1914$ kJ/mol.

100. Oxygen is not normally found in positive oxidation states, but when it is combined with fluorine in the compound oxygen difluoride, oxygen is in a +2 oxidation state. Oxygen difluoride is a strong oxidizing agent that oxidizes water to produce O_2 and HF.

$$OF_2(g) + H_2O(g) \longrightarrow 2\ HF(g) + O_2(g)$$

The standard molar enthalpy of formation of oxygen difluoride is 18 kJ/mol. Using this information and data from Appendix J, calculate the standard molar enthalpy change for the reaction of oxygen difluoride with water.

101. ■ Iron can react with oxygen to give iron(III) oxide. If 5.58 g Fe is heated in pure O_2 to give $Fe_2O_3(s)$, how much thermal energy is transferred out of this system (at constant pressure)?

102. The formation of aluminum oxide from its elements is highly exothermic. If 2.70 g Al metal is burned in pure O_2 to give Al_2O_3, how much thermal energy is evolved in the process (at constant pressure)?

Chemical Fuels

103. If you want to convert 56.0 g ice (at 0 °C) to water at 75.0 °C, how many grams of propane (C_3H_8) would you have to burn to supply the energy to melt the ice and then warm it to the final temperature (at 1 bar)?

104. Suppose you want to heat your house with natural gas (CH_4). Assume your house has 1800 ft^2 of floor area and that the ceilings are 8.0 ft from the floors. The air in the house has a molar heat capacity of 29.1 J mol^{-1} °C^{-1}. (The number of moles of air in the house can be found by assuming that the average molar mass of air is 28.9 g/mol and that the density of air at these temperatures is about 1.22 g/L.) How many grams of methane do you have to burn to heat the air from 15.0 °C to 22.0 °C?

105. Companies around the world are constantly searching for compounds that can be used as substitutes for gasoline in automobiles. One possibility is methanol, CH_3OH, a compound that can be made relatively inexpensively from coal. The alcohol has a smaller energy per gram than gasoline, but with its higher octane rating it burns more efficiently than gasoline in internal combustion engines. (It also contributes smaller quantities of some air pollutants.) Compare the quantity of thermal energy produced per gram of CH_3OH and C_8H_{18} (octane), the latter being representative of the compounds in gasoline. The $\Delta H_f°$ for octane is −250.1 kJ/mol.

106. Hydrazine and 1,1-dimethylhydrazine both react spontaneously with O_2 and can be used as rocket fuels.

$$\underset{\text{hydrazine}}{N_2H_4(\ell)} + O_2(g) \longrightarrow N_2(g) + 2\ H_2O(g)$$

$$\underset{\text{1,1-dimethylhydrazine}}{N_2H_2(CH_3)_2(\ell)} + 4\ O_2(g) \longrightarrow 2\ CO_2(g) + 4\ H_2O(g) + N_2(g)$$

The molar enthalpy of formation of liquid hydrazine is 50.6 kJ/mol, and that of liquid 1,1-dimethylhydrazine is 49.2 kJ/mol. By doing appropriate calculations, decide whether the reaction of hydrazine or 1,1-dimethylhydrazine with oxygen gives more heat per gram (at constant pressure). (Other enthalpy of formation data can be obtained from Table 6.2.)

Food and Energy

107. M&M candies consist of 70.% carbohydrate, 21% fat, and 4.6% protein as well as other ingredients that do not have caloric value. What quantity of energy transfer would occur if 34.5 g M&Ms were burned in a bomb calorimeter?

108. A particular kind of cracker contains 71.4% carbohydrate, 10.7% fat, and 14.3% protein. Calculate the caloric value in Cal/g and in kJ/g.

109. Suppose you eat a quarter-pound hamburger (no bread, cheese, or other items—just meat) and then take a walk. For how long will you need to walk to use up the caloric value of the hamburger?

110. If you eat a quarter-pound of cheese pizza and then go out and play soccer vigorously, how long will it take before you have used up the calories in the pizza you ate?

General Questions

111. The specific heat capacity of copper is 0.385 J g^{-1} °C^{-1}, whereas it is 0.128 J g^{-1} °C^{-1} for gold. Assume you place

100. g of each metal, originally at 25 °C, in a boiling water bath at 100 °C. If energy is transferred to each metal at the same rate, which piece of metal will reach 100 °C first?

112. Calculate the molar heat capacity, in J mol^{-1} $°C^{-1}$, for the four metals in Table 6.1. What observation can you make about these values? Are they very different or very similar? Using this information, can you estimate the heat capacity in the units J g^{-1} $°C^{-1}$ for silver? (The correct value for silver is 0.23 J g^{-1} $°C^{-1}$.)

113. Suppose you add 100.0 g water at 60.0 °C to 100.0 g ice at 0.00 °C. Some of the ice melts and cools the warm water to 0.00 °C. When the ice/water mixture has come to a uniform temperature of 0.00 °C, how much ice has melted?

114. Suppose you have 40.0 g ice at −25.0 °C and you add to it 60.0 g liquid water at 10.0 °C. What will be the composition and state (s or ℓ) that results? What will be the temperature? (Assume that there is no heat transfer of energy except that between the water and the ice.)

115. ■ The combustion of diborane, B_2H_6, proceeds according to the equation

$$B_2H_6(g) + 3\ O_2(g) \longrightarrow B_2O_3(s) + 3\ H_2O(\ell)$$

and 2166 kJ is liberated per mole of $B_2H_6(g)$ (at constant pressure). Calculate the molar enthalpy of formation of $B_2H_6(g)$ using this information, the data in Table 6.2, and the fact that the standard molar enthalpy of formation for $B_2O_3(s)$ is −1273 kJ/mol.

116. In principle, copper could be used to generate valuable hydrogen gas from water.

$$Cu(s) + H_2O(g) \longrightarrow CuO(s) + H_2(g)$$

(a) Is the reaction exothermic or endothermic?
(b) If 2.00 g copper metal reacts with excess water vapor at constant pressure, how much thermal energy transfer is involved (either into or out of the system) in the reaction?

117. P_4 ignites in air to give P_4O_{10} and a large thermal energy transfer to the surroundings. This is an important reaction, because the phosphorus oxide can then be treated with water to give phosphoric acid for use in making detergents, toothpaste, soft drinks, and other consumer products. About 500,000 tons of elemental phosphorus is made annually in the United States. If you oxidize just 1 ton of P_4 (9.08×10^5 g) to the oxide, how much thermal energy (in kJ) is evolved at constant pressure?

118. The combination of coke and steam produces a mixture called coal gas, which can be used as a fuel or as a starting material for other reactions. If we assume coke can be represented by graphite, the equation for the production of coal gas is

$$2\ C(s) + 2\ H_2O(g) \longrightarrow CH_4(g) + CO_2(g)$$

Determine the standard enthalpy change for this reaction from the following standard enthalpies of reaction:

$$C(s) + H_2O(g) \longrightarrow CO(g) + H_2(g) \qquad \Delta H° = 131.3\ kJ$$
$$CO(g) + H_2O(g) \longrightarrow CO_2(g) + H_2(g) \qquad \Delta H° = 41.2\ kJ$$
$$CH_4(g) + H_2O(g) \longrightarrow 3\ H_2(g) + CO(g) \qquad \Delta H° = 206.1\ kJ$$

119. These two thermochemical expressions are known:

$$2\ C\ (graphite) + 2\ H_2(g) \longrightarrow C_2H_2(g) \qquad \Delta H° = 52.3\ kJ$$
$$C_2H_4Cl_2(\ell) \longrightarrow Cl_2(g) + C_2H_4(g) \qquad \Delta H° = 217.5\ kJ$$

Calculate the molar enthalpy of formation of $C_2H_4Cl_2(\ell)$.

120. Given the following information and the data in Table 6.2, calculate the molar enthalpy of formation for liquid hydrazine, N_2H_4.

$$N_2H_4(\ell) + O_2(g) \longrightarrow N_2(g) + 2\ H_2O(g) \qquad \Delta H° = -534\ kJ$$

121. The standard molar enthalpy of combustion of methanol, $CH_3OH(\ell)$, to form carbon dioxide and water vapor is −676.485 kJ/mol. Use data from Table 6.2 to calculate the standard molar enthalpy of formation of methanol.

122. The standard molar enthalpy of combustion of formic acid, $CH_2O_2(\ell)$, to form carbon dioxide and water vapor is −210.607 kJ/mol. Use data from Table 6.2 to calculate the standard molar enthalpy of formation of formic acid.

123. In 1947 Texas City, Texas, was devastated by the explosion of a shipload of ammonium nitrate, a compound intended to be used as a fertilizer. When heated, ammonium nitrate can decompose exothermically to N_2O and water.

$$NH_4NO_3(s) \longrightarrow N_2O(g) + 2\ H_2O(g)$$

If the heat from this exothermic reaction is contained, higher temperatures are generated, at which point ammonium nitrate can decompose explosively to N_2, H_2O, and O_2.

$$2\ NH_4NO_3(s) \longrightarrow 2\ N_2(g) + 4\ H_2O(g) + O_2(g)$$

If oxidizable materials are present, fires can break out, as was the case at Texas City. Using the information in Appendix J, answer the following questions.
(a) How much thermal energy is evolved (at constant pressure and under standard conditions) by the first reaction?
(b) If 8.00 kg ammonium nitrate explodes (the second reaction), how much thermal energy is evolved (at constant pressure and under standard conditions)?

124. Uranium-235 is used as a fuel in nuclear power plants. Since natural uranium contains only a small amount of this isotope, the uranium must be enriched in uranium-235 before it can be used. To do this, uranium(IV) oxide is first converted to a gaseous compound, UF_6, and the isotopes are separated by a gaseous diffusion technique. Some key reactions are

$$UO_2(s) + 4\ HF(g) \longrightarrow UF_4(s) + 2\ H_2O(g)$$
$$UF_4(s) + F_2(g) \longrightarrow UF_6(g)$$

How much thermal energy transfer (at constant pressure) would be involved in producing 225 ton $UF_6(g)$ from $UO_2(s)$ (1 ton = 9.08×10^5 g)? Some necessary standard enthalpies of formation are

$$\Delta H_f°\{UO_2(s)\} = -1085\ kJ/mol$$
$$\Delta H_f°\{UF_4(s)\} = -1914\ kJ/mol$$
$$\Delta H_f°\{UF_6(g)\} = -2147\ kJ/mol$$

125. One method of producing H_2 on a large scale is this chemical cycle.

Step 1: $SO_2(g) + 2\ H_2O(g) + Br_2(g) \longrightarrow H_2SO_4(\ell) + 2\ HBr(g)$

Step 2: $H_2SO_4(\ell) \longrightarrow H_2O(g) + SO_2(g) + \frac{1}{2}\ O_2(g)$

Step 3: $2\ HBr(g) \longrightarrow H_2(g) + Br_2(g)$

Using the table of standard enthalpies of formation in Appendix J, calculate $\Delta H°$ for each step. What is the equation for the overall process, and what is its enthalpy change? Is the overall process exothermic or endothermic?

126. One reaction involved in the conversion of iron ore to the metal is

$$FeO(s) + CO(g) \longrightarrow Fe(s) + CO_2(g)$$

Calculate the standard enthalpy change for this reaction from these reactions of iron oxides with CO:

$$3\ Fe_2O_3(s) + CO(g) \longrightarrow 2\ Fe_3O_4(s) + CO_2(g) \quad \Delta H° = -47\ kJ$$

$$Fe_2O_3(s) + 3\ CO(g) \longrightarrow 2\ Fe(s) + 3\ CO_2(g) \quad \Delta H° = -25\ kJ$$

$$Fe_3O_4(s) + CO(g) \longrightarrow 3\ FeO(s) + CO_2(g) \quad \Delta H° = 19\ kJ$$

Applying Concepts

127. Based on your experience, when ice melts to liquid water, is the process exothermic or endothermic? When liquid water freezes to ice at 0 °C, is this exothermic or endothermic? (Assume that the ice/water is the system in each case.)

128. You pick up a six-pack of soft drinks from the floor, but it slips from your hand and smashes onto your foot. Comment on the work and energy involved in this sequence. What forms of energy are involved and at what stages of the process?

129. ■ Consider the following graph, which presents data for a 1.0-g mass of each of four substances, A, B, C, and D. Which substance has the highest specific heat capacity?

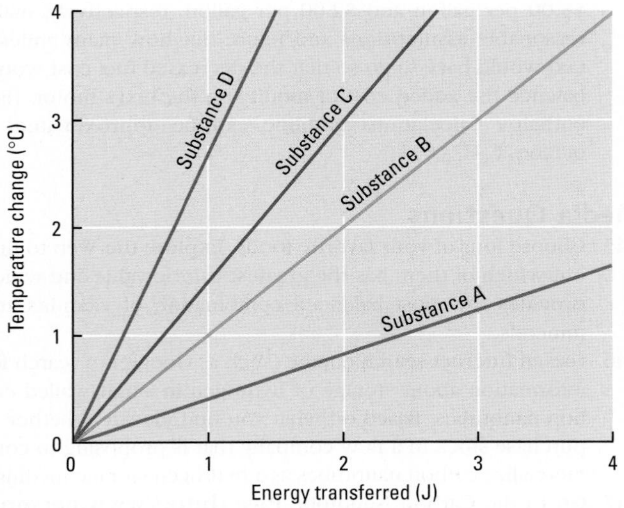

130. Based on the graph that accompanies Question 129, how much heat would need to be transferred to 10 g substance B to raise its temperature from 35 °C to 38 °C?

131. The sketch below shows two identical beakers with different volumes of water at the same temperature. Is the thermal energy content of beaker 1 greater than, less than, or equal to that of beaker 2? Explain your reasoning.

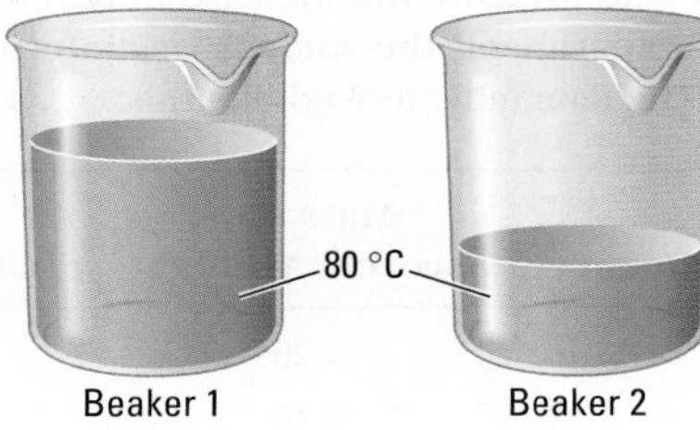

132. If the same quantity of thermal energy were transferred to each beaker in Question 131, would the temperature of beaker 1 be greater than, less than, or equal to that of beaker 2? Explain your reasoning.

133. Consider this thermochemical expression

$$2\ S(s) + 3\ O_2(g) \longrightarrow 2\ SO_3(g) \quad \Delta H° = -791\ kJ$$

and the standard molar enthalpy of formation for $SO_3(g)$ listed in Table 6.2. Why are the enthalpy values different?

134. In this chapter, the symbols $\Delta H_f°$ and $\Delta H°$ were used to denote a change in enthalpy. What is similar and what is different about the enthalpy changes they represent?

135. A fully inflated Mylar party balloon (the kind that does not expand once it is fully inflated) is heated, and 310 J transfers to the gas in the balloon. Calculate ΔE and w for the gas.

136. A sample of Dry Ice, $CO_2(s)$, is placed in a flask that is then tightly stoppered. Because the Dry Ice is very cold, 350 J transfers from the surroundings to the $CO_2(s)$. Calculate ΔE and w for the contents of the flask.

More Challenging Questions

137. Oxygen difluoride, OF_2, is a colorless, very poisonous gas that reacts rapidly and exothermically with water vapor to produce O_2 and HF.

$$OF_2(g) + H_2O(g) \longrightarrow 2\ HF(g) + O_2(g) \quad \Delta H° = -318\ kJ$$

Using this information and Table 6.2 or Appendix J, calculate the molar enthalpy of formation of $OF_2(g)$.

138. Suppose that 28.89 g $ClF_3(g)$ is reacted with 57.3 g Na(s) to form NaCl(s) and NaF(s). The reaction occurs at 1 bar and 25.0 °C. Calculate the quantity of energy transferred between the system and surroundings and describe in which direction the energy is transferred.

139. The four hydrocarbons of lowest molar mass are methane, ethane, propane, and butane. All are used extensively as fuels in our economy. Calculate the thermal energy transferred to the surroundings per gram (the fuel value) of each of these four fuels and rank them by this quantity.

140. For the four substances in the preceding question, calculate the energy density. Assume that substances that are gases at room temperature have been forced to condense to liquids by applying pressure and, if necessary, by lowering temperature. Obtain needed density information from the *CRC Handbook of Chemistry and Physics,* 85th ed. (London: Taylor & Francis CRC Press; 2004) **http://crcpress.com**.

141. A student had five beakers, each containing 100. mL of 0.500 M NaOH(aq) and all at room temperature (20.0 °C). The student planned to add a carefully weighed quantity of solid ascorbic acid, $C_6H_8O_6$, to each beaker, stir until it dissolved, and measure the increase in temperature. After the fourth experiment, the student was interrupted and called away. The data table looked like this:

Experiment	Mass of Ascorbic Acid (g)	Final Temperature (°C)
1	2.20	21.7
2	4.40	23.3
3	8.81	26.7
4	13.22	26.6
5	17.62	—

(a) Predict the temperature the student would have observed in experiment 5. Explain why you predicted this temperature.
(b) For each experiment indicate which is the limiting reactant, sodium hydroxide or ascorbic acid.
(c) When ascorbic acid reacts with NaOH, how many hydrogen ions are involved? One, as in the case of HCl? Two, as in the case of H_2SO_4? Or three, as in the case of phosphoric acid, H_3PO_4? Explain clearly how you can tell, based on the student's calorimeter data.

142. In their home laboratory, two students do an experiment (a rather dangerous one—don't try it without proper safety precautions!) with drain cleaner (Drano, a solid) and toilet bowl cleaner (The Works, a liquid solution). The students measure 1 teaspoon (tsp) of Drano into each of four Styrofoam coffee cups and dissolve the solid in half a cup of water. Then they wash their hands and go have lunch. When they return, they measure the temperature of the solution in each of the four cups and find it to be 22.3 °C. Next they measure into separate small empty cups 1, 2, 3, and 4 tablespoons (Tbsp) of The Works. In each cup they add enough water to make the total volume 4 Tbsp. After a few minutes they measure the temperature of each cup and find it to be 22.3 °C. Finally the two students take each cup of The Works, pour it into a cup of Drano solution, and measure the temperature over a period of a few minutes. Their results are reported in the table below.

Experiment	Volume of The Works (Tbsp)	Highest Temperature (°C)
1	1	28.0
2	2	33.6
3	3	39.3
4	4	39.4

Discuss these results and interpret them in terms of the thermochemistry and stoichiometry of the reaction. Is the reaction exothermic or endothermic? Why is more energy transferred in some cases than others? For each experiment, which reactant, Drano or The Works, is limiting? Why are the final temperatures nearly the same in experiments 3 and 4? What can you conclude about the stoichiometric ratio between the two reactants?

143. On March 4, 1996, five railroad tank cars carrying liquid propane derailed in Weyauwega, Wisconsin, forcing evacuation of the town for more than a week. Residents who lived within the square mile centered on the accident were unable to return to their homes for more than two weeks. Evaluate whether this evacuation was reasonable and necessary by considering the following questions.
(a) Estimate the volume of a railroad tank car. Obtain the density of liquid propane (C_3H_8) at or near its boiling point and calculate the mass of propane in the five tank cars. Obtain the data you need to calculate the energy transfer if all the propane burned at once. (Assume that the reaction takes place at room temperature.)
(b) The enthalpy of decomposition of TNT, $C_7H_5N_3O_6$, to water, nitrogen, carbon monoxide, and carbon is -1066.1 kJ/mol. How many metric kilotons (1 tonne = 1 metric ton = 1 Mg = 1×10^6 g) of TNT would provide energy transfer equivalent to that produced by combustion of propane in the five tank cars?
(c) Find the energy transfer (in kilotons of TNT) resulting from the nuclear fission bombs dropped on Hiroshima and Nagasaki, Japan, in 1945, and the energy transfer for modern fission weapons. What is the largest nuclear weapon thought to have been detonated to date? Compare the energy of the Hiroshima and Nagasaki bombs with the Weyauwega propane spill. What can you conclude about the wisdom of evacuating the town?
(d) Compare the energy that would have been released by burning the propane with the energy of a hurricane.

144. In some cities taxicabs run on liquefied propane fuel instead of gasoline. This practice extends the lifetime of the vehicle and produces less pollution. Given that it costs about $2000 to modify the engine of a taxicab to run on propane and that the cost of gasoline and liquid propane are $3.00 per gallon and $2.00 per gallon, respectively, make reasonable assumptions and figure out how many miles a taxi would have to go so that the decreased fuel cost would balance the added cost of modifying the taxi's motor. [For enthalpy calculations gasoline can be approximated as octane, $C_8H_{18}(\ell)$.]

Media Questions

145. Choose four of your favorite foods. Explore the Web to find out which of them has the greatest caloric value and which provides the most balanced combination of vitamins and minerals.

146. Use an Internet search engine (such as Google) to search for information about storage of hydrogen in single-walled carbon nanotubes. Based on what you find, decide whether to purchase stock in a new company that is proposing to commercialize carbon nanotubes as a hydrogen storage medium.

147. Go to the Carbon Nanotube Page (**http://www.personal.rdg.ac.uk/~scsharip/tubes.htm**) and find out the difference between a single-walled nanotube, a nanotube rope, a nanohorn, and a nano-test-tube.

148. Starting at the Carbon Nanotube Page (**http://www.personal.rdg.ac.uk/~scsharip/tubes.htm**), find out as much as you can about filling nanotubes with biological molecules.

Conceptual Challenge Problems

CP6.A (Section 6.2) Suppose a scientist discovered that energy was not conserved, but rather that $1 \times 10^{-7}\%$ of the energy transferred from one system vanishes before it enters another system. How would this affect electric utilities, thermochemical experiments in scientific laboratories, and scientific thinking?

CP6.B (Section 6.2) Suppose that someone were to tell your teacher during class that energy is not always conserved. This person states that he or she had previously learned that in the case of nuclear reactions, mass is converted into energy according to Einstein's equation $E = mc^2$. Hence, energy is continuously produced as mass is changed into energy. Your teacher quickly responds by giving the following assignment to the class: "Please write a paragraph or two to refute or clarify this student's thesis." What would you say?

CP6.C (Section 6.3) The specific heat capacities at 25 °C for three metals with widely differing molar masses are 3.6 J g^{-1} °C^{-1} for Li, 0.25 J g^{-1} °C^{-1} for Ag, and 0.11 J g^{-1} °C^{-1} for Th. Suppose that you have three samples, one of each metal and each containing the same number of atoms.

(a) Is the energy transfer required to increase the temperature of each sample by 1 °C significantly different from one sample to the next?

(b) What interpretation can you make about temperature based on the result you found in part (a)?

CP6.D (Section 6.4) During one of your chemistry classes a student asks the professor, "Why does hot water freeze more quickly than cold water?"

(a) What do you expect the professor to say in answer to the student's question?

(b) In one experiment, two 100.-g samples of water were placed in identical containers on the same surface 1 decimeter apart in a room at −25 °C. One sample had an initial temperature of 78 °C, while the second was at 24 °C. The second sample took 151 min to freeze, and the first took 166 min (only 10% longer) to freeze. Clearly the cooler sample froze more quickly, but not nearly as quickly as one might have expected. How can this be so?

CP6.E (Section 6.10) Assume that glass has the same properties as pure SiO_2. The thermal conductivity (the rate at which heat transfer occurs through a substance) for aluminum is eight times that for SiO_2.

(a) Is it more efficient in time and energy to bake brownies in an aluminum pan or a glass pan?

(b) It is said that things cook more evenly in a glass pan than in an aluminum pan. Are there scientific data that indicate that this statement is reasonable?

CP6.F (Section 6.11) Suppose that you are an athlete and exercise a lot. Consequently you need a large caloric intake each day. Choose at least ten foods that you normally eat and evaluate each one to find which provides the most calories per dollar.

7

Electron Configurations and the Periodic Table

The spectacular colors of fireworks are due to transition of electrons among different energy levels in various metal ions. Electron transitions in Sr^{2+} ions give bright red color; Ca^{2+} orange; Ba^{2+} green; and Cu^{2+} blue. Mixtures of Sr^{2+} and Cu^{2+} produce purple. This chapter includes a discussion of the electron transitions that lead to emission of visible light.

© Frank Leather, Eye Ubiquitous/Corbis

The periodic table was created by Dmitri Mendeleev to summarize experimental observations (⇐ **p. 64**). He had no theory or model to explain why, for example, all alkaline earth metals combine with oxygen in a 1:1 atom ratio—he just knew they did. In the early years of the twentieth century, however, it became evident that atoms contain electrons. As a result of these findings, explanations of periodic trends in physical and chemical properties began to be based on an understanding of the arrangement of electrons within atoms—on what we now call *electron configurations.* Studies of the interaction of light with atoms and molecules revealed that electrons in atoms are arranged in energy levels or shells. Soon it was understood that the occurrence of electrons in these shells is determined by the energies of the electrons. Electrons in the outermost shell are the *valence electrons;* the number of valence electrons and the shell in which they occur are the chief factors that determine chemical reactivity. This chapter describes the relationship of atomic electron configurations to atomic properties. Special emphasis is placed on the use of the periodic table to derive the electron configurations for atoms and ions.

ThomsonNOW
Throughout the text, this icon indicates an opportunity to test yourself on key concepts and to explore interactive modules by signing in to ThomsonNOW at **www.thomsonedu.com**.

7.1 Electromagnetic Radiation and Matter

Theories about the energy and arrangement of electrons in atoms are based on experimental studies of the interaction of matter with electromagnetic radiation, of which visible light is a familiar form. The human eye can distinguish the spectrum of colors that make up visible light. Interestingly, matter in some form is always associated with any color of light our eyes see. For example, the red glow of a neon sign comes from neon atoms excited by electricity, and fireworks displays are visible because of light emitted from metal ions excited by the heat of explosive reactions. How are these varied colors of light produced?

When atoms gain energy by absorbing light, they are described as "excited." The added energy is absorbed by electrons and then released in the form of electromagnetic radiation, some of which is light in the visible region. Electromagnetic radiation and its applications are familiar to all of us; sunlight, automobile headlights, dental X-rays, microwave ovens, and cell phones that we use for communications are a few examples (Figure 7.1). These kinds of radiation seem very different, but they are actually very similar. All **electromagnetic radiation** consists of oscillating perpendicular electric and magnetic fields that travel through space at the same rate (the "speed of light": 186,000 miles/second, or 2.998×10^8 m/s in a vacuum). Any of the various kinds of electromagnetic radiation can be described in terms of frequency (ν) and wavelength (λ). A **spectrum** is the distribution of intensities of wavelengths or frequencies of electromagnetic radiation emitted or absorbed by an object. Figure 7.1 gives wavelength and frequency values for several regions of the spectrum.

The speed of light through a substance (air, glass, or water, for example) depends on the chemical constitution of the substance and the wavelength of the light. This is the basis for using a glass prism to disperse light and is the explanation for rainbows.

Wavelength units are summarized in Table 7.1.

Table 7.1 Useful Wavelength Units for Different Regions of the Electromagnetic Spectrum

Wavelength Unit	Unit Length (m)	Radiation Type
Picometer, pm	10^{-12}	γ (gamma)
Ångström, Å	10^{-10}	X-ray
Nanometer, nm	10^{-9}	Ultraviolet, visible
Micrometer, μm	10^{-6}	Infrared
Millimeter, mm	10^{-3}	Infrared
Centimeter, cm	10^{-2}	Microwave
Meter, m	1	TV, radio

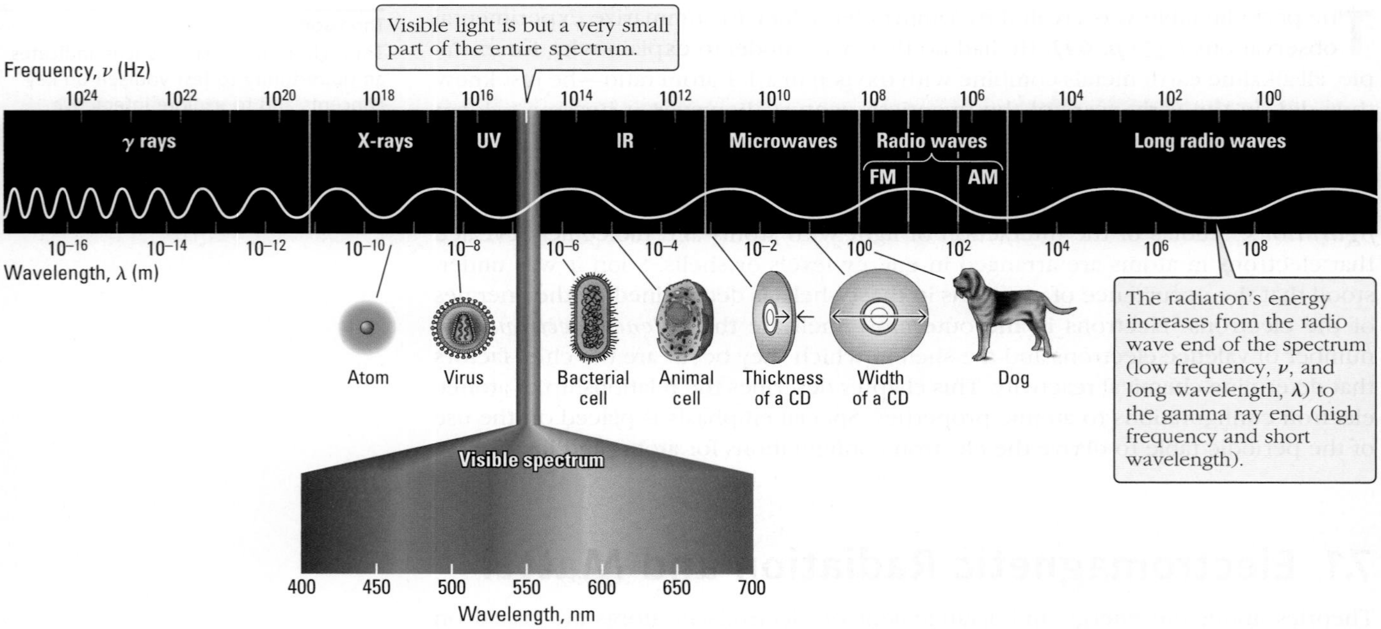

Figure 7.1 The electromagnetic spectrum. The size of wavelengths in the electromagnetic spectrum is compared with common objects. Visible light (enlarged section) is only a small part of the entire spectrum.

As illustrated in Figure 7.2, the **wavelength** is the distance between adjacent crests (or troughs) in a wave, and the **frequency** is the number of complete waves passing a point in a given period of time—that is, cycles per second or simply per second, 1/s. Reciprocal units such as 1/s are often represented in the negative exponent form, s^{-1}, which means "per second." A frequency of 4.80×10^{14} s^{-1} means that 4.80×10^{14} waves pass a fixed point every second. The unit s^{-1} is given the name *hertz* (Hz).

The hertz unit (cycles/s, or s^{-1}) was named in honor of Heinrich Hertz (1857–1894), a German physicist.

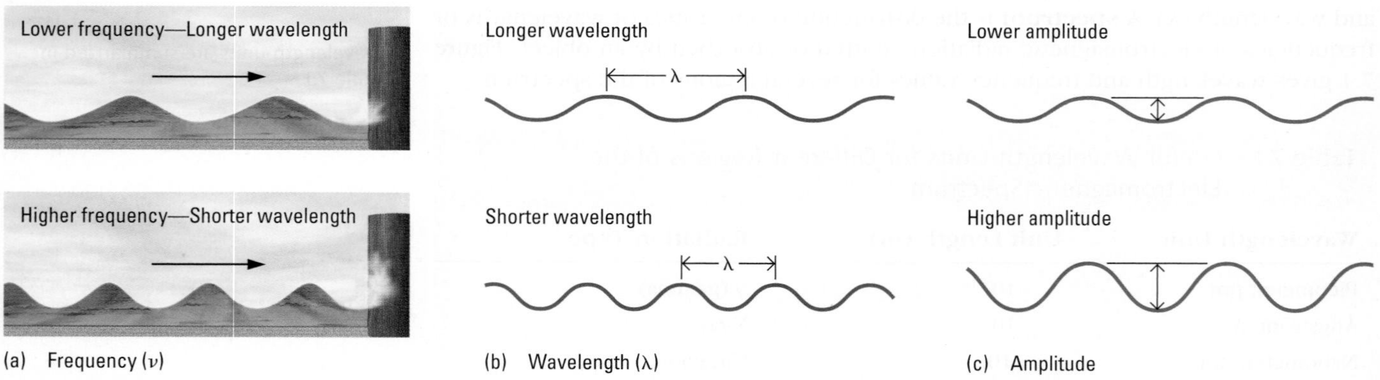

Figure 7.2 Wavelength, frequency, and amplitude of water waves. The waves are moving from left to right toward the post at the same speed.
(a) The upper wave has a long wavelength (large λ) and low frequency (the number of times per second the peak of the wave hits the post). The lower wave has a shorter wavelength and a higher frequency (its peaks hit the post more often in a given time). (b) Variation in wavelength. (c) Variation in amplitude.

If light is thought of as electromagnetic waves, the intensity of radiation (brightness for visible light) is related to the *amplitude* (height of the wave crest) (Figure 7.2). The higher the amplitude, the more intense is the radiation. For example, green light of a particular shade always has the same frequency and wavelength, but it can vary from bright (high amplitude) to dim (low amplitude).

The frequency of electromagnetic radiation is related to its wavelength by

$$\nu\lambda = c$$

where c is the speed of light, 2.998×10^8 m/s.

As Figure 7.1 shows, visible light is only a small portion of the electromagnetic spectrum. Radiation with shorter wavelengths includes ultraviolet radiation (the type that leads to sunburn), X-rays, and gamma (γ) rays (emitted in the process of radioactive disintegration of some atoms). Infrared radiation, the type that is sensed as heat from a fire, has wavelengths longer than those of visible light. Longer still is the wavelength of the radiation in a microwave oven or of television and radio transmissions, such as that used for cellular telephones.

Note that frequency and wavelength are *inversely* related; that is, as one decreases, the other increases. *Short-wavelength* radiation has a *high* frequency.

ThomsonNOW™
Go to the Coached Problems menu for a tutorial on **determining wavelength.**

PROBLEM-SOLVING EXAMPLE 7.1 Wavelength and Frequency

Microwaves from a home microwave oven have a frequency of 2.45×10^9 s^{-1}. Calculate the wavelength of this radiation in nanometers, nm.

Answer 1.22×10^8 nm

Strategy and Explanation Rearrange the equation relating frequency, the speed of light, and wavelength to calculate the wavelength of this radiation. Recall that 1 m = 1×10^9 nm.

$$\lambda = \frac{c}{\nu} = \frac{2.998 \times 10^8 \text{ m/s}}{2.45 \times 10^9 \text{ s}^{-1}} = 0.122 \text{ m}$$

Convert meters to nanometers:

$$0.122 \text{ m} \times \frac{1 \times 10^9 \text{ nm}}{1 \text{ m}} = 1.22 \times 10^8 \text{ nm}$$

✓ **Reasonable Answer Check** Compare the calculated wavelength (0.122 m) with the wavelength of the microwave region of the electromagnetic spectrum illustrated in Figure 7.1. The calculated wavelength falls within the microwave region and thus the answer is reasonable.

PROBLEM-SOLVING PRACTICE 7.1

A laser developed for use with digital video disc (DVD) players has a wavelength of 405 nm. Calculate the frequency of this radiation in hertz (Hz).

CONCEPTUAL EXERCISE 7.1 Frequency and Wavelength

A fellow chemistry student says that low-frequency radiation is short-wavelength radiation. You disagree. Explain why the other student is wrong.

CONCEPTUAL EXERCISE 7.2 Estimating Wavelengths

The size of a radio antenna is proportional to the wavelength of the radiation. Cellular phones have antennas often less than 0.076 m long, whereas submarine antennas are up to 2000 m long. Which is using higher-frequency radio waves?

7.2 Planck's Quantum Theory

Have you ever looked at the wires in a toaster as they heat up? Although you cannot see the metal atoms in the toaster wires, as electric energy flows through them, their atoms gain energy and then emit it as radiation. First the wires emit a slight amount of heat that you can feel (infrared radiation). As the wire gets hotter, it begins to glow, initially emitting red light, and then orange (Figure 7.3a). If a wire gets very hot, it appears almost white. Figure 7.3b shows the spectrum of a typical heated object.

In trying to explain the nature of these emissions from hot objects, late nineteenth-century scientists assumed that vibrating atoms in a hot wire caused the emission of electromagnetic vibrations (light waves). According to the laws of classical physics, the light waves could have any frequency along a continuously varying range. Using such laws, however, the scientists were unable to predict the experimentally observed spectrum.

In 1900, Max Planck (1858–1947) offered an explanation for the spectrum of a heated body. His ideas contained the seeds of a revolution in scientific thought. Planck made what was at that time an incredible assertion, one that departed dramatically from the laws of classical physics. He stated that when an atom in a hot object emits radiation, it does so only in packets having a minimum amount of energy. That is, there must be a small packet of energy such that no smaller quantity can be emitted, just as an atom is the smallest packet of an element. Planck called this packet of energy a **quantum.** He further asserted that the energy of a quantum is proportional to the frequency of the radiation according to the equation

A quantum is the smallest possible unit of a distinct quantity—for example, the smallest possible unit of energy for electromagnetic radiation of a given frequency.

$$E_{\text{quantum}} = h\nu_{\text{radiation}}$$

The proportionality constant h is called **Planck's constant** in his honor; it has a value of 6.626×10^{-34} J·s and relates the frequency of radiation to its energy *per quantum.*

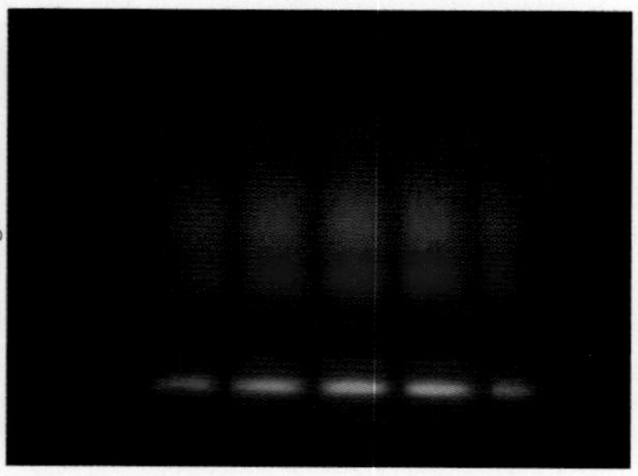

© Thomson Learning/Charles D. Winters

(a)

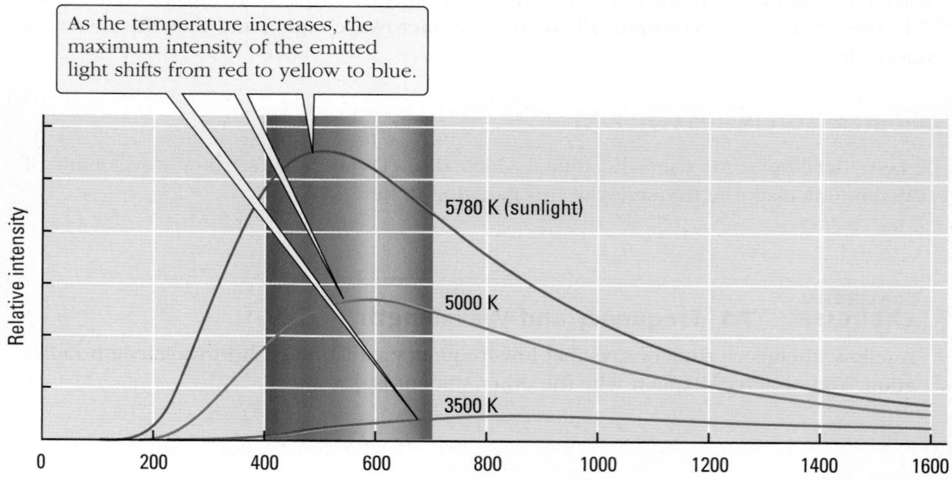

(b)

Figure 7.3 Heated objects and temperature. (a) A heated filament. The color of the hot filament and its continuous spectrum change as the temperature is increased. (b) The spectrum of radiation given off by a heated object. At very high temperatures, the heated object becomes "white hot" as all wavelengths of visible light become equally intense.

Orange light has a measured frequency of $4.80 \times 10^{14}\ s^{-1}$. The energy of *one* quantum of orange light is therefore

$$E = h\nu = (6.626 \times 10^{-34}\ J \cdot s)(4.80 \times 10^{14}\ s^{-1}) = 3.18 \times 10^{-19}\ J$$

The theory based on Planck's work is called the **quantum theory.** By using his quantum theory, Planck was able to calculate results that agreed very well with the experimentally measured spectra of heated objects, spectra for which the laws of classical physics had no explanation.

Max Planck won the 1918 Nobel Prize in Physics for his quantum theory.

PROBLEM-SOLVING EXAMPLE 7.2 Calculating Quantum Energies

In the stratosphere, ultraviolet radiation with a frequency of $1.36 \times 10^{15}\ s^{-1}$ can break C—Cl bonds in chlorofluorocarbons (CFCs), which can lead to stratospheric ozone depletion. Calculate the energy per quantum of this radiation.

Answer 9.01×10^{-19} J

Strategy and Explanation According to Planck's quantum theory, the energy and frequency of radiation are related by $E = h\nu$. Substituting the values for h and ν into the equation, followed by multiplying and canceling the units, gives the correct answer.

$$E = h\nu = (6.626 \times 10^{-34}\ J \cdot s)(1.36 \times 10^{15}\ s^{-1}) = 9.01 \times 10^{-19}\ J$$

ThomsonNOW™

Go to the Coached Problems menu for a tutorial on **calculating quantum energy.**

PROBLEM-SOLVING PRACTICE 7.2

Which has more energy,

(a) One quantum of microwave radiation or one quantum of ultraviolet radiation?

(b) One quantum of blue light or one quantum of green light?

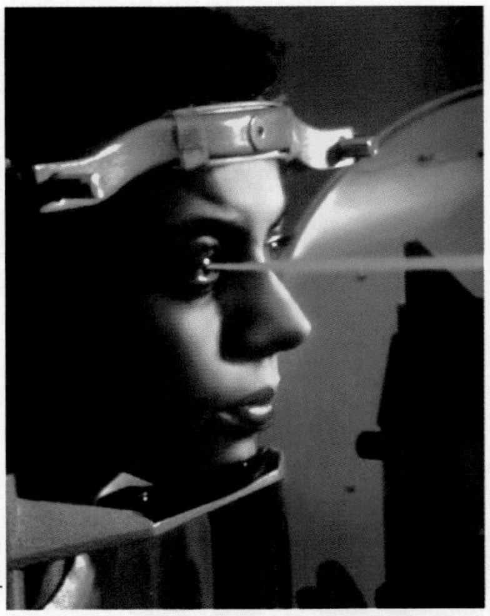

SuperStock

A laser being used to perform eye surgery.

There is a very important relationship between the energy and wavelength of a quantum of radiation. Since $E = h\nu$ and $\nu = c/\lambda$, then

$$E = \frac{hc}{\lambda}$$

where h is Planck's constant, c is the velocity of light (2.998×10^8 m/s), and λ is the wavelength of the radiation. Note that energy and wavelength are inversely proportional: ***The energy per quantum of radiation increases as the wavelength gets shorter.*** For example, red light and blue light have wavelengths of 656.3 nm and 434.1 nm, respectively. Because of its shorter wavelength, blue light has a higher energy per quantum than red light. We can calculate their different energies by applying the previous equation.

$$E_{red} = \frac{(6.626 \times 10^{-34}\ J \cdot s)(2.998 \times 10^8\ m/s)}{(656.3\ nm)(1\ m/10^9\ nm)} = 3.027 \times 10^{-19}\ J$$

$$E_{blue} = \frac{(6.626 \times 10^{-34}\ J \cdot s)(2.998 \times 10^8\ m/s)}{(434.1\ nm)(1\ m/10^9\ nm)} = 4.576 \times 10^{-19}\ J$$

EXERCISE 7.3 Energy, Wavelength, and Drills

A drilling method uses a microwave drill rather than a mechanical one. The apparatus contains a powerful source of 2.45-GHz microwave radiation. Calculate the wavelength and the energy of the microwaves emitted by such an apparatus.

ESTIMATION

Turning on the Light Bulb

You turn the switch and a living room lamp comes on. The lamp emits yellow light (585 nm), producing 20 J of energy in one second. Approximately how many quanta of yellow light are given off by the lamp in that time?

To find out, we first determine the energy of each 585-nm quantum by using the relationship $E = \frac{hc}{\lambda}$. We approximate by rounding the value of Planck's constant to 7×10^{-34} J·s and that of *c*, the speed of light, to 3×10^{8} m/s. The wavelength of the quanta we round to approximately 600×10^{-9} m; remember we have to convert nanometers to meters: 1 nm = 1×10^{-9} m. Therefore, the energy, *E*, of each quantum is

$$\frac{(7 \times 10^{-34}\ \text{J}\cdot\text{s})\ (3 \times 10^{8}\ \text{m/s})}{600 \times 10^{-9}\ \text{m}}$$

which is about 4×10^{-19} J per quantum. Using this value and the total energy generated in one second, we can calculate the number of quanta of yellow light emitted in that time.

$$\text{Number of quanta} = \frac{\text{total energy}}{\text{energy of each quantum}} =$$

$$\frac{20\ \text{J}}{4 \times 10^{-19}\ \text{J/quantum}} = 5 \times 10^{19}\ \text{quanta}$$

a considerable number.

ThomsonNOW™
Sign in to ThomsonNOW at **www.thomsonedu.com** to work an interactive module based on this material.

© Thomson Learning/Charles D. Winters

An application of photoelectric effect. The photoelectric effect is used in a light meter's sensors to determine exposure for photographic film.

The Photoelectric Effect

When a theory can accurately predict experimental results, the theory is usually regarded as useful. Planck's quantum theory was not widely accepted at first because of its radical assertion that energy is quantized. The quantum theory of electromagnetic energy was firmly accepted only after Planck's quanta were used by Albert Einstein to explain another phenomenon, the photoelectric effect.

In the early 1900s it was known that certain metals exhibit a **photoelectric effect**: They emit electrons when illuminated by light of certain wavelengths (Figure 7.4a). For each photosensitive metal there is a threshold wavelength below which no photoelectric effect is observed. For example, cesium (Cs) metal emits electrons when illuminated by red light, whereas some metals require yellow light, and others require ultraviolet light to cause emission of electrons. The differences occur because each type of light has a different wavelength and thus a different energy per quantum. Red light, for example, has a lower energy (longer wavelength) than yellow light or ultraviolet light. Light with energy that is below the threshold needed to eject electrons from the metal will not cause an electric current to flow, *no matter how bright the light.* Figure 7.4b illustrates how the electrons ejected from the photosensitive cathode are attracted to the anode in the photoelectric cell, causing an electric current to flow, resulting in a display on the meter. Figure 7.4c shows how an electric current suddenly increases when light of sufficient energy per quantum (short enough wavelength) shines on a photosensitive metal.

Albert Einstein explained these experimental observations by assuming that Planck's quanta were *massless* "particles" of light. Einstein called them **photons** instead of quanta. That is, light could be described as a stream of photons that had particle-like properties as well as wave-like properties. To remove one electron from a photosensitive metal surface requires a certain minimum quantity of energy; we call it E_{min}. Since each photon has an energy given by $E = h\nu$, only photons whose E is greater than E_{min} will have enough energy to knock an electron loose. Thus, no electrons are ejected until photons with high enough frequencies (and short enough wavelengths) strike the photosensitive surface. Photons with lower frequencies (left side of Figure 7.4c) do not have enough energy to remove electrons. This means that if a photosensitive metal requires photons of green light to eject electrons from its surface, then yellow light, red light, or light of any other lower

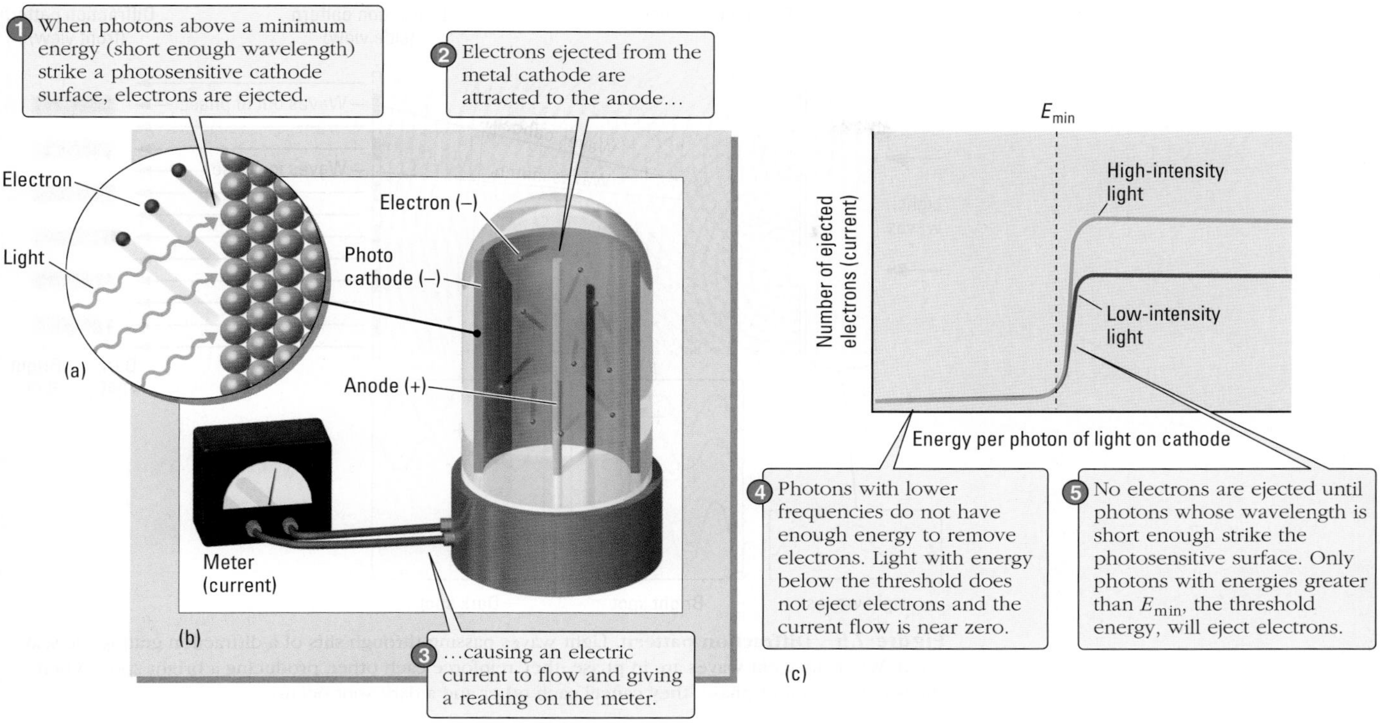

Active Figure 7.4 **The photoelectric effect.** (a) A photoelectric surface. (b) A photoelectric cell. Only photons with energies greater than the threshold energy will eject electrons from the photosensitive surface. (c) Ejected electrons and energy. Photons with lower energy (left side of Figure 7.4c) do not have enough energy to remove electrons. Note that the *number* of electrons ejected (the current) depends on the light's intensity, not its energy. **Go to the Active Figures menu at ThomsonNOW to test your understanding of the concepts in this figure.**

frequency (longer wavelength) will not have sufficient energy to cause the photoelectric effect with that metal. This brilliant deduction about the quantized nature of light and how it relates to light's interaction with matter won Einstein the Nobel Prize for physics in 1921.

A common misconception is that Einstein won the Nobel Prize for his theory of relativity.

The energies of photons are important for practical reasons. Photons of ultraviolet light can damage skin, while photons of visible light cannot. We use sunblocks containing molecules that selectively absorb ultraviolet photons to protect our skin from solar UV radiation. X-ray photons are even more energetic than ultraviolet photons and can disrupt molecules at the cellular level, causing genetic damage, among other effects. For this reason we try to limit our exposure to X-rays even more than we limit our exposure to ultraviolet light.

Look again at Figure 7.4c. Notice how a higher-intensity light source causes a higher photoelectric current. Higher intensities of ultraviolet light (or more time of exposure) can cause greater damage to the skin than lower intensities (or less exposure time). The same holds true for other high-energy forms of electromagnetic radiation, such as X-rays.

In the quantum theory the intensity of radiation is proportional to the number of photons. The total energy is proportional to the number of photons times the energy per photon.

Developments such as Einstein's explanation of the photoelectric effect led eventually to acceptance of what is referred to as the *dual nature* of light. Depending on the experimental circumstances, visible light and all other forms of electromagnetic radiation appear to have either "wave" or "particle" characteristics. However, both ideas are needed to fully explain light's behavior. Classical wave theory fails to explain the photoelectric effect. But it does explain quite well the *refraction,* or bending, of light by a prism and the diffraction of light by a diffraction grating, a device with a series of parallel, closely spaced small slits. When waves of light

Refraction is the bending of light as it crosses the boundary from one medium to another—for example, from air to water. Diffraction is the bending of light around the edges of objects, such as slits in a diffraction grating.

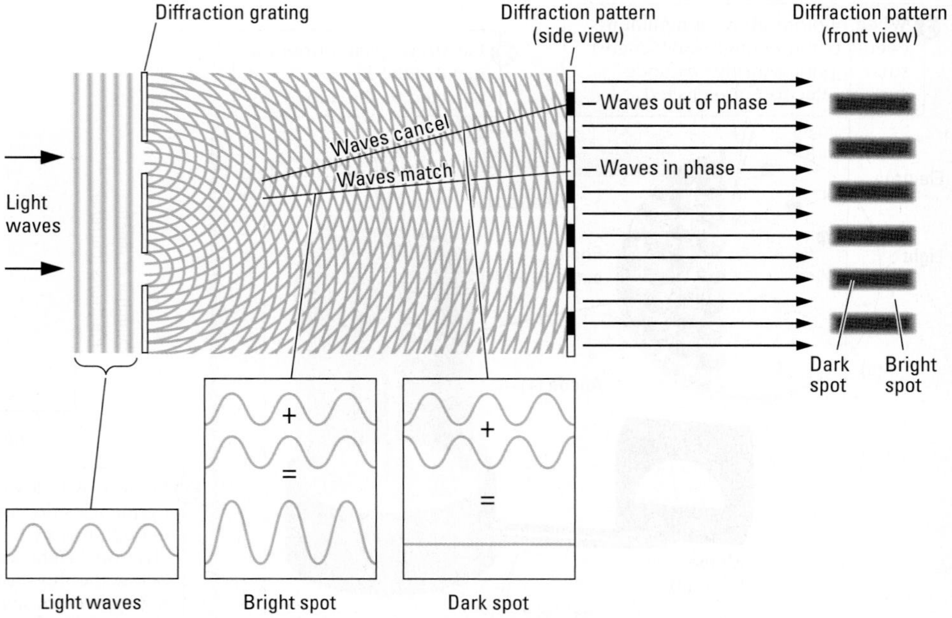

Figure 7.5 **Diffraction pattern.** Light waves passing through slits of a diffraction grating are scattered. When adjacent waves are in phase, they reinforce each other, producing a bright spot. When the waves are out of phase, they cancel each other and a dark spot occurs.

pass through such adjacent narrow slits, the waves are scattered so that the emerging light waves spread out, a phenomenon called *diffraction*. The semicircular waves emerging from the narrow slits can either amplify or cancel each other. Such behavior creates a diffraction pattern of dark and bright spots, as seen in Figure 7.5.

Prior to Einstein's explanation of the photoelectric effect, classical physics considered light as being only wave-like.

It is important to realize, however, that this "dual nature" description arises because of our attempts to explain observations by using inadequate models. Light is not changing back and forth from being a wave to being a particle, but has a single consistent nature that can be described by modern quantum theory. The dual-nature description arises when we try to explain our observations by using our familiarity with classical models for "wave" or "particle" behavior.

7.3 The Bohr Model of the Hydrogen Atom

Within just about a decade (1900–1911), three major discoveries were made about the atom and the nature of electromagnetic radiation. The first two, discussed in the previous section, were Max Planck's suggestion that energy was quantized and, five years later, Albert Einstein's application of the quantum idea to explain the photoelectric effect. The third came in 1911 when Ernest Rutherford demonstrated experimentally that atoms contain a dense positive core, the nucleus, surrounded by electrons. Niels Bohr linked these three powerful ideas when, in 1913, he used quantum theory to explain the behavior of the electron in a hydrogen atom. In doing so, Bohr developed a mathematical model to explain how excited hydrogen atoms emit or absorb only certain wavelengths of light, a phenomenon that had been unexplained for nearly a century. To understand what Bohr did, we turn first to the visible spectrum.

© Steve Taylor/Digital Vision/ Getty Images

The various colors of light emitted by neon-type signs are due to emissions from different gases.

The spectrum of white light, such as that from the sun or an incandescent light bulb, consists of a rainbow of colors, as shown in Figure 7.6. This **continuous spectrum** contains light of all wavelengths in the visible region.

If a high voltage is applied to a gaseous element at low pressure, the atoms absorb energy and are "excited." The excited atoms then emit, as electromagnetic radiation, the energy that was previously absorbed. A neon advertising sign, in which the neon atoms emit red-orange light, makes commercial use of the light from excited neon atoms. When light from such a source passes through a prism onto a white surface, only a few colored lines are seen in a **line emission spectrum,** characteristic of the element. The line spectra of the visible light emitted by excited atoms of hydrogen, mercury, and neon are shown in Figure 7.7.

Hydrogen has the simplest line emission spectrum. It was first studied in the 1880s. At that time, lines in the visible region of the spectrum and their wavelengths were accurately measured (Figure 7.7). Other series of lines in the ultraviolet region ($\lambda < 400$ nm) and in the infrared region ($\lambda > 700$ nm) were discovered subsequently.

Niels Bohr provided the first explanation of the line emission spectra of atoms by audaciously assuming that the single electron of a hydrogen atom moved in a circular orbit around its nucleus. He then related the energies of the electron to the radius of its orbit, but not by using the classic laws of physics. Such laws allowed the electron to have a wide range of energy. Instead, Bohr introduced quantum theory into his atomic model by invoking Planck's idea that energies are quantized. In the Bohr model, the electron could circle the nucleus in orbits of only certain radii, which correspond to specific energies. Thus, the energy of the electron is "quantized," and the electron is restricted to certain energy levels unless it gains or loses a certain amount of energy. Bohr referred to these energy levels as *orbits* and represented the energy difference between any two adjacent orbits as a specific quantity of energy. Each allowed orbit was assigned an integer, n, known as the **principal quantum number.**

In the Bohr model, the value of n for the possible orbits can be any integer from 1 to infinity (∞). *The energy of the electron and the size of its orbit increase as the value of n increases.* The orbit of lowest energy, $n = 1$, is closest to the nucleus, and the electron of a hydrogen atom is normally in this energy level. Any atom with its electrons arranged to give the lowest total energy is said to be in its **ground state.** Because the positive nucleus attracts the negative electron, an electron must absorb energy to go from a lower energy state (lower n value) to a higher energy state (higher n value), an excited state. Conversely, energy is emitted when the reverse process occurs—an electron going from a higher energy state to a lower energy state (Figure 7.8). Emission lines in the ultraviolet region result from electron transitions from a higher n value down to the $n = 1$ level. Emission lines in the

© Roger Antrobus/Corbis

Figure 7.6 A continuous spectrum from white light. When white light is passed through slits to produce a narrow beam and then refracted in a glass prism, the various colors blend smoothly into one another.

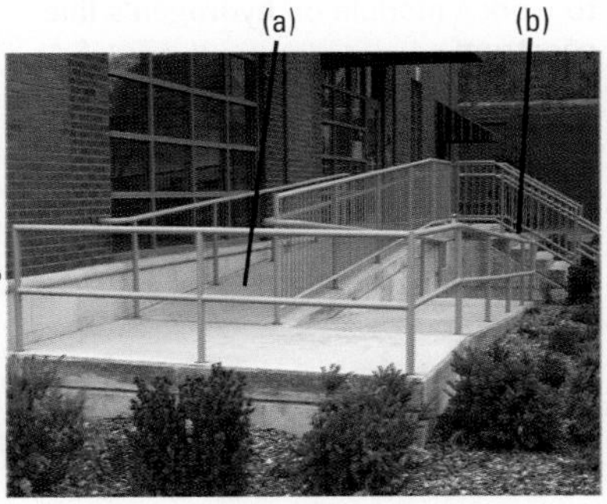

© Thomson Learning/Charles D. Winters

(a) A ramp (not quantized) (b) Stair steps (quantized)

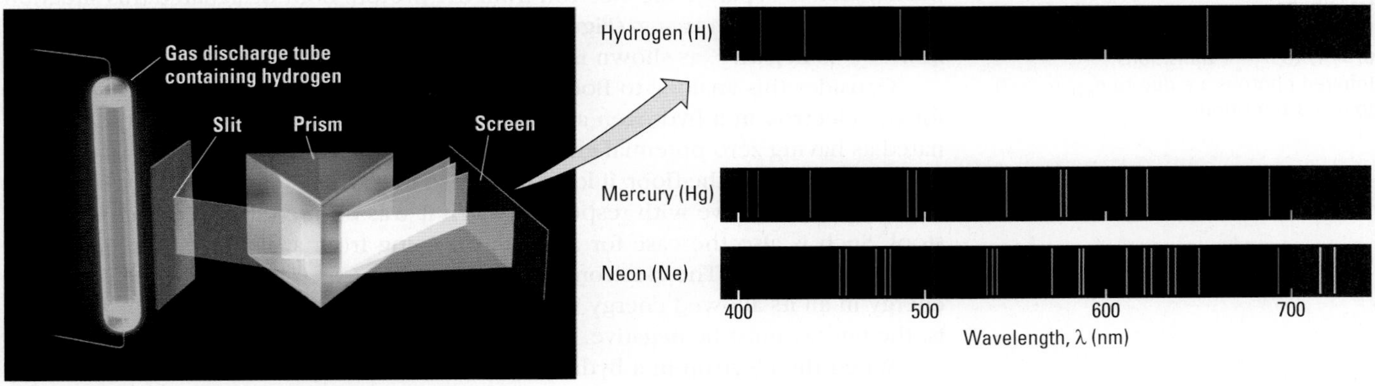

Figure 7.7 Line emission spectra of hydrogen, mercury, and neon. Excited gaseous elements produce characteristic spectra that can be used to identify the elements as well as to determine how much of an element is present in a sample.

The Bohr orbit model is analogous to a set of stairs in which the higher stairs are closer together. As you move up and down the stairs, you can stop at any step, *but not between steps* because the steps are quantized; only whole steps are allowed.

ThomsonNOW
Go to the Chemistry Interactive menu to work a module on **hydrogen's line spectrum.**

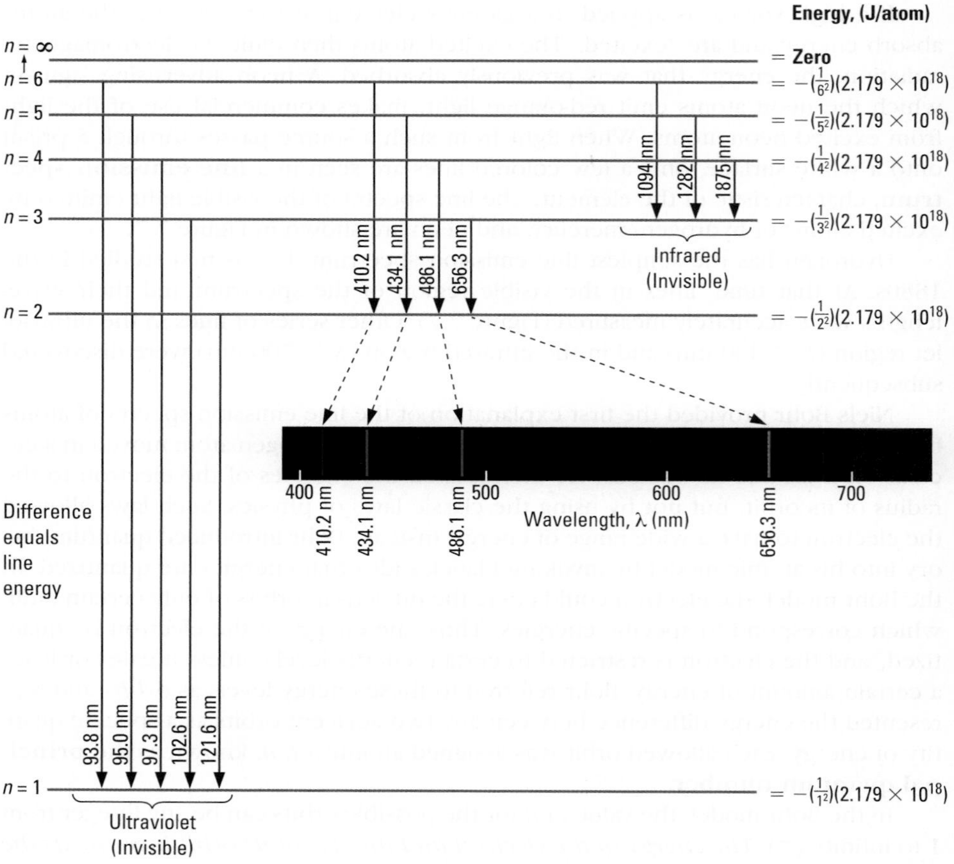

Figure 7.8 Electron transitions in an excited H atom. The lines in the ultraviolet region all result from transitions to the $n = 1$ level. Transitions from levels with values of $n > 2$ to the $n = 2$ level occur in the visible region. Lines in the infrared region result from the transitions from levels with values of $n > 3$ or 4 to the $n = 3$ or 4 levels (only the series for transitions to the $n = 3$ level is shown here).

For the hydrogen atom, visible photons are due to n_{high} ($n > 2$) to $n = 2$ transitions.
Ultraviolet photons are due to n_{high} ($n > 1$) to $n = 1$ transitions.
Infrared photons are due to n_{high} ($n > 3$) to $n = 3$ transitions.

visible region occur due to electron transitions from levels with values of $n > 2$ to the $n = 2$ level. Infrared radiation emission lines result from electron transitions from levels with $n > 3$ or 4 down to the $n = 3$ or $n = 4$ levels. The highest potential energy the electron in a hydrogen atom can have is when sufficient energy has been added to separate the electron from the proton. Bohr designated this situation as zero energy when $n = \infty$ (Figure 7.8). Thus, the potential energy of the electron in $n < \infty$ is negative, as shown in Figure 7.8.

Consider this analogy to Bohr's arbitrarily selecting zero as the highest energy for the electron in a hydrogen atom. A book resting on a table is arbitrarily designated as having zero potential energy. As the book falls from the table to a chair, to a stool, and then to the floor, it loses energy so that when it is on the floor, its potential energy is negative with respect to when it was on the table or the chair or the stool. Such is also the case for an electron going from a higher energy level to a lower energy level. The electron must lose energy. Correspondingly, the electron's energy in all its allowed energy states within the atom must be less than zero; that is, the energy must be negative.

When the electron in a hydrogen atom absorbs a quantized amount of energy and moves to an orbit with $n > 1$, the atom is said to be in an **excited state** in which it has more energy than in its ground state. Any excited state of any atom is unstable. When the electron returns to the ground state from an excited state, the electron emits the energy gained when it moved from the ground state to the excited state. The emitted energy is given off as photons of light having an energy of hc/λ. The energy of an emitted photon corresponds to the *difference* between two energy levels of the atom (Figure 7.8). According to Bohr, the light forming the lines in the emission spectrum of hydrogen (Figure 7.7) comes from electrons in hydrogen atoms moving from higher energy orbits to lower energy orbits closer to the nucleus (Figure 7.8).

© Royalty-Free/Corbis

Electron transitions in the visible region of the spectrum are responsible for the impressive displays of color in fireworks.

PROBLEM-SOLVING EXAMPLE 7.3 Electron Transitions

Four possible electron transitions in a hydrogen atom are given below.

	n_{initial}	n_{final}
(1)	2	5
(2)	5	3
(3)	7	2
(4)	4	6

(a) Which transition(s) represent a loss of energy?
(b) For which transition does the atom gain the greatest quantity of energy?
(c) Which transition corresponds to emission of the greatest quantity of energy?

Answer

(a) (2) and (3) (b) (1) (c) (3)

Strategy and Explanation First, consider the initial and final energy levels, and then whether the initial level is greater or less than the final one.

(a) Energy is emitted when electrons fall from a higher n level to a lower n level. The $n_7 \rightarrow n_2$ and $n_5 \rightarrow n_3$ transitions release energy.
(b) Energy is gained when electrons go from a lower n level to a higher n level. The $n_2 \rightarrow n_5$ transition requires more energy than the $n_4 \rightarrow n_6$ one.
(c) The $n_7 \rightarrow n_2$ transition is the most energetic (Figure 7.8). It represents the greatest energy difference between n energy levels.

PROBLEM-SOLVING PRACTICE 7.3

Identify two electron transitions in a hydrogen atom that would be of greater energy than any of those listed in Problem-Solving Example 7.3.

CONCEPTUAL EXERCISE 7.4 Many Spectral Lines, but Only One Kind of Atom

The hydrogen atom contains only one electron, but there are several lines in its line emission spectrum (Figure 7.7). How does the Bohr theory explain this?

EXERCISE 7.5 Electron Transitions

In which of these transitions in the hydrogen atom is energy emitted and in which is it absorbed?

(a) $n = 3 \rightarrow n = 2$ (b) $n = 1 \rightarrow n = 4$
(c) $n = 5 \rightarrow n = 3$ (d) $n = 6 \rightarrow n = 2$

ThomsonNOW

Go to the Coached Problems menu to work modules on:

- **hydrogen atom electron transitions**
- **atomic line spectra**

Through his calculations, Bohr found that the allowed energies of the electron in a hydrogen atom are restricted by n, the principal quantum number, according to the equation

$$E = -\frac{2.179 \times 10^{-18}\,\text{J}}{n^2} \qquad (n = 1, 2, 3, \ldots)$$

where the constant, 2.179×10^{-18} J, called the Rydberg constant, can be calculated from theory. The negative sign in the equation arises due to the choice Bohr made to select zero as the energy of a completely separated electron and proton ($n = \infty$). As a consequence of this choice, all energies for the electron in the atom are negative (Figure 7.8).

Division by infinity makes E equal to zero when $n = \infty$.

The energy of a ground-state hydrogen atom ($n = 1$) is

$$E = -2.179 \times 10^{-18}\,\text{J}\left(\frac{1}{n^2}\right) = -2.179 \times 10^{-18}\,\text{J}\left(\frac{1}{1^2}\right) = -2.179 \times 10^{-18}\,\text{J}$$

The difference in energy, ΔE, when the electron moves from its initial state, E_i, to its final state, E_f, can be calculated as $\Delta E = E_\text{f} - E_\text{i}$. When an electron moves from a higher energy state to a lower energy state, one with a lower n value, energy is emitted and ΔE is negative. When an electron moves from a lower energy state to a higher one, energy must be absorbed (ΔE is positive). These energy differences can be expressed in relation to the change in principal energy levels, where n_i and n_f are the initial and final energy states of the atom, respectively.

Think of the atom as the system and everything else as the surroundings (p. 220).

$$\Delta E = E_\text{f} - E_\text{i} = -2.179 \times 10^{-18}\,\text{J}\left(\frac{1}{n_\text{f}^2} - \frac{1}{n_\text{i}^2}\right)$$

If $n_\text{f} > n_\text{i}$, energy is absorbed; if $n_\text{f} < n_\text{i}$, energy is emitted.

In the Bohr model, only certain frequencies of light can be absorbed or emitted by an excited atom. The equation relating energy change and frequency, $\Delta E = h\nu$, and the previous equation can be rearranged into the following equation that relates the frequency of light absorbed or emitted to the n values of the initial (n_i) and final (n_f) states involved in the transition.

$$\nu = \frac{\Delta E}{h} = \frac{2.179 \times 10^{-18}\,\text{J}}{h}\left(\frac{1}{n_\text{i}^2} - \frac{1}{n_\text{f}^2}\right)$$

For example, the frequency of light absorbed in the $n = 2$ to $n = 3$ transition can be calculated using this equation.

$$\nu = \left(\frac{2.179 \times 10^{-18}\,\text{J}}{6.626 \times 10^{-34}\,\text{J}\cdot\text{s}}\right)\left(\frac{1}{2^2} - \frac{1}{3^2}\right)$$

$$= (3.289 \times 10^{15}\,\text{s}^{-1})\left(\frac{1}{4} - \frac{1}{9}\right)$$

$$= (3.289 \times 10^{15}\,\text{s}^{-1})(0.250 - 0.111) = 4.567 \times 10^{14}\,\text{s}^{-1}$$

The energy absorbed corresponding to this frequency can be calculated.

$$E = h\nu = (6.626 \times 10^{-34}\,\text{J}\cdot\text{s})(4.567 \times 10^{14}\,\text{s}^{-1}) = 3.026 \times 10^{-19}\,\text{J}$$

The positive sign indicates that energy was absorbed, which is as it should be because the electron moved from a lower ($n = 2$) to a higher ($n = 3$) level.

The wavelength (λ) of the light absorbed can be obtained from its frequency by using the relationship $\lambda = c/\nu$, where c is the velocity of light (2.998×10^8 m/s). For the $n = 2$ to $n = 3$ transition,

Table 7.2 Agreement Between Bohr's Theory and the Lines of the Hydrogen Emission Spectrum*

Changes in Energy Levels	Wavelength Predicted by Bohr's Theory (nm)	Wavelength Determined from Laboratory Measurement (nm)	Spectral Region
$2 \rightarrow 1$	121.6	121.7	Ultraviolet
$3 \rightarrow 1$	102.6	102.6	Ultraviolet
$4 \rightarrow 1$	97.28	97.32	Ultraviolet
$3 \rightarrow 2$	656.5	656.3	Visible red
$4 \rightarrow 2$	486.5	486.1	Visible blue-green
$5 \rightarrow 2$	434.3	434.1	Visible blue
$4 \rightarrow 3$	1876	1876	Infrared

*These lines are typical; other lines could be cited as well, with equally good agreement between theory and experiment. The unit of wavelength is the nanometer (nm), 10^{-9} m.

American Institute of Physics

Niels Bohr
1885–1962

Born in Copenhagen, Denmark, Bohr worked with J. J. Thomson and Ernest Rutherford in England, where he began to develop the ideas that led to the publication of his explanation of atomic spectra. He received the Nobel Prize in physics in 1922 for this work.

As the director of the Institute of Theoretical Physics in Copenhagen, Bohr was a mentor to many young physicists, seven of whom later received Nobel Prizes for their studies in physics or chemistry, including Werner Heisenberg, Wolfgang Pauli, and Linus Pauling.

$$\lambda = \frac{2.998 \times 10^{8}\ \text{m/s}}{4.567 \times 10^{14}\ \text{s}^{-1}} = 6.565 \times 10^{-7}\ \text{m} = 656.5\ \text{nm}$$

This is in the red region of visible light.

There is exceptional agreement between the experimentally measured wavelengths and those calculated by the Bohr theory (Table 7.2). Thus, Niels Bohr had tied the unseen (the atom) to the seen (the observable lines of the hydrogen emission spectrum)—a fantastic achievement!

PROBLEM-SOLVING EXAMPLE 7.4 Electron Transitions

(a) Calculate the frequency and wavelength (nm) corresponding to the $n = 2$ to $n = 5$ transition in a hydrogen atom.

(b) In what region of the spectrum does this transition occur?

Answer

(a) $6.907 \times 10^{14}\ \text{s}^{-1}$; 434.1 nm (b) Visible region

Strategy and Explanation

(a) We first calculate the frequency of the transition from which the wavelength can then be determined. In this case, $n_i = 2$ and $n_f = 5$.

$$\nu = \frac{2.179 \times 10^{-18}\ \text{J}}{h}\left(\frac{1}{n_i^2} - \frac{1}{n_f^2}\right)$$

$$= \left(\frac{2.179 \times 10^{-18}\ \text{J}}{6.626 \times 10^{-34}\ \text{J}\cdot\text{s}}\right)\left(\frac{1}{2^2} - \frac{1}{5^2}\right)$$

$$= \left(\frac{2.179 \times 10^{-18}\ \text{J}}{6.626 \times 10^{-34}\ \text{J}\cdot\text{s}}\right)\left(\frac{1}{4} - \frac{1}{25}\right) = (3.289 \times 10^{15}\ \text{s}^{-1})(0.2500 - 0.04000)$$

$$= (3.289 \times 10^{15}\ \text{s}^{-1})(0.2100) = 6.907 \times 10^{14}\ \text{s}^{-1}$$

Convert the frequency to wavelength.

$$\lambda = \frac{c}{\nu} = \frac{2.998 \times 10^{8}\ \text{m/s}}{6.907 \times 10^{14}\ \text{s}^{-1}} = 4.341 \times 10^{-7}\ \text{m} = 434.1\ \text{nm}$$

Spectroscopy is the science of measuring spectra. Many kinds of spectroscopy have emerged since the first studies of simple line spectra. Some spectral measurements are done for quantitative analytical purposes; others are done to determine molecular structure.

CHEMISTRY YOU CAN DO

Using a Compact Disc (CD) as a Diffraction Grating

Seeing the visible spectrum by using a prism to refract visible light is a familiar experiment (Figure 7.6). Less familiar is the use of a diffraction grating for the same purpose. A diffraction grating consists of many equally spaced parallel lines—thousands of lines per centimeter. A grating that transmits diffracted light is made by cutting thousands of grooves on a piece of glass or clear plastic; a grating that reflects diffracted light is made by cutting the grooves on a piece of metal or opaque plastic.

You can get an idea of how diffraction gratings work by using a compact disc as a diffraction grating. Compare the spectra of light from two different sources—a mercury vapor lamp and a white incandescent light bulb. Stand about 20 to 60 m away from a mercury street lamp and hold the CD about waist high with the print side down. Tilt the CD down until you see the reflected image of the street lamp. Close one eye, and view along the line from the light source to your body as you slowly tilt the CD up toward you. Use the same procedure with an incandescent light bulb as the light source.

1. What colors do you see with the mercury vapor lamp?
2. Do you see the same colors with the incandescent light? Explain your results.

SOURCE: Mebane, R. C., and Rybolt, T. R. Atomic Spectroscopy with a Compact Disc. *Journal of Chemical Education*, Vol. 69, 1992; p. 401.

(b) Checking Figure 7.8 shows that electron transitions between any higher n level and the $n = 2$ level emit radiation in the visible region ($\lambda > 400$ nm; $\nu < 7.5 \times 10^{14}\ s^{-1}$).

PROBLEM-SOLVING PRACTICE 7.4

(a) Calculate the frequency and the wavelength of the line for the $n = 6$ to $n = 4$ transition.

(b) Is this wavelength longer or shorter than that of the $n = 7$ to $n = 4$ transition?

CONCEPTUAL EXERCISE 7.6 Conversions

Show that the value of the Rydberg constant per photon, 2.179×10^{-18} J, is equivalent to 1312 kJ/mol photons.

7.4 Beyond the Bohr Model: The Quantum Mechanical Model of the Atom

The Bohr atomic model was accepted almost immediately. Bohr's success with the hydrogen atom soon led to attempts by him and others to extend the same model to more complex atoms. Before long it became apparent, however, that line spectra for elements other than hydrogen had more lines than could be explained by the simple Bohr model. A totally different approach was needed to explain electron behavior in atoms or ions with more than one electron. The new approach again took a radical departure from classical physics.

In 1924, the young physicist Louis de Broglie posed the question: *If light can be viewed in terms of both wave and particle properties, why can't particles of matter, such as electrons, be treated the same way?* And so de Broglie proposed the revolutionary idea that electrons could have wave-like properties. The wavelength (λ) of the electron (or any other particle) would depend on its mass (m) and its velocity (v) according to the relationship

$$\lambda = \frac{h}{mv}$$

where h is Planck's constant. The product of $m \times v$ for any object, including electrons, is the **momentum** of the object. Note that particles of very small mass, such as the electron (mass = 9.11×10^{-28} g), have wavelengths that are measurable. Objects of ordinary size, such as a tennis ball (mass = 56.7 g), have wavelengths too short to be observed.

Momentum = mass × velocity

© Alastair Grant/Rueters/CORBIS

A served tennis ball. Even when the ball is served at 125 mi/h, the wavelength of the tennis ball is too short to be observed.

PROBLEM-SOLVING EXAMPLE 7.5 Tennis Balls and Electrons

At Wimbledon, tennis serves routinely reach more than 100 mi/h. Compare the de Broglie wavelength (nm) of an electron moving at a velocity of 5.0×10^6 m/s with that of a tennis ball traveling at 56.0 m/s (125 mi/h). Masses: electron = 9.11×10^{-31} kg; tennis ball = 0.0567 kg.

Answer The wavelength of the electron is *much* longer than that of the tennis ball: electron = 0.15 nm; tennis ball = 2.09×10^{-25} nm.

Strategy and Explanation We can substitute the mass and velocity into the de Broglie wave equation to calculate the corresponding wavelength. Planck's constant, h, is

$$6.626 \times 10^{-34}\ \text{J}\cdot\text{s, and } 1\ \text{J} = \frac{1\ \text{kg}\cdot\text{m}^2}{\text{s}^2} \text{ so that } h = 6.626 \times 10^{-34}\ \text{kg}\cdot\text{m}^2\ \text{s}^{-1}.$$

For the electron:

$$\lambda = \frac{6.626 \times 10^{-34}\ \text{kg}\cdot\text{m}^2\ \text{s}^{-1}}{(9.11 \times 10^{-31}\ \text{kg})(5.0 \times 10^6\ \text{m/s})} = 1.5 \times 10^{-10}\ \text{m} \times \frac{1\ \text{nm}}{10^{-9}\ \text{m}} = 0.15\ \text{nm}$$

For the tennis ball:

$$\lambda = \frac{6.626 \times 10^{-34}\ \text{kg}\cdot\text{m}^2\ \text{s}^{-1}}{(0.0567\ \text{kg})(56.0\ \text{m/s})} = 2.09 \times 10^{-34}\ \text{m} \times \frac{1\ \text{nm}}{10^{-9}\ \text{m}} = 2.09 \times 10^{-25}\ \text{nm}$$

The wavelength of the electron is in the X-ray region of the electromagnetic spectrum (Figure 7.1, p. 274). The wavelength of the tennis ball is far too short to observe.

ThomsonNOW™
Go to the Coached Problems menu for a tutorial on **calculating wavelength for matter waves.**

PROBLEM-SOLVING PRACTICE 7.5

Calculate the de Broglie wavelength of a neutron moving at 10% the velocity of light. The mass of a neutron is 1.67×10^{-24} g.

Many scientists found de Broglie's concept hard to accept, much less believe. But experimental support for de Broglie's hypothesis was soon produced. In 1927, C. Davisson and L. H. Germer, working at the Bell Telephone Laboratories, found that a beam of electrons is diffracted by planes of atoms in a thin sheet of metal foil (Figure 7.9) in the same way that light waves are diffracted by a diffraction grating. Since diffraction is readily explained by the wave properties of light, it followed that electrons also can be described by the equations of waves under some circumstances.

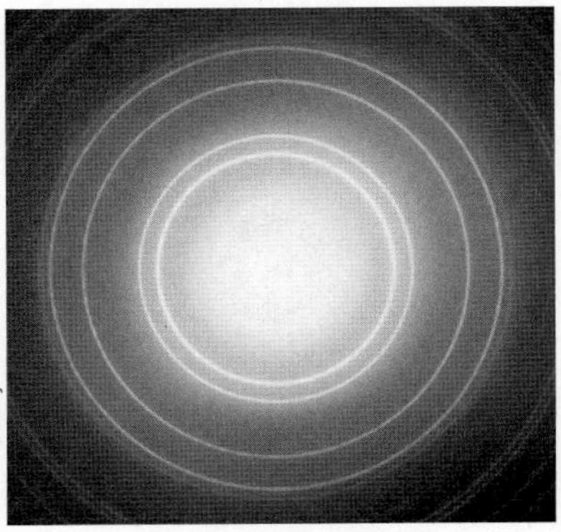

Sarnoff Library in Princeton

Figure 7.9 **Electron diffraction pattern obtained from aluminum foil.**

A few years after de Broglie's hypothesis about the wave nature of the electron, Werner Heisenberg (1901–1976) proposed the **uncertainty principle,** which states that *it is impossible to simultaneously determine the exact position and the exact momentum of an electron.* This limitation is not a problem for a macroscopic object because the energy of photons used to locate such an object does not cause a measurable change in the position or momentum of that object. However, the very act of measurement would affect the position and momentum of the electron because of its very small size and mass. High-energy photons would be required to locate the small electron; when such photons collide with the electron, the momentum of the electron would be changed. If lower-energy photons were used to avoid affecting the momentum, little information would be obtained about the location of the electron. Consider an analogy in photography. If you take a picture at a higher

Bill Beatty/Visuals Unlimited, Inc.
Al Bello/Allsport/Getty Images, Inc.

A speeding race car. (a) Photo taken at high shutter speed. (b) Photo taken at low shutter speed.

Electron density is also called probability density.

shutter speed setting of a car race, you get a clear picture of the cars but you can't tell how fast they are going or even whether they are moving. With a slow shutter speed, you can tell from the blur of the car images something about the speed and direction, but you have less information about where the car is.

The Heisenberg uncertainty principle illustrated another inadequacy in the Bohr model—its representation of the electron in the hydrogen atom in terms of well-defined orbits about the nucleus. In practical terms, the best we can do is to represent the *probability* of finding an electron of a given energy and momentum within a given space. This probability-based model of the atom is what chemists now use.

In 1926 Erwin Schrödinger (1877–1961) combined de Broglie's hypothesis with classic equations for wave motion. From these and other ideas he derived a new equation called the *wave equation* to describe the behavior of an electron in the hydrogen atom. Solutions to the wave equation are called *wave functions* and are represented by the Greek letter psi, ψ. Wave functions predict the allowed energy states of an electron and the probability of finding that electron in a given region of space. Only certain wave functions are satisfactory for an electron in an atom.

The wave function is a complex mathematical equation that has no direct physical meaning. However, the square of the wave function, ψ^2, can be represented in graphical form as a picture of the three-dimensional region of the atom where an electron with a given energy state is most likely to be found. That is, ψ^2 is related to the probability of finding the electron in a given region of space. This probability, known as the **electron density,** can be visualized as an array of dots, each dot representing the possible location of the electron with a given energy in relation to the nucleus. Figure 7.10 is an electron density distribution, sometimes called an electron cloud picture, for a ground state hydrogen atom. In such a plot, the density of the dots indicates the probability of the electron being there. The cloud of dots is denser nearer the nucleus than farther from it, indicating that the probability of finding the electron is higher nearer the nucleus than farther from it. The electron-cloud density decreases as the distance from the nucleus increases, illustrating the probability of finding the electron as distance from the nucleus increases.

Solving the Schrödinger wave equation results in a set of wave functions called **orbitals.** Each orbital contains information about the region of space where an electron of a given energy is most likely located because ψ^2 represents electron probability density. Another way to represent an electron is to draw a surface within which there is a 90% probability that the electron will be found. That is, nine times out of ten an electron will be somewhere inside such a **boundary surface;** there is one chance in ten that the electron will be outside of it. A 100% probability is not chosen because such a surface would have no definite boundary. Consider that a typical dart board has a finite size, and normally, players in a dart game hit the board more than 90% of the time. But if you wanted to be certain that any player, no matter how far away, would be able to hit the board on 100% of his or her throws, then the board would have to be considerably larger. By similar reasoning, a boundary surface in which there would be a 100% probability of finding a given kind of electron would have to be infinitely large. Boundary-surface diagrams are given in Figure 7.11. This figure will be discussed in detail in Section 7.5.

Note that an *orbital* (quantum mechanical model) is not the same as an *orbit* (Bohr model). In the quantum mechanical model, the principal quantum number, n, is a measure of the most probable distance of the electron from the nucleus, not the radius of a well-defined orbit.

We turn next to describing quantum numbers, which define the orbitals and energy states available to an electron in an atom. Following that, we will relate quantum numbers to the shapes of atomic orbitals.

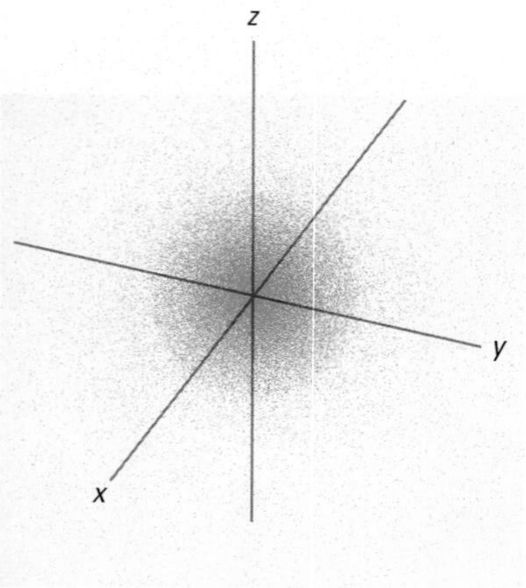

Figure 7.10 Electron density distribution in a ground-state hydrogen atom.

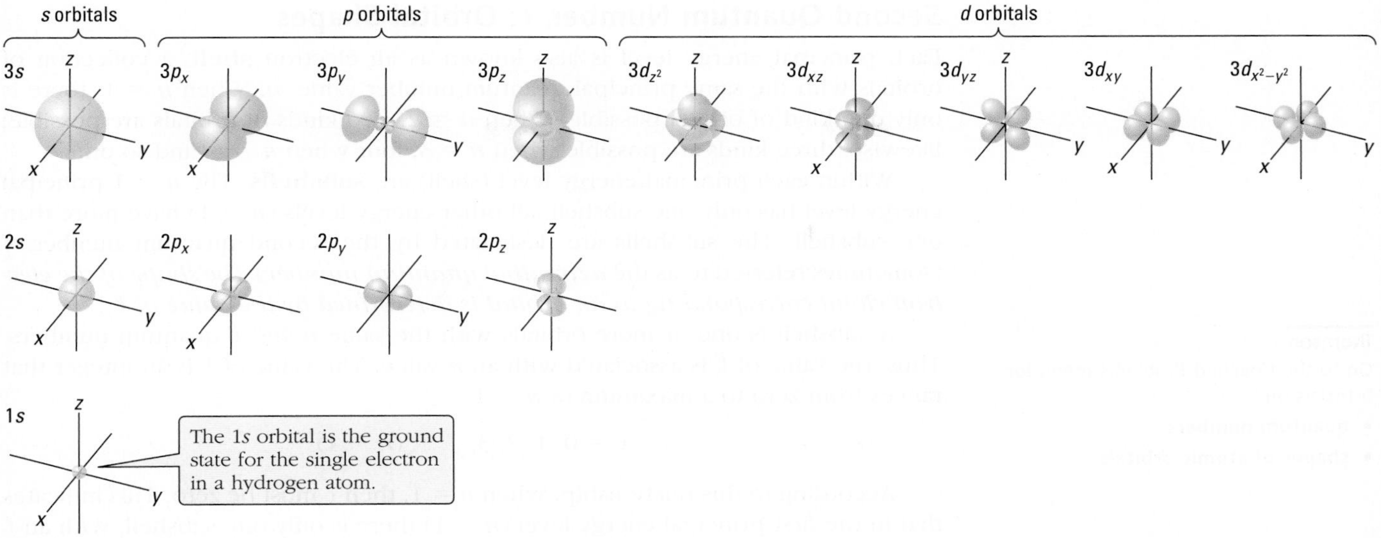

Figure 7.11 **Orbitals**. Boundary-surface diagrams for electron densities of 1*s*, 2*s*, 2*p*, 3*s*, 3*p*, and 3*d* orbitals of a hydrogen atom (generated by a computer).

7.5 Quantum Numbers, Energy Levels, and Atomic Orbitals

In their quantum mechanical calculations, Schrödinger and others found that a set of three integers, called **quantum numbers**—the principal quantum number n and two others, ℓ and m_ℓ—are needed to describe the three-dimensional coordinates of an electron's motion in the orbitals in a hydrogen atom. The need for a fourth quantum number, m_s, was identified in subsequent work by others. Thus, a set of four quantum numbers—n, ℓ, m_ℓ, and m_s—is used to denote the energy and the shape of the electron cloud for each electron.

We can apply quantum numbers to electrons in any atom, not just hydrogen. The quantum numbers, their meanings, and the quantum number notations used for atomic orbitals are given in the following subsection.

First Quantum Number, n: Principal Energy Levels

The first quantum number, n, the principal quantum number, is the most important one in determining the energy of an electron. The quantum number n has only integer values, starting with 1:

$$n = 1, 2, 3, 4, \ldots$$

The value of n corresponds to a **principal energy level** so that an electron is in the first principal energy level when $n = 1$, in the second principal level when $n = 2$, and so on. As n increases, the energy of the electron increases as well, and the electron, on average, is farther away from the nucleus and is less tightly bound to it.

Second Quantum Number, ℓ: Orbital Shapes

Each principal energy level is also known as an electron **shell**, a collection of orbitals with the same principal quantum number value, n. When $n = 1$, there is only one kind of orbital possible. When $n = 2$, two kinds of orbitals are possible; likewise, three kinds are possible when $n = 3$, four when $n = 4$, and so on.

Within each principal energy level (shell) are **subshells**. The $n = 1$ principal energy level has only one subshell; all other energy levels ($n > 1$) have more than one subshell. The subshells are designated by the second quantum number, ℓ (sometimes referred to as the *azimuthal quantum number*). *The shape of the electron cloud corresponding to an orbital is determined by the value of* ℓ.

ThomsonNOW™
Go to the Coached Problems menu for tutorials on:
- **quantum numbers**
- **shapes of atomic orbitals**

A subshell is one or more orbitals with the same n and ℓ quantum numbers. Thus, the value of ℓ is associated with an n value. The value of ℓ is an integer that ranges from zero to a maximum of $n - 1$:

$$\ell = 0, 1, 2, 3, \ldots, (n - 1)$$

According to this relationship, when $n = 1$, then ℓ must be zero. This indicates that in the first principal energy level ($n = 1$) there is only one subshell, with an ℓ value of 0. The second principal energy level ($n = 2$) has two subshells—one with an ℓ value of 0 and a second with an ℓ value of 1. Continuing in this manner,

$$n = 3; \quad \ell = 0, 1, \text{ or } 2 \quad \text{(three subshells)}$$

$$n = 4; \quad \ell = 0, 1, 2 \text{ or } 3 \quad \text{(four subshells)}$$

As mentioned earlier, a boundary surface for an orbital can be drawn within which there is a 90% probability that an electron can be found. Note in Figure 7.11 (p. 289) that as n increases, two things happen: (1) orbitals become larger and (2) there is an increase in the number and types of orbitals within a given level. ***The number of orbital types within a principal energy level equals n.*** Thus, in the $n = 3$ level, there are three different types of subshells—that is, s, p, and d orbitals. *Atomic orbitals with the same n and* ℓ *values are in the same subshell.*

Rather than using ℓ values, subshells are more commonly designated by letters: *s, p, d,* or *f*. The first four subshells are known as the *s* subshell, *p* subshell, *d* subshell, and *f* subshell.

The letters *s, p, d,* and *f* derived historically from spectral lines called *s*harp, *p*rincipal, *d*iffuse, and *f*undamental.

ℓ value	0	1	2	3
Subshell	*s*	*p*	*d*	*f*

A number (the n value) and a letter (*s, p, d,* or *f*) are used to designate the principal energy level locations of specific subshells.

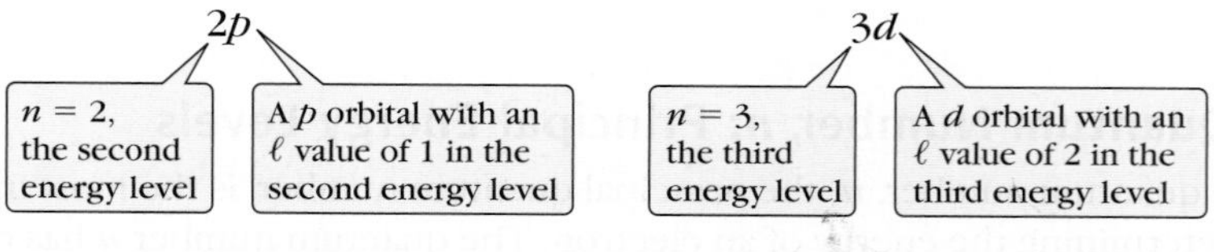

For the first four principal energy levels, these designations are as follows.

n	1	2		3			4			
ℓ	0	0	1	0	1	2	0	1	2	3
Level	1*s*	2*s*	2*p*	3*s*	3*p*	3*d*	4*s*	4*p*	4*d*	4*f*

For atoms with two or more electrons, orbitals in different subshells but with the same n value have different energies. The energies of subshells within a given principal energy level always increase in the order $ns < np < nd < nf$. Consequently, a 3*p* subshell has a higher energy than a 3*s* subshell but less energy than a

$3d$ subshell, which would have the highest energy in the $n = 3$ level. Figure 7.12 shows the relative energies of orbitals in many-electron atoms through the $4p$ orbitals.

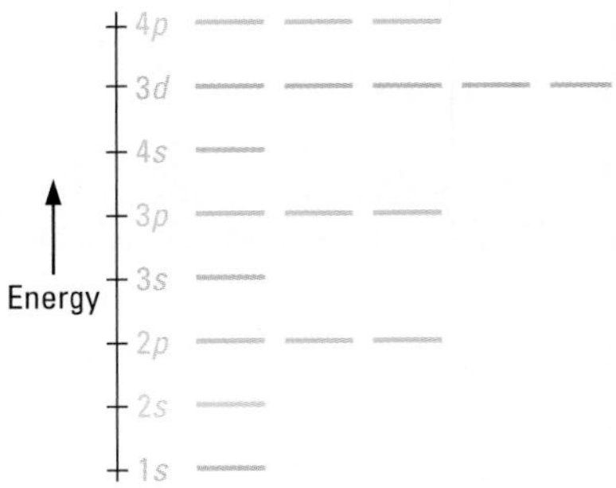

Figure 7.12 The ordering of orbital energy levels in a many-electron atom from the 1*s* level through the 4*p* sublevels. Orbitals in different sublevels of the same level have different energy.

EXERCISE 7.7 Subshell Designations

Give the subshell designation for an electron with these quantum numbers.

(a) $n = 5, \ell = 2$ (b) $n = 4, \ell = 3$ (c) $n = 6, \ell = 1$

EXERCISE 7.8 Subshell Designations

Explain why $3f$ is an incorrect subshell designation. Likewise, why is $n = 2, \ell = 2$ incorrect for a subshell?

Third Quantum Number, m_ℓ: Orientation of Atomic Orbitals

The magnetic quantum number, m_ℓ, can have any integer value between ℓ and $-\ell$, including zero. Thus,

$$m_\ell = \ell, \ldots, +1, 0, -1, \ldots, -\ell$$

For an s subshell, which has an ℓ value of zero, m_ℓ has only one value—zero. Therefore, an s subshell, regardless of its n value—1*s*, 2*s*, and so on—contains only one orbital, whose m_ℓ value is zero. For a p subshell, ℓ equals 1, and so m_ℓ can be $+1$, 0, or -1. This means that within each p subshell there are three *different* types of orbitals: one with $m_\ell = +1$, another with $m_\ell = 0$, and a third with $m_\ell = -1$. In general, for a subshell of quantum number ℓ, there is a total of $2\ell + 1$ orbitals within that subshell. Orbitals within the same *subshell* have essentially the same energy.

Table 7.3 summarizes the relationships among n, ℓ, and m_ℓ. ***The total number of orbitals in a shell equals n^2.*** For example, an $n = 3$ shell has a total of nine orbitals: one $3s$ + three $3p$ + five $3d$.

Table 7.3 Relationships Among n, ℓ, and m_ℓ for the First Four Principal Energy Levels

n Value	ℓ Value	Subshell Designation	m_ℓ Values	Number of Orbitals in Subshell, $2\ell + 1$	Total Number of Orbitals in Shell, n^2
1	0	1*s*	0	1	1
2	0	2*s*	0	1	
2	1	2*p*	1, 0, −1	3	4
3	0	3*s*	0	1	
3	1	3*p*	1, 0, −1	3	
3	2	3*d*	2, 1, 0, −1, −2	5	9
4	0	4*s*	0	1	
4	1	4*p*	1, 0, −1	3	
4	2	4*d*	2, 1, 0, −1, −2	5	
4	3	4*f*	3, 2, 1, 0, −1, −2, −3	7	16

In terms of an atomic orbital, the quantum number

- n relates to the orbital's size.
- ℓ relates to the orbital's shape.
- m_ℓ relates to the orbital's orientation.

The m_ℓ value, in conjunction with the ℓ value, is related to the shape and orientation of an orbital in space. The *s* orbitals are spherical; their size enlarges as n increases (Figure 7.11, p. 289).

Beginning with the second principal energy level ($n = 2$) and at each higher n level, each energy level has three *p* orbitals. The three *p* orbitals are dumbbell-shaped and oriented at right angles to each other, with maximum electron density directed along either the *x*-, *y*-, or *z*-axis, as shown in Figure 7.11. They are sometimes designated as p_x, p_y, and p_z orbitals. The five *d* orbitals in the 3*d* sublevel ($\ell = 2$) are also illustrated in Figure 7.11. We will discuss *d* orbitals further in Chapter 22 in connection with their role in the chemistry of transition metal ions.

We leave the discussion of *f* orbitals, which are very complex, to subsequent courses.

In summary,

- ***The principal energy level (shell) has a quantum number $n = 1, 2, 3, \ldots$***
- ***Within each principal energy level there are subshells equal in number to n and designated as the s, p, d, and f subshells.***
- ***The number of orbitals in each subshell is $2\ell + 1$: one s orbital ($\ell = 0$), three p orbitals ($\ell = 1$), five d orbitals ($\ell = 2$), and seven f orbitals ($\ell = 3$).***
- ***Within a principal energy level n there are n^2 orbitals.***
- ***Within a principal energy level n there is a maximum of $2n^2$ electrons.***

PROBLEM-SOLVING EXAMPLE 7.6 Quantum Numbers, Subshells, and Atomic Orbitals

Consider the $n = 4$ principal energy level.

(a) Without referring to Table 7.3, predict the number of subshells in this level.

(b) Identify each of the subshells by its number and letter designation (as in 1*s*) and give its ℓ values.

(c) Use the $2\ell + 1$ rule to calculate how many orbitals each subshell has and identify the m_ℓ value for each orbital.

(d) What is the total number of orbitals in the $n = 4$ level?

Answer

(a) Four subshells

(b) 4*s*, 4*p*, 4*d*, and 4*f*; $\ell = 0, 1, 2$, and 3, respectively

(c) One 4*s* orbital, three 4*p* orbitals, five 4*d* orbitals, and seven 4*f* orbitals

(d) 16 orbitals

Strategy and Explanation

(a) There are n subshells in the nth level. Thus, the $n = 4$ level contains four subshells.

(b) The number refers to the principal quantum number, n; the letter is associated with the ℓ quantum number. The four sublevels correspond to the four possible ℓ values:

Sublevels	4*s*	4*p*	4*d*	4*f*
ℓ value	0	1	2	3

(c) There are a total of $2\ell + 1$ orbitals within a sublevel. Only one 4*s* orbital is possible ($\ell = 0$, so m_ℓ must be zero). There are three 4*p* orbitals ($\ell = 1$) with m_ℓ values of 1, 0, or -1. There are five 4*d* orbitals ($\ell = 2$) corresponding to the five allowed values for m_ℓ: 2, 1, 0, −1, and −2. There are seven 4*f* orbitals ($\ell = 3$), each with one of the seven permitted values of m_ℓ: 3, 2, 1, 0, −1, −2, and −3.

(d) The total number of orbitals in a level is n^2. Therefore, the $n = 4$ level has a total of 16 orbitals.

PROBLEM-SOLVING PRACTICE 7.6

(a) Identify the subshell with $n = 6$ and $\ell = 2$.
(b) How many orbitals are in this subshell?
(c) What are the m_ℓ values for these orbitals?

Fourth Quantum Number, m_s: Electron Spin

When spectroscopists more closely studied emission spectra of hydrogen and sodium atoms, they discovered that what were originally thought to be single lines were actually very closely spaced pairs of lines. In 1925 the Dutch physicists George Uhlenbeck and Samuel Goudsmit proposed that the line splitting could be explained by assuming that each electron in an atom can exist in one of two possible spin states. To visualize these states, consider an electron as a charged sphere rotating about an axis through its center (Figure 7.13). Such a spinning charge generates a magnetic field, so that each electron acts like a tiny bar magnet with north and south magnetic poles. Only two directions of spin are possible in relation to the direction of an external magnetic field—clockwise or counterclockwise. Spins in opposite directions produce oppositely directed magnetic fields, which result in two slightly different energies. This slight difference in energy splits the spectral lines into closely spaced pairs.

Thus, to describe an electron in an atom completely, a fourth quantum number, m_s, called the *spin quantum number*, is needed in conjunction with the other three quantum numbers.

The spin quantum number can have just one of two values: $+\frac{1}{2}$ or $-\frac{1}{2}$. Electrons are said to have *parallel* spins if they have the same m_s quantum number (both $+\frac{1}{2}$ or both $-\frac{1}{2}$). Electrons are said to be *paired* when they are in the same orbital and have opposite spins—one has an m_s of $+\frac{1}{2}$ and the other has a $-\frac{1}{2}$ value.

To make quantum theory consistent with experiment, Wolfgang Pauli stated in 1925 what is now known as the **Pauli exclusion principle:** ***No more than two electrons can occupy the same orbital in an atom, and these electrons must have opposite spins.*** This is equivalent to saying that no two electrons in the same atom can have the same set of four quantum numbers n, ℓ, m_ℓ, and m_s. For example, two electrons can occupy the same 3*p* orbital only if their spins are paired ($+\frac{1}{2}$ and $-\frac{1}{2}$). In such a case, the electrons would have the same first three quantum numbers, for example, 3, 1, +1, but would differ in their m_s values.

ThomsonNOW™
Go to the Chemistry Interactive menu to work modules on:
- **orbital shape**
- **electron spin and magnetic fields**

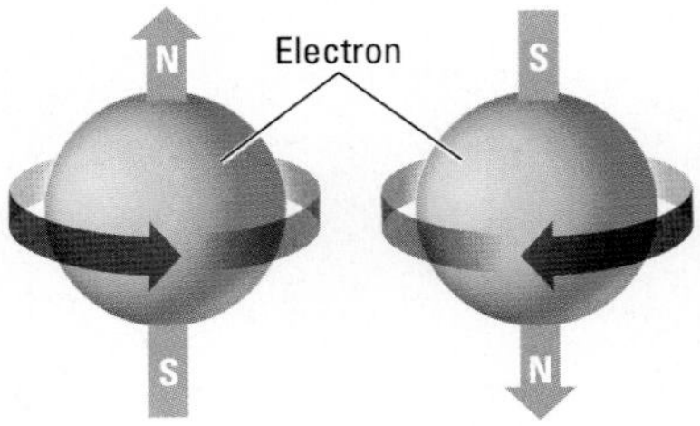

Figure 7.13 Spin directions. The electron can be pictured as though it were a charged sphere spinning about an axis through its center. The electron can have only two directions of spin; any other position is forbidden. Therefore, the spin of the electron is said to be quantized.

EXERCISE 7.9 Quantum Numbers

Give the set of four quantum numbers for each electron in a 3*s* orbital in a sodium atom.

CONCEPTUAL EXERCISE 7.10 Orbitals and Quantum Numbers

Give sets of four quantum numbers for two electrons that are (a) in the same level and subshell, but in different orbitals, and (b) in the same level, but in different subshells and in different orbitals.

CHEMISTRY IN THE NEWS

Single-Electron Spin Measurement

By combining the powerful instrumental technologies of magnetic resonance imaging and atomic force microscopy, scientists at the IBM Almaden Research Center in California have measured the force associated with the spin of a single electron. Atomic force microscopy can image the surface of individual atoms in a sample and magnetic resonance imaging can determine structural details about the interior of the sample. The very small force of the spin of a single electron, only 2×10^{-18} Newton (N), was detected within a specially fabricated silica (SiO_2) chip.

The IBM team used a flexible cantilever only 85 μm long and just 100 nm thick fitted with a 150-nm-wide tip of SmCo, a powerful magnet. Irradiation of the silica with gamma rays broke Si—O bonds in the silica and created unpaired electrons, whose spin was measured. With the cantilever tip suspended about 100 nm above the silica surface, a high-frequency magnetic field was applied simultaneously, allowing an interferometer to measure the small changes in the vibration frequency created by the interaction of the electron spin with the magnetic tip. This breakthrough in imaging technology could lead to the development of three-dimensional composite pictures of molecules.

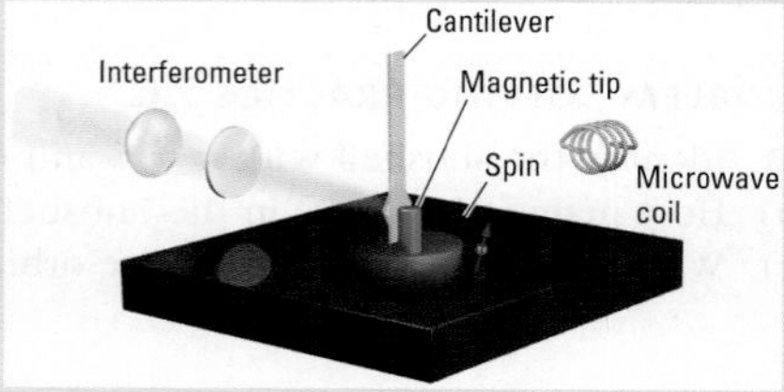

Electron spin detector. Device used to detect the force associated with the spin of a single electron.

SOURCES:

Mitch Jacoby, "A Spin on Magnetic Resonance Imaging," *Chemical & Engineering News*, July 19, 2004, p. 4.

Erik Stokstad, "Single-Electron Spin Measurement Heralds Deeper Look at Atoms." 16 July 2004, Vol. 305, *Science*, p. 322.

EXERCISE 7.11 Quantum Number Comparisons

Two electrons in the same atom have these sets of quantum numbers: electron_a: 3, 1, 0, $+\frac{1}{2}$; electron_b: 3, 1, −1, $+\frac{1}{2}$. Show that these two electrons are not in the same orbital. Which subshell are these electrons in?

The restriction that only two electrons can occupy a single orbital has the effect of establishing the maximum number of electrons for each principal energy level, *n*, as summarized in Table 7.4. Since each orbital can hold a maximum of two paired electrons, the general rule is that ***each principal energy level, n, can accommodate a maximum number of $2n^2$ electrons.*** For example, the $n = 2$ energy level has one *s* and three *p* orbitals, each of which can accommodate two paired electrons. Therefore, this level can accommodate a total of eight electrons (two in the 2*s* orbital and three pairs in the three 2*p* orbitals).

EXERCISE 7.12 Maximum Number of Electrons

(a) What is the maximum number of electrons in the $n = 3$ level? Identify the orbital of each electron.
(b) What is the maximum number of electrons in the $n = 5$ level? Identify the orbital of each electron. (*Hint: g* orbitals follow *f* orbitals.)

CONCEPTUAL EXERCISE 7.13 *g* Orbitals

Using the same reasoning as was developed for *s, p, d,* and *f* orbitals, what should be the *n* value of the first shell that could contain *g* orbitals, and how many *g* orbitals would be in that shell?

Table 7.4 Number of Electrons Accommodated in Electron Shells and Subshells

Electron Shell (n)	Number of Subshells Available ($=n$)	Number of Orbitals Available ($=2\ell + 1$)	Number of Electrons Possible in Subshell	Maximum Electrons for nth Shell ($=2n^2$)
1	s	1	2	2
2	s	1	2	
	p	3	6	8
3	s	1	2	
	p	3	6	
	d	5	10	18
4	s	1	2	
	p	3	6	
	d	5	10	
	f	7	14	32
5	s	1	2	
	p	3	6	
	d	5	10	
	f	7	14	
	g*	9	18	50
6	s	1	2	
	p	3	6	
	d	5	10	
	f*	7	14	
	g*	9	18	
	h*	11	22	72
7	s	1	2	

*These orbitals are not used in the ground state of any known element.

The results expressed in this table were predicted by the Schrödinger theory and have been confirmed by experiment.

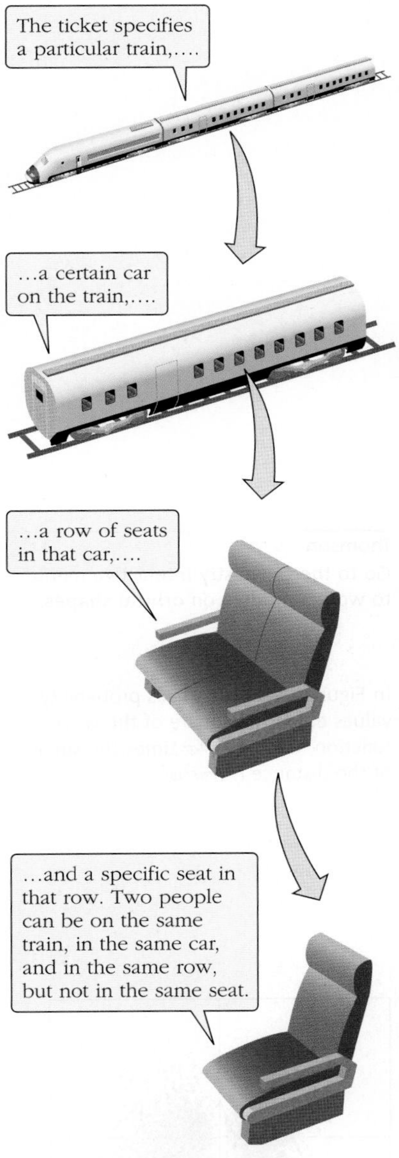

A quantum number analogy. A ticket for a reserved seat on a train is analogous to a set of four quantum numbers, n, ℓ, m_ℓ, and m_s. The ticket specifies a particular train, a certain car on the train, a row of seats in that car, and a specific seat in that row. The row is analogous to an atomic orbital, and the occupants of the row are like two electrons in the same orbital (same train, car, and row), but with opposite spins (different seats).

7.6 Shapes of Atomic Orbitals

As noted in the previous section, the ℓ and m_ℓ quantum numbers relate to the shapes and spatial orientations of atomic orbitals. We now consider these in more detail.

s Orbitals ($\ell = 0$)

Electron density plots, such as that shown in Figure 7.10, are one way to depict atomic orbitals. In Figure 7.14a, the dot-density diagram of the 1*s* orbital of a hydrogen atom is shown with its electron density decreasing rapidly as the distance from the nucleus increases. The value r_{90} in the figure is the radius of the sphere in which the electron is found 90% of the time. Note from Figure 7.14a that the probability of finding a 1*s* electron is the same *in any direction* at the same distance from the nucleus. Thus, the 1*s* orbital is spherical.

In Figure 7.14a the electron density illustrates that the probability of finding the 1*s* electron in a hydrogen atom varies throughout space. This probability can be

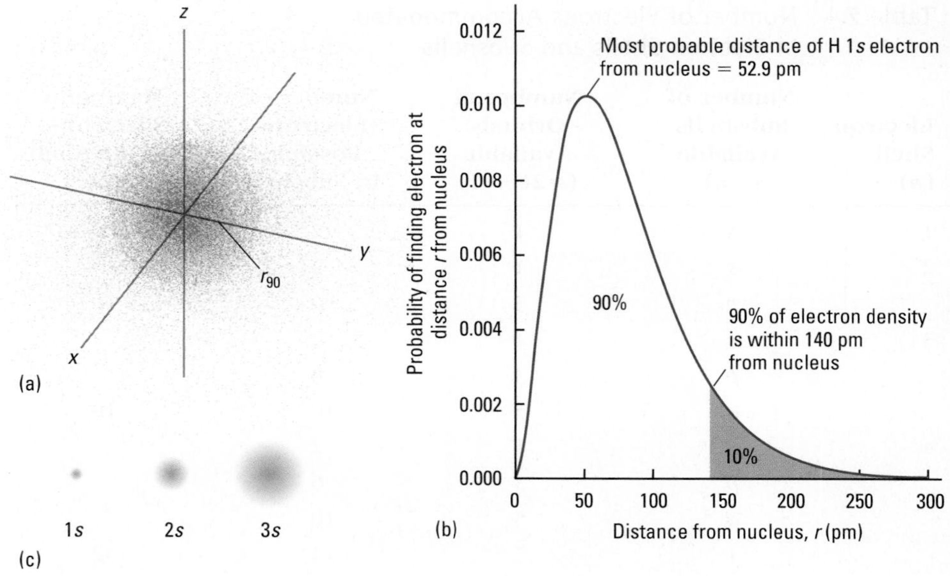

Figure 7.14 Depicting *s* atomic orbitals. (a) An electron density illustration of a 1*s* orbital. The density of dots represents the probability of finding the electron in any region of the diagram. (b) A radial distribution plot as a function of distance from the nucleus for a 1*s* orbital of hydrogen. (c) The relative sizes of the boundary surfaces of *s* orbitals.

ThomsonNOW
Go to the Chemistry Interactive menu to work a module on **orbital shapes.**

In Figure 7.14b, the *y*-axis probability values equal the square of the wave function, ψ^2, times 4π times the square of the distance *r*: $4\pi r^2\psi^2$.

represented in another way known as a **radial distribution plot**, as shown in Figure 7.14b. In this case, the *y*-axis represents the probability of finding the electron at a given distance, *r*, from the nucleus (*x*-axis). The probability is zero at the nucleus; that is, there is no probability of finding the electron at the nucleus. The greatest probability of finding the 1*s* electron in a ground-state hydrogen atom has been determined to be at 0.0529 nm (52.9 pm) from the nucleus. Note from the figure that at larger distances the probability drops very close to zero, but does not quite become zero. This indicates that although it is extremely small, there is a finite probability of the electron being at a considerable distance from the nucleus.

As the *n* value increases, the shape of *s* orbitals remains the same; they are all spherical. Their sizes, however, increase as *n* increases, as shown in Figure 7.14c. For example, the boundary surface of a 3*s* orbital has a greater volume (and radius) than that of a 2*s* orbital, which is greater than that of a 1*s* orbital.

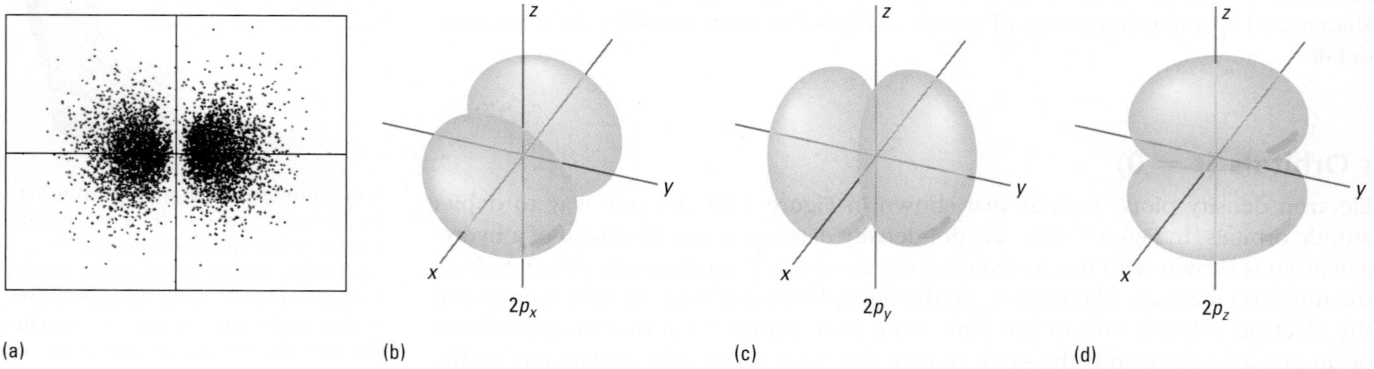

Figure 7.15 Depicting *p* atomic orbitals. (a) Electron density distribution of a 2*p* atomic orbital. (b), (c), and (d) Boundary surfaces for the set of three 2*p* orbitals. (From Zumdahl and Zumdahl, *Chemistry* 6th ed., Fig. 7.14, p. 310. Reprinted by permission of Houghton Mifflin Co.)

p Orbitals ($\ell = 1$)

Unlike *s* atomic orbitals, which are all spherical, the *p* atomic orbitals, those for which $\ell = 1$, are all dumbbell-shaped (Figure 7.15). In a *p* orbital, there are two lobes with electron density on either side of the nucleus. The *p* orbitals within a given subshell (same n and ℓ value) differ from each other in their orientation in space; each set of three *p* orbitals within the same subshell are mutually perpendicular to each other along the *x*-, *y*-, and *z*-axes. These orientations correspond to the three allowed m_ℓ values of $+1$, 0, and -1.

d Orbitals ($\ell = 2$)

Each energy level with $n \geqslant 3$ contains a subshell for which $\ell = 2$ consisting of five *d* atomic orbitals with corresponding m_ℓ values of $+2$, $+1$, 0, -1, and -2. The *d* orbitals consist of two different types of shapes and spatial orientations. Three of them (d_{xz}, d_{yz}, and d_{xy}) each have four lobes that lie in the plane of but between the designated *x*-, *y*-, or *z*-axes; the other pair—the $d_{x^2-y^2}$ and d_{z^2} orbitals—have their principal electron density along the designated axes. The shapes of five *d* orbitals, along with those of *s* and *p* orbitals, are illustrated in Figure 7.16. We will discuss *d* orbitals further in Chapter 22 in connection with their role in the chemistry of transition metal ions.

7.7 Atom Electron Configurations

The complete description of the orbitals occupied by all the electrons in an atom or ion is called its **electron configuration.** The periodic table can serve as a guide to determine the electron configurations of atoms. As you will see, the chemical similarities of elements in the same periodic table group are explained by the similar electron configurations of their atoms.

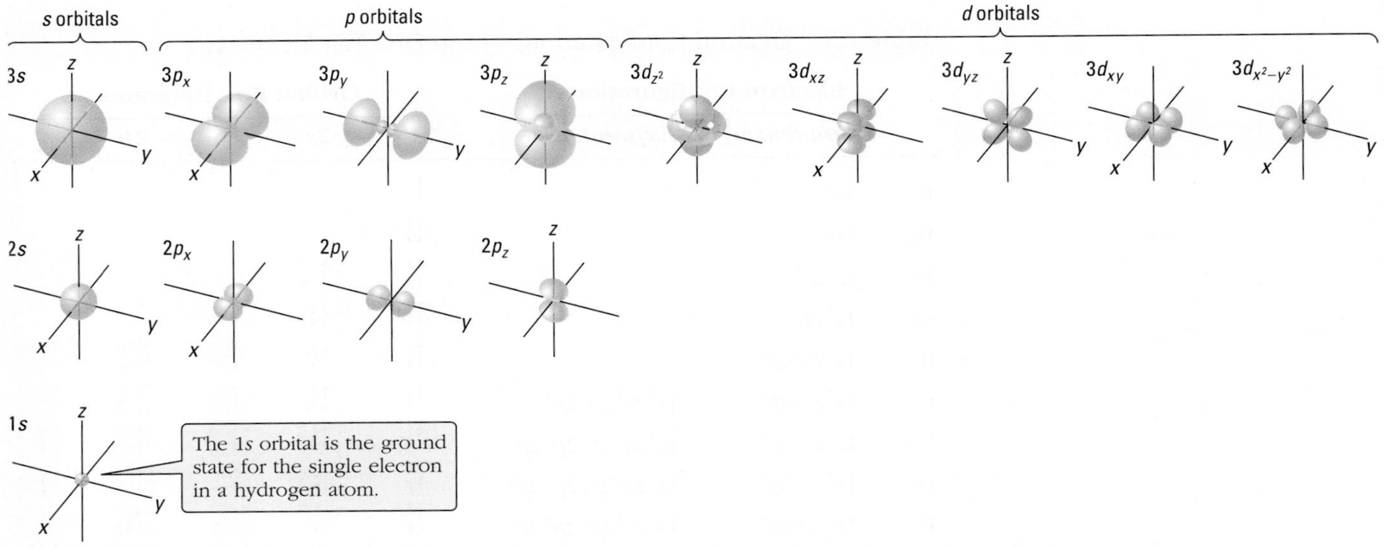

Figure 7.16 Depicting atomic orbitals. Boundary-surface diagrams for electron densities of 1*s*, 2*s*, 2*p*, 3*s*, 3*p*, and 3*d* atomic orbitals.

ThomsonNOW

Go to the Chemistry Interactive menu to work modules on:

- **single-electron versus multielectron subshell energies**
- **electron configurations and their corresponding periodic table blocks**
- **Hund's rule**

Electron Configurations of Main Group Elements

The atomic numbers of the elements increase in numerical order throughout the periodic table. As a result, atoms of a particular element each contain one more electron (and proton) than atoms of the preceding element. How do we know which shell and orbital each new electron occupies? An important principle for answering this question is the following: *For an atom in its ground state, electrons are found in the energy shells, subshells, and orbitals that produce the lowest energy for the atom.* In other words, electrons fill orbitals starting with the $1s$ orbital and work upward in the subshell energy order starting with $n = 1$.

To better understand how this filling of orbitals works, consider the experimentally determined electron configurations of the first ten elements, which are written in three different ways in Table 7.5—condensed, expanded, and orbital box diagram. Since electrons assigned to the $n = 1$ shell are closest to the nucleus and therefore lowest in energy, electrons are assigned to it first (H and He). At the left in Table 7.5, the occupied orbitals and the number of electrons in each orbital are represented by this notation:

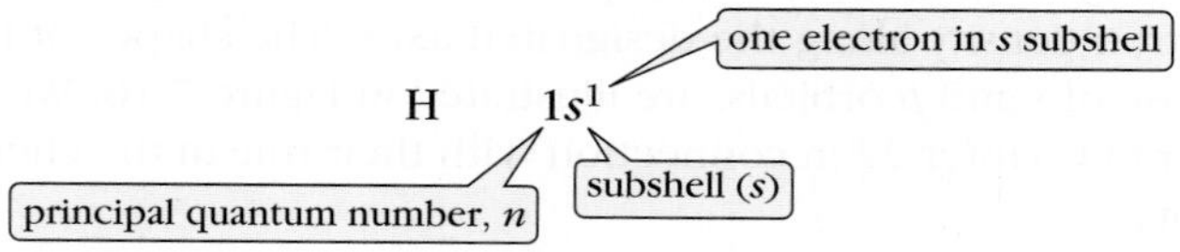

At the right in the table, each occupied orbital is represented by a box in which electrons are shown as arrows: ↑ for a single electron in an orbital and ↑↓ for paired electrons in an orbital.

In helium the two electrons are paired in the $1s$ orbital so that the lowest energy shell ($n = 1$) is filled. After the $n = 1$ shell is filled, electrons are assigned to the next lowest unoccupied energy level (Table 7.5), the $n = 2$ shell, beginning with lithium. This second shell can hold eight electrons ($2n^2$), and its orbitals are occupied sequentially in the eight elements from lithium to neon. Notice in the periodic table inside the front cover that these are the eight elements of the second period.

As happens in each principal energy level (and each period), the first two electrons fill the s orbital. In the second period this occurs in Li ($1s^2 2s^1$) and Be ($1s^2 2s^2$), which has the $2s$ orbital filled. The next element is boron, B ($1s^2 2s^2 2p^1$), and the

Table 7.5 Electron Configurations of the First Ten Elements

	Electron Configurations		**Orbital Box Diagrams**				
	Condensed	***Expanded***	**1*s***	**2*s***	**2*p***		
H	$1s^1$		↑				
He	$1s^2$		↑↓				
Li	$1s^2 2s^1$		↑↓	↑			
Be	$1s^2 2s^2$		↑↓	↑↓			
B	$1s^2 2s^2 2p^1$		↑↓	↑↓	↑		
C	$1s^2 2s^2 2p^2$	$1s^2 2s^2 2p^1 2p^1$	↑↓	↑↓	↑	↑	
N	$1s^2 2s^2 2p^3$	$1s^2 2s^2 2p^1 2p^1 2p^1$	↑↓	↑↓	↑	↑	↑
O	$1s^2 2s^2 2p^4$	$1s^2 2s^2 2p_x^2 2p^1 2p^1$	↑↓	↑↓	↑↓	↑	↑
F	$1s^2 2s^2 2p^5$	$1s^2 2s^2 2p^2 2p^2 2p^1$	↑↓	↑↓	↑↓	↑↓	↑
Ne	$1s^2 2s^2 2p^6$	$1s^2 2s^2 2p^2 2p^2 2p^2$	↑↓	↑↓	↑↓	↑↓	↑↓

fifth electron goes into a $2p$ orbital. The three $2p$ orbitals are of equal energy, and it does not matter which $2p$ orbital is occupied first. Adding a second p electron for the next element, carbon ($1s^22s^22p^2$), presents a choice. Does the second $2p$ electron in the carbon atom pair with the existing electron in a $2p$ orbital, or does it occupy a $2p$ orbital by itself? It has been shown experimentally that both $2p$ electrons have the same spin. (The electrons are said to have parallel spins.) Hence, they must occupy different $2p$ orbitals; otherwise, they would violate the Pauli exclusion principle. The expanded electron configurations in the middle of Table 7.5 show the locations of the p electrons individually in the boron, carbon, and nitrogen atoms' $2p$ orbitals.

Because electrons are negatively charged particles, electron configurations where electrons have parallel spins also minimize electron–electron repulsions, making the total energy of the set of electrons as low as possible. **Hund's rule** summarizes how subshells are filled: The most stable arrangement of electrons in the same subshell has the maximum number of unpaired electrons, all with the same spin. ***Electrons pair only after each orbital in a subshell is occupied by a single electron.*** The general result of Hund's rule is that in p, d, or f orbitals, each successive electron enters a different orbital of the subshell until the subshell is half-full, after which electrons pair in the orbitals one by one. We can see this in Table 7.5 for the elements that follow boron—carbon, nitrogen, oxygen, fluorine, and neon.

ThomsonNOW™
Go to the Coached Problems menu for a tutorial on **electron configurations of atoms.**

Suppose you need to know the electron configuration of a phosphorus atom. Checking the periodic table (inside the front cover), you find that phosphorus has atomic number 15 and therefore has 15 electrons. The electron configuration can be derived by using the general relationships among periodic table position, shells (n), subshells, and electron configuration as summarized in Figure 7.17. Phosphorus is in the third period ($n = 3$). From Figure 7.17 we see that the $n = 1$ and $n = 2$ shells are filled in the first two periods, giving the first ten electrons in phosphorus the configuration $1s^22s^22p^6$ (the same as neon). The next two electrons are assigned to the $3s$ orbital, giving $1s^22s^22p^63s^2$ so far. The final three electrons have to be assigned to the $3p$ orbitals, so the electron configuration for phosphorus is

$$\text{P} \quad 1s^22s^22p^63s^23p^3$$

The electron configurations of all the elements are given in Appendix D. In that appendix, an abbreviated representation of the configurations called the **noble gas notation** is used in which the symbol of the preceding noble gas represents filled

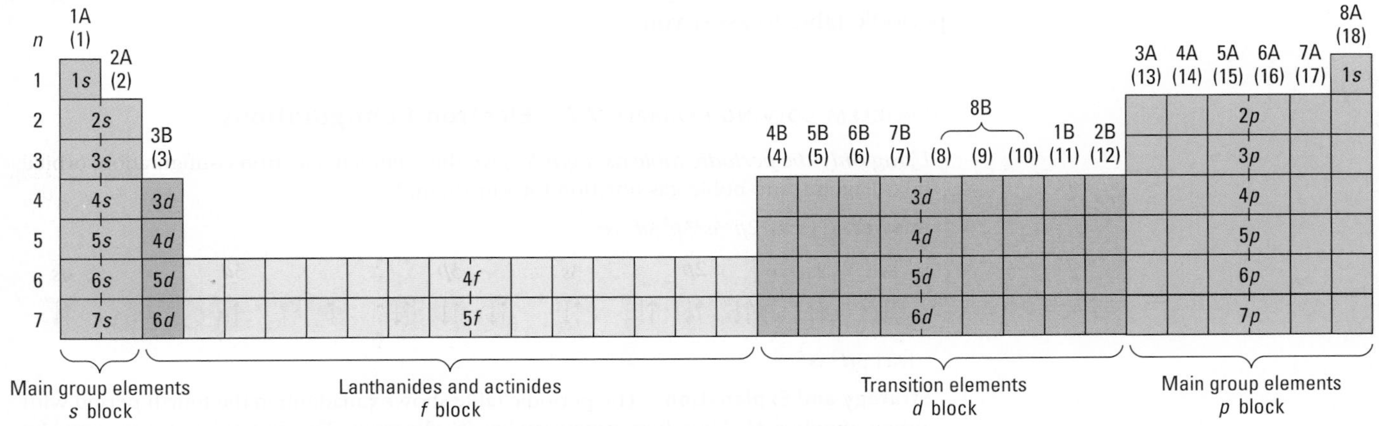

Figure 7.17 Electron configuration and the periodic table. Electron configurations can be generated by assigning electrons to the subshells shown here starting at H and moving through this table in atomic number order until the desired element is reached. The electron configurations in atomic number order are given in Appendix D.

subshells. Using the noble gas notation, the electron configuration of phosphorus is [Ne] $3s^2 3p^3$.

According to Hund's rule, the three electrons in the $3p$ orbitals of the phosphorus atom must be unpaired. To show this, you can write the *expanded* electron configuration

$$\text{P} \qquad 1s^2 2s^2 2p^2 2p^2 2p^2 3s^2 3p^1 3p^1 3p^1$$

or the orbital box diagram

P	1*s*	2*s*	2*p*	3*s*	3*p*
	↑↓	↑↓	↑↓ ↑↓ ↑↓	↑↓	↑ ↑ ↑

Thus, all the electrons are paired except for the three electrons in $3p$ orbitals. These three electrons each occupy different $3p$ orbitals, and they have parallel spins. The partial orbital box diagram of elements in Period 3 is given in Figure 7.18.

Atomic number/ element	Partial orbital box diagram (3*s* and 3*p* sublevels only) 3*s*	3*p*	Electron configuration	Noble gas notation
$_{11}$Na	[↑]	[ ] [ ] [ ]	$[1s^2 2s^2 2p^6]\ 3s^1$	[Ne] $3s^1$
$_{12}$Mg	[↑↓]	[ ] [ ] [ ]	$[1s^2 2s^2 2p^6]\ 3s^2$	[Ne] $3s^2$
$_{13}$Al	[↑↓]	[↑] [ ] [ ]	$[1s^2 2s^2 2p^6]\ 3s^2 3p^1$	[Ne] $3s^2 3p^1$
$_{14}$Si	[↑↓]	[↑] [↑] [ ]	$[1s^2 2s^2 2p^6]\ 3s^2 3p^2$	[Ne] $3s^2 3p^2$
$_{15}$P	[↑↓]	[↑] [↑] [↑]	$[1s^2 2s^2 2p^6]\ 3s^2 3p^3$	[Ne] $3s^2 3p^3$
$_{16}$S	[↑↓]	[↑↓] [↑] [↑]	$[1s^2 2s^2 2p^6]\ 3s^2 3p^4$	[Ne] $3s^2 3p^4$
$_{17}$Cl	[↑↓]	[↑↓] [↑↓] [↑]	$[1s^2 2s^2 2p^6]\ 3s^2 3p^5$	[Ne] $3s^2 3p^5$
$_{18}$Ar	[↑↓]	[↑↓] [↑↓] [↑↓]	$[1s^2 2s^2 2p^6]\ 3s^2 3p^6$	[Ne] $3s^2 3p^6$

Figure 7.18 **Partial orbital diagrams for Period 3 elements.**

At this point, you should be able to write electron configurations and orbital box diagrams for main group elements through Ca, atomic number 20, using the periodic table to assist you.

PROBLEM-SOLVING EXAMPLE 7.7 Electron Configurations

Using only the periodic table as a guide, give the complete electron configuration, orbital box diagram, and noble gas notation for vanadium, V.

Answer $1s^2 2s^2 2p^6 3s^2 3p^6 3d^3 4s^2$

1*s*	2*s*	2*p*	3*s*	3*p*	3*d*	4*s*
↑↓	↑↓	↑↓ ↑↓ ↑↓	↑↓	↑↓ ↑↓ ↑↓	↑ ↑ ↑ [ ] [ ]	↑↓

[Ar] $3d^3 4s^2$

Strategy and Explanation The periodic table shows vanadium in the fourth period with atomic number 23. Therefore, vanadium has 23 electrons. The first 18 are represented by $1s^2 2s^2 2p^6 3s^2 3p^6$, the electron configuration of argon, Ar, the noble gas that precedes vanadium. The last five electrons in vanadium have the configuration $3d^3 4s^2$. The orbital box diagram shown above follows from the total electron configuration.

PROBLEM-SOLVING PRACTICE 7.7

(a) Write the electron configuration of silicon in the noble gas notation.
(b) Determine how many unpaired electrons a silicon atom has by drawing the orbital box diagram.

EXERCISE 7.14 Highest Energy Electrons in Ground State Atoms

Give the electron configuration of electrons in the highest occupied principal energy level (highest *n*) in a ground state chlorine atom. Do the same for a selenium atom.

We move now from considering the electron configuration of all electrons in an atom to those electrons of primary importance to the chemical reactivity of an element, its valence electrons in the outermost orbitals of the atom.

Valence Electrons

The chemical reactivity of an element is not determined by the total number of electrons in each of its atoms. If such were the case, chemical reactivity would increase sequentially with increasing atomic number. Instead, chemically similar behavior occurs among elements within a group in the periodic table, and differs among groups. As early as 1902, Gilbert N. Lewis (1875–1946) hit upon the idea that electrons in atoms might be arranged in shells, starting close to the nucleus and building outward. Lewis explained the similarity of chemical properties for elements in a given group by assuming that atoms of all elements in that group have the same number of electrons in their outer shell. These electrons are known as **valence electrons** for the main group elements. The electrons in the filled inner shells of these elements are called **core electrons.** For elements in the fourth and higher periods of Groups 3A to 7A, electrons in the filled *d* subshell are also core electrons. Using this notation, the core electrons of As are represented by [Ar] $3d^{10}$. A few examples of core and valence electrons are the following:

Element	Core Electrons	Total Electron Configuration	Valence Electrons	Periodic Group
Na	$1s^22s^22p^6$, ([Ne])	[Ne] $3s^1$	$3s^1$	1A
Si	$1s^22s^22p^6$, ([Ne])	[Ne] $3s^23p^2$	$3s^23p^2$	4A
As	$1s^22s^22p^63s^23p^6$, ([Ar])	[Ar] $3d^{10}4s^24p^3$	$4s^24p^3$	5A

For transition elements (*d*-block) and *f*-block elements, the *d* and *f* electrons of inner shells may also be valence electrons. (See p. 302.)

While teaching his students about atomic structure, Lewis used the element's symbol to represent the atomic nucleus together with the core electrons. He introduced the practice of representing the valence electrons as dots. The dots are placed around the symbol one at a time until they are used up or until all four sides are occupied; any remaining electron dots are paired with ones already there. The result is a **Lewis dot symbol.** Table 7.6 shows Lewis dot symbols for the atoms of the elements in Periods 2 and 3.

Main group elements in Groups 1A and 2A are known as ***s*-block elements,** and their valence electrons are *s* electrons (ns^1 for Group 1A, ns^2 for Group 2A). Elements in the main groups at the right in the periodic table, Groups 3A through 8A, are known as ***p*-block elements.** Their valence electrons include the outermost *s*

Table 7.6 Lewis Dot Symbols for Atoms

	1A ns^1	2A ns^2	3A ns^2np^1	4A ns^2np^2	5A ns^2np^3	6A ns^2np^4	7A ns^2np^5	8A ns^2np^6
Period 2	Li·	·Be·	·B·	·C·	·N·	:O·	:F·	:Ne:
Period 3	Na·	·Mg·	·Al·	·Si·	·P·	:S·	:Cl·	:Ar:

and *p* electrons. Notice in Table 7.6 how the Lewis dot symbols show that *in each A group the number of valence electrons is equal to the group number.*

PROBLEM-SOLVING EXAMPLE 7.8 Valence Electrons

(a) Using the noble gas notation, write the electron configuration for bromine. Identify its core and valence electrons.

(b) Write the Lewis dot symbol for bromine.

Answer

(a) [Ar] $3d^{10}4s^24p^5$ Core electrons are [Ar]$3d^{10}$; valence electrons are $4s^24p^5$.

(b) :Br·

Strategy and Explanation Bromine is element 35, a Group 7A element. Its first 18 electrons are represented by [Ar], as shown in Table 7.6. These, along with the ten $3d$ electrons, make up the core electrons. Because it is in Group 7A, bromine has seven valence electrons, as given by $4s^24p^5$ and shown in the Lewis dot symbol.

PROBLEM-SOLVING PRACTICE 7.8

Use the noble gas notation to write electron configurations and Lewis dot symbols for Se and Te. What do these configurations illustrate about elements in the same main group?

Electron Configurations of Transition Elements

The **transition elements** are those in the B groups in Periods 4 through 7 in the middle of the periodic table. In these metallic elements, a *d* subshell is being filled as shown in Figure 7.17 (p. 299). In addition to *s* and *p* electrons in the outermost shells of these atoms, electrons in an incompletely filled $(n - 1)d$ subshell are valence electrons.

In each period in which they occur, the transition elements are immediately preceded by two *s*-block elements. As shown in Figure 7.17, once the $4s$ subshell is filled, the next subshell filled is $3d$ (not $4p$, as you might expect). ***In general, $(n - 1)d$ orbitals are filled after ns orbitals and before filling of np orbitals begins.***

In atoms more complex than hydrogen (multielectron atoms), the subshell energies depend on both n and ℓ, not simply n. Subshells are filled sequentially in order of increasing $n + \ell$. When two subshells have the same $n + \ell$ value, the electrons are first assigned to the subshell with the lower n value (Figure 7.19). For example, the sequence for $3d$, $4s$, and $4p$ subshells for manganese, element 25, is that the $4s$ subshell ($n + \ell = 4 + 0 = 4$) is filled before the $3d$ subshell ($n + \ell = 3 + 2 = 5$), which fills before the $4p$ subshell ($n + \ell = 4 + 1 = 5$). The electron configuration for manganese is [Ar] $3d^54s^2$. The $3d$ and $4p$ subshells have the same

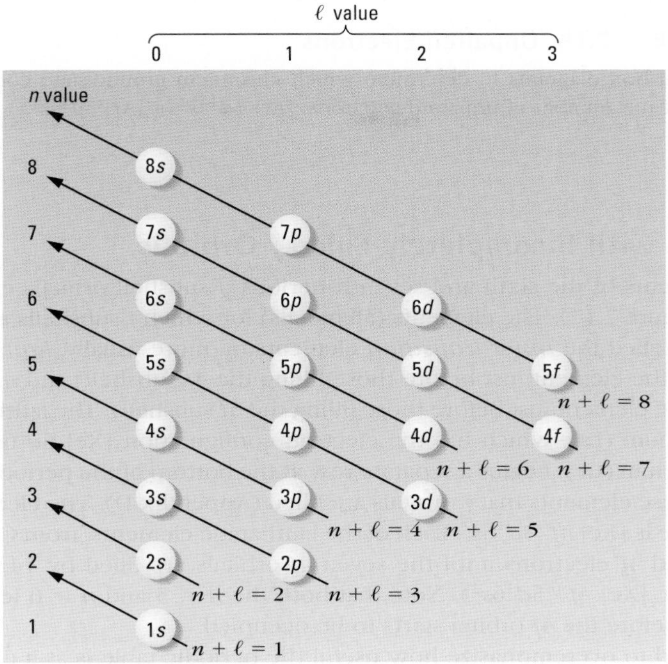

Figure 7.19 **Order of subshell filling.** As n increases, the energies of electron shells also increase. The energies of subshells within a shell increase with ℓ. Subshells are filled in increasing order of $n + \ell$. When two subshells have the same sum of $n + \ell$, the subshell with the lower n value is filled first.

$n + \ell$ value, but because of its lower n value, the five electrons enter the $3d$ subshell before the $4p$ subshell. Manganese has seven valence electrons.

The use of d orbitals begins with the $n = 3$ level and therefore with the first transition metal, scandium, which has the configuration [Ar] $3d^14s^2$. After scandium comes titanium with [Ar] $3d^24s^2$ and vanadium with [Ar] $3d^34s^2$. We would expect the configuration of the next element, chromium, to be [Ar] $3d^44s^2$, but that turns out to be incorrect. The correct configuration is [Ar] $3d^54s^1$, based on spectroscopic and magnetic measurements. This illustrates one of several anomalies that occur in predicting electron configurations for transition and f subshell-filling elements. When half-filled d subshells are possible, they are sometimes favored (an illustration of Hund's rule). As a result, transition elements that have a half-filled s orbital and half-filled or filled d orbitals have stable electron configurations. Chromium (s^1d^5) and copper (s^1d^{10}) are examples. The electron configuration for copper, the next-to-last element in the first transition series, is [Ar] $3d^{10}4s^1$ instead of the expected [Ar] $3d^94s^2$.

This also occurs with silver and gold, elements that are in the same group as copper.

The number of unpaired electrons for atoms of most transition elements can be predicted according to Hund's rule by placing valence electrons in orbital diagrams. For example, the electron configuration of Co ($Z = 27$) is [Ar] $3d^74s^2$, and the number of unpaired electrons is three, corroborated by experimental measurements, and seen from the following orbital box diagram.

	$3d$					$4s$
Co [Ar]	↑↓	↑↓	↑	↑	↑	↑↓

EXERCISE 7.15 Unpaired Electrons

Use orbital box diagrams to determine which chromium ground-state configuration has the greater number of unpaired electrons: [Ar] $3d^44s^2$ or [Ar] $3d^54s^1$.

Elements with Incompletely Filled *f* Orbitals

In the elements of the sixth and seventh periods, *f* subshell orbitals exist and can be filled (Figure 7.17). The elements (all metals) for which *f* subshells are filling are sometimes called the *inner transition* elements or, more usually, *lanthanides* (for lanthanum, the element just before those filling the 4*f* subshell) and *actinides* (for actinium, the element just before those filling the 5*f* subshell). The lanthanides start with lanthanum (La), which has the electron configuration [Xe] $5d^16s^2$. The next element, cerium (Ce), begins a separate row at the bottom of the periodic table, and it is with these elements that *f* orbitals are filled (Appendix D). The electron configuration of Ce is [Xe] $4f^15d^16s^2$. Each of the lanthanide elements, from Ce to Lu, continues to add 4*f* electrons until the seven 4*f* orbitals are filled by 14 electrons in lutetium (Lu, [Xe] $4f^{14}5d^16s^2$). Note that both the $n = 5$ and $n = 6$ levels are partially filled before the 4*f* orbital starts to be occupied.

It is hard to overemphasize how useful the periodic table is as a guide to electron configurations. As another example, using Figure 7.17 as a guide we can find the configuration of Te. Because tellurium is in Group 6A, by now you should immediately recognize that it has *six* valence electrons with an outer electron configuration of ns^2np^4. And, because Te is in the fifth period, $n = 5$. Thus, the complete electron configuration is given by starting with the electron configuration of krypton [$1s^22s^22p^63s^23p^63d^{10}4s^24p^6$], the noble gas at the end of the fourth period. Then add the filled $4d^{10}$ subshell and the six valence electrons of Te ($5s^25p^4$) to give $1s^22s^22p^63s^23p^63d^{10}4s^24p^64d^{10}5s^25p^4$, or [Kr] $4d^{10}5s^25p^4$. To predict the number of unpaired electrons, look at the outermost subshell's electron configuration, because the inner shells (represented by [Kr] in this case) are completely filled with paired electrons. For Te, [Kr] $4d^{10}5s^25p^25p^15p^1$ indicates two *p* orbitals with unpaired electrons for a total of two unpaired electrons.

7.8 Ion Electron Configurations

In studying ionic compounds **(*p. 89*)**, you learned that atoms from Groups 1A through 3A form positive ions (cations) with charges equal to their group numbers—for example, Li^+, Mg^{2+}, and Al^{3+}. Nonmetals in Groups 5A through 7A that form ions do so by adding electrons to form negative ions (anions) with *charges equal to eight minus the A group number.* Examples of such anions are N^{3-}, O^{2-}, and F^-. Here's the explanation. When atoms from *s*- and *p*-block elements form ions, electrons are removed or added so that a noble gas configuration is achieved. Atoms from Groups 1A, 2A, and 3A *lose* 1, 2, or 3 valence electrons to form 1+, 2+, or 3+ ions, respectively; the positive ions have the electron configurations of the *preceding* noble gas. Atoms from Groups 7A, 6A, and some in 5A *gain* 1, 2, or 3 valence electrons to form 1−, 2−, or 3− ions, respectively; the negative ions have the electron configurations of the *next* noble gas. ***Metal atoms lose electrons to form cations with a positive charge equal to the group number; nonmetals gain electrons to form anions with a negative charge equal to the A group number minus eight.*** This relationship holds for Groups 1A to 3A and 5A to 7A. Atoms and ions that have the same electron configuration are said to be **isoelectronic**.

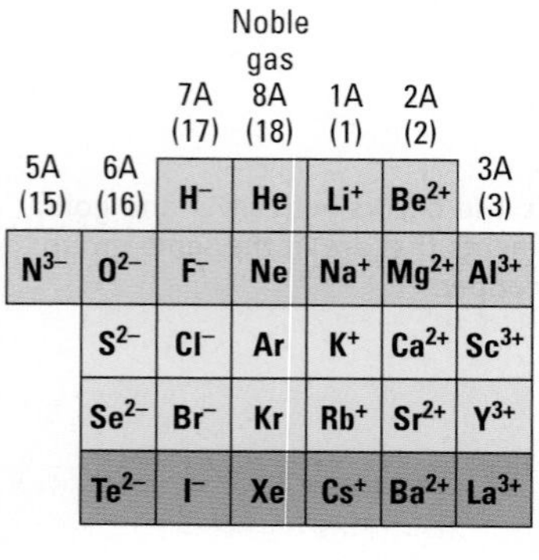

Cations, anions, and atoms with ground state noble gas configurations.
Atoms and ions shown in the same color are isoelectronic, that is, they have the same electron configuration.

PROBLEM-SOLVING EXAMPLE 7.9 Atoms and Their Ions

Complete this table.

Neutral Atom	Neutral Atom Electron Configuration	Ion	Ion Electron Configuration
Se	______	______	[Kr]
Ba	______	Ba^{2+}	______
Br	______	Br^{-}	______
______	[Kr] $5s^1$	Rb^{+}	______
______	[Ne] $3s^23p^3$	______	[Ar]

Answer

Neutral Atom	Neutral Atom Electron Configuration	Ion	Ion Electron Configuration
Se	[Ar] $3d^{10}4s^24p^4$	Se^{2-}	[Kr]
Ba	[Xe] $6s^2$	Ba^{2+}	[Xe]
Br	[Ar] $3d^{10}4s^24p^5$	Br^{-}	[Kr]
Rb	[Kr] $5s^1$	Rb^{+}	[Kr]
P	[Ne] $3s^23p^3$	P^{3-}	[Ar]

Strategy and Explanation A neutral Se atom has the electron configuration [Ar] $3d^{10}4s^24p^4$; Se is in Group 6A, so it gains two electrons in the 4*p* sublevel to form Se^{2-} and achieve the noble gas configuration of krypton, Kr (36 electrons). Barium is a Group 2A element and loses the two 6*s* electrons to acquire the electron configuration of xenon (54 electrons), the preceding noble gas. Therefore, Ba is [Xe] $6s^2$ and Ba^{2+} is [Xe]. Bromine is in Group 7A and will gain one electron to form Br^{-}, which has the electron configuration of krypton, the next noble gas. An electron configuration of [Kr] $5s^1$ indicates 37 electrons in the neutral atom, which is a rubidium atom, Rb. A neutral Rb atom loses the $5s^1$ electron to form an Rb^{+} ion, which has a [Kr] configuration. The [Ne] $3s^23p^3$ configuration is for an element with 15 electrons, which is a phosphorus atom, P. By gaining three electrons, a neutral phosphorus atom becomes a P^{3-} ion with the [Ar] configuration.

PROBLEM-SOLVING PRACTICE 7.9

(a) What Period 3 anion with a 3− charge has the [Ar] electron configuration?

(b) What Period 4 cation with a 2+ charge has the electron configuration of argon?

Table 7.7 lists some isoelectronic ions and the noble gas atom that has the same electron configuration. The table emphasizes that ***metal ions are isoelectronic with the preceding noble gas atom, while nonmetal ions have the electron configuration of the next noble gas atom.***

Table 7.7 Noble Gas Atoms and Their Isoelectronic Ions

(All $1s^2$)	He, Li^{+}, Be^{2+}, H^{-}
(All $1s^22s^22p^6$)	Ne, Na^{+}, Mg^{2+}, Al^{3+}, F^{-}, O^{2-}
(All $1s^22s^22p^63s^23p^6$)	Ar, K^{+}, Ca^{2+}, Cl^{-}, S^{2-}
(All $1s^22s^22p^63s^23p^63d^{10}4s^24p^6$)	Kr, Rb^{+}, Sr^{2+}, Br^{-}, Se^{2-}
(All $1s^22s^22p^63s^23p^63d^{10}4s^24p^64d^{10}5s^25p^6$)	Xe, Cs^{+}, Ba^{2+}, I^{-}, Te^{2-}

Transition Metal Ions

The closeness in energy of the $4s$ and $3d$ subshells was mentioned earlier in connection with the electron configurations of transition metal atoms. The $5s$ and $4d$ subshells are also close to each other in energy, as are the $6s$, $4f$, and $5d$ subshells and the $7s$, $5f$, and $6d$ subshells. The ns and $(n-1)d$ subshells are so close in energy that once d electrons are added, the $(n-1)d$ subshell becomes slightly lower in energy than the ns subshell. As a result, ***the ns electrons are at higher energy and are always removed before (n−1)d electrons when transition metals form cations***. A simple way to remember this is that when a transition metal atom loses electrons to form an ion, the electrons in the outermost shell are lost first.

For example, a nickel atom, Ni: [Ar] $3d^8 4s^2$, will lose its two $4s$ electrons to form a Ni^{2+} ion.

$$Ni \rightarrow Ni^{2+} + 2e^-$$

That two $4s$ electrons are lost, and not two electrons from the $3d$ subshell, is corroborated by the experimental evidence that Ni^{2+} has two unpaired electrons. This is shown by the following box diagrams.

		3d					4s
Ni^0	[Ar]	↑↓	↑↓	↑↓	↑	↑	↑↓

Nickel atom: [Ar] $3d^8 4s^2$

		3d					4s
Ni^{2+}	[Ar]	↑↓	↑↓	↑↓	↑	↑	

Ni^{2+} ion: [Ar] $3d^8$ (correct)

If two electrons had been removed from the $3d$ subshell rather than the $4s$ subshell, a Ni^{2+} ion would have four unpaired electrons, which is inconsistent with experimental evidence.

		3d					4s
Ni^{2+}	[Ar]	↑↓	↑	↑	↑	↑	↑↓

Ni^{2+} ion: [Ar] $3d^6 4s^2$ (incorrect)

Iron, [Ar] $3d^6 4s^2$, which forms Fe^{2+} and Fe^{3+} ions, is another example. The Fe atom loses its two $4s$ electrons to form an Fe^{2+} ion:

$$\underset{[Ar]\ 3d^6 4s^2}{Fe} \longrightarrow \underset{[Ar]\ 3d^6}{Fe^{2+}} + 2e^-$$

and then Fe^{3+} is formed from Fe^{2+} by loss of a $3d$ electron.

$$\underset{[Ar]\ 3d^6}{Fe^{2+}} \longrightarrow \underset{[Ar]\ 3d^5}{Fe^{3+}} + e^-$$

There are five unpaired electrons in the Fe^{3+} ion, compared with only four unpaired electrons for Fe^{2+}, as shown by using orbital box diagrams for the $3d$ electrons:

		3d
Fe^{2+}	[Ar]	↑↓ ↑ ↑ ↑ ↑
Fe^{3+}	[Ar]	↑ ↑ ↑ ↑ ↑

Atoms or ions of inner transition elements (lanthanides and actinides) can have as many as seven unpaired electrons in the *f* subshell, as occurs in Eu^{2+} and Gd^{3+} ions.

PROBLEM-SOLVING EXAMPLE 7.10 Electron Configurations for Transition Elements and Ions

(a) Write the electron configuration for the Co atom using the noble gas notation. Then draw the orbital box diagram for the electrons beyond the preceding noble gas configuration.

(b) Cobalt commonly exists as 2+ and 3+ ions. How does the orbital box diagram given in part (a) have to be changed to represent the outer electrons of Co^{2+} and Co^{3+}?

(c) How many unpaired electrons do Co, Co^{2+}, and Co^{3+} each have?

Answer

(a)

	3d	4s
$[Ar]3d^7 4s^2$; [Ar]	↑↓ ↑↓ ↑ ↑ ↑	↑↓

(b) For Co^{2+}, remove the two 4*s* electrons from Co to give

		3d
Co^{2+}	[Ar]	↑↓ ↑↓ ↑ ↑ ↑

For Co^{3+}, remove the two 4*s* electrons and one of the paired 3*d* electrons from Co to give

		3d
Co^{3+}	[Ar]	↑↓ ↑ ↑ ↑ ↑

(c) Co has three unpaired electrons; Co^{2+} has three unpaired electrons; Co^{3+} has four unpaired electrons.

Strategy and Explanation

(a) Co, with an atomic number of 27, is in the fourth period. It has nine more electrons than Ar, with two of the nine in the 4*s* subshell and seven in the 3*d* subshell, so its electron configuration is [Ar] $3d^7 4s^2$. For the orbital box diagram, all *d* orbitals get one electron before pairing occurs (Hund's rule).

(b) To form Co^{2+}, two electrons are removed from the outermost shell (4*s* subshell). To form Co^{3+} from Co^{2+}, one of the paired electrons is removed from a 3*d* orbital.

(c) Looking at the orbital box diagrams, you should see that the numbers of unpaired electrons are three for Co, three for Co^{2+}, and four for Co^{3+}.

PROBLEM-SOLVING PRACTICE 7.10

Use the electron configuration of a neutral ground state copper atom to explain why copper readily forms the Cu^+ ion.

Paramagnetism and Unpaired Electrons

The magnetic properties of a spinning electron were described in Section 7.5. In atoms and ions that have filled shells, all the electrons are paired (opposite spins) and their magnetic fields effectively cancel each other. Such substances are called

ThomsonNOW™

Go to the Coached Problems menu for exercises on:

- **electron configurations of ions**
- **electron configurations and magnetism**

TOOLS OF CHEMISTRY

Nuclear Magnetic Resonance and Its Applications

In Section 7.5, the magnetic field created by the spinning electron was mentioned in connection with the discussion of the quantized spin of electrons. The nuclei of certain isotopes have the same property. For example, a ^{1}H nucleus (the hydrogen nucleus or proton) can spin in either of two directions. In the absence of a magnetic field, the two spin states have the same energy. When a strong external magnetic field is applied, those ^{1}H nuclei spinning in such a way as to be aligned with the external magnetic field are slightly lower in energy than those that are aligned against the magnetic field. At first it might appear that this energy difference, ΔE, between the two nuclear spin states would be the same for all of the hydrogen atoms in a molecule. This is not the case. Neighboring atoms of the hydrogen atoms in a molecule cause the hydrogens to see effective magnetic fields that are slightly different from the external magnetic field. The value of ΔE is small enough that radiation in the radio wave region of the electromagnetic spectrum (***Figure 7.1, p. 274***) can change the direction of spin.

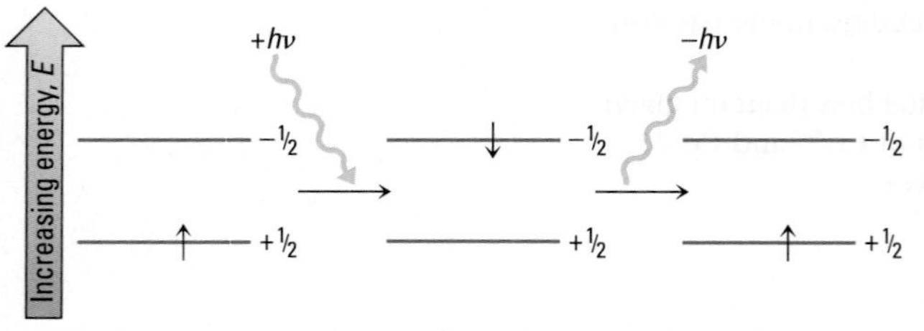

Absorption of radio frequency energy changes the direction and energy of spin of a proton. Emission of the energy returns the proton to its original spin.

Picture the aligned hydrogen nuclei absorbing a particular radio frequency that changes their spin to the less stable direction. When the nuclei return to the more stable spin direction, the same radio frequency is emitted and can be measured with a radio receiver. This phenomenon, known as **nuclear magnetic resonance (NMR),** provides an extremely valuable tool for studying molecular structure.

NMR is used extensively by chemists because the radio frequency absorbed and then emitted depends on the chemi-

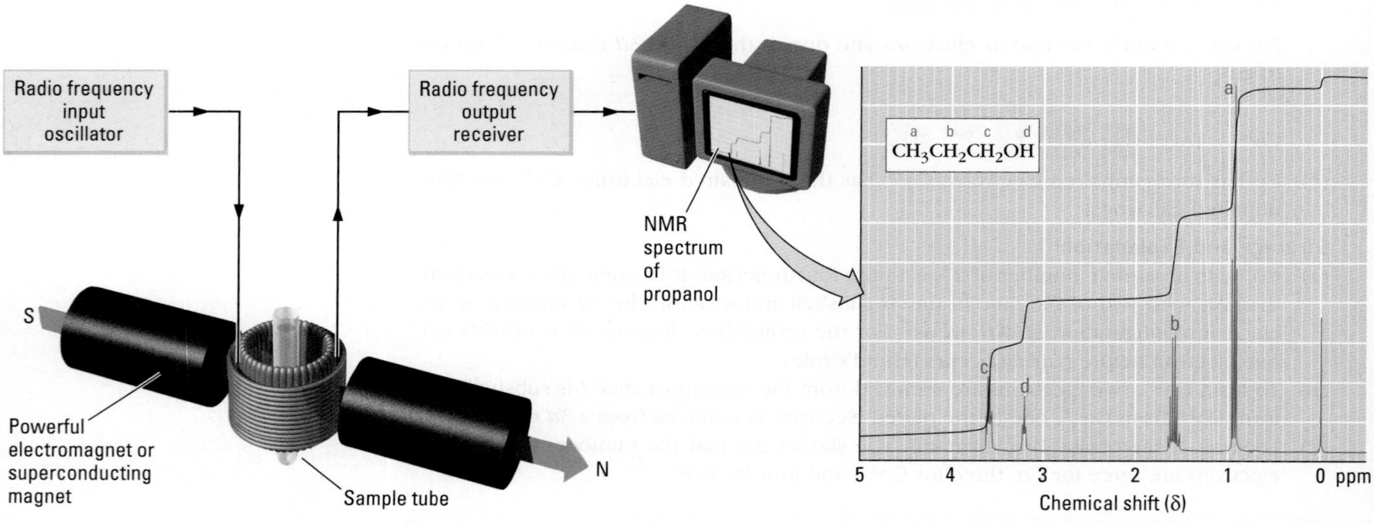

Schematic diagram of a modern NMR spectrometer. (a) A modern NMR spectrometer is a highly automated, computer-controlled instrument. (b) The spectrum pictured here is of propanol, showing the four different types of protons (hydrogen nuclei) present in the molecule. The chemical shift (symbolized by δ and given in parts per million) is the position of the absorption relative to a defined zero point and the strength of the instrument.

diamagnetic. Atoms or ions with unpaired electrons are attracted to a magnetic field; the more unpaired electrons, the greater is the attraction. Such substances are called **paramagnetic.** For example, the greater paramagnetism of chromium with six unpaired electrons rather than four is experimental evidence that Cr has the electron configuration [Ar] $3d^5 4s^1$, rather than [Ar] $3d^4 4s^2$.

cal environment of the atoms with nuclear spin states in the sample. The study of hydrogen atoms with NMR (known as *proton* nuclear magnetic resonance, ^{1}H NMR) has quickly developed into an indispensable structural and analytical tool, particularly for organic chemists. Plots of the intensity of energy absorption versus the magnetic field strength are called *NMR spectra;* from such spectra chemists deduce the kinds of atoms bonded to hydrogen as well as the number of hydrogen atoms present in a molecule.

Because hydrogen is the most common element in the body and H atoms give a strong NMR signal, ^{1}H is the most logical candidate for the application of NMR to medical imaging. The first use of NMR for this purpose was reported in 1973. The delay between the discovery of NMR and its application in medicine was related to the technical difficulties associated with getting a uniform magnetic field with a diameter large enough to enclose a patient. In addition, advances in computer technology for analysis of data and construction of an image from these data were needed.

NMR imaging in medicine is based on the time it takes for the protons (hydrogen nuclei) in the unstable high-energy nuclear spin position to "relax" or return to the low-energy nuclear spin position. These *relaxation times* are different for protons in muscle (see *Proteins,* Section 12.9), blood, and bone because of differences in the chemical environments. These differences in relaxation times are enhanced by the computer to produce a magnetic resonance image.

The use of NMR in medical imaging is now referred to as magnetic resonance imaging (MRI). The name "nuclear" was dropped because it frightened some people due to its association with weapons and radioactivity. In magnetic resonance imaging, the patient is placed in the opening of a large magnet. The magnetic field aligns the magnetic spin of the protons (as well as those of other magnetic nuclei). A radio frequency transmitter coil is placed in position near the region of the body to be examined. The radio frequency energy absorbed by the spinning hydrogen nuclei causes the aligned nuclei to flip to the less stable, high-energy spin direction. When the nuclei flip back to the more stable spin state, photons of radio frequency electromagnetic radiation are emitted. The intensity of the emitted signal is related to the density of hydrogen nuclei in the region being examined. The time it takes for the signal to be emitted (relaxation time) is related to the type of tissue. The emitted radio frequency signal is received by a radio receiver coil, which then sends it to a computer for mathematical construction of the image. MRI can readily image organs, detect small tumors or blockage in blood vessels, and assess damage to bones and vertebrae.

Mauro Fermariello/Science Photo Library/Photo Researchers, Inc.

The MRI method. A patient undergoing an MRI scan.

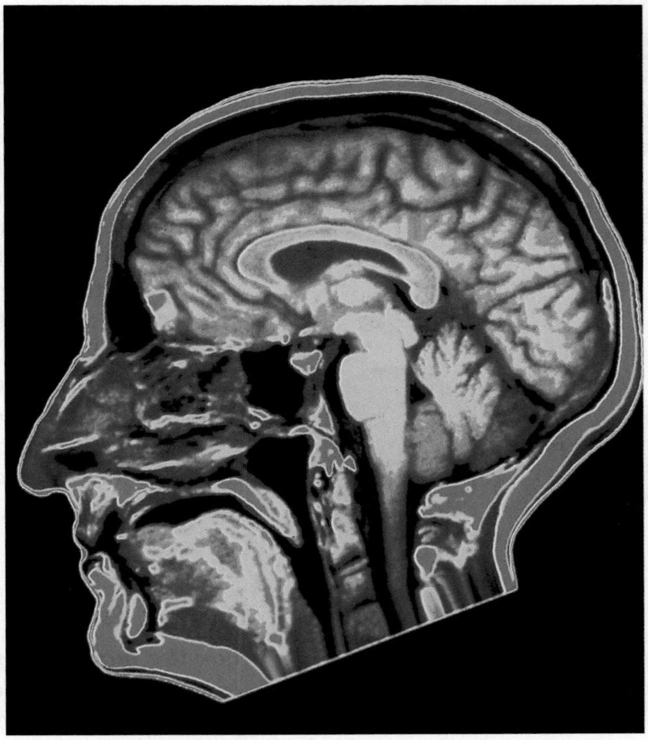

Scott Camazine/Photo Researchers, Inc.

An MRI image. An MRI scan of a normal human brain.

Ferromagnetic substances are permanent magnets; they retain their magnetism. The magnetic effect in ferromagnetic materials is much larger than that in paramagnetic materials. Ferromagnetism occurs when the spins of unpaired electrons in a cluster of atoms (called a domain) in a solid are aligned in the same direction (Figure 7.20). Only the metals of the iron, cobalt, and nickel subgroups in the periodic

This answers the question posed in Chapter 1 (***p. 3***), "Why is iron strongly attracted to a magnet, but most substances are not?"

table exhibit this property. They are also unique in that, once the domains are aligned in a magnetic field, the metal is permanently magnetized. In such a case, the magnetism can be eliminated only by heating or shaping the metal to rearrange the electron spin domains. Many alloys, such as alnico (an alloy of aluminum, nickel, and cobalt), exhibit greater ferromagnetism than do the pure metals themselves. Some metal oxides, such as CrO_2 and Fe_3O_4, are also ferromagnetic and are used in magnetic recording tape. Computer discs use ferromagnetic materials to store data in a binary code of zeroes and ones. Very small magnetic domains store bits of binary code as a magnetized region that represents a one and an unmagnetized region that represents a zero.

Paramagnetism: The atoms or ions with magnetic moments are not aligned. If the substance is in a magnetic field, they align with and against the field. Magnetism is weak.

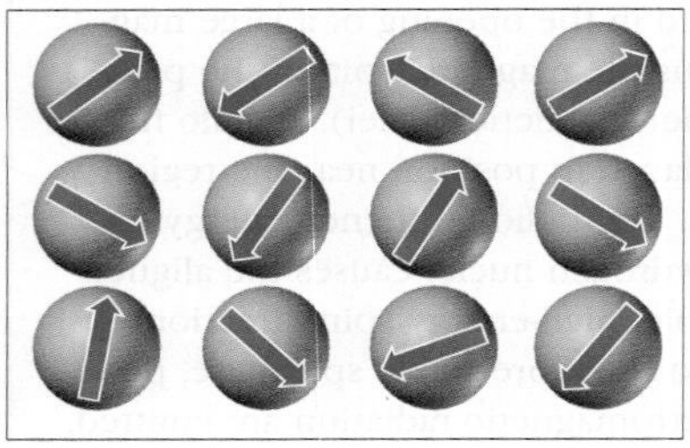

Ferromagnetism: The spins of unpaired electrons in clusters of atoms or ions are aligned in the same direction. In a magnetic field these domains all align and stay aligned when the field is removed.

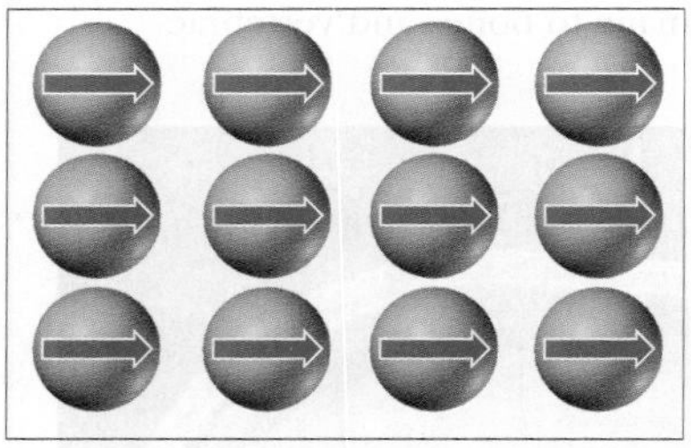

Figure 7.20 Types of magnetic behavior.

CONCEPTUAL EXERCISE 7.16 Unpaired Electrons

The acetylacetonate ion, acac$^-$, which has no unpaired electrons, forms compounds with Fe^{2+} and Fe^{3+} ions. Their formulas are $Fe(acac)_2$ and $Fe(acac)_3$ respectively. Which one will have the greater attraction to a magnetic field? Explain.

7.9 Periodic Trends: Atomic Radii

Using knowledge of electron configurations, we can now answer fundamental questions about why atoms of different elements fit as they do in the periodic table, as well as explain the trends in the properties of the elements in the table.

For atoms that form simple diatomic molecules, such as Cl_2, the **atomic radius** can be defined experimentally by finding the distance between the centers of the two atoms in the molecule. Assuming the atoms to be spherical, one-half of this distance is a good estimate of the atom's radius. In the Cl_2 molecule, the atom-to-atom distance (the distance from the center of one atom to the center of the other) is 200 pm. Dividing by 2 shows that the Cl radius is 100 pm. Similarly, the C—C distance in diamond is 154 pm, so the radius of the carbon atom is 77 pm. To test these estimates, we can add them together to estimate the distance between Cl and C in CCl_4. The estimated distance of 177 pm (100 pm + 77 pm) is in good agreement with the experimentally measured C—Cl distance of 176 pm.

This approach can be extended to other atomic radii. The radii of O, C, and S atoms can be estimated by measuring the O—H, C—Cl and H—S distances in H_2O, CCl_4, and H_2S, and then subtracting the H and Cl radii found from H_2 and Cl_2. By this and other techniques, a reasonable set of atomic radii for main group elements has been assembled (Figure 7.21).

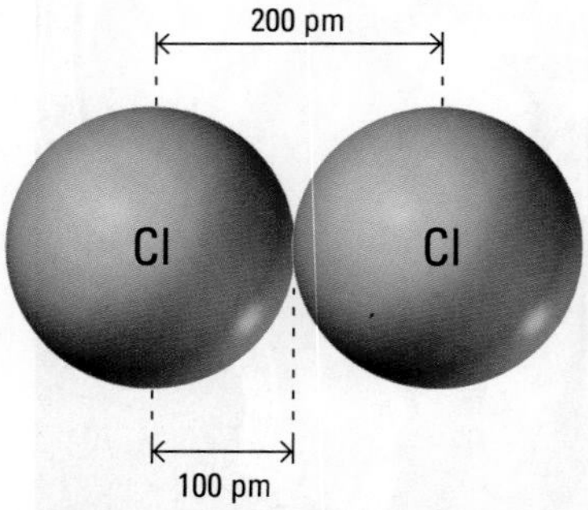

Atomic radius of chlorine. The atomic radius is taken to be one half of the internuclear distance in the Cl_2 molecule.

Atomic Radii of the Main Group Elements

For the main group elements, atomic radii increase going down a group in the periodic table and decrease going across a period (Figure 7.21). These trends reflect three important effects:

The main group elements are those in the A groups in the periodic table (Figure 7.17, p. 299).

- From the top to the bottom of a group in the periodic table, the atomic radii increase because electrons occupy orbitals that are successively larger as the value of *n*, the principal quantum number, increases.
- The atomic radii decrease from left to right across a period. The *n* value of the outermost orbitals stays the same, so we might expect the radii of the occupied orbitals to remain approximately constant. However, in crossing a period, as each successive electron is added, the nuclear charge also increases by the addition of one proton. The result is an increased attraction between the nucleus and electrons that is somewhat stronger than the increasing repulsion between electrons, causing atomic radii to decrease (Figure 7.21).

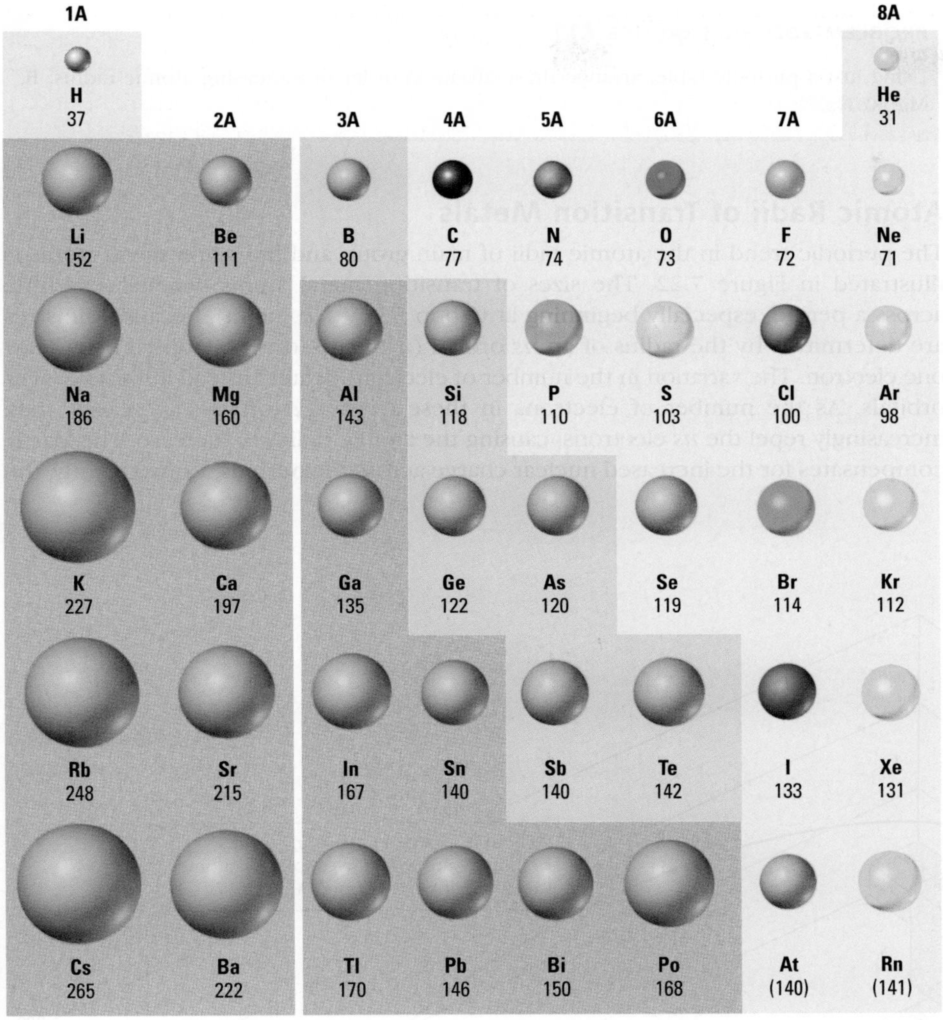

Figure 7.21 **Atomic radii of the main group elements** (in picometers; 1 pm = 10^{-12} m).

- There is a large increase in atomic radius going from any noble gas atom to the following Group 1A atom, where the outermost electron is assigned to the next higher energy level (the next larger shell, higher *n* value). For example, compare the atomic radii of Ne (71 pm) and Na (186 pm) or Ar (98 pm) and K (227 pm).

PROBLEM-SOLVING EXAMPLE 7.11 Atomic Radii and Periodic Trends

Using only a periodic table, list these atoms in order of decreasing size: Br, Cl, Ge, K, S.

Answer K > Ge > Br > S > Cl

Strategy and Explanation Based on the periodic trends in atomic size, we expect the radius of Cl to be smaller than that of Br, which is below it in Group 7A; S in Period 3 should be smaller than Br, which is in Period 4. Because size decreases across a period, we expect Cl to be smaller than S. Of the Period 4 atoms, Ge is earlier in the period than Br and therefore larger than it, but smaller than K, which starts the period. From these trends we can summarize the relative sizes of the radii, from largest to smallest, as K > Ge > Br > S > Cl.

PROBLEM-SOLVING PRACTICE 7.11

Using just a periodic table, arrange these atoms in order of increasing atomic radius: B, Mg, K, Na.

Atomic Radii of Transition Metals

The periodic trend in the atomic radii of main group and transition metal atoms is illustrated in Figure 7.22. The sizes of transition metal atoms change very little across a period, especially beginning at Group 5B (V, Nb, or Ta), because the sizes are determined by the radius of an *ns* orbital (n = 4, 5, or 6) occupied by at least one electron. The variation in the number of electrons occurs instead in the $(n - 1)d$ orbitals. As the number of electrons in these $(n = 1)d$ orbitals increases, they increasingly repel the *ns* electrons, causing the atomic radius to increase. This partly compensates for the increased nuclear charge across the periods. Consequently, the

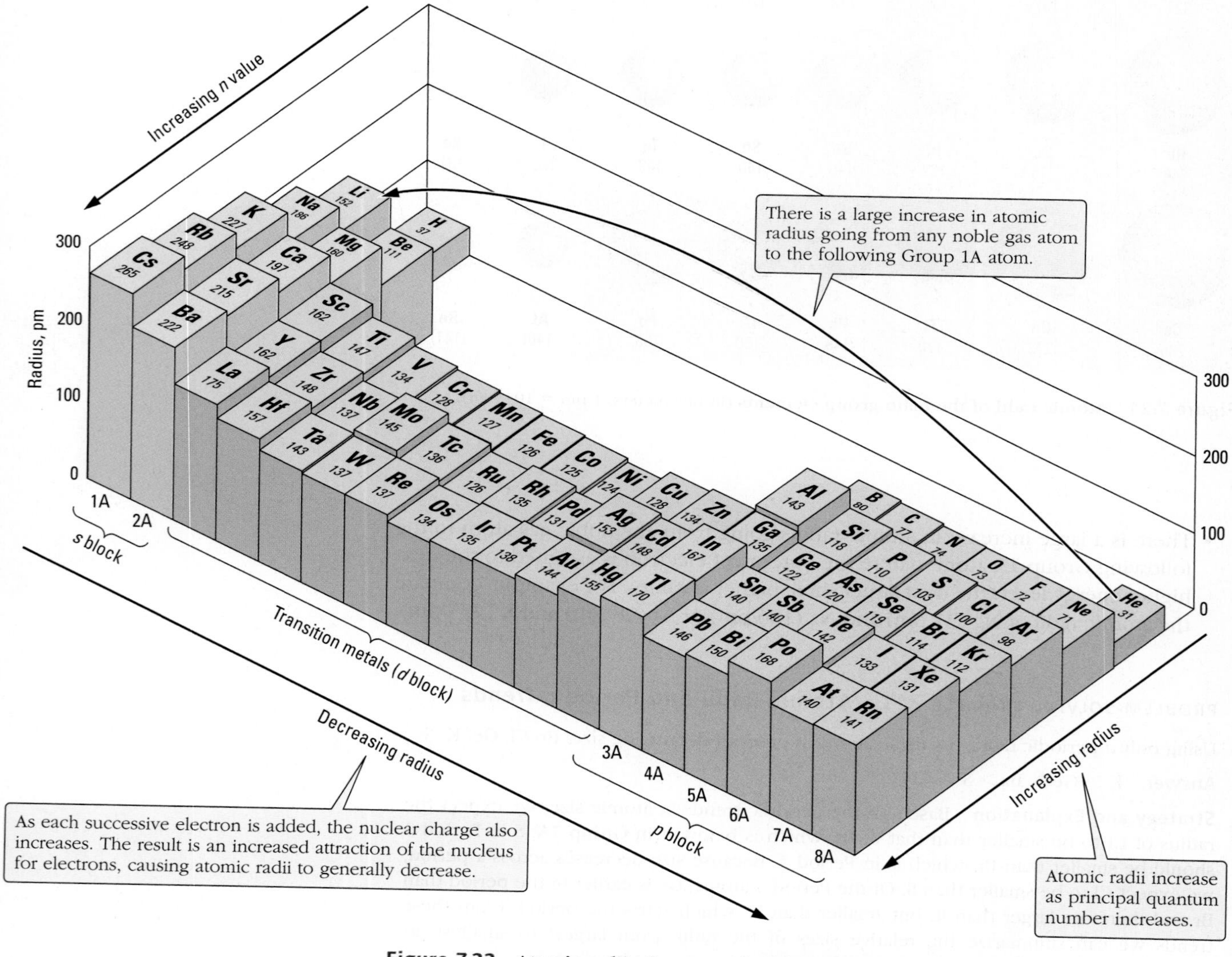

Figure 7.22 **Atomic radii of *s*-, *p*-, and *d*-block elements** (in picometers, pm; 1 pm = 10^{-12} m). Note the slight change in atomic radii for the transition elements (*d* block) across a period.

ns electrons experience only a slightly increasing nuclear attraction, and the radii remain nearly constant until the slight rise at the copper and zinc groups due to the continually increasing electron-to-electron repulsions as the *d* subshell is filled.

The similar radii of the transition metals and the similar sizes of their ions have an important effect on their chemistry—they tend to be more alike in their properties than other elements in their respective groups. The nearly identical radii of the fifth- and sixth-period transition elements lead to difficult problems in separating them from one another. The metals Ru, Os, Rh, Ir, Pd, and Pt are called the "platinum group metals" because they occur together in nature. Their radii and chemistry are so similar that their minerals are similar and are found in the same geologic zones.

Effective Nuclear Charge

We have seen that the atomic radii of main group elements decrease across a period, as the number of protons and electrons increases with each element. This change in radii can be explained by **effective nuclear charge,** the nuclear positive charge experienced by outer-shell electrons in a many-electron atom. The effective nuclear charge felt by outer-shell electrons is less than the actual nuclear positive charge. Outer electrons are shielded from the full nuclear positive charge by intervening inner electrons, those closer to the nucleus (lower *n* values). These electrons repel outer electrons and this repulsion partially offsets the attraction of the nucleus for outer-shell electrons. Therefore, $Z^* = Z - \sigma$, where Z^* is the effective nuclear charge, Z is the number of protons in the nucleus (the actual nuclear charge), and σ is the amount of screening, the amount by which the actual nuclear charge is reduced. This decrease is called the **screening effect.** The effective nuclear charge increases across a period and outer electrons are pulled closer to the nucleus causing the decrease of atomic radii across a period.

ThomsonNOW™
Go to the Coached Problems menu to work modules on:
- **orbital energies**
- **atomic size**
- **effective nuclear charge**

7.10 Periodic Trends: Ionic Radii

As shown in Figure 7.23, the periodic trends in the **ionic radii** parallel the trends in atomic radii within the same periodic group: ***positive ions of elements in the same group increase in size down the group***—for example, Li^+ to Rb^+ in Group 1A. ***This also occurs with negative ions in the same group*** (see F^- to I^-, Group 7A). But take time to compare the two types of entries in Figure 7.23. When an electron is removed from an atom to form a cation, the size shrinks considerably; ***the radius of a cation is always smaller than that of the atom from which it is derived.*** The radius of Li is 152 pm, whereas that for Li^+ is only 90 pm. This is understandable, because when an electron is removed from a lithium atom, the nuclear charge remains the same (3+), but there are fewer electrons repelling each other. Consequently, the positive nucleus can attract the two remaining electrons more strongly, causing the electrons to contract toward the nucleus. The decrease in ion size is especially great when the electron removed comes from a higher energy level than the new outer electron. This is the case for Li, for which the "old" outer electron was from a 2*s* orbital and the "new" outer electron in Li^+ is in a 1*s* orbital.

The shrinkage is also great when two or more electrons are removed—for example, Mg^{2+} and Al^{3+}.

Mg atom (radius = 160 pm)	Mg^{2+} cation (radius = 86 pm)
$1s^22s^22p^63s^2$	$1s^22s^22p^6$
Al atom (radius 143 pm)	Al^{3+} cation (radius = 68 pm)
$1s^22s^22p^63s^23p^1$	$1s^22s^22p^6$

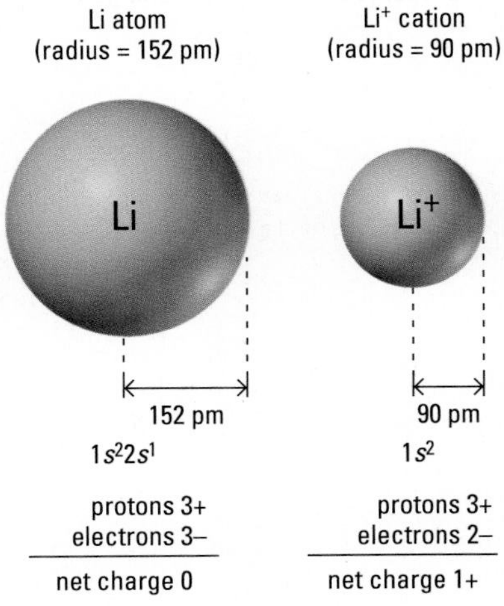

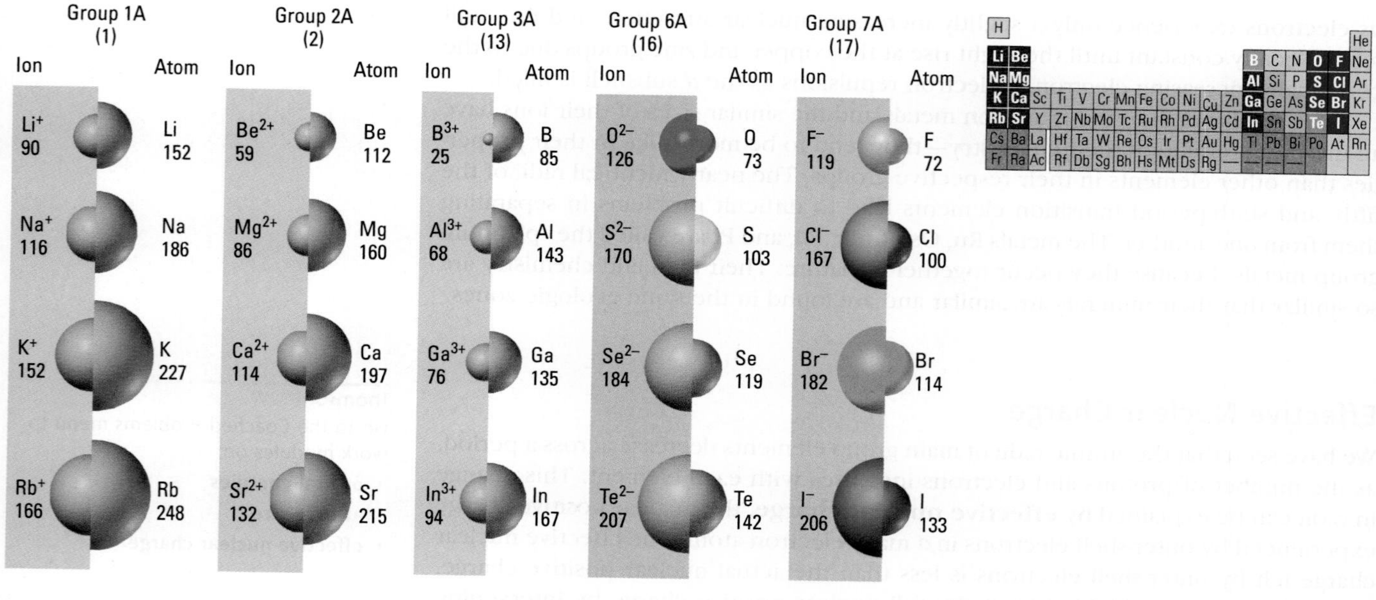

Figure 7.23 **Sizes of ions and their neutral atoms.** Radii are given in picometers (1 pm = 10^{-12} m).

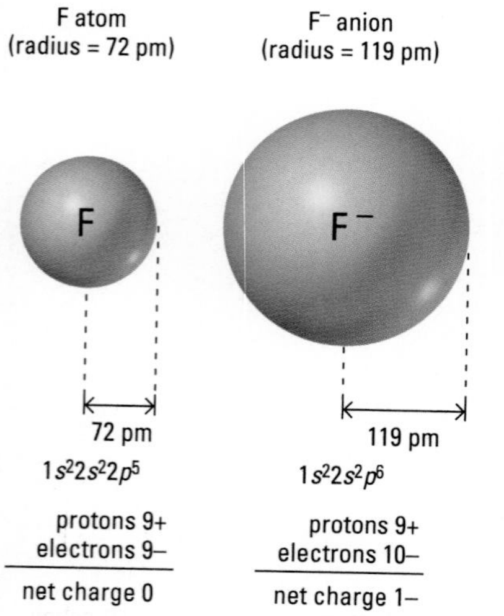

From Figure 7.23 you can see that ***anions are always larger than the atoms from which they are derived.*** Here the argument is the opposite of that used to explain the radii of cations. For anions, the nuclear charge is unchanged, but the added electron(s) introduce new repulsions and the electron clouds swell. The F atom has nine protons and nine electrons. When it forms the F^- anion, the nuclear charge is still 9+ but there are now ten electrons in the anion. The F^- ion (119 pm) is much larger than the F atom (72 pm) because of increased electron-to-electron repulsions.

The oxide ion, O^{2-}, and fluoride ion, F^-, are *isoelectronic;* they both have the same electron configuration (the neon configuration). However, the oxide ion is larger than the fluoride ion because the O^{2-} ion has only eight protons available to attract ten electrons, whereas F^- has more protons (nine) to attract the same number of electrons. The effect of nuclear charge is evident when the sizes of isoelectronic ions across the periodic table are compared. Consider O^{2-}, F^-, Na^+, and Mg^{2+}.

Isoelectronic Ions	O^{2-}	F^-	Na^+	Mg^{2+}
Ionic radius (pm)	126	119	116	86
Number of protons	8	9	11	12
Number of electrons	10	10	10	10

Each ion contains ten electrons. However, the O^{2-} ion has only eight protons in its nucleus to attract these electrons, while F^- has nine, Na^+ has eleven, and Mg^{2+} has twelve. Thus, there is an increasing number of protons to attract the same number of electrons (10). As the electron-to-proton ratio decreases in an isoelectronic series of ions, such as those given, the overall electron cloud is attracted more tightly to the nucleus and the ion size shrinks, as seen for O^{2-} to Mg^{2+}.

PROBLEM-SOLVING EXAMPLE 7.12 Trends in Ionic Sizes

For each of these pairs, choose the smaller atom or ion:
(a) A Cu atom or a Cu^{2+} ion
(b) A Se atom or a Se^{2-} ion
(c) A Cu^{+} ion or a Cu^{2+} ion

Answer
(a) Cu^{2+} ion (b) Se atom (c) Cu^{2+} ion

Strategy and Explanation Consider the differences in the sizes of atoms and their corresponding ions based on electron loss or gain.
(a) A cation is smaller than its parent atom; therefore, Cu^{2+} is smaller than a Cu atom.
(b) Anions are larger than their parent atoms, so a Se^{2-} ion is larger than a selenium atom.
(c) Both copper ions contain 26 protons, but Cu^{2+} has one fewer electron than does Cu^{+}. Correspondingly, the radius of Cu^{2+} is smaller than that of Cu^{+}.

PROBLEM-SOLVING PRACTICE 7.12

Which of these isoelectronic ions, Ba^{2+}, Cs^{+}, or La^{3+}, will be (a) the largest? (b) the smallest?

7.11 Periodic Trends: Ionization Energies

An element's chemical reactivity is determined, in part, by how easily valence electrons are removed from its atoms, a process that requires energy. The **ionization energy** of an atom is the energy needed to remove an electron from that atom in the gas phase. For a gaseous sodium atom, the ionization process is

$$Na(g) \longrightarrow Na^{+}(g) + e^{-} \qquad \Delta E = \text{ionization energy (IE)}$$

Because energy is always required to remove an electron, the process is endothermic, and the sign of the ionization energy is always positive. The more difficult an electron is to remove, the greater its ionization energy. ***For s- and p-block elements, first ionization energies (the energy needed to remove one electron from the neutral atom) generally decrease down a group and increase across a period*** (Figures 7.24 and 7.25). The decrease down a group reflects the increasing radii of the atoms—it is easier to remove a valence electron from a larger atom because the force of attraction between the electron and the nucleus is small due to the greater separation. Thus, for example, the ionization energy of Rb (403 kJ/mol) is less than that of K (419 kJ/mol) or Na (496 kJ/mol). Ionization energies increase across a period for the same reason that the radii decrease. Increasing nuclear charge attracts electrons in the same shell more tightly. However, as shown in Figure 7.25, the trend across a given period is not always smooth, as in the second, third, fourth, and fifth periods. The single *np* electron of the Group 3A element is more easily removed than one of the two *ns* electrons in the preceding Group 2A element. Another deviation occurs with Group 6A elements (ns^2np^4), which have smaller ionization energies than the Group 5A elements that precede them in the second, third, and fourth periods. Beginning in Group 6A, two electrons are assigned to the same *p* orbital. Thus, greater electron repulsion is experienced by the fourth *p* electron, making it easier to remove.

Ionization energies increase much more gradually across the period for the transition and inner transition elements than for the main group elements (Figure 7.24). Just as the atomic radii of transition elements change very little across a period, the ionization energy for the removal of an *ns* electron also shows small changes, until the *d* orbitals are filled (Zn, Cd, Hg).

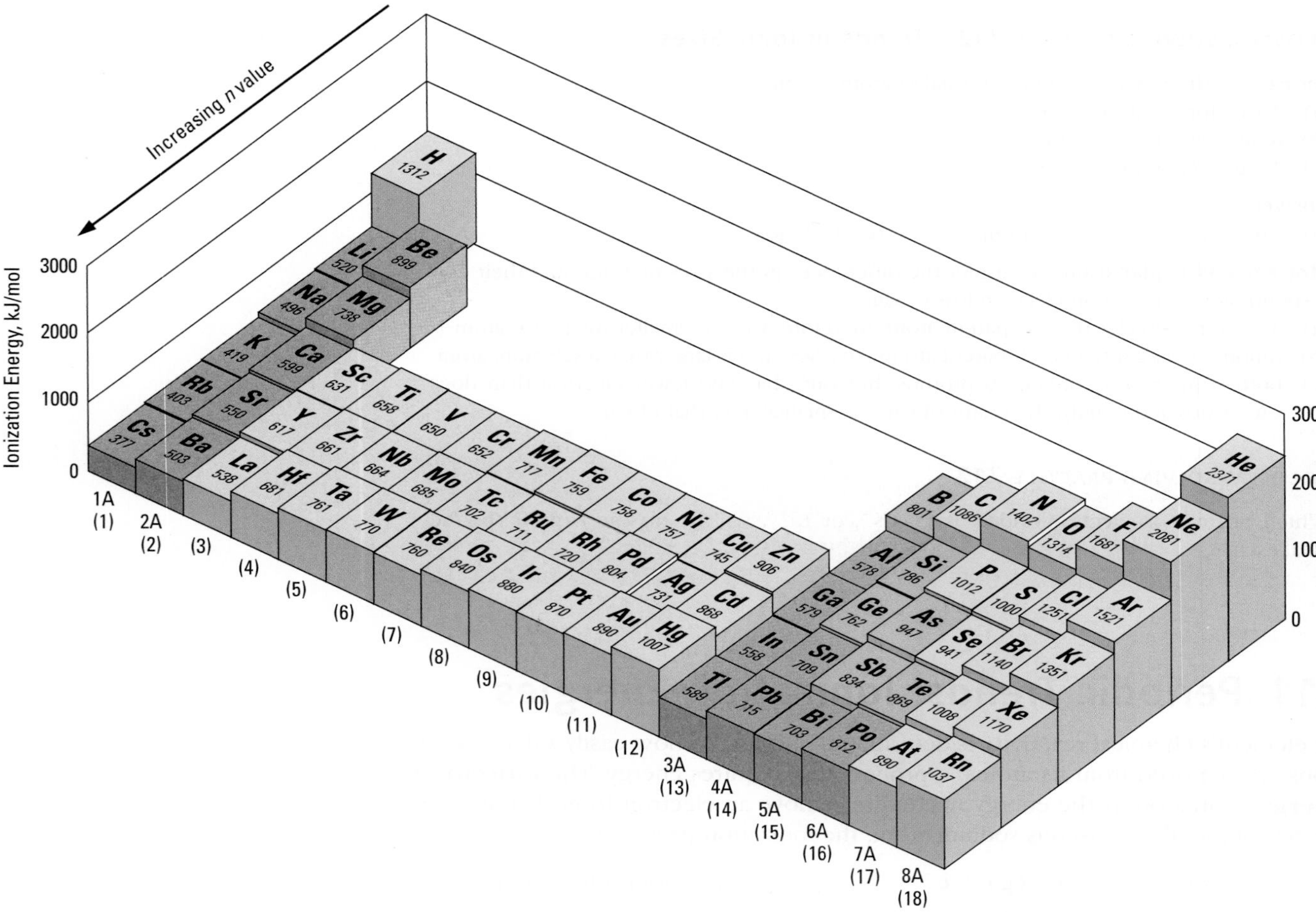

Figure 7.24 First ionization energies for elements in the first six periods.

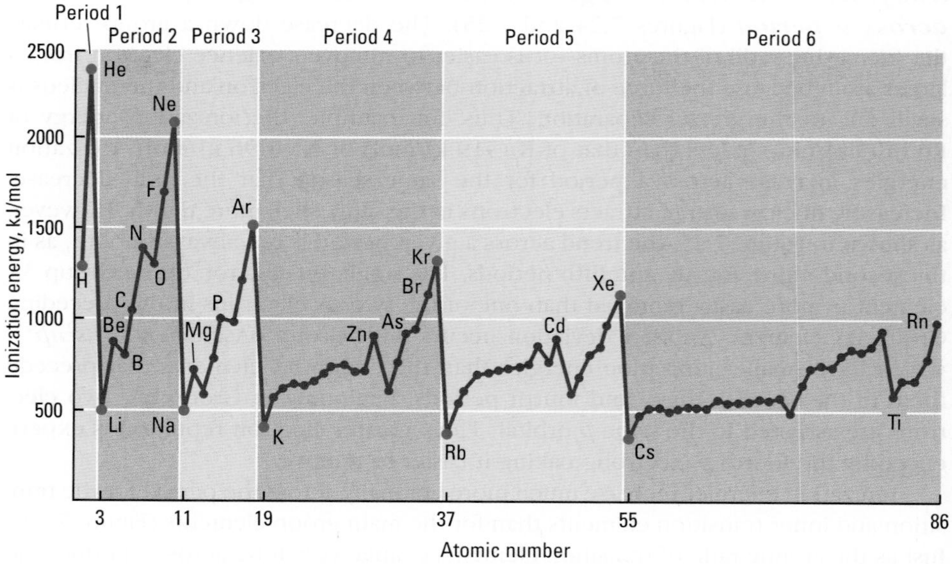

Figure 7.25 First ionization energies for elements in the first six periods plotted against atomic number.

Every atom except hydrogen has a series of ionization energies, since more than one electron can be removed. For example, the first three ionization energies of Mg in the gaseous state are

$$Mg(g) \longrightarrow Mg^+(g) + e^- \qquad IE_1 = 738 \text{ kJ/mol}$$
$$1s^22s^22p^63s^2 \qquad 1s^22s^22p^63s^1$$

$$Mg^+(g) \longrightarrow Mg^{2+}(g) + e^- \qquad IE_2 = 1450 \text{ kJ/mol}$$
$$1s^22s^22p^63s^1 \qquad 1s^22s^22p^6$$

$$Mg^{2+}(g) \longrightarrow Mg^{3+}(g) + e^- \qquad IE_3 = 7734 \text{ kJ/mol}$$
$$1s^22s^22p^6 \qquad 1s^32s^32p^5$$

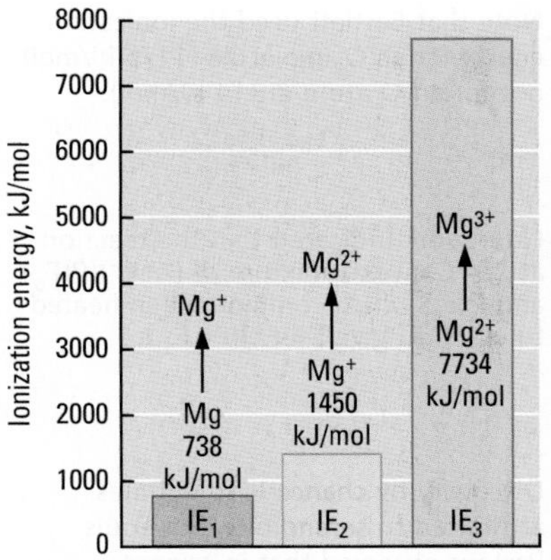

First three ionization energies for Mg.

Notice that removing each subsequent electron requires more energy, and the jump from the second (IE_2) to the third (IE_3) ionization energy of Mg is particularly great. The first electron removed from a magnesium atom comes from the 3*s* orbital. The second ionization energy corresponds to removing a 3*s* electron from a Mg^+ ion. As expected, the second ionization energy is higher than the first ionization energy because the electron is being removed from a positive ion, which strongly attracts the electron. The third ionization energy corresponds to removing a 2*p* electron, a core electron, from a filled *p* subshell in Mg^{2+}. The great difference between the second and third ionization energies for Mg is excellent experimental evidence for the existence of electron shells in atoms. Removal of the first core electron requires much more energy than removal of a valence electron. Table 7.8 gives the successive ionization energies of the second-period elements.

ThomsonNOW™
Go the Coached Problems menu to work a module on **ionization energy.**

Using Ionization Energies—The Discovery of Noble Gas Compounds

Earlier textbooks described these elements, all gases, as being inert—unreactive.

Due to their high ionization energies, helium and the other members of Group 8A were once considered to be completely inert to normal chemical attack by oxidizing agents, acids, and other reactants. All that changed in 1962 when Neil Bartlett, while studying PtF_6, noticed, quite by accident, that it reacted with oxygen to form $[O_2^+][PtF_6^-]$. In this compound, an oxygen molecule has lost an electron to form the

Table 7.8 Ionization Energies Required to Remove Successive Electrons from Second-Period Atoms

Ionization Energy (10^6 J/mol)	Li $1s^22s^1$	Be $1s^22s^2$	B $1s^22s^22p^1$	C $1s^22s^22p^2$	N $1s^22s^22p^3$	O $1s^22s^22p^4$	F $1s^22s^22p^5$	Ne $1s^22s^22p^6$
IE_1	0.52	0.90	0.80	1.09	1.40	1.31	1.68	2.08
IE_2	7.30	1.76	2.43	2.35	2.86	3.39	3.37	3.95
IE_3	11.81	14.85	3.66	4.62	4.58	5.30	6.05	6.12
IE_4		21.01	25.02	6.22	7.48	7.47	8.41	9.37
IE_5			32.82	37.83	9.44	10.98	11.02	12.18
IE_6				47.28	53.27	13.33	15.16	15.24
IE_7					64.37	71.33	17.87	20.00
IE_8		Core electrons				84.08	92.04	23.07
IE_9							106.43	115.38
IE_{10}								131.43

Note: In each of these elements the core electrons are those in the 1*s* orbital.

Note that Bartlett used the ionization energy for an O_2 molecule (1175 kJ/mol), not for an O atom (1314 kJ/mol).

O_2^+ ion. Bartlett realized that the ionization energy of O_2 (1175 kJ/mol) is almost the same as the ionization energy for the noble gas xenon (1170 kJ/mol). He suspected that if an oxygen molecule could lose an electron to form O_2^+ when 1175 kJ/mol was added, then an Xe atom could also lose an electron. When he tried the experiment, PtF_6 quickly reacted with Xe gas to form a red crystalline solid, which was assigned the formula $[Xe^+][PtF_6^-]$.

Later work indicated that the reaction at 25 °C gives a mixture of $[XeF^+][PtF_6^-]$ and PtF_5, which combine when heated to 60 °C to give $[XeF^+][Pt_2F_{11}^-]$.

As soon as Bartlett's discovery was announced, chemists in other laboratories quickly discovered that xenon would even react directly with fluorine at room temperature in sunlight to form XeF_2.

$$Xe(g) + F_2(g) \longrightarrow XeF_2(s)$$

Discovery by chance is sometimes attributed to serendipity, but Louis Pasteur observed that in science ". . . chance favors *only* the prepared mind."

This discovery was particularly enlightening for chemists, because it made them realize that something they had believed for 60 years—that noble gases do not react to form compounds—was not true. It illustrated how careful use of knowledge of periodic properties of the elements can advance what we know about chemistry.

PROBLEM-SOLVING EXAMPLE 7.13 Ionization Energies

Using only a periodic table, arrange these atoms in order of increasing first ionization energy: Al, Ar, Cl, Na, K, Si.

Answer K < Na < Al < Si < Cl < Ar

Strategy and Explanation Since ionization energy increases across a period, we expect the ionization energies for Ar, Al, Cl, Na, and Si, which are all in Period 3, to be in the order Na < Al < Si < Cl < Ar. Because K is below Na in Group 1A, the first ionization energy of K is less than that of Na. Therefore, the final order is K < Na < Al < Si < Cl < Ar.

PROBLEM-SOLVING PRACTICE 7.13

Use only a periodic table to arrange these elements in decreasing order of their first ionization energy: Na, F, N, P.

7.12 Periodic Trends: Electron Affinities

The **electron affinity** of an element is the energy change when an electron is added to a gaseous atom to form a 1− ion. As the term implies, the electron affinity (EA) is a measure of the attraction an atom has for an additional electron. For example, the electron affinity of fluorine is −328 kJ/mol.

$$\underset{[He]\,2s^22p^5}{F(g)} + e^- \longrightarrow \underset{[He]\,2s^22p^6}{F^-(g)} \qquad \Delta E = EA = -328 \text{ kJ/mol}$$

Two sign conventions are used for electron affinity—the one used here and an alternative one. The latter uses the opposite sign—for example, +328 kJ/mol for the electron affinity of fluorine.

This large negative value indicates that fluorine atoms readily accept an electron. As expected, fluorine and the rest of the halogens have large negative electron affinities because, by acquiring an electron, the halogen atoms achieve a stable octet of valence electrons, ns^2np^6 (Table 7.9). Notice from Table 7.9 that electron affinities generally become more negative across a period toward the halogen, which is only one electron away from a noble gas configuration.

Some elements have a positive electron affinity, meaning that the negative ion is less stable than the neutral atom. Such electron affinity values are difficult to obtain experimentally, and the electron affinity is simply indicated as > 0, as in the case of neon.

$$\underset{[He]\,2s^22p^6}{Ne} + e^- \longrightarrow \underset{[He]\,2s^22p^63s^1}{Ne^-} \qquad EA > 0 \text{ kJ/mol}$$

Table 7.9 Electron Affinities (kJ/mol)

1A (1)	2A (2)	3A (13)	4A (14)	5A (15)	6A (16)	7A (17)	8A (18)
H −73							He >0
Li −60	Be >0	B −27	C −122	N >0	O −141	F −328	Ne >0
Na −53	Mg >0	Al −43	Si −134	P −72	S −200	Cl −349	Ar >0
K −48	Ca −2	Ga −30	Ge −119	As −78	Se −195	Br −325	Kr >0
Rb −47	Sr −5	In −30	Sn −107	Sb −103	Te −190	I −295	Xe >0

The Ne^- ion would revert back to the neutral neon atom and an electron. From their electron configurations we can understand why the Ne^- ion would be less stable than the neutral neon atom; the anion would exceed the stable octet of valence electrons of Ne atoms.

7.13 Ion Formation and Ionic Compounds

Energy is released when an alkali metal and a nonmetal react to form a salt. For example, the vigorous reaction of sodium metal and chlorine gas forms sodium chloride, NaCl, along with the transfer of energy to the surroundings (Figure 7.26).

$$Na(s) + \tfrac{1}{2} Cl_2(g) \longrightarrow NaCl(s) \qquad \Delta H_f^\circ = -410.9 \text{ kJ}$$

As described in Chapter 3, solid sodium chloride contains Na^+ and Cl^- ions grouped in a crystal lattice of alternating cations and anions (Figure 7.27). Sodium atoms have low ionization energy and readily lose their $3s^1$ outer electron; chlorine atoms have a high electron affinity and accept the electron into a $3p$ orbital. Thus, electron transfer occurs from sodium metal atoms to chlorine atoms during NaCl formation (⇐ ***Figure 3.1, p. 90***). The transfer of electrons converts sodium and chlorine atoms into Na^+ and Cl^- ions, each of which has an octet of outer electrons, a very stable configuration.

$$Na\ 1s^22s^22p^63s^1 \longrightarrow Na^+\ 1s^22s^22p^6 + e^- \qquad \text{Ionization energy} = 496 \text{ kJ}$$

$$Cl\ 1s^22s^22p^63s^23p^5 + e^- \longrightarrow Cl\ 1s^22s^22p^63s^23p^6 \qquad \text{Electron affinity} = -349 \text{ kJ}$$

7.14 Energy Considerations in Ionic Compound Formation

As seen in Figure 7.26, energy changes occur during the formation of an ionic compound such as NaCl. These energy changes can be considered by applying Hess's law to a series of reactions (⇐ ***p. 246***) including ionization energy and electron affinity. Consider, for example, potassium fluoride, an ionic compound containing

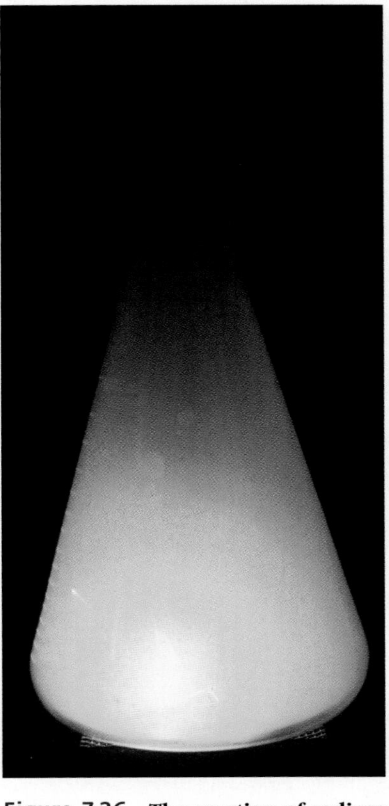

© Thomson Learning/Charles D. Winters

Figure 7.26 The reaction of sodium with chlorine. The reaction liberates heat and light and forms Na^+ and Cl^- ions.

Figure 7.27 **A sodium chloride crystal illustrating the arrangement of Na^+ and Cl^- ions in a lattice structure.**

ThomsonNOW
Go to the Coached Problems menu to work a module on **ion charge.**

K^+ and F^- ions, formed by the reaction of potassium, a very reactive alkali metal, and fluorine, a highly reactive halogen. The standard molar enthalpy of formation, ΔH_f°, of KF is −567.27 kJ/mol.

$$K(s) + \tfrac{1}{2}F_2(g) \longrightarrow KF(s) \qquad \Delta H_f^\circ = -567.27 \text{ kJ}$$

Electron configurations: K [Ar] $4s^1$; F [He] $2s^22p^5$; K^+ [Ar]; F^- [Ne]

If you write the electron configuration for K and F, you will see that in this reaction electron transfer occurs from potassium atoms to fluorine atoms to yield K^+ and F^- ions, each with an octet of outer electrons. These ions aggregate to form KF, an ionic crystalline solid. We can evaluate the energy required to form the ions and the solid compound by applying Hess's law to a series of five hypothetical steps, known as the **Born-Haber cycle,** as outlined below and illustrated in Figure 7.28. When combined with the thermochemical expression for enthalpy of formation, such a hypothetical multistep sequence allows the calculation of the lattice energy of the crystal.

This cycle is named for Max Born and Fritz Haber, two Nobel Prize–winning German scientists.

Step 1: *Convert solid potassium to gaseous potassium atoms.* This is the enthalpy of sublimation, ΔH_1, which is +89 kJ for 1 mol potassium.

$$K(s) \longrightarrow K(g) \qquad \Delta H_1 = +89 \text{ kJ/mol}$$

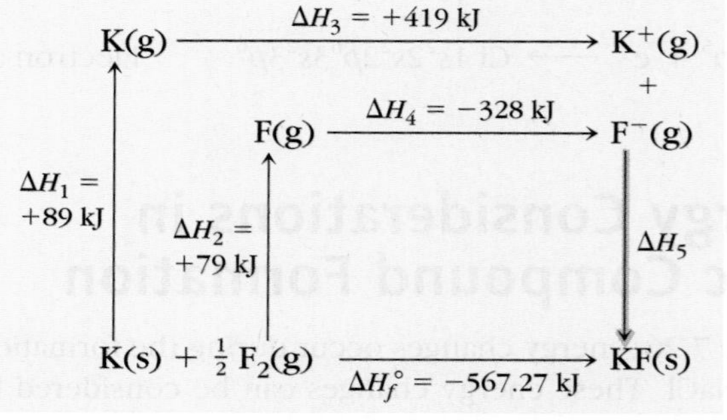

Figure 7.28 **Born-Haber cycle for KF.**

Step 2: *Dissociate F_2 molecules into F atoms.* One mol of KF contains 1 mol fluorine, so $\frac{1}{2}$ mol F_2 is required. Breaking the bonds in diatomic fluorine molecules requires energy. This energy, ΔH_2, is +79 kJ, one half of the bond enthalpy of F_2, that is, $\frac{1}{2}$ (158 kJ/mol).

$$\tfrac{1}{2}\ F_2(g) \longrightarrow F(g)$$

$$\Delta H_2 = \tfrac{1}{2}\ \text{BE of } F_2 = \tfrac{1}{2}\ \text{mol}\ (+158\ \text{kJ/mol}) = +79\ \text{kJ}$$

Step 3: *Convert gaseous potassium atoms to gaseous potassium ions.* The energy, ΔH_3, required to remove the $4s^1$ electron is the first ionization energy, IE_1, of potassium, +419 kJ, which can be obtained from Figure 7.24, page 316.

$$K(g) \longrightarrow K^+(g) + e^- \qquad \Delta H_3 = IE_1 = +419\ \text{kJ/mol}$$

Step 4: *Form F^- ions from F atoms.* The addition of a sixth electron to the $2p$ subshell completes the octet of valence electrons for F^-. For the formation of 1 mol F^- ions, this energy, ΔH_4, is the electron affinity (EA) of F, −328 kJ, which can be obtained from Table 7.9, page 319.

$$F(g) + e^- \longrightarrow F^-(g) \qquad \Delta H_4 = EA = -328\ \text{kJ}$$

Step 5: *Consolidate gaseous K^+ and F^- ions into a crystal.* The cations and anions assemble into a crystal, releasing a significant amount of energy due to the attraction between oppositely charged ions. This energy, ΔH_5, known as the **lattice energy**, is the enthalpy change when 1 mol of an ionic solid is formed from its separated gaseous ions.

$$K^+(g) + F^-(g) \longrightarrow KF(s) \qquad \Delta H_5 = \text{lattice energy of KF}$$

Therefore, the sum of the enthalpy changes in the five steps of the Born-Haber cycle represents the total enthalpy change in the overall reaction of solid potassium metal with gaseous fluorine to produce potassium fluoride. According to Hess's law, the sum of these enthalpy changes must equal the standard molar enthalpy of formation (ΔH_f°) of KF, which is experimentally measured as −567.27 kJ (see thermochemical expressions, p. 320).

$$\Delta H_f^\circ = -567.27\ \text{kJ} = \Delta H_1 + \Delta H_2 + \Delta H_3 + \Delta H_4 + \Delta H_5$$

Data for Steps 1–4 can be determined experimentally, but lattice energies cannot easily be measured directly. Instead, we can apply Hess's law in a Born-Haber cycle to calculate the lattice energy for KF, ΔH_5, using data from Steps 1–4 and the enthalpy of formation, −567.27 kJ.

$$-567.27\ \text{kJ} = 89\ \text{kJ} + 79\ \text{kJ} + 419\ \text{kJ} + (-328\ \text{kJ}) + \Delta H_5$$

$$\begin{aligned}\Delta H_5 &= \text{lattice energy of KF} \\ &= (-567.27\ \text{kJ}) + (-89\ \text{kJ}) + (-79\ \text{kJ}) + (-419\ \text{kJ}) + (328\ \text{kJ}) \\ &= -826\ \text{kJ}\end{aligned}$$

ThomsonNOW
Go to the Chemistry Interactive menu to work modules on:
- **formation of ionic solids**
- **Born-Haber cycle**

Notice that the formation of the gaseous cations and anions from the respective elements (Steps 1–4) is not energetically favorable (Figure 7.28). The net enthalpy change for these four steps in the cycle is positive, +259 kJ. The solid compound forms because of the very large lattice energy released during the assembling of the gaseous cations and anions into the solid. It is the lattice energy, not the formation of K^+ and F^- ions, that drives the formation of solid KF (Figure 7.28).

The strength of the ionic bonding in a crystal—its lattice energy—depends on the strength of the electrostatic interactions among the crystal's cations and anions. In a crystal lattice there are attractive forces between oppositely charged ions and

Table 7.10 Effect of Ion Size and Charge on Lattice Energy and Melting Point

Compound	Charges of Ions	$r_+ + r_-$	Lattice Energy (kJ/mol)	Melting Point (K)
NaCl	1+, 1−	116 pm + 167 pm = 283 pm	−786	1073
BaO	2+, 2−	149 pm + 126 pm = 275 pm	−3054	2193
MgO	2+, 2−	86 pm + 126 pm = 212 pm	−3791	3073

repulsive forces between ions of like charge. All of these forces obey Coulomb's law (⟵ ***p. 93***). Both attractive and repulsive forces are affected in the same proportion by two factors:

- *The sizes of the charges on the cation and the anion.* As the charges get larger (from 1+ and 1− to 2+ and 2−, etc.), both attractive and repulsive forces among the ions increase.
- *The distances among the ions.* The forces increase as the distances decrease. The shortest distance is $r_+ + r_-$, where r_+ is the cation radius and r_- is the anion radius. The distances among ions of like charge increase or decrease in proportion to this shortest distance. The smaller the ionic radii, the shorter the distances among the ions.

Ions are arranged in a crystal lattice so that the attractive forces predominate over the repulsive forces. This makes the energy lower when the ions are in a crystal lattice than when they are completely separated from one another. Because the energy of the crystal lattice is lower than for the separated ions (that is, a mole of KF(s) is lower in energy than a mole of separated K^+ and F^- ions), the lattice energy is negative. The stronger the net ionic attractions are, the more negative the lattice energy is and the more stable the crystal lattice is. Thus, crystal lattices are more stable for small ions of large charge.

Compounds with large negative lattice energies have high melting points. The entries in Table 7.10 exemplify this trend. Consider NaCl and BaO. In both compounds the sum of the ionic radii of the cation and anion is about the same; it is 283 pm for NaCl and 275 pm for BaO. However, the product of the charges differs by a factor of four [(1+) × (1−)] for NaCl versus [(2+) × (2−)] for BaO. This charge factor of four is reflected in a lattice energy (−3054 kJ/mol) and a melting point (2193 K) for BaO that are much larger than the lattice energy (−786 kJ/mol) and the melting point (1073 K) of NaCl. The effect of cation size can be seen by comparing MgO and BaO. Because Mg^{2+} ($r_+ = 86$ pm) is much smaller than Ba^{2+} ($r_+ = 149$ pm), the 2+ charge on magnesium ion is more concentrated (higher charge density) than the 2+ charge on barium ion. Consequently, the net attractive force between Mg^{2+} and O^{2-} is greater than the net attractive force between Ba^{2+} and O^{2-}, and the lattice energy for MgO is more negative. This results in a higher melting point for MgO (3073 K) than for BaO (2193 K).

SUMMARY PROBLEM

(a) Without looking back in the chapter, draw and label the first five energy levels of a hydrogen atom. Next, indicate the $2 \rightarrow 1$, $3 \rightarrow 1$, $5 \rightarrow 2$, and $4 \rightarrow 3$ transitions in a hydrogen atom. Look in Table 7.2 to get the measured wavelengths and spectral regions for these transitions. Now calculate the frequencies (ν) for these transitions. Next, calculate the energies of the photons that are produced in these transitions.

(b) The photoelectric threshold is the minimum wavelength a photon must have to produce a photoelectric effect for a metal. These three metals exhibit photoelectric effects when photons of sufficient energies strike their surfaces.

Element	Photoelectric Threshold (nm)
Lithium	540
Potassium	550
Cesium	660

Which photon energies calculated in part (a) would be sufficient to cause a photoelectric effect in lithium, in potassium, and in cesium?

(c) Vanadium, V, is a transition element named after Vanadis, the Scandinavian goddess of beauty, because of the range of beautiful colors observed among vanadium compounds. Vanadium forms a series of oxides in which vanadium ions are V^{2+} (in VO), V^{3+} (in V_2O_3), V^{4+} (in VO_2), and V^{5+} (in V_2O_5).

(i) Write the full electron configuration for a vanadium atom.

(ii) Using the noble gas notation, write the electron configuration for a V^{2+} ion.

(iii) Write the orbital box diagram for a V^{3+} ion.

(iv) How many unpaired electrons are in the V^{4+} ion?

(v) Write the set of four quantum numbers for each valence electron in a V^{2+} ion.

(vi) Is the V^{5+} ion paramagnetic? Explain.

(d) An element is brittle with a steel-gray appearance. It is a relatively poor electrical conductor and forms a volatile molecular chloride and a molecular hydride that decomposes at room temperature. Is the element an alkaline earth metal, a transition metal, a metalloid, or a halogen? Explain your answer.

(e) Give two ways in which *p* orbitals and *d* orbitals are (i) alike; (ii) different.

IN CLOSING

ThomsonNOW™
Sign in to ThomsonNOW at **www.thomsonedu.com** to check your readiness for an exam by taking the Pre-Test and exploring the modules recommended in your Personalized Learning Plan.

Having studied this chapter, you should be able to . . .

- Use the relationships among frequency, wavelength, and the speed of light for electromagnetic radiation (Section 7.1). ThomsonNOW homework: Study Questions 14, 16
- Explain the relationship between Planck's quantum theory and the photoelectric effect (Section 7.2). ThomsonNOW homework: Study Question 32
- Use the Bohr model of the atom to interpret line emission spectra and the energy absorbed or emitted when electrons in atoms change energy levels (Section 7.3). ThomsonNOW homework: Study Question 40
- Calculate the frequency, energy, or wavelength of an electron transition in a hydrogen atom and determine in what region of the electromagnetic spectrum the emission would occur (Section 7.3). ThomsonNOW homework: Study Question 44

- Explain the use of the quantum mechanical model of the atom to represent the energy and probable location of electrons (Section 7.4). ThomsonNOW homework: Study Question 58
- Apply quantum numbers (Section 7.5). ThomsonNOW homework: Study Questions 52, 54
- Understand the spin properties of electrons and how they affect electron configurations and the magnetic properties of atoms (Section 7.5). ThomsonNOW homework: Study Question 87
- Describe and explain the relationships among shells, subshells, and orbitals (Section 7.5). ThomsonNOW homework: Study Question 56
- Describe how the shapes of *s*, *p*, and *d* orbitals and their sets of the first three quantum numbers differ (Section 7.6).
- Use the periodic table to write the electron configurations of atoms and ions of main group and transition elements (Sections 7.7 and 7.8). ThomsonNOW homework: Study Questions 66, 69, 74
- Explain variations in valence electrons, electron configurations, ion formation, and paramagnetism of transition metals (Section 7.8). ThomsonNOW homework: Study Question 76
- Explain how nuclear magnetic resonance works and how it is used in chemical analysis and medical diagnosis (*Tools of Chemistry*). ThomsonNOW homework: Study Question 91
- Describe trends in atomic radii, based on electron configurations (Section 7.9). ThomsonNOW homework: Study Question 94
- Describe the role of effective nuclear charge in the trend of atomic radii across a period (Section 7.9).
- Describe trends in ionic radii and explain why ions differ in size from their atoms (Section 7.10). ThomsonNOW homework: Study Question 96
- Use electron configurations to explain trends in the ionization energies of the elements (Section 7.11). ThomsonNOW homework: Study Questions 98, 102
- Describe electron affinity (Section 7.12).
- Describe the relationship between ion formation and the formation of ionic compounds (Section 7.13).
- Discuss the energy changes that occur during the formation of an ionic compound from its elements (Section 7.14).
- Use a Born-Haber cycle to determine the lattice energy of an ionic compound (Section 7.14). ThomsonNOW homework: Study Question 110

KEY TERMS

atomic radius *(7.9)*
Born-Haber cycle *(7.14)*
boundary surface *(7.4)*
continuous spectrum *(7.3)*
core electrons *(7.7)*
diamagnetic *(7.8)*
effective nuclear charge *(7.9)*
electromagnetic radiation *(7.1)*
electron affinity *(7.12)*
electron configuration *(7.7)*
electron density *(7.4)*
excited state *(7.3)*
ferromagnetic *(7.8)*
frequency *(7.1)*
ground state *(7.3)*
Hund's rule *(7.7)*
ionic radii *(7.10)*
ionization energy *(7.11)*
isoelectronic *(7.8)*
lattice energy *(7.14)*
Lewis dot symbol *(7.7)*
line emission spectrum *(7.3)*
momentum *(7.4)*
noble gas notation *(7.7)*

nuclear magnetic resonance (NMR) *(p. 308)*
orbital *(7.4)*
orbital shape *(7.6)*
paramagnetic *(7.8)*
Pauli exclusion principle *(7.5)*
***p*-block elements** *(7.7)*
photoelectric effect *(7.2)*
photons *(7.2)*
Planck's constant *(7.2)*
principal energy level *(7.5)*
principal quantum number *(7.3)*
quantum *(7.2)*
quantum number *(7.5)*
quantum theory *(7.2)*
radial distribution plot *(7.6)*
***s*-block elements** *(7.7)*
screening effect *(7.9)*
shell *(7.5)*
spectrum *(7.1)*
subshell *(7.5)*
transition elements *(7.7)*
uncertainty principle *(7.4)*
valence electrons *(7.7)*
wavelength *(7.1)*

QUESTIONS FOR REVIEW AND THOUGHT

■ denotes questions available in ThomsonNOW and assignable in OWL.

Blue-numbered questions have short answers at the back of this book and fully worked solutions in the *Student Solutions Manual*.

ThomsonNOW™
Assess your understanding of this chapter's topics with sample tests and other resources found by signing in to ThomsonNOW at **www.thomsonedu.com**.

Review Questions

1. How is the frequency of electromagnetic radiation related to its wavelength?
2. Light is given off by a sodium- or mercury-containing streetlight when the atoms are excited in some way. The light you see arises for which of these reasons?
   (a) Electrons moving from a given quantum level to one of higher n.
   (b) Electrons being removed from the atom, thereby creating a metal cation.
   (c) Electrons moving from a given quantum level to one of lower n.
   (d) Electrons whizzing about the nucleus in an absolute frenzy.
3. What is Hund's rule? Give an example of the use of this rule.
4. Explain what it means when an electron occupies the $3p_x$ orbital.
5. Tell what happens to atomic size and ionization energy across a period and down a group.
6. Why is the radius of Na^+ much smaller than the radius of Na? Why is the radius of Cl^- much larger than the radius of Cl?
7. Write electron configurations to show the first two ionization steps for potassium. Explain why the second ionization energy is much larger than the first.
8. Explain how the sizes of atoms change and why they change across a period of the periodic table.
9. Write the electron configurations for the valence electrons of elements in the first three periods in Groups 1A through 8A.

Topical Questions

Electromagnetic Radiation

10. Electromagnetic radiation that is high in energy consists of waves that have __________ (long or short) wavelengths and __________ (high or low) frequencies. Give an example of radiation from the high-energy end of the electromagnetic spectrum.
11. Electromagnetic radiation that is low in energy consists of waves that have __________ (long or short) wavelengths and __________ (high or low) frequencies. Give an example of radiation from the low-energy end of the electromagnetic spectrum.
12. The regions of the electromagnetic spectrum are shown in Figure 7.1. Answer these questions on the basis of this figure.
    (a) Which type of radiation involves less energy, radio waves or infrared radiation?
    (b) Which radiation has the higher frequency, radio waves or microwaves?
13. The colors of the visible spectrum and the wavelengths corresponding to the colors are given in Figure 7.1.
    (a) Which colors of light involve photons with less energy than yellow light?
    (b) Which color of visible light has photons of greater energy, green or violet?
    (c) Which color of light has the greater frequency, blue or green?
14. ■ Assume that a microwave oven operates at a frequency of $1.00 \times 10^{11}\ s^{-1}$.
    (a) What is the wavelength of this radiation in meters?
    (b) What is the energy in joules per photon?
    (c) What is the energy per mole of photons?
15. IBM scientists have developed a prototype computer chip that operates at 350 GHz (1 GHz = 10^9 Hz).
    (a) What is its wavelength in meters? In nanometers (nm)?
    (b) Calculate its energy in joules.
16. ■ Place these types of radiation in order of increasing energy per photon.
    (a) Green light from a mercury lamp
    (b) X-rays from a dental X-ray
    (c) Microwaves in a microwave oven
    (d) An FM music station broadcasting at 89.1 MHz

17. Place these types of radiation in order of increasing energy per photon.
    (a) Radio signals
    (b) Radiation from a microwave oven
    (c) Gamma rays from a nuclear reaction
    (d) Red light from a neon sign
    (e) Ultraviolet radiation from a sun lamp
18. If green light has a wavelength of 495 nm, what is its frequency?
19. What kind of radiation has a frequency of 5×10^{12} Hz? What is its wavelength?
20. What is the energy of one photon of blue light that has a wavelength of 450 nm?
21. Which has more energy,
    (a) One photon of infrared radiation or one photon of microwave radiation?
    (b) One photon of yellow light or one photon of orange light?
22. Which kinds of electromagnetic radiation can interact with molecules at the cellular level?
23. What is the energy and wavelength associated with one quantum of laser light that has a frequency of $4.57 \times 10^{14}\ s^{-1}$?
24. Stratospheric ozone absorbs damaging UV-C radiation from the sun, preventing the radiation from reaching the earth's surface. Calculate the frequency and energy of UV-C radiation that has a wavelength of 270 nm.
25. When someone uses a sunscreen, which kind of radiation will be blocked? How does the sunscreen protect your skin from this type of radiation?
26. Calculate the energy of one photon of X-radiation having a wavelength of 2.36 nm, and compare it with the energy of one photon of orange light (3.18×10^{-19} J).
27. Green light of wavelength 516 nm is absorbed by an atomic gas. Calculate the energy difference between the two quantum states involved with this absorption.
28. Calculate the energy possessed by one mole of X-ray photons of wavelength 1.00×10^{-9} m.

Photoelectric Effect

29. Describe the role Einstein's explanation of the photoelectric effect played in the development of the quantum theory.
30. Light of very long wavelength strikes a photosensitive metallic surface and no electrons are ejected. Explain why increasing the intensity of this light on the metal still will not cause the photoelectric effect.
31. Photons of light with sufficient energy can eject electrons from a gold surface. To do so requires photons with a wavelength equal to or shorter than 257 nm. Will photons in the visible region of the spectrum dislodge electrons from a gold surface?
32. ■ To eject electrons from the surface of potassium metal requires a minimum energy of 3.69×10^{-19} J. When 600.-nm photons shine on a potassium surface, will they cause the photoelectric effect?
33. A bright red light strikes a photosensitive surface and no electrons are ejected, even though dim blue light ejects electrons from the surface. Explain.

Atomic Spectra and the Bohr Atom

34. How does a line emission spectrum differ from sunlight?
35. Any atom with its electrons in their lowest energy levels is said to be in a(n) __________ state.
36. Energy is emitted from an atom when an electron moves from the __________ state to the __________ state. The energy of the emitted radiation corresponds to the __________ between the two energy levels.
37. Which transition involves the emission of less energy in the H atom, an electron moving from $n = 4$ to $n = 3$ or an electron moving from $n = 3$ to $n = 1$? (See Figure 7.8.)
38. For which of these transitions in a hydrogen atom is energy absorbed? Emitted?
    (a) $n = 1$ to $n = 3$ (b) $n = 5$ to $n = 1$
    (c) $n = 2$ to $n = 4$ (d) $n = 5$ to $n = 4$
39. For the transitions in Question 38:
    (a) Which ones involve the ground state?
    (b) Which one involves the greatest energy change?
    (c) Which one absorbs the most energy?
40. ■ If energy is absorbed by a hydrogen atom in its ground state, the atom is excited to a higher energy state. For example, the excitation of an electron from the energy level with $n = 1$ to a level with $n = 4$ requires radiation with a wavelength of 97.3 nm. Which of these transitions would require radiation of a wavelength longer than this? (See Figure 7.8.)
    (a) $n = 2$ to $n = 4$ (b) $n = 1$ to $n = 3$
    (c) $n = 1$ to $n = 5$ (d) $n = 3$ to $n = 5$
41. (a) Calculate the wavelength, in nanometers, of the emission line that results from the $n = 2$ to $n = 1$ transition in hydrogen.
    (b) The emitted radiation is in what region of the electromagnetic spectrum?
42. Spectroscopists have observed He^+ in the outer space. This ion is a one-electron species like a neutral hydrogen atom. Calculate the energy emitted for the transition from the $n = 5$ to the $n = 3$ state in this ion using the equation $E_n = -\frac{Z^2}{n^2}(2.179 \times 10^{-18}\text{ J})$. Z is the positive charge of the nucleus and n is principal quantum number. In what part of the electromagnetic spectrum does this radiation lie?
43. The Brackett series of emissions has $n_f = 4$.
    (a) Calculate the wavelength, in nanometers, of the $n = 7$ to $n = 4$ electron transition.
    (b) The emitted radiation is in what region of the electromagnetic spectrum?
44. ■ The Bohr equation for hydrogen can be modified to apply to one-electron species other than neutral hydrogen atoms, for example Li^{2+}, to calculate the energy of electron transitions in the ion. The modified equation is $E_n = -\frac{Z^2}{n^2}(2.179 \times 10^{-18}\text{ J})$. Z is the positive charge of the nucleus and n is the principal quantum number. Calculate the energy emitted for the transition from the $n = 4$ to the $n = 1$ state in this ion. In what region of the electromagnetic spectrum does it lie?
45. Calculate the energy and the wavelength of the electron transition from $n = 1$ to $n = 4$ in the hydrogen atom.
46. Calculate the energy and wavelength for the electron transition from $n = 2$ to $n = 5$ in the hydrogen atom.

de Broglie Wavelength

47. Calculate the de Broglie wavelength of a 4400-lb sport-utility vehicle moving at 75 miles per hour.
48. Calculate the de Broglie wavelength of an electron moving at 5% the speed of light.

Quantum Numbers

49. Assign a set of four quantum numbers for
    (a) *Each* electron in a nitrogen atom.
    (b) The valence electron in a sodium atom.
    (c) A $3d$ electron in a nickel atom.
50. Assign a correct set of four quantum numbers for
    (a) *Each* electron in a boron atom.
    (b) The $3s$ electrons in a magnesium atom.
    (c) A $3d$ electron in an iron atom.
51. One electron has the set of quantum numbers $n = 3$, $\ell = 1$, $m_\ell = -1$, and $m_s = +\frac{1}{2}$; another electron has the set $n = 3$, $\ell = 1$, $m_\ell = 1$, and $m_s = +\frac{1}{2}$.
    (a) Could the electrons be in the same atom? Explain.
    (b) Could they be in the same orbital? Explain.
52. ■ Some of these sets of quantum numbers (n, ℓ, m_ℓ, m_s) could not occur. Explain why.
    (a) 2, 1, 2, $+\frac{1}{2}$ (b) 3, 2, 0, $-\frac{1}{2}$
    (c) 1, 0, 0, 1 (d) 3, 3, 2, $-\frac{1}{2}$
    (e) 2, 0, 0, $+\frac{1}{2}$
53. Give the n, ℓ, and m_ℓ values for
    (a) Each orbital in the $6f$ sublevel.
    (b) Each orbital in the $n = 5$ level.
54. ■ Assign a correct set of four quantum numbers for the circled electrons in these orbital diagrams.

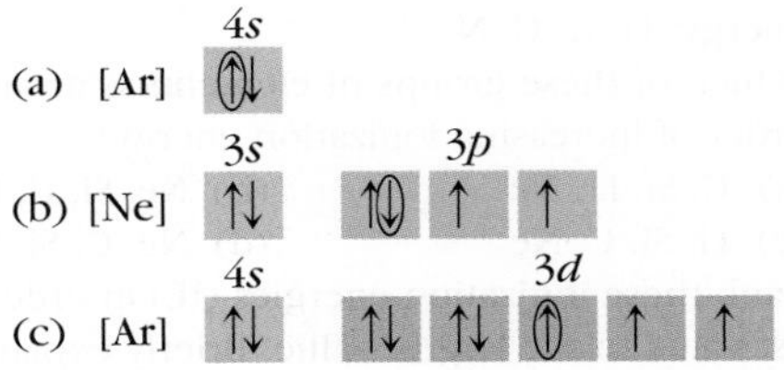

Quantum Mechanics

55. From memory, sketch the shape of the boundary surface for each of these atomic orbitals:
    (a) $2p_z$ (b) $4s$
56. ■ How many subshells are there in the electron shell with the principal quantum number $n = 4$?
57. How many subshells are there in the electron shell with the principal quantum number $n = 5$?
58. ■ Bohr pictured the electrons of the atom as being located in definite orbits about the nucleus, just as planets orbit the sun. Criticize this model in view of the quantum mechanical model.
59. Radiation is not the only thing that has both wave-like and particle-like characteristics. What component of matter can also be described in the same way?
60. How did the Heisenberg uncertainty principle illustrate the fundamental flaw in Bohr's model of the atom?
61. The three-dimensional boundary surfaces describing the probability of finding an electron and the energy of an electron can both be obtained from the ____________ of the electron.
62. Which type of orbitals are found in the $n = 3$ shell? How many orbitals altogether are found in this shell?

Electron Configurations

63. ■ Write electron configurations for Mg and Cl atoms.
64. Write electron configurations for Al and S atoms.
65. Write electron configurations for these atoms.
    (a) Strontium (Sr), named for a town in Scotland.
    (b) Tin (Sn), a metal used in the ancient world. Alloys of tin (solder, bronze, and pewter) are important.
66. ■ Germanium had not been discovered when Mendeleev formulated his ideas of chemical periodicity. He predicted its existence, however, and germanium was found in 1886 by Winkler. Write the electron configuration of germanium.
67. Name an element of Group 3A. What does the group designation tell you about the electron configuration of the element?
68. Name an element of Group 6A. What does the group designation tell you about the electron configuration of the element?
69. ■ (a) Which ions in this list are likely to be formed: K^{2+}, Cs^+, Al^{4+}, F^{2-}, Se^{2-}?
    (b) Which, if any, of these ions have a noble gas configuration?
70. These ground state orbital diagrams are incorrect. Explain why they are incorrect and how they should be corrected.

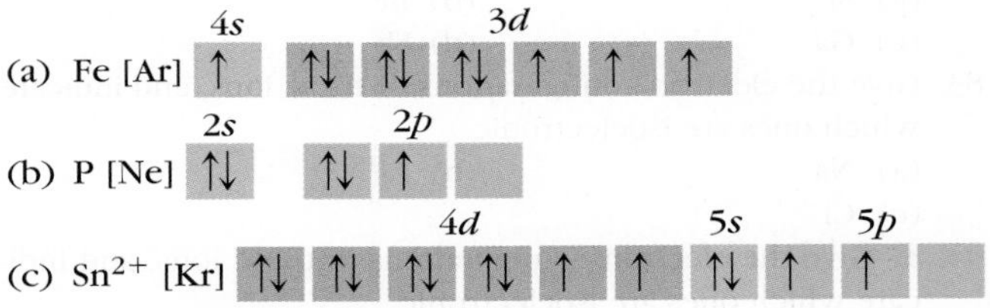

71. Write the orbital diagrams for
    (a) A nitrogen atom and a nitride, N^{3-}, ion.
    (b) The $3p$ electrons of a sulfur atom and a sulfide, S^{2-}, ion.
72. Write the orbital diagram for the $4s$ and $3d$ electrons in a
    (a) Vanadium atom. (b) V^{2+} ion.
    (c) V^{4+} ion.
73. Write the orbital diagram for the $4s$ and $3d$ electrons in a
    (a) Manganese atom. (b) Mn^+ ion.
    (c) Mn^{5+} ion.
74. ■ How many elements are there in the fourth period of the periodic table? Explain why it is not possible for there to be another element in this period.
75. When transition metals form ions, electrons are lost first from which type of orbital? Why?
76. ■ Give the electron configurations of Mn, Mn^{2+}, and Mn^{3+}. Use orbital box diagrams to determine the number of unpaired electrons for each species.

77. Write the electron configurations of chromium: Cr, Cr^{2+}, and Cr^{3+}. Use orbital box diagrams to determine the number of unpaired electrons for each species.
78. Write the electron configuration of sulfur, S. The element was known to the ancients as brimstone.
79. Write electron configurations for these elements.
(a) Zirconium (Zr). This metal is exceptionally resistant to corrosion and so has important industrial applications. Moon rocks show a surprisingly high zirconium content compared with rocks on earth.
(b) Rhodium (Rh), used in jewelry and in industrial catalysts.
80. The lanthanides, or rare earths, are only "medium rare." All can be purchased for a reasonable price. Give electron configurations for atoms of these lanthanides.
(a) Europium (Eu), the most expensive of the rare earth elements; 1 g can be purchased for about $90.
(b) Ytterbium (Yb). Less expensive than Eu, Yb costs only about $12 per gram. It was named for the village of Ytterby in Sweden, where a mineral source of the element was found.

Valence Electrons

81. Locate these elements in the periodic table, and draw a Lewis dot symbol that represents the number of valence electrons for an atom of each element.
(a) F (b) In
(c) Te (d) Cs
82. ■ Locate these elements in the periodic table, and draw a Lewis dot symbol that represents the number of valence electrons for an atom of each element.
(a) Sr (b) Br
(c) Ga (d) Sb
83. Give the electron configurations of these ions, and indicate which ones are isoelectronic.
(a) Na^+ (b) Al^{3+}
(c) Cl^-
84. ■ Give the electron configurations of these ions, and indicate which ones are isoelectronic.
(a) Ca^{2+} (b) K^+
(c) O^{2-}
85. What is the electron configuration for
(a) A bromine atom? (b) A bromide ion?
86. (a) What is the electron configuration for an atom of tin?
(b) What are the electron configurations for Sn^{2+} and Sn^{4+} ions?

Paramagnetism and Unpaired Electrons

87. ■ (a) In the first transition series (in row four of the periodic table), which elements would you predict to be diamagnetic?
(b) Which element in this series has the greatest number of unpaired electrons?
88. What is ferromagnetism?
89. Which groups of elements in the periodic table are ferromagnetic?
90. How do the spins of unpaired electrons from paramagnetic and ferromagnetic materials differ in their behavior in a magnetic field?

Tools of Chemistry: NMR and MRI

91. ■ What kind of electromagnetic radiation is used in nuclear magnetic resonance (NMR)?
92. In magnetic resonance imaging (MRI), the intensity of the emitted signal is related to the __________ of hydrogen nuclei and the relaxation time is related to the type of tissue being examined.

Periodic Trends

93. Arrange these elements in order of increasing size: Al, B, C, K, Na. (Try doing it without looking at Figure 7.21 and then check yourself by looking up the necessary atomic radii.)
94. ■ Arrange these elements in order of increasing size: Ca, Rb, P, Ge, Sr. (Try doing it without looking at Figure 7.21 and then check yourself by looking up the necessary atomic radii.)
95. Select the atom or ion in each pair that has the larger radius.
(a) Cl or Cl^- (b) Ca or Ca^{2+}
(c) Al or N (d) Cl^- or K^+
(e) In or Sn
96. ■ Select the atom or ion in each pair that has the smaller radius.
(a) Cs or Rb (b) O^{2-} or O
(c) Br or As (d) Ba or Ba^{2+}
(e) Cl^- or Ca^{2+}
97. Write electron configurations to show the first two ionization steps for sodium. Explain why the second ionization energy is much larger than the first.
98. ■ Arrange these atoms in order of increasing first ionization energy: F, Al, P, Mg.
99. Arrange these atoms in order of increasing first ionization energy: Li, K, C, N.
100. Which of these groups of elements is arranged correctly in order of increasing ionization energy?
(a) C, Si, Li, Ne (b) Ne, Si, C, Li
(c) Li, Si, C, Ne (d) Ne, C, Si, Li
101. Rank these ionization energies (IE) in order from the smallest value to the largest value. Briefly explain your answer.
(a) First IE of Be (b) First IE of Li
(c) Second IE of Be (d) Second IE of Na
(e) First IE of K
102. ■ Predict which of these elements would have the greatest difference between the first and second ionization energies: Si, Na, P, Mg. Briefly explain your answer.
103. Compare the elements Li, K, C, N.
(a) Which has the largest atomic radius?
(b) Place the elements in order of increasing first ionization energy.
104. ■ Compare the elements B, Al, C, Si.
(a) Which has the most metallic character?
(b) Which has the largest atomic radius?
(c) Place the three elements B, Al, and C in order of increasing first ionization energy.
105. Explain why the transition elements in a row are more alike in their properties than other elements in the same groups.
106. Select the atom or ion in each pair that has the larger radius. Explain your choice.
(a) H^+ or H^- (b) N or N^{3-}
(c) F^- or Ne

107. Explain why nitrogen has a higher first ionization energy than does carbon, the preceding element in the periodic table.
108. The first electron affinity of oxygen is negative, the second is positive. Explain why this change in sign occurs.
109. Which group of the periodic table has elements with high first ionization energies *and* very negative electron affinities? Explain this behavior.

Born-Haber Cycle

110. ■ Determine the lattice energy for LiCl(s) given these data: Enthalpy of sublimation of Li, 161 kJ; IE_1 for Li, 520 kJ; BE of $Cl_2(g)$, 242 kJ; electron affinity of Cl, −349 kJ; enthalpy of formation of LiCl(s), −408.7 kJ.
111. The lattice energy of KCl(s) is −719 kJ/mol. Use data from the text to calculate the enthalpy of formation of KCl.

General Questions

112. Arrange these colors of the visible region of the electromagnetic spectrum in order of increasing energy per photon: green, red, yellow, and violet.
113. A neutral atom has two electrons with $n = 1$, eight electrons with $n = 2$, eight electrons with $n = 3$, and one electron with $n = 4$. Assuming this element is in its ground state, supply its
(a) Atomic number and name.
(b) Total number of *s* electrons.
(c) Total number of *p* electrons.
(d) Total number of *d* electrons.
114. How many *p* orbital electron pairs are there in an atom of selenium (Se) in its ground state?
115. Give the symbol of all the ground state elements that have
(a) No *p* electrons.
(b) From two to four *d* electrons.
(c) From two to four *s* electrons.
116. Give the symbol of the ground state element that
(a) Is in Group 8A but has no *p* electrons.
(b) Has a single electron in the 3*d* subshell.
(c) Forms a 1+ ion with a $1s^22s^22p^6$ electron configuration.
117. Answer these questions about the elements X and Z, which have the electron configurations shown.

$$X = [Kr]\ 4d^{10}5s^1 \qquad Z = [Ar]\ 3d^{10}4s^24p^4$$

(a) Is element X a metal or a nonmetal?
(b) Which element has the larger atomic radius?
(c) Which element would have the greater first ionization energy?
118. (a) Rank these in order of increasing atomic radius: O, S, F.
(b) Which has the largest first ionization energy: P, Si, S, Se?
119. (a) Place these in order of increasing radius: Ne, O^{2-}, N^{3-}, F^-.
(b) Place these in order of increasing first ionization energy: Cs, Sr, Ba.
120. Name the element corresponding to each of these characteristics.
(a) The element whose atoms have the electron configuration $1s^22s^22p^63s^23p^4$
(b) The element in the alkaline earth group that has the largest atomic radius
(c) The element in Group 5A whose atoms have the largest first ionization energy
(d) The element whose 2^+ ion has the configuration [Kr] $4d^6$
(e) The element whose neutral atoms have the electron configuration [Ar] $3d^{10}4s^1$
121. The ionization energies for the removal of the first electron from atoms of Si, P, S, and Cl are listed in the following table. Briefly rationalize this trend.

Element	First Ionization Energy (kJ/mol)
Si	780
P	1060
S	1005
Cl	1255

122. Answer these questions about the elements with the electron configurations shown.

$$X = [Ar]\ 3d^84s^2 \qquad Z = [Ar]\ 3d^{10}4s^24p^5$$

(a) An atom of which element is expected to have the larger first ionization energy?
(b) An atom of which element would be the smaller of the two?
123. Place these atoms and ions in order of decreasing size: Ar, K^+, Cl^-, S^{2-}, Ca^{2+}.
124. Which of these ions are unlikely, and why: Cs^+, In^{4+}, V^{6+}, Te^{2-}, Sn^{5+}, I^-?
125. Rank these in order of increasing first ionization energy: Zn, Ca, Ca^{2+}, Cl^-. Briefly explain your answer.
126. Classify these statements as being either true or false. If a statement is false, correct it to make it true.
(a) The wavelength of green light is longer than that of red light.
(b) Photons of green light have greater energy than those of red light.
(c) The frequency of green light is greater than that of red light.
(d) In the electromagnetic spectrum, frequency and wavelength of radiation are directly related.
127. Classify these statements as being either true or false. If a statement is false, correct it to make it true.
(a) A 3*f* orbital can hold a maximum of 14 electrons.
(b) The ground state electron configuration of a sulfur atom is $1s^22s^22p^63s^23p^4$.
(c) A ground state sulfur atom has four unpaired electrons.
(d) A Mg^{2+} ion has an argon electron configuration.
(e) A N^{3-} ion and a P^{3-} ion have the same ground-state electron configuration.
128. Criticize these statements.
(a) The energy of a photon is inversely related to its frequency.
(b) The energy of the hydrogen electron is inversely proportional to its principal quantum number *n*.
(c) Electrons start to enter the fourth energy level as soon as the third level is full.
(d) Light emitted by an $n = 4$ to $n = 2$ transition will have a longer frequency than that from an $n = 5$ to $n = 2$ transition.

129. A general chemistry student tells a chemistry classmate that when an electron goes from a $2d$ orbital to a $1s$ orbital, it emits more energy than that for a $2p$ to $1s$ transition. The other student is skeptical and says that such an energy change is not possible and explains why. What explanation was given?

130. Which of these types of radiation—infrared, visible, or ultraviolet—is required to ionize a hydrogen atom? Explain.

131. A certain minimum energy, E_{min}, is required to eject an electron from a photosensitive surface. Any energy absorbed beyond this minimum gives kinetic energy to the ejected electron. When 540-nm light falls on a cesium surface, an electron is ejected with a kinetic energy of 6.69×10^{-20} J. When the wavelength is 400 nm, the kinetic energy is 1.96×10^{-19} J.
   (a) Calculate E_{min} for cesium, in joules.
   (b) Calculate the longest wavelength, in nanometers, that will eject an electron from cesium.

132. Suppose a new element, extraterrestrium, tentatively given the symbol Et, has just been discovered. Its atomic number is 120.
   (a) Write the electron configuration of the element.
   (b) Name another element you would expect to find in the same group as Et.
   (c) Give the formulas for the compounds of Et with O and Cl.

133. When sulfur dioxide reacts with chlorine, the products are thionyl chloride ($SOCl_2$) and dichlorine monoxide (OCl_2).

$$SO_2(g) + 2\,Cl_2(g) \longrightarrow SOCl_2(g) + OCl_2(g)$$

   (a) In what period of the periodic table is S located?
   (b) Give the complete electron configuration of S. Do *not* use the noble gas notation.
   (c) An atom of which element involved in this reaction (O, S, or Cl) should have the smallest first ionization energy? The smallest radius?
   (d) If you want to make 675 g $SOCl_2$, what mass in grams of Cl_2 is required?
   (e) If you use 10.0 g SO_2 and 20.0 g Cl_2, what is the theoretical yield of $SOCl_2$?

Applying Concepts

134. Write the electron configuration for the product of the first ionization of the smallest halogen.

135. ■ Write the electron configuration for the product of the second ionization of the third largest alkaline earth metal.

136. What compound will most likely form between chlorine and element X, if element X has the electronic configuration $1s^22s^22p^63s^1$?

137. Write the formula for the compound that most likely forms between potassium and element Z, if element Z has the electronic configuration $1s^22s^22p^63s^23p^4$.

138. ■ Which of these electron configurations are for atoms in the ground state? In excited states? Which are impossible?
   (a) $1s^22s^1$ (b) $1s^22s^22p^3$
   (c) [Ne] $3s^23p^34s^1$ (d) [Ne] $3s^23p^64s^33d^2$
   (e) [Ne] $3s^23p^64f^4$ (f) $1s^22s^22p^43s^2$

139. Which of these electron configurations are for atoms in the ground state? In excited states? Which are impossible?
   (a) $1s^22s^2$ (b) $1s^22s^23s^1$
   (c) [Ne] $3s^23p^84s^1$ (d) [He] $2s^22p^62d^2$
   (e) [Ar] $4s^23d^3$ (f) [Ne] $3s^22p^54s^1$

140. Using the information in Appendix D and Figure 7.17, write the electron configuration for the undiscovered element with an atomic number of 164. Where would this element be located in the periodic table?

141. These questions refer to the graph below.

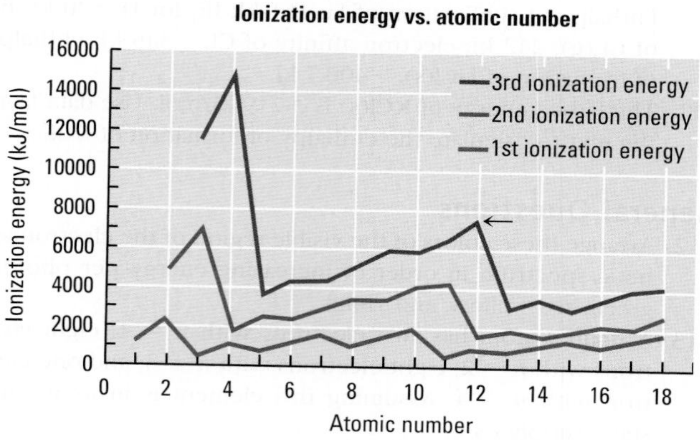

   (a) Based on the graphic data, ionization energies ________ (decrease, increase) left to right and ________ (decrease, increase) top to bottom on the periodic table.
   (b) Which element has the largest first ionization energy?
   (c) A plot of the fourth ionization energy versus atomic number for elements 1 through 18 would have peaks at which atomic numbers?
   (d) Why is there no third ionization energy for helium?
   (e) What is the reason for the large second ionization energy for lithium?
   (f) Find the arrow pointing to the third ionization energy curve. Write the equation for the process corresponding to this data point.

142. Use Coulomb's law to predict which substance in each of these pairs has the larger lattice energy.
   (a) CaO or KI (b) CaF_2 or BaF_2
   (c) KCl or LiBr

More Challenging Questions

143. An element has an ionization energy of 1.66×10^{-18} J. The three longest wavelengths in its absorption spectrum are 253.7 nm, 185.0 nm, and 158.5 nm.
   (a) Construct an energy-level diagram similar to Figure 7.8 for this element.
   (b) Indicate all possible emission lines. Start from the highest energy level on the diagram.

144. The energy of a photon needed to cause ejection of an electron from a photoemissive metal is expressed as the sum of the binding energy of the photon plus the kinetic energy of the emitted electron. When photons of 4.00×10^{-7} m light

strike a calcium metal surface, electrons are ejected with a kinetic energy of 6.3×10^{-20} J.

(a) Calculate the binding energy of the calcium electrons.

(b) The minimum frequency at which the photoelectric effect occurs for a metal is that for which the emitted electron has no kinetic energy. Calculate the minimum frequency required for the photoelectric effect to occur with calcium metal.

145. Calculate the kinetic energy of an electron that is emitted from a strontium metal surface irradiated with photons of 4.20×10^{-7} m light. The binding energy of strontium is 4.39×10^{-19} J. See Question 144 for a statement about binding energy.

146. Ionization energy is the minimum energy required to remove an electron from a ground state atom. According to Niels Bohr, the total energy of an electron in a stable orbit of quantum number n is equal to

$$E_n = -\frac{Z^2}{n^2}(2.18 \times 10^{-18}\text{ J})$$

where Z is the atomic number. Calculate the ionization energy for the electron in a ground state hydrogen atom.

147. Ionization energy is the minimum energy required to remove an electron from a ground state atom. According to the relationship developed by Niels Bohr, the total energy, E_n, of an electron in a stable orbit of quantum number n is equal to $E_n = -[Z^2/n^2]$ $(2.18 \times 10^{-18}$ J) where Z is the atomic number. Calculate the ionization energy for the electron in a ground state He^+ ion.

148. Oxygen atoms are smaller than nitrogen atoms, yet oxygen has a lower first ionization energy than nitrogen. Explain.

149. Beryllium atoms are larger than boron atoms, yet boron has a lower first ionization energy than beryllium. Explain.

150. The element Meitnerium, Mt, honors Lise Meitner for her role in the discovery of nuclear fission.

(a) Meitnerium atoms have the same outer electron configuration as what transition metal?

(b) Using the noble gas notation, write the electron configuration for a ground state Mt atom.

151. Suppose two electrons in the same system each have $n = 3$, $\ell = 0$.

(a) How many different electron arrangements would be possible if the Pauli exclusion principle did not apply in this case?

(b) How many would apply if it is operative?

152. Although yet unnamed, element 112 is known and its existence verified.

(a) The chemical properties of the element can be expected to be those of what kind of element—main group, transition metal, lanthanide, or actinide?

(b) Using the noble gas notation, write the electron configuration for a ground state atom of element 112 to corroborate your answer to part (a).

153. You are given the atomic radii of 110 pm, 118 pm, 120 pm, 122 pm, and 135 pm, but do not know to which element (As, Ga, Ge, P, Si) these values correspond. Which must be the value for Ge?

Conceptual Challenge Problems

CP7.A (Section 7.2) Planck stated in 1900 that the energy of a single photon of electromagnetic radiation was directly proportional to the frequency of the radiation ($E = h\nu$). The constant h is known as Planck's constant and has a value of 6.626×10^{-34} J · s. Soon after Planck's statement, Einstein proposed his famous equation ($E = mc^2$), which states that the total energy in any system is equal to its mass times the speed of light squared.

According to the de Broglie relation, what is the apparent mass of a photon emitted by an electron undergoing a change from the second to the first energy level in a hydrogen atom? How does the photon mass compare with the mass of the electron (9.109×10^{-31} kg)?

CP7.B (Section 7.7) When D. I. Mendeleev proposed a periodic law around 1870, he asserted that the properties of the elements are a periodic function of their atomic weights. Later, after H. G. J. Moseley measured the charge on the nuclei of atoms, the periodic law could be revised to state that the properties of the elements are a periodic function of their atomic numbers. What would be another way to define the periodic function that relates the properties of the elements?

CP7.C (Sections 7.3 and 7.11) Figure 7.8 shows a diagram of the energy states that an electron can occupy in a hydrogen atom. Use this diagram to show that the first ionization energy for hydrogen, given in Figure 7.24, is correct.

8 Covalent Bonding

Human body cells are made up of many thousands of compounds, most of which consist of atoms covalently bonded by sharing electron pairs. The chapter explains aspects of these kinds of bonds—their lengths, strengths, and polarities—and describes some molecular compounds and their covalent bonding.

© David DeLossy/Photodisc Green/Getty Images

Atoms of elements are rarely found uncombined in nature. Only the noble gases consist of individual atoms. Most nonmetallic elements consist of molecules, and in a solid metallic element each atom is closely surrounded by eight or twelve neighbors. What makes atoms stick to one another? Interactions among valence electrons of bonded atoms form the glue, but how? In ionic compounds, the transfer of one or more valence electrons from an atom of a metal to the valence shell of an atom of a nonmetal produces ions whose opposite charges hold the ions in a crystal lattice. Ionic compounds conduct an electric current when melted due to the mobile cations and anions present. But many other compounds, molecular compounds, do not conduct electricity when in the liquid state and correspondingly do not consist of ions. Examples are carbon monoxide (CO), water (H_2O), methane (CH_4), and the millions of organic compounds.

In these molecular compounds atoms are held together by bonds consisting of one or more pairs of electrons *shared* between the bonded atoms. The attraction of positively charged nuclei for electrons between them pulls the nuclei together. This simple idea can account for the bonding in nearly all molecular compounds, allowing us to correlate their structures with their physical and chemical properties. This chapter describes the bonding found in molecules ranging from simple diatomic gases to hydrocarbons and more complex molecules.

ThomsonNOW™
Throughout the text, this icon indicates an opportunity to test yourself on key concepts and to explore interactive modules by signing in to ThomsonNOW at **www.thomsonedu.com**.

8.1 Covalent Bonding

Previously we have seen that cations and anions form substances such as NaCl (Na^+ and Cl^-) and CaO (Ca^{2+} and O^{2-}) with characteristic properties (**p. 89**). Many everyday substances, such as CO_2, CH_4, and $C_6H_{12}O_6$ (glucose) are composed of molecules however, not ions. Molecular compounds have properties different from those of ionic compounds. For example, ionic compounds are solids at room temperature, but the molecular compound water, H_2O, is formed by the reaction of gaseous hydrogen (H_2) and oxygen (O_2), both diatomic molecules.

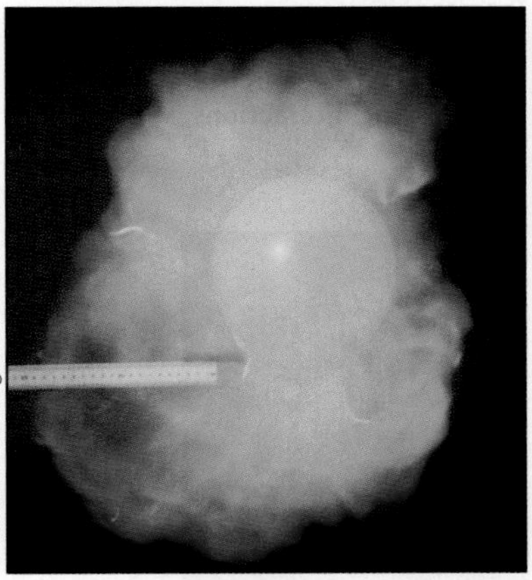

© Thomson Learning/Charles D. Winters

Hydrogen. A hydrogen-filled balloon burning in air forms water.

An explanation of bonding in the simplest molecule H_2 was proposed in 1916 by G. N. Lewis, who suggested that valence electrons rearrange to give noble gas electron configurations when atoms join together chemically. Lewis regarded the lack of reactivity of the noble gases as due to their stable electron configuration, a filled outermost shell. Lewis proposed that an attractive force called a **covalent bond** results when one or more pairs of electrons are shared between the bonded atoms. ***Covalent bonds, which are shared electron pairs, connect the atoms in molecular (covalent) compounds.*** For example, the two H atoms in H_2 and the H and Cl atoms in HCl are held together by covalent bonds.

But why does sharing electrons provide an attractive force between bonded atoms? Consider the formation of the simplest stable molecule, H_2. If the two hydrogen atoms are widely separated, there is little if any interaction between them. When the two atoms get close enough, however, their 1*s* electron clouds overlap.

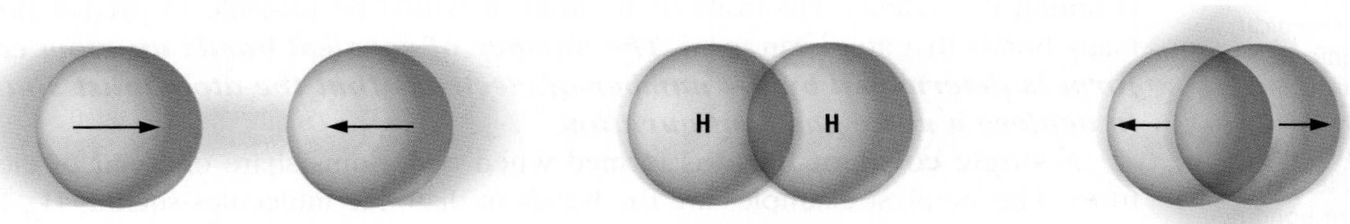

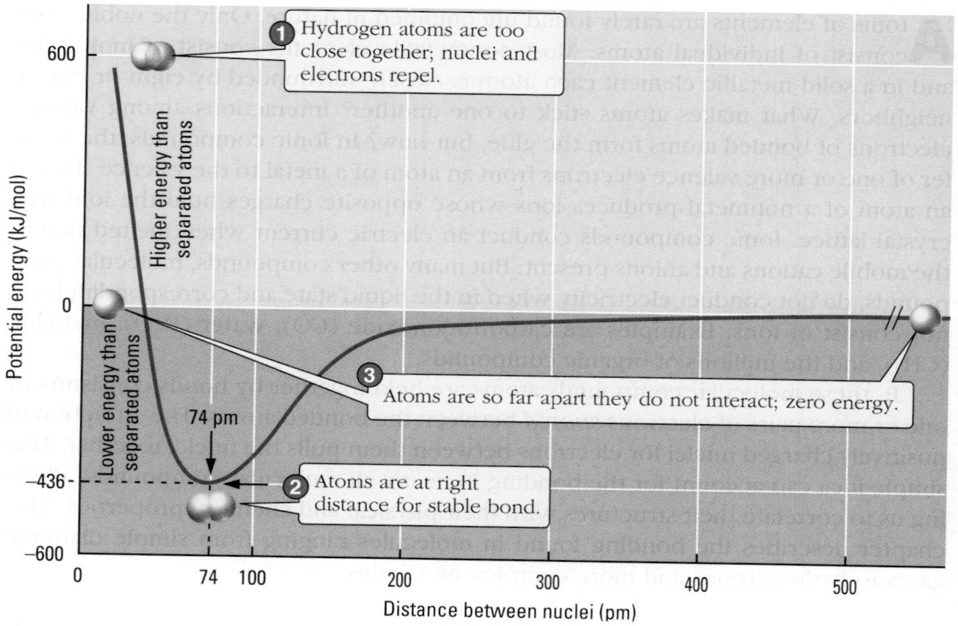

Figure 8.1 H—H bond formation from isolated H atoms. Energy is at a minimum at an internuclear distance of 74 pm, where there is a balance between electrostatic attractions and repulsions.

Lowering potential energy is favorable to bond formation.

ThomsonNOW™
Go to the Chemistry Interactive menu to work a module on **interatomic electrostatic interactions.**

This overlap allows the electron from each atom to be attracted by the other atom's nucleus, causing a net attraction between the two atoms. Experimental data and calculations indicate that an H_2 molecule has its lowest potential energy and is therefore most stable when the nuclei are 74 pm apart (Figure 8.1). At that distance, the attractive and repulsive electrostatic forces are balanced. If the nuclei get closer than 74 pm, repulsion of each nucleus by the other begins to take over. When the H nuclei are 74 pm apart—*the bond length*—it takes 436 kJ of energy to break the hydrogen-to-hydrogen covalent bonds when a mole of gaseous H_2 molecules is converted into isolated H atoms. This energy is the *bond energy* of H_2 **(⟸ p. 241)**.

Oesper Collection in the History of Chemistry, University of Cincinnati

Gilbert Newton Lewis
1875–1946

In 1916, G. N. Lewis introduced the theory of the shared electron pair chemical bond in a paper published in the *Journal of the American Chemical Society*. His theory revolutionized chemistry, and it is in honor of this contribution that we refer to "electron dot" structures as Lewis structures. Of particular interest in this text is the extension of his theory of bonding to a generalized theory of acids and bases (Section 16.9).

8.2 Single Covalent Bonds and Lewis Structures

The shared electron pairs of covalent bonds occupy the same shell as the valence electrons of each atom. For main group elements, the electrons commonly contribute to a noble gas configuration on each atom. Lewis further proposed that by counting the valence electrons of an atom, it would be possible to predict how many bonds that atom can form. ***The number of covalent bonds an atom can form is determined by the number of electrons that the atom must share to achieve a noble gas configuration.***

A **single covalent bond** is formed when two atoms share one pair of electrons. The simplest examples are the bonds in diatomic molecules such as H_2, F_2, and Cl_2, which, like other simple molecules, can be represented by Lewis structures. A **Lewis structure** for a molecule shows all valence electrons as dots or lines that represent covalent bonds.

Lewis structures are drawn by starting with the Lewis dot symbols for the atoms (⇐ ***p. 302, Table 7.6***) and arranging the valence electrons until each atom in the molecule has a noble gas configuration. For example, the Lewis structure for H_2 shows two bonding electrons shared between two hydrogen atoms.

ThomsonNOW
Go to the Coached Problems menu for a tutorial on **interpreting Lewis electron dot structures.**

H:H or H—H

The shared electron pair of a *single* covalent bond is often represented by a line instead of a pair of dots. Note that *each* hydrogen atom shares the pair of electrons, thereby achieving the same two-electron configuration as helium, the simplest noble gas.

Atoms with more than two valence electrons achieve a noble gas structure by sharing enough electrons to attain an octet of valence electrons. This is known as the **octet rule:** ***To form bonds, main group elements gain, lose, or share electrons to achieve a stable electron configuration characterized by eight valence electrons.*** To obtain the Lewis structure for F_2, for example, we start with the Lewis dot symbol for a fluorine atom. Fluorine, in Group 7A, has seven valence electrons, so there are seven dots, one less than an octet. If each F atom in F_2 shares one valence electron with the other F atom to form a shared electron pair, a single covalent bond forms, and each fluorine atom achieves an octet. ***Shared electrons are counted with each of the atoms in the bond.***

Achieving a noble gas configuration is also referred to as "obeying the octet rule" because all noble gases except helium have eight valence electrons.

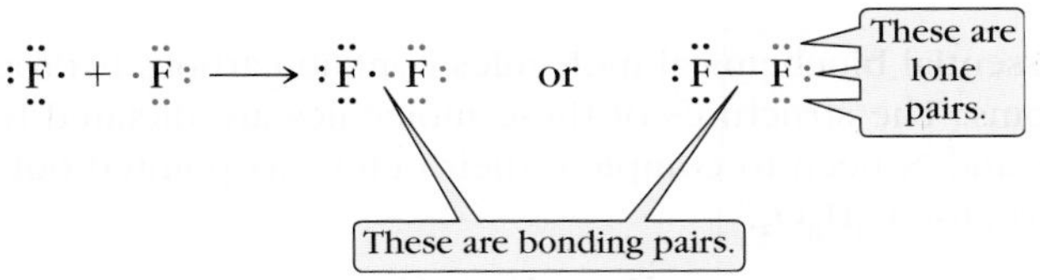

A Lewis structure such as that for F_2 shows valence electrons in a molecule as **bonding electrons** (shared electron pairs) and **lone pair electrons** (unshared pairs). In a Lewis structure the atomic symbols, such as F, represent the nucleus and core (nonvalence) electrons of each atom in the molecule. The pair of electrons shared between the two fluorine atoms is a *bonding electron pair.* The other three pairs of electrons on each fluorine atom are *lone pair electrons.* In writing Lewis structures, the bonding pairs of electrons are usually indicated by lines connecting the atoms they hold together; lone pairs are usually represented by pairs of dots.

The term "lone pairs" will be used in this text to refer to unshared electron pairs.

Magnetic measurements (Section 7.7) support the concept that each electron in a pair of electrons (bonding or lone pair) has its spin opposite that of the other electron.

What about Lewis structures for molecules such as H_2O or NH_3? Oxygen (Group 6A) has six valence electrons and must share two electrons to satisfy the octet rule. This can be accomplished by forming covalent bonds with two hydrogen atoms.

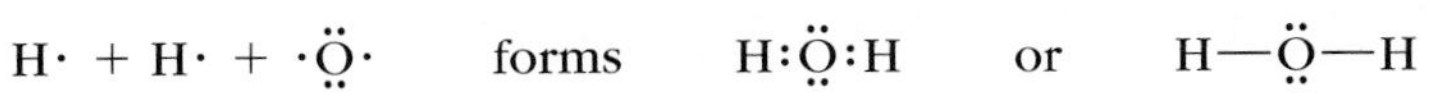

Nitrogen (Group 5A) in NH_3 must share three electrons to achieve a noble gas configuration, which can be done by forming covalent bonds with three hydrogen atoms.

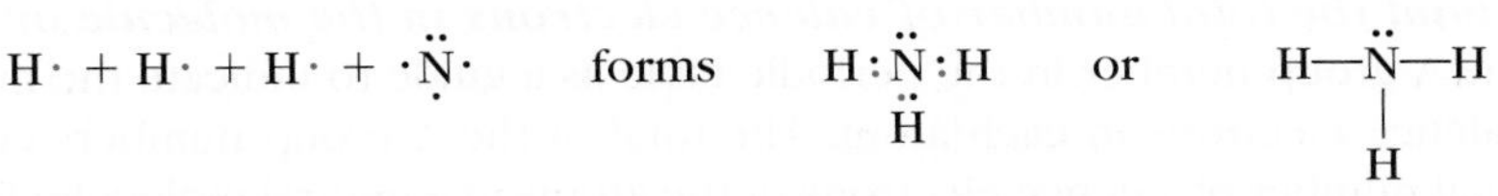

From the Lewis structures of F_2, H_2O, and NH_3, we can make an important generalization: ***The number of electrons that an atom of a main group element must share to achieve an octet equals eight minus its A group number.*** Carbon, for example, which is in Group 4A, needs to share four electrons to reach an octet.

Main group elements are those in the groups labeled "A" in the periodic table inside the front cover of this book.

Group Number	Number of Valence Electrons	Number of Electrons Shared to Complete an Octet (8 − A group number)	Example
4A	4	4	C in CH_4 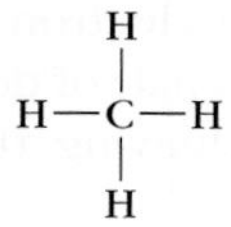
5A	5	3	N in NF_3 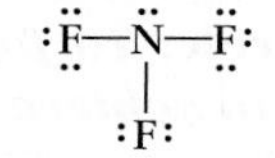
6A	6	2	O in H_2O 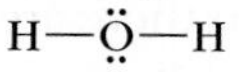
7A	7	1	F in HF 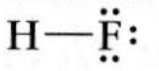

Many essential biochemical molecules contain carbon, hydrogen, oxygen, and nitrogen atoms. The structures of these molecules are dictated by the number of bonds C, O, and N need to complete their octets, as pointed out in the table. For example, glycerol, $C_3H_8O_3$,

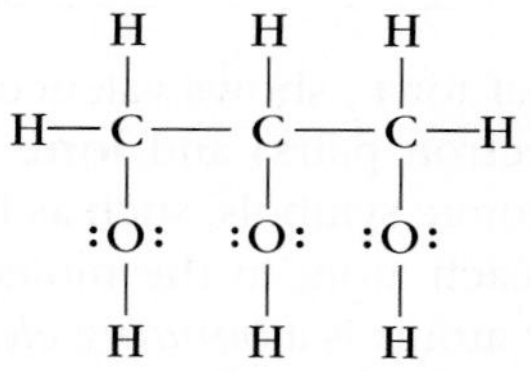

glycerol

is vital to the formation and metabolism of fats. In glycerol, each carbon atom has four shared pairs to complete an octet; each oxygen atom completes an octet by sharing two pairs and having two lone pairs; and hydrogen is satisfied by sharing two electrons. The same type of electron sharing occurs in deoxyribose, $C_5H_{10}O_4$, an essential component of DNA (deoxyribonucleic acid). Four of the carbon atoms are joined in a ring with an oxygen atom.

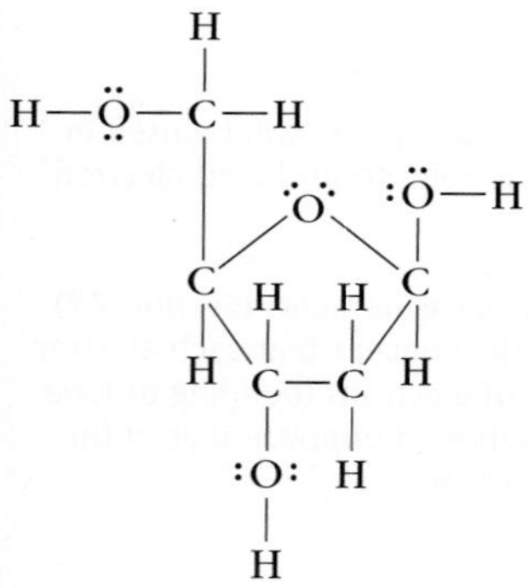

deoxyribose

ThomsonNOW
Go to the Coached Problems menu for a tutorial on **drawing Lewis structures.**

Guidelines for Writing Lewis Structures

Guidelines have been developed for writing Lewis structures correctly, and we will illustrate using these guidelines to write the Lewis structure for PCl_3.

1. ***Count the total number of valence electrons in the molecule or ion.*** Use the A group number in the periodic table as a guide to indicate the number of valence electrons in each atom. The total of the A group numbers equals the total number of valence electrons of the atoms in a neutral molecule. For a negative ion, add electrons equal to the ion's charge. For a positive ion, subtract the number of electrons equal to the charge. For example, add one electron for the negative charge of OH^- (total of eight valence electrons); subtract one electron for the positive charge of NH_4^+ (total of eight valence electrons: $5 + 4(1) - 1$).

   Because PCl_3 is a neutral molecule, its number of valence electrons is five for P (it is in Group 5A) and seven for *each* Cl (chlorine is in Group 7A): Total number of valence electrons $= 5 + (3 \times 7) = 26$.

2. ***Use atomic symbols to draw a skeleton structure by joining the atoms with shared pairs of electrons (a single line).*** A skeleton structure indicates the attachment of terminal atoms to a central atom. The central atom is usually the one written first in the molecular formula and is the one that can form the most bonds, such as Si in $SiCl_4$ and P in PO_4^{3-}. Hydrogen, oxygen, and the halogens are often terminal atoms. In PCl_3, the central atom is phosphorus, so we draw a skeleton structure with P as the central atom and the three terminal chlorine atoms arranged around it. The three bonding pairs account for six of the total of 26 valence electrons.

Although H is given first in the formulas of H_2O and H_2O_2, for example, it is not the central atom. H is never the central atom in a molecule or ion because hydrogen atoms form only one covalent bond.

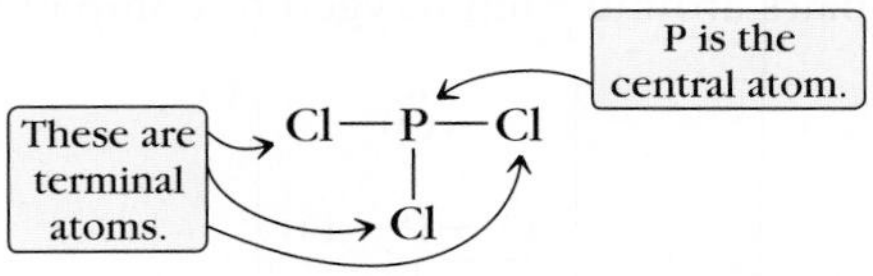

3. ***Place lone pairs of electrons around each atom (except H) to satisfy the octet rule, starting with the terminal atoms.*** Using lone pairs in this way on the Cl atoms accounts for 18 of the remaining 20 valence electrons, leaving two electrons for a lone pair on the P atom. When you check for octets, remember that shared electrons are counted as "belonging" to *each* of the atoms bonded by the shared pair. Thus, each P—Cl bond has two shared electrons that count for phosphorus and also count for chlorine.

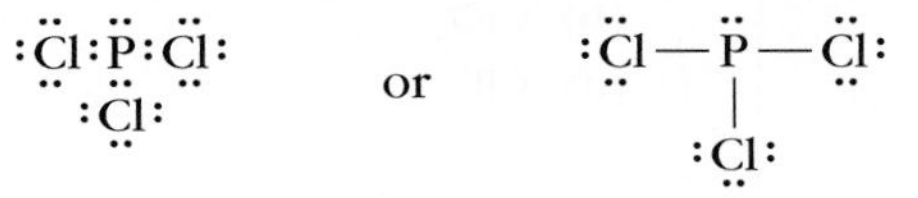

Counting dots and lines in the Lewis structure above shows 26 electrons, accounting for all valence electrons. This is the correct Lewis structure for PCl_3.

The next two steps apply when Steps 1 through 3 result in a structure that does not use all the valence electrons or fails to give an octet of electrons to each atom that should have an octet.

4. ***Place any leftover electrons on the central atom, even if it will give the central atom more than an octet.*** If the central atom is from the third or a higher period, it can accommodate more than an octet of electrons (Section 8.10). Sulfur tetrafluoride, SF_4, is such a molecule. It has a total of 34 valence electrons—six for S (Group 6A) plus seven for each F (Group 7A). In the Lewis structure, each F atom has an octet of electrons giving a total of 32. The remaining two valence electrons are on the central S atom, which, as a third-period element, can accommodate more than an octet of electrons.

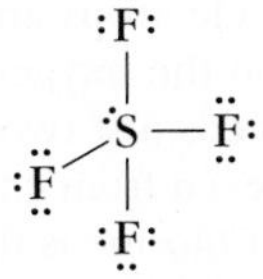

5. ***If the number of electrons around the central atom is less than eight, change single bonds to the central atom to multiple bonds.*** Some atoms can share more than one pair of electrons, resulting in a double covalent bond (two shared pairs) or a triple covalent bond (three shared pairs), known as *multiple bonds* (Section 8.4). Where multiple bonds are needed to complete an octet, use one or more lone pairs of electrons from the terminal atoms to form *double* (two shared pairs) or *triple* (three shared pairs) covalent bonds until the central atom and all terminal atoms have octets. This guideline does not apply to PCl_3, but will be illustrated in Section 8.4.

Double bond: two shared pairs of electrons, as in C=C.

Triple bond: three shared electron pairs, as in C≡N.

We apply these guidelines to write the Lewis structure of phosphate ion, PO_4^{3-}, which has a total of 32 valence electrons (five from P, six from each O, and three for the 3− charge). Phosphorus is the central atom and oxygens are the terminal atoms, giving a skeleton structure of

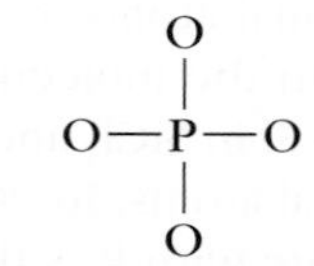

The four single P—O bonds account for eight of the valence electrons and provide phosphorus with an octet of electrons. The remaining 24 valence electrons are distributed as three lone pairs around each oxygen to complete their octets.

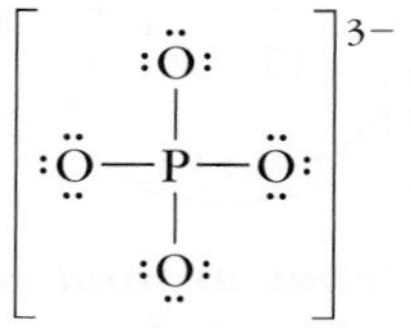

This is the correct Lewis structure for phosphate ion.

PROBLEM-SOLVING EXAMPLE 8.1 Lewis Structures

Write Lewis structures for these molecules or ions.

(a) HOCl (b) ClO_3^-

(c) SF_6 (d) ClF_4^+

Answer

(a) 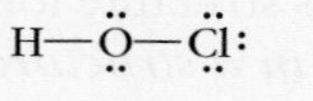 (b) 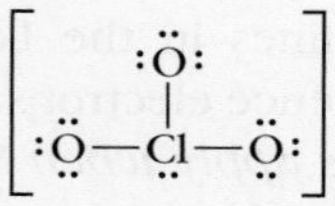

(c) 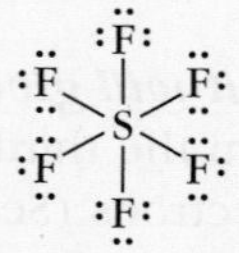 (d) 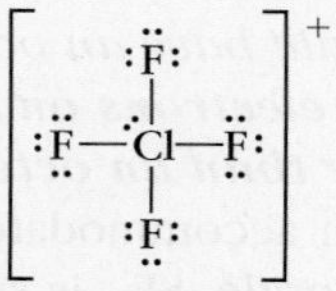

Strategy and Explanation Count up the total valence electrons and distribute them in such a way that each atom (except hydrogen) has an octet of electrons.

(a) There are 14 valence electrons, one from hydrogen (Group 1A), six from oxygen (Group 6A), and seven from chlorine (Group 7A). The central atom is O and the skeleton structure is H—O—Cl. This arrangement uses four of the 14 valence electrons. The remaining ten valence electrons are used by placing three lone pairs on the chlorine and two lone pairs on the oxygen, thereby satisfying the octet rule for oxygen and chlorine; hydrogen needs just two electrons.

(b) There are 26 valence electrons—seven from chlorine and six from each oxygen, plus one for the 1− charge of the ion. Chlorine is the central atom with the three oxygen atoms each single bonded to it. The bonding uses six of the 26 valence electrons, leaving 20 for lone pairs. Placing three lone pairs on each oxygen and a lone pair on chlorine satisfies the octet rule for each atom and uses up the remaining valence electrons.

(c) Sulfur forms more bonds than fluorine does, so sulfur is the central atom. There is a total of 48 valence electrons: six from sulfur (Group 6A) and seven from each fluorine (Group 7A) for a total of 42 from fluorine. Because sulfur is a Period 3 nonmetal, it can expand its octet to accommodate six fluorine atoms around it, an exception to the octet rule. The 48 valence electrons are distributed as six bonding pairs in S—F bonds and the remaining 36 valence electrons as three lone pairs around each of the six fluorine atoms.

(d) Chlorine, a Period 3 element, can accommodate more than an octet of electrons and is the central atom. There are 34 valence electrons: seven from chlorine, seven for each fluorine, and one subtracted for the 1+ charge. The 34 valence electrons are distributed as four pairs in the four Cl—F bonds and the remaining 26 valence electrons as three lone pairs on each fluorine and one lone pair on the chlorine, making chlorine in this case an exception to the octet rule.

PROBLEM-SOLVING PRACTICE 8.1

Write the Lewis structures for (a) NF_3, (b) N_2H_4, and (c) ClO_4^-.

Although Lewis structures are useful for predicting the number of covalent bonds an atom will form, they do not give an accurate representation of where electrons are located in a molecule. Bonding electrons do not stay in fixed positions between nuclei, as Lewis's dots might imply. Instead, quantum mechanics tells us that there is a high probability of finding the bonding electrons between the nuclei. Also, Lewis structures do not convey the shapes of molecules. The angle between the two O—H bonds in a water molecule is not 180°, as the Lewis structure in the margin seems to imply. However, Lewis structures can be used to predict geometries by a method based on the repulsions between valence shell electron pairs (Section 9.1).

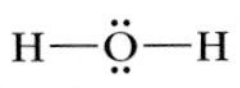

8.3 Single Covalent Bonds in Hydrocarbons

In hydrocarbons, carbon's four valence electrons are shared with hydrogen atoms or other carbon atoms. In methane, CH_4, the simplest hydrocarbon, the four valence electrons are shared with electrons from four hydrogen atoms, forming four single covalent bonds. The bonding in methane is represented by a Lewis structure and an *electron density model.* In an electron density model, a ball-and-stick model is surrounded by a space-filling model that represents the distribution of electron density on the surface of the molecule. ***Red indicates regions of higher electron density, and blue indicates regions of lower electron density.***

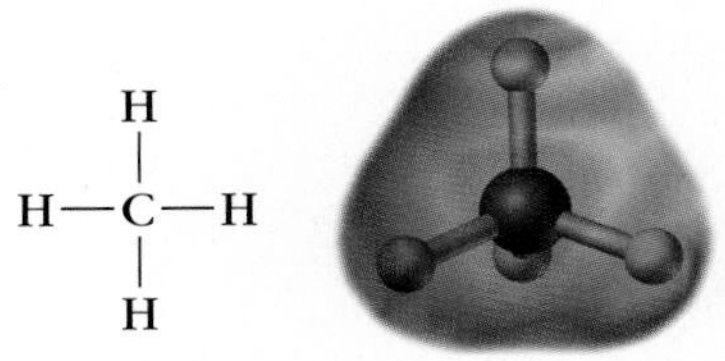

An electron density model of methane.

Carbon is unique among the elements because of the ability of its atoms to form strong bonds with one another as well as with atoms of hydrogen, oxygen, nitrogen, sulfur, and the halogens. The strength of the carbon-carbon bond permits long chains to form:

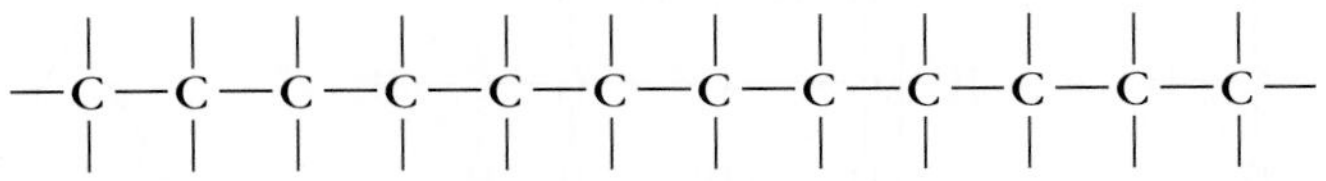

Because each carbon atom can form four covalent bonds, such chains contain numerous sites to which other atoms (including more carbon atoms) can bond, leading to isomeric structures ***(p. 86)*** and the great variety of carbon compounds.

Hydrocarbons contain only carbon and hydrogen atoms ***(p. 84).*** Alkanes, which contain only C—H and C—C single covalent bonds, are often referred to as **saturated hydrocarbons** because each carbon is bonded to a maximum number of hydrogen atoms ***(p. 84).***

Review the discussion on alkanes in Section 3.4. See Table 3.4 for a list of selected alkanes.

The carbon atoms in alkanes with four or more carbon atoms per molecule can be arranged in either a straight chain or a branched chain ***(p. 87).***

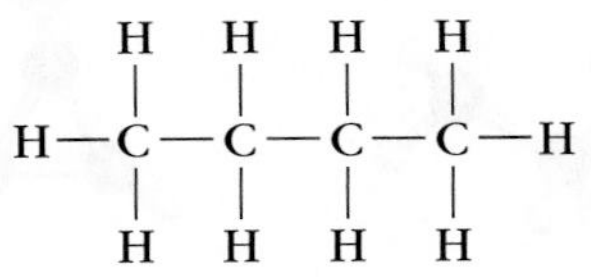

butane

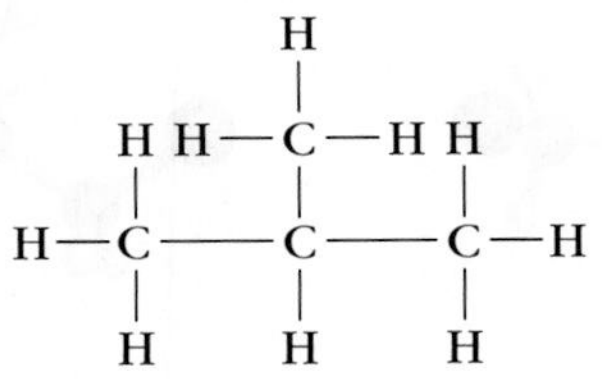

2-methylpropane

Rules for naming organic compounds are given in Appendix E.

In addition to straight-chain and branched-chain alkanes, there are *cycloalkanes,* saturated hydrocarbon compounds consisting of carbon atoms joined in rings of —CH_2— units. Cycloalkanes are commonly represented by polygons in which each corner represents a carbon atom and two hydrogen atoms and each line represents a C—C bond. The C—H bonds usually are not shown, but are understood to be present. The simplest cycloalkane is cyclopropane; other common cycloalkanes include cyclobutane, cyclopentane, and cyclohexane.

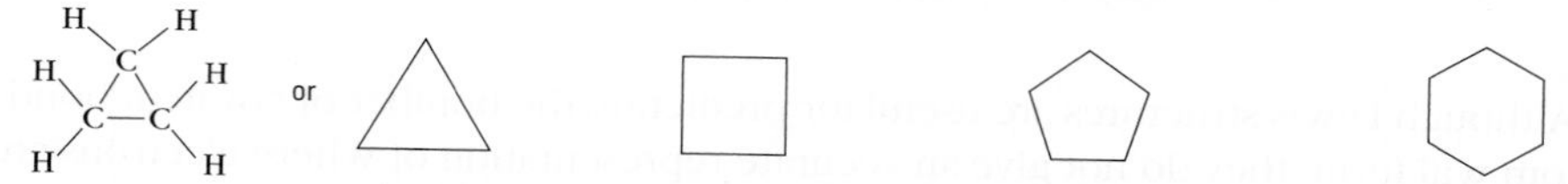

cyclopropane C_3H_6 | cyclobutane C_4H_8 | cyclopentane C_5H_{10} | cyclohexane C_6H_{12}

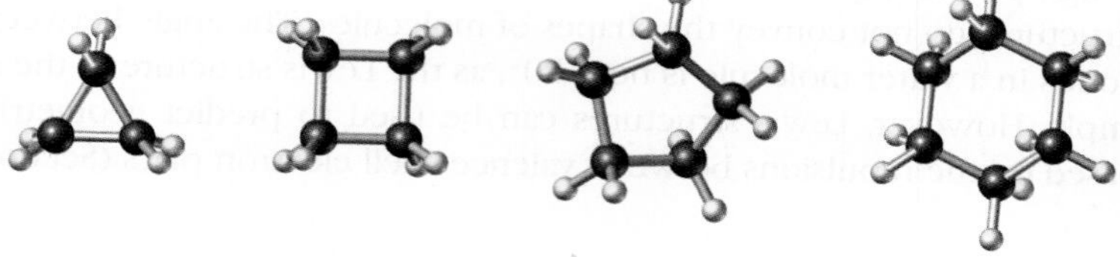

EXERCISE 8.1 Cyclic Hydrocarbons

Write the Lewis structure and the polygon that represents cyclooctane. Write the molecular formula for this compound.

When we say that a chlorine atom replaces a hydrogen atom we are referring to the different bonding pattern in the molecule, not to a chemical reaction of the hydrocarbon molecule with a chlorine atom.

The great variety of organic compounds can also be accounted for by the fact that one or many carbon-hydrogen bonds in hydrocarbons can be replaced by bonds between carbon and other atoms. For example, the new bonds to carbon can connect to individual halogen atoms, thus creating entirely different compounds. Consider the new substances that result when a chlorine atom replaces a hydrogen atom in ethane, 2-methylbutane, and cyclopropane.

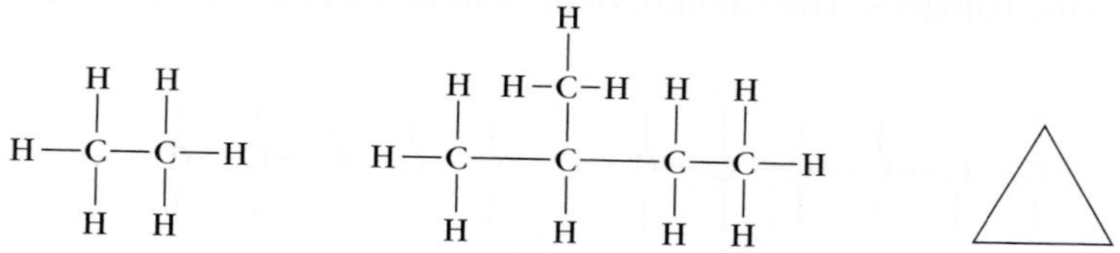

ethane | 2-methylbutane | cyclopropane

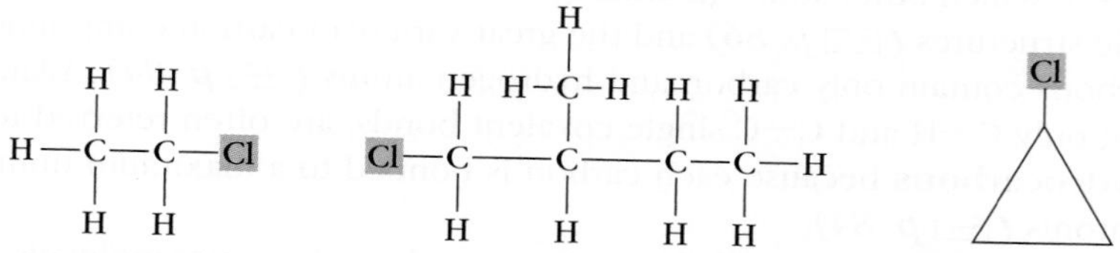

chloroethane | 1-chloro-2-methylbutane | chlorocyclopropane

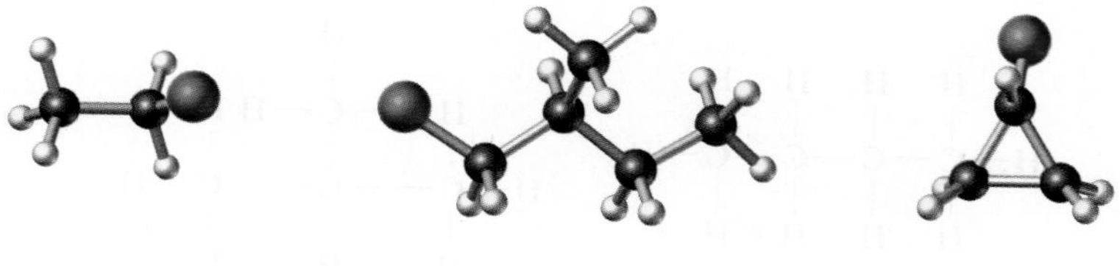

In another case, consider how an —OH functional group can replace one or more hydrogen atoms in an alkane. A **functional group** is a distinctive group of atoms in an organic molecule that imparts characteristic chemical properties to the molecule. The —OH functional group is characteristic of alcohols. A molecule of ethanol can be thought of as a molecule of ethane in which a hydrogen atom has been replaced by an —OH group. Replacing two hydrogen atoms on adjacent carbon atoms in ethane with —OH groups results in a molecule of ethylene glycol. In the structure of glycerol, three hydrogen atoms in propane are replaced by —OH groups.

The —OH group in an alcohol is not an ion; it is different from the OH^- ion in a base.

Chapter 12 describes additional functional groups. Appendix E.2 includes a list of functional groups.

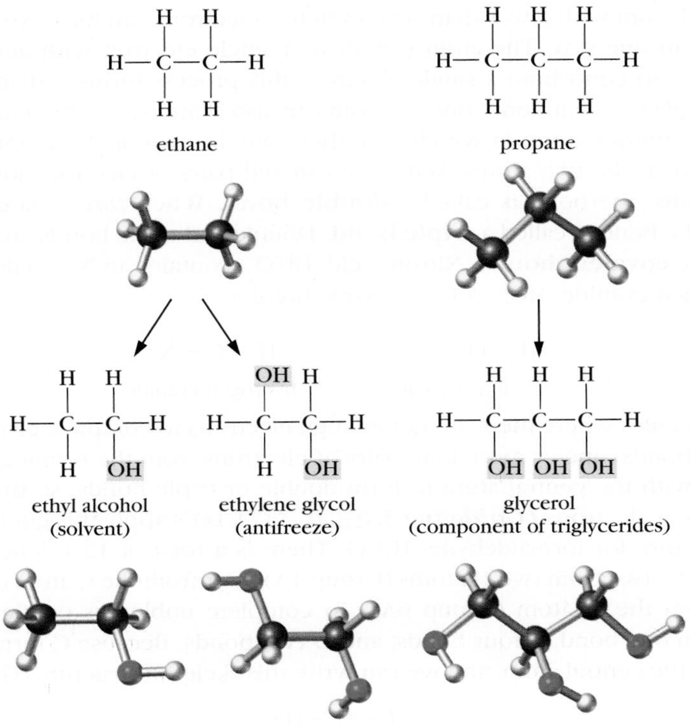

PROBLEM-SOLVING EXAMPLE 8.2 Structural Formulas and Cl Substitution

Three hydrogens in propane can be replaced with three Cl atoms to form five different structures. Draw the structural formulas for two of five possible compounds.

Answer

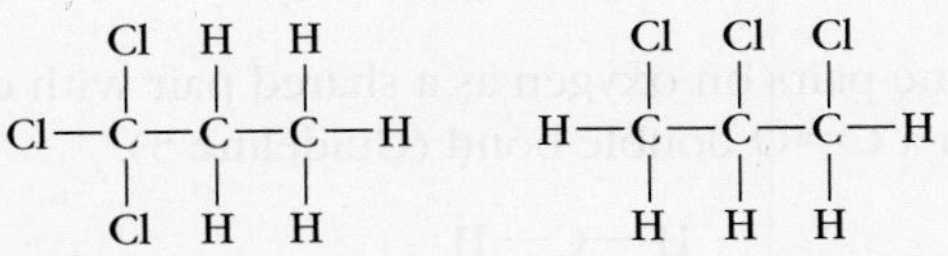

Strategy and Explanation One of the three Cl atoms can be placed on each of the carbons, or all three Cl atoms could be put on a terminal carbon atom, one at the end of the carbon chain. Two possibilities are

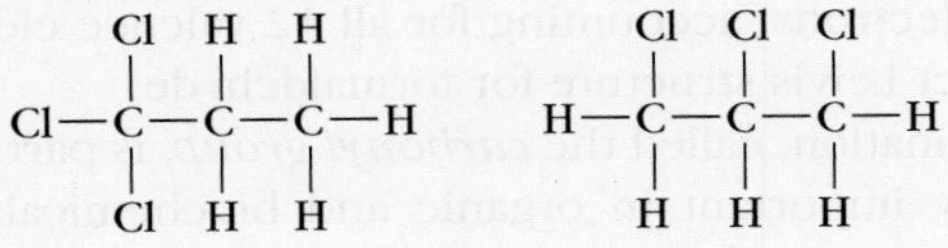

PROBLEM-SOLVING PRACTICE 8.2

There are three other possible structures for three Cl atoms on a three-carbon chain. Draw these structures.

8.4 Multiple Covalent Bonds

A nonmetal atom with fewer than seven valence electrons can form covalent bonds in more than one way. The atom can share a single electron with another atom, which can also contribute a single electron; this process forms a shared electron pair—a *single* covalent bond. But the atom can also share two or three pairs of electrons with another atom, in which case there will be two or three bonds, respectively, between the two atoms. When *two* shared pairs of electrons join the same pair of atoms, the bond is called a **double bond.** When *three* shared pairs are involved, the bond is called a **triple bond.** Double and triple bonds are referred to as **multiple covalent bonds.** Nitrous acid, HNO_2, contains an N=O double bond, and hydrogen cyanide, HCN, a C≡N triple bond.

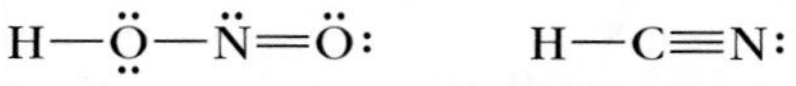

nitrous acid   hydrogen cyanide

In molecules where there are not enough electrons to complete all octets using just single bonds, one or more lone pairs of electrons from the terminal atoms can be shared with the central atom to form double or triple bonds, so that all atoms have octets of electrons ***(Guideline 5, p. 337).*** Let's apply this guideline to the Lewis structure for formaldehyde, H_2CO. There is a total of 12 valence electrons (Guideline 1): two from two H atoms (Group 1A), four from the C atom (Group 4A), and six from the O atom (Group 6A). To complete noble gas configurations, H should form one bond, C four bonds, and O two bonds. Because C forms the most bonds, it is the central atom, and we can write this skeleton structure (Guideline 2).

You might have written the skeleton structure O—C—H—H, but remember that H forms only one bond. Another possible skeleton is H—O—C—H, but with this skeleton it is impossible to achieve an octet around carbon without having more than two bonds to oxygen.

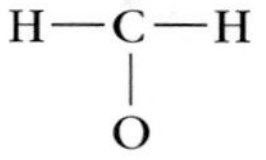

Putting bonding pairs and lone pairs in the skeleton structure according to Guideline 3 yields a structure using all 12 valence electrons in which oxygen has an octet, but carbon does not.

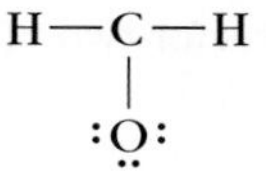

We use one of the lone pairs on oxygen as a shared pair with carbon to change the C—O single bond to a C=O double bond (Guideline 5).

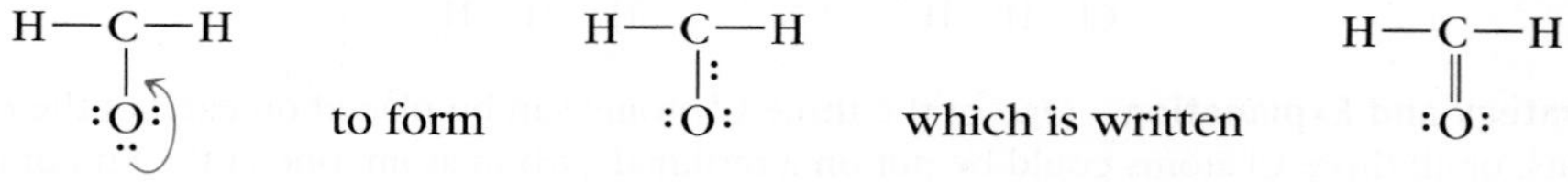

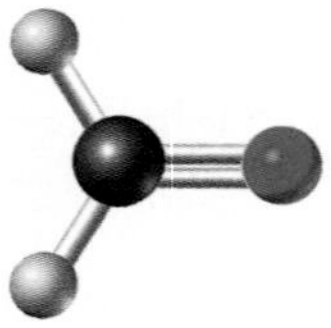

Formaldehyde

This gives carbon and oxygen a share in an octet of electrons, and each hydrogen has a share of two electrons, accounting for all 12 valence electrons and verifying that this is the correct Lewis structure for formaldehyde.

The C=O combination, called the *carbonyl group,* is part of several functional groups that are very important in organic and biochemical molecules (Section 12.5.) The carbonyl-containing —CHO group that appears in formaldehyde is known as the *aldehyde functional group.*

Formaldehyde is produced in vast quantities (over a million tons annually in the United States), primarily to make hard plastics (Section 12.7) and in adhesives used to bind wood chips to produce particle board and plywood. An aqueous solution of formaldehyde (formalin) has been used as an antiseptic and embalming fluid, but its use for these purposes has declined because formaldehyde is a suspected carcinogen.

Formaldehyde, a gas at room temperature, is the simplest compound with an aldehyde functional group.

As another example of multiple bonds, let's write the Lewis structure for molecular nitrogen, N_2. There is a total of ten valence electrons (five from each N). If two nonbonding pairs of electrons (one pair from each N) become bonding pairs to give a triple bond, the octet rule is satisfied. This is the correct Lewis structure of N_2.

N—N to form :N≡N:

CONCEPTUAL EXERCISE 8.2 Lewis Structures

Why is :N̈—N̈: an incorrect Lewis structure for N_2?

A molecule can have more than one multiple bond, as in carbon dioxide, where carbon is the central atom. There is a total of 16 valence electrons in CO_2, and the skeleton structure uses four of them (two shared pairs):

O—C—O

Adding lone pairs to give each O an octet of electrons uses up the remaining 12 electrons, but leaves C needing four more valence electrons to complete an octet.

:Ö—C—Ö:

With no more valence electrons available, the only way that carbon can have four more valence electrons is to use one lone pair of electrons on each oxygen to form a covalent bond to carbon. In this way the 16 valence electrons are accounted for, and each atom has an electron octet.

:Ö—C—Ö: forms :O=C=O:

PROBLEM-SOLVING EXAMPLE 8.3 Lewis Structures

Write Lewis structures for (a) carbon monoxide, CO, an air pollutant; (b) nitrosyl chloride, ClNO, an unstable solid; (c) N_3^-, a polyatomic ion; and (d) HCN, a poison.

Answer

(a) :C≡O:

(b) :C̈l—N̈=Ö:

(c) [N̈=N=N̈]⁻

(d) H—C≡N:

Strategy and Explanation Follow the steps given previously to write proper Lewis structures.

(a) The molecule CO contains ten valence electrons (four from C and six from O). We start with a single C—O bond as a skeleton structure.

C—O

Putting lone pairs around the carbon and oxygen atoms satsfies the octet rule for one of the atoms, but not both. Therefore, lone pairs must become bonding pairs to make up this deficiency and achieve an appropriate Lewis structure.

:C—Ö: to form :C≡O:

(b) In ClNO, nitrogen is the central atom (it can form more bonds than can oxygen or chlorine) and there are 18 valence electrons (five from N, six from O, and seven from Cl). The skeleton structure is

Cl—N—O

Placing lone pairs on the terminal atoms and a lone pair on the N atom uses the remaining valence electrons, but leaves the N atom without an octet.

:Cl—N—O:

Converting a lone pair on the oxygen to a bonding pair results in the correct Lewis structure, with each atom having an octet of electrons.

:Cl—N=O:

(c) There are 16 valence electrons in N_3^- (15 from three N atoms and one for the ion's 1− charge). The skeleton structure with lone pairs on all nitrogen atoms uses all 16 valence electrons.

$[N{=}N{=}N]^-$

is a plausible Lewis structure.

(d) Hydrogen cyanide has a total of ten valence electrons (four from C, five from N, plus one from H.)

H—C≡N:

PROBLEM-SOLVING PRACTICE 8.3

Write Lewis structures for these: (a) nitrosyl ion, NO^+; (b) carbonyl chloride, $COCl_2$.

CONCEPTUAL EXERCISE 8.3 Lewis Structures

Which of these are appropriate Lewis structures and which are not? Explain what is wrong with the incorrect ones.

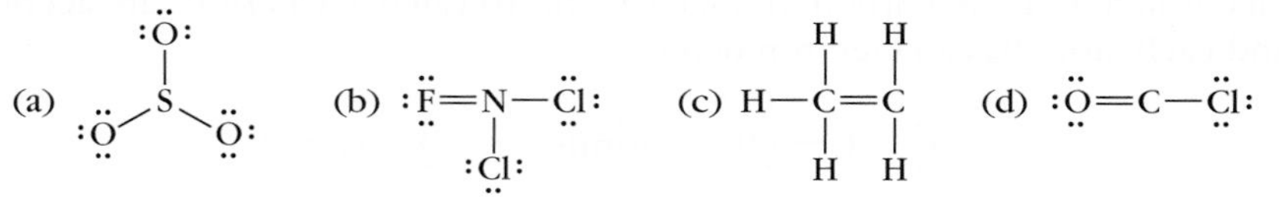

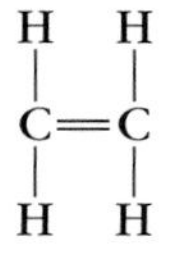

ethylene

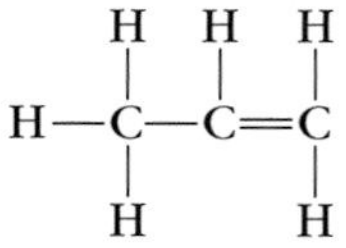

propylene

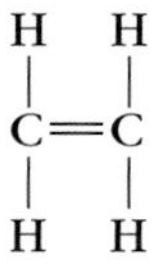

unsaturated

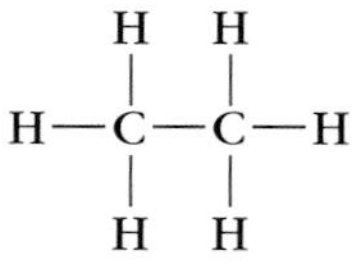

saturated

8.5 Multiple Covalent Bonds in Hydrocarbons

Carbon atoms are connected by double bonds in some compounds and triple bonds in others as well as by single bonds. **Alkenes** *are hydrocarbons that have one or more carbon-carbon double bonds,* C=C. The general formula for alkenes with one double bond is C_nH_{2n}, where $n = 2, 3, 4$, and so on. The first two members of the alkene series are ethene ($CH_2{=}CH_2$) and propene ($CH_3CH{=}CH_2$), commonly called ethylene and propylene, particularly when referring to the polymers polyethylene and polypropylene, which will be discussed in Section 12.7.

Alkenes are said to be **unsaturated hydrocarbons.** The carbon atoms connected by double bonds are the *unsaturated sites*—they contain fewer hydrogen atoms than the corresponding alkanes (ethylene, $CH_2{=}CH_2$; ethane, $CH_3{-}CH_3$).

Alkenes are named by using the name of the corresponding alkane *(⇐ p. 84)* to indicate the number of carbons and the suffix *-ene* to indicate one or more double bonds. The first member, ethylene (ethene), is the most important raw material in the organic chemical industry, where it is used in making polyethylene, antifreeze (ethylene glycol), ethanol, and other chemicals.

CONCEPTUAL EXERCISE 8.4 Alkenes

(a) Write the molecular formula and structural formula of an alkene with five carbon atoms and one C═C double bond.

(b) How many different alkenes have five carbon atoms and one C═C double bond?

Hydrocarbons with one or more triple bonds, —C≡C—, per molecule are **alkynes.** The general formula for alkynes with one triple bond is C_nH_{2n-2}, where $n = 2, 3, 4$, and so on. The simplest one is ethyne, commonly called acetylene (C_2H_2).

H—C≡C—H

acetylene

Roger Ressmeyer/Corbis

An oxyacetylene torch cutting steel. An oxyacetylene torch cuts through the steel door of a Titan II missile silo that is being retired as part of a disarmament treaty. A mixture of acetylene and oxygen burns with a flame hot enough (3000 °C) to cut steel.

Double Bonds and Isomerism

The C═C double bond creates an important difference between alkanes and alkenes—the degree of flexibility of the carbon-carbon bonds in the molecules. The C—C single bonds in alkanes allow the carbon atoms to rotate freely along the C—C bond axis (Figure 8.2). But in alkenes, the C═C double bond prevents such free rotation. This limitation is responsible for the *cis-trans* isomerism of alkenes.

Two or more compounds with the same molecular formula but different arrangements of atoms are known as isomers (***p. 86***). *Cis-trans* isomerism occurs when molecules differ in their arrangement of atoms on either side of a C═C double bond because there is no rotation around the C═C double bond. When two atoms or groups of atoms are attached on the *same* side of the C═C bond, the groups or atoms are said to be *cis* to each other and the compound is the ***cis* isomer;** when two atoms or groups of atoms are on opposite sides, they are *trans* to each other and the compound is the ***trans* isomer.** An example is the *cis* and *trans* isomers of ClHC═CHCl, 1,2-dichloroethene. Because of their different geometries, the two isomers have different physical properties, including melting point, boiling point, and density.

Cis-trans isomerism is also called geometric isomerism.

The 1 and 2 indicate that the two chlorine atoms are attached to the first and second carbon atoms, respectively.

Cis-trans* isomerism** in alkenes is possible ***only when each of the carbon atoms connected by the double bond has two different groups attached. (For the sake of simplicity, the word "groups" refers to both atoms and groups of atoms.) For example, two chlorine atoms can also bond to the *first* carbon to give 1,1-dichloroethene, which does not have *cis* and *trans* isomers because each carbon

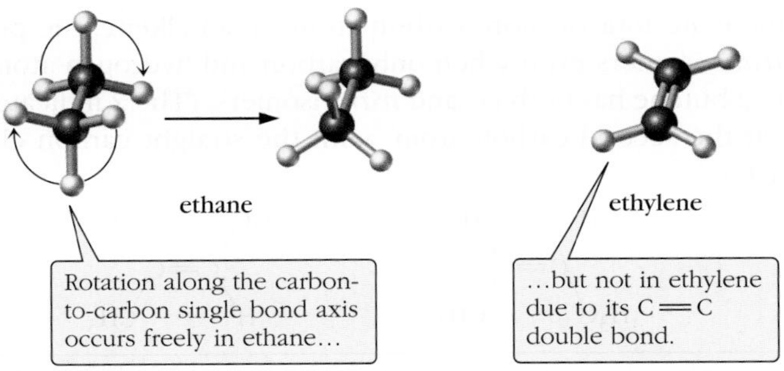

Figure 8.2 Nonrotation around C═C. At room temperature, rotation along the carbon-to-carbon axis occurs freely in ethane, but not in ethylene because of its double bond.

atom is attached to two identical atoms (one carbon to two chlorines, the other carbon to two hydrogens).

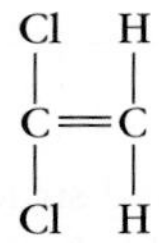

1,1-dichloroethene

The *cis* isomer has two chlorine atoms on the *same* side of the double bond; the *trans* isomer has two chlorine atoms on *opposite* sides of the double bond.

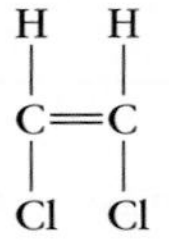

cis-1,2-dichloroethene

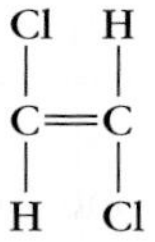

trans-1,2-dichloroethene

Physical Property	***cis*-1,2-dichloroethene**	***trans*-1,2-dichloroethene**
Melting point	−80.0 °C	−49.8 °C
Boiling point (at 1 atm)	60.1 °C	48.7 °C
Density (at 20 °C)	1.284 g/mL	1.265 g/mL

If free rotation could occur around a carbon-carbon double bond, these two molecules would be the same. Therefore, there would only be a single compound.

CONCEPTUAL EXERCISE 8.5 *Cis-Trans* Isomerism and Biomolecules

Maleic acid and fumaric acid are very important biomolecules that undergo different reactions in metabolism because they are *cis-trans* isomers.

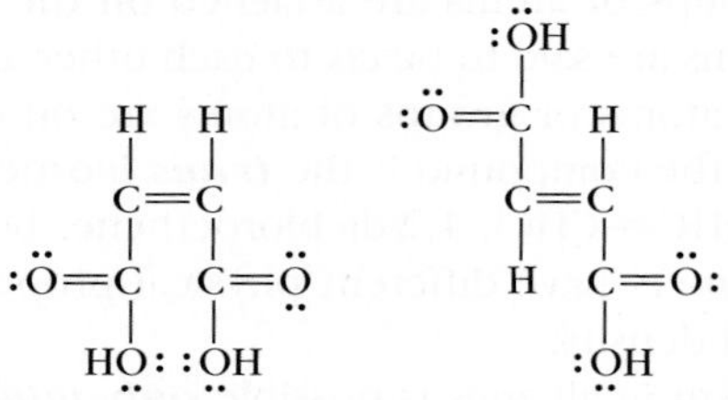

maleic acid

fumaric acid

Identify the *cis* isomer and the *trans* isomer.

The importance of *cis-trans* isomerism in biologically important molecules is discussed in Section 12.6.

When there are four or more carbon atoms in an alkene, the possibility exists for *cis* and *trans* isomers even when only carbon and hydrogen atoms are present. For example, 2-butene has both *cis* and *trans* isomers. (The 2 indicates that the double bond is at the second carbon atom, with the straight carbon chain beginning with carbon 1.)

Physical Property	***cis*-2-butene**	***trans*-2-butene**
Melting point	−138.9 °C	−105.5 °C
Boiling point (at 1 atm)	3.7 °C	0.88 °C

PROBLEM-SOLVING EXAMPLE 8.4 *Cis* and *Trans* Isomers

Which of these molecules can have *cis* and *trans* isomers? For those that do, write the structural formulas for the two isomers and label them *cis* and *trans*.

(a) $(CH_3)_2C{=}CCl_2$ (b) $CH_3ClC{=}CClCH_3$
(c) $CH_3BrC{=}CClCH_3$ (d) $(CH_3)_2C{=}CBrCl$

Answer (b) and (c)

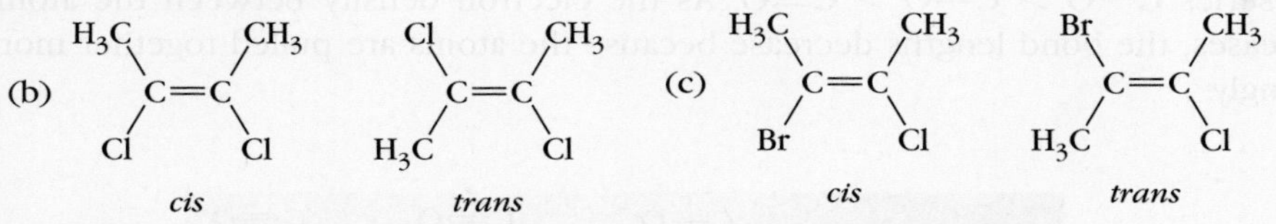

Strategy and Explanation Recall that molecules having two identical groups on a C=C carbon cannot be *cis* and *trans* isomers. Because both of the groups on each carbon are the same, (a) cannot have *cis* and *trans* isomers. In (b), the two $—CH_3$ groups and the two Cl atoms can both be on the same side of the C=C bond (the *cis* form) or on opposite sides (the *trans* form). The same holds true for the $—CH_3$ groups in (c). There are two CH_3 groups on the same carbon in (d), so *cis* and *trans* isomers are not possible.

Cis-trans isomerism plays a vital role in vision through the *cis-trans* conversion of retinal. A *Chemistry You Can Do* in Chapter 13 (Kinetics and Vision) explores this conversion.

PROBLEM-SOLVING PRACTICE 8.4

Which of these molecules can have *cis* and *trans* isomers? For those that do, write the structural formulas for the two isomers and label them *cis* and *trans*.

(a) 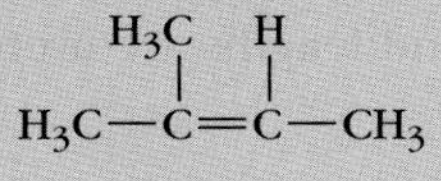

(b) 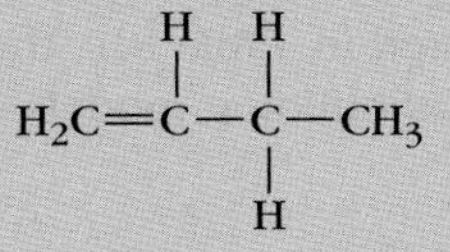

(c) 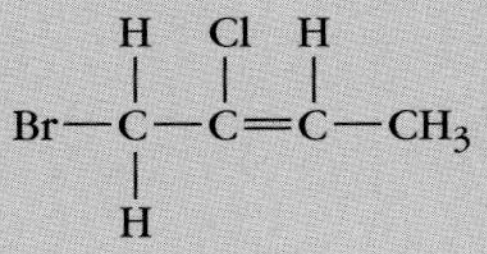

8.6 Bond Properties: Bond Length and Bond Energy

Bond Length

The most important factor determining **bond length**, the distance between nuclei of two bonded atoms, is the sizes of the atoms themselves ***(⇐ p. 310)***. The bond length can be considered as the sum of the atomic radii of the two bonded atoms. Bond lengths are given in Table 8.1. As expected, the bond length is greater for larger atoms. Figure 8.3 illustrates the change in atomic size across Periods 2 and 3, and down Groups 4A–6A. Thus, single bonds with carbon increase in length along the series:

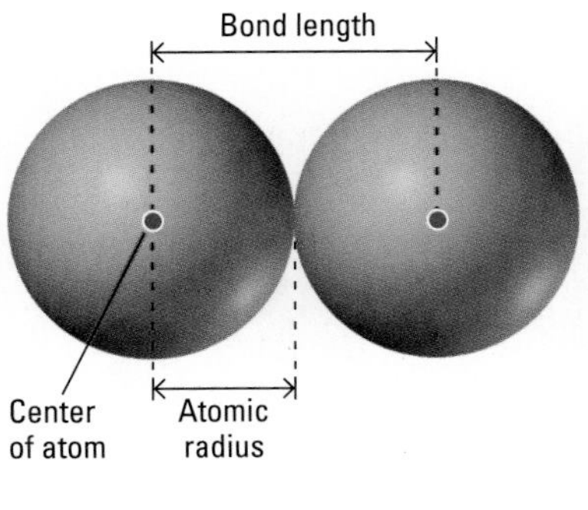

C—N < C—C < C—P

Increase in bond length ⟶

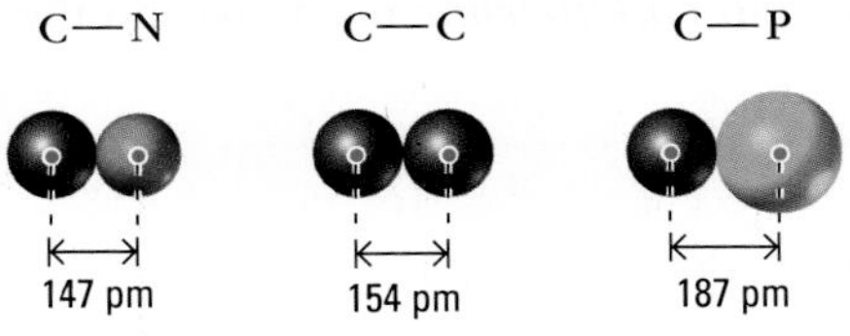

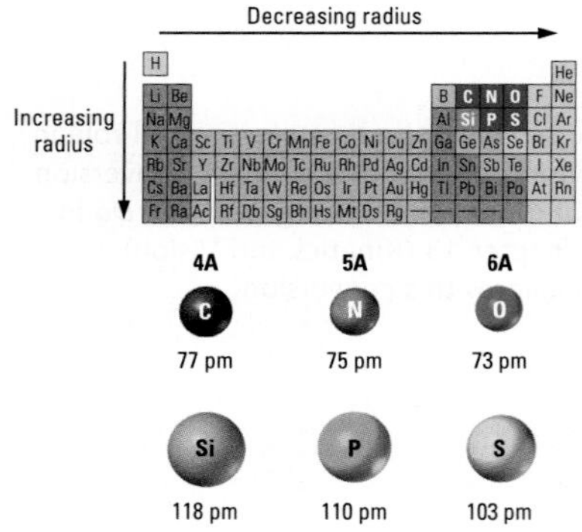

Figure 8.3 Relative atom sizes for second- and third-period elements in Groups 4A, 5A, and 6A.

In the case of multiple bonds, a C=O bond will be shorter than a C=S bond because S is a larger atom than O. Likewise, a C≡N bond is shorter than a C≡C bond because N is a smaller atom than C (Figure 8.3). Each of these trends can be predicted from the relative sizes shown in Figure 8.3 and is confirmed by the average bond lengths given in Table 8.1 (p. 349).

The effect of bond type is evident when bonds between the same two atoms are compared. For example, structural data show that the bonds become shorter in the series C—O $>$ C=O $>$ C≡O. As the electron density between the atoms increases, the bond lengths decrease because the atoms are pulled together more strongly.

Bond	C—O	C=O	C≡O
	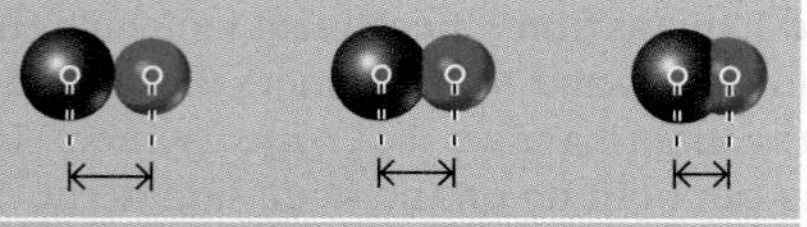		
Bond length (pm)	143 pm	122 pm	113 pm

Bond lengths are given in picometers (pm) in Table 8.1, but many scientists use nanometers (1 nm = 10^3 pm) or the older unit of Ångströms (Å). 1 Å equals 100 pm. A C—C single bond is 0.154 nm, 1.54 Å, or 154 pm in length.

The bond lengths in Table 8.1 are average values, because variations in neighboring parts of a molecule can affect the length of a particular bond. For example, the C—H bond has a length of 105.9 pm in acetylene, HC≡CH, but a length of 109.3 pm in methane, CH_4. Although there can be a variation of as much as 10% from the average values listed in Table 8.1, the average bond lengths are useful for estimating bond lengths and building models of molecules.

PROBLEM-SOLVING EXAMPLE 8.5 Bond Lengths

In each pair of bonds, predict which will be shorter.

(a) P—O or S—O
(b) C≡C or C=C
(c) C=O or C=S

Answer The shorter bonds will be (a) S—O, (b) C≡C, (c) C=O

Strategy and Explanation Apply the periodic trends in atomic radii to determine the relative sizes of the atoms in the question and consequently their relative bond distances.

(a) S—O is shorter than P—O because a P atom is larger than an S atom.
(b) C≡C is shorter than C=C because the more electrons that are shared by atoms, the more closely the atoms are pulled together.
(c) C=O is shorter than C=S because an O atom is smaller than an S atom.

PROBLEM-SOLVING PRACTICE 8.5

Explain the increasing order of bond lengths in these pairs of bonds.

(a) C—S is shorter than C—Si.
(b) C—Cl is shorter than C—Br.
(c) N≡O is shorter than N=O.

Bond Enthalpies

In any chemical reaction, bonds are broken and new bonds are formed. The energy required to break bonds (an *endothermic* reaction) and the energy released when

Table 8.1 Some Average Single and Multiple Bond Lengths (in picometers, pm)*

Single Bonds

	I	Br	Cl	S	P	Si	F	O	N	C	H
H	161	142	127	132	138	145	92	94	98	110	74
C	210	191	176	181	187	194	141	143	147	154	
N	203	184	169	174	180	187	134	136	140		
O	199	180	165	170	176	183	130	132			
F	197	178	163	168	174	181	128				
Si	250	231	216	221	227	234					
P	243	224	209	214	220						
S	237	218	203	208							
Cl	232	213	200								
Br	247	228									
I	266										

Multiple Bonds

N=N	120	C=C	134
N≡N	110	C≡C	121
C=N	127	C=O	122
C≡N	115	C≡O	113
O=O (in O_2)	112	N≡O	108
N=O	115		

*1 pm = 10^{-12} m.

bonds are formed (an *exothermic* reaction) contribute to the enthalpy change for the overall reaction (***p. 241***). **Bond enthalpy (bond energy)** *is the enthalpy change that occurs when the bond between two bonded atoms in the gas phase is broken and the atoms are separated completely at constant pressure.*

You have seen that as the number of bonding electrons between a pair of atoms increases (single to double to triple bonds), the bond length decreases. It is therefore reasonable to expect that multiple bonds are stronger than single bonds. ***As the electron density between two atoms increases, the bond gets shorter and stronger.*** For example, the bond energy of C=O in CO_2 is 803 kJ/mol and that of C≡O is 1073 kJ/mol. In fact, the C≡O triple bond in carbon monoxide is the strongest known covalent bond. Data on the strengths of bonds between atoms in gas phase molecules are summarized in Table 8.2.

The data in Table 8.2 can help us understand why an element such as nitrogen, which forms many compounds with oxygen, is unreactive enough to remain in the earth's atmosphere as N_2 molecules even though there is plenty of O_2 to react with. The two N atoms are connected by a very strong bond (946 kJ/mol). Reactions in which N_2 combines with other elements are less likely to occur, because they require breaking a very strong N≡N bond. This allows us to inhale and exhale N_2 without its undergoing any chemical change. If this were not the case and N_2 reacted readily at body temperature (37 °C) to form oxides and other compounds, there would be severe consequences for us. In fact, life on earth as we know it would not be possible.

ThomsonNOW™
Go to the Coached Problems menu for a tutorial on **bond energy and enthalpy change.**

The two terms "bond enthalpy" and "bond energy" are used interchangeably, although they are not quite equal.

The quantity of energy released when 1 mol of a particular bond is made equals that needed when 1 mol of that bond is broken. For example, the H—Cl bond energy is 431 kJ/mol, indicating that 431 kJ must be supplied to break 1 mol H—Cl bonds ($\Delta H° = +431$ kJ). Conversely, when 1 mol H—Cl bonds is formed, 431 kJ is released ($\Delta H° = -431$ kJ).

Table 8.2 Average Bond Enthalpies (in kJ/mol)*

Single Bonds

	I	Br	Cl	S	P	Si	F	O	N	C	H
H	299	366	431	347	322	323	566	467	391	416	436
C	213	285	327	272	264	301	486	336	285	356	
N	—	—	193	—	~200	335	272	201	160		
O	201	—	205	—	~340	368	190	146			
F	—	—	255	326	490	582	158				
Si	234	310	391	226	—	226					
P	184	264	319	—	209						
S	—	213	255	226							
Cl	209	217	242								
Br	180	193									
I	151										

Multiple Bonds

N═N	418	C═C	598
N≡N	946	C≡C	813
C═N	616	C═O (as in CO_2, O═C═O)	803
C≡N	866	C═O (as in H_2C═O)	695
O═O (in O_2)	498	C≡O	1073

*Data from Cotton, F. A., Wilkinson, G., and Gaus, P. L. *Basic Inorganic Chemistry,* 3rd ed. New York: Wiley, 1995; p. 12.

The bond enthalpies in Table 8.2 are for gas phase reactions. If liquids or solids are involved, there are additional energy transfers for the phase changes needed to convert the liquids or solids to the gas phase. We shall restrict our use of bond enthalpies to gas phase reactions for that reason.

Bond enthalpy is represented by the letter *D* because it refers to *d*issociation of a bond.

We can use data from Table 8.2 to estimate $\Delta H°$ for reactions such as the reaction of hydrogen gas with chlorine gas. Breaking the covalent bond of H_2 requires an input to the system of 436 kJ/mol; breaking the covalent bond in Cl_2 requires 242 kJ/mol. In both cases, the sign of the enthalpy change is positive. Forming a covalent bond in HCl transfers 431 kJ/mol out of the system. Since 2 mol HCl bonds are formed, there will be 2 mol × 431 kJ/mol = 862 kJ transferred *out,* which makes the sign of this enthalpy change negative (−862 kJ). If we represent bond enthalpy by the letter *D*, with a subscript to show which bond it refers to, the net transfer of energy is

$$\begin{aligned}\Delta H° &= \{[(1 \text{ mol H—H}) \times D_{\text{H—H}}] + [(1 \text{ mol Cl—Cl}) \times D_{\text{Cl—Cl}}]\} \\ &\quad - [(2 \text{ mol H—Cl}) \times D_{\text{H—Cl}}] \\ &= [(1 \text{ mol H—H})(436 \text{ kJ/mol})] + [(1 \text{ mol Cl—Cl})(242 \text{ kJ/mol})] \\ &\quad - (2 \text{ mol H—Cl})(431 \text{ kJ/mol}) \\ &= -184 \text{ kJ}\end{aligned}$$

This differs only very slightly from the experimentally determined value of −184.614 kJ.

As illustrated in Figure 8.4, we can think of the process in the calculation in terms of breaking all the bonds in each reactant molecule and then forming all the bonds in the product molecules. Each bond enthalpy was multiplied by the number of moles of bonds that were broken or formed. For bonds in reactant molecules, we added the bond enthalpies because breaking bonds is endothermic. For products, we subtracted the bond enthalpies because bond formation is an exothermic process. This can be summarized in the following equation:

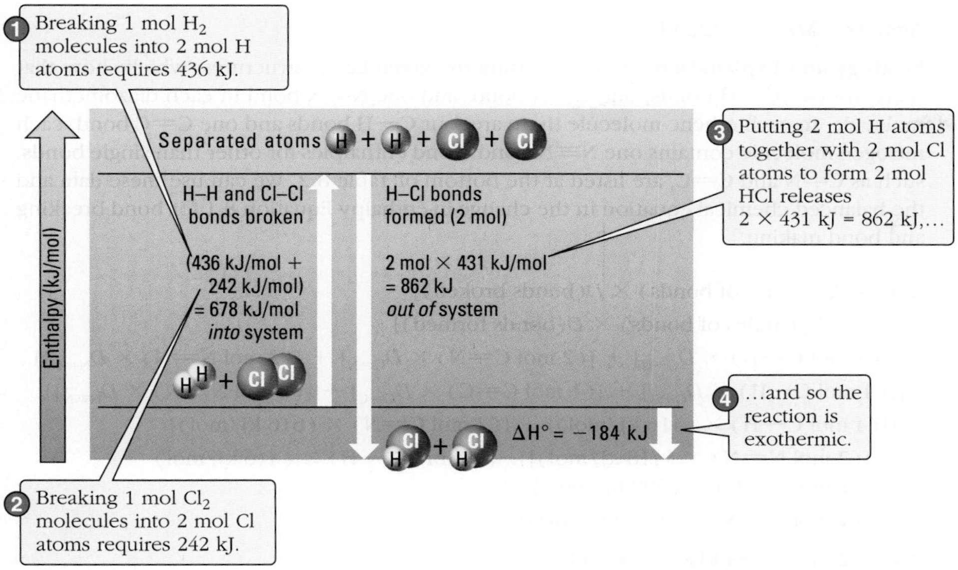

Active Figure 8.4 **Stepwise energy changes in the reaction of hydrogen with chlorine.** The enthalpy change for the reaction is −184 kJ; $\Delta H° = 436\text{ kJ} + 242\text{ kJ} - 862\text{ kJ} = -184\text{ kJ}$. **Go to the Active Figures menu at ThomsonNOW to test your understanding of the concepts in this figure.**

$$\Delta H° = \sum[(\text{moles of bonds}) \times D(\text{bonds broken})] - \sum[(\text{moles of bonds}) \times D(\text{bonds formed})] \quad [8.1]$$

The Σ (Greek capital letter *sigma*) represents summation. We add the bond enthalpies for all bonds broken, and we subtract the bond enthalpies for all bonds formed. This equation and the values in Table 8.2 allow us to estimate enthalpy changes for a wide variety of gas phase reactions.

There are several important points about the bond enthalpies in Table 8.2:

- The enthalpies listed are often average bond enthalpies and may vary depending on the molecular structure. For example, the enthalpy of a C—H bond is given as 413 kJ/mol, but C—H bond strengths are affected by other atoms and bonds in the same molecule. Depending on the structure of the molecule, the energy required to break a mole of C—H bonds may vary by 30 to 40 kJ/mol, so the values in Table 8.2 can be used only to estimate an enthalpy change, not to calculate it exactly.
- The enthalpies in Table 8.2 are for breaking bonds in molecules in the gaseous state. If a reactant or a product is in the liquid or solid state, the energy required to convert it to or from the gas phase will also contribute to the enthalpy change of a reaction and should be accounted for.
- Multiple bonds, shown as double and triple lines between atoms, are listed at the bottom of Table 8.2. In some cases, different enthalpies are given for multiple bonds in specific molecules such as $O_2(g)$ or $CO_2(g)$.

PROBLEM-SOLVING EXAMPLE 8.6 Estimating $\Delta H°$ from Bond Enthalpies

The conversion of diazomethane to ethene and nitrogen is given by this equation:

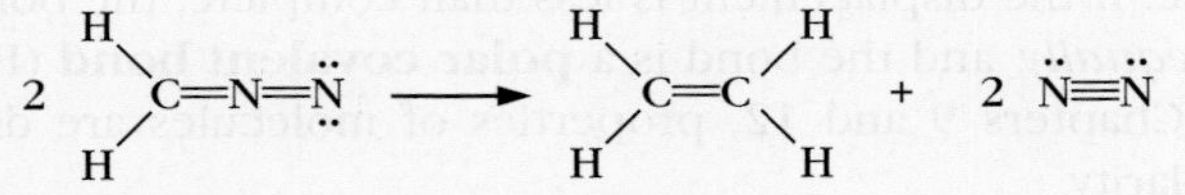

Using the bond enthalpies in Table 8.2, calculate the $\Delta H°$ for this reaction.

Answer $\Delta H^\circ = -422$ kJ

Strategy and Explanation Begin by using the given Lewis structures, which show that there are two C—H bonds, one C═N bond, and one N═N bond in each diazomethane molecule. In each ethene molecule there are four C—H bonds and one C═C bond; each nitrogen molecule contains one N≡N bond. Bond enthalpies for other than single bonds, such as C═N and C═C, are listed at the bottom of Table 8.2. We can use these data and the balanced chemical equation in the change-in-enthalpy Equation 8.1 for bond breaking and bond making.

$$\Delta H^\circ = \Sigma[(\text{moles of bonds}) \times D(\text{bonds broken})]$$
$$-\Sigma[(\text{moles of bonds}) \times D(\text{bonds formed})]$$
$$= \{[(4 \text{ mol C—H}) \times D_{\text{C—H}}] + [(2 \text{ mol C═N}) \times D_{\text{C═N}}] + [(2 \text{ mol N═N}) \times D_{\text{N═N}}]\}$$
$$-\{[(4 \text{ mol C—H}) \times D_{\text{C—H}}] + [(1 \text{ mol C═C}) \times D_{\text{C═C}}] + [(2 \text{ mol N≡N}) \times D_{\text{N≡N}}]\}$$
$$= \{[(4 \text{ mol C—H}) \times (416 \text{ kJ/mol})] + [(2 \text{ mol C═N}) \times (616 \text{ kJ/mol})]$$
$$+ [(2 \text{ mol N═N}) \times (418 \text{ kJ/mol})]\} - \{[(4 \text{ mol C—H}) \times (416 \text{ kJ/mol})$$
$$+ [(1 \text{ mol C═C}) \times (598 \text{ kJ/mol})]$$
$$+ [(2 \text{ mol N≡N}) \times (946 \text{ kJ/mol})]\}$$
$$= (3732 \text{ kJ} - 4154 \text{ kJ}) = -422 \text{ kJ}$$

✓ **Reasonable Answer Check** Note that the energy for the bond-breaking steps in the reactants (3732 kJ) is less than the energy given off during bond formation in the products (4154 kJ). Therefore, the reaction is exothermic as indicated by the negative ΔH° value. This means that the bonds in the products are stronger than those of the reactants. Thus, the potential energy of the products is lower than that of the reactants and so ΔH° will be negative.

© Thomson Learning/Charles D. Winters

Burning methane in a Bunsen burner. Combustion of methane is highly exothermic, releasing energy to the surroundings for every mole of CH_4 that burns.

PROBLEM-SOLVING PRACTICE 8.6

Use Equation 8.1 and values from Table 8.2 to estimate the enthalpy change when methane, CH_4, and oxygen combine according to the equation:

$$CH_4(g) + 2\,O_2(g) \longrightarrow CO_2(g) + 2\,H_2O(g)$$

CONCEPTUAL EXERCISE 8.6 Bond Length

Arrange C═N, C≡N, and C—N in order of decreasing bond length. Is the order for decreasing bond energy the same or the reverse order? Explain.

The measured value for the enthalpy of combustion of methane is −802 kJ; the average bond enthalpies used in Problem-Solving Practice 8.6 give a good estimate.

8.7 Bond Properties: Bond Polarity and Electronegativity

In a molecule such as H_2 or F_2, where both atoms are the same, there is *equal* sharing of the bonding electron pair and the bond is a **nonpolar covalent bond.** When two different atoms are bonded, however, the sharing of the bonding electrons is usually *unequal* and results in a displacement of the bonding electrons toward one of the atoms. If the displacement is complete, electron transfer occurs and the bond is ionic. If the displacement is less than complete, the bonding electrons are shared *unequally,* and the bond is a **polar covalent bond** (Figure 8.5). As you will see in Chapters 9 and 12, properties of molecules are dramatically affected by bond polarity.

Linus Pauling, in 1932, first proposed the concept of electronegativity based on an analysis of bond energies. **Electronegativity** represents the ability of an atom in a covalent bond to attract *shared* electrons to itself.

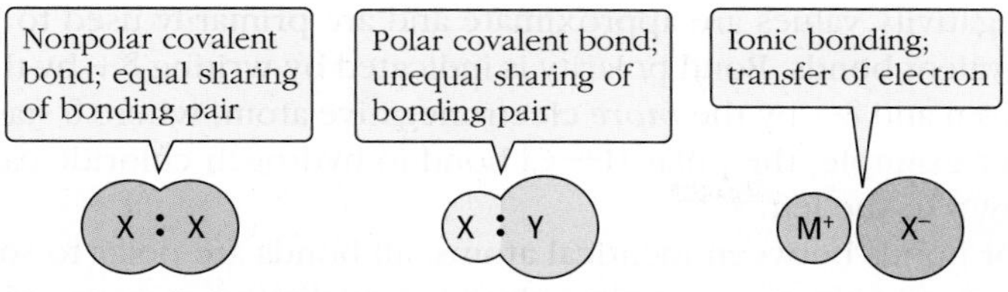

Figure 8.5 **Nonpolar covalent, polar covalent, and ionic bonding.**

Pauling's electronegativity values (Figure 8.6) are relative numbers with an arbitrary value of 4.0 assigned to fluorine, the most electronegative element. The nonmetal with the next highest electronegativity is oxygen, with a value of 3.5, followed by chlorine and nitrogen, each with the same value of 3.0. Elements with electronegativities of 2.5 or more are all nonmetals in the upper-right corner of the periodic table. By contrast, elements with electronegativities of 1.3 or less are all metals on the left side of the periodic table. These elements are often referred to as the most electropositive elements; *they are the metals that invariably form ionic compounds.* Between these two extremes are most of the remaining metals (largely transition metals) with electronegativities between 1.4 and 1.9, the metalloids with electronegativities between 1.8 and 2.1, and some nonmetals (P, Se) with electronegativities between 2.1 and 2.4.

Electronegativities show a periodic trend (Figure 8.6): Electronegativity *increases* across a period and *decreases* down a group. ***In general, electronegativity increases diagonally upward and to the right in the periodic table.*** Because metals typically lose electrons, they are the least electronegative elements. Nonmetals, which have a tendency to gain electrons, are the most electronegative.

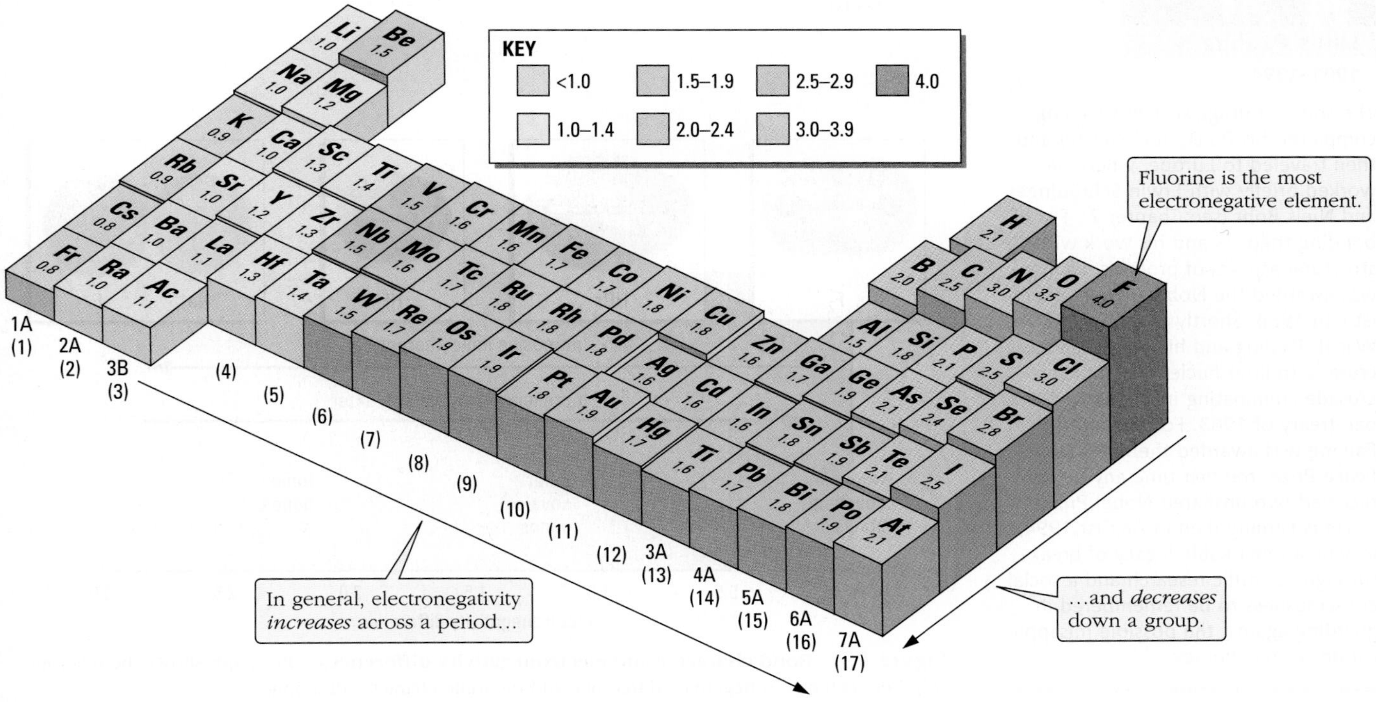

Figure 8.6 **Periodic trends in electronegativities.**

$\delta+$ $\delta-$
H—Cl

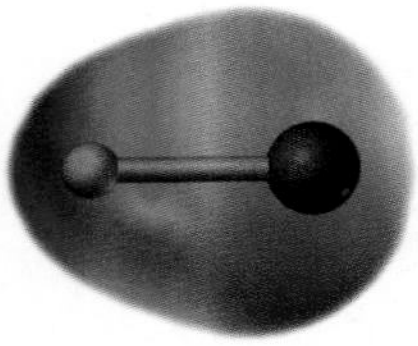

Polar H—Cl bond in hydrogen chloride. Red indicates regions of higher electron density; blue represents regions of lower electron density.

Electronegativity values are approximate and are primarily used to predict the polarity of covalent bonds. Bond polarity is indicated by writing $\delta+$ by the *less* electronegative atom and $\delta-$ by the *more* electronegative atom, where δ stands for partial charge. For example, the polar H—Cl bond in hydrogen chloride can be represented as shown to the left.

Except for bonds between identical atoms, all bonds are polar to some extent, and the difference in electronegativity values is a qualitative measure of the degree of polarity. ***The greater the difference in electronegativity between two atoms, the more polar will be the bond between them.*** The change from nonpolar covalent bonds to slightly polar covalent bonds to very polar covalent bonds to ionic bonds can be regarded as a continuum (Figure 8.7). Examples are F_2 (nonpolar), HBr (slightly polar), HF (very polar), and Na^+F^- (ionic).

PROBLEM-SOLVING EXAMPLE 8.7 Bond Polarity

For each of these bond pairs, indicate the partial positive and negative atoms and tell which is the more polar bond.

(a) Cl—F and Br—F
(b) N—Cl and P—Cl

Answer

(a) $\overset{\delta+}{\text{Br}}$—$\overset{\delta-}{\text{F}}$ (more polar); $\overset{\delta-}{\text{F}}$—$\overset{\delta+}{\text{Cl}}$ (b) $\overset{\delta+}{\text{P}}$—$\overset{\delta-}{\text{Cl}}$ (more polar);

Strategy and Explanation Compare the electronegativities of the two bonded atoms by using Figure 8.6. The atom with the lesser electronegativity will have a partial positive charge and the one with the greater electronegativity will bear a partial negative charge.

(a) The Br—F bond is more polar because the difference in electronegativity is greater between Br and F (1.2) than between Cl and F (1.0). The F atom is the partial negative end in BrF; because F is more electronegative than Cl, the F atom is the partial negative end in ClF.

(b) P—Cl is more polar than N—Cl because P is less electronegative than N, so the electronegativity difference is greater between P and Cl (0.9) than between N and Cl (zero).

Oesper Collection in the History of Chemistry, University of Cincinnati

Linus Pauling
1901–1994

The son of a druggist, Linus Pauling completed his Ph.D. in chemistry and then traveled to Europe, where he worked briefly with Erwin Schrödinger and Niels Bohr (see Chapter 7). For his bonding theories and his work with structural aspects of proteins, Pauling was awarded the Nobel Prize in chemistry in 1954. Shortly after World War II, Pauling and his wife began a crusade to limit nuclear weapons, a crusade culminating in the limited test ban treaty of 1963. For this effort, Pauling was awarded the 1963 Nobel Peace Prize, the first time any person received two unshared Nobel Prizes.

Linus Pauling died in August 1994, leaving a remarkable legacy of breakthrough scientific research and a social consciousness to be remembered in guarding against the possible misapplications of technology.

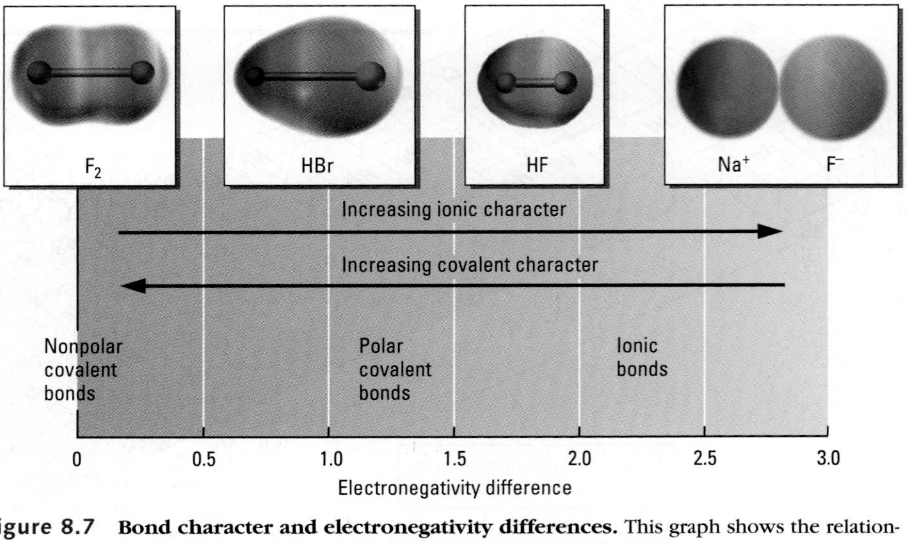

Figure 8.7 Bond character and electronegativity differences. This graph shows the relationship between electronegativity difference and the ionic character of a bond.

PROBLEM-SOLVING PRACTICE 8.7

For each of these pairs of bonds, decide which is the more polar. For each polar bond, indicate the partial positive and partial negative atoms.

(a) B—C and B—Cl (b) N—H and O—H

CONCEPTUAL EXERCISE 8.7 Bond Types

Use Figures 8.6 and 8.7 to explain why:

(a) NaCl is considered to be an ionic compound rather than a polar covalent compound.

(b) BrF is considered to be a polar covalent compound rather than an ionic compound.

In moving across the third period from sodium to sulfur, changes in electronegativity difference cause a significant shift in the properties of compounds of these elements with chlorine. The third period begins with the ionic compounds NaCl and $MgCl_2$; both are crystalline solids at room temperature. The electronegativity differences between the metal and chlorine are 2.0 and 1.8, respectively. Aluminum chloride is less ionic; with an aluminum-chlorine electronegativity difference of 1.5, its bonding is highly polar covalent. As electronegativity increases across the period, the remaining Period 3 chlorides—$SiCl_4$, PCl_3, and S_2Cl_2—are molecular compounds, with decreasing electronegativity differences between the nonmetal and chlorine from Si to S. This results in a decrease in bond polarity from Si—Cl to P—Cl to S—Cl bonds, culminating in no electronegativity difference in Cl—Cl bonds.

Compound	$SiCl_4$	PCl_3	S_2Cl_2	Cl_2
Bond	Si—Cl	P—Cl	S—Cl	Cl—Cl
Electronegativity difference	1.2	0.9	0.5	0.0

Electronegativities: Si = 1.8; P = 2.1; S = 2.5; Cl = 3.0.

8.8 Formal Charge

Lewis structures depict how valence electrons are distributed in a molecule or ion. For some molecules or ions, more than one Lewis structure can be written, each of which obeys the octet rule. Which of the structures is more correct? How do you decide? Using formal charge is one way to do so. **Formal charge *is the charge a bonded atom would have if its bonding electrons were shared equally.*** In calculating formal charges, the following assignments are made:

- ***All of the lone pair electrons are assigned to the atom on which they are found.***
- ***Half of the bonding electrons are assigned to each atom in the bond.***
- ***The sum of the formal charges must equal the actual charge: zero for molecules and the ionic charge for an ion.***

Thus, in assigning formal charge to an atom in a Lewis structure,

$$\text{Formal charge} = [\textit{number valence electrons in an atom}] - [(\textit{number lone pair electrons}) + (\tfrac{1}{2}\ \textit{number bonding electrons})]$$

Applying these rules, we can, for example, calculate the formal charges of the atoms in a cyanate ion, $[:N{\equiv}C{-}\ddot{\underset{..}{O}}:]^-$

	N	C	O
Valence electrons	5	4	6
Lone pair electrons	2	0	6
$\frac{1}{2}$ shared electrons	3	4	1
Formal charge	0	0	−1

ThomsonNOW™
Go to the Coached Problems menu for a tutorial on **calculating formal charge.**

Note that the sum of the formal charges equals −1, the charge on the ion. The −1 formal charge is on oxygen, the most electronegative atom in the ion.

It is important to recognize that formal charges do *not* indicate actual charges on atoms. Formal charge is a useful way to determine the most likely structure from among several Lewis structures. In evaluating possible structures with different formal charge distributions, the following principles apply:

- ***Smaller formal charges are more favorable than larger ones.***
- ***Negative formal charges should reside on the more electronegative atoms.***
- ***Like charges should not be on adjacent atoms.***

PROBLEM-SOLVING EXAMPLE 8.8 Formal Charges

(a) Two possible Lewis structures for N_2O are $:\ddot{O}{=}N{=}\ddot{N}:$ and $:\ddot{\underset{..}{O}}{-}N{\equiv}N:$. Determine the formal charges on each atom and the preferred structure.

(b) Determine the formal charges on each atom of these two Lewis structures of dichlorine monoxide, Cl_2O. Which structure is preferred?

Structure 1 $:\ddot{\underset{..}{O}}{-}\ddot{\underset{..}{Cl}}{-}\ddot{\underset{..}{Cl}}:$

Structure 2 $:\ddot{\underset{..}{Cl}}{-}\ddot{\underset{..}{O}}{-}\ddot{\underset{..}{Cl}}:$

Answer

(a) $\overset{0}{:\ddot{O}}{=}\overset{+1}{N}{=}\overset{-1}{\ddot{N}:}$ $\quad$ $\overset{-1}{:\ddot{\underset{..}{O}}}{-}\overset{+1}{N}{\equiv}\overset{0}{N:}$ (preferred)

(b) $\overset{-1}{:\ddot{\underset{..}{O}}}{-}\overset{+1}{\ddot{Cl}}{-}\overset{0}{\ddot{\underset{..}{Cl}}:}$ $\quad$ $\overset{0}{:\ddot{\underset{..}{Cl}}}{-}\overset{0}{\ddot{\underset{..}{O}}}{-}\overset{0}{\ddot{\underset{..}{Cl}}:}$ (preferred)

Strategy and Explanation Count the valence electrons, account for the number of lone pair electrons, and assign half the bonding electrons to each atom in the bond. The formal charges should add up to zero for N_2O and in Cl_2O because they are both neutral molecules.

(a) In the first N_2O structure, $:\ddot{O}{=}N{=}\ddot{N}:$, the formal charges for the atoms in order in the structure are 0, +1, and −1. The sum of the formal charges is $0 + (+1) + (-1) = 0$. This is as it should be for a neutral molecule. Applying the rules for assigning electrons to the second structure, $:\ddot{\underset{..}{O}}{-}N{\equiv}N:$, the formal charges are (in order) −1, +1, and 0. The sum of the formal charges in this structure is also zero.

	Structure 1			Structure 2		
	O	N	N	O	N	N
Valence electrons	6	5	5	6	5	5
Lone pair electrons	4	0	4	6	0	2
$\frac{1}{2}$ shared electrons	2	4	2	1	4	3
Formal charge	0	+1	−1	−1	+1	0

Formal charges are low in both structures, but the second structure is preferred because it has the negative charge on the more electronegative atom (O) rather than on the less electronegative N, as in the first structure.

(b)

	Structure 1			Structure 2		
	O	Cl	Cl	Cl	O	Cl
Valence electrons	6	7	7	7	6	7
Lone pair electrons	6	4	6	6	4	6
$\frac{1}{2}$ shared electrons	1	2	1	1	2	1
Formal charge	−1	+1	0	0	0	0

In both cases, the total formal charge is zero, which it should be for a neutral molecule. Structure 2 is preferred because it has all zero formal charges.

PROBLEM-SOLVING PRACTICE 8.8

A third Lewis structure can be written for N_2O, which also obeys the octet rule. Write this other Lewis structure and determine the formal charges on its atoms.

CONCEPTUAL EXERCISE 8.8 Formal Charge

Determine the formal charge of each atom in hydrazine, H_2NNH_2.

8.9 Lewis Structures and Resonance

Ozone, O_3, is an unstable, pale blue, diamagnetic gas with a pungent odor. Depending on its location, ozone can be either beneficial or harmful. A low-concentration, but very important, layer of ozone in the stratosphere protects the earth and its inhabitants from intense ultraviolet solar radiation (Section 10.11), but ozone pollution in the lower atmosphere causes respiratory problems (Section 10.12).

As you have seen, the number of bonding electron pairs between two atoms is important in determining bond length and strength. The experimentally measured lengths for the two oxygen-oxygen bonds in ozone are the same, 127.8 pm, implying that both bonds contain the same number of bond pairs. However, using the guidelines for writing Lewis structures, you might come to a different conclusion. Two possible Lewis structures are

:Ö=Ö—Ö: and :Ö—Ö=Ö:

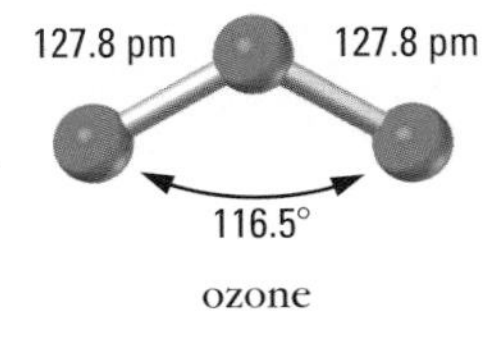

ozone

Each structure shows a double bond on one side of the central O atom and a single bond on the other side. If either one were the actual structure of O_3, then one bond (O=O) should be shorter than the other (O—O), but this is not the case. That the oxygen-to-oxygen bonds in ozone are neither double bonds nor single bonds is supported by the fact that the experimentally determined 127.8 pm bond length is longer than that for O=O (112 pm), but shorter than that for O—O (132 pm). Therefore, no single Lewis structure can be written that is consistent with all of the experimental data. When this situation arises, the concept of *resonance* is invoked to reconcile the experimental observation with two or more Lewis structures for the same molecule. Each of the Lewis structures, called **resonance structures,** is thought of as contributing to the true structure that cannot be written. The actual structure of O_3 is neither of the Lewis structures above, but a composite called a **resonance hybrid.** It is conventional to connect the resonance structures with a

ThomsonNOW™
Go to the Coached Problems menu for a tutorial on **drawing resonance structures.**

double-headed arrow, ↔, to emphasize that the actual bonding is a composite of these structures.

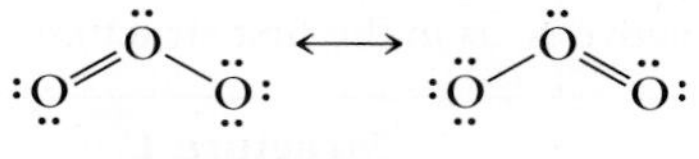

Resonance structures of ozone

The resonance concept is useful whenever there is a choice about which of two or three atoms contribute lone pairs to achieve an octet of electrons about a central atom by multiple bond formation.

When applying the concept of resonance, keep several important things in mind:

- Lewis structures contributing to the resonance hybrid structure differ only in the assignment of electron pair positions; the positions of the atoms don't change.
- Contributing Lewis structures differ in the number of bond pairs between one or more specific pairs of atoms.
- The resonance hybrid structure represents a single composite structure, not different structures that are continually changing back and forth.

"Resonance" truly is an unfortunate term, because it implies that the molecule somehow "resonates," moving in some way to form different kinds of molecules, which is not true. There is only one kind of ozone molecule.

To further illustrate the use of resonance, consider what happens in writing the Lewis structure of the carbonate ion, CO_3^{2-}, which has 24 valence electrons (four from C, 18 from three O atoms, and two for the 2− charge). Writing the skeleton structure and putting in lone pairs so that each O has an octet uses all 24 electrons but leaves carbon without an octet:

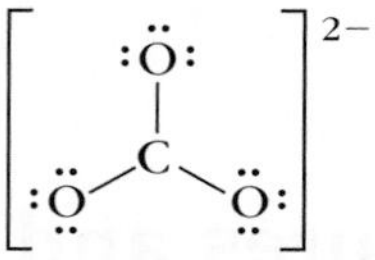

To give carbon an octet requires changing a single bond to a double bond, which can be done in three equivalent ways:

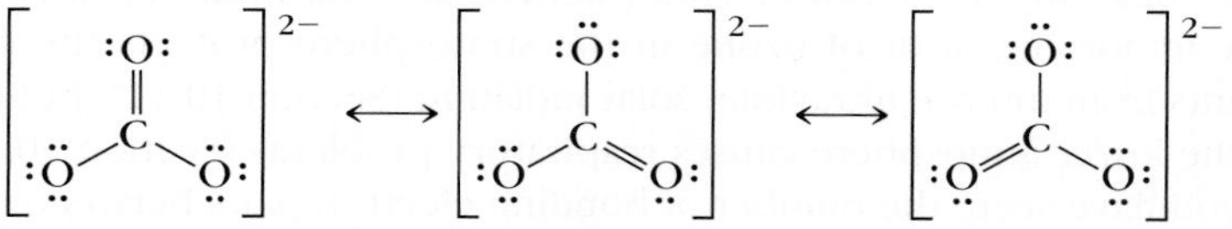

Writing the Lewis structures of oxygen-containing anions often requires using resonance.

The three resonance structures contribute to the resonance hybrid. As with ozone, there are no single and double bonds in the carbonate ion. All three carbon-oxygen bond distances are 129 pm, intermediate between the C—O single bond (143 pm) and the C=O double bond (122 pm) distances.

Resonance and the Structure of Benzene

To nineteenth-century chemists, the C_6H_6 molecular formula of benzene implied that it was an unsaturated compound because it lacked the ratio of carbon to hydrogen found in saturated noncyclic hydrocarbons (C_nH_{2n+2}). A six-membered ring structure with alternating double bonds uses all the available valence electrons and gives each carbon atom an octet of valence electrons.

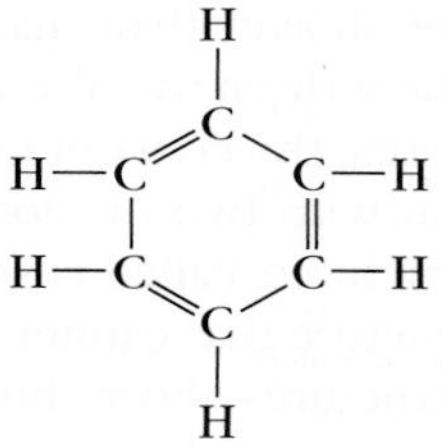

or

This structure implies that alternating C—C single bonds and C═C double bonds are present. But benzene reacts with bromine in a way that incorporates bromine atoms by a *substitution* reaction, not an addition reaction as C═C bonds do under the same conditions. Rather, a bromine atom replaces (substitutes for) a hydrogen of benzene to produce bromobenzene, and the displaced hydrogen combines with the free bromine atom to form hydrogen bromide (HBr). This is strong experimental evidence that benzene does not contain C═C double bonds.

Addition reaction (occurs only with C═C double bonds):

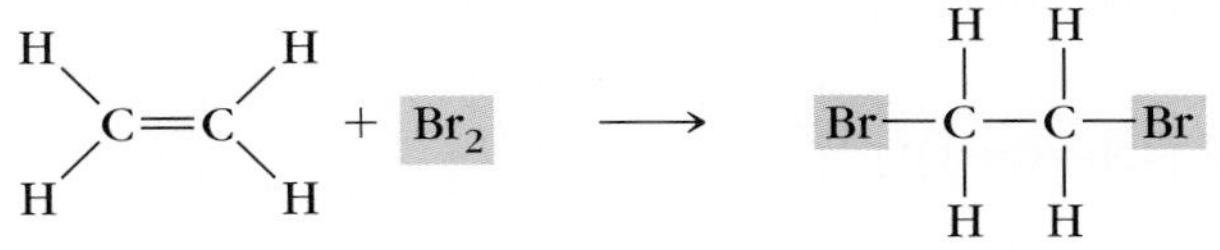

Substitution reaction:

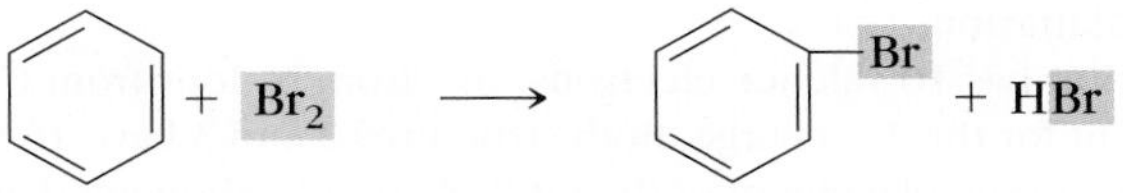

In 1872 Friedrich A. Kekulé proposed that benzene could be represented by a combination of two structures, now called resonance structures, indicated by the double-headed arrow.

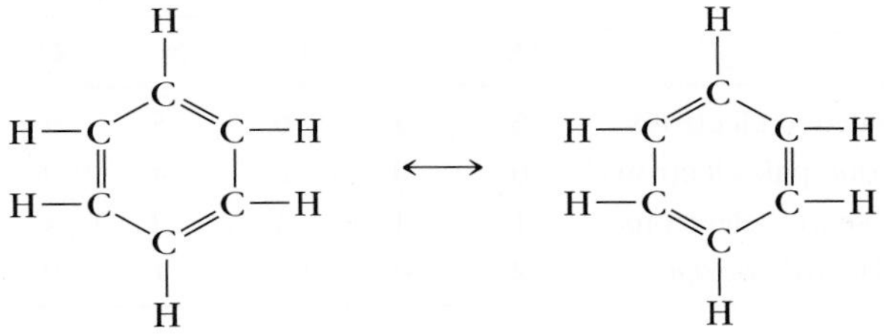

Neither of these alternating single- and double-bond resonance structures, however, accurately represents benzene. Experimental structural data for benzene indicate a planar, symmetric molecule in which all carbon-carbon bonds are equivalent. Each carbon-carbon bond is 139 pm long, intermediate between the length of a C—C single bond (154 pm) and a C═C double bond (134 pm). Benzene is a resonance hybrid of these resonance structures—it is a molecule in which the six electrons of the suggested three double bonds are actually delocalized uniformly around the ring, with the six **delocalized electrons** shared equally by all six carbon atoms. When hydrogen and carbon atoms are not shown, the benzene ring is sometimes written as a hexagon with a circle in the middle. The circle represents the six delocalized electrons spread evenly over all of the carbon atoms. Each corner in the hexagon represents one carbon atom and one hydrogen atom, and each line represents a single C—C bond.

Bonding in benzene can be described better using the molecular orbital theory (see Section 8.12).

Sometimes a dotted circle rather than a solid circle is used to represent the delocalized electrons.

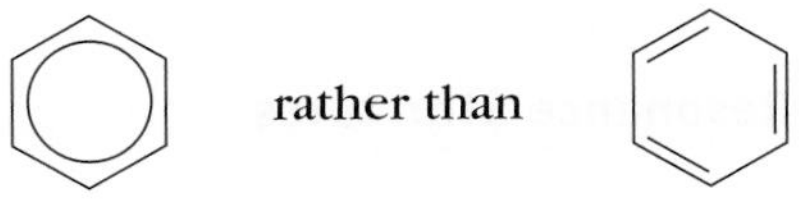

Unlike the resonance structures of CO_3^{2-} and benzene, which are similar and contribute equally to the resonance hybrid, some resonance structures are significantly different and cannot make equal contributions to the hybrid. As demonstrated in Problem-Solving Example 8.9, formal charge is useful in determining which resonance structures are most plausible.

PROBLEM-SOLVING EXAMPLE 8.9 Writing Resonance Structures

The Lewis structure for cyanate ion was given previously as $\left[:N{\equiv}C{-}\ddot{\underset{\cdot\cdot}{O}}:\right]^-$ (⇐ p. 356). This is just one of three possible resonance structures for cyanate ion.

(a) Draw the Lewis structures for the two other resonance structures.

(b) Use formal charges to determine which resonance structure is preferred.

Answer

(a) Structure 2: $\left[:\ddot{\underset{\cdot\cdot}{N}}{-}C{\equiv}O:\right]^-$

Structure 3: $\left[:\ddot{N}{=}C{=}\ddot{O}:\right]^-$

(b) The initial structure, $\left[:N{\equiv}C{-}\ddot{\underset{\cdot\cdot}{O}}:\right]^-$, is preferred.

Strategy and Explanation

(a) The cyanate ion has 16 valence electrons: five from N, four from C, six from O, and one to account for the 1− charge. Both structures 2 and 3 have 16 valence electrons and differ only in the placement of the multiple bonds, showing that they are correct resonance structures.

(b) The formal charges on the atoms in structures 2 and 3 are shown in the table below. The table for the initial structure is on p. 356.

	Structure 2			Structure 3		
	N	**C**	**O**	**N**	**C**	**O**
Valence electrons	5	4	6	5	4	6
Lone pair electrons	6	0	2	4	0	4
$\frac{1}{2}$ shared electrons	1	4	3	2	4	2
Formal charge	−2	0	+1	−1	0	0

The formal charges in structures 2 and 3 add up to −1, as they must for the 1− cyanate ion. Oxygen, the most electronegative atom, should bear the negative charge. Structure 2 would be least preferred because it has an atom with a high formal charge (−2 on N) and a positive charge on oxygen. The initial structure $\left[:N{\equiv}C{-}\ddot{\underset{\cdot\cdot}{O}}:\right]^-$ is the one in which oxygen has the negative charge (⇐ p. 356). Thus, it is the preferred one.

PROBLEM-SOLVING PRACTICE 8.9

The nitrogen-oxygen bond lengths in NO_2^- are both 124 pm. Compare this with the bond distances given in Table 8.1 for N—O and N═O bond lengths. Account for any difference.

CONCEPTUAL EXERCISE 8.9 Resonance Structures

Why is $\left[:\ddot{\underset{\cdot\cdot}{N}}{-}O{\equiv}C:\right]^-$ not a resonance structure for cyanate ion?

8.10 Exceptions to the Octet Rule

Many molecules and polyatomic ions have structures that are not consistent with the octet rule (⇐ *p. 335*). Consideration of the electron configurations of their central atoms demonstrates why three kinds of exceptions occur: (1) molecules or ions with central atoms having fewer than eight electrons; (2) molecules or ions with an odd number of valence electrons; and (3) molecules or ions with central atoms having more than an octet of electrons.

Fewer Than Eight Valence Electrons

Boron trifluoride, BF_3, is a molecule with less than an octet of valence electrons around the central boron atom. Boron, a Group 3A element, has only three valence electrons; each fluorine contributes seven, for a total of 24 valence electrons. Although the Lewis structure has an octet around each fluorine atom, there are only six electrons around the B atom, an exception to the octet rule.

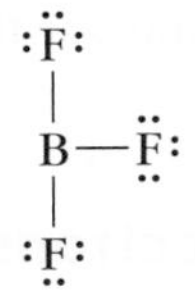

Because it lacks an octet around boron, BF_3 is very reactive—for example, it readily combines with NH_3 to form a compound with the formula BF_3NH_3. The bonding between BF_3 and NH_3 can be explained by using the lone pair of electrons on N to form a covalent bond with B in BF_3. In this case, the nitrogen lone pair provides *both* of the shared electrons, resulting in an octet of electrons for both B and N.

The type of bond in which both electrons are provided by the same atom is known as a coordinate covalent bond. It is discussed further in Section 22.6.

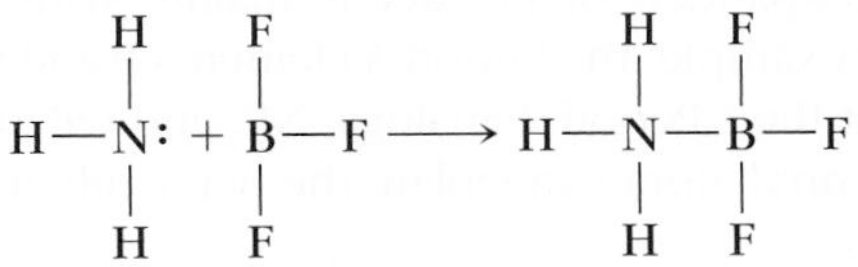

Odd Number of Valence Electrons

All the molecules we have discussed up to this point have contained only *pairs* of valence electrons. However, a few stable molecules have an odd number of valence electrons. For example, NO has 11 valence electrons, and NO_2 has 17 valence electrons. The most plausible Lewis structures for these molecules are

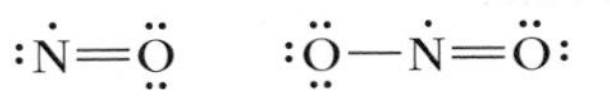

Oxygen is more electronegative than nitrogen, so oxygen has the octet of electrons.

Atoms and molecules that have an unpaired electron are known as **free radicals.** How do unpaired electrons affect reactivity? Simple free radicals such as atoms of H· and Cl· are very reactive and readily combine with other atoms to give molecules such as H_2, Cl_2, and HCl. Therefore, we would expect free radical molecules to be more reactive than molecules that have all paired electrons, and they are. A free radical either combines with another free radical to form a more stable molecule in which the electrons are paired, or it reacts with other molecules to produce new free radicals. These kinds of reactions are central to the formation of addition

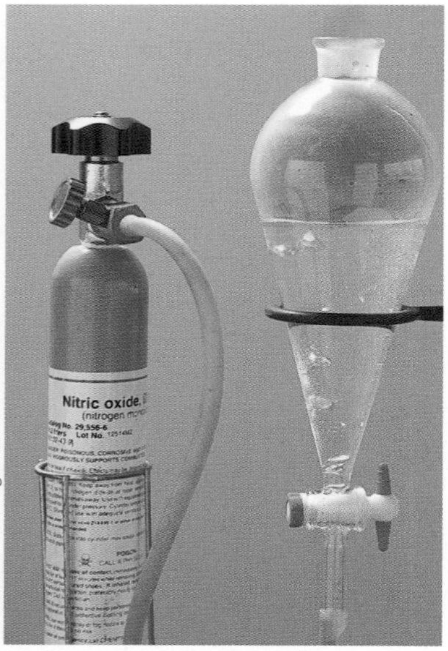

© Thomson Learning/Charles D. Winters

Nitrogen dioxide formation. As it emerges from water, colorless nitrogen monoxide (also called nitric oxide) reacts with oxygen to form reddish-brown NO_2.

NO_2 is a free radical; N_2O_4 is not because it has no unpaired valence electrons.

polymers (Section 12.7) and air pollutants (Section 10.10). For example, when gaseous NO and NO_2 are released in vehicle exhaust, the colorless NO reacts with O_2 in the air to form brown NO_2. The NO_2 decomposes in the presence of sunlight to give NO and O, both of which are free radicals.

$$:\ddot{O}-\dot{N}=\ddot{O}: \xrightarrow{\text{sunlight}} :\dot{N}=\ddot{O} + \cdot\ddot{O}\cdot$$

The free O atom reacts with O_2 in the air to give ozone, O_3, an air pollutant that affects the respiratory system (Section 10.12). Free radicals also have a tendency to combine with themselves to form dimers, substances made from two smaller units. For example, when NO_2 gas is cooled it dimerizes to N_2O_4.

As expected, NO and NO_2 are paramagnetic (⇐ ***p. 307***) because of their odd numbers of electrons. Experimental evidence indicates that O_2 is also paramagnetic (Figure 8.8) with two unpaired electrons and a double bond. The predicted Lewis structure for O_2 shows a double bond, but in that case all the electrons would be paired. It is impossible to write a conventional Lewis structure of O_2 that is in agreement with the experimental results. The molecular orbital theory (Section 8.12) explains bonding in a way that accounts for the paramagnetism of O_2.

More Than Eight Valence Electrons

Exceptions to the octet rule are most common among molecules or ions with an "expanded octet"—that is, more than eight electrons in the valence shell around a central atom. For example, sulfur and phosphorus commonly form stable molecules and ions in which S or P is surrounded by more than an octet of valence electrons. Expanded octets are not found with elements in the first or second period. The octet rule is reliable for predicting stable molecules that contain only H, C, N, O, or F.

Third-period elements can also satisfy the octet rule by using just 3*s* and 3*p* orbitals, such as in PF_3.

See Suidan, L., *et al. Journal of Chemical Education* 1995, **72**, 583 for a discussion of bonding in exceptions to the octet rule.

Compounds with expanded octets occur mainly with elements in the third period and beyond. For example, the Period 3 elements P and S form the known compounds PF_5 and SF_4, but their Period 2 analogs, NF_5 and OF_4, do not exist. For example, phosphorus as a central atom can violate the octet rule to form PF_5 and PF_6^-.

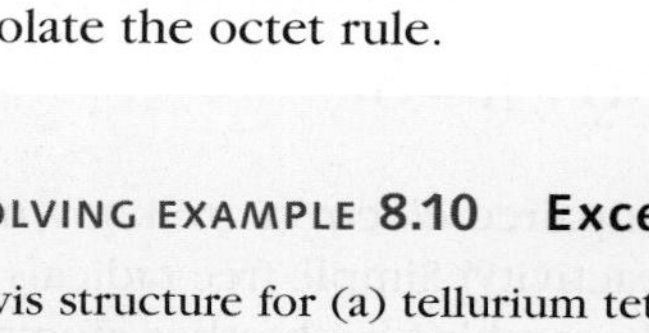

phosphorus pentafluoride

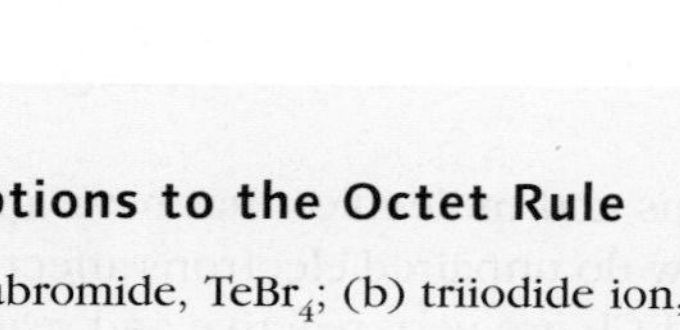

phosphorus hexafluoride ion

Table 8.3 illustrates molecules and ions of central atoms beyond the second period that violate the octet rule.

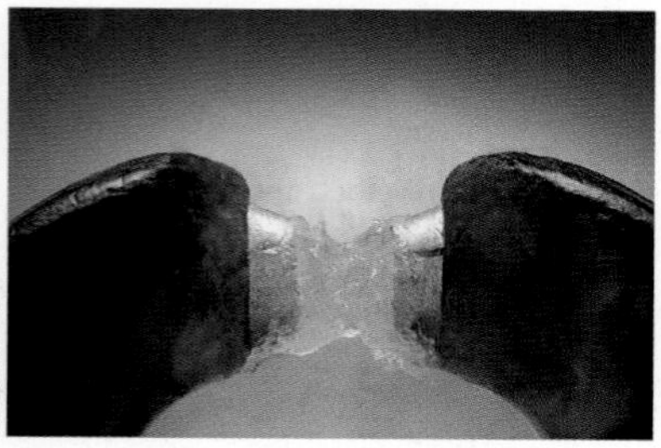

Ruven Smith

Figure 8.8 Paramagnetism of liquid oxygen. Liquid oxygen, the solid between the poles of the magnet, can be suspended between the poles of a magnet because O_2 is paramagnetic. Paramagnetic substances are attracted into a magnetic field.

PROBLEM-SOLVING EXAMPLE 8.10 Exceptions to the Octet Rule

Write the Lewis structure for (a) tellurium tetrabromide, $TeBr_4$; (b) triiodide ion, I_3^-; and (c) boric acid, $B(OH)_3$.

Answer

(a)

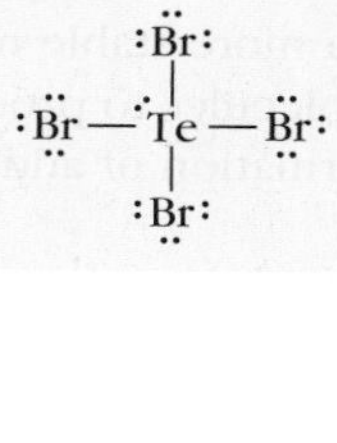

(b)

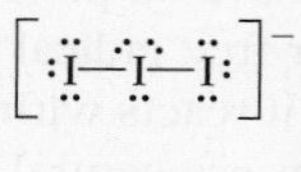

(c)

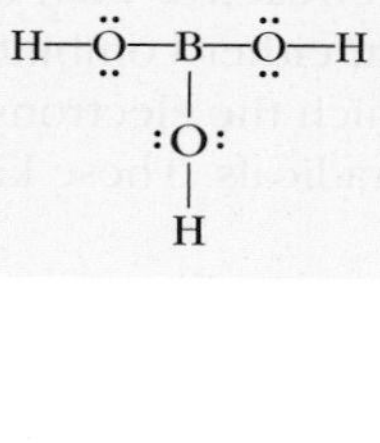

Table 8.3 Lewis Structures for Some Ions and Molecules with More Than Eight Electrons Around the Central Atom*

	Group 4A	Group 5A	Group 6A	Group 7A	Group 8A
Central atoms with five valence pairs		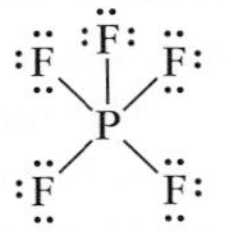	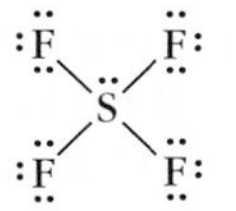	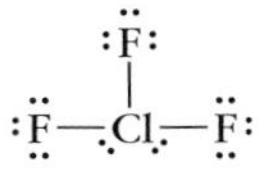	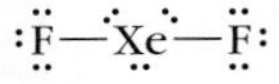
	—	PF_5	SF_4	ClF_3	XeF_2
Bonding pairs	—	5	4	3	2
Lone pairs	—	0	1	2	3
Central atoms with six valence pairs	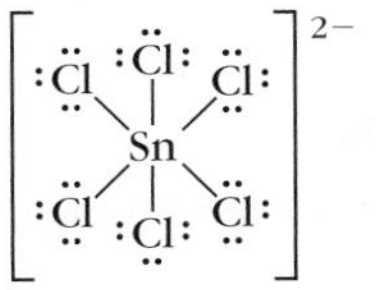	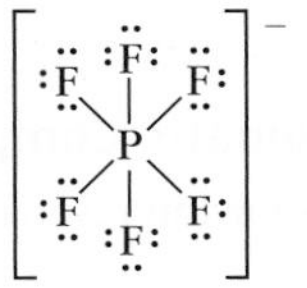	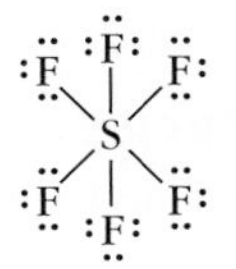	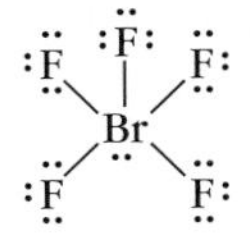	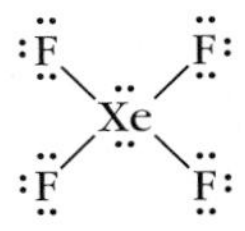
	$SnCl_6^{2-}$	PF_6^-	SF_6	BrF_5	XeF_4
Bonding pairs	6	6	6	5	4
Lone pairs	0	0	0	1	2

*In each case, the numbers of bond pairs and lone pairs about the central atom are given.

Strategy and Explanation

(a) $TeBr_4$ has 34 valence electrons, eight of which are distributed among four Te—Br bonds. Of the remaining 26 lone pair electrons, 24 complete octets for the Br atoms. The other two electrons form a lone pair on Te, which has a total of ten electrons (five pairs: four shared, one unshared) around it, acceptable for a Period 5 element.

(b) There are a total of 22 valence electrons: seven from each iodine atom and one for the 1− charge on the ion. Forming two I—I single bonds with the central I atom and then distributing six of the remaining nine electron pairs as lone pairs on terminal I atoms to satisfy the octet rule uses a total of eight electron pairs. The remaining three electron pairs are placed on the central iodine, which can accommodate more than eight electrons because it is from the fifth period.

(c) $B(OH)_3$ uses six of its 24 valence electrons to form three B—O bonds and an additional six electrons for three O—H bonds. The remaining 12 electrons complete two lone pairs on each oxygen atom, giving them an octet. This leaves boron with only three electron pairs, an exception to the octet rule.

PROBLEM-SOLVING PRACTICE **8.10**

Write the Lewis structure for each of these molecules or ions. Indicate which central atoms break the octet rule, and why.

(a) BeF_2 (b) ClO_2 (c) PCl_5
(d) BH_2^+ (e) IF_7

ThomsonNOW™
Go to the Coached Problems menu for a tutorial on **identifying electron-deficient compounds.**

8.11 Aromatic Compounds

Benzene, C_6H_6, is an important industrial chemical that is used, along with its derivatives, to manufacture plastics, detergents, pesticides, drugs, and other organic chemicals. It is the simplest member of a very large family of compounds known as **aromatic compounds,** which are compounds containing one or more benzene or

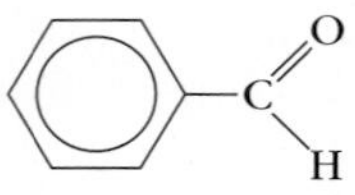

benzaldehyde

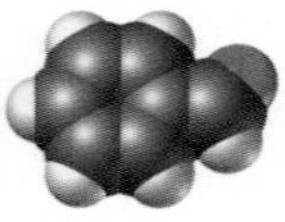

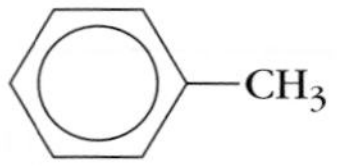

toluene

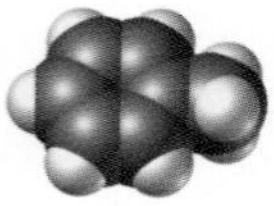

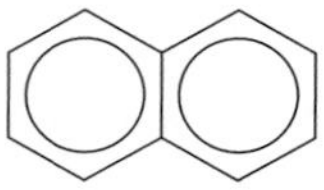

naphthalene

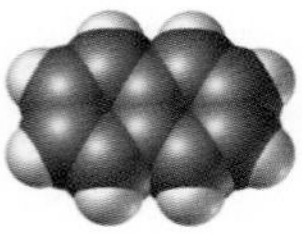

Ortho—a prefix indicating that two substituents are on *adjacent* carbon atoms on a benzene ring. *Meta*—two substituents attached to carbon atoms *separated by one carbon atom* on a benzene ring. *Para*—two substituents attached to carbon atoms *separated by two carbon atoms* on a benzene ring.

benzene-like rings. The word "aromatic" is derived from "aroma," which describes the rather strong and often pleasant odors of these compounds.

As noted earlier (⇐ *p. 359*), the benzene ring can be represented by a hexagon with a circle in the middle. Whenever you see a formula with one or more carbon rings, each with a central circle or alternating double and single bonds throughout, the compound is aromatic, like benzene. Benzaldehyde and toluene are examples of the many aromatic compounds with functional groups or alkyl groups bonded to the aromatic ring. Naphthalene is representative of a large group of aromatic compounds with more than one ring joined by common carbon-carbon bonds. Benzaldehyde is used in synthetic almond and cherry food flavoring; toluene and benzene boost the octane rating of gasoline; and naphthalene is a moth repellant in one kind of moth balls.

EXERCISE 8.10 Aromatic Compounds

Write the Lewis structures for the resonance structures of toluene.

Constitutional Isomers of Aromatic Compounds

Because benzene is a planar molecule, constitutional isomers are possible when two or more groups are substituted for hydrogen atoms on the benzene ring. If two groups are substituted for two hydrogen atoms on the benzene ring, three constitutional isomers are possible. When the two groups are methyl groups, the compound is called xylene. The prefixes *ortho-*, *meta-*, and *para-* are used to differentiate the three isomers of any disubstituted benzene.

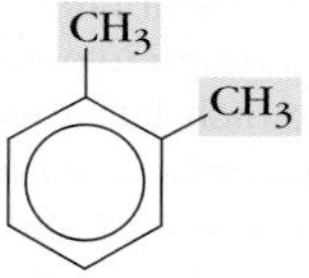

ortho-xylene

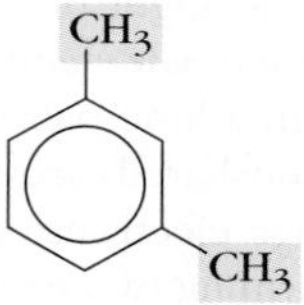

meta-xylene

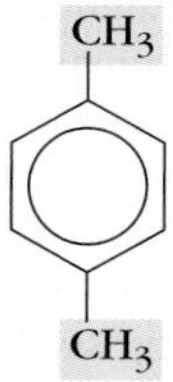

para-xylene

These constitutional isomers differ in melting point, boiling point, density, and other physical properties.

Physical Property	*ortho*-xylene	*meta*-xylene	*para*-xylene
Melting point, °C	−25.2	−47.8	13.2
Boiling point, °C	144.5	139.1	138.4
Density, g/mL	0.876	0.860	0.857

If more than two groups are attached to the benzene ring, numbers must be used to identify them and their positions, as for the three trichlorobenzenes:

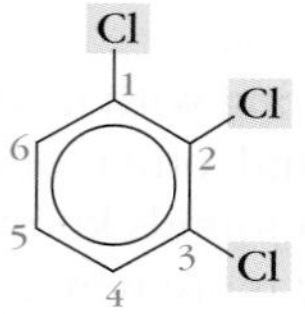

1,2,3-trichlorobenzene

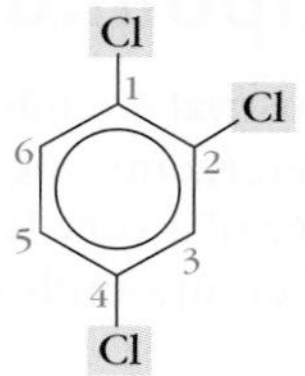

1,2,4-trichlorobenzene

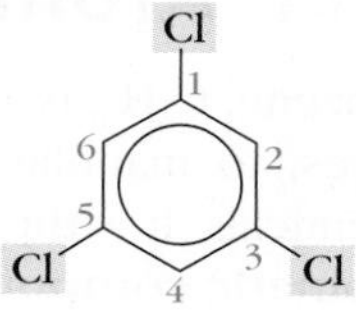

1,3,5-trichlorobenzene

There is no other way to attach three chlorine atoms to a benzene ring, and only three trichlorobenzenes exist.

EXERCISE 8.11 Constitutional Isomers of Aromatic Compounds

Write the structural formula of 1,2,4-trimethylbenzene. Explain why 1,5,6-trimethylbenzene is not different from 1,2,3-trimethylbenzene

Throughout this chapter, you have seen simple as well as complex structural formulas. The structural formulas of many biochemically active molecules are large and seemingly quite complicated. But, by closely examining the structural formulas, you can recognize the individual parts of the molecule. For example, by looking at the structural formulas of vitamins A and E that follow, you should recognize that the molecules are almost entirely assembled from structural parts that you now understand—rings and chains of carbon atoms, including an aromatic ring, C=C double bonds, and an alcohol group. There is also a six-membered ring containing one oxygen atom instead of one of the carbon atoms.

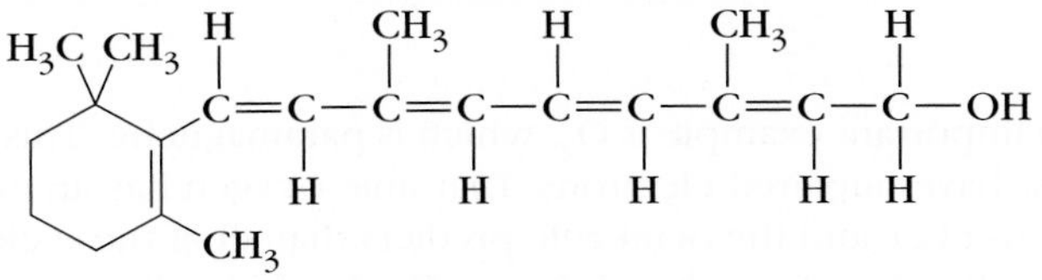

vitamin A

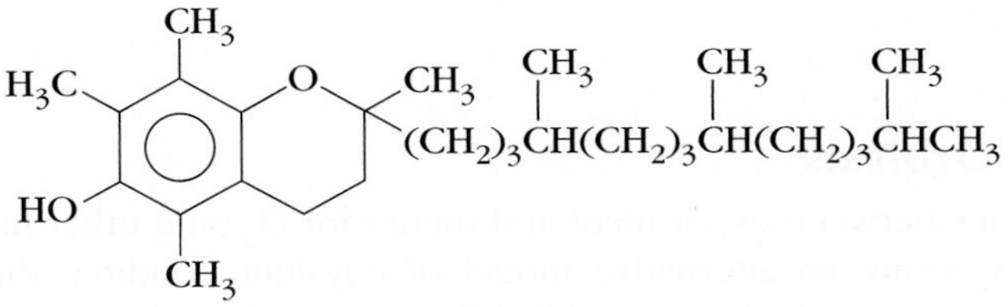

vitamin E

CONCEPTUAL EXERCISE 8.12 Knowing Your Vitamins

1. Use the structural formula for vitamin A to answer these questions.
   (a) How many carbon atoms and how many hydrogen atoms does it contain?
   (b) Locate the carbon atom that is bonded directly to four carbon atoms.
   (c) How many C=C double bonds are there in this molecule?
2. Consider the structural formula for vitamin E.
   (a) What is its molecular formula?
   (b) How many C=C double bonds does it have?
   (c) Which is likely to be the most polar bond in the molecule?

8.12 Molecular Orbital Theory

Earlier in this chapter, we used electron-pair bonds to explain bonding in molecules, accounting qualitatively for the stability of the covalent bond in terms of the overlap of atomic orbitals. Where more than one Lewis structure could be drawn for the same arrangement of atomic nuclei, as in SO_2, the concept of resonance (⇐ *p. 357*) was used to account for observed properties of molecules.

A major weakness of the valence bond theory presented earlier in this chapter is that the theory does not always correctly predict the magnetic properties of

CHEMISTRY IN THE NEWS

Olive Oil and Ibuprofen

Chemists at the Monell Chemical Sense Center in Philadelphia identified oleocanthal, a compound in freshly pressed extra-virgin olive oil that has the same pharmaceutical activity as ibuprofen, the nonsteroidal anti-inflammatory drug. The serendipitous discovery was made when a biologist at the center realized that the fresh extra-virgin olive oil produced a definitive stinging sensation in the back of his throat, the same sensation that occurred when he swallowed ibuprofen solutions during a previous ibuprofen study. The chemists subsequently synthesized oleocanthal, which produces the same stinging sensation. Further experiments indicated that the compound inhibits cyclooxygenase enzymes, just as ibuprofen does. The daily amount of oleocanthal ingested in a typical Mediterranean diet is estimated to be about 10% of the dose of ibuprofen recommended for headache relief.

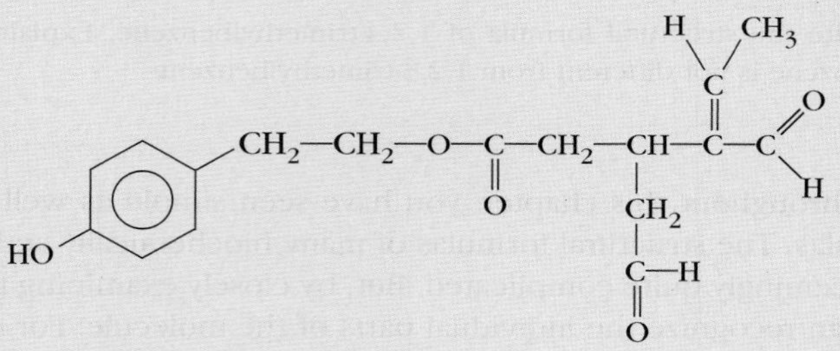

Structural formula of oleocanthal.

SOURCE: Steve Ritter, "Olive Oil Compound Acts Like Ibuprofen," *Chemical & Engineering News*, September 5, 2005: p. 15.

substances. An important example is O_2, which is paramagnetic. This means that O_2 molecules must have unpaired electrons. Diatomic oxygen has an even number of valence electrons (12), and the octet rule predicts that all of these electrons should be paired. According to valence bond theory, O_2 should be diamagnetic, but experimental measurements show that it is not.

Molecular Orbitals

This discrepancy between experiment and theory for O_2 (and other molecules) can be resolved by using an alternative model of covalent bonding, the **molecular orbital** (MO) approach. *Molecular orbital theory* treats bonding in terms of orbitals that can extend over an entire molecule. Thus, the molecular orbitals are not confined to two atoms at a time. The MO approach involves three basic operations.

Step 1: Combine the valence atomic orbitals of all atoms in the molecule to give a new set of molecular orbitals (MOs) that are characteristic of the molecule as a whole. *The number of MOs formed is equal to the number of atomic orbitals combined.* For example, when two H atoms combine to form H_2, two *s* orbitals, one from each atom, yield two molecular orbitals. For O_2 there are one *s* orbital and three *p* orbitals in the valence shell of each of the two oxygen atoms. This gives eight atomic orbitals, which combine to give eight MOs.

Step 2: Arrange the MOs in order of increasing energy, as will be illustrated later in this section for second-period elements (Figure 8.11 on p. 369). The relative energies of MOs are usually deduced from experiments involving spectral and magnetic properties.

Step 3: Distribute the *valence electrons* of the molecule among the available MOs, filling the lowest-energy MO first and continuing to build up the electron configuration of the molecule in the same way that electron configurations of atoms are built up (***⇐ p. 298***). As electrons are added,

(a) *Each MO can hold a maximum of two electrons.* In a filled molecular orbital the two electrons have opposed spins, in accordance with the Pauli exclusion principle (***⇐ p. 293***).

ThomsonNOW™

Go to the Chemistry Interactive menu to work modules on **formation of bonding and antibonding orbitals of H_2.**

(b) *Electrons go into the lowest-energy MO available.* A higher-energy molecular orbital starts to fill only when each molecular orbital below it has its quota of two electrons.

(c) *Hund's rule is obeyed.* When two molecular orbitals of equal energy are available to two electrons, one electron goes into each, giving two half-filled molecular orbitals.

Molecular Orbitals for Diatomic Molecules

To illustrate molecular orbital theory, we apply it to the diatomic molecules of the elements in the first two periods of the periodic table.

Hydrogen and Helium (Combining Two 1s Orbitals)

When two hydrogen atoms (or two helium atoms) come close together, two 1*s* orbitals overlap and combine to give two MOs. One MO has an energy lower than that of the atomic orbitals from which it was formed; the other MO is of higher energy (Figure 8.9). A molecule that has two electrons in the lower-energy MO is lower in energy (more stable) than the isolated atoms. That lowering of energy corresponds to the bond energy. For that reason the lower-energy MO in Figure 8.9a is called a **bonding molecular orbital.** If electrons are placed in the higher-energy MO, the molecule's energy is higher than the energy of the isolated atoms. This unstable situation is the opposite of bonding; the higher-energy MO is called an **antibonding molecular orbital.**

When two atomic orbitals of equal energy combine, the resulting MOs lie above and below the energy of the atomic orbitals.

The electron density in these MOs is shown in Figure 8.9b. The bonding MO has higher electron density between the nuclei than the sum of the individual atomic orbitals. This attracts the nuclei together and forms the bond. In the antibonding orbital, the electron density between the nuclei is smaller than it would have been in the atoms alone. The positively charged nuclei have less electron "glue" to hold them together, they repel each other, and the molecule flies apart—the opposite of a bond.

The electron density in both MOs is symmetrical along a line connecting the two nuclei, which means that both are sigma orbitals. In MO notation, the 1*s* bonding orbital is designated as σ_{1s}. The antibonding orbital is given the symbol σ^{*}_{1s}. An asterisk designates an antibonding molecular orbital.

In the H_2 molecule, there are two 1*s* electrons. They fill the σ_{1s} orbital, giving a single bond. If an He_2 molecule could form, there would be four electrons—two from each atom. These would fill the bonding and antibonding orbitals. One bond

ThomsonNOW™
Go to the Coached Problems menu for exercises on:
- **identifying bonding and antibonding orbitals**
- **homonuclear, diatomic molecules**

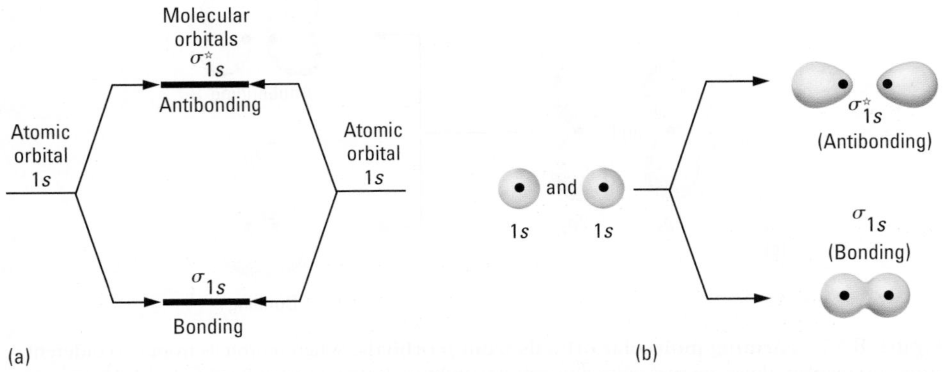

Figure 8.9 Molecular orbital formation. Two MOs are formed by combining two 1*s* atomic orbitals (a) Energy level diagram. (b) Orbital overlap diagram. (Black dots in (b) represent atomic nuclei.)

and one antibond give a *bond order* (number of bonds) of zero in He_2. The bond order is calculated as

$$\text{Bond order} = \text{number of bonds} = \frac{n_B - n_A}{2}$$

where n_B is the number of electrons in bonding molecular orbitals, n_A is the number of electrons in antibonding molecular orbitals, and dividing by 2 accounts for the fact that two electrons are needed for a bond. In H_2, $n_B = 2$ and $n_A = 0$, so we have one bond. For He_2, $n_B = n_A = 2$, so the number of bonds is zero. The MO theory predicts that the He_2 molecule should not exist, and it does not.

Second-Period Elements (Combining 2s and 2p Orbitals)

Three of the elements in the second period form familiar diatomic molecules: N_2, O_2, and F_2. Less common, but also known, are Li_2, B_2, and C_2, which have been observed as gases. The molecules Be_2 and Ne_2 are either highly unstable or nonexistent. To see what MO theory predicts about the stability of diatomic molecules from the second period, consider the valence atomic orbitals, 2*s* and 2*p*.

Combining two 2*s* atomic orbitals, one from each atom, gives two MOs. These are very similar to the ones shown in Figure 8.9. They are designated as σ_{2s} (sigma, bonding, 2*s*) and σ^*_{2s} (sigma, antibonding, 2*s*).

In an isolated atom, there are three 2*p* orbitals, oriented at right angles to each other. We call these atomic orbitals p_x, p_y, and p_z (Figure 8.10a). Assume that two

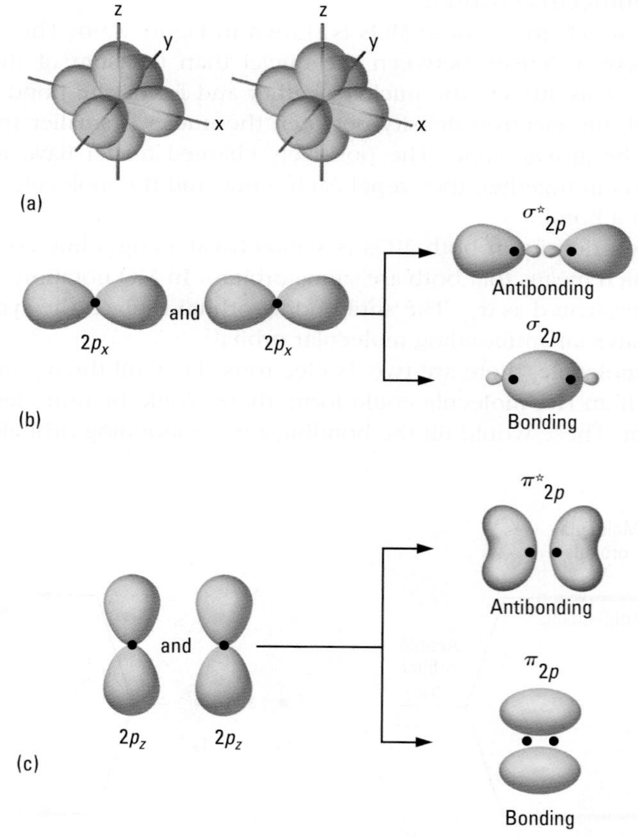

Figure 8.10 Forming molecular orbitals from *p* orbitals. When *p* orbitals from two different atoms (a) overlap, there are two quite different possibilities. If they overlap head to head (b), two σ MOs are produced. If, on the other hand, they overlap side to side (c), two π MOs result. In this example, both p_z and p_y orbitals can overlap to form π MOs. Only p_z overlap is shown. (Black dots represent atomic nuclei.)

atoms approach along the x-axis. The two p_x atomic orbitals overlap head to head to form two orbitals that are symmetric around the line connecting the two nuclei (Figure 8.10b). That is, they form a sigma bonding orbital, σ_{2p}, and a sigma antibonding orbital, $\sigma^{\star}_{2p}$.

The situation is quite different when the p_z orbitals overlap. Because they are oriented parallel to one another, they overlap side to side (Figure 8.10c). The two MOs formed in this case are pi orbitals; one is a bonding MO, π_{2p}, and the other is an antibonding MO, $\pi^{\star}_{2p}$. Similarly, the p_y orbitals of the two atoms interact to form another pair of pi MOs, π_{2p} and $\pi^{\star}_{2p}$, which are not shown in Figure 8.10.

If you look down the internuclear axis, a π molecular orbital looks like a p atomic orbital.

The relative energies of the MOs available for occupancy by the valence electrons of diatomic molecules formed from second-period atoms are shown in Figure 8.11. To obtain the MO structure of the diatomic molecules of the elements in the second period, we fill the available MOs in order of increasing energy. The results are shown in Table 8.4. Note that MO theory correctly predicts the number of unpaired electrons in each molecule and the bonding in the molecule.

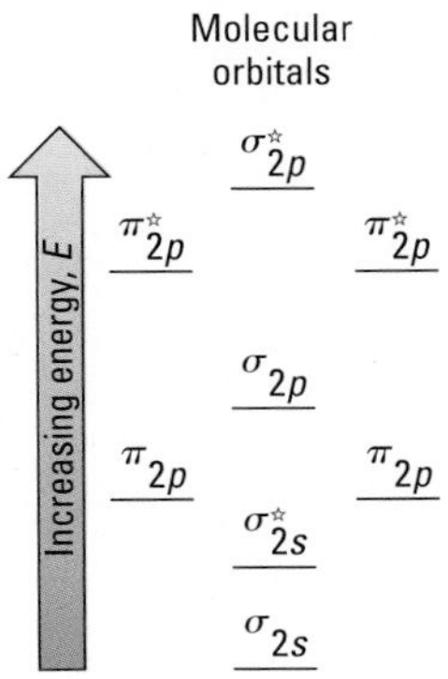

Figure 8.11 Relative order of filling molecular orbitals. The energies of MOs formed by combining $2s$ and $2p$ atomic orbitals increase from bottom to top of the diagram. This order of energies applies to Li_2 through N_2, but for O_2 and F_2 the energy of the σ_{2p} orbital drops below the energy of the two π_{2p} orbitals. This does not affect the filling order, because in O_2 and F_2 the σ_{2p} and π_{2p} orbitals are filled.

PROBLEM-SOLVING EXAMPLE 8.11 Filling Molecular Orbitals

Without consulting Table 8.4, apply the energy diagram in Figure 8.11 to C_2 and fill the molecular orbitals appropriately. Verify that the results correspond to the number of unpaired electrons and the bond order listed for C_2 in Table 8.4.

Answer See Table 8.4.

Table 8.4 Predicted and Observed Properties of Diatomic Molecules of Second-Period Elements

Occupancy of Orbitals

	σ_{2s}	$\sigma^{\star}_{2s}$	π_{2p}	π_{2p}	σ_{2p}	$\pi^{\star}_{2p}$	$\pi^{\star}_{2p}$	$\sigma^{\star}_{2p}$
Li_2	(↑↓)	( )	( )	( )	( )	( )	( )	( )
Be_2	(↑↓)	(↑↓)	( )	( )	( )	( )	( )	( )
B_2	(↑↓)	(↑↓)	(↑)	(↑)	( )	( )	( )	( )
C_2	(↑↓)	(↑↓)	(↑↓)	(↑↓)	( )	( )	( )	( )
N_2	(↑↓)	(↑↓)	(↑↓)	(↑↓)	(↑↓)	( )	( )	( )
O_2	(↑↓)	(↑↓)	(↑↓)	(↑↓)	(↑↓)	(↑)	(↑)	( )
F_2	(↑↓)	(↑↓)	(↑↓)	(↑↓)	(↑↓)	(↑↓)	(↑↓)	( )
Ne_2	(↑↓)	(↑↓)	(↑↓)	(↑↓)	(↑↓)	(↑↓)	(↑↓)	(↑↓)

	Predicted Properties		Observed Properties	
	Number of Unpaired e^-	Bond Order	Number of Unpaired e^-	Bond Energy (kJ/mol)
Li_2	0	1	0	105
Be_2	0	0	0	Unstable
B_2	2	1	2	289
C_2	0	2	0	598
N_2	0	3	0	946
O_2	2	2	2	498
F_2	0	1	0	158
Ne_2	0	0	0	Nonexistent

Strategy and Explanation First, determine the number of valence electrons and then use the MO diagram in Figure 8.11 to fill the MOs in proper order of increasing energy. There are a total of eight valence electrons, four from each carbon atom. The correct orbital diagram is given in Table 8.4. The correct bond order is 2, as calculated from (6 − 2)/2 = 2. There are no unpaired electrons.

PROBLEM-SOLVING PRACTICE 8.11

Repeat Problem-Solving Example 8.11, but use N_2 instead of C_2.

There is also a general correlation between the predicted bond order, $(n_B - n_A)/2$, and the experimental bond energy. The bond order of two for C_2 and O_2 implies a double bond, which is expected to be stronger than the single bonds in Li_2, B_2, and F_2 (bond order = 1). The bond order of three for N_2 (triple bond) implies a still stronger bond. A major triumph of MO theory is its ability to explain the properties of O_2. The bond order of two and the presence of two unpaired electrons in the two π^*_{2p} MOs explain how the molecule can have a double bond and at the same time be paramagnetic.

PROBLEM-SOLVING EXAMPLE 8.12 Electron Structure of Peroxide Ion

Using MO theory, predict the bond order and number of unpaired electrons in the peroxide ion, O_2^{2-}.

Answer Bond order = 1; there are no unpaired electrons.

Strategy and Explanation First, find the number of valence electrons. Then, construct an orbital diagram, filling the available MOs (Figure 8.11) in order of increasing energy.

Recall that oxygen is in Group 6A of the periodic table, so an oxygen atom has six valence electrons. The peroxide ion has two oxygen atoms and two extra electrons (2− charge). The total number of valence electrons is 2(6) + 2 = 14. The molecular orbital diagram is

	σ_{2s}	σ^*_{2s}	π_{2p}	π_{2p}	σ_{2p}	π^*_{2p}	π^*_{2p}	σ^*_{2p}
O_2^{2-}	(↑↓)	(↑↓)	(↑↓)	(↑↓)	(↑↓)	(↑↓)	(↑↓)	( )

The bond order is (8 − 6)/2 = 1. There are no unpaired electrons. These conclusions are in agreement with the Lewis structure (valence bond theory) for the peroxide ion: $(:\ddot{\underset{..}{O}}-\ddot{\underset{..}{O}}:)^{2-}$

PROBLEM-SOLVING PRACTICE 8.12

Use MO theory to predict the bond order and the number of unpaired electrons in the superoxide ion, O_2^-.

Molecular orbital theory can also be applied to predict the properties of molecules containing different kinds of atoms, such as NO. There are 11 valence electrons in this molecule (five from nitrogen and six from oxygen). These 11 valence electrons are placed into molecular orbitals of increasing energy in the molecular orbital diagram:

	σ_{2s}	σ^*_{2s}	π_{2p}	π_{2p}	σ_{2p}	π^*_{2p}	π^*_{2p}	σ^*_{2p}
NO	(↑↓)	(↑↓)	(↑↓)	(↑↓)	(↑↓)	(↑)	( )	( )

There are eight electrons in bonding orbitals (two in σ_{2s}, four in π_{2p}, two in σ_{2p}) and three electrons in antibonding orbitals (two in $\sigma^{\star}_{2s}$, one in $\pi^{\star}_{2p}$). Therefore there is one unpaired electron (in the $\pi^{\star}_{2p}$ molecular orbital). The bond order is

$$\text{Number of bonds} = \frac{8 - 3}{2} = \frac{5}{2} = 2.5$$

Polyatomic Molecules; Delocalized π Electrons

The bonding in molecules containing more than two atoms can also be described in terms of MOs. We will not attempt to do this; the energy level structure is considerably more complex than that for diatomic molecules. However, one point is worth mentioning: In polyatomic species, *the MOs can be spread over the entire molecule* rather than being localized between two atoms.

The nitrate ion is known from experiment to be triangular planar, with three N—O bonds whose lengths are equal. However, a single Lewis structure for nitrate ion does not predict three equal-length bonds.

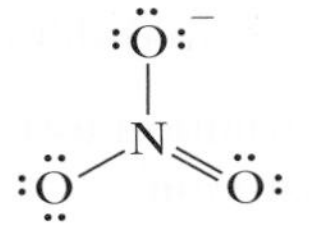

Valence bond theory invokes three contributing resonance structures to explain the fact that the three N—O bonds are identical. In each contributing structure there is a double bond from N to a different O atom. MO theory, on the other hand, considers that the skeleton of the nitrate ion involves three sigma bonds, but the fourth electron pair (the second pair in the double bond) is in a pi orbital that is delocalized; it is shared by all of the atoms in the ion. That is, this pair of electrons is shared equally among the three O atoms. According to MO theory, a similar interpretation applies with all of the resonance hybrids described in this chapter.

Ozone (O_3) is a molecule for which two resonance structures can be written (⇐ *p. 357*), each of which contains two sigma bonds and one pi bond. The sigma bonds are localized electron pairs between adjacent oxygen atoms. The pi electrons can be considered to be delocalized over the entire three-oxygen chain of the molecule.

Benzene (C_6H_6) is another species in which delocalized pi orbitals play an important role. There are 30 valence electrons—15 electron pairs—in this molecule; 12 of the electron pairs form the sigma bond framework:

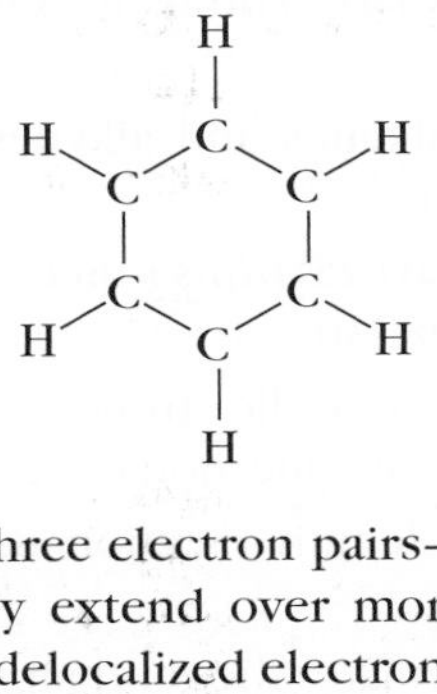

The remaining six electrons—three electron pairs—are located in three π orbitals, which according to MO theory extend over more than two atoms. Figure 8.12 shows the three π MOs. These delocalized electrons are spread over all six C atoms and are represented simply as

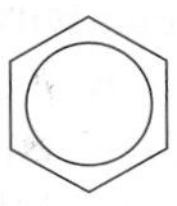

Figure 8.12 Electron delocalization in benzene. Three of the 15 valence electron pairs in the benzene molecule occupy three π MOs that are delocalized in regions above and below the plane of the benzene ring. These three electron pairs in π MOs add 0.5 to the bond order between each pair of carbon atoms, giving a total of $6 \times 0.5 = 3$ additional bonds.

SUMMARY PROBLEM

Glycine, $C_2H_5NO_2$, is a naturally occurring amino acid with this Lewis structure,

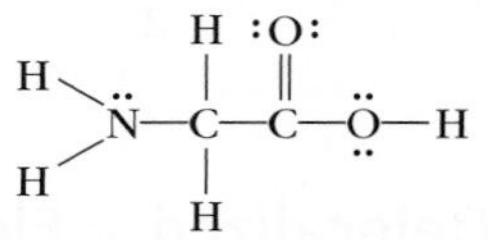

that contains the amine functional group, $—NH_2$, and a carboxylic acid functional group, —COOH.

(a) List the C—H, O—H, C—N, N—H, C—C, C—O, and C=O bonds in glycine in order of increasing bond length.

(b) List the C—H, O—H, C—N, C—C, C—O, and C=O bonds in glycine in order of increasing bond strength.

(c) Arrange these bonds in glycine in order of increasing bond polarity: C—N, C—O, C—H, O—H, and C—C in order of increasing bond polarity.

(d) The ionization of glycine in solution forms H^+ and glycinate ions. Write the structural formula for glycinate ion.

(e) Glycinate ion is an example of a resonance hybrid. Write two Lewis structures that contribute to this resonance hybrid.

(f) Glycine also forms a zwitterion. In the zwitterion an H^+ is released by the carboxylic acid group and attaches to the nitrogen of the amine group. Write the Lewis structure of the zwitterion form of glycine.

(g) Using the Lewis structure drawn for part (f), calculate the formal charges on each of its atoms. What is the net charge of the zwitterion?

ThomsonNOW™
Sign in to ThomsonNOW at **www.thomsonedu.com** to check your readiness for an exam by taking the Pre-Test and exploring the modules recommended in your Personalized Learning Plan.

IN CLOSING

Having studied this chapter, you should be able to . . .

- Recognize the different types of covalent bonding (Sections 8.1–8.3 and 8.9).
- Use Lewis structures to represent covalent bonds in molecules and polyatomic ions (Sections 8.1–8.3, 8.8, 8.10). ThomsonNOW homework: Study Questions 14, 18
- Describe multiple bonds in alkenes and alkynes (Section 8.5). ThomsonNOW homework: Study Question 26
- Recognize molecules that can have *cis-trans* isomerism (Section 8.5). ThomsonNOW homework: Study Questions 28, 30
- Predict bond lengths from periodic trends in atomic radii (Section 8.6). ThomsonNOW homework: Study Questions 34, 38, 82
- Relate bond energy to bond length (Section 8.6). ThomsonNOW homework: Study Question 82
- Use bond enthalpies to calculate the enthalpy of a reaction (Section 8.6). ThomsonNOW homework: Study Question 42
- Predict bond polarity from electronegativity trends (Section 8.7). ThomsonNOW homework: Study Questions 46, 48, 78
- Use formal charges to compare Lewis structures (8.8). ThomsonNOW homework: Study Questions 52, 56
- Use resonance structures to model multiple bonding in molecules and polyatomic ions (Section 8.9). ThomsonNOW homework: Study Questions 60, 65

- Recognize three types of exceptions to the octet rule (Section 8.10). ThomsonNOW homework: Study Question 67
- Describe bonding and constitutional isomerism in aromatic compounds (Section 8.11).
- Use molecular orbital theory to explain bonding in diatomic molecules and ions (Section 8.12). ThomsonNOW homework: Study Question 75

KEY TERMS

alkenes *(8.5)*
alkynes *(8.5)*
aromatic compounds *(8.11)*
antibonding molecular orbital *(8.12)*
bond enthalpy (bond energy) *(8.6)*
bond length *(8.6)*
bonding electrons *(8.2)*
bonding molecular orbital *(8.12)*
cis **isomer** *(8.5)*
cis-trans **isomerism** *(8.5)*
covalent bond *(8.1)*
delocalized electrons *(8.9)*
double bond *(8.4)*
electronegativity *(8.7)*
formal charge *(8.8)*
free radicals *(8.10)*
functional group *(8.3)*
Lewis structure *(8.2)*
lone pair electrons *(8.2)*
molecular orbital *(8.12)*
multiple covalent bonds *(8.4)*
nonpolar covalent bond *(8.7)*
octet rule *(8.2)*
polar covalent bond *(8.7)*
resonance hybrid *(8.9)*
resonance structures *(8.9)*
saturated hydrocarbons *(8.3)*
single covalent bond *(8.2)*
trans **isomer** *(8.5)*
triple bond *(8.4)*
unsaturated hydrocarbons *(8.5)*

QUESTIONS FOR REVIEW AND THOUGHT

■ denotes questions available in ThomsonNOW and assignable in OWL.

Blue-numbered questions have short answers at the back of this book and fully worked solutions in the *Student Solutions Manual.*

ThomsonNOW
Assess your understanding of this chapter's topics with sample tests and other resources found by signing in to ThomsonNOW at **www.thomsonedu.com**.

Review Questions

1. Explain the difference between an ionic bond and a covalent bond.
2. What kind of bonding (ionic or covalent) would you predict for the products resulting from the following combinations of elements?
   (a) $Na + I_2$ (b) $C + S$
   (c) $Mg + Br_2$ (d) $P_4 + Cl_2$
3. What characteristics must atoms A and X have if they are able to form a covalent bond A—X with each other? A polar covalent bond with each other?
4. Indicate the difference among alkanes, alkenes, and alkynes by giving the structural formula of a compound in each class that contains three carbon atoms.
5. Refer to Table 8.3 and answer these questions:
   (a) Do any molecules with more than eight electrons have a second-period element as the central atom?
   (b) What is the maximum number of bond pairs and lone pairs that surround the central atom in any of these molecules?
6. While sulfur forms the compounds SF_4 and SF_6, no equivalent compounds of oxygen, OF_4 and OF_6, are known. Explain.
7. Which of these molecules have an odd number of valence electrons: NO_2, SCl_2, NH_3, NO_3?
8. Write resonance structures for NO_2^-. Predict a value for the N—O bond length based on bond lengths given in Table 8.1, and explain your answer.
9. Consider these structures for the formate ion, HCO_2^-. Designate which two are resonance structures and which is equivalent to one of the resonance structures.

(a)
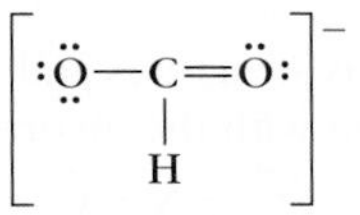
(b)
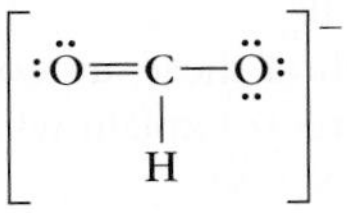
(c)
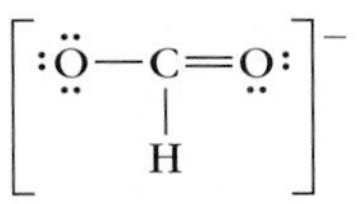

10. Consider a series of molecules in which the C atom is bonded to atoms of second-period elements: C—O, C—F, C—N, C—C, and C—B. Place these bonds in order of increasing bond length.
11. What are the trends in bond length and bond energy for a series of related bonds—for instance, single, double, and triple carbon-to-oxygen bonds?
12. Why is *cis-trans* isomerism not possible for alkynes?

Topical Questions

Lewis Structures

13. Write the Lewis structures of (a) dichlorine monoxide, Cl_2O; (b) hydrogen peroxide, H_2O_2; (c) borohydride ion, BH_4^-; (d) phosphonium ion, PH_4^+; and (e) PCl_5.
14. ■ Write Lewis structures for these molecules or ions.
    (a) ClF (b) H_2Se
    (c) BF_4^- (d) PO_4^{3-}
15. Write Lewis structures for these molecules.
    (a) $CHClF_2$, one of several chlorofluorocarbons that has been used in refrigeration
    (b) Methyl alcohol, CH_3OH
    (c) Methyl amine, CH_3NH_2
16. Write Lewis structures for these molecules or ions.
    (a) CH_3Cl (b) SiO_4^{4-}
    (c) ClF_4^+ (d) C_2H_6
17. Write Lewis structures for these molecules.
    (a) Formic acid, HCOOH, in which atomic arrangement is

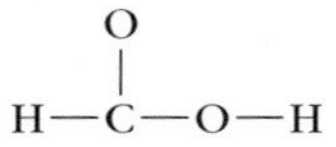

    (b) Acetonitrile, CH_3CN
    (c) Vinyl chloride, CH_2CHCl, the molecule from which PVC plastics are made
18. ■ Write Lewis structures for these molecules.
    (a) Tetrafluoroethylene, C_2F_4, the molecule from which Teflon is made
    (b) Acrylonitrile, CH_2CHCN, the molecule from which Orlon is made
19. Write Lewis structures for:
    (a) N_2^+
    (b) XeF_7^-
    (c) tetracyanoethane, C_6N_4
20. Write Lewis structures for:
    (a) Disulfur dichloride, S_2Cl_2
    (b) Nitrous acid, HNO_2, which has no oxygen-to-oxygen bonds
    (c) ClF_6^+
21. Which of these are correct Lewis structures and which are incorrect? Explain what is wrong with the incorrect ones.

(a) 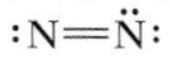
N_2

(b) 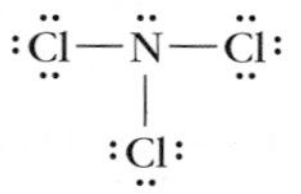
NCl_3

(c) 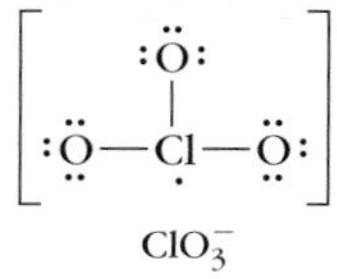
ClO_3^-

(d) 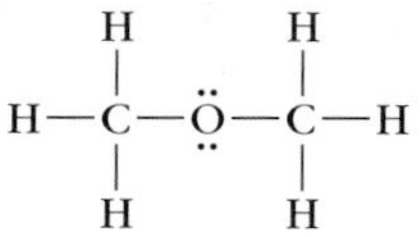
$(CH_3)_2O$

(e) 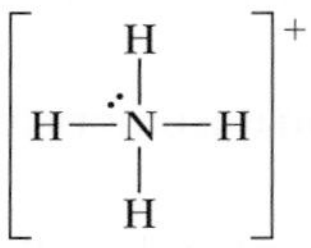

22. Which of these are correct Lewis structures and which are incorrect? Explain what is wrong with the incorrect ones.

(a) 
OF_2

(b) 
O_2

(c) 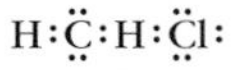
CH_3Cl

(d) 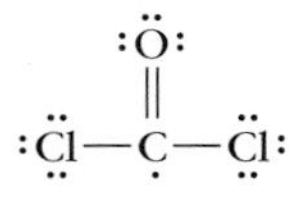
CCl_2O

(e) 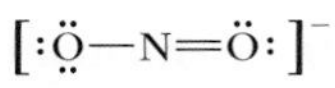
NO_2^-

Bonding in Hydrocarbons

23. Write the structural formulas for all the branched-chain compounds with the molecular formula C_4H_{10}.
24. Write the structural formulas for all the branched-chain compounds with the molecular formula C_6H_{14}.
25. Write structural formulas for two straight-chain alkenes with the formula C_5H_{10}. Are these the only two structures that meet these specifications?
26. ■ From their molecular formulas, classify each of these straight-chain hydrocarbons as an alkane, an alkene, or an alkyne.
    (a) C_5H_8 (b) $C_{24}H_{50}$ (c) C_7H_{14}
27. From their molecular formulas, classify each of these straight-chain hydrocarbons as an alkane, an alkene, or an alkyne.
    (a) $C_{21}H_{44}$ (b) C_4H_6 (c) C_8H_{16}
28. ■ Write the structural formulas for the *cis* and *trans* isomers of 2-pentene.
29. The structural formulas are given for these *cis* or *trans* alkenes.

(a) 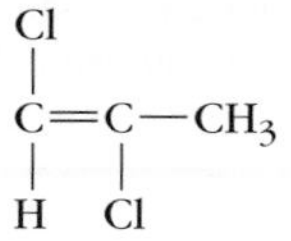
trans-1,2-dichloropropene

(b) 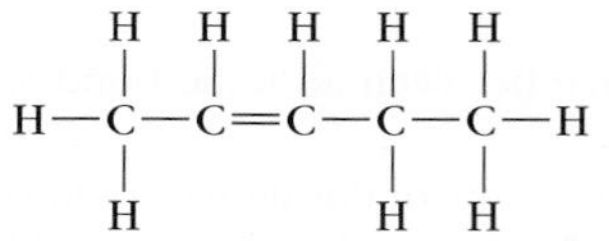
cis-2-pentene

(c) 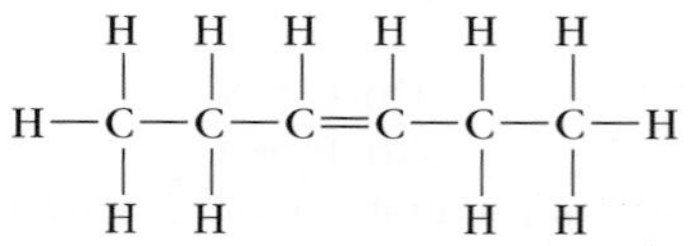
cis-3-hexene

(d) 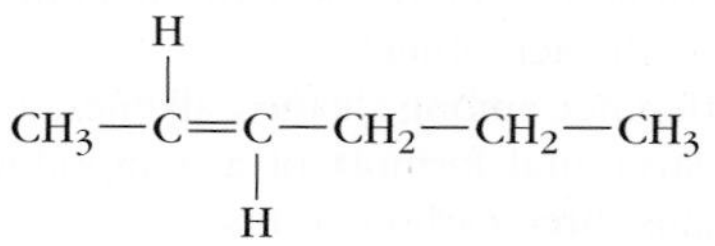
trans-2-hexene

Write the structural formula for
(a) *cis*-1,2-dichloropropene
(b) *trans*-2-pentene
(c) *trans*-3-hexene
(d) *cis*-2-hexene

30. ■ In each case, tell whether *cis* and *trans* isomers exist. If they do, write structural formulas for the two isomers and label each *cis* or *trans.*
(a) Br_2CH_2
(b) $CH_3CH_2CH{=}CHCH_2CH_3$
(c) $CH_3CH{=}CHCH_3$
(d) $CH_2{=}CHCH_2CH_3$

31. ■ Which of these molecules can have *cis* and *trans* isomers? For those that do, write the structural formulas of the two isomers and label each *cis* or *trans.* For those that cannot have these isomers, explain why.
(a) $CH_3CH_2BrC{=}CBrCH_3$
(b) $(CH_3)_2C{=}C(CH_3)_2$
(c) $CH_3CH_2IC{=}CICH_2CH_3$
(d) $CH_3ClC{=}CHCH_3$
(e) $(CH_3)_2C{=}CHCH_3$

32. Oxalic acid has this structural formula.

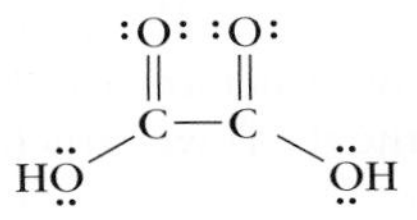

Is *cis-trans* isomerism possible for oxalic acid? Explain your answer.

33. 2-methyl propene has this Lewis structure.

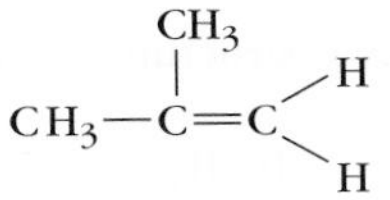

Is *cis-trans* isomerism possible for this molecule? Explain your answer.

Bond Properties

34. ■ For each pair of bonds, predict which will be the shorter.
(a) B—Cl or Ga—Cl
(b) C—O or Sn—O
(c) P—S or P—O
(d) The C=C or the C=O bond in acrolein

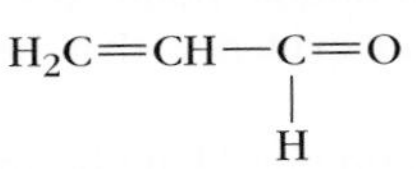

35. For each pair of bonds, predict which will be the shorter.
(a) Si—N or P—O
(b) Si—O or C—O
(c) C—F or C—Br
(d) The C=C or the C≡N bond in acrylonitrile, $H_2C{=}CH{-}C{\equiv}N$

36. ■ Using only a periodic table (not a table of bond energies), decide which of these is likely to be the strongest bond.
(a) Si—F (b) P—S (c) P—O

37. Compare the nitrogen-nitrogen bonds in hydrazine, N_2H_4, and in "laughing gas," N_2O. In which molecule is the nitrogen-nitrogen bond shorter? In which should the nitrogen-nitrogen bond be stronger?

38. ■ Consider the carbon-oxygen bonds in formaldehyde, H_2CO, and in carbon monoxide, CO. In which molecule is the carbon-oxygen bond shorter?

39. Which bond will require more energy to break, the carbon-oxygen bond in formaldehyde, H_2CO, or the CO bond in carbon monoxide, CO?

40. ■ Compare the carbon-oxygen bond lengths in the formate ion, HCO_2^-, and in the carbonate ion, CO_3^{2-}. In which ion is the bond longer? Explain briefly.

41. Compare the nitrogen-oxygen bond lengths in NO_2^+ and in NO_3^-. In which ion are the bonds longer? Explain briefly.

Bond Energies and Enthalpy Changes

42. ■ Estimate $\Delta H°$ for forming 2 mol ammonia from molecular nitrogen and molecular hydrogen. Is this reaction exothermic or endothermic? (N_2 has a triple bond.)

43. Estimate $\Delta H°$ for the conversion of 1 mol carbon monoxide to carbon dioxide by combination with molecular oxygen. Is this reaction exothermic or endothermic? (CO has a triple bond.)

44. Which of the four molecules HF, HCl, HBr, and HI has the strongest chemical bond? Using bond energies, estimate $\Delta H°$ for the reaction of molecular hydrogen with each of the gaseous molecular halogens: fluorine, chlorine, bromine, and iodine. Which is the most exothermic reaction?

Electronegativity and Bond Polarity

45. For each pair of bonds, indicate the more polar bond and use $\delta+$ or $\delta-$ to show the partial charge on each atom.
(a) C—O and C—N
(b) B—O and P—S
(c) P—H and P—N
(d) B—H and B—I

46. ■ Given the bonds C—N, C—H, C—Br, and S—O,
(a) Which atom in each is the more electronegative?
(b) Which of these bonds is the most polar?

47. For each pair of bonds, identify the more polar one and use $\delta+$ or $\delta-$ to indicate the partial charge on each atom.
(a) B—Cl and B—O (b) O—F and O—Se
(c) S—Cl and B—F (d) N—H and N—F

48. ■ The molecule below is urea, a compound used in plastics and fertilizers.

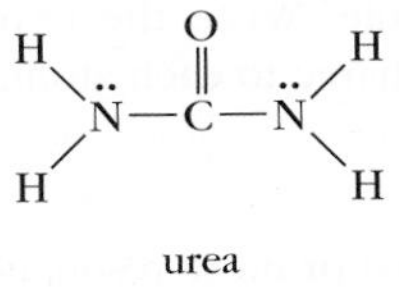

urea

(a) Which bonds in the molecule are polar and which are nonpolar?
(b) Which is the most polar bond in the molecule? Which atom is the partial negative end of this bond?

49. The molecule below is acrolein, the starting material for certain plastics.

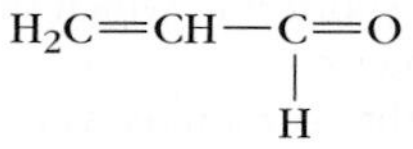

acrolein

(a) Which bonds in the molecule are polar and which are nonpolar?
(b) Which is the most polar bond in the molecule? Which atom is the partial negative end of this bond?

Formal Charge

50. What is the total formal charge of a molecule? Of an ion?
51. What is the relationship between formal charge and electronegativity?
52. ■ Write correct Lewis structures and assign a formal charge to each atom.
(a) SO_3
(b) C_2N_2 (atoms bonded in the order NCCN)
(c) NO_2^-
53. Write correct Lewis structures and assign a formal charge to each atom.
(a) OCS
(b) HNC (atoms bonded in that order)
(c) CH_3^-
54. Write correct Lewis structures and assign a formal charge to each atom.
(a) CH_3CHO
(b) N_3^-
(c) CH_3CN
55. Write correct Lewis structures and assign a formal charge to each atom.
(a) KrF_4
(b) ClO_3^-
(c) SO_2Cl_2
56. ■ Write the correct Lewis structure and assign a formal charge to each atom in fulminate ion, $(CNO)^-$.
57. Peroxydisulfate ion, $S_2O_8^{2-}$, is reduced to two sulfate ions, SO_4^{2-}. Write the correct Lewis structures and assign a formal charge to each atom in the peroxydisulfate and sulfate ions.
58. Two Lewis structures can be written for nitrosyl chloride, which contains one nitrogen, one oxygen, and one chlorine atom per molecule. Write the two Lewis structures and assign a formal charge to each atom.
59. Two Lewis structures can be written for nitrosyl fluoride, which contains one nitrogen, one oxygen, and one fluorine atom per molecule. Write the two Lewis structures and assign a formal charge to each atom.

Resonance

60. ■ These have two or more resonance structures. Write all the resonance structures for each.
(a) Nitric acid

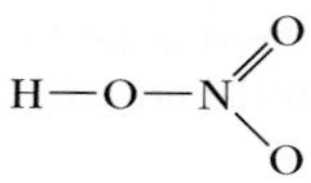

(b) Nitrate ion, NO_3^-

61. These have two or more resonance structures. Write all the resonance structures for each molecule or ion.
(a) SO_3 (b) SCN^-
62. Several Lewis structures can be written for perbromate ion, BrO_4^-, the central Br with all single Br—O bonds, or with one, two, or three Br=O double bonds. Draw the Lewis structures of these possible resonance forms, and use formal charges to predict the most plausible one.
63. Use formal charges to predict which of the resonance forms is most plausible for
(a) SO_3 and (b) HNO_3 (See Question 60.)
64. Write the resonance structures for adenine, which is the nitrogen-containing organic base portion of the nucleic acid ATP (adenosine triphosphate).

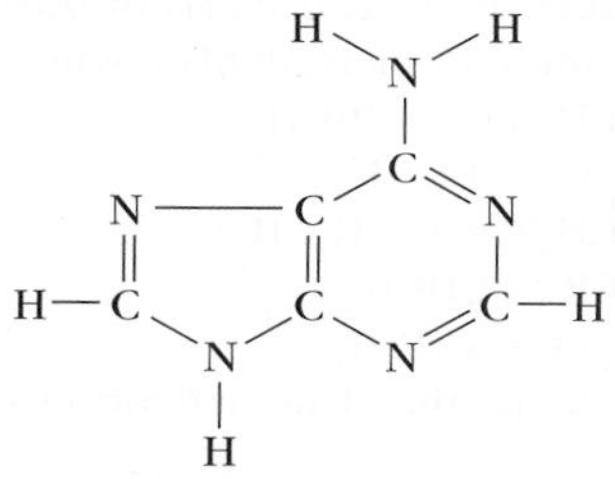

65. ■ Several Lewis structures can be written for thiosulfate ion, $S_2O_3^{2-}$. Write the Lewis structures of these possible resonance forms.
66. Use formal charges to predict the most plausible Lewis structure for thiosulfate ion, $S_2O_3^{2-}$. (See Question 65.)

Exceptions to the Octet Rule

67. ■ Write the Lewis structure for each of these molecules or ions.
(a) BrF_5 (b) IF_5 (c) IBr_2^-
68. Write the Lewis structure for each of these molecules or ions.
(a) BrF_3 (b) I_3^- (c) XeF_4
69. Which of these elements can form compounds with five or six pairs of valence electrons surrounding their atoms?
(a) C (b) P (c) O
(d) F (e) Cl (f) B
(g) Se (h) Sn

Aromatic Compounds

70. Carbon-to-carbon double bonds (C=C) react by addition. Cite experimental evidence that benzene does not have C=C bonds.
71. All carbon-to-carbon bond lengths are identical in benzene. Does this argue for or against the presence of C=C bonds in benzene? Explain.
72. Three dibromobenzenes are known. Write the Lewis structure and name for each compound.
73. The structural formula of anthracene is

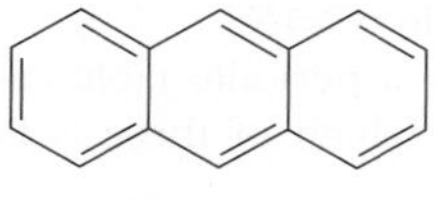

anthracene

What is its molecular formula?

74. Write the structural formula for 1,2-diiodobenzene (also known as *ortho*-diiodobenzene). Write the structural formulas for the *meta* and *para* isomers as well.

Molecular Orbital Theory

75. ■ Use MO theory to predict the MO diagram, the number of bonds, and the number of unpaired electrons in the nitrosyl ion, NO^+.
76. Use MO theory to predict the number of electrons in each of the 2*s* and 2*p* molecular orbitals, the number of bonds, and the number of unpaired electrons in:
(a) CO (b) F_2^- (c) NO^-
77. Use MO theory to predict the number of bonds and the number of unpaired electrons in each of these ions:
(a) B_2^+ (b) Li_2^+ (c) O_2^+

General Questions

78. ■ Using just a periodic table (not a table of electronegativities), decide which of these is likely to be the most polar bond. Explain your answer.
(a) C—F (b) S—F
(c) Si—F (d) O—F
79. The C—Br bond length in CBr_4 is 191 pm; the Br—Br distance in Br_2 is 228 pm. Estimate the radius of a C atom in CBr_4. Use this value to estimate the C—C distance in ethane, $H_3C—CH_3$. How does your calculated bond length agree with the measured value of 154 pm? Are radii of atoms exactly the same in every molecule?
80. Is it a good generalization that elements that are close together in the periodic table form covalent bonds, whereas elements that are far apart form ionic bonds? Why or why not?
81. Write Lewis structures for:
(a) CS_2
(b) NH_2OH
(c) S_2Cl_2 (contains S—S bond)
(d) NS_2^+
82. ■ The molecule pictured below is acrylonitrile, the building block of the synthetic fiber Orlon.

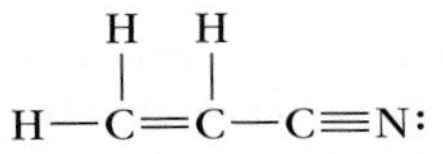

(a) Which is the shorter carbon-carbon bond?
(b) Which is the stronger carbon-carbon bond?
(c) Which is the most polar bond and what is the partial negative end of the bond?
83. In nitryl chloride, NO_2Cl, there is no oxygen-oxygen bond. Write a Lewis structure for the molecule. Write any resonance structures for this molecule.
84. Write Lewis structures for:
(a) SCl_2
(b) Cl_3^+
(c) $ClOClO_3$ (contains Cl—O—Cl bond)
(d) $SOCl_2$
85. Arrange these bonds in order of increasing length (shortest first). List all the factors responsible for each placement: O—H, O—O, Cl—O, O=O, O=C.
86. List the bonds in Question 85 in order of increasing bond *strength*.
87. Chlorine trifluoride, ClF_3, is one of the most reactive compounds known. Write the Lewis structure for ClF_3.
88. Judging from the number of carbon and hydrogen atoms in their formulas, which of these formulas represent alkanes? Which are likely aromatic? Which fall into neither category? (It may help to write structural formulas.)
(a) C_8H_{10} (b) $C_{10}H_8$ (c) C_6H_{12}
(d) C_6H_{14} (e) C_8H_{18} (f) C_6H_{10}

Applying Concepts

89. A student drew this incorrect Lewis structure for ClO_3^-. What errors were made when determining the number of valence electrons?

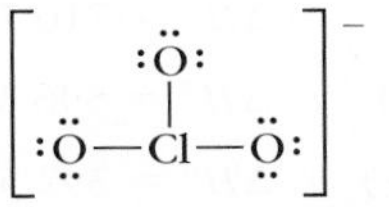

90. This Lewis structure for SF_5^+ is drawn incorrectly. What error was made when determining the number of valence electrons?

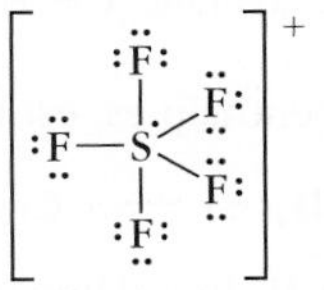

91. Tribromide, Br_3^-, and triiodide, I_3^-, ions exist, but trifluoride ion, F_3^-, is not known. Explain.
92. Explain why nonmetal atoms in Period 3 and beyond can accommodate greater than an octet of electrons and those in Period 2 cannot do so.
93. When asked to give an example of resonance structures, a student drew these Lewis structures. Why is this example incorrect?

$$:\ddot{N}{=}N{-}\ddot{\underset{..}{O}}: \longleftrightarrow :\ddot{N}{-}O{-}\ddot{\underset{..}{N}}:$$

94. Why is this not an example of resonance structures?

$$[:\ddot{N}{=}S{=}\ddot{C}:]^- \longleftrightarrow [:\ddot{N}{=}C{-}\ddot{\underset{..}{S}}:]^-$$

95. How many bonds would you expect the elements in Groups 3A through 7A to form if they obeyed the octet rule?
96. In another universe, elements try to achieve a nonet (nine valence electrons) instead of an octet when forming chemical bonds. As a result, covalent bonds form when a trio of electrons are shared between two atoms. Draw Lewis structures for the compounds that would form between (a) hydrogen and oxygen and (b) hydrogen and fluorine.
97. Elemental phosphorus has the formula P_4. Propose a Lewis structure for this molecule. [*Hints:* (1) Each phosphorus atom is bonded to three other phosphorus atoms. (2) Visualize the structure three-dimensionally, not flat on a page.]
98. ■ The elements As, Br, Cl, S, and Se have electronegativity values of 2.1, 2.4, 2.5, and 3.0, but not in that order. Using the periodic trend for electronegativity, assign the values to the elements. Which assignments are you certain about? Which are you not?

99. A substance is analyzed and found to contain 85.7% carbon and 14.3% hydrogen by weight. A gaseous sample of the substance is found to have a density of 1.87 g/L, and 1 mol of it occupies a volume of 22.4 L. What are two possible Lewis structures for molecules of the compound? (*Hint:* First determine the empirical formula and molar mass of the substance.)

100. Which of these molecules is least likely to exist: NF_5, PF_5, SbF_5, or IF_5? Explain why.

101. When we estimate $\Delta H°$ from bond enthalpies we assume that all bonds of the same type (single, double, triple) between the same two atoms have the same energy, regardless of the molecule in which they occur. The purpose of this problem is to show you that this is only an approximation. You will need the following standard enthalpies of formation:

C(g)	$\Delta H° = 716.7$ kJ/mol
CH(g)	$\Delta H° = 596.3$ kJ/mol
CH_2(g)	$\Delta H° = 392.5$ kJ/mol
CH_3(g)	$\Delta H° = 146.0$ kJ/mol
H(g)	$\Delta H° = 218.0$ kJ/mol

(a) What is the average C—H bond energy in methane, CH_4?

(b) Using bond enthalpies, estimate $\Delta H°$ for the reaction

$$CH_4(g) \longrightarrow C(g) + 2\,H_2(g)$$

(c) By heating CH_4 in a flame it is possible to produce the reactive gaseous species CH_3, CH_2, CH, and even carbon atoms, C. Experiments give these values of $\Delta H°$ for the reactions shown:

$$CH_3(g) \longrightarrow C(g) + H_2(g) + H(g) \qquad \Delta H° = 788.7 \text{ kJ}$$

$$CH_2(g) \longrightarrow C(g) + H_2(g) \qquad \Delta H° = 324.2 \text{ kJ}$$

$$CH(g) \longrightarrow C(g) + H(g) \qquad \Delta H° = 338.3 \text{ kJ}$$

For each of these reactions, draw a diagram similar to Figure 8.4. Then calculate the average C—H bond energy in CH_3, CH_2, and CH. Comment on any trends you see.

102. Write the Lewis structure for nitrosyl fluoride, FNO. Using only a periodic table, identify:
(a) Which is the longest bond.
(b) Which is the strongest bond.
(c) Which is the most polar bond.

103. Write the Lewis structure for nitrosyl chloride, ClNO. Using only a periodic table, identify:
(a) Which is the longest bond.
(b) Which is the strongest bond.
(c) Which is the most polar bond.

104. Methylcyanoacrylate is the active ingredient in "super" glues. Its Lewis structure is

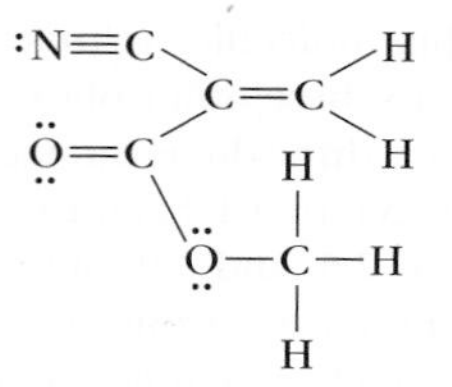

In this molecule, which is the:
(a) Weakest carbon-containing bond?
(b) Strongest carbon-containing bond?
(c) Most polar bond?

105. Acrylonitrile is used to made synthetic carpets and wigs. Its Lewis structure is

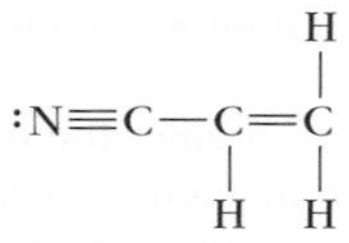

In this molecule, which is the:
(a) Strongest carbon-containing bond?
(b) Second strongest carbon-containing bond?
(c) Most polar bond?

More Challenging Questions

106. Write the Lewis structure for:
(a) tetraboron tetrachloride, B_4Cl_4
(b) hyponitrous acid, $H_2N_2O_2$

107. Nitrosyl azide, N_4O, is a pale yellow solid first synthesized in 1993. Write the Lewis structure for nitrosyl azide.

108. Write the Lewis structures for:
(a) $(Cl_2PN)_3$
(b) $(Cl_2PN)_4$

109. Write the Lewis structures for:
(a) dithiocyanogen, $(NCS)_2$
(b) tetrahydrofuran, C_4H_8O

110. In sulfuric acid production, sulfur trioxide is combined with sulfuric acid to produce oleum, which contains $H_2S_2O_7$. Write the Lewis structure for this compound.

111. Tetrasulfur tetranitride, S_4N_4, can be converted to disulfur dinitride, S_2N_2. Write the Lewis structures for these compounds.

112. Write the Lewis structures for:
(a) hyponitrite ion, $(N_2O_2)^{2-}$
(b) $(SO_3)_3$

113. Write the Lewis structures for:
(a) S_2F_{10}
(b) $FXeN(SO_2F)_2$

114. Experimental evidence indicates the existence of HC_3N molecules in interstellar clouds. Write a plausible Lewis structure for this molecule.

115. Molecules of SiC_3 have been discovered in interstellar clouds. Write a plausible Lewis structure for this molecule.

116. For many people, tears flow when they cut raw onions. The tear-inducing agent is thiopropionaldehyde-S-oxide, C_3H_6OS. Write the Lewis structure for this compound.

117. One of the structural isomers of C_3H_6OS is the compound that is the offending odorant released by striped skunks. Write Lewis structures for two isomers of this compound.

118. Phosphorus and sulfur form a series of compounds, one of which is tetraphosphorus trisulfide. Write the Lewis structure for this compound.

119. Piperine, the active ingredient in black pepper, has the structural formula given below.

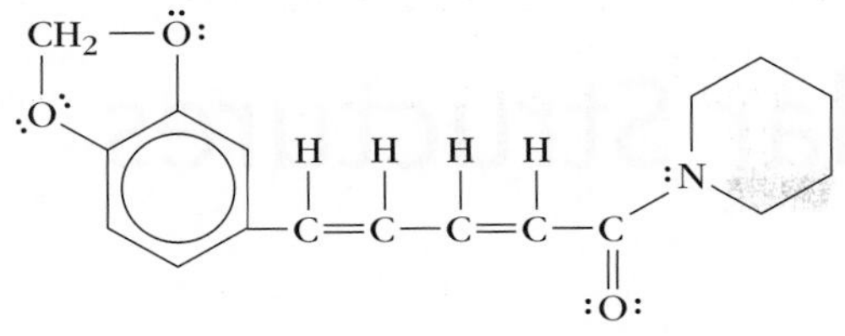

(a) Write the molecular formula of piperine.
(b) Identify the shortest carbon-to-carbon bond in piperine.
(c) Identify the shortest carbon-to-oxygen bond in piperine.
(d) Identify the stongest carbon-to-carbon bond in piperine.
(e) Identify the most polar bond in piperine.

120. Gamma-aminobutanoic acid, $C_4H_9O_2N$, is a neurotransmitter. The molecule contains a four-carbon chain.
(a) Write the Lewis structure for this molecule.
(b) Which bond is the longest?
(c) Which bond is the most polar?
(d) Which bond is the strongest?

121. Suppose in building up molecular orbitals, the π_{2p} were placed above the σ_{2p}. Prepare a diagram similar to Figure 8.11 based on these changes. For which species in Table 8.4 would this change in relative energies of the MOs affect the prediction of number of bonds and number of unpaired electrons?

Conceptual Challenge Problems

CP8.A (Section 8.2) What deficiency is acknowledged by chemists when they write the formula for silicon dioxide as $(SiO_2)_n$ but write CO_2 for carbon dioxide?

CP8.B (Section 8.7) Without referring to the periodic table, write an argument to predict how the electronegativities of elements change based on the composition of their atoms.

CP8.C (Section 8.7) How would you rebut the statement, "There are no ionic bonds, only polar covalent bonds"?

9 Molecular Structures

The bark of the Pacific yew tree (above) contains paclitaxel, a highly effective anti-cancer drug. The ball-and-stick model illustrates the shape of part of the paclitaxel molecule. By a detailed study of its molecular shape, researchers were able to determine the mechanism for the drug's anti-cancer activity *(⟵ p. 5)*. This chapter explains aspects of the shapes of molecules, such as paclitaxel's, using the valence-shell electron-pair repulsion (VSEPR) model.

Left: © Ray Pfortner/Peter Arnold, Inc.; right: © Scott Camazine/Photo Resarchers, Inc.

Although the composition, empirical formula, molecular formula, and Lewis structure of a substance provide important information, they are not sufficient to predict or explain the properties of most molecular compounds. Also important are the arrangement of the atoms and how they occupy three-dimensional space—the shape of a molecule. Because of differences in the sequence in which their atoms are joined, molecules can have the same numbers of the same kinds of atoms, yet have different properties. For example, ethanol (in alcoholic beverages) and dimethyl ether (a refrigerant) have the same molecular formula, C_2H_6O. But the C, H, and O atoms are arranged so differently in molecules of these two compounds that their melting points differ by 27 °C and their boiling points by 103 °C.

ThomsonNOW™
Throughout the text, this icon indicates an opportunity to test yourself on key concepts and to explore interactive modules by signing in to ThomsonNOW at **www.thomsonedu.com**.

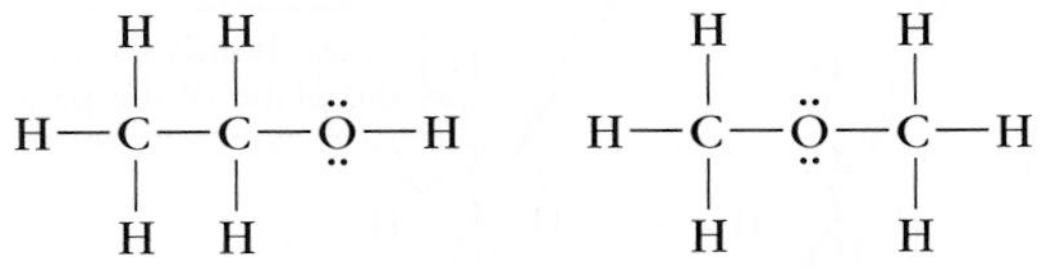

ethanol   dimethyl ether

	Ethanol	Dimethyl ether
Melting Pts. °C	−114.1	−141.5
Boiling Pts. °C	78.3	−24.8

The ideas about molecular shape presented in this chapter are crucial to understanding the relationships between the structure and properties of molecules, properties related to the behavior of molecules in living organisms, the design of molecules that are effective drugs, and many other aspects of modern chemistry.

9.1 Using Molecular Models

Molecules are three-dimensional aggregates of atoms, much too small to examine visually. Our ability to understand three-dimensional molecular structures is helped by the use of molecular models. Probably the best example of the impact a model can have on the advancement of science is the double helix model of DNA used by James Watson and Francis Crick, which revolutionized the understanding of human heredity and genetic disease. We will discuss DNA (Section 9.7) after considering molecular shapes (Section 9.2) and noncovalent interactions (Section 9.6), both of which are essential to DNA function.

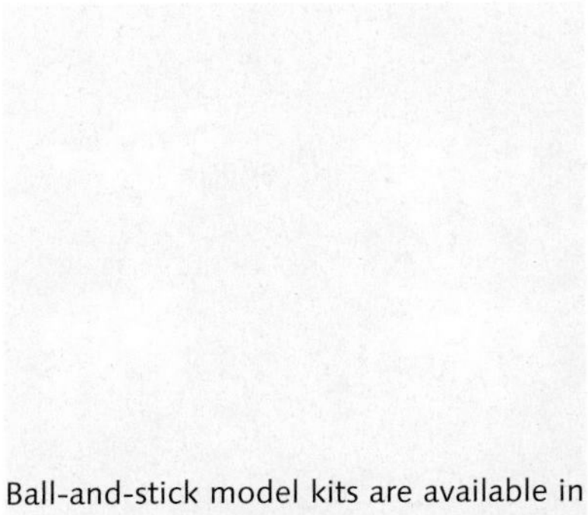

Ball-and-stick model kits are available in many campus bookstores. The models are easy to assemble and will help you to visualize the molecular geometries described in this chapter. Ball-and-stick models are relatively inexpensive compared with space-filling models.

Watson and Crick's DNA model was a physical model assembled atom by atom, like those for water shown below on the left. The ball-and-stick model uses balls to represent atoms and short rods of wood or plastic to represent bonds. For example, the ball-and-stick model for water has a red ball representing oxygen, with holes at the correct angles connected by sticks to two white balls representing hydrogen atoms. In the space-filling physical model, the atomic models are scaled according to the experimental values for atom sizes, and the links between parts of the model are not visible when the model is assembled. This gives a better representation of the actual space occupied by atoms.

This book uses many computer-generated pictures of molecular models, like those for water shown below. The computer programs that generate these pictures

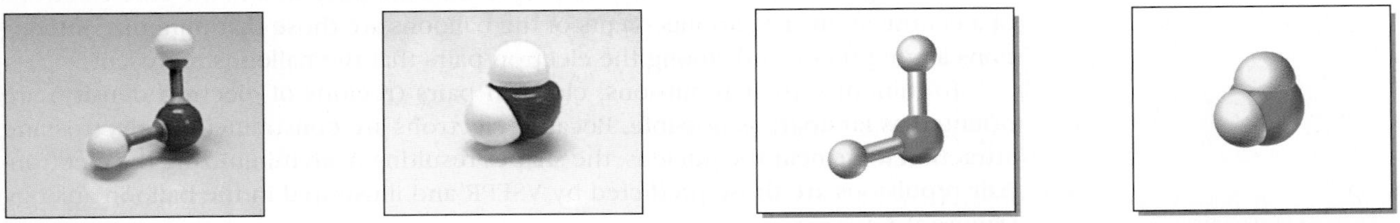

Photos: © Thomson Learning/Charles D. Winters

Ball-and-stick   Space-filling   Ball-and-stick   Space-filling

Physical molecular models   Computer-generated molecular models

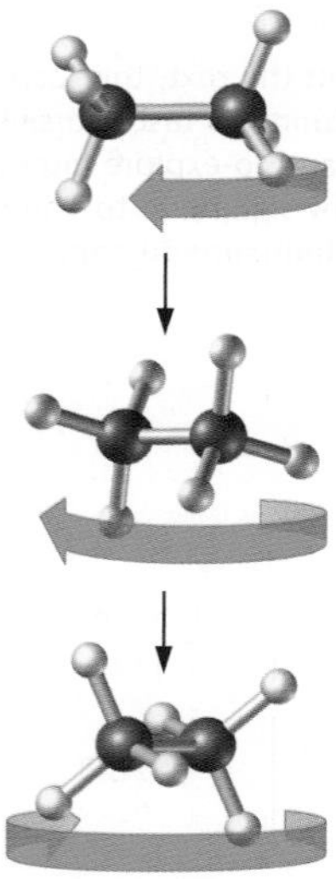

Figure 9.1 **Rotation around an axis perpendicular to the C—C bond axis in an ethane molecule (C_2H_6).**

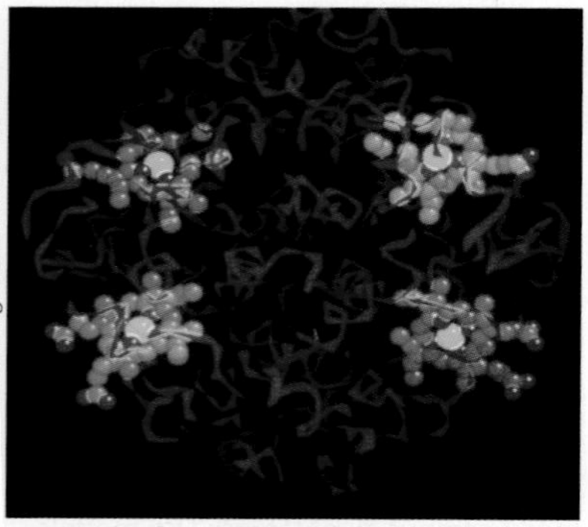

© Thomson Learning/Charles D. Winters

Figure 9.2 **Hemoglobin, a protein essential to human life.** An Fe^{2+} ion shown in yellow is at the center of each green heme cluster.

rely on the most accurate experimentally derived data on atomic radii, bond lengths, and bond angles.

To convey a three-dimensional perspective for a molecule drawn on a flat surface, such as the page of a book, we can also make a perspective drawing that uses solid wedges (▶) to represent bonds extending in front of the page, and dashed lines (----) or dashed wedges (⦙⦙⦙) to represent bonds behind the page. Bonds that lie in the plane of the page are indicated by a line (—), as illustrated in the following perspective drawing for methane, a tetrahedral molecule:

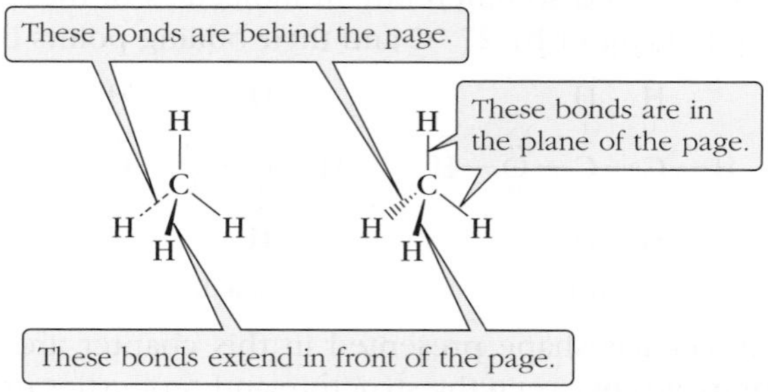

Computers can draw and also rotate molecules so that they can be viewed from any angle, as illustrated in Figure 9.1 for ethane.

Advances in computer graphics have made it possible to draw scientifically accurate pictures of extremely complex molecules, as well as to study interactions between molecules. Figure 9.2 is a computer-generated model of hemoglobin, the remarkable and essential protein in the blood that takes up and releases oxygen. This vital protein is made up of two folded sets of pairs of long chains of atoms, indicated by the red ribbons. In a hemoglobin molecule, oxygen binds to Fe^{2+} ions (yellow) at four sites shown in green, red, and blue in Figure 9.2. Computer graphics can rotate such computer-generated models to provide different views of the molecule.

9.2 Predicting Molecular Shapes: VSEPR

Because molecular shape is so important to the reactivity and function of molecules, it is essential to have a simple, reliable method for predicting the shapes of molecules and polyatomic ions. The **valence-shell electron-pair repulsion (VSEPR)** model is such a method. The VSEPR model is based on the idea that repulsions occur among regions of electron density, such as the repulsions among pairs of bonding and lone pair electrons. Such repulsions control the angles between bonds from a central atom to other atoms surrounding it.

How do repulsions among electron pairs result in different shapes? Imagine that the volume of a balloon represents the repulsive force of an electron pair that prevents other electron pairs from occupying the same space. When two or more balloons are tied together at a central point, the cluster of balloons assumes the shapes shown in Figure 9.3. The central point represents the nucleus and the core electrons of a central atom. The arrangements of the balloons are those that minimize interactions among them, and among the electron pairs that the balloons represent.

To minimize their repulsions, electron pairs (regions of electron density) are oriented as far apart as possible. Because electrons are constrained by electrostatic attraction to be near the nucleus, the shapes resulting from minimizing the electron-pair repulsions are those predicted by VSEPR and illustrated in the balloon analogy (Figure 9.3.)

Photos: © Thomson Learning/ Charles D. Winters

Figure 9.3 Balloon models of the geometries predicted by the VSEPR model.

Central Atoms with Only Bonding Pairs

The simplest application of VSEPR is to molecules and polyatomic ions having a central atom that has only shared electron pairs to bond it to other atoms (terminal atoms) by only single bonds. In such cases, the central atom has no lone pairs. We can summarize this using an AXE-based shorthand notation: A (the central atom) is bonded to X_n (the terminal atoms); E_m represents the number of lone pair electrons on the central atom. When there are no lone pairs, the symbolism is E_0. For example, an AX_3E_0 designation denotes a central atom (A) with no lone pairs (E_0) and whose shared pairs are bonded to three terminal atoms (X_3), such as in BF_3.

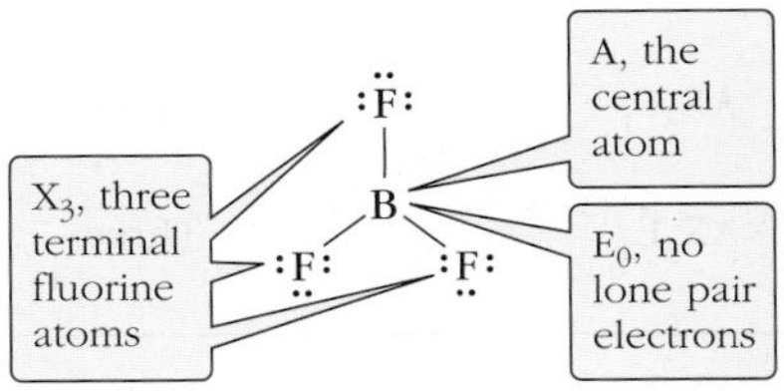

Using the AX_3E_0 designation for boron trifluoride.

Figure 9.4 illustrates the geometries predicted by the VSEPR model for molecules of types AX_2E_0 to AX_6E_0. (Table 9.1 also summarizes this information.)

Notice in Figure 9.4 that there are two categories of geometries—electron-pair geometry and molecular geometry. In a molecule or polyatomic ion, the **electron-pair geometry** is determined by the number and arrangement of the electron pairs around the central atom. By contrast, the **molecular geometry** is the arrangement of the atoms in space. *For molecules whose central atoms have no lone pairs, the electron-pair geometry and the molecular geometry are the same.* When lone pairs are present on the central atom, the electron-pair and molecular geometries are not the same, as will be discussed shortly. **Bond angles,** as shown in Figure 9.4, are the angles between the bonds of two atoms that are bonded to the same third atom. In a methane molecule, CH_4, for example, all the H—C—H bond angles are 109.5°.

The term "molecular shape" is sometimes used rather than "molecular geometry."

The predicted bond angles given in the examples in Figure 9.4 are in agreement with experimental values obtained from structural studies.

Molecular model	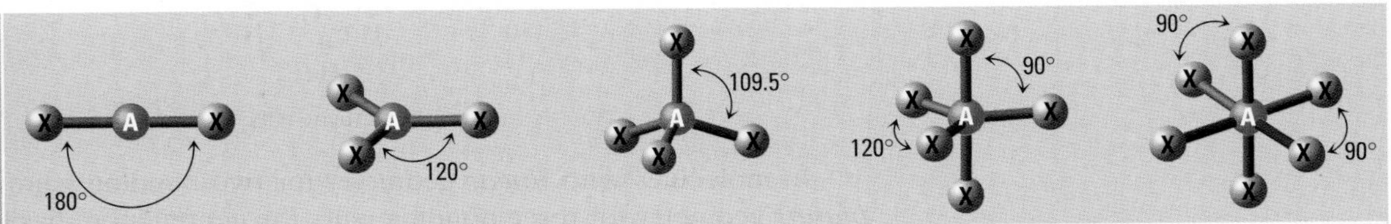				
Type	AX_2E_0	AX_3E_0	AX_4E_0	AX_5E_0	AX_6E_0
Electron-pair geometry	Linear	Triangular planar	Tetrahedral	Triangular bipyramidal	Octahedral
Molecular geometry	Linear	Triangular planar	Tetrahedral	Triangular bipyramidal	Octahedral
Example molecule	BeF_2	BF_3	CH_4	PCl_5	SF_6

Figure 9.4 Geometries predicted by the VSEPR model for molecules of types AX_2E_0 through AX_6E_0 that contain only single covalent bonds and no lone pairs on the central atom, A.

Table 9.1 Examples of Electron-Pair Geometries and Molecular Geometries Predicted by the VSEPR Model

Type (X = atoms bonded to central atom A; E = lone pairs on central atom)	Number of X Atoms on Central Atom	Number of Lone Pairs on Central Atom	Electron-Pair Geometry	Molecular Geometry	Example
AX_2E_0	Two	None	Linear	Linear	CO_2, $BeCl_2$
AX_2E_1	Two	One	Triangular planar	Angular (bent)	$SnCl_2$
AX_2E_2	Two	Two	Tetrahedral	Angular (bent)	H_2O, OCl_2
AX_2E_3	Two	Three	Triangular bipyramidal	Linear	XeF_2
AX_3E_0	Three	None	Triangular planar	Triangular planar	BCl_3, CO_3^{2-}
AX_3E_1	Three	One	Tetrahedral	Triangular pyramidal	NCl_3
AX_3E_2	Three	Two	Triangular bipyramidal	T-shaped	ClF_3
AX_4E_0	Four	None	Tetrahedral	Tetrahedral	CH_4, $SiCl_4$
AX_4E_1	Four	One	Triangular bipyramidal	Seesaw	SF_4
AX_4E_2	Four	Two	Octahedral	Square planar	XeF_4
AX_5E_0	Five	None	Triangular bipyramidal	Triangular bipyramidal	PF_5
AX_5E_1	Five	One	Octahedral	Square pyramidal	BrF_5
AX_6E_0	Six	None	Octahedral	Octahedral	SF_6

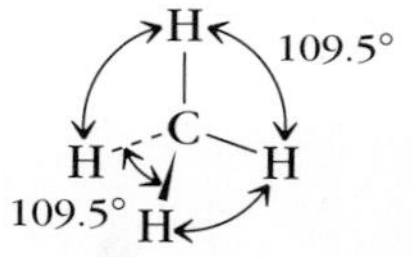

methane (CH_4)

Central atoms from Period 2 are too small to accommodate more than four atoms bonded to them.

ThomsonNOW™
Go to the Chemistry Interactive menu to work a module on **ideal electron-pair geometries.**

In molecules with *linear* geometry for two bonding pairs and the *triangular planar* geometry for three bonding pairs the central atom has less than an octet of electrons around it **(⇐ *p. 361*).** The central atom in a *tetrahedral* molecule obeys the octet rule with four bonding pairs (Figure 9.4). The central atoms in *triangular bipyramidal* and *octahedral* molecules do not obey the octet rule because they have five and six bonding pairs, respectively. Hence, triangular bipyramidal and octahedral geometries would be expected only when the central atom is an element in Period 3 or higher **(⇐ *p. 361*).** The geometries illustrated in Figure 9.4 are by far the most common in molecules and polyatomic ions, and you should be thoroughly familiar with them.

Suppose you want to use VSEPR concepts to predict the shape of $SiCl_4$. First, draw the Lewis structure, with Si as the central atom. From the Lewis structure, you can see that there are four bonding pairs from the terminal Cl atoms to the central Si atom forming four single bonds to Si, and no lone pairs on Si. Therefore, $SiCl_4$ is an AX_4E_0 type of molecule (Figure 9.4) and you would predict a tetrahedral electron-pair geometry and a tetrahedral molecular geometry for the molecule. This is in agreement with structural studies of $SiCl_4$, which indicate a tetrahedral molecule with all Cl—Si—Cl bond angles 109.5°.

In this case, A is Si, X is Cl, and X_4 indicates four Cl atoms bonded to A; E_0 denotes no lone pairs on A (Si), the central atom.

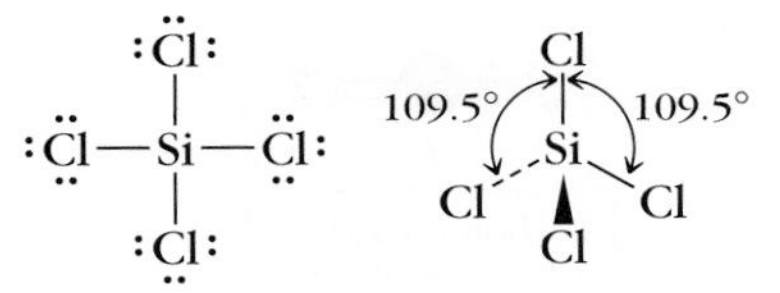

PROBLEM-SOLVING EXAMPLE 9.1 Molecular Geometry

Use the VSEPR model to predict the electron-pair geometry, molecular geometry, and bond angles of (a) BF_3 and (b) CBr_4.

Answer

(a) Triangular planar electron-pair and molecular geometries with 120° F—B—F bond angles

(b) Tetrahedral electron-pair and molecular geometries with 109.5° Br—C—Br bond angles

Strategy and Explanation The first step in using VSEPR is to write the correct Lewis structure and classify the molecule according to the number of bonding electron pairs and lone pairs on the central atom.

(a) The Lewis structure is

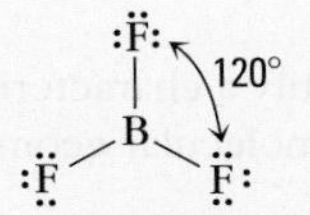

BF_3 is an AX_3E_0-type molecule (three bonding pairs, no lone pairs around the central B atom; see Figure 9.4). The molecule has three B—F single bonds around the central boron atom, arranged at 120° angles from each other. Therefore, BF_3 has a triangular planar electron-pair geometry and molecular geometry with all the atoms lying in the same plane.

(b) Being an AX_4E_0-type molecule, CBr_4 will be a tetrahedral molecule with 109.5° Br—C—Br bond angles. The electron pair and molecular geometries are tetrahedral.

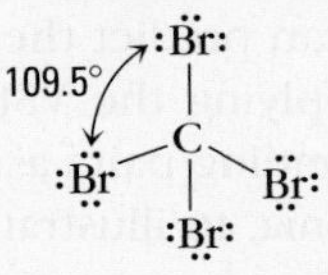

PROBLEM-SOLVING PRACTICE 9.1

Identify the electron-pair geometry, the molecular geomety, and the bond angles for BeF_2.

Multiple Bonds and Molecular Geometry

Although double bonds and triple bonds are shorter and stronger than single bonds, this has only a minor effect on predictions of molecular shape. Why? Electron pairs involved in a multiple bond are all shared between the same two nuclei and therefore occupy the same region of space. Because they must remain in that region, two electron pairs in a double bond or three electron pairs in a triple bond are like a single, slightly fatter balloon, rather than two or three balloons. Hence, ***for the purpose of determining molecular geometry, the electron pairs in a multiple***

bond constitute a single region of electron density as in a single bond. For example, compare BeF_2 (Figure 9.4) with CO_2. BeF_2 is a linear molecule with the two Be—F single bonds 180° apart. In CO_2, each C=O double bond is a single region of electron density, just as each Be—F single bond is, so the structure of CO_2 is also linear.

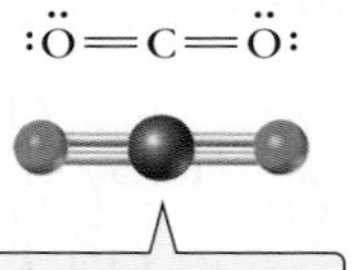

ThomsonNOW

Go to the Coached Problems menu for tutorials on:

- **ideal repulsion shapes**
- **molecular shapes**

When resonance structures are possible, the geometry can usually be predicted from *any* of the Lewis resonance structures or from the resonance hybrid structure. For example, the geometry of the CO_3^{2-} ion is predicted to be triangular planar because the carbon atom has three sets of bonds and no lone pairs. It can be predicted from the Lewis structure.

This structural formula is one of three resonance forms for carbonate ion ***(⇐ p. 357).***

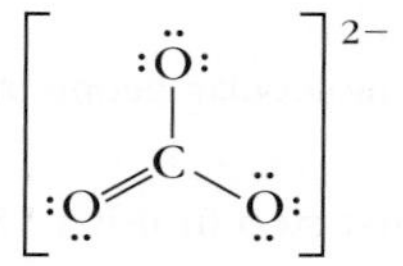

CONCEPTUAL EXERCISE 9.1 Geometries

Based on the discussion so far, identify a characteristic that is common to all situations where electron-pair geometry and molecular geometry are the same for a molecule or a polyatomic ion.

Central Atoms with Bonding Pairs and Lone Pairs

How does the presence of lone pairs on the central atom affect the geometry of a molecule or polyatomic ion? The easiest way to visualize this situation is to return to the balloon model and notice that the electron pairs on the central atom do not all have to be bonding pairs. We can predict the electron-pair geometry, molecular geometry, and bond angles by applying the VSEPR model to the total number of valence electron pairs—that is, bonding pairs as well as lone pairs around the central atom. We will use NH_3, ammonia, to illustrate guidelines for doing so.

1. ***Draw the Lewis structure.*** The Lewis structure for NH_3 is

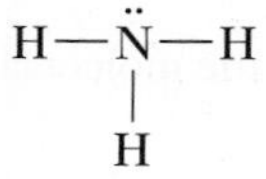

2. ***Determine the number of bonds and the number of lone pairs around each atom.*** In the case of NH_3, there are three bonding pairs and one lone pair; thus, NH_3 is an AX_3E_1-type molecule (Table 9.1). Any electron pairs in a multiple bond contribute to the molecular geometry in a similar manner as those in a single bond. The central N atom in NH_3 has no multiple bonds, only three H—N single covalent bonds.

In ammonia, A is N, X is H, and X_3 indicates three H atoms bonded to A, the central atom; E_1 denotes one lone pair on A.

3. ***Pick the appropriate electron-pair geometry around each central atom, and then choose the molecular shape that matches the total number of bonds and lone pairs.*** The *electron-pair geometry* around a central atom includes the spatial positions of all bond pairs and lone pairs. Because

there are three bonding pairs and one lone pair for a total of four pairs of electrons, we predict that the electron-pair geometry of NH_3 is tetrahedral. To represent this geometry, draw a tetrahedron with N as the central atom and the three bonding pairs represented by lines, since they are single covalent bonds. The lone pair is drawn as a balloon shape to indicate its spatial position in the tetrahedron.

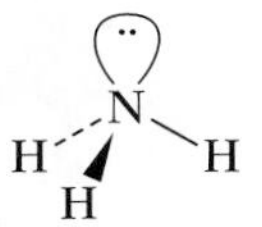

The positions of the lone pairs are *not* specified when describing the molecular geometry of molecules. The *molecular geometry* of ammonia is described as a triangular pyramid because the three hydrogen atoms form a triangular base with the nitrogen atom at the apex of the pyramid. (This can be seen by covering up the lone pair of electrons and looking at the molecular geometry—the location of the three H atoms and the N atoms.)

4. ***Predict the bond angles, remembering that lone pairs occupy more volume than do bonding pairs.*** Bonding pairs are concentrated in the bonding region between two atoms by the strong attractive forces of two positive nuclei and are, therefore, relatively compact, or "skinny." For a lone pair, there is only one nucleus attracting the electron pair. As a result, lone pairs are less compact. Using the balloon analogy, a lone pair is like a fatter balloon that takes up more room and squeezes the thinner balloons closer together. The relative strengths of electron-pair repulsions are

   lone pair–lone pair > lone pair–bonding pair > bonding pair–bonding pair

   This listing predicts that lone pairs will force bonding pairs closer together and decrease the angles between the bonding pairs. Recognizing this, we can predict that bond angles adjacent to lone pairs will be smaller than those predicted for perfect geometric shapes. The determination of electron-pair geometry and molecular geometry for NH_3 is summarized by this sequence:

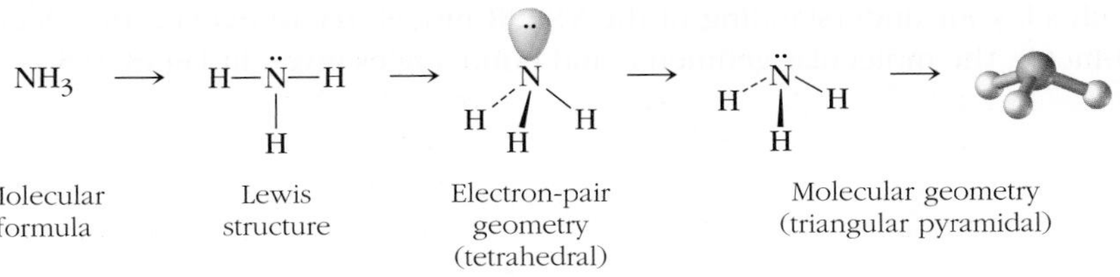

The success of the VSEPR model in predicting molecular shapes indicates that it is appropriate to account for the effects of lone pairs in this way.

   Because the electron-pair geometry is tetrahedral, we would expect the H—N—H bond angles to be 109.5°. However, the experimentally determined bond angles in NH_3 are 107.5°. This is attributed to the bulkier lone pair forcing the bonding pairs closer together, thereby reducing the bond angle from 109.5° to 107.5°. Table 9.1 (p. 384) summarizes the electron-pair geometry and molecular geometry for cases of zero, one, two, or three lone pairs on the central atom.

The effect that increasing numbers of lone pairs on the central atom have on bond angles is shown on page 388 for CH_4, NH_3, and H_2O. Note from the series of molecules that as the number of lone pairs on the central atom increases, the bond angle decreases. The three molecules all have tetrahedral electron-pair geometry because each has four electron pairs around the central atom. Each molecule, however, has slightly different bond angles due to the lone pair effect. There are bonding pair–bonding pair repulsions in all three molecules, and also bonding pair–lone pair repulsions in NH_3, and additionally lone pair–lone pair repulsions in water. This results in tetrahedral molecular geometry for CH_4 (109.5°), triangular pyramidal molecular geometry for NH_3 (107.5°), and angular (bent) molecular geometry for H_2O (104.5°).

Sometimes the term "bent" is used rather than "angular" to describe this molecular geometry.

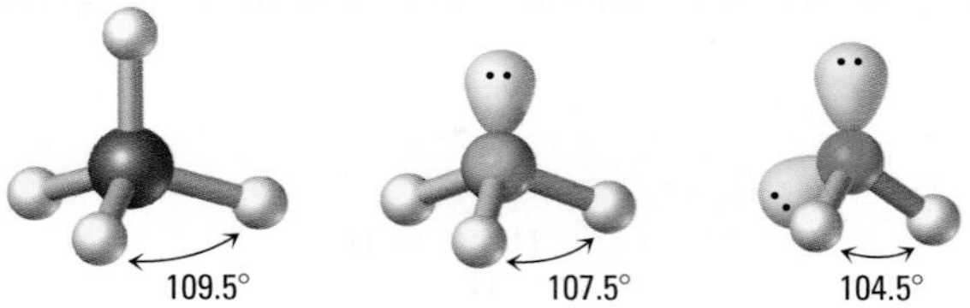

methane CH_4 ammonia NH_3 water H_2O

Methane, which has a tetrahedral shape, is the smallest member of the large family of saturated hydrocarbons called alkanes (⇐ p. 339). It is important to recognize that every carbon atom in an alkane has a tetrahedral environment. For example, notice below that the carbon atoms in propane and in the much longer carbon chain of hexadecane do not lie in a straight line because of the tetrahedral geometry about each carbon atom. The tetrahedron is arguably the most important shape in chemistry because of its predominance in the chemistry of carbon and the carbon-based chains that form the backbone of many biomolecules.

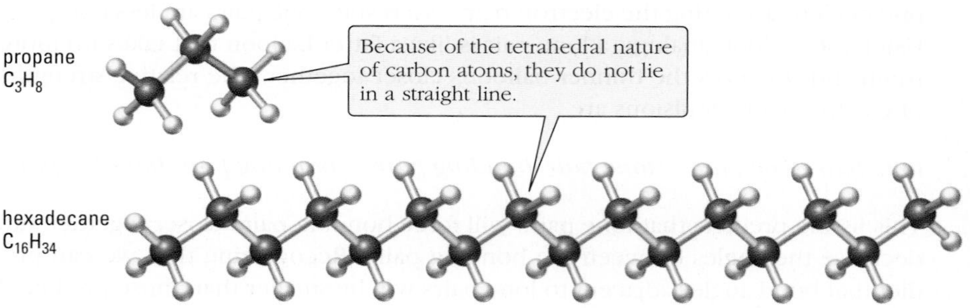

Figure 9.5 gives additional examples of electron-pair and molecular geometries for molecules or ions with three and four electron pairs around the central atom. To check your understanding of the VSEPR model, try to explain the electron-pair geometry, the molecular geometry, and bond angles given in Figure 9.5.

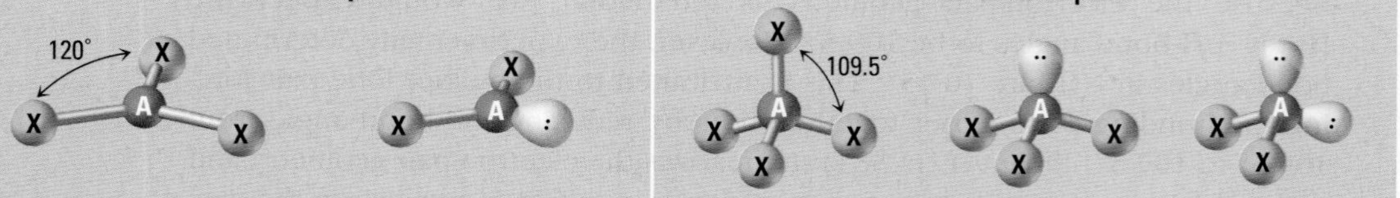

	Three electron pairs		Four electron pairs		
Molecular model	No lone pairs	One lone pair	No lone pairs	One lone pair	Two lone pairs
Type	AX_3E_0	AX_2E_1	AX_4E_0	AX_3E_1	AX_2E_2
Electron-pair geometry	Triangular planar	Triangular planar	Tetrahedral	Tetrahedral	Tetrahedral
Molecular geometry	Triangular planar	Angular	Tetrahedral	Triangular pyramidal	Angular
Example	BCl_3	$GeCl_2$	CCl_4	NCl_3	OF_2

Figure 9.5 Three and four electron pairs around a central atom. Examples are shown of electron-pair geometries and molecular shapes for molecules and polyatomic ions with three and four electron pairs around the central atom.

PROBLEM-SOLVING EXAMPLE 9.2 Molecular Structure

Use the VSEPR model to predict the electron-pair geometry and the molecular geometry of (a) ClF_2^+, (b) $SnCl_3^-$, (c) SeO_3, and (d) CS_2.

Answer

Electron-Pair Geometry	Molecular Geometry
(a) Tetrahedral	Angular
(b) Tetrahedral	Triangular pyramidal
(c) Triangular planar	Triangular planar
(d) Linear	Linear

Strategy and Explanation Writing the correct Lewis structures identifies the central atom in each ion or molecule. The Lewis structures are

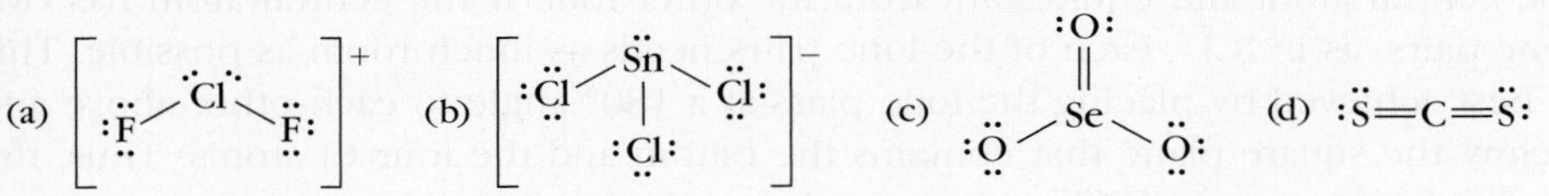

(a) The Lewis structure of ClF_2^+ reveals that the central Cl atom has four electron pairs: two bonding pairs to terminal fluorine atoms and two lone pairs. Consequently, the ion is an AX_2E_2 type and has a tetrahedral electron-pair geometry and an angular (bent) molecular geometry.

(b) The central tin atom is surrounded by three bonding pairs and one lone pair (AX_3E_1 type). These four electron pairs give a tetrahedral electron-pair geometry. The molecular geometry is triangular pyramidal. The lone pair pushes the Sn—Cl bonds closer together than the purely 109.5° tetrahedral angle expected for four bonding pair–bonding pair repulsions.

(c) The two bonding pairs in the Se=O double bond are counted as one region of electron density for determining the geometry of the molecule, giving three bonding regions around Se (AX_3E_0 type). Because there are no lone pairs around Se, the electron-pair and molecular geometries are the same, triangular planar.

(d) For determining molecular structure, each C=S double bond is treated as one region of electron density. There are no lone pairs on the central C atom (AX_2E_0 type). Therefore, the electron-pair geometry and molecular geometry are both linear.

PROBLEM-SOLVING PRACTICE 9.2

Use Lewis structures and the VSEPR model to determine electron-pair and molecular geometries for (a) BrO_3^-, (b) SeF_2, and (c) NO_2^-.

Expanded Octets: Central Atoms with Five or Six Electron Pairs

Analysis of electron-pair and molecular geometries becomes more complicated if a central atom has five or six electron pairs, some of which are lone pairs. Let's look first at the entries in Figure 9.6 for the case of five electron pairs. The three angles in the triangular plane are all 120°. The angles between any of the pairs in this plane and an upper or lower pair are only 90°. Thus, the *triangular bipyramidal* structure has two sets of positions that are not equivalent. Because the positions in the triangular plane lie in the equator of an imaginary sphere around the central atom, they are called **equatorial positions.** The north and south poles are called **axial positions.** Each equatorial position is next to only two electron pairs at 90° angles, the axial ones, while an axial position is proximate to three electron pairs, the equatorial

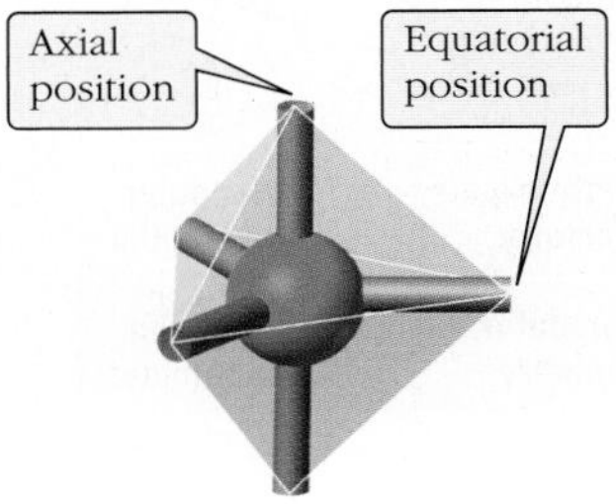

Triangular bipyramidal structure

ones. This means that *any lone pairs, because they are more extensive than bonding pairs, will occupy equatorial positions rather than axial positions.* For example, consider the ClF_3 molecule, which has three bonding pairs and two lone pairs, as shown in Figure 9.6. The two lone pairs in ClF_3 are equatorial; two bonding pairs are axial, with a third occupying an equatorial position, so the molecular geometry is T-shaped (Figure 9.6). (Given our viewpoint of axial positions lying on a vertical line, the T of the molecule is actually on its side ⊢.)

The electron-pair geometry for six electron pairs is an *octahedron* with each angle 90°. Unlike the triangular bipyramid, the octahedron has no distinct axial and equatorial positions; all six positions around the central atom are equivalent. As shown in Figure 9.6, six atoms bonded to the central atom in an octahedron can occupy three axes at right angles to one another (the *x*-, *y*-, and *z*-axes). All six atoms are *equidistant* from the central atom. Thus, if a molecule with octahedral electron-pair geometry has one lone pair on the central atom, it makes no difference which apex the lone pair occupies. An example is BrF_5, whose molecular geometry is *square pyramidal* (Figure 9.6). There is a *square plane* containing the central atom and four of the atoms bonded to it, with the other bonded atom directly above the central atom and equidistant from the other four. If the central atom has two lone pairs, as in ICl_4^-, each of the lone pairs needs as much room as possible. This is best achieved by placing the lone pairs at a 180° angle to each other above and below the square plane that contains the I atom and the four Cl atoms. Thus, the molecular geometry of ICl_4^- is *square planar* (Figure 9.6).

In Figure 9.6, the lone pair in BrF_5 could have been located in any one of the six positions around Br. We arbitrarily chose the "down" position.

An example of the power of the VSEPR model is its use to correctly predict the shape of XeF_4. At one time the noble gases were not expected to form compounds because their atoms have a stable octet of valence electrons (⇐ ***p. 334***). The synthesis of XeF_4 was a surprise to chemists, but you can use the VSEPR model to predict the correct geometry. The molecule has 36 valence electrons (eight from Xe and seven from each of four F atoms). There are eight electrons in four bonding pairs around Xe, and a total of 24 electrons in the lone pairs on the four F atoms. That leaves four electrons in two lone pairs on the Xe atom.

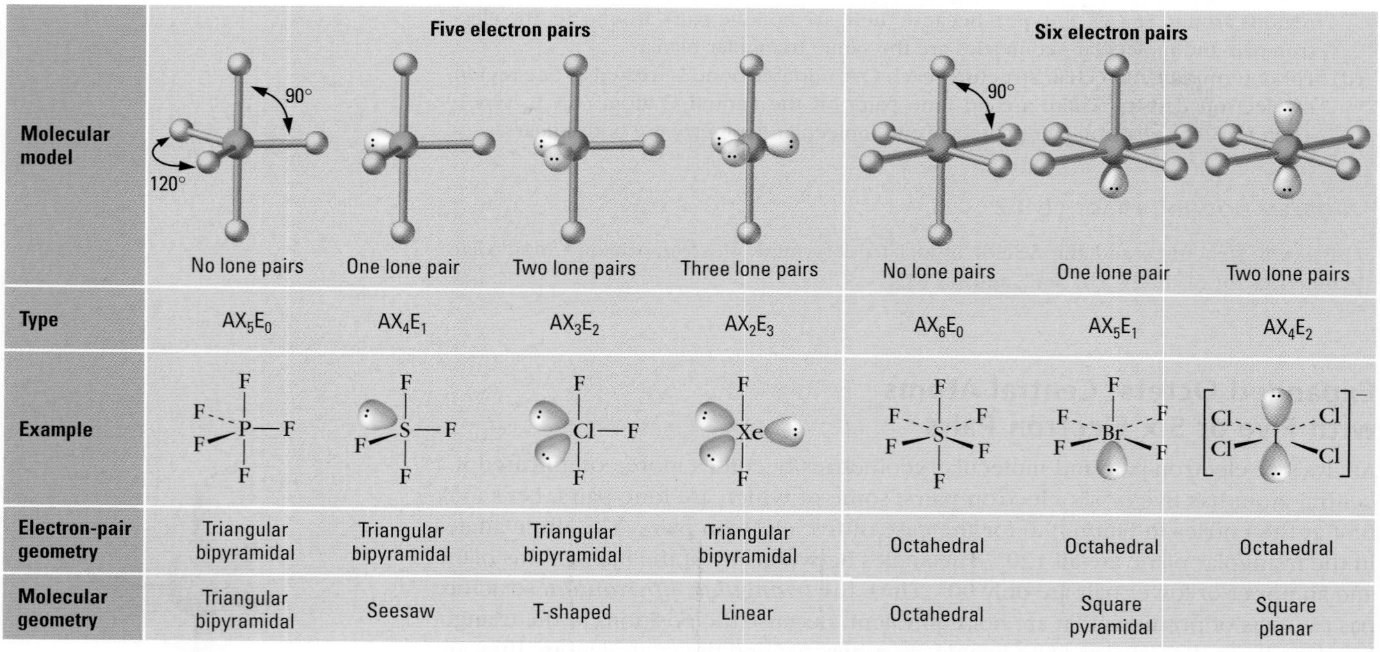

Figure 9.6 Five and six electron pairs around a central atom. Molecules and polyatomic ions with five and six electron pairs around the central atom can have these electron-pair geometries and molecular shapes.

Because Xe is in Period 5, it can accommodate more than an octet of electrons (**p. 362**). The total of six electron pairs on Xe leads to a prediction of an octahedral *electron-pair geometry* (AX_4E_2 type). Where do you put the lone pairs? As explained earlier for the ICl_4^- ion, the lone pairs are placed at opposite corners of the octahedron to minimize repulsion by keeping them as far apart as possible. The result is a square planar *molecular geometry* for the XeF_4 molecule (cover the lone pairs in the drawing for ICl_4^- in Figure 9.6 to see this). This shape agrees with experimental structural results. A number of other xenon compounds have been prepared, and the VSEPR model has been useful in predicting their geometries as well.

Argonne National Laboratory, managed and operated by UChicago Argonne, LLC, for the U.S. Dept of Energy under contract No. DE-AC02-06CH11357

Xenon tetrafluoride crystals.

CONCEPTUAL EXERCISE 9.2 Two Dissimilar Shapes

Triangular bipyramidal and square pyramidal molecular geometries each have a central atom with five terminal atoms around it, but the molecular shapes are different. Explain how and why these two shapes differ.

Table 9.1 (p. 384) gives additional examples of molecules and ions whose shapes can be predicted by using the VSEPR model. The model also can be used to predict the geometry around atoms in molecules with more than one central atom. Consider, for example, lactic acid, a compound important in carbohydrate metabolism. The molecular structure of lactic acid is

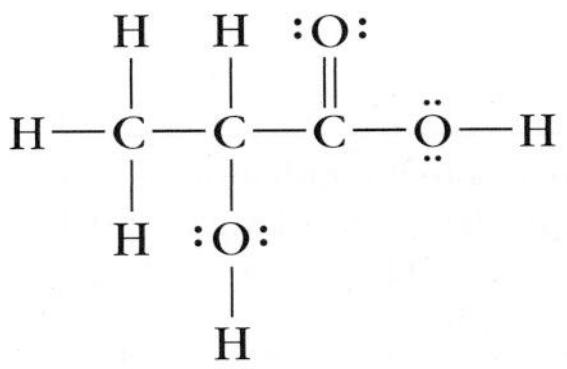

Around C in the $—CH_3$ group are four bonding pairs and no lone pairs, so its molecular geometry is tetrahedral (109.5° bond angles). The middle carbon also has four bonding pairs associated with it and so also has tetrahedral geometry (109.5° bond angles). The remaining carbon atom has four bonding pairs—two in single bonds and two in a C=O double bond—giving, for molecular geometry purposes, three bonding regions around it and a triangular planar geometry (120° bond angles). The single-bonded oxygens, in each case, have two bonding pairs and two lone pairs, creating an angular molecular geometry around each single-bonded oxygen atom (with a bond angle of less than 109.5°). The combined effect of these geometries is shown in the molecular models below.

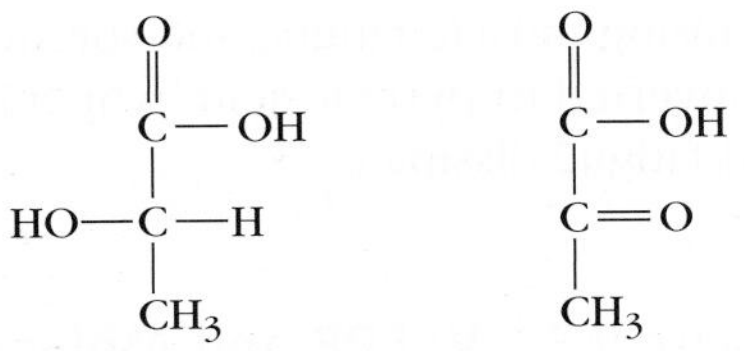

lactic acid   pyruvic acid

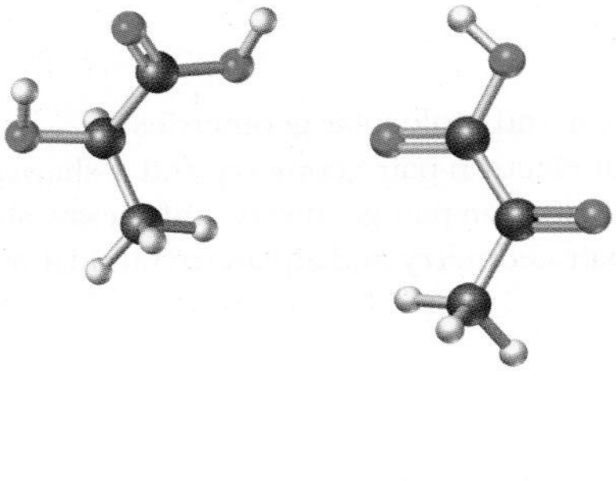

TOOLS OF CHEMISTRY

Infrared Spectroscopy

How are molecular structures determined? Many methods rely on the interaction of electromagnetic radiation with matter. Probing matter with electromagnetic radiation is called **spectroscopy,** and each area of the electromagnetic spectrum *(⇐ p. 274)* can be used as the basis for a particular spectroscopic method. Recall from Section 7.1 that electromagnetic radiation is emitted or absorbed in quantized packets of energy called photons and that the energy of the photon is represented by $E = h\nu$, where ν is the frequency of the light. Molecules may absorb several different electromagnetic radiation frequencies depending on the energy differences between their allowed energy levels. Each frequency absorbed must provide the exact packet of energy needed to lift a molecule from one energy level to another. Infrared (IR) spectroscopy uses the interaction of infrared radiation with matter to study molecular structure. It is particularly useful for learning about molecular structure because the energy of the internal motions of molecules is similar to the energy of photons whose frequency is in the infrared region. Covalent bonds between atoms in a molecule can be considered to be like springs that can bend or stretch only in specified amounts.

For example, bending or stretching of the bonds of the water molecule, as shown, occurs at specific frequencies corresponding to specific energy levels. The strength of the

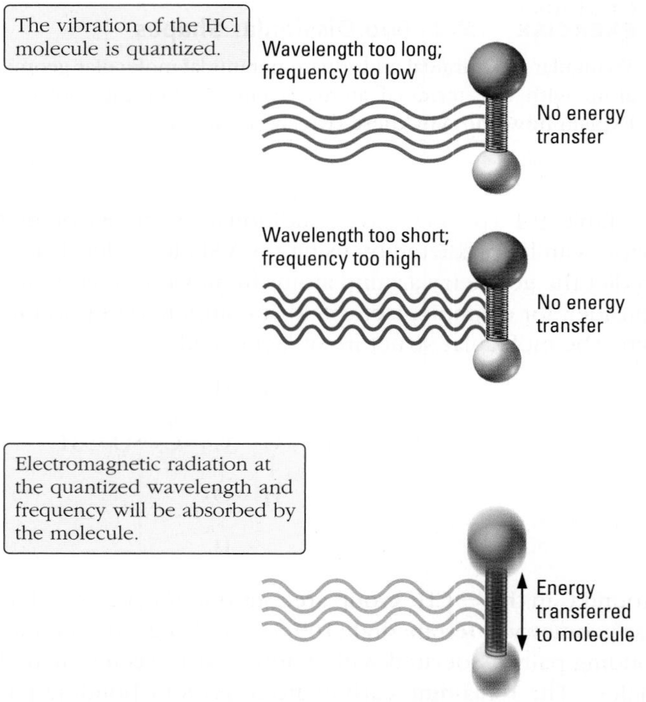

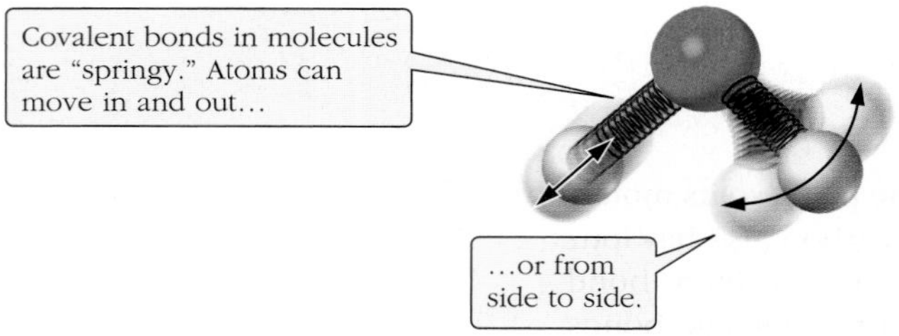

Olivier Prevosto/Corbis

Lactic acid has built up in the cells of these sprinters.

Lactic acid, a waste product of glucose metabolism, builds up rapidly in muscles during strenuous short-term exercise such as sprinting (100 to 800 m) and swimming (100 or 200 m). During such exercise, the accumulated lactic acid irritates the muscle tissue, causing muscle fatigue and soreness. But after the exercise stops, the lactic acid is converted to pyruvic acid, which is removed from the muscles, and the soreness and fatigue dissipate.

PROBLEM-SOLVING EXAMPLE 9.3 VSEPR and Molecular Shape

What are the electron-pair and the molecular geometries of (a) SeF_6, (b) IF_3, (c) TeF_4, and (d) XeF_5^+?

Answer

(a) Octahedral electron-pair and molecular geometries
(b) Triangular bipyramidal electron-pair geometry and T-shaped molecular geometry
(c) Triangular bipyramidal electron-pair geometry and seesaw-shaped molecular geometry
(d) Octahedral electron-pair geometry and square pyramidal molecular geometry

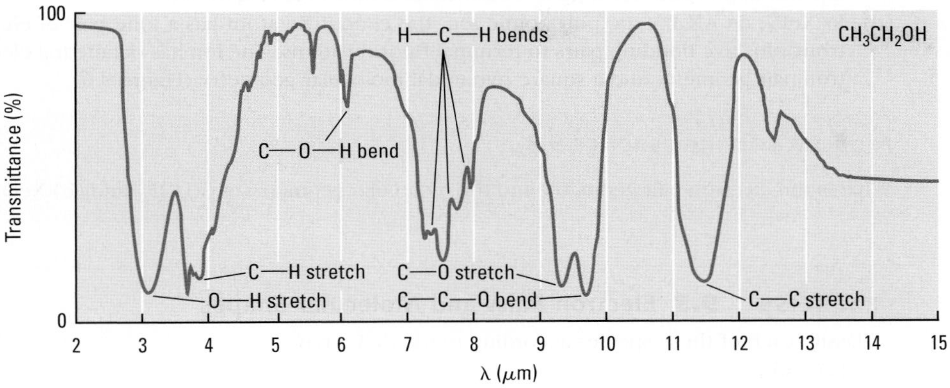

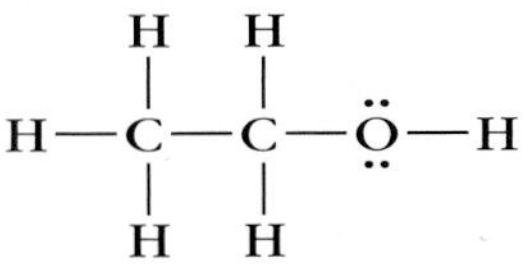

ethanol

Ethanol and its infrared spectrum.

covalent bonds determines what frequency of infrared light is necessary for changing from one stretching or bending energy level to another. The molecule must be excited from one of these allowed energy states to another by an exact quantity of energy.

As another example, a hydrogen chloride molecule vibrates at a specific energy. Photons that are too low or too high in energy do not cause vibration at the next higher energy level, and the radiation passes through the molecule without being absorbed. In contrast, photons of the proper energy are absorbed and increase the molecule's vibrational energy.

Because the covalent bonds in molecules differ in strength and number, the molecular motions and the number of vibrational energy levels vary; hence, the wavelengths of infrared radiation that are absorbed by different molecules differ. As a result, infrared spectroscopy can be used to learn about the structures of molecules and even to analyze an unknown material by matching its infrared spectrum with that of a known compound. In fact, the infrared frequencies absorbed by a molecule are so characteristic of the bending and stretching of various bonds that the infrared spectrum of a molecule is regarded as its *fingerprint.*

An example of the use of infrared spectroscopy in the identification of ethanol is shown above, where each of the absorption peaks is labeled with the type of bond action that causes it. To obtain such an IR absorption spectrum, infrared radiation is passed through a sample. The frequency of the IR radiation striking the sample is varied and the sample absorbs or transmits the IR radiation at each frequency. Peaks (drops in transmittance) occur when the sample absorbs IR radiation of a particular frequency. The overall result is an absorption spectrum, as shown for ethanol.

Strategy and Explanation First, draw the Lewis structures, then use them as a guide to determine the electron-pair and molecular geometries. The Lewis structures are

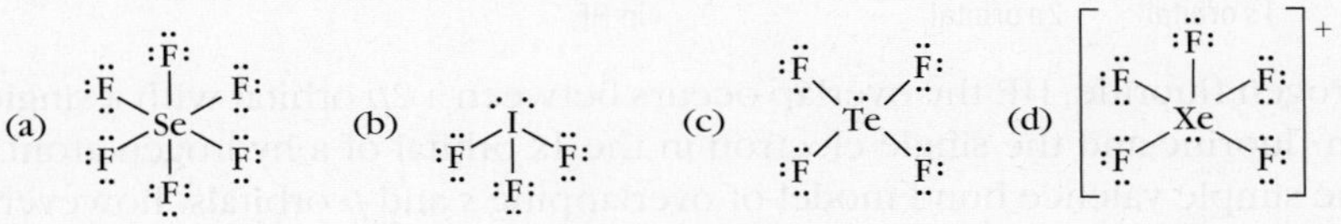

(a) The 48 valence electrons are used for six single bonds from the central Se to the terminal fluorine atoms and three lone pairs around each fluorine. Because SeF_6 is an AX_6E_0-type molecule, there are six bonding pairs around Se and no lone pairs. The electron-pair geometry and the molecular geometry are octahedral.

(b) IF_3 is an AX_3E_2-type molecule. There are five electron pairs around I, giving a triangular bipyramidal electron-pair geometry. As noted in Figure 9.6, the two lone pairs will be in equatorial positions. One bonding pair is equatorial, while the remaining two bonding pairs are axial. The molecule is T-shaped.

(c) In TeF_4, an AX_4E_1-type molecule, the central Te atom is surrounded by five electron pairs, giving it a triangular bipyramidal electron-pair geometry. The lone pair is in an equatorial position, creating a seesaw-shaped molecule (Figure 9.6).
(d) In XeF_5^+, an AX_5E_1-type polyatomic ion, the central Xe atom has a lone pair of electrons plus five bonding pairs to terminal fluorine atoms. The ion has octahedral electron-pair geometry and a square pyramidal molecular geometry (Figure 9.6).

PROBLEM-SOLVING PRACTICE 9.3

What is the electron-pair geometry and the molecular geometry of (a) ClF_2^- and (b) XeO_3?

EXERCISE 9.3 Electron Pairs and Molecular Shapes

Classify each of these species according to its AX_nE_m type:
(a) XeF_2
(b) NI_3
(c) I_3^-

9.3 Orbitals Consistent with Molecular Shapes: Hybridization

Although Lewis structures are helpful in assigning molecular geometries, they indicate nothing about the orbitals occupied by the bonding and lone pair electrons. A theoretical model of covalent bonding, referred to as the **valence bond model,** does so by describing a covalent bond as the result of an overlap of orbitals on each of two bonded atoms. For H_2, for example, the bond is a shared electron pair located in the overlapping *s* atomic orbitals.

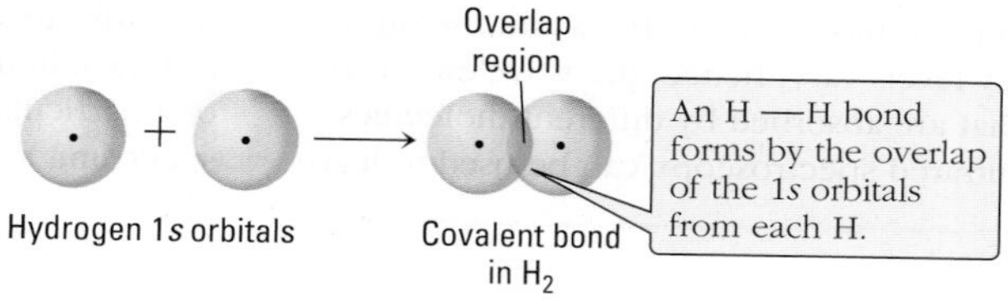

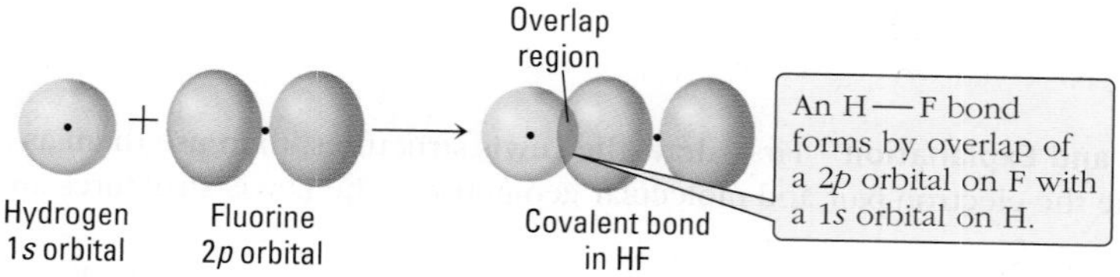

In hydrogen fluoride, HF, the overlap occurs between a 2*p* orbital with a single electron on fluorine and the single electron in the 1*s* orbital of a hydrogen atom.

The simple valence bond model of overlapping *s* and *p* orbitals, however, must be modified to account for bonding in molecules with central atoms, such as Be, B, and C. Consider the electron configurations for Be, B, and C atoms:

			1s	2s	2p		
Be	$1s^2 2s^2$		↑↓	↑↓			
B	$1s^2 2s^2 2p^1$		↑↓	↑↓	↑		
C	$1s^2 2s^2 2p^2$	$1s^2 2s^2 2p_x^1 2p_y^1$	↑↓	↑↓	↑	↑	

The simple valence bond model would predict that Be, with an outer s^2 configuration like He, should form no covalent bonds; B, with one unpaired electron ($2p^1$) should form only one bond; and C ($2p^2$) should form only two bonds with its two unpaired 2*p* electrons. But BeF_2, BF_3, and CF_4 all exist, as well as other Be, B, and C compounds in which these atoms have two, three, and four bonds, respectively.

To account for molecules like CH_4, in which the actual molecular geometry is incompatible with simple overlap of *s* and *p* orbitals, valence bond theory is modified to include a new kind of atomic orbital. Atomic orbitals of the proper energy and orientation in the same atom are **hybridized,** meaning that the atomic orbitals are combined to form **hybrid orbitals.** The resulting hybrid orbitals all have the same shape. Consequently, they are better able to overlap with bonding orbitals on other atoms. Hybrid atomic orbitals result in more bonds, stronger bonds, or both between atoms than do the unhybridized atomic orbitals from which they are formed. We turn now to a discussion of several types of hybrid orbitals. ***The total number of hybrid orbitals formed is always equal to the number of atomic orbitals that are hybridized.***

Hybridization is described by a combination of mathematical functions that represent *s*, *p*, or *d* orbitals to give new functions that predict shapes of the hybrid orbitals.

Another theory, the *molecular orbital theory,* is also used to describe chemical bonding, as well as the magnetic properties of molecules. Molecular orbital theory was discussed in Section 8.12.

sp Hybrid Orbitals

The simplest hybrid orbitals are ***sp* hybrid orbitals** formed by the combination of one *s* orbital and one *p* orbital; these *two* atomic orbitals combine to form *two sp* hybrid orbitals (Figure 9.7).

One *s* atomic orbital + one *p* atomic orbital→ two *sp* hybrid orbitals

In BeF_2, for example, a 2*s* and a 2*p* orbital on Be are hybridized to form two *sp* hybrid orbitals that are 180° from each other. That is, the hybrid orbitals are oriented exactly the same way we predicted earlier for two regions of electron density.

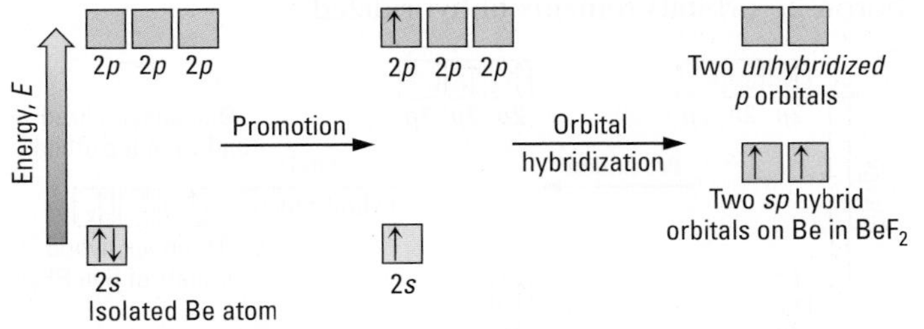

Each *sp* hybrid orbital has one electron that is shared with an electron from a fluorine atom to form two equivalent Be—F bonds. The remaining two 2*p* orbitals in Be are *unhybridized* and are 90° to each other and to the two *sp* hybrid orbitals.

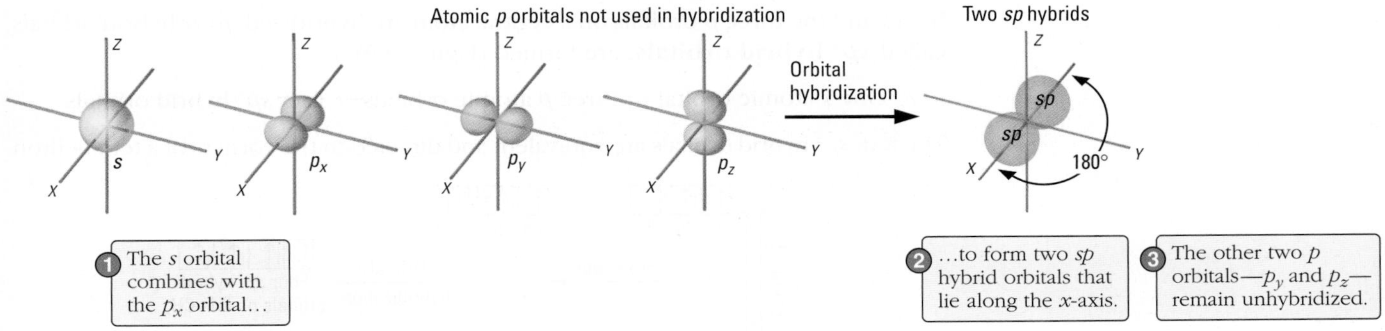

Active Figure 9.7 **Formation of two *sp* hybrid orbitals.** An *s* orbital combines with a *p* orbital in the same atom, say, p_x, to form two *sp* hybrid orbitals that lie along the *x*-axis. The angle between the two *sp* orbitals is 180°. The other two *p* orbitals remain unhybridized. **Go to the Active Figures menu at ThomsonNOW to test your understanding of the concepts in this figure.**

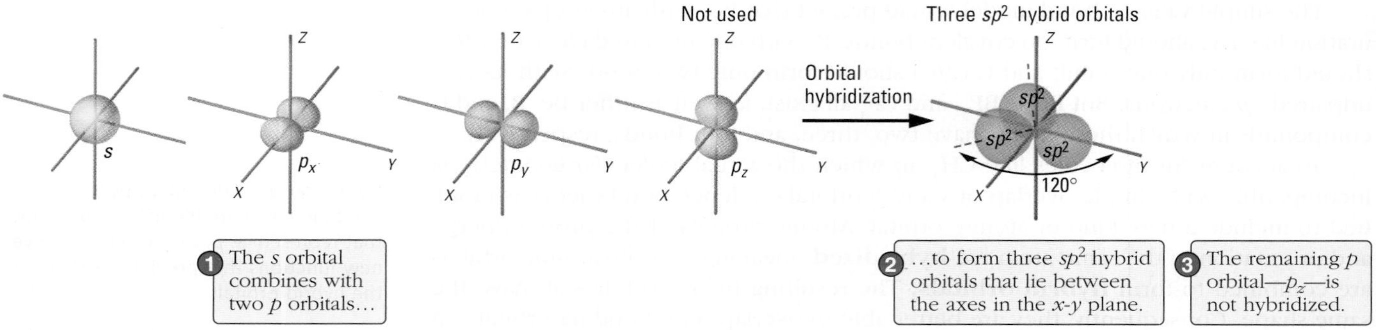

Active Figure 9.8 **Formation of three sp^2 hybrid orbitals.** An *s* orbital combines with two *p* orbitals in the same atom, say, p_x and p_y, to form three sp^2 hybrid orbitals that lie in the *x-y* plane. The angle between the three sp^2 orbitals is 120°. The other *p* orbital is unhybridized. **Go to the Active Figures menu at ThomsonNOW to test your understanding of the concepts in this figure.**

sp^2 Hybrid Orbitals

In BF_3, three atomic orbitals on the central B atom—a 2*s* and two 2*p* orbitals—are hybridized to form *three* **sp^2 hybrid orbitals** (Figure 9.8). The superscript sum (1 + 2 = 3) indicates the number of orbitals that have hybridized—three in this case: one *s* and two *p* orbitals.

One *s* atomic orbital + two *p* atomic orbitals→ three sp^2 hybrid orbitals

The three sp^2 hybridized orbitals on boron are 120° apart in a plane, each with an electron shared with a fluorine atom electron to form three equivalent B—F bonds. One of the boron 2*p* orbitals remains unhybridized.

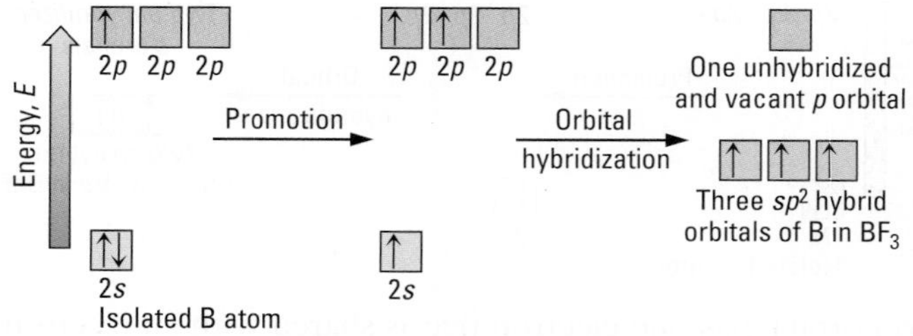

sp^3 Hybrid Orbitals

If an *s* and the three *p* orbitals on a central atom are hybridized, *four* hybrid orbitals, called **sp^3 hybrid orbitals,** are formed (Figure 9.9).

One *s* atomic orbital + three *p* atomic orbitals→ four sp^3 hybrid orbitals

The four sp^3 hybrid orbitals are equivalent and directed to the corners of a tetrahedron.

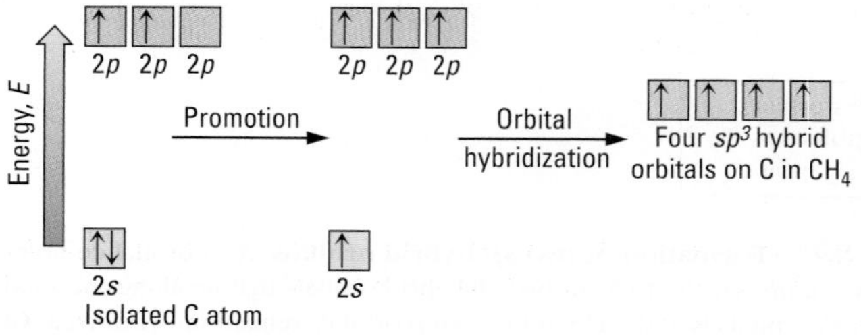

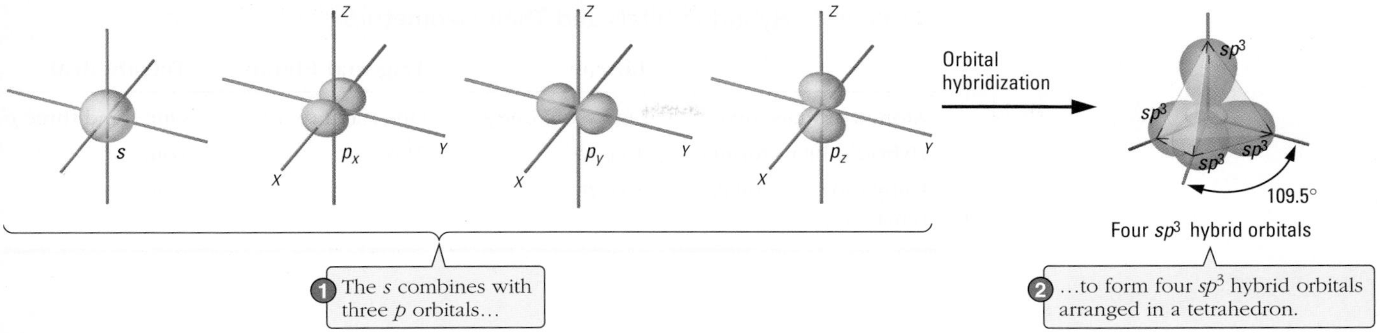

Active Figure 9.9 **Formation of four sp^3 hybrid orbitals.** An *s* orbital combines with three *p* orbitals to form four hybrid sp^3 orbitals that are directed to the corners of a tetrahedron. The angle between the four sp^3 orbitals is 109.5°. The bonds of carbon atoms with four single bonds are described as formed by sp^3 hybrid orbitals. **Go to the Active Figures menu at ThomsonNOW to test your understanding of the concepts in this figure.**

The sp^3 hybridization is consistent with the fact that carbon forms four tetrahedral bonds in CF_4 and in all other single-bonded carbon compounds. Overlap of each half-filled sp^3 hybrid orbital on carbon with half-filled orbitals from four fluorine atoms forms four equivalent C—F bonds. The central atoms of Periods 2 and 3 elements that obey the octet rule commonly have sp^3 hybridization.

Because the bond angles in NH_3 and H_2O are close to those in CF_4 and CH_4, this suggests that in general, lone pairs as well as bonding electron pairs can occupy hybrid orbitals. For example, according to the valence bond model, the four electron pairs surrounding the nitrogen atom in ammonia and the oxygen atom in water occupy sp^3 hybrid orbitals like those in CF_4 and CH_4. In NH_3, three shared pairs on nitrogen occupy three of these orbitals, with a lone pair filling the fourth. In H_2O, two of the sp^3 hybrid orbitals on oxygen contain bonding pairs, and two contain lone pairs (Figure 9.10).

Geometry	Hybrid Orbitals
Linear	Two *sp*
Triangular planar	Three sp^2
Tetrahedral	Four sp^3

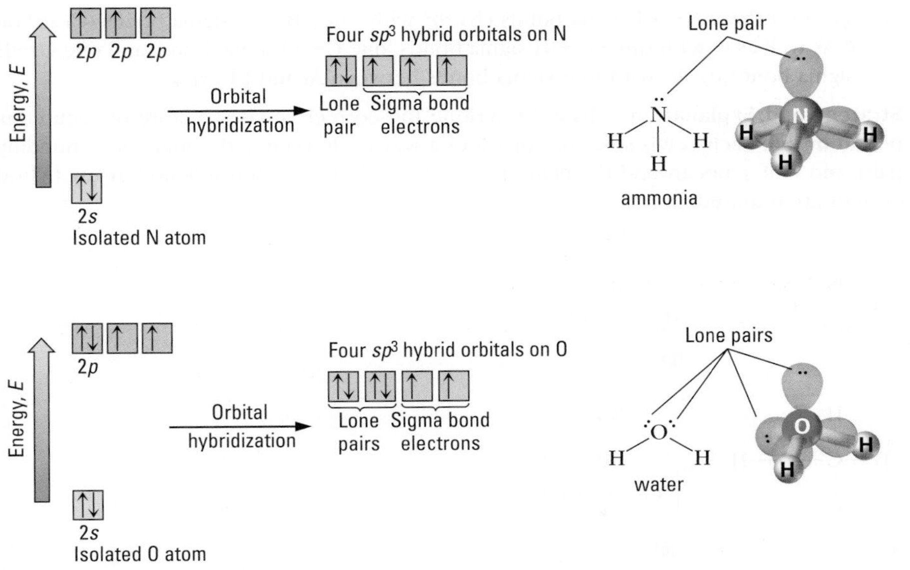

Figure 9.10 **Hybridization of nitrogen in ammonia and oxygen in water.** Nitrogen and oxygen are both sp^3 hybridized in these ammonia and water molecules. The lone pair electrons are in sp^3 hybrid orbitals.

Table 9.2 Hybrid Orbitals and Their Geometries

	Linear	Trigonal Planar	Tetrahedral
Atomic orbitals mixed	One *s* and one *p*	One *s* and two *p*	One *s* and three *p*
Hybrid orbitals formed	Two *sp*	Three sp^2	Four sp^3
Unhybridized orbitals remaining	Two *p*	One *p*	None

It is important for you to recognize that because hybrid orbitals are oriented as far apart as possible to minimize repulsions, they are consistent with the molecular geometries predicted using VSEPR theory. Table 9.2 summarizes information about hybrid orbitals formed from *s* and *p* atomic orbitals.

Bonds in which there is head-to-head orbital overlap so that the electron density of the bond lies along the bonding axis are called **sigma bonds** (σ bonds). The single bonds in diatomic molecules such as H_2 and Cl_2 and also those in the molecules illustrated in Figure 9.10 and BeF_2, BF_3, and CF_4 are all sigma bonds. The N—H and O—H bonds in ammonia and water, respectively, are also sigma bonds.

ThomsonNOW

Go to the Chemistry Interactive menu to work a module on the **formation of sigma bonds between hydrogen 1*s* and carbon sp^3 orbitals in methane.**

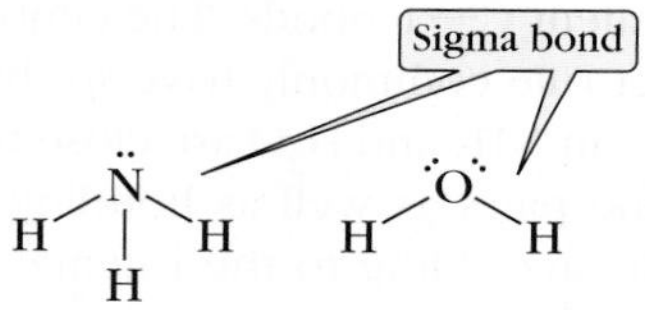

PROBLEM-SOLVING EXAMPLE 9.4 Hybridization of Atomic Orbitals

Describe the hybridization around the central atom and the bonding in

(a) NCl_3 (b) BCl_3

(c) CH_3OH (hybridization of C and O) (d) $AlCl_4^-$

Answer

(a) sp^3 with three N—Cl sigma bonds (b) sp^2 with three B—Cl sigma bonds (c) sp^3 on C as well as O with three C—H sigma bonds, one C—O sigma bond, and one O—H sigma bond (d) sp^3 with four sigma bonds between Al and Cl atoms

Strategy and Explanation Begin by writing the correct Lewis structure of each compound or ion. Each Lewis structure provides a way to determine the number of bonding pairs and lone pairs around the central atom, a number that indicates how many hybrid orbitals are required.

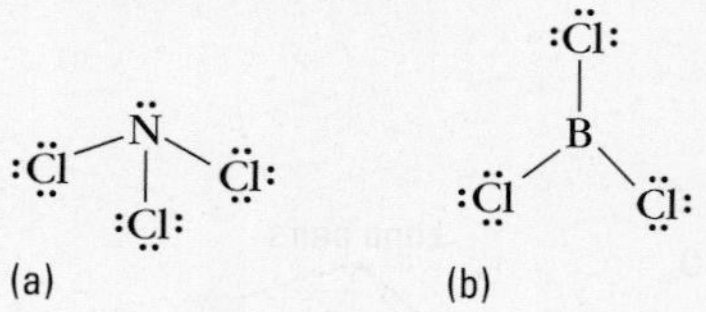

(a) (b)

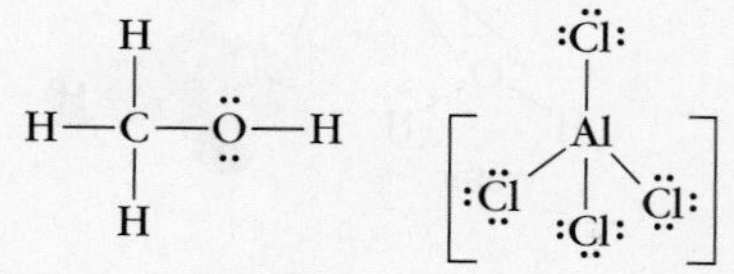

(c) (d)

(a) There are four electron pairs around nitrogen in NCl_3, a compound analogous to NH_3. Three of the pairs are bonding pairs and the other is a lone pair. Each electron pair is in an sp^3 hybrid orbital. The three N—Cl bonds are sigma bonds formed by the head-to-head overlap of three half-filled sp^3 hybrid orbitals on nitrogen with those of chlorine. The lone pair on nitrogen is in a filled sp^3 hybrid orbital.

(b) BCl_3 is analogous to BF_3 and, therefore, boron has sp^2 orbital hybridization with boron forming three sigma bonds to chlorine.

(c) Carbon forms four sigma bonds in CH_3OH (three to hydrogen atoms and one to oxygen) and so has four bonding pairs, all in sp^3 hybrid orbitals. Oxygen has two sigma bonds formed by the head-to-head overlap of two half-filled sp^3 hybrid orbitals on oxygen with one on carbon and one on hydrogen. The two lone pairs on oxygen are in filled sp^3 hybrid orbitals.

(d) The four sigma bonds in $AlCl_4^-$ are due to four bonding pairs being in sp^3 hybrid orbitals on aluminum that overlap head-to-head with the chlorine atoms.

PROBLEM-SOLVING PRACTICE 9.4

Describe the hybridization around the central atom and the bonding in

(a) $BeCl_2$ (b) NH_4^+

(c) CH_3OCH_3 (hybridization of C and O) (d) BF_4^-

Hybridization in Expanded Octets

Central atoms from the third and subsequent periods can accommodate more than four electron pairs—that is, an expanded octet (p. 389). Bonding pairs and lone electron pairs are accommodated in these atoms by hybridizing *d* as well as *s* and *p* atomic orbitals. By including *d* atomic orbitals, two additional types of hybrid orbitals result: the $\boldsymbol{sp^3d}$ and $\boldsymbol{sp^3d^2}$ **hybrid orbitals** (Figure 9.11).

Orbital hybridization is one way to describe bonding in molecules with expanded octets. Another way to consider bonding in these molecules is to use molecular orbital theory. The application of this theory to such molecules is complex and beyond the scope of a general chemistry course. Accurate application of this theory shows that there is little or no participation of *d* orbitals in trigonal bipyramidal and octahedral bonding when nonmetals are the central atoms. See, for example, Laila Suidan, Jay K. Badenhoop, Eric D. Glendening, and Frank Weinhold, *Journal of Chemical Education*, Vol. 72, p. 583, 1995.

One *s* atomic orbital + three *p* atomic orbitals + one *d* atomic orbital⟶

five sp^3d hybrid orbitals

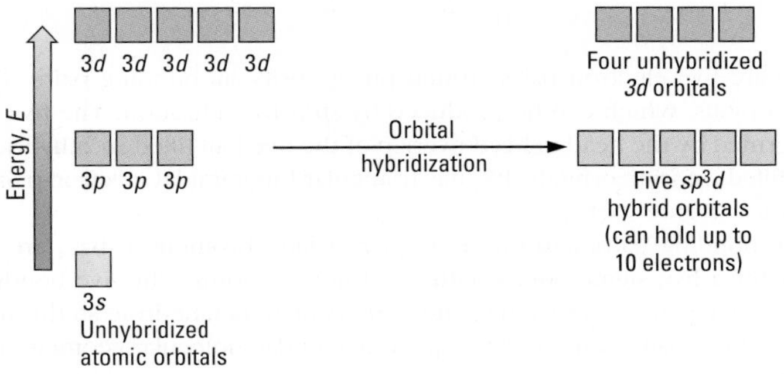

One *s* atomic orbital + three *p* atomic orbitals + two *d* atomic orbitals ⟶

six sp^3d^2 hybrid orbitals

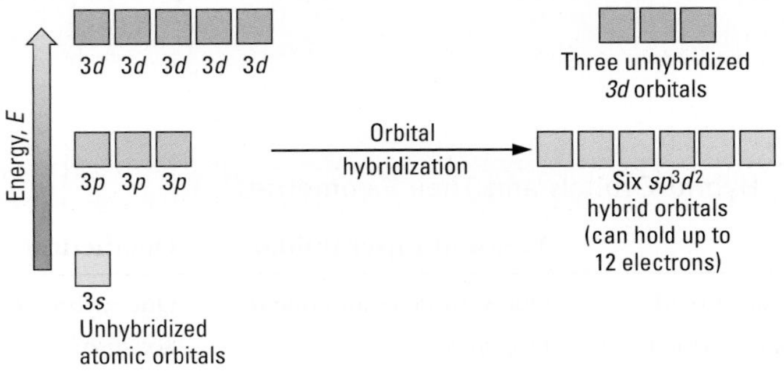

Hybridizing the appropriate five atomic orbitals yields five sp^3d hybrid orbitals. Hybridizing the suitable six atomic orbitals yields six sp^3d^2 hybrid orbitals.

Hybridization of *s*, *p*, and *d* orbitals coincides with the molecular geometry expected from VSEPR theory (Figure 9.11). Table 9.3 summarizes information about hybrid orbitals formed from *s*, *p*, and *d* atomic orbitals.

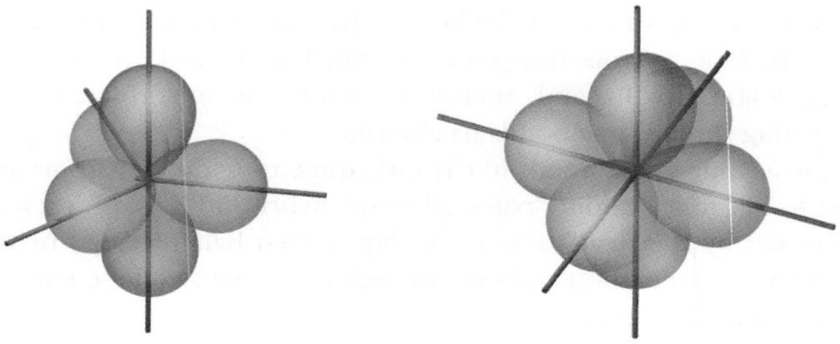

(a) Triangular bipyramidal sp^3d hybridization

(b) Octahedral sp^3d^2 hybridization

Figure 9.11 Hybridization using *d* orbitals to form (a) sp^3d and (b) sp^3d^2 hybrid orbitals. The five sp^3d hybrid orbitals form from hybridizing one *d* orbital, one *s* orbital, and three *p* orbitals. Six sp^3d^2 hybrid orbitals come from hybridizing two *d*, one *s*, and three *p* orbitals.

ThomsonNOW™
Go to the Coached Problems menu for a tutorial on **determining hybrid orbitals.**

PROBLEM-SOLVING EXAMPLE 9.5 Hybridization and Expanded Octets

Describe the hybridization around the central atom and the bonding in PF_5 and BrF_5.

Answer PF_5: sp^3d, five sigma bonds; BrF_5: sp^3d^2, five sigma bonds

Strategy and Explanation Start by writing the correct Lewis structure of each molecule, which allows the number of bonding pairs and lone pairs around the central atom to be determined. This number indicates how many hybrid orbitals are required.

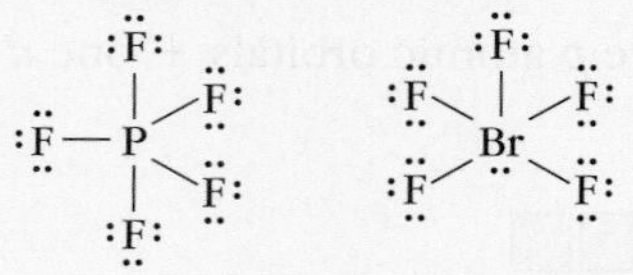

In PF_5 there are five electron pairs around phosphorus, all bonding pairs. This requires five hybrid orbitals, which can be produced by sp^3d hybridization. The five P—F sigma bonds are formed by the head-to-head overlap of the five half-filled sp^3d hybrid orbitals on P with half-filled fluorine orbitals. PF_5 has triangular bipyramidal electron-pair and molecular geometries (Figure 9.6).

The five bonding pairs and one lone pair around bromine in BrF_5 are in six sp^3d^2 orbitals that form five sigma bonds with five fluorine atoms. The five bonding electron pairs and one lone pair are directed to the corners of an octahedron, so this molecule has octahedral electron-pair geometry and square pyramidal molecular geometry (Figure 9.6).

PROBLEM-SOLVING PRACTICE 9.5

Describe the hybridization of the central atom and bonding in (a) PF_6^-, (b) IF_3, and (c) ICl_4^-.

Table 9.3 Hybrid Orbitals and Their Geometries

	Trigonal Bipyramidal	Octahedral
Atomic orbitals mixed	One *s*, three *p*, and one *d*	One *s*, three *p*, and two *d*
Hybrid orbitals formed	Five sp^3d	Six sp^3d^2
Unhybridized orbitals remaining	Four *d*	Three *d*

9.4 Hybridization in Molecules with Multiple Bonds

When using hybrid orbitals to account for molecular shapes, it must be recognized that in a multiple bond, the shared electron pairs do *not* all occupy hybrid orbitals. On a central atom with a multiple bond, the hybrid orbitals contain

- The electron pairs in single bonds to central atoms
- All lone pairs
- Only *one* of the shared electron pairs in a double or triple bond

The electrons in ***unhybridized*** atomic orbitals are used to form the second bond of a double bond and the second and third bonds in a triple bond. Such bonds, called **pi bonds (π bonds),** are formed by the *sideways* (edgewise) overlap of *parallel* atomic *p* orbitals, as shown in Figure 9.12. In contrast to sigma bonds, in which there is overlap along the bond axis, pi bonds result when *parallel p* orbitals (such as a p_y on one atom and a p_y on the other atom) overlap above and below the bond axis.

It is also possible for *d* orbitals to overlap above and below a bond axis, forming a pi bond.

ThomsonNOW™
Go to the Coached Problems menu for a tutorial on **bonding in molecules with multiple bonds.**

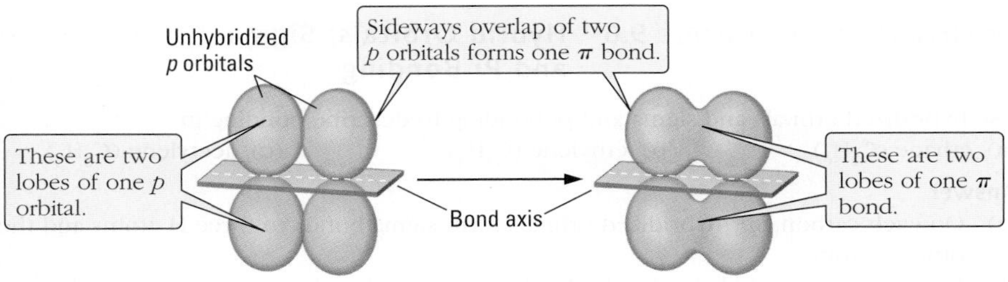

Figure 9.12 Pi bonding. Pi bonding occurs by sideways overlap of two adjacent *p* orbitals to make one pi (π) bond.

The bonding in formaldehyde, H_2CO, exemplifies sigma and pi bonding. Formaldehyde has two C—H single bonds and one C=O double bond.

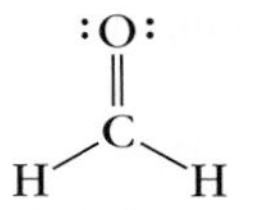

formaldehyde

The triangular planar electron-pair geometry suggests sp^2 hybridization of the carbon atom to supply three sp^2 orbitals for three sigma bonds. As seen in Figure 9.13,

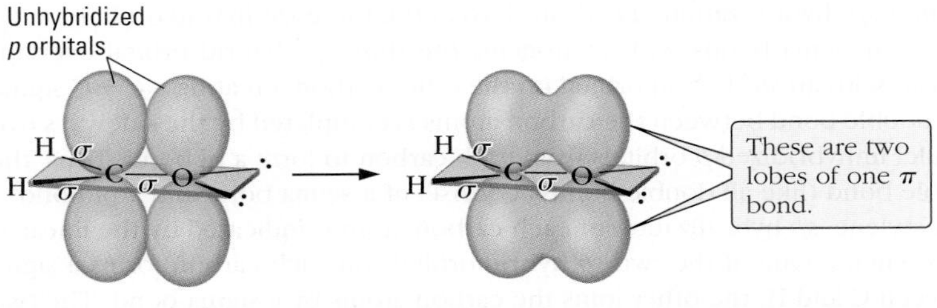

Figure 9.13 Sigma and pi bonding in formaldehyde. In formaldehyde, the C and O atoms are sp^2 hybridized. The C—O sigma bond forms from the end-to-end overlap of two sp^2 hybrid orbitals. The sp^2 hybridization leaves a half-filled unhybridized *p* orbital on each C and O atom. These orbitals overlap edgewise to form the carbon-oxygen pi bond.

two of these sp^2 hybrid orbitals on carbon form two sigma bonds with half-filled 1*s* H orbitals; the third sp^2 hybrid orbital on carbon forms a sigma bond with a half-filled oxygen orbital. The *unhybridized p* orbital on carbon overlaps sideways with an unhybridized *p* orbital on oxygen to form a pi bond, thus completing a double bond between carbon and oxygen.

Bond energies are given in Table 8.2 (*← p. 350*).

Because pi bonds have less orbital overlap than sigma bonds, pi bonds are generally weaker than sigma bonds. Thus, a C═C double bond is stronger (and shorter) than a C—C single bond, but not twice as strong; correspondingly, a C≡C triple bond, although stronger (and shorter) than a C═C double bond, is not three times stronger than a C—C single bond.

Consider what would happen if one end of a pi bond were to rotate around the sigma bond axis relative to the other end. Because the *p* orbitals need to be parallel to overlap, the pi bond would be broken and the molecule containing the pi bond would be less stable by an amount of energy equal to the strength of the pi bond. The resulting instability means that significant energy is required to rotate around a pi bond. This is the reason that we stated earlier that at room temperature there is no rotation around a double bond. A consequence of this barrier to rotation is *cis-trans* isomerism.

ThomsonNOW™

Go to the Chemistry Interactive menu to work modules on:

- **formation of sigma and pi bonds**
- **sigma and pi bonds in ethene**
- **structure and bonding of allene and benzene**

PROBLEM-SOLVING EXAMPLE 9.6 Hybrid Orbitals; Sigma and Pi Bonding

Use hybridized orbitals and sigma and pi bonding to describe bonding in
(a) ethane (C_2H_6) (b) ethylene (C_2H_4) (c) acetylene (C_2H_2)

Answer

(a) On each carbon, sp^3 hybridized orbitals form sigma bonds to three H atoms and the other C atom.

(b) On each carbon, sp^2 hybridized orbitals form sigma bonds to two H atoms and to the other C atom; the unhybridized 2*p* orbitals form one pi bond between C atoms.

(c) The *sp* hybridized orbitals on each carbon atom form sigma bonds to one H atom and to the other C; the two unhybridized 2*p* orbitals on each carbon atom form two pi bonds between C atoms.

Strategy and Explanation The Lewis structures can be used to derive the number of sigma and pi bonds, which indicate where and what type of hybridization must occur. The Lewis structures for the three compounds are

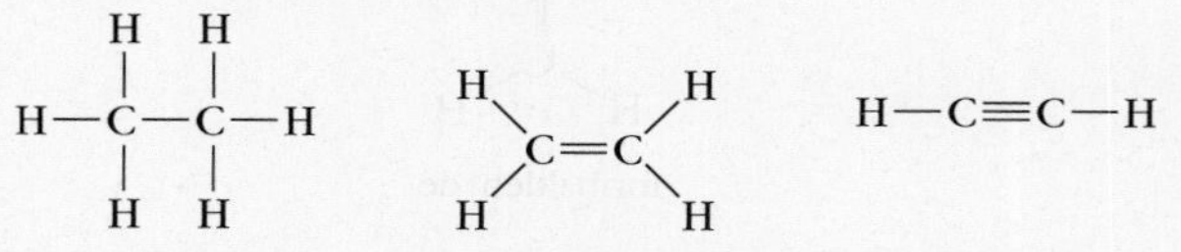

ethane ethylene acetylene

(a) Consistent with the tetrahedral bond angles for single-bonded carbon atoms, each carbon atom in ethane is sp^3 hybridized and all bonds are sigma bonds.

(b) The C═C double bond in ethylene, like the C═O double bond in formaldehyde, requires sp^2 hybridization of carbon. Two of the three sp^2 hybrid orbitals on each carbon form sigma bonds with hydrogens; the third sp^2 hybrid orbital overlaps head-to-head with an sp^2 hybrid orbital on the other carbon, creating a C—C sigma bond. The double bond between the carbon atoms is completed by the sideways overlap of parallel unhybridized *p* orbitals from each carbon to form a pi bond. Thus, the C═C double bond (like all double bonds) consists of a sigma bond and a pi bond.

(c) In acetylene, *sp* hybridization of each carbon atom is indicated by the linear molecular geometry. One of the two *sp* hybrid orbitals on each carbon forms a sigma bond between C and H; the other joins the carbon atoms by a sigma bond. The two unhybridized *p* orbitals on each carbon overlap sideways to form two pi bonds, completing the triple bond. Therefore, the triple bond consists of one sigma and two pi bonds in which the pi bonds are at right angles (90°) to each other (Figure 9.14).

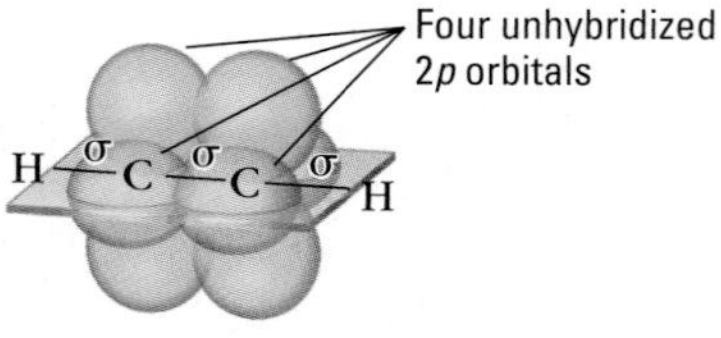

(a) Sigma bonds in acetylene

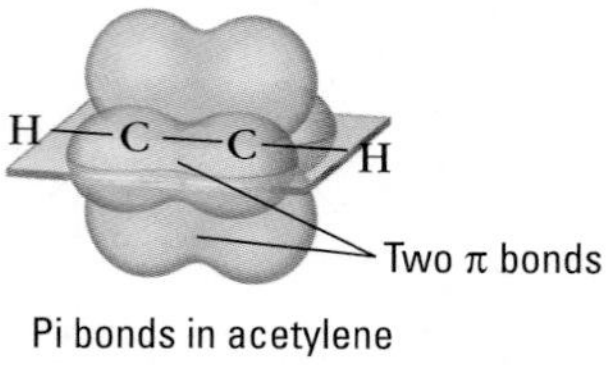

(b) Pi bonds in acetylene

Figure 9.14 Sigma and pi bonding in acetylene. (a) The carbon atoms in acetylene are *sp* hybridized. (b) Thus, each contains two unhybridized *p* orbitals, one from each carbon atom, which overlap sideways to form two pi bonds. There is also a sigma bond formed by the head-to-head overlap of two *sp* hybrid orbitals.

PROBLEM-SOLVING PRACTICE 9.6

Using hybridization and sigma and pi bonding, explain the bonding in (a) HCN and (b) H_2CNH.

CONCEPTUAL EXERCISE 9.4 Pi Bonding

Explain why pi bonding is not possible for an sp^3 hybridized carbon atom.

9.5 Molecular Polarity

A molecule that has polar bonds ***(⟵ p. 352)*** may or may not be polar. If the polar bonds are oriented so that their polarities cancel each other, such as in CO_2, a **nonpolar molecule** results. If electron density is concentrated at one end of the molecule, as in HCl, the result is a **polar molecule.** A polar molecule is a *permanent* dipole with a partial negative charge (δ−) where the electron density is concentrated, and a partial positive (δ+) charge at the opposite end, as illustrated in Figure 9.15.

Before examining the factors that determine whether a molecule is polar, let's look at the experimental measurement of the polarity of molecules. Polar molecules experience a force in an electric field that tends to align them with the field (Figure 9.16). In an electric field created by a pair of oppositely charged plates, the partial positive end of each polar molecule is attracted toward the negative plate, and the partial negative end is attracted toward the positive plate. The extent to which the molecules line up with the field depends on their **dipole moment** (μ), which is defined as the product of the magnitude of the partial charges (δ−) and (δ+) times the distance of separation between them. The derived unit of the dipole moment is the coulomb-meter (C · m); a more convenient derived unit is the debye (D), defined as $1\ D = 3.34 \times 10^{-30}\ C \cdot m$. Some typical experimental values are listed in Table 9.4. Nonpolar molecules have a zero dipole moment ($\mu = 0$); ***the dipole moments for polar molecules are always greater than zero and increase with greater molecular polarity.***

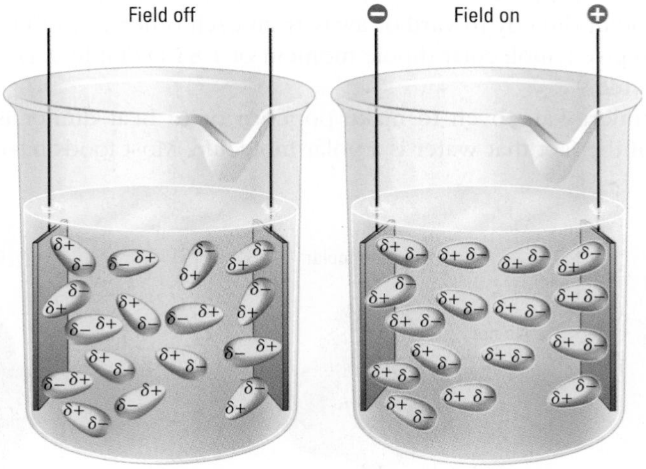

Figure 9.16 Polar molecules in an electric field. Polar molecules experience a force in an electric field that tends to align them so that oppositely charged ends of adjacent molecules are closer to each other.

© Thomson Learning/Charles D. Winters

Chlorine gas

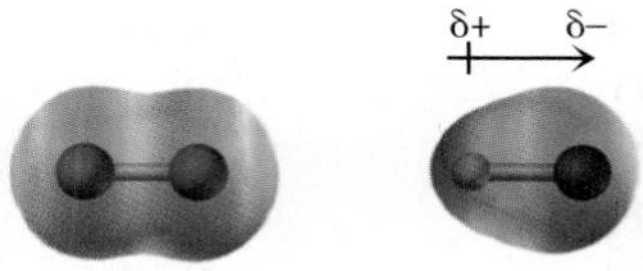

Figure 9.15 Nonpolar (Cl_2) and polar (HCl) molecules. The red color indicates higher electron density; the blue color indicates lower electron density.

Copyright Nobel Foundation

Peter Debye
1884–1966

Peter Debye was one of the leading figures in physical chemistry during the early- to mid-twentieth century. His many contributions included the first major X-ray diffraction studies with randomly oriented microcrystals, the seminal theoretical work in conjunction with Hückel on interactions of ionic solutes in solution, and the defining research on molecular polarities. After receiving the 1936 Nobel Prize in chemistry, Debye left Germany in 1940 due to increasing Nazi influence, accepting an invitation to join the chemistry faculty at Cornell University where he remained until the end of his career.

Table 9.4 Dipole Moments of Selected Molecules

Molecule	Dipole Moment, μ (D)
H_2	0
HF	1.78
HCl	1.07
HBr	0.79
HI	0.38
ClF	0.88
BrF	1.29
BrCl	0.52
H_2O	1.85
H_2S	0.95
CO_2	0
NH_3	1.47
NF_3	0.23
NCl_3	0.39
CH_4	0
CH_3Cl	1.92
CH_2Cl_2	1.60
$CHCl_3$	1.04
CCl_4	0

To predict whether a molecule is polar, we need to consider two factors: (1) whether the molecule has polar bonds, and (2) how those bonds are positioned relative to one another, that is, the molecular geometry. *The net dipole moment of a molecule is the sum of its bond dipoles.* A diatomic molecule is, of course, linear. If its atoms differ in electronegativity, then the bond and the molecule will be polar, with the partial negative charge at the more electronegative atom, as in HCl (Figure 9.15). In polyatomic molecules, the individual bonds can be polar, but because of the molecular shape, there may be no net dipole ($\mu = 0$); if so, the *molecule* is nonpolar. In other nondiatomic molecules, the bond polarity and molecular shape combine to give a net dipole ($\mu > 0$) and a polar molecule. We can correlate the types of molecular geometry with dipole moment by applying a general rule to a molecule of the type AB_n where A is the central atom, B represents a terminal atom or group of atoms, and n is the number of terminal atoms or groups. Such a molecule will *not* be polar if it meets *both* of the following conditions:

- All the terminal atoms or groups are the same, *and*
- All the terminal atoms or groups are symmetrically arranged around the central atom, A, in the molecular geometries given in Figure 9.4 (p. 383) or the AX_5E_0 and AX_6E_0 geometries given in Figure 9.6 (p. 390).

These conditions mean that molecules with the molecular geometries given in Figures 9.4 and 9.6 will never be polar if all their terminal atoms or groups are the same. The dipoles of the individual bonds will cancel due to the symmetry of the molecular structure.

Nonpolar molecules have a dipole moment of zero.

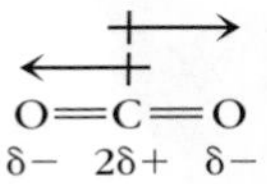

Consider, for example, carbon dioxide, CO_2, a linear triatomic molecule. Each C=O bond is polar because O is more electronegative than C, so O is the partial negative end of the bond dipole. The dipole moment contribution from each bond (the bond dipole) is represented by the symbol ↦, in which the plus sign indicates the partial positive charge and the arrow points to the partial negative end of the bond. We can use the arrows to help estimate whether a molecule is polar. In CO_2, the O atoms are at the same distance from the C atom, both have the same $\delta-$ charge, and they are symmetrically on opposite sides of C. Therefore, their bond dipoles cancel each other, resulting in a molecule with a zero molecular dipole moment. Even though each C=O bond is polar, CO_2 is a nonpolar molecule due to its linear shape.

The situation is different for water, a triatomic, but an angular molecule. Here, both O—H bonds are polar, with the H atoms having the same $\delta+$ charge (Figure 9.17). Note, however, that the two bond dipoles are not symmetrically arranged; they do not point directly toward or away from each other, as in CO_2, but augment each other to give a molecular dipole moment of 1.85 D (Table 9.4). Thus, water is a polar molecule.

Combining bond dipoles to obtain a molecular dipole involves addition of vectors (the bond dipoles) to obtain a resultant vector (the molecular dipole).

Using a microwave oven to make popcorn or to heat dinner is an everyday application of the fact that water is a polar molecule. Most foods have a high water

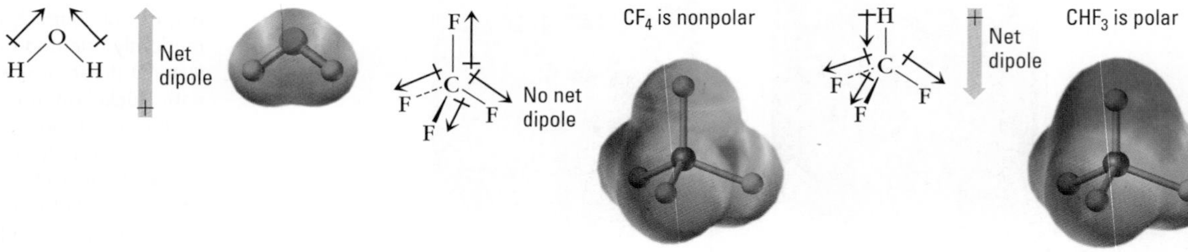

Figure 9.17 **Water (μ = 1.85) and CHF_3 (μ = 1.65) are polar molecules; CF_4 (μ = 0) is a nonpolar molecule.**

content. When water molecules in foods absorb microwave radiation, they rotate, turning so that the dipoles align with the crests and troughs of the oscillating microwave radiation. The radiation generator (the magnetron) in the oven creates microwave radiation that oscillates at 2.45 GHz (2.45 gigahertz, $2.45 \times 10^9\ s^{-1}$), very nearly the optimum frequency to rotate water molecules. So the leftover pizza warms up in a hurry for a late-night snack.

Now consider the differing dipole moments of CF_4 ($\mu = 0$ D) and CF_3H ($\mu = 1.60$ D). Both molecules have the same geometry, with their atoms tetrahedrally arranged around a central carbon atom (Figure 9.17). The terminal F atoms are all the same in CF_4 and thus have the same partial charges. However, the terminal atoms in CF_3H are not the same; F is more electronegative than C, but H is less electronegative than C, so that the bond dipoles reinforce each other in CF_3H. Consequently, CF_4 is a nonpolar molecule and CF_3H is polar.

PROBLEM-SOLVING EXAMPLE 9.7 Molecular Polarity

Are boron trifluoride (BF_3) and dichloromethane (CH_2Cl_2) polar or nonpolar? If polar, indicate the direction of the net dipole.

Answer BF_3 is nonpolar; CH_2Cl_2 is polar, with the partial negative end at the Cl atoms.

Strategy and Explanation To decide whether a molecule is polar requires knowing the geometry of the molecule, the polarity of its bonds, and whether the bonds, if polar, are arranged symmetrically or unsymmetrically. As predicted for a molecule with three electron pairs around the central atom, BF_3 is triangular planar.

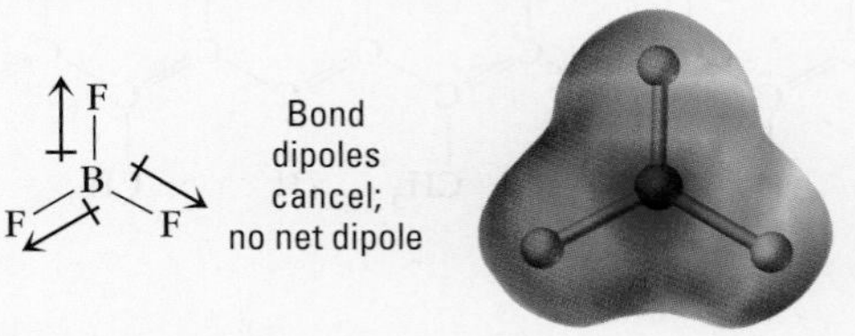

Because F is more electronegative than B, the B—F bonds are polar, with F being the partial negative end. The molecule is nonpolar, though, because the three terminal F atoms are identical, they have the same partial charge, and they are arranged symmetrically around the central B atom. The bond dipole of each B—F is canceled by the bond dipoles of the other two B—F bonds.

From the Lewis structure for CH_2Cl_2 in the margin, you might be tempted to say that CH_2Cl_2 is nonpolar because the hydrogens appear across from each other, as do the chlorines. In fact, CH_2Cl_2 is a tetrahedral molecule in which neither hydrogen nor chlorine is directly across from each other.

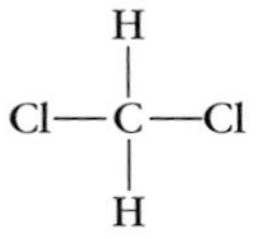

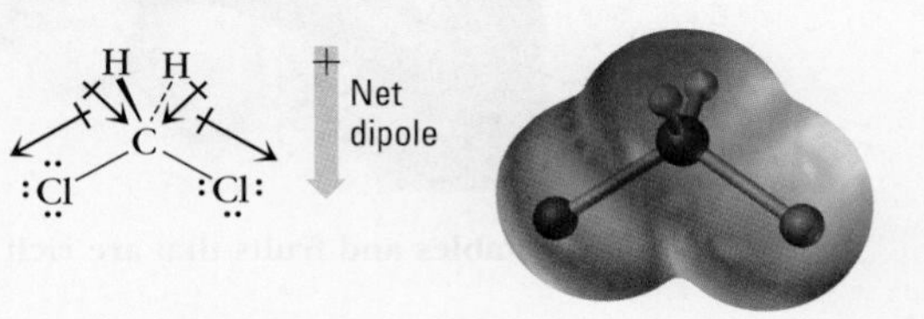

Because Cl is more electronegative than C, while H is less electronegative, negative charge is drawn away from H atoms and toward Cl atoms. As a result, CH_2Cl_2 has a net dipole ($\mu = 1.60$ D), with the partial negative end at the Cl atoms and the partial positive end between the H atoms.

PROBLEM-SOLVING PRACTICE 9.7

For each of these molecules, decide whether the molecule is polar and, if so, which region is partially positive and which is partially negative.

(a) $BFCl_2$ (b) NH_2Cl (c) SCl_2

ThomsonNOW™
Go to the Coached Problems menu for an exercise on **determining molecular polarity.**

TOOLS OF CHEMISTRY

Ultraviolet-Visible Spectroscopy

When a molecule absorbs radiation in the ultraviolet (UV) or visible region, the absorbed energy promotes an electron from a lower energy orbital in the ground state molecule to a higher energy orbital in the excited state molecule. The maximum UV-visible absorption occurs at a wavelength characteristic of the molecule's structure. This absorption can be determined from a UV-visible spectrum, a plot of the absorbance, which is the intensity of radiation absorbed by the molecule, versus the wavelength at which the absorbance occurred.

Ultraviolet-visible spectral data can be used to account for several structural features, including (1) differentiation of *cis* from *trans* isomers, because a *trans* isomer generally absorbs UV-visible radiation at a longer wavelength than the *cis* isomer, (2) confirmation of the presence (or absence) of carbonyl 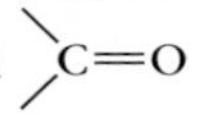 and aromatic groups in organic compounds, because they absorb UV radiation at characteristic wavelengths, and (3) specific transitions of electrons between *d* orbitals in transition metal compounds.

Ultraviolet-visible spectroscopy can also be used to study the molecular structures of colored compounds, those that absorb radiation in the visible region of the spectrum. Generally, organic compounds containing only sigma bonds are colorless; that is, they do not absorb light in the visible region. On the other hand, brightly colored pigments, such as beta-carotene, have an extended sequence of alternating single and double bonds, called a *conjugated* system. When visible light is absorbed, electron transitions occur among the pi electrons in the conjugated double bonds. Carrots look yellow-orange because electron transitions in their beta-carotene absorb in the 400- to 500-nm region, which is blue-green. We then see the remaining unabsorbed (reflected) portion of the visible spectrum, which is yellow-orange.

beta-carotene

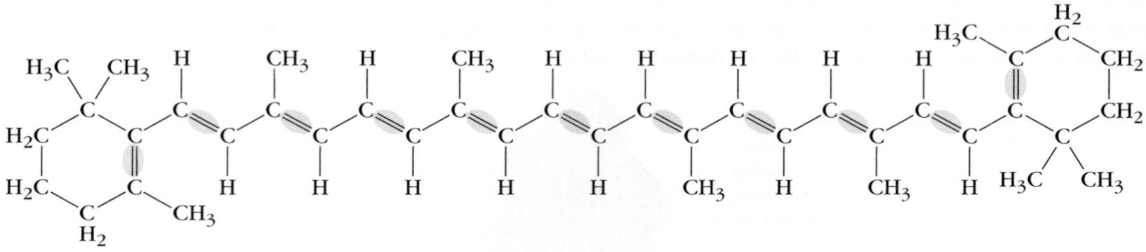

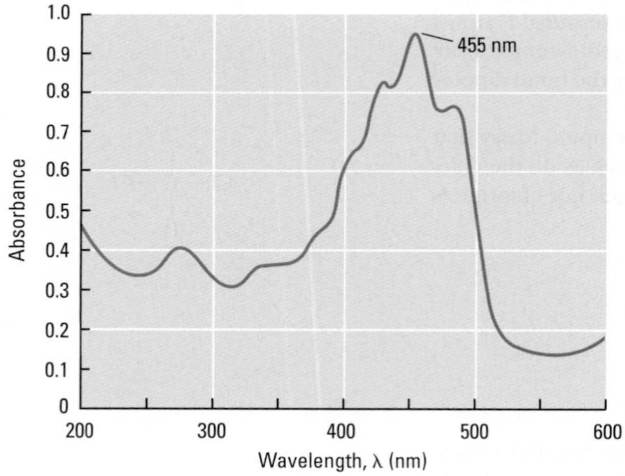

The UV-visible spectrum of beta-carotene. Beta-carotene absorbs in the blue-green region of the visible spectrum, indicated by a maximum absorbance at 455 nm. This peak is caused by transitions of pi electrons in the conjugated double bonds of the beta-carotene molecule.

© Thomson Learning/Charles D. Winters

Some vegetables and fruits that are rich in beta-carotene.

EXERCISE 9.5 Dipole Moments

Explain the differences in the dipole moments of

(a) HI (0.38 D) and HBr (0.79 D)

(b) CH_3Cl (1.92 D), CH_3Br (1.81 D), and CH_3I (1.62 D)

9.6 Noncovalent Interactions and Forces Between Molecules

Molecules are attracted to one another. If there were no attractions, then there would be no liquid or solid compounds, only gaseous ones. The attraction between molecules is always the result of an attraction between opposite charges, regardless of whether the charges are permanent or temporary. Polar molecules attract each other due to their permanent dipoles. Even nonpolar molecules, those without a permanent dipole, have some attraction for one another, as you will see in this section.

Atoms within the same molecule are held together by covalent chemical bonds with strengths ranging from 150 to 1000 kJ/mol. Covalent bonds are strong forces. For example, it takes 1656 kJ to break 4 mol C—H covalent bonds and separate the one C atom and four H atoms in all the molecules in 1 mol methane molecules:

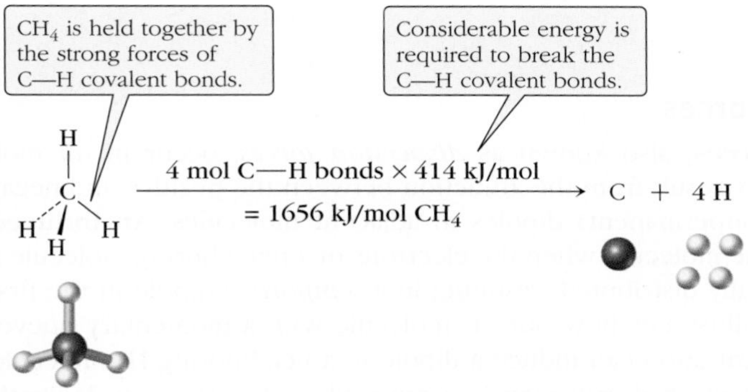

Weaker forces attract one molecule to another molecule. In contrast to the 1656 kJ/mol it takes to atomize methane, only 8.9 kJ is required to pull 1 mol of methane molecules that are close together in liquid methane away from each other to evaporate liquid methane to a gas.

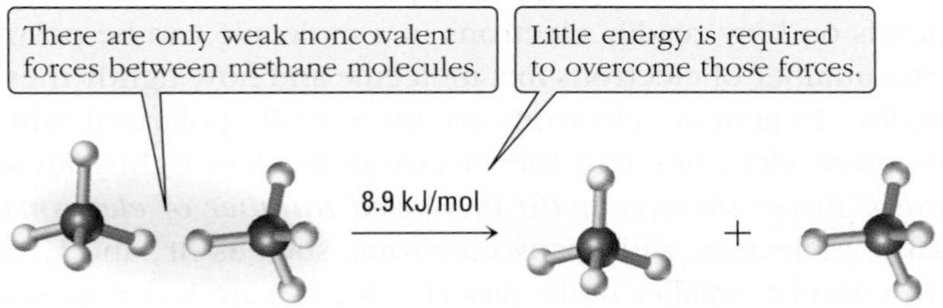

We use the term **noncovalent interactions** to refer to all forces of attraction other than covalent, ionic, or metallic bonding (*metallic bonding* is discussed in Section 11.9). When noncovalent interactions act between one molecule and another, they are referred to as **intermolecular forces.** Because intermolecular forces do not result from the sharing of electron pairs between atoms, they are weaker than covalent bonds. The strengths of noncovalent interactions between molecules (*inter*molecular forces) account for melting points, boiling points, and

*Intra*molecular means *within* a single molecule; *inter*molecular means *between* two or more separate molecules.

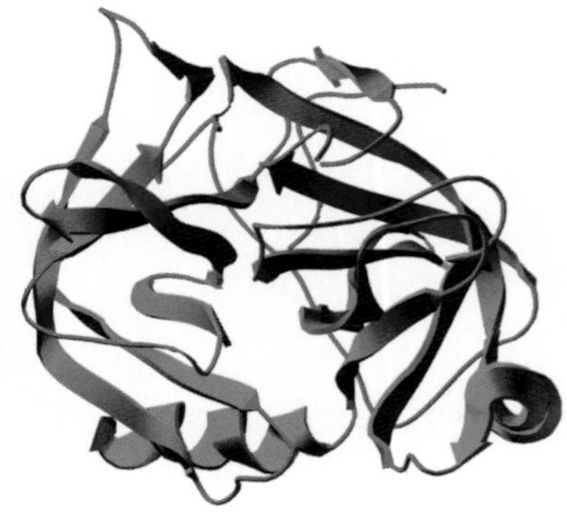

Figure 9.18 A ribbon model of a chymotrypsin molecule. Noncovalent interactions help fold chymotrypsin into its biochemically active shape.

other properties of molecular substances. Noncovalent interactions between different parts of the same large molecule (*intra*molecular forces) maintain biologically important molecules in the exact shapes required to carry out their functions. Chymotrypsin, an enzyme with a molecular weight of more than 22,000, is folded into its biochemically active shape with the assistance of noncovalent interactions between strategically placed atoms. Figure 9.18 shows a ribbon model of chymotrypsin. Red and green ribbons show portions where the protein chain is folded into helical or sheet structures, respectively; the narrow purple ribbons represent simpler, unfolded protein regions. Noncovalent interactions help maintain the shapes of thousands of different kinds of protein molecules in our bodies.

The next few sections explore three types of noncovalent interactions: London forces, dipole-dipole attractions, and hydrogen bonding.

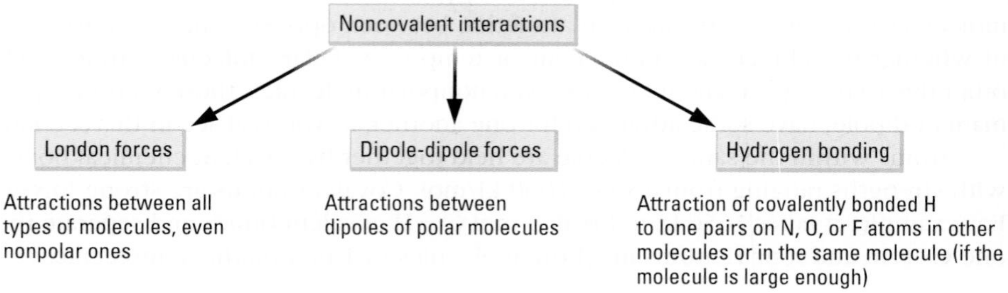

London forces are named to recognize the work of Fritz London, who extensively studied the origins and nature of such forces. London forces are also called *dispersion forces.*

London Forces

London forces, also known as *dispersion forces,* occur in *all* molecular substances. They result from the attraction between the positive and negative ends of *induced* (nonpermanent) dipoles in adjacent molecules. An **induced dipole** is caused in one molecule when the electrons of a neighboring molecule are momentarily unequally distributed, resulting in a *temporary* dipole in the first molecule. Figure 9.19 illustrates how one H_2 molecule with a momentary unevenness in its electron distribution can induce a dipole in a neighboring H_2 molecule. This kind of shift in electron distribution in a molecule is known as **polarization.** Due to polarization, even noble gas atoms, molecules of diatomic gases such as oxygen, nitrogen, and chlorine (all of which must be nonpolar), and nonpolar hydrocarbon molecules such as CH_4 and C_2H_6 have these fleeting dipoles. Such London forces are the *only* noncovalent interactions among nonpolar molecules.

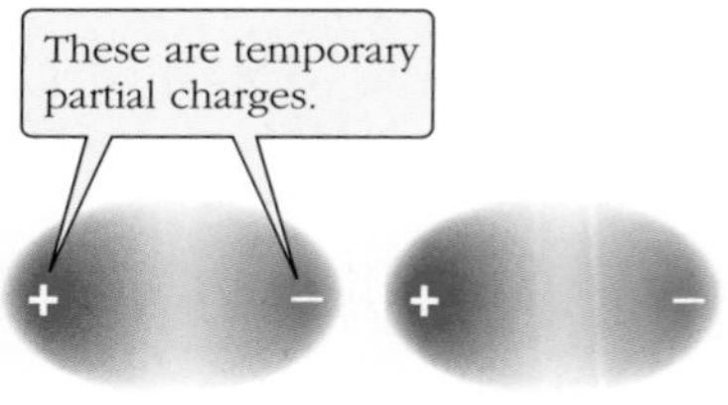

Figure 9.19 Origin of London forces. Such attractive forces originate when electrons are momentarily distributed unevenly in the molecule, such as the one on the right. The molecule has a temporary positive charge that is close to the molecule on the left. The positive charge attracts electrons in the left-hand molecule, temporarily creating an induced dipole (an unbalanced electron distribution) in that molecule.

London forces range in energy from approximately 0.05 to 40 kJ/mol. Their strength depends on how readily electrons in a molecule can be polarized, which depends on the number of electrons in a molecule and how tightly they are held by nuclear attraction. In general, electrons are more easily polarized when the molecule contains more electrons and the electrons are less tightly attracted to the nucleus; *London forces increase with increased number of electrons in a molecule.* Thus, large molecules with many electrons, such as Br_2 and I_2, are relatively polarizable. In contrast, smaller molecules (F_2, N_2, O_2) are less polarizable because they have fewer electrons.

ThomsonNOW
Go to the Chemistry Interactive menu to work modules on:
- **dipole-induced dipole forces**
- **induced dipoles in neighboring I_2 molecules**

When we look at the boiling points of several groups of nonpolar molecules (Table 9.5), the effect of the total number of electrons becomes readily apparent: *Boiling points increase as the total number of electrons increases.* (This effect also correlates with molar mass—the heavier an atom or molecule, the more electrons it has.) For a liquid to boil, its molecules must have enough energy to overcome their noncovalent intermolecular attractive forces. Thus, *the boiling point of a liq-*

Table 9.5 Effect of Number of Electrons on Boiling Points of Nonpolar Molecular Substances

Noble Gases			Halogens			Hydrocarbons		
	No. e's	bp (°C)		No. e's	bp (°C)		No. e's	bp (°C)
He	2	−269	F_2	18	−188	CH_4	10	−161
Ne	10	−246	Cl_2	34	−34	C_2H_6	18	−88
Ar	18	−186	Br_2	70	59	C_3H_8	26	−42
Kr	36	−152	I_2	106	184	C_4H_{10}*	34	0

*Butane.

© Thomson Learning/Charles D. Winters

Lava lamps take advantage of differences in the intermolecular forces within the liquid and within the solid in the lamp, and those intermolecular forces between them.

uid depends on the nature and strength of intermolecular forces. If more energy is required to overcome the intermolecular attractions between molecules of liquid A than the intermolecular attractions between molecules of liquid B, then the boiling point of A will be higher than that of B. Such is the case for Cl_2 (bp = −34 °C) compared with F_2 (bp = −188 °C) due to weaker London forces between diatomic fluorine molecules than between diatomic chlorine molecules. Conversely, weaker intermolecular attractions result in lower boiling points. For example, the boiling point of Br_2 (59 °C) is higher than that of Cl_2 (−34 °C), indicating stronger London forces among Br_2 molecules than among Cl_2 molecules.

Interestingly, molecular shape can also play a role in London forces. Two of the isomers of pentane—straight-chain pentane and 2,2-dimethylpropane (both with the molecular formula C_5H_{12})—differ in boiling point by 27 °C. The linear shape of the pentane molecule allows close contact with adjacent molecules over its entire length, resulting in stronger London forces, while the more compact 2,2-dimethylpropane molecule does not allow as much close contact.

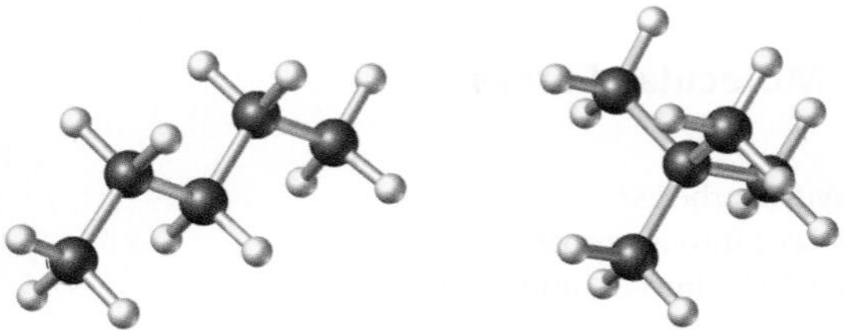

pentane, bp = 36.0 °C   2,2-dimethylpropane, bp = 9.5 °C

Structure and boiling point. The boiling points of pentane and 2,2-dimethylpropane differ because of differences in their molecular structures even though the total number of electrons in each molecule is the same.

Dipole-Dipole Attractions

Polar molecules have *permanent* dipoles that create a **dipole-dipole attraction,** a noncovalent interaction between two *polar* molecules or two polar groups in the same large molecule. Molecules that are dipoles attract each other when the partial positive region of one is close to the partial negative region of another (Figure 9.20).

The boiling points of several nonpolar and polar substances with comparable numbers of electrons, and therefore comparable London forces, are given in Table

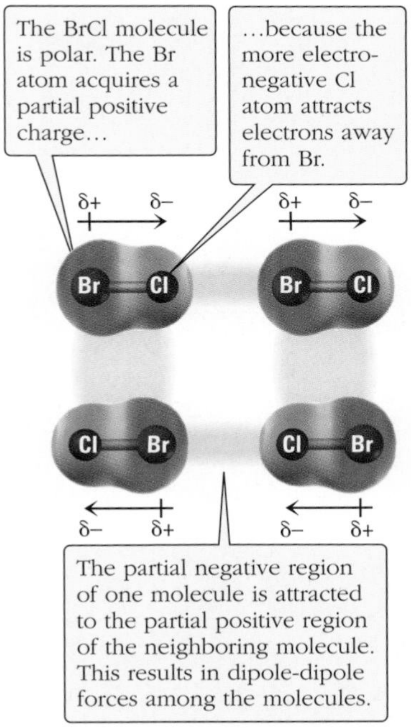

Figure 9.20 Dipole-dipole attractions between BrCl molecules.

Bromine vapor and liquid bromine.

Table 9.6 Numbers of Electrons and Boiling Points of Nonpolar and Polar Substances

Nonpolar Molecules			Polar Molecules		
	No. e's	bp (°C)		No. e's	bp (°C)
SiH_4	18	−112	PH_3	18	−88
GeH_4	36	−90	AsH_3	36	−62
Br_2	70	59	ICl	70	97

9.6. In general, the more polar its molecules, the higher the boiling point of a substance, provided the London forces are similar (molecules with similar numbers of electrons). The lower boiling points of nonpolar substances compared with those of polar substances in Table 9.6 reflect this relationship. Dipole-dipole forces range from 5 to 25 kJ/mol, but London forces (0.05 to 40 kJ/mol) can be stronger. For example, the greater London forces in HI cause it to have a higher boiling point (−36 °C) than HCl (−85 °C), even though HCl is more polar. When London forces are similar, however, a more polar substance will have stronger intermolecular attractions than a less polar one. An example of this is the difference in boiling points of polar ICl with dipole-dipole attractions (97 °C) and nonpolar Br_2 with only London forces (59 °C), even though the substances have approximately the same London forces due to their similar number of electrons (Table 9.6).

CONCEPTUAL EXERCISE 9.6 Dipole-Dipole Forces

Draw a sketch, like that in Figure 9.20, of four CO molecules to indicate dipole-dipole forces between the CO molecules.

PROBLEM-SOLVING EXAMPLE 9.8 Molecular Forces

Which forces must be overcome to

(a) Evaporate gasoline, a mixture of hydrocarbons?
(b) Convert solid carbon dioxide (Dry Ice) into a vapor?
(c) Decompose ammonium nitrate, NH_4NO_3, into N_2 and H_2O?
(d) Boil ClF?
(e) Convert P_4 to P_2?

Answer

(a) and (b) London forces
(c) Covalent bonds between N and H atoms, and O and N atoms; ionic attractions between NH_4^+ and NO_3^- ions.
(d) London forces and dipole-dipole forces
(e) Covalent bonds between phosphorus atoms

Strategy and Explanation Changing the physical state of a molecular substance requires breaking noncovalent intermolecular attractions between molecules. If the molecules are polar, dipole-dipole forces are involved, and possibly hydrogen bonding, depending on the molecular structure. London forces are present to some extent between all molecules, but are the only intermolecular forces between nonpolar molecules. London forces can be significant between large molecules. The decomposition of a molecular substance is drastically different, requiring breaking covalent bonds *within* the molecules.

(a) Gasoline is a mixture of hydrocarbons, which are nonpolar molecules. To evaporate, the hydrocarbon molecules must overcome London forces among them in the liquid to escape from each other and enter the gas phase.
(b) Solid carbon dioxide converts to a vapor when the thermal energy becomes great enough to overcome some of the noncovalent forces of attraction (London forces) among the nonpolar CO_2 molecules. Noncovalent forces still exist in the gaseous CO_2.
(c) Decomposing ammonium nitrate into N_2 and H_2O requires breaking the N—H and N—O covalent bonds in the NH_4^+ and NO_3^- polyatomic ions and rearranging the atoms to form nitrogen and water. These bond-breaking changes involve much greater energy (the bond enthalpy) than that needed to melt the compound, which involves overcoming ionic interactions.
(d) Dipole-dipole forces, like those between BrCl molecules in Figure 9.20, attract the polar ClF molecules to each other in the liquid. London forces are also present. These collective forces must be overcome so that ClF molecules can get away from their neighbors at the surface of the liquid and enter the gaseous state.
(e) Covalent bonds must be broken between phosphorus atoms in P_4.

ThomsonNOW
Go to the Coached Problems menu for an exercise on **identifying intermolecular forces.**

PROBLEM-SOLVING PRACTICE 9.8

Explain the principal type of forces that must be overcome for
(a) Kr to melt.
(b) Propane to release C and H_2.

Hydrogen Bonds

A hydrogen bond is an especially significant type of dipole-dipole force. A **hydrogen bond** is the attraction between a partially positive hydrogen atom in a molecule and a lone electron pair on a small, very electronegative atom (generally F, O, or N) in another molecule or in a different part of the same molecule. Electron density within molecules shifts toward F, O, or N because of their high electronegativity, giving these atoms *partial negative charges.* As a result, a hydrogen atom bonded to the nitrogen, oxygen, or fluorine atom acquires a *partial positive charge.* In a hydrogen bond, a partially positive hydrogen atom bonded covalently to one of the electronegative atoms (X) is attracted electrostatically to the negative charge of a lone pair on the other atom (Z). Hydrogen bonds are typically shown as dotted lines (· · ·) between the atoms:

This represents a hydrogen bond.

X—H · · · :Z—

X = N, O, F   Z = N, O, F

The hydrogen bond forms a "bridge" between a hydrogen atom and a highly electronegative atom, which may be in a different molecule or in the same molecule, if the molecule is large enough. This type of bridge from hydrogen to nitrogen and hydrogen to oxygen plays an essential role in determining the folding (three-dimensional structure) of large protein molecules.

Hydrogen bonds can form between molecules or within a molecule. These are known as *inter*molecular and *intra*molecular hydrogen bonds, respectively.

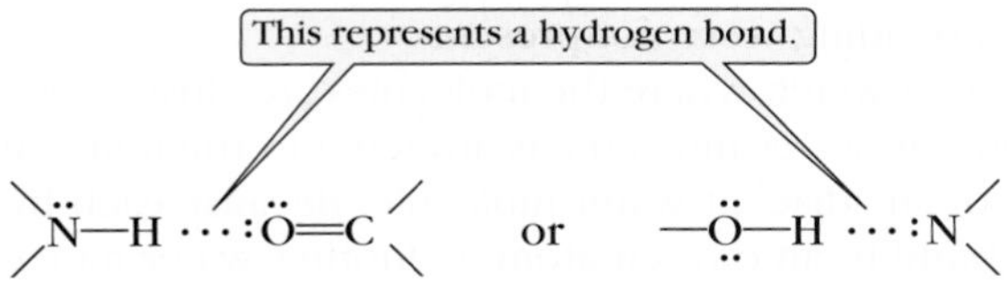

The greater the electronegativity of the atom connected to H, the greater the partial positive charge on H and hence the stronger the hydrogen bond.

Noncovalent interactions in ethanol and dimethyl ether. The molecules have the same number of electrons, so London forces are roughly the same. An ethanol molecule has an —OH group, which means that there are both dipole forces and hydrogen bond forces attracting ethanol molecules to each other. A dimethyl ether molecule is polar, but there is no hydrogen bonding, so the noncovalent intermolecular noncovalent forces are weaker than in ethanol.

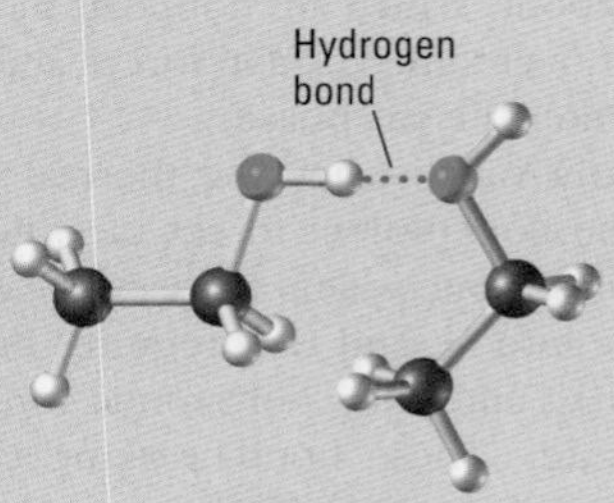

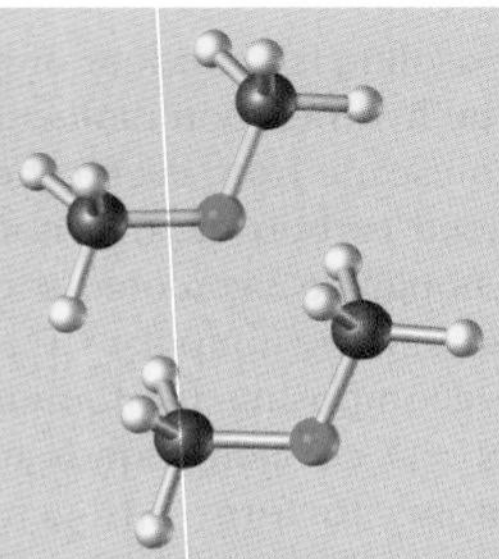

	ethanol CH_3CH_2OH	dimethyl ether CH_3OCH_3
Molecular model	(see above)	(see above)
Dipole moment, D	1.69	1.30
Melting point, °C	–114.1	–141.5
Boiling point, °C	78.29	–24.8

Type of Force	**Magnitude of Force (kJ/mol)**
Covalent bond	150–1000
London force	0.05–40
Dipole-dipole	5–25
Hydrogen bond	10–40

The H atom is very small and its partial positive charge is concentrated in a very small volume, so it can come very close to the lone pair to form an especially strong dipole-dipole force through hydrogen bonding. Hydrogen-bond strengths range from 10 to 40 kJ/mol, less than those of covalent bonds. However, a great many hydrogen bonds often occur in a sample of matter, and the overall effect can be very dramatic. An example of this effect can be seen in the melting and boiling points of ethanol. This chapter began by noting the very different melting and boiling points of ethanol and dimethyl ether, both of which have the same molecular formula, C_2H_6O, and thus the same number of electrons and roughly the same London forces. Both molecules are polar (dipole moment > 0), so there are dipole-dipole forces in each case. The differences in melting and boiling points arise because of hydrogen bonding in ethanol. The O—H bonds in ethanol make intermolecular hydrogen bonding possible, while this is not possible in dimethyl ether because it has no O—H bonds.

The hydrogen halides also illustrate the significant effects of hydrogen bonding (Figure 9.21). The boiling point of hydrogen fluoride (HF), the lightest hydrogen halide, is much higher than expected; this is attributed to hydrogen bonding, which does not occur significantly in the other hydrogen halides.

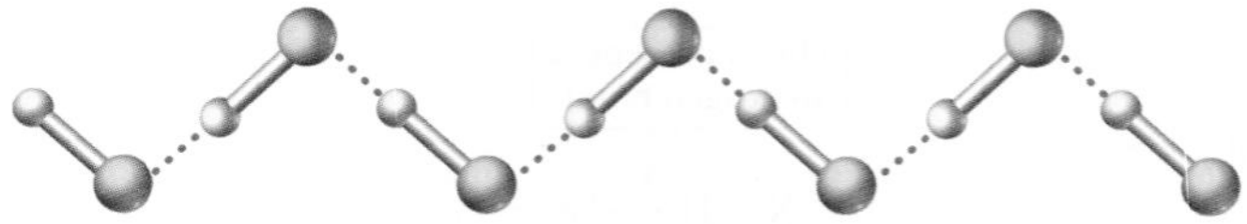

Hydrogen bonding in solid HF

Hydrogen bonding is especially strong among water molecules and is responsible for many of the unique properties of water (Section 11.4). Hydrogen compounds of oxygen's neighbors and family members in the periodic table are gases at room temperature: CH_4, NH_3, H_2S, H_2Se, H_2Te, PH_3, HF, and HCl. But H_2O is a liquid at room temperature, indicating a strong degree of intermolecular attraction. Figure 9.21 shows that the boiling point of H_2O is about 200 °C higher than would be predicted if hydrogen bonding were not present.

The structure of solid water is described in Section 11.4.

In liquid and solid water, where the molecules are close enough to interact, the hydrogen atom on one water molecule is attracted to the lone pair of electrons on the oxygen atom of an adjacent water molecule. Because each hydrogen atom can form a hydrogen bond to an oxygen atom in another water molecule, and because each oxygen atom has two lone pairs, every water molecule can participate in four hydrogen bonds to four other water molecules (Figure 9.22). The result is a tetrahedral cluster of water molecules around the central water molecule.

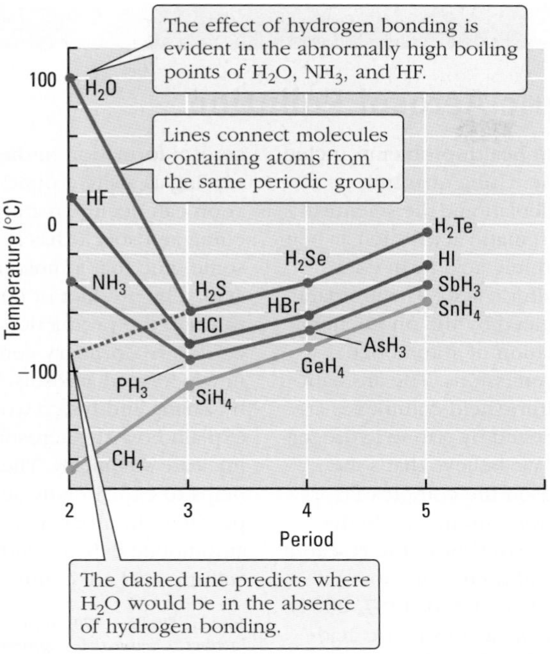

Figure 9.21 Boiling points of some simple hydrogen-containing binary compounds.

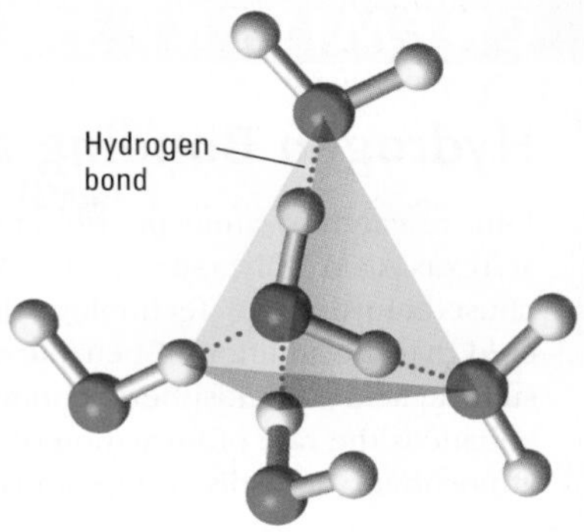

Figure 9.22 Hydrogen bonding between one water molecule and its neighbors. Each water molecule can participate in four hydrogen bonds—one for each hydrogen atom and two through the two lone pairs of oxygen. Since each hydrogen bond is shared between two water molecules, there are two hydrogen bonds per molecule ($\frac{1}{2} \cdot 4$).

© Scott Camazine/Photo Researchers, Inc.

Ice crystals.

CONCEPTUAL EXERCISE

9.7 Strengths of Hydrogen Bonds

Which of these three hydrogen bonds, F—H · · · F—H, O—H · · · N—C, and N—H · · · O=C, is the strongest? Explain why.

PROBLEM-SOLVING EXAMPLE 9.9 Molecular Forces

What are the types of forces, in addition to London forces, that are overcome in these changes? Using structural formulas, make a sketch representing the major type of force in each case.

(a) The evaporation of liquid ethanol, CH_3CH_2OH

(b) The decomposition of ammonia, NH_3, into N_2 and H_2

(c) The sublimation of iodine, I_2, that is, its conversion from a solid directly into a vapor

(d) The boiling of liquid NH_3

Answer

(a) Hydrogen bonding and dipole forces:

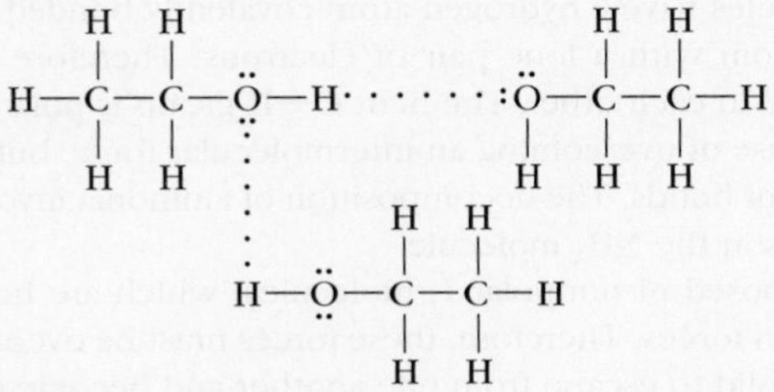

(b) Covalent bonds between N—H:

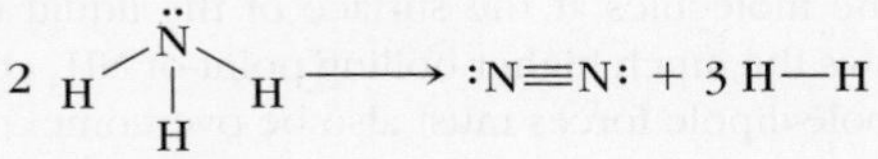

CHEMISTRY IN THE NEWS

Hydrogen Bonding and Atmospheric Aerosol Pollution

Joint research by atmospheric scientists at Texas A&M University and the Massachusetts Institute of Technology discovered that the addition of benzoic acid to sulfuric acid at atmospheric conditions enhances the rate of formation of atmospheric aerosols, compounds implicated in human health problems, including lung disease. Using quantum mechanical calculations, the scientists showed that aromatic acids such as benzoic acid and toluic acid form complexes with sulfuric acid. The aromatic acids are produced by the photochemical oxidation of automobile exhaust emissions. The aromatic acid–sulfuric acid complexes are characterized by strong hydrogen bonds. "We believe that's the main reason the complex favors particle formation," says Renyi Zhang, a coauthor of the research paper published in the journal *Science* (Vol. 304, p. 1487, 2004). The benzoic acid–sulfuric acid complex is believed to boost aerosol formation in the atmosphere by serving as a site around which nucleation can occur, creating health-threatening aerosols. It has been known for some time that atmospheric sulfuric acid, a by-product of burning coal through the production of sulfur oxides, is a primary component of newly formed aerosols. The discovery by Zhang and his co-workers helps to explain how the aerosol particles can nucleate so quickly. The research also helps to explain why aerosols are so prevalent in urban areas, places where automobile exhaust and atmospheric sulfuric acid are common.

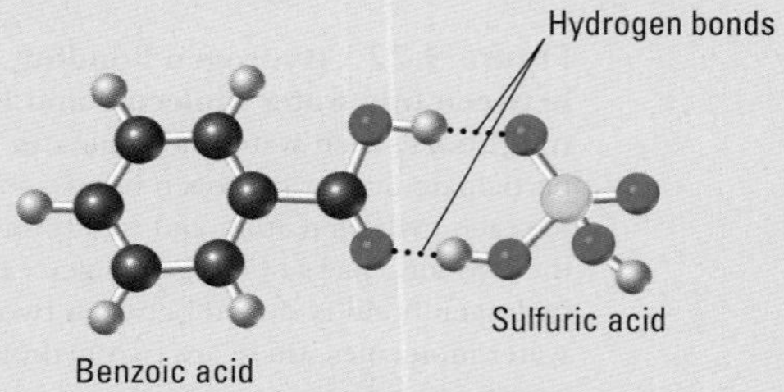

Structural formula of a benzoic acid–sulfuric acid complex. Hydrogen bonds are shown as dashed lines.

SOURCE: Elizabeth Wilson, "Car and Coal Emissions Interact," *Chemical & Engineering News*, June 7, 2004, p. 10.

© Thomson Learning/Charles D. Winters

Sublimation of iodine.

(c) London forces between I_2 molecules:

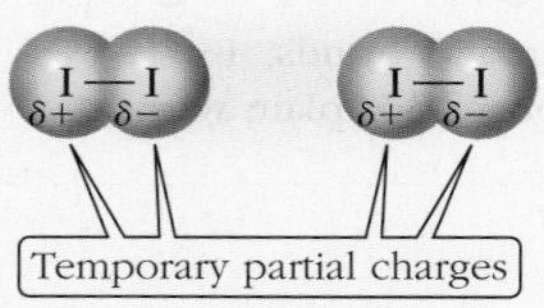

(d) Hydrogen bonding and dipole forces:

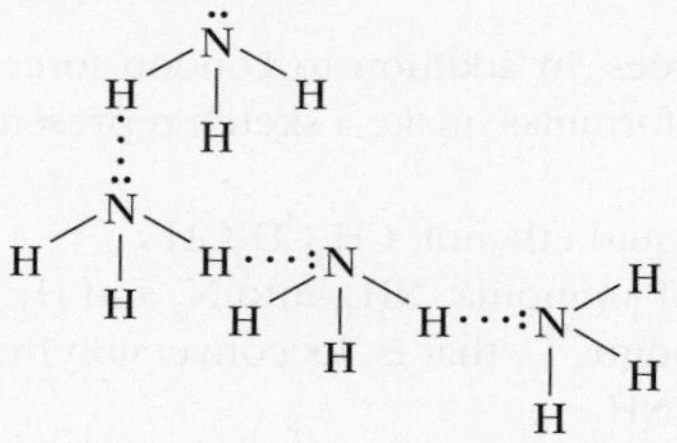

Strategy and Explanation In each case identify the force to be overcome. Where the change involves an intermolecular force, consider the particular kind of force.

(a) Ethanol molecules have a hydrogen atom covalently bonded to a highly electronegative oxygen atom with a lone pair of electrons. Therefore, ethanol molecules can hydrogen bond to each other. The bent O—H group is polar also.

(b) This is not a case of overcoming an intermolecular force, but rather an *intra*molecular one, covalent bonds. The decomposition of ammonia involves breaking the N—H covalent bonds in the NH_3 molecule.

(c) Iodine is composed of nonpolar I_2 molecules, which are held to each other in the solid by London forces. Therefore, these forces must be overcome for the iodine molecules in the solid to escape from one another and become gaseous.

(d) Ammonia molecules are held together in the liquid by hydrogen bonds, which must be broken for the molecules at the surface of the liquid to escape into the vapor. (Figure 9.21 shows the much higher boiling point of NH_3 compared to PH_3.) Because NH_3 is polar, dipole-dipole forces must also be overcome.

CHEMISTRY YOU CAN DO

Molecular Structure and Biological Activity

Noncovalent forces (London forces, hydrogen bonds, and dipole-dipole forces) are important in biochemical reactions for bringing together reactants in proper orientations. This is particularly the case for enzymes—biomolecules that help to speed up the rates of biochemical reactions (Section 13.9). Noncovalent forces often bind the reactant to an enzyme's *active site,* the particular region of the enzyme where its reactivity occurs.

Lactase, which acts on lactose, is such an enzyme. Lactose, a disaccharide (Section 12.8), is also known as milk sugar because it is present in the milk of humans, cows, and other mammals. Lactose can make up to about 40% of an infant's diet during the first year. Lactase accelerates the decomposition of lactose to its component monosaccharides glucose and galactose. A portion of the lactase molecule has a region whose shape matches only that of lactose. Therefore, the enzyme acts selectively on lactose and not on sucrose or maltose, two other dietary disaccharides whose shapes do not match that required by lactase.

Infants have a more active form of the enzyme than do adults. Consequently, nearly 20% of adults in the United States and nearly 70% worldwide suffer some degree of lactose intolerance, the inability to rapidly digest lactose in milk and dairy products. Lactaid, an over-the-counter product that contains lactase, can be used by lactose-intolerant individuals to break down lactose in milk.

In this activity, you will use Lactaid to study the conversion of lactose in milk to glucose and galactose. Do this experiment with several friends. You will need:

- One quart of 2% milk
- One package of Lactaid drops (not caplets), available at most pharmacies
- Two one-pint (16-oz) containers that can be closed
- Four to eight small glasses

Taste a drop of Lactaid and record its taste.

Pour two samples for yourself and two for each friend. For the samples pour half the milk into one container as a control and close the container. Pour the remainder of the milk into the second container, add 3 to 4 drops of Lactaid, close the container, and shake it to mix its contents. Mark the Lactaid containers to identify them. Refrigerate all containers for about 48 hours.

Take the containers from the refrigerator and pour samples of the Lactaid-treated and untreated milk into separate glasses. Each person should taste his or her two samples of milk and record any differences in their taste.

1. What difference in taste was there between the untreated and the Lactaid-treated samples?
2. Explain the difference in taste to the others who have done this exercise.

SOURCE: Richman, R. "Detection of Catalysis by Taste." *Journal of Chemical Education,* Vol. 75, 1998; p. 315.

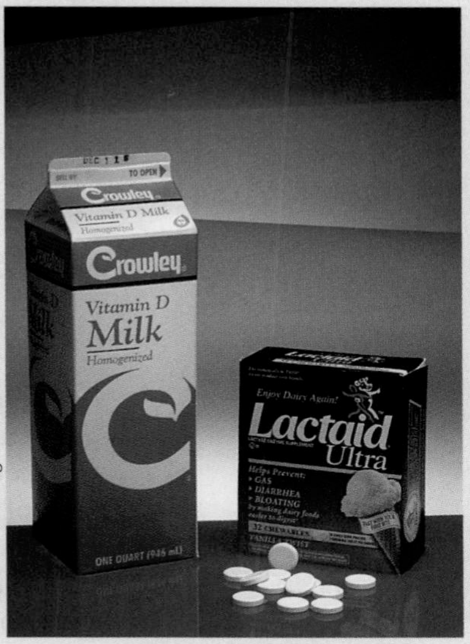

© Thomson Learning/Charles D. Winters

Lactaid.

PROBLEM-SOLVING PRACTICE 9.9

Decide what types of intermolecular forces are involved in the attraction between molecules of (a) N_2 and N_2, (b) CO_2 and H_2O, and (c) CH_3OH and NH_3.

Noncovalent Forces in Living Cells

Noncovalent forces are important in biological structures, including cell membranes. The basic structure of a cell membrane, known as a **lipid bilayer,** is two aligned layers of phospholipids. **Phospholipids** are glycerol derivatives having two long, nonpolar fatty acid chains and a polar phosphate derivative at the head of the molecule (Figure 9.23).

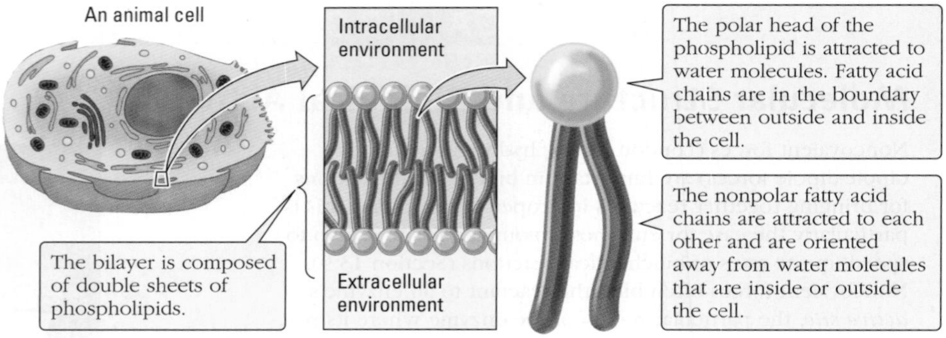

Figure 9.23 **Lipid bilayer in cell membranes.**

The polar end of phospholipid molecules is **hydrophilic,** that is, "water-loving," because of its attraction to water molecules. The polar end is oriented toward the aqueous environments of the cell and its surroundings. The long, nonpolar chains of the fatty acids are **hydrophobic,** or "water-hating." They point away from the aqueous environments and are held together by London forces. The result is separation of the interior of a cell from the surrounding fluids, a separation that allows control over which ions or molecules enter a cell and which chemical reactions can occur there.

In our bodies, noncovalent interactions bring metabolic products, drugs, hormones, and neurotransmitters (nervous system messengers) into contact with cellular receptors. The receptors are often proteins embedded in the cell membrane's lipid bilayer. Dipole-dipole forces, hydrogen bonding, and London forces help to align the target molecule with its particular site on the receptor surface. Once a chemical messenger connects with its receptor, the messenger may enter the cell to initiate a chemical reaction, or a reaction may occur as a result of changes initiated by the receptor.

DOE/Science Source/Photo Researchers, Inc.

Francis H. C. Crick *(right)* and James Watson. Working in the Cavendish Laboratory at Cambridge, England, Watson and Crick built a scale model of the double-helical structure, based on X-ray data. Knowing distances and angles between atoms, they compared the task to working on a three-dimensional jigsaw puzzle. Watson, Crick, and Maurice Wilkins received the 1962 Nobel Prize for their work relating to the structure of DNA.

9.7 Biomolecules: DNA and the Importance of Molecular Structure

Nowhere do the shape of a molecule and noncovalent forces play a more intriguing and important role than in the structure and function of **DNA (deoxyribonucleic acid),** the molecule that stores the genetic code. Whether you are male or female, have blue or brown eyes, or have curly or straight hair depends on your genetic makeup. These and all your other physical traits are determined by the composition of the approximately 1.8 m of coiled DNA that makes up the 23 double-stranded chromosomes in the nucleus of each of your cells.

Nucleotides of DNA

DNA is a **polymer,** a molecule composed of many small, repeating units bonded together. Each repeating unit in DNA, called a **nucleotide,** has the three connected parts shown in Figure 9.24—one sugar unit, one phosphate group (phosphoric acid unit), and a cyclic nitrogen compound known as a *nitrogen base.* In DNA the sugar is always deoxyribose and the base is one of four bases—*adenine (A), thymine (T),*

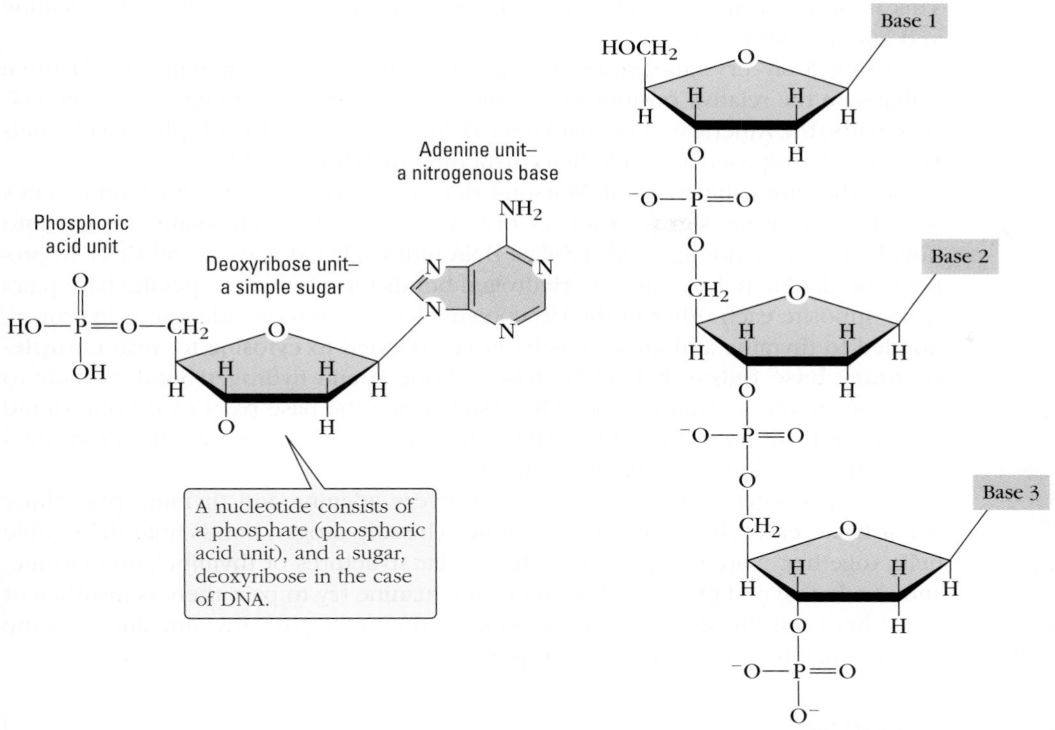

Figure 9.24 **Nucleotides and DNA.** The phosphate groups and the deoxyribose sugar groups form the *backbone* of DNA. The genetic code is carried by the nitrogenous bases.

guanine (G), or *cytosine (C)*. The bases are often referred to by their single-letter abbreviations.

A DNA segment with nucleotides bonded together is shown in Figure 9.24. The phosphate units join nucleotides into a polynucleotide chain that has a backbone of alternating deoxyribose and phosphate units in a long strand with the various bases extending out from the sugar-phosphate backbone. The order of the nucleotides (and thus the particular sequence of bases) along the DNA strand carries the genetic code from one generation to the next.

A DNA nucleotide is a combination of a phosphate group, deoxyribose, and a nitrogen base.

The deoxyribose units in the backbone chain are joined through phosphate diester linkages. Phosphoric acid is H_3PO_4, $O{=}P(OH)_3$.

phosphoric acid

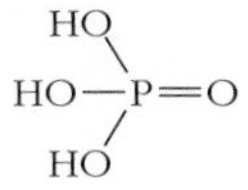

Replacing two H atoms with two CH_3 groups gives a phosphate diester, $O{=}P(OH)(OCH_3)_2$.

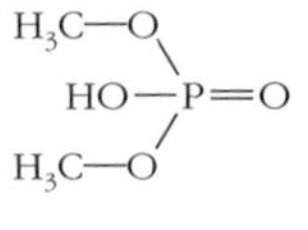

phosphate diester

The Double Helix: The Watson-Crick Model

In the 1950s, Erwin Chargaff made the important discovery that the adenine/thymine and guanine/cytosine ratios are constant in any given organism, from a human genius to a bacterium. Based on this analysis, it was apparent that in any given organism,

- The base composition is the same in all cells of an organism and is characteristic of that organism.
- The amounts of adenine and thymine are equal, as are the amounts of guanine and cytosine.
- The amount of the bases adenine plus guanine equals that of the bases cytosine plus thymine.

© Photo Researchers, Inc.

Rosalind Franklin
1920–1958

A member of a prominent London banking family, Rosalind Franklin received her degrees from Cambridge University. Her most famous work was the first X-ray photographs of DNA, done in collaboration with Maurice Wilkins at King's College in London, showing two forms of DNA, one of them a helix. By interpreting these X-ray data, James Watson and Francis Crick derived their now-famous double helix model of DNA for which they, along with Wilkins, received the 1962 Nobel Prize in chemistry. Rosalind Franklin's untimely death of ovarian cancer at the age of 37 resulted in her not sharing that award. Nobel Prizes are not awarded posthumously.

The Double Helix by James Watson chronicles this discovery.

This information implied that the bases occurred in pairs: adenine with thymine and guanine with cytosine.

Using X-ray crystallography data gathered by Rosalind Franklin and Maurice Wilkins on the relative positions of atoms in DNA, plus the concept of A-T and G-C base pairs, the American biologist James D. Watson and the British physicist Francis H. C. Crick proposed a double helix structure for DNA in 1953.

In the three-dimensional Watson-Crick structure, two polynucleotide DNA strands wind around each other to form a double helix. Remarkable insight into how hydrogen bonding could stabilize DNA ultimately led Watson and Crick to propose the double helix structure. Hydrogen bonds form between specific base pairs lying opposite each other in the two polynucleotide strands. Adenine is hydrogen-bonded to thymine and guanine is hydrogen-bonded to cytosine to form **complementary base pairs;** that is, the bases of one strand hydrogen-bond strongly to those of the other (Figure 9.25). The result is that the base pairs (A on one strand with T on the other strand, or C with G) are stacked one above the other in the interior of the double helix (*blue* in Figure 9.25).

Two hydrogen bonds occur between every adenine and thymine pair; three occur between each guanine and cytosine. These hydrogen bonds hold the double helix together. Note in Figure 9.26 the similar structures of thymine and cytosine, and of adenine and guanine. If adenine and guanine try to pair, there is insufficient space between the strands to accommodate the bulky pair; thymine and cytosine are too small to pair and to align properly.

CONCEPTUAL EXERCISE 9.8 Hydrogen Bonding and DNA

Only one hydrogen bond is possible between G and T or between C and A. Use the structural formulas for these compounds to indicate where such hydrogen bonding can occur in these base pairs (see Figure 9.26).

The Genetic Code and DNA Replication

In the historic scientific journal article describing their revolutionary findings, Watson and Crick wrote, "It has not escaped our notice that the specific pairing we have postulated immediately suggests a possible copying mechanism for the genetic material." This bit of typical British understatement belies the enormous impact that deciphering DNA's structure had on establishing the molecular basis of heredity. It

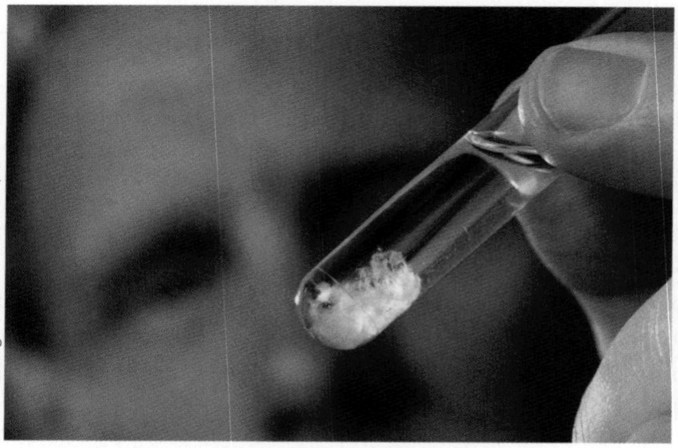

© Volker Steger/Photo Researchers, Inc.

DNA. Solid DNA is precipitated from solution.

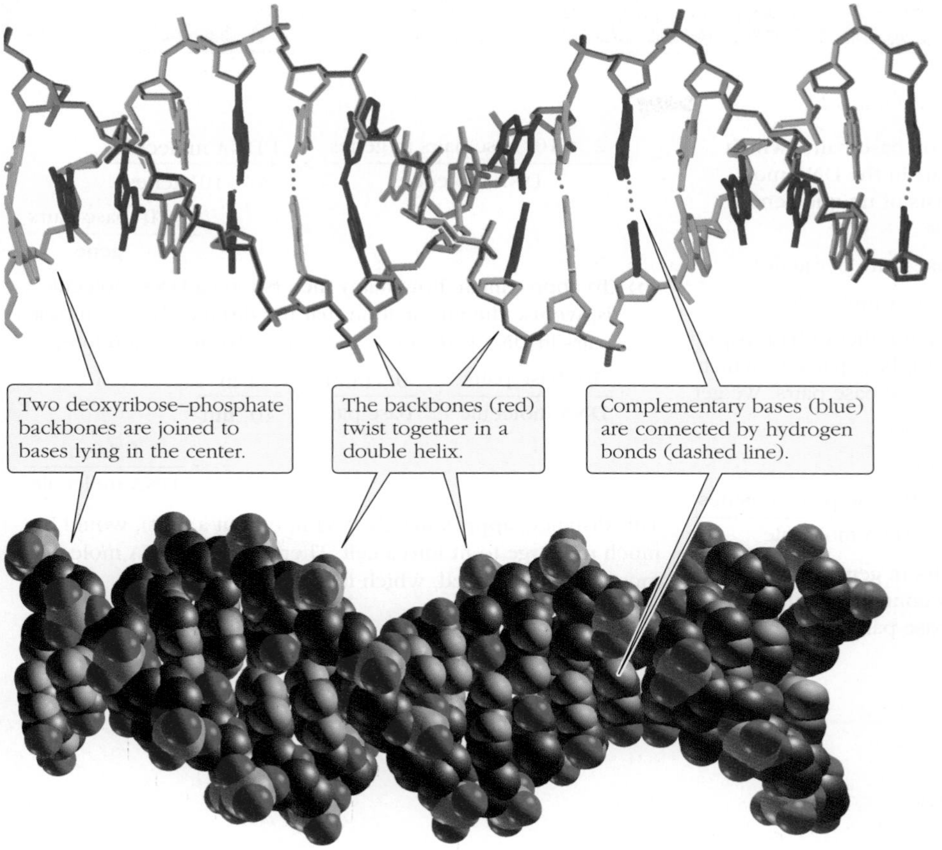

Figure 9.25 Double-stranded DNA. The illustration shows the deoxyribose-phosphate backbone of each strand as phosphate groups (orange and red) linking five-membered rings of deoxyribose joined to bases. The complementary bases *(shown in blue)* are connected by hydrogen bonds: two between adenine and thymine, and three for guanine and cytosine.

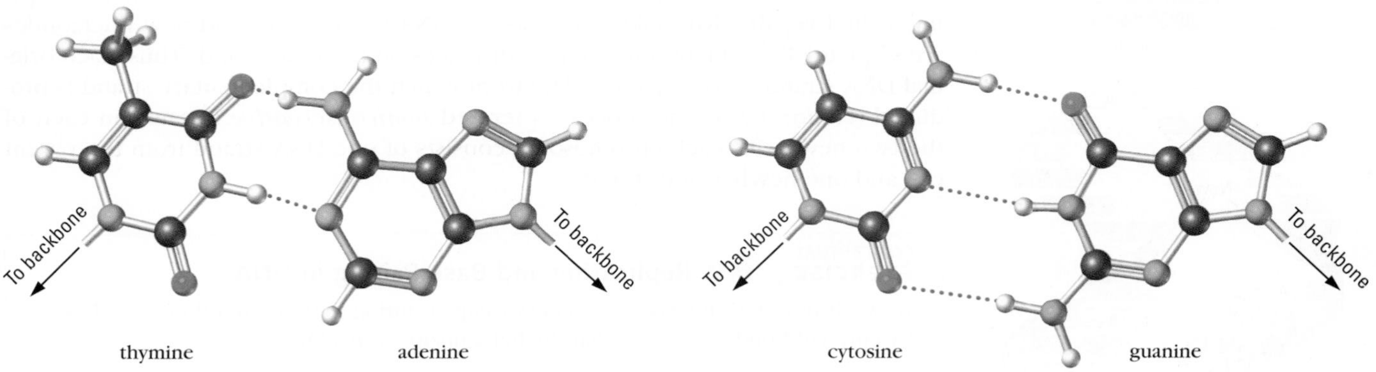

Figure 9.26 Hydrogen bonding between T-A and C-G in DNA.

was now clear that the DNA sequence of base pairs in the nucleus of a cell represents a genetic code that controls the inherited characteristics of the next generation, as well as most of the life processes of an organism.

The total sequence of base pairs in a plant or animal cell is called its genome.

In humans, the double-stranded DNA forms 46 chromosomes (23 chromosome pairs). The **gene** that accounts for a particular hereditary trait is usually located in the same position on the same chromosome. Each gene is distinguished by a unique

ESTIMATION

Base Pairs and DNA

Human DNA contains about three billion base pairs, which are an average distance of 0.34 nm apart in the DNA molecule. Only about 2% of this DNA consists of unique genes. The number of genes is estimated to be 3×10^4.

(a) What is the average number of base pairs per gene?

(b) Approximately how long (m) is a DNA molecule?

(a) We begin by calculating the average number of base pairs/gene, starting with approximately 10^9 base pairs, of which there are 2 base pairs in genes per 100 base pairs. We get

$$\frac{10^9 \text{ base pairs}}{\text{DNA molecule}} \times \frac{2 \text{ base pairs in genes}}{100 \text{ base pairs}} = \frac{2 \times 10^7 \text{ base pairs in genes}}{\text{DNA molecule}}$$

Thus, there are about 2×10^7 base pairs in genes/DNA. Using this information and the fact that DNA contains about 3×10^4 genes, there are roughly 1×10^3 base pairs/gene.

$$\frac{2 \times 10^7 \text{ base pairs in genes}}{\text{DNA molecule}} \times \frac{1 \text{ DNA molecule}}{3 \times 10^4 \text{ genes}} \approx \frac{10^3 \text{ base pairs}}{\text{gene}}$$

(b) To approximate how many meters long a DNA molecule is, we use the information that the distance between base pairs in DNA is 0.34 nm and 1 m = 10^9 nm. Therefore,

$$\frac{10^9 \text{ base pairs}}{\text{DNA molecule}} \times \frac{0.34 \text{ nm}}{\text{base pair}} \times \frac{1 \text{ m}}{10^9 \text{ nm}} \approx \frac{0.34 \text{ m}}{\text{DNA molecule}}$$

This distance, approximately 0.34 m (about a foot), would be much too large to fit into a cell. Therefore, the DNA molecule must be tightly coiled, which it is.

ThomsonNOW
Sign in to ThomsonNOW at **www.thomsonedu.com** to work an interactive module based on this material.

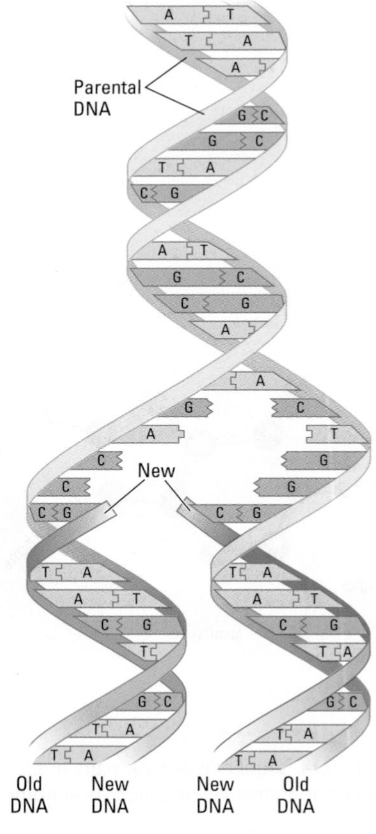

Figure 9.27 DNA replication. When the original DNA helix (*orange*) unwinds, each half is a template on which to assemble nucleotides from the cell environment to produce a complementary strand (*green*).

sequence of bases that codes for the synthesis of a single protein within the body. The protein then goes on to play its role in the growth and functioning of the individual. (Proteins are discussed in Section 12.8.)

Each organism (except viruses) begins life as a single cell. The DNA in that cell consists of a single strand from each parent. During regular cell division, both DNA strands are accurately copied, with a remarkably low incidence of error. The copying, called **replication,** takes place as the DNA helix unzips and new nucleotides are sequentially brought into the proper places on the new strand. Thus, each original DNA strand serves as a template from which the complementary strand is produced (Figure 9.27). The process is termed *semiconservative* because in each of the two new cells, each chromosome consists of one DNA strand from the parent cell and one newly made strand.

CONCEPTUAL EXERCISE 9.9 Replication and Base Pairing in DNA

How easily would the base pairs in DNA unpair during replication if they were linked by covalent bonds? How is it that the helix unzips so readily?

SUMMARY PROBLEM

Part 1

Write the Lewis structures and give the electron-pair geometry, the shape and bond angles, and the hybridization of the central atom of these polyatomic ions:

(a) BrF_2^+ (b) BrF_4^- (c) BrF_6^+ (d) $IBrCl_3^-$

Part 2

Aspartame is a commonly used artificial sweetener (NutraSweet®) that was discovered accidentally by a chemist in the laboratory carelessly licking his fingers after synthesizing a new compound (aspartame). The sweetener's popularity stems from the fact that aspartame tastes over 100 times sweeter than sugar. Aspartame has this structural formula.

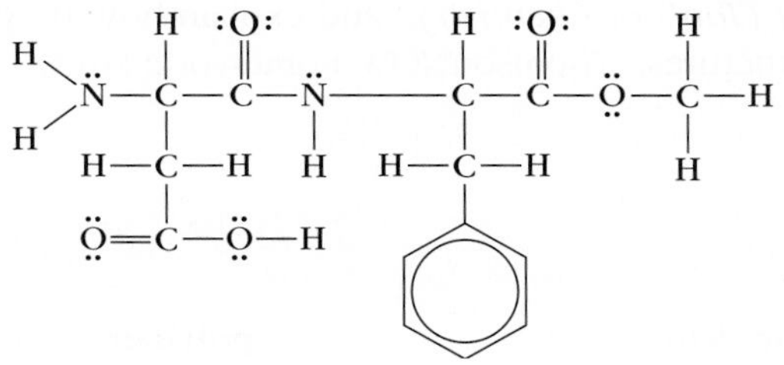

(a) Write the molecular formula of aspartame.

(b) Identify the hybridization of each nitrogen atom.

(c) Identify the hybridization of carbon in the CH_2 groups.

(d) Identify the hybridization of the carbon atom in the C=O group.

(e) Identify the hybridization of the oxygen atom to which a methyl (—CH_3) group is attached.

(f) Label each of the sigma and pi bonds involving carbon and those involving nitrogen.

Part 3

The structural formula for the open-chain form of glucose is

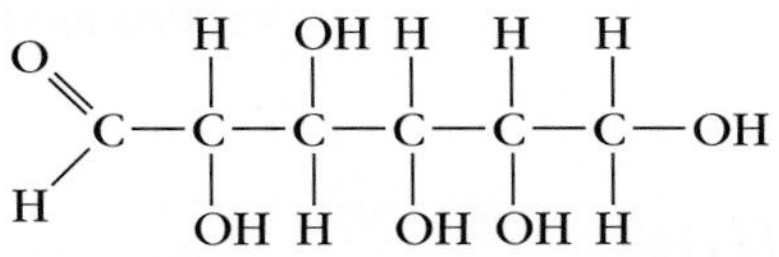

Glucose dissolves readily in water. Use molecular structure principles to explain why glucose is so water-soluble.

IN CLOSING

Having studied this chapter, you should be able to . . .

- Recognize the various ways that the shapes of molecules are represented by models and on the printed page (Section 9.1).
- Predict shapes of molecules and polyatomic ions by using the VSEPR model (Section 9.2). ThomsonNOW homework: Study Questions 17, 19, 21, 23, 76
- Determine the orbital hybridization of a central atom and the associated molecular geometry (Section 9.3). ThomsonNOW homework: Study Questions 29, 31, 33, 40
- Describe in terms of sigma and pi bonding the orbital hybridization of a central atom and the associated molecular geometry for molecules containing multiple bonds (Section 9.4). ThomsonNOW homework: Study Question 42
- Describe covalent bonding between two atoms in terms of sigma or pi bonds, or both (Section 9.3). ThomsonNOW homework: Study Question 44
- Use molecular structure and electronegativities to predict the polarities of molecules (Section 9.5). ThomsonNOW homework: Study Questions 46, 48, 52

ThomsonNOW

Sign in to ThomsonNOW at **www.thomsonedu.com** to check your readiness for an exam by taking the Pre-Test and exploring the modules recommended in your Personalized Learning Plan.

- Describe the different types of noncovalent interactions and use them to explain melting points and boiling points (Section 9.6). ThomsonNOW homework: Study Questions 58, 62
- Identify the major components in the structure of DNA (Section 9.7). ThomsonNOW homework: Study Question 68
- Describe the basis of infrared spectroscopy *(Tools of Chemistry)* and UV-visible spectroscopy *(Tools of Chemistry)* and explain how they are used to determine molecular structures. ThomsonNOW homework: Study Question 66

KEY TERMS

axial positions *(9.2)*
bond angle *(9.2)*
complementary base pairs *(9.7)*
deoxyribonucleic acid (DNA) *(9.7)*
dipole-dipole attraction *(9.6)*
dipole moment *(9.5)*
electron-pair geometry *(9.2)*
equatorial positions *(9.2)*
gene *(9.7)*
hybrid orbital *(9.3)*
hybridized *(9.3)*
hydrogen bond *(9.6)*
hydrophilic *(9.6)*
hydrophobic *(9.6)*
induced dipole *(9.6)*
intermolecular forces *(9.6)*
lipid bilayer *(9.6)*
London forces *(9.6)*
molecular geometry *(9.2)*
noncovalent interactions *(9.6)*
nonpolar molecule *(9.5)*
nucleotide *(9.7)*
phospholipid *(9.6)*
pi bond, π bond *(9.4)*
polar molecule *(9.5)*
polarization *(9.6)*
polymer *(9.7)*
replication *(9.7)*
sigma bond, σ bond *(9.3)*
***sp* hybrid orbital** *(9.3)*
sp^2 hybrid orbital *(9.3)*
sp^3 hybrid orbital *(9.3)*
sp^3d hybrid orbital *(9.3)*
sp^3d^2 hybrid orbital *(9.3)*
spectroscopy (Tools of Chemistry, pp. 392, 406)
valence bond model *(9.3)*
valence-shell electron-pair repulsion (VSEPR) model *(9.2)*

QUESTIONS FOR REVIEW AND THOUGHT

■ denotes questions available in ThomsonNOW and assignable in OWL.

Blue-numbered questions have short answers at the back of this book and fully worked solutions in the *Student Solutions Manual.*

ThomsonNOW
Assess your understanding of this chapter's topics with sample tests and other resources found by signing in to ThomsonNOW at **www.thomsonedu.com**.

Review Questions

1. What is the VSEPR model? What is the physical basis of the model?
2. What is the difference between the electron-pair geometry and the molecular geometry of a molecule? Use the water molecule as an example in your discussion.
3. Designate the electron-pair geometry for each case from two to six electron pairs around a central atom.
4. What are the molecular geometries for each of these?

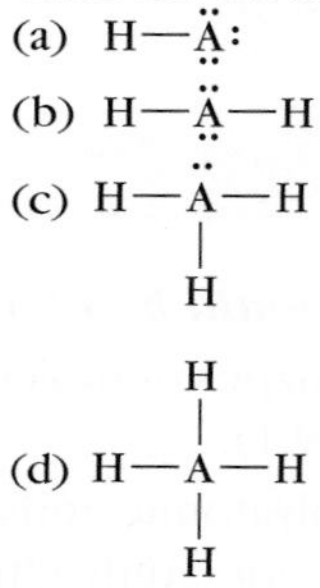

Give the H—A—H bond angle for each of the last three.
5. If you have three electron pairs around a central atom, how can you have a triangular planar molecule? An angular molecule? What bond angles are predicted in each case?
6. Use VSEPR to explain why ethylene is a planar molecule.
7. How can a molecule with polar bonds be nonpolar? Give an example.
8. Explain the significance of Erwin Chargaff's research to the understanding of the structure of DNA.

9. (a) Describe how nucleotides are joined into a polynucleotide chain in DNA.
   (b) Explain how the nitrogen bases are joined in the DNA helix.
10. Explain why the infrared spectrum of a molecule is referred to as its "fingerprint."
11. For infrared energy to be absorbed by a molecule, what frequency of motion must the molecule have?

Topical Questions

Molecular Shape

12. Use the various molecular modeling techniques (ball-and-stick, space-filling, two-dimensional pictures using wedges and dashed lines) to illustrate these simple molecules:
    (a) NH_3 (b) H_2O
    (c) CO_2
13. All of these molecules have central atoms with only bonding pairs of electrons. After drawing the Lewis structure, identify the molecular shape of each molecule.
    (a) BeH_2 (b) CH_2Cl_2
    (c) BH_3 (d) $SeCl_6$
    (e) PF_5
14. Draw the Lewis structure for each of these molecules or ions. Describe the electron-pair geometry and the molecular geometry.
    (a) NH_2Cl (b) OCl_2
    (c) SCN^- (d) HOF
15. Use the VSEPR model to predict the electron-pair geometry and the molecular geometry of
    (a) PH_4^+ (b) OCl_2
    (c) SO_3 (d) H_2CO
16. In each of these molecules or ions, two oxygen atoms are attached to a central atom. Draw the Lewis structure for each one, and then describe the electron-pair geometry and the molecular geometry. Comment on similarities and differences in the series.
    (a) CO_2 (b) NO_2^-
    (c) SO_2 (d) O_3
    (e) ClO_2^-
17. ■ In each of these ions, three oxygen atoms are attached to a central atom. Draw the Lewis structure for each one, and then describe the electron-pair geometry and the molecular geometry. Comment on similarities and differences in the series.
    (a) BO_3^{3-} (b) CO_3^{2-}
    (c) SO_3^{2-} (d) ClO_3^-
18. These are examples of molecules and ions that do not obey the octet rule. After drawing the Lewis structure, describe the electron-pair geometry and the molecular geometry for each.
    (a) ClF_2^- (b) ClF_3
    (c) ClF_4^- (d) ClF_5
19. ■ These are examples of molecules and ions that do not obey the octet rule. After drawing the Lewis structure, describe the electron-pair geometry and the molecular geometry for each.
    (a) SiF_6^{2-} (b) SF_4
    (c) PF_5 (d) XeF_4
20. Iodine forms three compounds with chlorine: ICl, ICl_3, and ICl_5. Draw the Lewis structures and determine the molecular shapes of these three molecules.
21. ■ Give the approximate values for the indicated bond angles. The figures given are not the actual molecular shapes, but are used only to show the bonds being considered.
    (a) O—S—O angle in SO_2
    (b) F—B—F angle in BF_3
    (c) 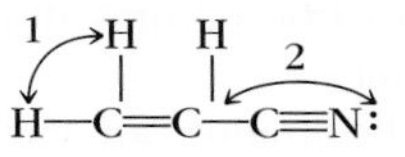
    (d) 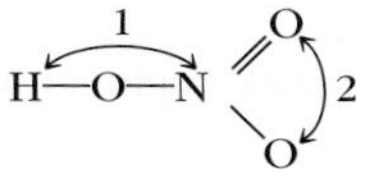
22. Give approximate values for the indicated bond angles. The figures given are not the actual molecular shapes, but are used only to show the bonds being considered.
    (a) Cl—S—Cl angle in SCl_2
    (b) N—N—O angle in N_2O
    (c) 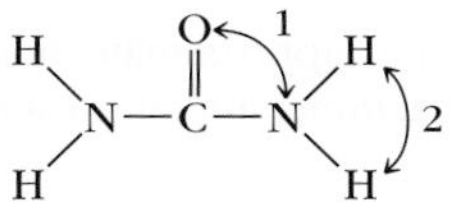
    (d) 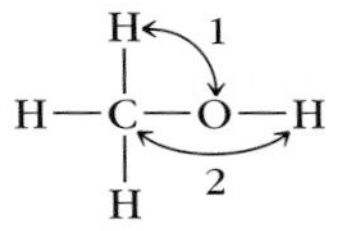
23. ■ Give approximate values for the indicated bond angles.
    (a) F—Se—F angles in SeF_4
    (b) O—S—F angles in SOF_4 (The O atom is in an equatorial position.)
    (c) F—Br—F angles in BrF_5
24. Give approximate values for the indicated bond angles.
    (a) F—S—F angles in SF_6
    (b) F—Xe—F angle in XeF_2
    (c) F—Cl—F angle in ClF_2^-
25. Which would have the greater O—N—O bond angle, NO_2 or NO_2^+? Explain your answer.
26. Compare the F—Cl—F angles in ClF_2^+ and ClF_2^-. From Lewis structures, determine the approximate bond angle in each ion. Explain which ion has the greater angle and why.

Hybridization

27. What designation is used for the hybrid orbitals formed by these combinations of atomic orbitals?
    (a) One *s* and three *p*
    (b) One *s*, three *p*, and two *d*
    (c) One *s* and two *p*
28. How many hybrid orbitals are formed in each case in Question 27?
29. ■ Describe the geometry and hybridization of carbon in chloroform, $CHCl_3$.
30. Describe the geometry and hybridization for each inner atom in ethylene glycol, $HOCH_2CH_2OH$, the main component in antifreeze.
31. ■ Describe the hybridization around the central sulfur atom and the bonding in SF_4 and SF_6.

32. Determine the Lewis structures, geometries, and hybridizations of GeF_4, SeF_4, and XeF_4.
33. ■ Determine the geometry and hybridization of the three phosphorus-chlorine species: PCl_4^+, PCl_5, and PCl_6^-.
34. Describe the bond angles generally associated with each of the hybrid orbitals described in Question 27.
35. On a general chemistry exam, a student mistakenly drew up a set of sp^2d hybrid orbitals formed only from orbitals for which $n = 2$. What was the student's mistake?
36. The hybridization of the two carbon atoms differs in an acetic acid, CH_3COOH, molecule.
    (a) Designate the correct hybridization for each carbon atom in this molecule.
    (b) What is the approximate bond angle around each carbon?
37. The hybridization of the two nitrogen atoms differs in NH_4NO_3.
    (a) Designate the correct hybridization for each nitrogen atom.
    (b) What is the approximate bond angle around each nitrogen?
38. What are the hybridization and approximate bond angles for the N, C, and O atoms in alanine, an amino acid, whose Lewis structure is

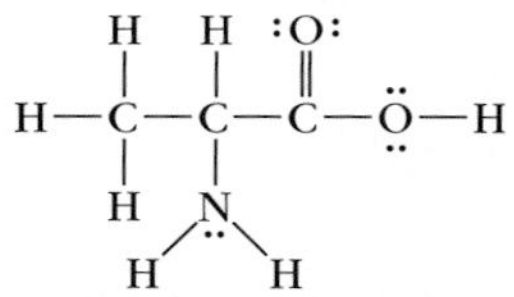

39. Identify the type of hybridization, geometry, and approximate bond angle for each carbon atom in an alkane.
40. ■ (a) Identify the type of hybridization and approximate bond angle for each carbon atom in CH_3CH_2CCH.
    (b) Which is the shortest carbon-to-carbon bond length in this molecule?
    (c) Which is the strongest carbon-to-carbon bond in this molecule?
41. Write the Lewis structure and designate which are sigma and pi bonds in each of these molecules.
    (a) HCN
    (b) N_2H_2
    (c) HN_3
42. ■ Write the Lewis structure and designate which are sigma and pi bonds in each of these molecules.
    (a) OCS (b) NH_2OH
    (c) CH_2CHCHO (d) $CH_3CH(OH)COOH$
43. Methylcyanoacrylate is the active ingredient in "super glues." Its Lewis structure is

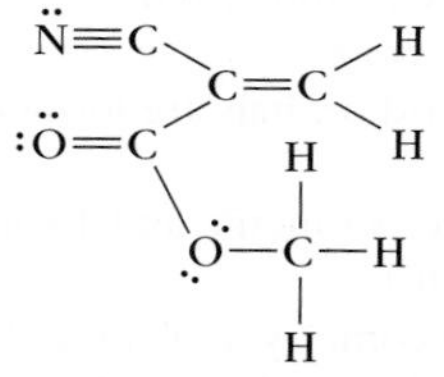

    (a) How many sigma bonds are in the molecule?
    (b) How many pi bonds are in the molecule?
    (c) What is the hybridization of the carbon atom bonded to nitrogen?
    (d) What is the hybridization of the carbon atom bonded to oxygen?
    (e) What is the hybridization of the double-bonded oxygen?
44. ■ Acrylonitrile is polymerized to manufacture carpets and wigs. Its Lewis structure is

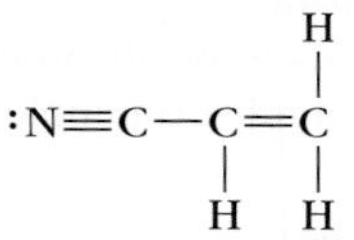

    (a) Locate the sigma bonds in the molecule. How many are there?
    (b) Locate the pi bonds in the molecule. How many are there?
    (c) What is the hybridization of the carbon atom that is bonded to nitrogen?
    (d) What is the hybridization of the nitrogen atom?
    (e) What is the hybridization of the hydrogen-bearing carbon atoms?

Molecular Polarity

45. Consider these molecules: CH_4, NCl_3, BF_3, CS_2.
    (a) In which compound are the bonds most polar?
    (b) Which compounds in the list are not polar?
46. ■ Consider these molecules: H_2O, NH_3, CO_2, ClF, CCl_4.
    (a) In which compound are the bonds most polar?
    (b) Which compounds in the list are not polar?
    (c) Which atom in ClF has a partial negative charge?
47. Which of these molecules is (are) not polar? Which molecule has the most polar bonds?
    (a) CO (b) PCl_3
    (c) BCl_3 (d) GeH_4
    (e) CF_4
48. ■ Which of these molecules is (are) polar? For each polar molecule, what is the direction of polarity; that is, which is the partial negative end and which is the partial positive end of the molecule?
    (a) CO_2 (b) HBF_2
    (c) CH_3Cl (d) SO_3
49. Which of these molecules have a dipole moment? For each of these polar molecules, indicate the direction of the dipole in the molecule.
    (a) XeF_2 (b) H_2S
    (c) CH_2Cl_2 (d) HCN
50. Explain the differences in the dipole moments of
    (a) BrF (1.29 D) and BrCl (0.52 D)
    (b) H_2O (1.86 D) and H_2S (0.95 D)
51. Which of these molecules has a dipole moment? For each of the polar molecules, indicate the direction of the dipole in the molecule.
    (a) Nitrosyl fluoride, FNO
    (b) Disulfur difluoride, S_2F_2
52. ■ Which of these molecules is polar? For each of the polar molecules, indicate the direction of the dipole in the molecule.
    (a) Hydroxylamine, NH_2OH
    (b) Sulfur dichloride, SCl_2, an unstable, red liquid

Noncovalent Interactions

53. Explain in terms of noncovalent interactions why water and ethanol are miscible, but water and cyclohexane are not.
54. Construct a table covering all the types of noncovalent interactions and comment about the distance dependence for each. (In general, the weaker the force, the closer together the molecules must be to feel the attractive force of nearby molecules.) You should also include an example of a substance that exhibits each type of noncovalent interaction in the table.
55. Explain the trends seen in the diagram below for the boiling points of some main group hydrogen compounds.
    (a) Group IV: CH_4, SiH_4, GeH_4, SnH_4
    (b) Group V: NH_3, PH_3, AsH_3, SbH_3
    (c) Group VI: H_2O, H_2S, H_2Se, H_2Te
    (d) Group VII: HF, HCl, HBr, HI

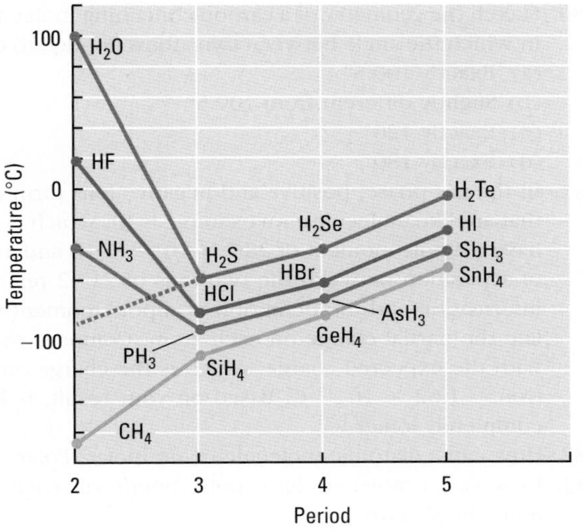

56. Explain why water "beads up" on a freshly waxed car, but not on a dirty, unwaxed car.
57. Explain why water will not remove tar from your shoe, but kerosene will.
58. ■ Which of these will form hydrogen bonds?
    (a) CH_2Br_2 (b) $CH_3OCH_2CH_3$
    (c) H_2NCH_2COOH (d) H_2SO_3
    (e) CH_3CH_2OH
59. Arrange the noble gases in order of increasing boiling point. Explain your reasoning.
60. The structural formula for vitamin C is

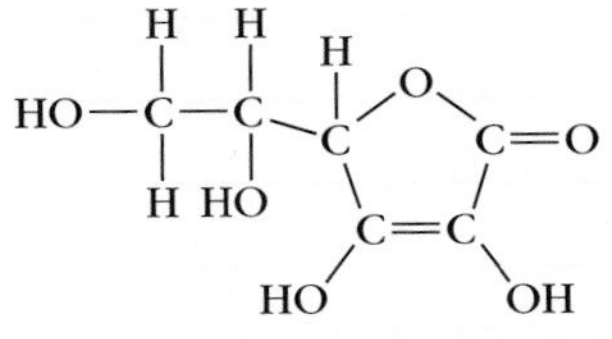

Give a molecular-level explanation why vitamin C is a water-soluble rather than a fat-soluble vitamin.

61. Which of these would you expect to be most soluble in cyclohexane (C_6H_{12})? The least soluble? Explain your reasoning.
    (a) NaCl (b) CH_3CH_2OH
    (c) C_3H_8
62. ■ What are the types of forces that must be overcome in these changes?
    (a) The sublimation of solid $C_{10}H_8$
    (b) The melting of propane, C_3H_8
    (c) The decomposition of water into H_2 and O_2
    (d) The evaporation of liquid PCl_3
    (e) Unzipping the DNA double helix during replication
63. The structural formula of alpha-tocopherol, a form of vitamin E, is

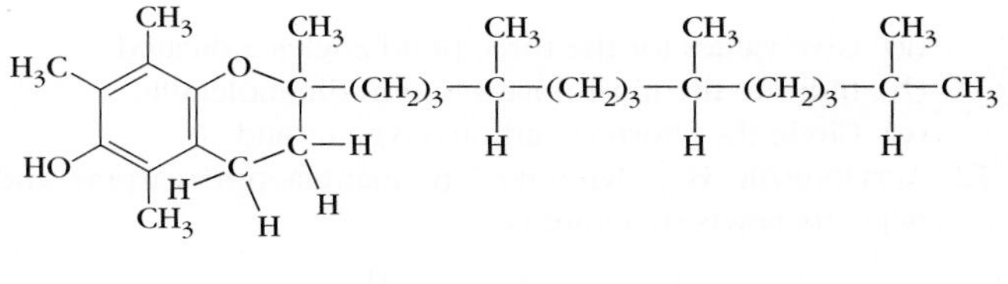

Give a molecular-level explanation why alpha-tocopherol dissolves in fat, but not in water.

Molecular Structure Determination by Spectroscopy

64. Ultraviolet and infrared spectroscopies probe different aspects of molecules.
    (a) Ultraviolet radiation is energetic enough to cause transitions in the energies of which electrons in an atom?
    (b) What does infrared spectroscopy tell us about a given molecule?
65. ■ The infrared spectrum of ethanol is given on page 393.
    (a) Which stretching requires the lowest amount of energy?
    (b) The highest amount of energy?
66. Compare IR and UV spectroscopy in these ways:
    (a) Energy of radiation
    (b) Wavelength of radiation
    (c) Frequency of radiation
67. ■ The UV-visible spectrum of beta-carotene given on page 406 shows a maximum absorbance at 455 nm. Estimate the wavelengths of two other peaks in the spectrum and indicate which peak identifies the more energetic electron transition.

Biomolecules

68. Discuss the differences between the extent of hydrogen bonding for the pairs G-C and A-T in nucleic acids. If a strand of DNA has more G-C pairs than A-T pairs in the double helix, the melting point (unwinding point) increases. The melting point for strands with more A-T pairing will decrease in comparison. Explain.
69. One strand of DNA contains the base sequence T-C-G. Draw a structure of this section of DNA that shows the hydrogen bonding between the base pairs of this strand and its complementary strand.

General Questions

70. The formula for nitryl chloride is NO_2Cl. Draw the Lewis structure for the molecule, including all resonance structures. Describe the electron-pair and molecular geometries, and give values for all bond angles.

71. ■ Methylcyanoacrylate is the active ingredient in "super glues." Its Lewis structure is

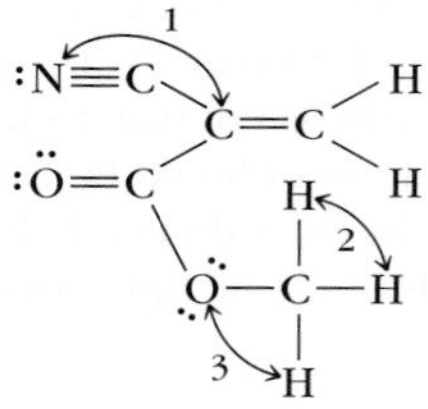

(a) Give values for the three bond angles indicated.
(b) Indicate the most polar bond in the molecule.
(c) Circle the shortest carbon-oxygen bond.

72. Acrylonitrile is polymerized to manufacture carpets and wigs. Its Lewis structure is

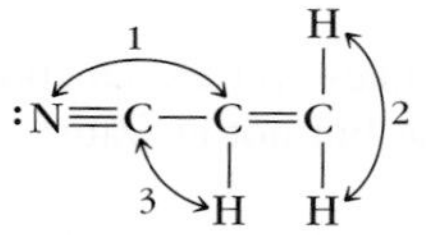

(a) Give approximate values for the indicated bond angles.
(b) Which are the most polar bonds in the molecule?

73. In addition to CO and CO_2, there are other carbon oxides. One is tricarbon dioxide, C_3O_2, also called carbon suboxide, a foul-smelling gas.
(a) Write the Lewis structure of this compound.
(b) What is the value of the C-to-C-to-O bond angle in carbon suboxide?
(c) What is the value of the C-to-C-to-C bond angle in tricarbon dioxide?

74. In addition to CO, CO_2, and C_3O_2, there is another molecular oxide of carbon, pentacarbon dioxide, C_5O_2, a yellow solid.
(a) What is the value of the C-to-C-to-O bond angle in pentacarbon dioxide?
(b) What is the value of the C-to-C-to-C bond angle in this compound?

75. Cyanidin chloride is an anthocyanin found in strawberries, apples, and cranberries.

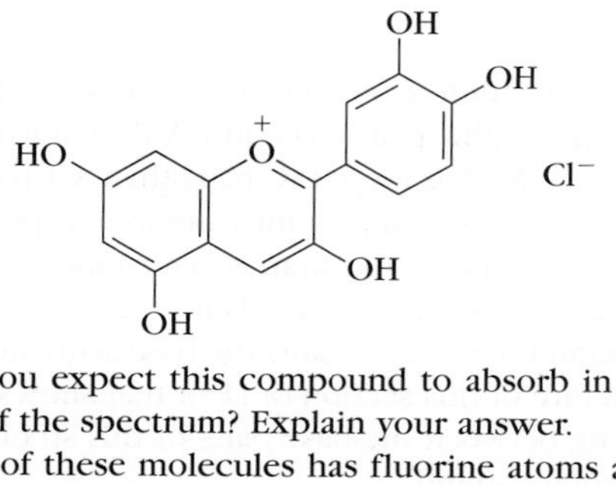

Would you expect this compound to absorb in the visible region of the spectrum? Explain your answer.

76. ■ Each of these molecules has fluorine atoms attached to an atom from Group 1A or 3A to 6A. Draw the Lewis structure for each one and then describe the electron-pair geometry and the molecular geometry. Comment on similarities and differences in the series.
(a) BF_3 (b) CF_4
(c) NF_3 (d) OF_2
(e) HF

77. Carbon and oxygen form the squarate ion, a polyatomic ion with the formula $C_4O_4^{2-}$.
(a) Write the Lewis structure for this ion.
(b) Describe the hybridization of each carbon atom.

78. In addition to carbonate ion, carbon and oxygen form the croconate ion, a polyatomic ion with the formula $C_5O_5^{2-}$.
(a) Write the Lewis structure for this ion.
(b) Describe the hybridization of each carbon atom.

79. The dipole moment of the HCl molecule is 3.43×10^{-30} C·m, and the bond length is 127.4 pm; the dipole moment of HF is 6.37×10^{-30} C·m, with bond length of 91.68 pm. Use the definition of dipole moment as a product of partial charge on each atom times the distance of separation (Section 9.5) to calculate the quantity of charge in coulombs that is separated by the bond length in each dipolar molecule. Use your result to show that fluorine is more electronegative than chlorine.

80. Sketch the geometry of a carbon-containing molecule or ion in which the angle between two atoms bonded to carbon is
(a) Exactly 109.5°
(b) Slightly different from 109.5°
(c) Exactly 120°
(d) Exactly 180°

81. In the gas phase, positive and negative ions form ion pairs that are like molecules. An example is KF, which is found to have a dipole moment of 28.7×10^{-30} C · m and a distance of separation between the two ions of 217.2 pm. Use this information and the definition of dipole moment to calculate the partial charge on each atom. Compare your result with the expected charge, which is the charge on an electron, -1.62×10^{-19} C. Based on your result, is KF really completely ionic?

82. How can a diatomic molecule be nonpolar? Polar?

83. How can a molecule have polar bonds yet have a dipole moment of zero?

Applying Concepts

84. Complete this table.

Molecule or Ion	Electron-Pair Geometry	Molecular Geometry	Hybridization of the Iodine Atom
ICl_2^+			
I_3^-			
ICl_3			
ICl_4^-			
IO_4^-			
IF_4^+			
IF_5			
IF_6^+			

85. Complete this table.

Molecule or Ion	Electron-Pair Geometry	Molecular Geometry	Hybridization of the Sulfur Atom
SO_2			
SCl_2			
SO_3			
SO_3^{2-}			
SF_4			
SO_4^{2-}			
SF_5^+			
SF_6			

86. What are the types of forces, in addition to London forces, that are overcome in these changes? Using structural formulas, make a sketch representing the major type of force in each case.
(a) The evaporation of liquid methanol, CH_3OH
(b) The decomposition of hydrogen peroxide (H_2O_2) into water and oxygen
(c) The melting of urea, H_2NCONH_2
(d) The boiling of liquid HCl

87. Name a Group 1A to 8A element that could be the central atom (X) in these compounds.
(a) XH_3 with one lone pair of electrons
(b) XCl_3
(c) XF_5
(d) XCl_3 with two lone pairs of electrons

88. Name a Group 1A to 8A element that could be the central atom (X) in these compounds.
(a) XCl_2
(b) XH_2 with two lone pairs of electrons
(c) XF_4 with one lone pair of electrons
(d) XF_4

89. What is the maximum number of water molecules that could hydrogen-bond to an acetic acid molecule? Draw in the water molecules and use dotted lines to show the hydrogen bonds.

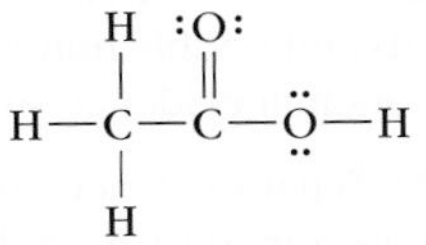

90. What is the maximum number of water molecules that could hydrogen-bond to an ethylamine molecule? Draw in the water molecules and use dotted lines to show the hydrogen bonds.

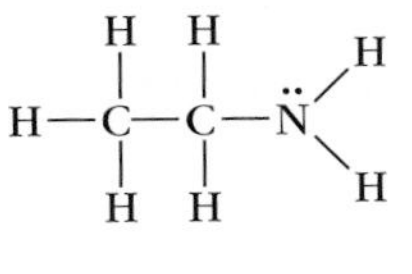

91. These are responses students wrote when asked to give an example of hydrogen bonding. Which are correct?
(a) H—H···H—H
(b) 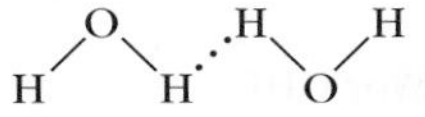
(c) H—F
(d) 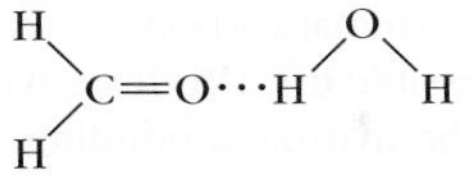

92. Which of these are examples of hydrogen bonding?
(a) 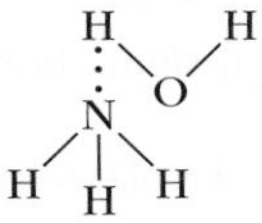
(b) H—H
(c) 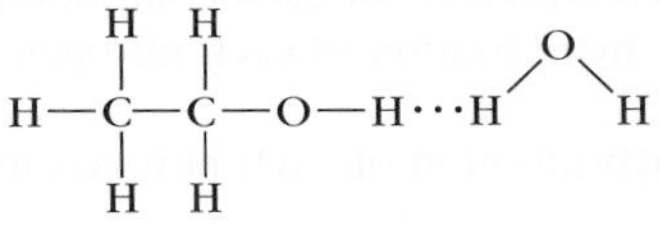
(d) 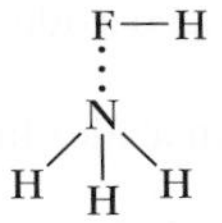

93. In another universe, elements try to achieve a nonet (nine valence electrons) instead of an octet when forming chemical bonds. As a result, covalent bonds form when a trio of electrons is shared between two atoms. Two compounds in this other universe are H_3O and H_2F. Draw their Lewis structures, then determine their electron-trio geometry and molecular geometry.

More Challenging Questions

94. One of the three isomers of dichlorobenzene, $C_6H_4Cl_2$, has a dipole moment of zero. Draw the structural formula of the isomer and explain your choice.

95. There are three isomers with the formula $C_6H_6O_2$. Each isomer contains a benzene ring to which two —OH groups are attached.
(a) Write the Lewis structures for the three isomers.
(b) Taking their molecular structure and the likelihood of hydrogen bonding into account, list them in order of increasing melting point.

96. Halomethane, which had been used as an anesthetic, has the molecular formula $CHBrClCF_3$.
(a) Write the Lewis structure for halomethane.
(b) Is halomethane a polar molecule? Explain your answer.
(c) Does hydrogen bonding occur in halomethane? Explain.

97. Ketene, C_2H_2O, is a reactant for synthesizing cellulose acetate, which is used to make films, fibers, and fashionable clothing.
(a) Write the Lewis structure of ketene. Ketene does not contain an —OH bond.
(b) Identify the geometry around each carbon atom and all the bond angles in the molecule.
(c) Identify the hybridization of each carbon and oxygen atom.
(d) Is the molecule polar or nonpolar? Use appropriate data to support your answer.

98. Gamma hydroxybutyric acid, GHB, infamous as a "date rape" drug, is used illicitly because of its effects on the nervous system. The condensed molecular formula for GHB is $HO(CH_2)_3COOH$.
   (a) Write the Lewis structure for GHB.
   (b) Identify the hybridization of the carbon atom in the CH_2 groups and of the terminal carbon.
   (c) Is hydrogen bonding possible in GHB? If so, write Lewis structures to illustrate the hydrogen bonding.
   (d) Which carbon atoms are involved in sigma bonds? In pi bonds?
   (e) Which oxygen atom is involved in sigma bonds? In pi bonds?

99. There are two compounds with the molecular formula HN_3. One is called hydrogen azide; the other is cyclotriazene.
   (a) Write the Lewis structure for each compound.
   (b) Designate the hybridization of each nitrogen in hydrogen azide.
   (c) What is the hybridization of each nitrogen in cyclotriazene?
   (d) How many sigma bonds are in hydrogen azide? In cyclotriazene?
   (e) How many pi bonds are in hydrogen azide? In cyclotriazene?
   (f) Give approximate values for the N-to-N-to-N bond angles in each molecule.

100. Nitrosyl azide, a yellow solid first synthesized in 1993, has the molecular formula N_4O.
   (a) Write its Lewis structure.
   (b) What is the hybridization on the terminal nitrogen?
   (c) What is the hybridization on the "central" nitrogen?
   (d) Which is the shortest nitrogen-nitrogen bond?
   (e) Give the approximate bond angle between the three nitrogens, beginning with the nitrogen that is bonded to oxygen.
   (f) Give the approximate bond angle between the last three nitrogens, those not involved in bonding to oxygen.
   (g) How many sigma bonds are there? How many pi bonds?

101. ■ Piperine, the active ingredient in black pepper, has this Lewis structure.

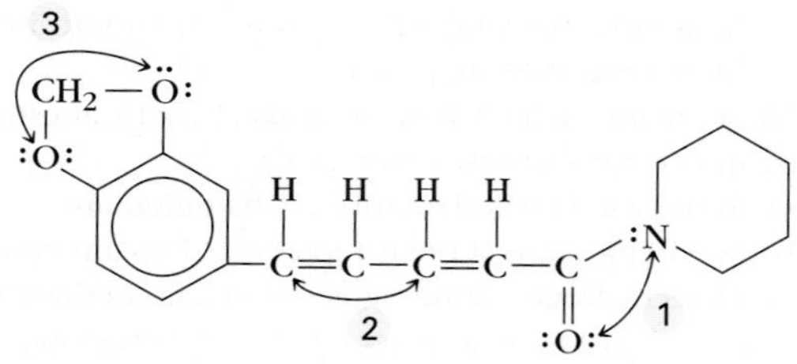

   (a) Give the values for the indicated bond angles.
   (b) What is the hybridization of the nitrogen?
   (c) What is the hybridization of the oxygens?

102. This compound is commonly called acetylacetone. As shown, it exists in two forms, one called the *enol* form and the other called the *keto* form.

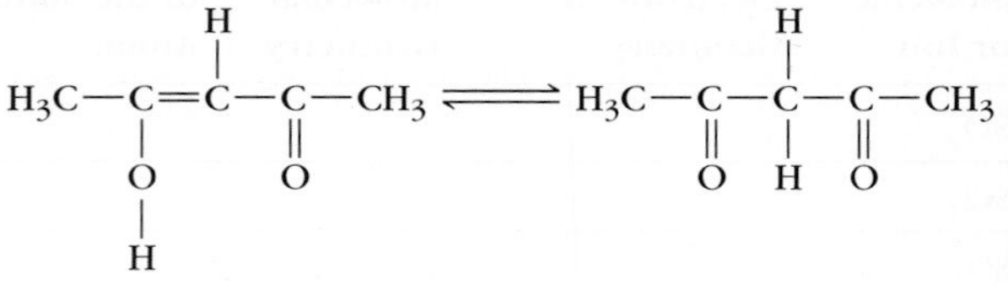

enol form *keto* form

While in the *enol* form, the molecule can lose H^+ from the —OH group to form an anion. One of the most interesting aspects of this anion (sometimes called the *acac* ion) is that one or more of them can react with a transition metal cation to give very stable, highly colored compounds.

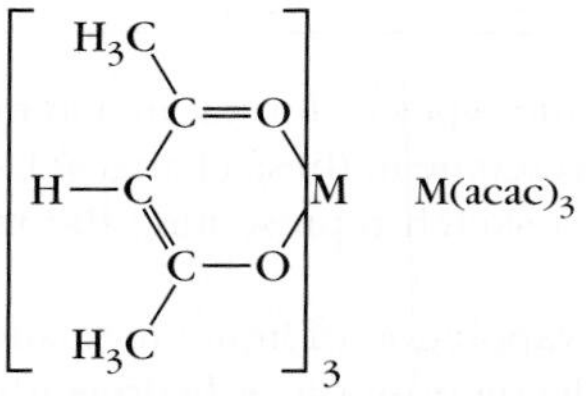

   (a) Using bond enthalpies, calculate the enthalpy change for the *enol* to *keto* change. Is the reaction exothermic or endothermic?
   (b) What are the electron-pair and "molecular" geometries around each C atom in the *keto* and *enol* forms? What changes (if any) occur when the *keto* form changes to the *enol* form?
   (c) If you wanted to prepare 15.0 g deep red $Cr(acac)_3$ using the following reaction,

$$CrCl_3 + 3\ H_3C{-}C(OH){=}CH{-}C(OH){-}CH_3 + 3\ NaOH \rightarrow Cr(acac)_3 + 3\ H_2O + 3\ NaCl$$

   how many grams of each of the reactants would you need?

Conceptual Challenge Problems

CP9.A (Section 9.2) What advantages does the VSEPR model of chemical bonding have compared with the Lewis dot formulas predicted by the octet rule?

CP9.B (Section 9.2) The VSEPR model does not differentiate between single bonds and double bonds for predicting molecular shapes. What experimental evidence supports this?

CP9.C (Section 9.3) What evidence could you present to show that two carbon atoms joined by a single sigma bond are able to rotate about an axis that coincides with the bond, but two carbon atoms bonded by a double bond cannot rotate about an axis along the double bond?

10 Gases and the Atmosphere

The Breitling Orbiter 3 became the first balloon to fly around the world nonstop in March 1999. The 20-day trip covered 28,431 miles. During its flight, the balloon attained an altitude of 36,000 feet and was driven by the jet stream. The balloon combined an outer hot-air chamber with an inner helium-filled chamber. As the temperature and pressure of the air and the helium changed, the volumes occupied by the gases changed, and the balloon rose and fell in elevation in response to these changes. The black object hanging beneath the gondola is a set of solar panels that supplied the necessary power for telecommunication and navigation instruments during the flight. The Breitling Orbiter 3 gondola in this picture is now on display at the Smithsonian National Air and Space Museum in Washington, DC.

© Breitling

ThomsonNOW™
Throughout the text, this icon indicates an opportunity to test yourself on key concepts and to explore interactive modules by signing in to ThomsonNOW at **www.thomsonedu.com**.

Early chemists studied gases and their chemistry extensively. They carried out reactions that generated gases, bubbled the gases through water into glass containers, and transferred the gases to animal bladders for storage. They mixed gases together to see whether the gases would react and, if so, how much of each gas would be consumed or formed. They discovered that gases have many properties in common, much more so than liquids or solids. All gases are transparent, although some are colored. (F_2 is light yellow, Cl_2 is greenish yellow, Br_2 and NO_2 are reddish brown, and I_2 vapor is violet.) All gases are also mobile, that is, they expand to fill all space available, and they mix together physically in any proportions. The volume of a gas sample can easily be altered by changing its temperature, its pressure, or both. Thus, gas densities (mass/volume) are quite variable, depending on the conditions. At first this might seem to make the study of gases complicated, but it really does not. The way that gas volume depends on temperature and pressure is essentially the same for all gases, so it is easy to formulate an expression that accounts for the dependence.

Compared to the size of the earth, the atmosphere is about the thickness of an apple skin compared to the size of the apple.

The earth is surrounded by a layer of gases we call the atmosphere. Many different chemical reactions take place in this gas mixture, many of them driven by energy from solar photons. Although many of these reactions are beneficial to the earth's inhabitants, some produce undesirable products. This chapter contains fundamental facts and concepts about gases as well as information about atmospheric reactions. The relationships among pressure, temperature, and amount of a gas and its volume are expressed in the ideal gas law. Other quantitative treatments of gases in chemical reactions are introduced, and adjustments to the ideal gas law to account for real gas behaviors are described. The chapter concludes with discussions of chemistry in the atmosphere.

A metric ton is 1000 kg.

The 5.3×10^{15} metric tons of the atmosphere has about the same mass as a cube of water 100 km on a side.

10.1 The Atmosphere

Earth is enveloped by a few vertical miles of atoms and molecules that compose the atmosphere, the gaseous medium in which we exist, a perfect place to begin the study of gases. Everything on the surface of the earth experiences the atmosphere's pressure. The atmosphere's total mass is approximately 5.3×10^{15} metric tons, a huge figure, but still only about one millionth of the earth's total mass. Close to the earth's surface the atmosphere is mostly nitrogen and life-sustaining oxygen, but a fraction of a percent of other chemicals can make a difference in the quality of life, even its very existence. Extra water in the atmosphere can support a rain forest, a little less water produces a balanced rainfall, and practically no water results in a desert. Air pollutants, which are present in such small quantities that they are outnumbered by oxygen and nitrogen molecules by 100,000 to 1 or more (Section 10.12), can lower our quality of life and generally prove harmful to people with respiratory disorders.

© Thomson Learning/Charles D. Winters

Figure 10.1 Combustion in pure oxygen. When a glowing wood splint is inserted into the mouth of a vessel containing pure oxygen, the high oxygen concentration causes the splint to burn much faster.

The two major chemicals in our atmosphere are nitrogen, a rather unreactive gas, and oxygen, a highly reactive one. In dry air at sea level, nitrogen is the most abundant atmospheric gas, followed by oxygen, and then 13 other gases, each at less than 1% by volume (Table 10.1). For every 100 volume units of air, 21 units are oxygen. When it is pure, oxygen supports very rapid combustion (Figure 10.1). When it is diluted with nitrogen at moderate temperatures such as in the atmosphere, however, oxygen's oxidizing capability is tamed somewhat. The atmosphere is our only source for most of the noble gases—argon, neon, krypton, and xenon. Helium is an exception; it is obtained from wells in the U.S. southern great plains.

Due to the force of gravity, molecules making up the atmosphere are most concentrated near the earth's surface. In addition to the percentages by volume used in Table 10.1, *parts per million (ppm)* and *parts per billion (ppb)* by volume are used

Table 10.1 The Composition of Dry Air at Sea Level

Gas	Percentage by Volume	Gas	Percentage by Volume
Nitrogen	78.084	Krypton	0.0001
Oxygen	20.948	Carbon monoxide†	0.00001
Argon	0.934	Xenon	0.000008
Carbon dioxide*	0.033	Ozone†	0.000002
Neon	0.00182	Ammonia	0.000001
Hydrogen	0.0010	Nitrogen dioxide†	0.0000001
Helium	0.00052	Sulfur dioxide†	0.00000002
Methane*	0.0002		

*The greenhouse gases carbon dioxide and methane are discussed in Section 10.13 as they relate to fuels and the burning of fuels for energy production.

†Trace gases of environmental importance.

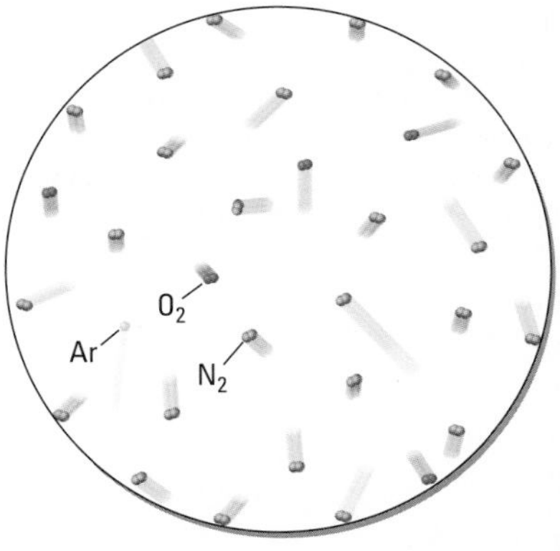

Nanoscale view of air. This instantaneous view of a sample of air at the nanoscale shows nitrogen, oxygen, and argon in rapid, random motion.

to describe the concentrations of components of the atmosphere. Since volume is proportional to the number of molecules, ppm and ppb units also give a ratio of molecules of one kind to another kind. For example, "10 ppm SO_2" means that for every 1 million molecules in air, 10 of them are SO_2 molecules. This may not sound like much until you consider that in just 1 cm^3 of air there are about 2.7×10^{13} million molecules. If this 1 cm^3 of air contains 10 ppm SO_2, then it contains 2.7×10^8 million SO_2 molecules.

To convert percent to ppm, multiply by 10,000. Divide by 10,000 to convert ppm to percent.

EXERCISE 10.1 Calculating the Mass of a Gas

Calculate the mass of the SO_2 molecules found in 1 cm^3 of air that contains 10 ppm SO_2.

The Troposphere and the Stratosphere

The earth's atmosphere can be roughly divided into layers, as shown in Figure 10.2. From the surface to an altitude of about 10 km, in the region named the **troposphere,** the temperature of the atmosphere decreases with increasing altitude. In this region the most violent mixing of air and the biggest variations in moisture content and temperature occur. Winds, clouds, storms, and precipitation are the result, the phenomena we know as weather. The troposphere is where we live. A commercial jet airplane flying at an altitude of about 10 km (approximately 33,000 ft) is still in the troposphere, although near its upper limits. The composition of the troposphere is roughly that of dry air near sea level (see Table 10.1), but the concentration of water vapor varies considerably, with an average of about 10 ppm.

Just above the troposphere, from about 12 to 50 km above the earth's surface, is the **stratosphere.** The pressures in the stratosphere are extremely low, and little mixing occurs between the stratosphere and the troposphere. The lower limit of the stratosphere varies from night to day over the globe, and in the polar regions it may be as low as 8 to 9 km above the earth's surface. About 75% of the mass of the atmosphere is in the troposphere, and 99.9% of the atmosphere's mass is below 50 km, in the troposphere and stratosphere.

NASA

Planet earth.

The troposphere was named by the British meteorologist Sir Napier Shaw from the Greek word *tropos,* meaning "turning."

The stratosphere was named by the French meteorologist Leon Phillipe Treisserenc de Bort, who believed this region consisted of orderly layers with no turbulence or mixing. *Stratum* is a Latin word meaning "layer."

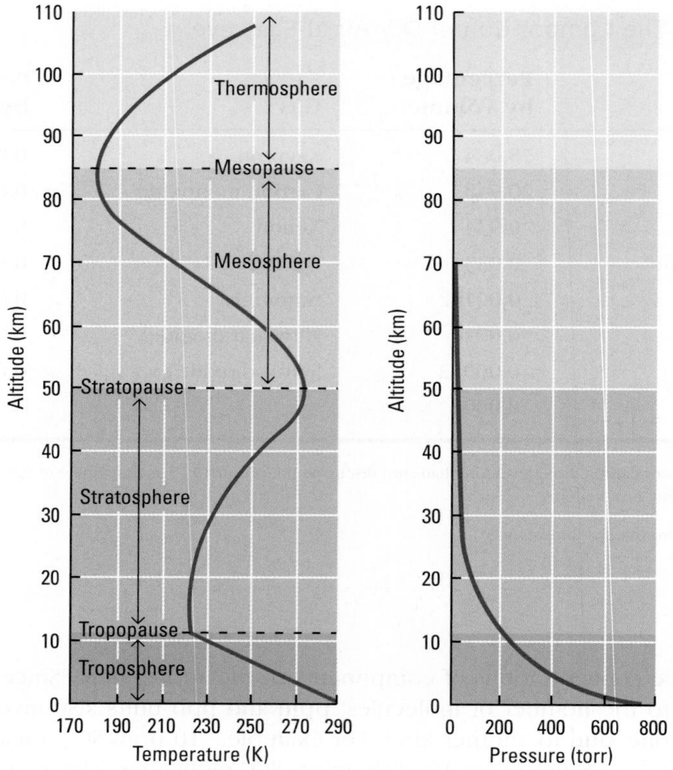

Figure 10.2 **Pressure and temperature changes in earth's atmosphere.**

10.2 Properties of Gases

Many molecular compounds are gases under ordinary conditions of temperature and pressure. The air we breathe consists mostly of diatomic nitrogen and oxygen molecules. Other elements that exist as gases at normal temperature and pressure include H_2, Cl_2, F_2, and the noble gases. Some examples of small molecular compounds that are also gases are shown in Table 10.2. At sufficiently high temperatures, many other compounds that are normally liquids or solids become gases.

All gases have a number of properties in common:

- ***Gases can be compressed.*** We often pump compressed air into an automobile or bicycle tire. Compressed air occupies less volume than the noncompressed air (Figure 10.3).
- ***Gases exert pressure on whatever surrounds them.*** A gas sample inside a balloon or a storage cylinder exerts pressure on its surroundings. If the container cannot sustain the pressure, some of the gas sample will escape, perhaps by bursting the container.
- ***Gases expand into whatever volume is available.*** The gaseous contents of a container will escape when it is opened.
- ***Gases mix completely with one another.*** Once gases are mixed, they do not separate spontaneously. The gases in the atmosphere are an example.
- ***Gases are described in terms of their temperature and pressure, the volume occupied, and the amount (numbers of molecules or moles) of gas present.*** For example, a hot gas in a fixed volume exerts a greater pressure than does the same sample of gas when it is cold.

Table 10.2 Some Common Gases and Their Uses

Gas	Formula	Typical Use
Acetylene (ethyne)	C_2H_2	Welding torch fuel
Ammonia	NH_3	Fertilizer
Argon	Ar	Filling for light bulbs
Butane	C_4H_{10}	Fuel for space heating (LP gas)
Carbon dioxide	CO_2	Carbonation of beverages
Chlorine	Cl_2	Disinfectant, bleach
Ethylene (ethene)	C_2H_4	Polymer manufacturing (polyethylene)
Helium	He	Lighter-than-air aircraft
Hydrogen	H_2	Hydrogenation of oils; possible fuel of the future
Methane	CH_4	Fuel (natural gas)
Nitrous oxide	N_2O	Anesthetic
Propane	C_3H_8	Fuel for space heating (LP gas)
Sulfur dioxide	SO_2	Preservative, disinfectant

The kinetic-molecular theory (***⇐ p. 20***) can be used to explain all these properties of gases on the nanoscale. You will see in Section 10.3 that using this theory makes gases fairly easy to understand and will enable you to predict accurately many of the properties of a gas sample. Let's look at some gas properties in more detail.

Gases Exert Pressure

The firmness of a balloon filled with air indicates that the gas inside exerts pressure caused by gas molecules striking the balloon's inner surface with each collision exerting a force on the surface. The force per unit area is the **pressure** of the gas. A gas exerts pressure on every surface it contacts, no matter what the direction of contact.

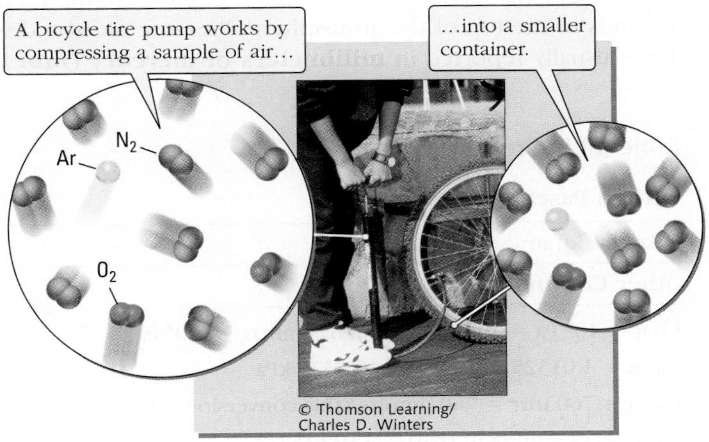

Figure 10.3 **Compression of gases.**

ESTIMATION

Thickness of Earth's Atmosphere

In the photograph of earth on page 431, the earth's diameter is about 5 cm. About 99.9% of the atmosphere is contained within 50 km of the earth's surface. To draw a circle around the photo properly relating the diameter of the earth with the thickness of the atmosphere, how thick should the line be drawn?

The diameter of earth is about 7900 miles, which is 12,700 km. Set up an equation that equates the ratio of the diameter of the photo to the diameter of earth with the ratio of the sought line width (x) to the thickness of the atmosphere.

$$\frac{5 \text{ cm}}{12{,}700 \text{ km}} = \frac{x}{50 \text{ km}}$$

$$x = 0.020 \text{ cm} = 0.2 \text{ mm}$$

If the circle representing the earth is 5 cm in diameter, then the line width that properly shows the relative thickness of the atmosphere would be only 0.2 mm, less than the width of the period at the end of this sentence. The proportions are about the same as the skin on an apple in relation to the apple. The atmosphere of earth is really quite thin.

ThomsonNOW™

Sign in to ThomsonNOW at **www.thomsonedu.com** to work an interactive module based on this material.

$$\text{Pressure} = \frac{\text{force}}{\text{area}}$$

A force can accelerate an object, and the force equals the mass of the object times its acceleration.

$$\text{Force} = \text{mass} \times \text{acceleration}$$

The SI units for mass and acceleration are kilograms (kg) and meters per second per second (m/s^2), respectively, so force has the units kg m/s^2. A force of 1 kg m/s^2 is defined as a **newton (N)** in the International System of Units (SI). A pressure of one newton per square meter (N/m^2) is defined as a **pascal (Pa).** Table 10.3 provides units of pressure and conversion factors among units.

1 kPa = 10^3 Pa

The earth's atmosphere exerts pressure on everything with which it comes into contact. Atmospheric pressure can be measured with a **barometer,** which can be made by filling a tube closed at one end with a liquid and then inverting the tube in a dish containing the same liquid. Figure 10.4 shows a mercury barometer—a glass tube filled with mercury, inverted, and placed in a container of mercury. At sea level the height of the mercury column is 760 mm above the surface of the mercury in the dish. The pressure at the bottom of a column of mercury 760 mm tall is balanced by the pressure at the bottom of the column of air surrounding the dish—a column that extends to the top of the atmosphere. Pressure measured with a mercury barometer is usually reported in **millimeters of mercury (mm Hg),** a unit

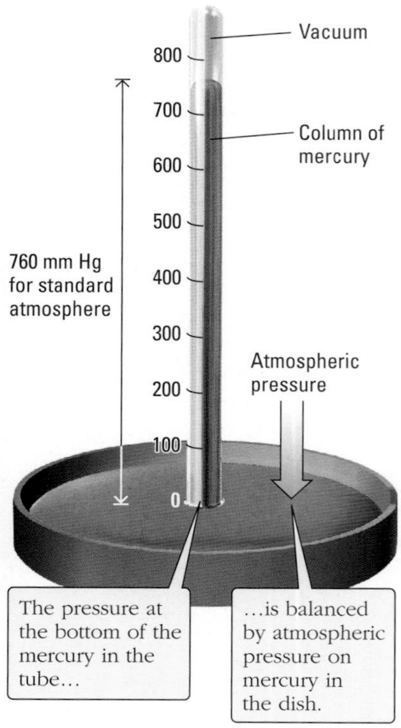

Figure 10.4 A Torricellian barometer.

Table 10.3 Pressure Units

SI Unit: Pascal (Pa)
1 Pa = 1 kg m^{-1} s^{-2} = 1 N/m^2
Other Common Units
1 bar = 10^5 Pa = 100 kPa; 1 millibar (mbar) = 10^2 Pa
1 atm = 1.01325 × 10^5 Pa = 101.325 kPa
1 atm = 760 torr = 760 mm Hg (this conversion is exact)*
1 atm = 14.7 lb/inch^2 (psi) = 1.01325 bar

*Exact conversion factors do not limit the number of significant figures in calculations.

that is also called the **torr** after Evangelista Torricelli, who invented the mercury barometer in 1643. The **standard atmosphere (atm)** is defined as

1 standard atmopshere = 1 atm = 760 mm Hg (exactly) = 101.325 kPa

The pressure of the atmosphere at sea level is about 101,300 Pa (101.3 kPa). A related unit, the **bar,** equal to 100,000 Pa, is sometimes used for atmospheric pressure. The standard thermodynamic properties (**⟵ p. 233**) are given for a gas pressure of 1 bar.

PROBLEM-SOLVING EXAMPLE 10.1 Converting Pressure Units

Convert a pressure reading of 0.988 atm to (a) mm Hg, (b) kPa, (c) bar, (d) torr, and (e) psi.

Answer (a) 751. mm Hg (b) 100. kPa (c) 1.00 bar (d) 751. torr (e) 14.5 psi

Strategy and Explanation We use the unit equivalencies shown in Table 10.3 as conversion factors.

(a) mm Hg: $0.988 \text{ atm} \times \dfrac{760. \text{ mm Hg}}{1 \text{ atm}} = 751. \text{ mm Hg}$

(b) kPa: $0.988 \text{ atm} \times \dfrac{101.31 \text{ kPa}}{1 \text{ atm}} = 100. \text{ kPa}$

(c) bar: $0.988 \text{ atm} \times \dfrac{1.013 \text{ bar}}{1 \text{ atm}} = 1.00 \text{ bar}$

(d) torr: $0.988 \text{ atm} \times \dfrac{760. \text{ torr}}{1 \text{ atm}} = 751. \text{ torr}$

(e) psi: $0.988 \text{ atm} \times \dfrac{14.7 \text{ psi}}{1 \text{ atm}} = 14.5 \text{ psi}$

PROBLEM-SOLVING PRACTICE 10.1

A TV weather person says the barometric pressure is "29.5 inches of mercury." What is this pressure in (a) atm, (b) mm Hg, (c) bar, and (d) kPa?

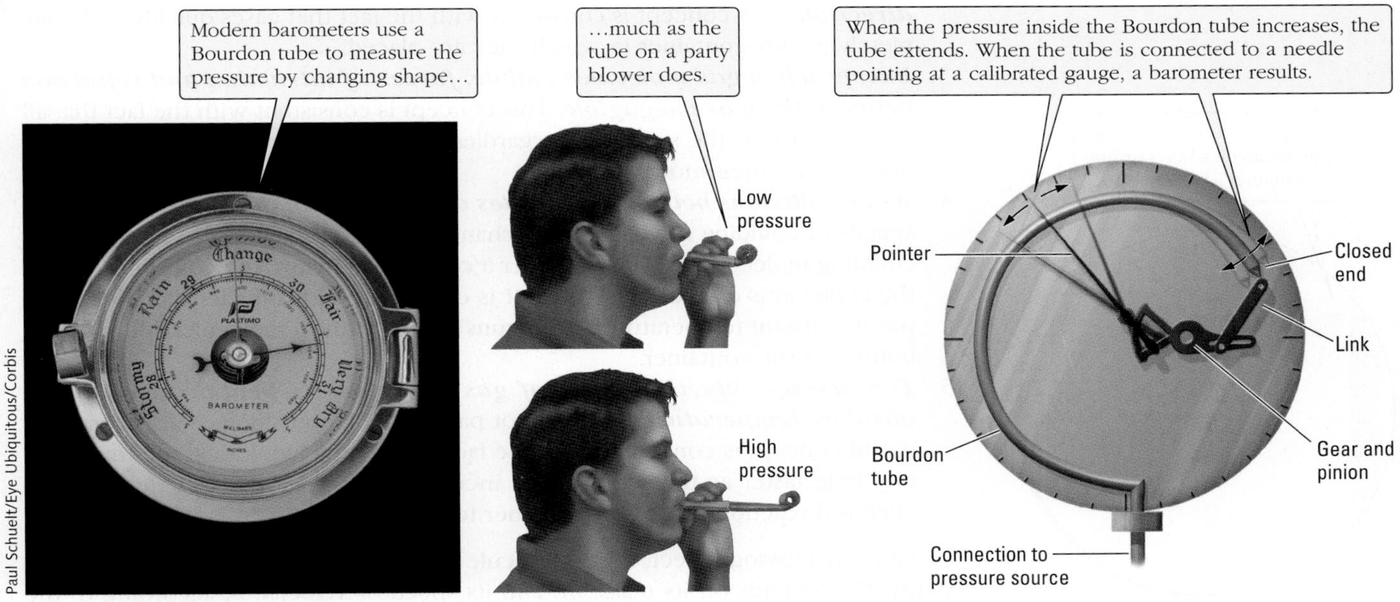

Barometers and the Bourdon gauge.

© Thomson Learning/Charles D. Winters

An old well pump. Old-fashioned water pumps like this one depend on atmospheric pressure to lift water from the well. They can only lift water from a depth of about 33 feet at sea level. At higher elevations this depth is lessened because the atmospheric pressure is lower.

Any liquid can be used in a barometer, but the height of the column depends on the density of the liquid. The atmosphere can support a column of mercury that is 760 mm high, or a column of water almost 34 ft high since water (1.0 g/cm^3) is much less dense than mercury (13.55 g/cm^3). A water barometer would be between 33 and 34 ft high, far too tall to be practical. Many water wells (especially in regions of the world without readily available electricity) bring up water from rock strata less than 33 ft below the surface. A simple hand pump can reduce the pressure at the top of the well, enabling the atmospheric pressure acting on the water at the bottom of the well to force the water upward. Before the invention of submersible electric pumps, well diggers knew from experience that if water was found deeper than 33 ft below the surface, a hole large enough for a bucket would have to be dug. The bucket would then have to be lowered and filled with water because atmospheric pressure alone could not push the water higher than 33 ft.

10.3 Kinetic-Molecular Theory

To explain why gases behave as they do, we first look at the nanoscale behavior of gas molecules. The fact that all gases behave in very similar ways can be interpreted by means of the *kinetic-molecular theory,* a theory that applies to the properties of liquids and solids as well as gases. According to the kinetic-molecular theory, a gas consists of tiny molecules in constant, rapid, random motion. The pressure a gas exerts on the walls of its container results from the continual bombardment of the walls by rapidly moving gas molecules (Figure 10.5).

In the kinetic-molecular theory the word "molecule" is taken to include atoms of the monatomic noble gases He, Ne, Ar, Kr, and Xe.

Four fundamental concepts form the foundation of the kinetic-molecular theory, and a fifth is closely associated with it. Each is consistent with the results of experimental studies of gases.

1. ***A gas is composed of molecules whose size is much smaller than the distances between them.*** This concept accounts for the ease with which gases can be compressed and for the fact that gases at ordinary temperature and pressure mix completely with each other. These facts imply that there must be much unoccupied space in gases that provides substantial room for additional molecules in a sample of gas.
2. ***Gas molecules move randomly at various speeds and in every possible direction.*** This concept is consistent with the fact that gases quickly and completely fill any container in which they are placed.
3. ***Except when gas molecules collide, forces of attraction and repulsion between them are negligible.*** This concept is consistent with the fact that all gases behave in the same way, regardless of the types of noncovalent interactions among their molecules.
4. ***When collisions between molecules occur, the collisions are elastic.*** The speeds of colliding molecules may change, but the total kinetic energy of two colliding molecules is the same after a collision as before the collision. That is, the collision is elastic. This concept is consistent with the fact that a gas sample at constant temperature never "runs down," with all molecules falling to the bottom of the container.
5. ***The average kinetic energy of gas molecules is proportional to the absolute temperature.*** Though not part of the kinetic-molecular theory, this useful concept is consistent with the fact that gas molecules escape through a tiny hole faster as the temperature increases, and with the fact that rates of chemical reactions are faster at higher temperatures.

Figure 10.5 Kinetic-molecular theory and pressure.

Like any moving object, a gas molecule has kinetic energy. An object's kinetic energy, E_k, depends on its mass, m, and its speed or velocity, v, according to the equation ***(⟸ p. 215)***

$$E_k = \frac{1}{2}(\text{mass})(\text{speed})^2 = \frac{1}{2}mv^2$$

CHEMISTRY IN THE NEWS

Nitrogen in Tires

Usually, we fill our automobile tires with compressed air because it is cheap. But race cars, jet aircraft, and some heavy trucks use nitrogen. For the ordinary motorist, many tire shops now offer to fill car's tires with nitrogen for about $5.00 each. Is it worth it? What advantages might nitrogen have over air?

Many bogus claims are being made about such fillings. For example, some claim that nitrogen will leak out of your tires more slowly than air because the molecules are bigger, which is false.

Some good reasons for using nitrogen also exist. For example, nitrogen is relatively inert and will not support combustion in case of a fire around the tires. Pure nitrogen contains no oxygen, whereas air does, so corrosion of rims and the insides of tires is said to be decreased. The generation units used to provide the nitrogen produce very dry nitrogen, whereas the air going through a typical gas station compressor contains substantial amounts of moisture, which could aid in corrosion.

Overall, it seems that most professionals recommend using compressed air to fill automobile tires except in specialized applications.

© Royalty-Free/Corbis

Landing gear on a Boeing 747. Jet aircraft use nitrogen in the tires.

SOURCE: *Chemical & Engineering News,* 10/25/04; p. 88.

All the molecules in a gas are moving, but they do not all move at the same speed, so they do not all have the same kinetic energy. At any given time a few molecules are moving very quickly, most are moving at close to the average speed, and a few may be in the process of colliding with a surface, in which case their speed is momentarily zero. The speed of any individual molecule changes as it collides with and exchanges energy with other molecules.

The relative number of molecules of a gas that have a given speed can be measured experimentally. Figure 10.6 is a graph of the number of molecules plotted versus their speed. The higher a point on the curve, the greater the number of molecules

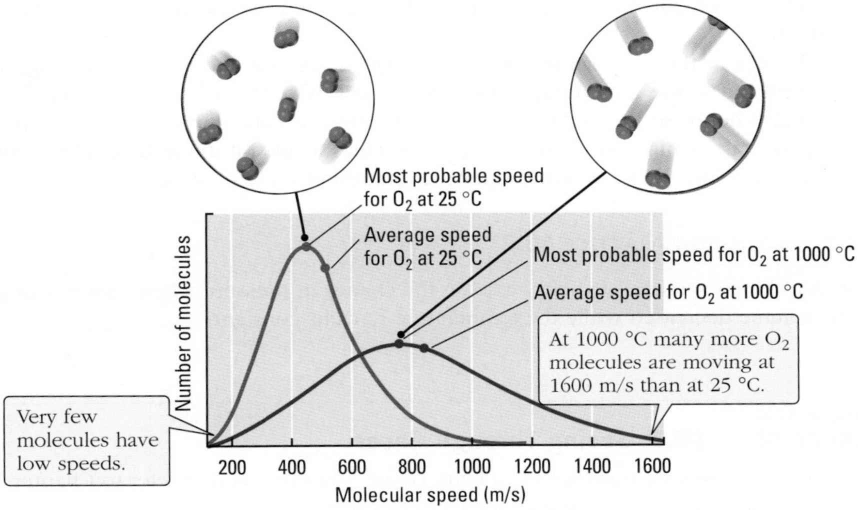

Active Figure 10.6 **Distribution of molecular speeds.** A plot of the relative number of oxygen molecules with a given speed versus that speed. **Go to the Active Figures menu at ThomsonNOW to test your understanding of the concepts in this figure.**

moving at that speed. Notice in the plot that some molecules are moving quickly (have high kinetic energy) and some are moving slowly (have low kinetic energy). The maximum in the distribution curve is the most probable speed. For oxygen gas at 25 °C, for example, the maximum in the curve occurs at a speed of about 400 m/s (1000 mph), and most of the molecules' speeds are in the range from 200 m/s to 700 m/s. Notice that the curves are not symmetric. A consequence of this asymmetry is that the average speed (shown in Figure 10.6 for O_2) is a little faster than the most probable speed. Molecules with speeds higher than the most probable speed outnumber those with speeds lower than the most probable speed, moving the average speed toward a somewhat higher value.

Graphs of molecular speeds (or energies) versus numbers of molecules are called Boltzmann distribution curves. They are named after Ludwig Boltzmann (1844–1906), an Austrian physicist who helped develop the kinetic-molecular theory of gases.

Also notice in Figure 10.6 that as temperature increases, the most probable speed increases, and the number of molecules moving very quickly increases. The areas under the two curves representing the two oxygen samples at different temperatures are the same because the total number of oxygen molecules is the same in both samples.

Since $E_k = \frac{1}{2}mv^2$ and the average kinetic energy of the molecules of any gas is the same at a given temperature, the larger m is, the smaller the average v must be. That is, heavier molecules have slower average speed than lighter ones. Figure 10.7 illustrates this relationship. The peaks in the curves for the heavier molecules, O_2 and N_2, occur at a much lower speed than that for the lightest molecule, He. You can also see from the graph that average speeds range from a few hundred to a few thousand meters per second.

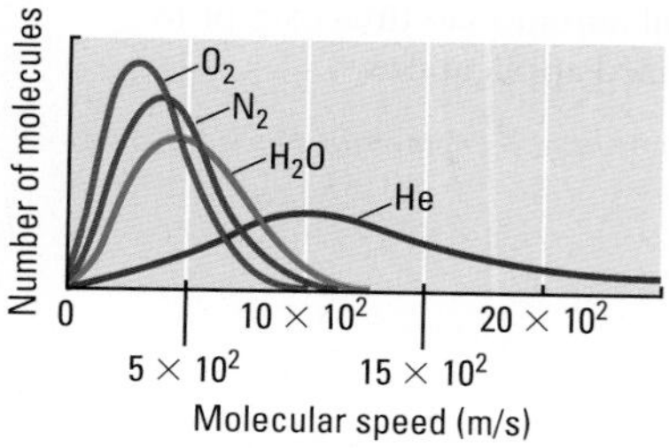

Figure 10.7 The effect of molar mass on the distribution of molecular speeds at a given temperature. On average, heavier molecules move slower than lighter ones.

PROBLEM-SOLVING EXAMPLE 10.2 Kinetic-Molecular Theory

Consider a sample of oxygen gas, $O_2(g)$, at 25 °C. Use the kinetic-molecular theory to answer these questions:

(a) How would the pressure of the gas change if the temperature were raised to 40 °C?

(b) If some of the O_2 molecules were removed from the sample (at constant T and P), how would the pressure change?

Answer (a) The pressure would increase. (b) The pressure would decrease.

Strategy and Explanation We use the fundamental concepts of kinetic-molecular theory to answer each question.

(a) Raising the temperature of the O_2 molecules causes them to move at higher average speed and higher average kinetic energy. At the higher temperature the molecules would hit the container walls harder and more often, which would yield a higher pressure.

(b) Molecules in the new sample of O_2, one with fewer gas molecules than originally present but at the same temperature, would still have the same average speed and average energy, so they would hit the walls with the same impact after the removal of part of the sample. However, the gas molecules would hit the walls less frequently, so the pressure would be lower after the removal of some of the gas.

PROBLEM-SOLVING PRACTICE 10.2

How does kinetic-molecular theory explain the change in pressure when a sample of gas has its volume decreased while the temperature remains constant?

CONCEPTUAL EXERCISE 10.2 Seeing Through Gases

Explain why gases are transparent to light. (*Hint:* You may need to refer to Chapter 7 in addition to using some of the concepts in this section.)

CONCEPTUAL EXERCISE 10.3 The Kinetic-Molecular Theory

Use the kinetic-molecular theory to explain why the pressure goes up when gas molecules are added to a sample of gas in a fixed-volume container at constant temperature.

EXERCISE 10.4 Molecular Kinetic Energies

Arrange these gaseous substances in order of increasing average kinetic energy of their molecules at 25 °C: Cl_2, H_2, NH_3, SF_6.

CONCEPTUAL EXERCISE 10.5 Molecular Kinetic Energies

Using Figure 10.7 as a source of information, first draw a plot of the number of molecules versus molecular speed for a sample of helium at 25 °C. Now assume that an equal number of molecules of argon, also at 25 °C, are added to the helium. What would the distribution curve for the mixture of gases look like (one distribution curve for all molecules in the mixture)?

CONCEPTUAL EXERCISE 10.6 Molecular Motion

Suppose you have two helium-filled balloons of about equal size, put one of them in the freezer compartment of your refrigerator, and leave the other one out in your room. After a few hours you take the balloon from the freezer and compare it to the one left out in the room. Based on the kinetic-molecular theory, what differences would you expect to see (a) immediately after taking the balloon from the freezer and (b) after the cold balloon warms to room temperature?

ThomsonNOW™

Go to the Coached Problems menu for guided simulations on:

- **kinetic-molecular theory**
- **Boltzmann distributions**
- **average molecular speed**
- **effusion**
- **diffusion**

The dependence of molecular speeds on molecular mass leads to some interesting phenomena. One is **effusion,** the escape of gas molecules from a container through a tiny hole into a vacuum. The rate of effusion of a gas is inversely proportional to the square root of its molar mass: rate $\propto 1/\sqrt{M}$. Therefore, He will effuse much faster than N_2, and a balloon filled with He will deflate faster than one filled with air. A related phenomenon is **diffusion,** the spread of gas molecules of one type through those of another type—for example, a pleasant odor spreading throughout a room. Diffusion is more complicated than effusion because the spreading gas molecules are colliding with the second type of gas molecules. Nevertheless, diffusion follows the same relationship between rate and molar mass. Diffusion was employed in the Manhattan project during World War II to purify uranium for the atomic bomb because the gaseous UF_6 molecules diffuse at slightly different rates due to the difference in masses of the two uranium isotopes, ^{235}U and ^{238}U.

© Thomson Learning/Charles D. Winters

He (red balloon), with its lower molar mass, effuses through tiny holes in a balloon surface faster than N_2 (blue balloon), with its higher molar mass. The lower frame shows the two balloons when first filled, and the upper frame shows the two balloons after several hours have passed.

10.4 The Behavior of Ideal Gases

The kinetic-molecular theory explains gas behavior on the nanoscale. On the macroscale, gases have been studied for hundreds of years, and the properties that all gases display have been summarized into *gas laws* that are named for their discoverers. Using the variables pressure, volume, temperature, and amount (number of moles), we can write equations that explain how gases behave. A gas that behaves exactly as described by these equations is called an **ideal gas.** At room temperature and atmospheric pressure, most gases behave nearly ideally. However, at pressures much higher than 1 atm or at temperatures just above the boiling point, gases deviate substantially from ideal behavior (Section 10.9). Each of the gas laws described in this section can be explained by the kinetic-molecular theory.

The Pressure-Volume Relationship: Boyle's Law

***Boyle's law** states that the volume (V) of an ideal gas varies inversely with the applied pressure (P) when temperature (T) and amount (n, moles) are constant.*

The symbol $\propto$ means "proportional to."

$$V \propto \frac{1}{P} \qquad \text{(unchanging } T \text{ and } n\text{)}$$

$$V = \text{constant} \times \frac{1}{P} \qquad PV = \text{constant}$$

Boyle's law explains how expanding and contracting your chest cavity (changing its volume) leads to inhalation and exhalation of air.

The value of the constant depends on the temperature and the amount of the gas. The inverse relationship between V and P is shown graphically in Figure 10.8a. Plotting V versus $1/P$ yields a linear relationship, as shown in Figure 10.8b. For a gas sample under two sets of pressure and volume conditions, Boyle's law can be written as $P_1V_1 = P_2V_2$.

In terms of the kinetic-molecular theory, a decrease in volume of a gas increases its pressure because there is less room for the gas molecules to move around before they collide with the walls of the container. Thus, there are more frequent collisions with the walls. These collisions produce pressure on the container walls, and more collisions mean a higher pressure. When you pump up a tire with a bicycle pump, the gas in the pump is squeezed into a smaller volume by application of pressure. This property is called *compressibility*. In contrast to gases, liquids and solids are only slightly compressible.

Robert Boyle studied the compressibility of gases in 1661 by pouring mercury into a J-shaped tube containing a sample of trapped gas. Each time he added more mercury, at constant temperature, the volume of the trapped gas decreased (Figure

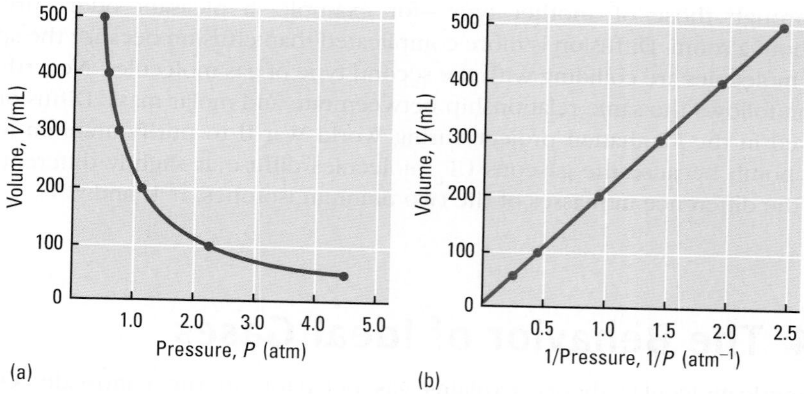

Figure 10.8 Graphical illustration of Boyle's law. (a) Volume (V) versus pressure (P). This curve shows the inverse proportionality between volume and pressure. As pressure increases, volume decreases. (b) V versus $1/P$. A linear plot results.

10.9). The mercury additions increased the pressure on the gas and changed the gas volume in a predictable fashion.

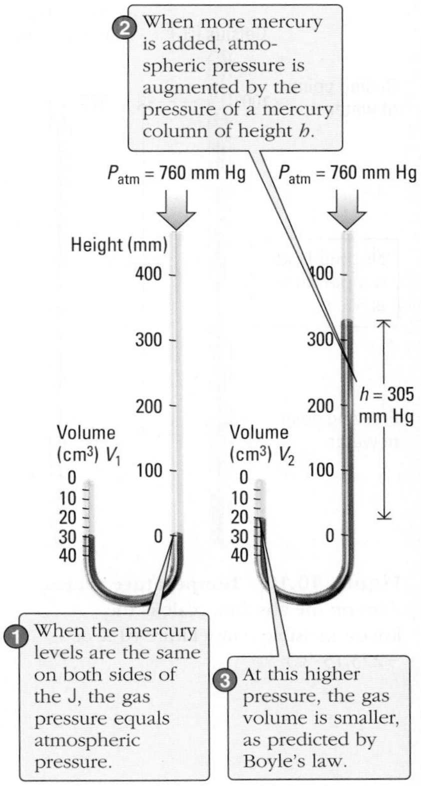

Figure 10.9 **Boyle's law.** Boyle's experiment showing the compressibility of gases.

CONCEPTUAL EXERCISE **10.7 Visualizing Boyle's Law**

Many cars have gas-filled shock absorbers to give the car and its occupants a smooth ride. If a four-passenger car is loaded with four NFL linemen, describe the gas inside the shock absorbers compared with that when the car has no passengers.

The Temperature-Volume Relationship: Charles's Law

***Charles's law** states that the volume (V) of an ideal gas varies directly with absolute temperature (T) when pressure (P) and amount (n, moles) are constant.*

$$V \propto T \qquad \text{(unchanging } P \text{ and } n)$$

$$V = \text{constant} \times T \qquad \frac{V}{T} = \text{constant}$$

The value of the constant depends on pressure and the amount of the gas. If the volume, V_1, and temperature, T_1, of a sample of gas are known, then the volume, V_2, at some other temperature, T_2, at the same pressure is given by

$$\frac{V_1}{T_1} = \frac{V_2}{T_2} \qquad (P \text{ and } n \text{ constant})$$

In terms of the kinetic-molecular theory, higher temperature means faster molecular motion and a higher average kinetic energy. The more rapidly moving molecules therefore strike the walls of a container more often, and each collision exerts greater force. For the pressure to remain constant, the volume of the container must expand.

When using the gas law relationships, temperature must be expressed in terms of the **absolute temperature scale.** The zero on this scale is the lowest possible temperature. The unit of the absolute temperature scale is the kelvin, symbol K (with no degree sign). The relationship between the absolute scale and the Celsius scale is shown in Figure 10.10. The kelvin is the same size as a degree Celsius. Thus, when ΔT is calculated by subtracting one temperature from another, the result is the same on both scales, even though the numbers involved are different. The lowest possible temperature, 0 K, known as **absolute zero,** is −273.15 °C. Temperature on the Celsius scale T(°C) and on the absolute scale T(K) are related as follows:

$$T(\text{K}) = T(°\text{C}) + 273.15$$

Thus, 25.00 °C (a typical room temperature) is the same as 298.15 K.

In 1787, Jacques Charles discovered that the volume of a fixed quantity of a gas at constant pressure increases with increasing temperature. Figure 10.11 shows how the volume of 1.0 mol H_2 and the volume of 0.55 mol O_2 change with the temperature (pressure remains constant at 1.0 atm). When the plots of volume versus temperature for different gases are extended toward lower temperatures, they all reach zero volume at the same temperature, −273.15 °C, which is 0 K.

Suppose you want to calculate the new volume when 450.0 mL of a gas is cooled from 60.0 °C to 20.0 °C, at constant pressure. First, convert the temperatures to kelvins by adding 273.15 to the Celsius values: 60.0 °C becomes 333.2 K

ThomsonNOW™

Go to the Chemistry Interactive menu to work modules on:

- **Boyle's law**
- **Charles's law**

The absolute temperature scale is also called the **Kelvin temperature scale.** The kelvin is the SI unit of temperature.

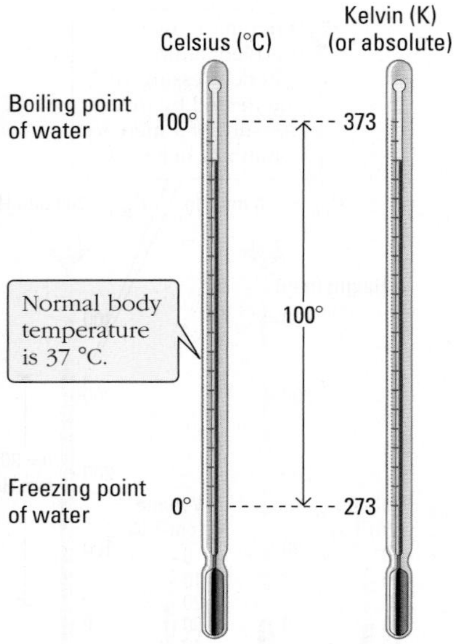

Figure 10.10 Temperature scales. Zero on the absolute scale is the lowest possible temperature (0 K or −273.15 °C).

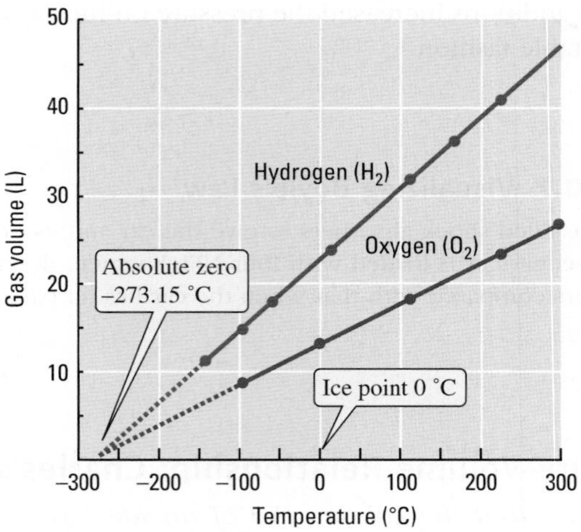

Figure 10.11 Charles's law. The volumes of two different samples of gases decrease with decreasing temperature (at constant pressure and constant molar amount). These graphs (as would those of all gases) intersect the temperature axis at about −273 °C.

and 20.0 °C becomes 293.2 K. Using Charles's law for the two sets of conditions at constant pressure gives

$$V_2 = \frac{V_1 T_2}{T_1} = \frac{450.0\ \text{mL} \times 293.2\ \text{K}}{333.2\ \text{K}} = 396.0\ \text{mL}$$

CONCEPTUAL EXERCISE 10.8 Visualizing Charles's Law

Consider a collection of gas molecules at temperature T_1. Now increase the temperature to T_2. Use the ideas of the kinetic-molecular theory and explain why the volume would have to be larger if the pressure remains constant. What would have to be done to maintain a constant volume if the temperature increased?

The Amount-Volume Relationship: Avogadro's Law

***Avogadro's law** states that the volume (V) of an ideal gas varies directly with amount (n) when temperature (T) and pressure (P) are constant.*

$$V \propto n \qquad \text{(unchanging } T \text{ and } P\text{)}$$

$$V = \text{constant} \times n \qquad \frac{V}{n} = \text{constant}$$

The value of the constant depends on the temperature and the pressure. Avogadro's law means, for example, that at constant temperature and pressure, if the number of moles of gas doubles, the volume doubles. It also means that at the same temperature and pressure, the volumes of two different amounts of gases are related as follows:

$$\frac{V_1}{n_1} = \frac{V_2}{n_2} \qquad (T \text{ and } P \text{ constant})$$

The volume of any gas would appear to be zero at −273.15 °C. However, at sufficiently high pressure, all gases liquefy before reaching this temperature.

ThomsonNOW™
Go to the Chemistry Interactive menu to work a module on **Avogadro's law.**

In terms of the kinetic-molecular theory, increasing the number of gas molecules at a constant temperature means that the added molecules have the same average molecular kinetic energy as the molecules to which they were added. As a result, the number of collisions with the container walls increases in proportion to the number of molecules. This would increase the pressure if the volume were held constant. To maintain constant pressure, the volume must increase.

Another way to state the relationship between the amount of gas and its volume is *Avogadro's hypothesis: Equal volumes of gases contain equal numbers of molecules at the same temperature and pressure.* Experiments show that at 0 °C and 1 atm pressure, 22.4 L of any gas will contain 1 mol of the gas (6.02×10^{23} gas molecules). This is illustrated in Figure 10.12.

The Law of Combining Volumes

In 1809 the French scientist Joseph Gay-Lussac (1778–1850) conducted experiments in which he measured the volumes of gases reacting with one another to form gaseous products. He found that, at constant temperature and pressure, the volumes of reacting gases were always in the *ratios of small whole numbers.* This is known as the **law of combining volumes.** For example, the reaction of 2 L H_2 with 1 L O_2 produces 2 L water vapor. Similarly, the reaction of 4 L H_2 with 2 L O_2 produces 4 L water vapor.

	$2\ H_2(g)$	+	$O_2(g)$	→	$2\ H_2O(g)$
Experiment 1	2 L		1 L		2 L
Experiment 2	4 L		2 L		4 L

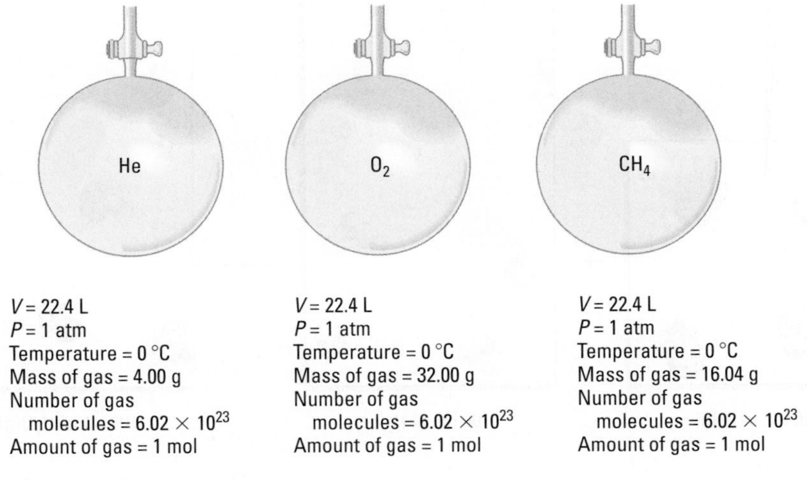

Figure 10.12 Comparison of volumes and amounts of gases illustrating Avogadro's hypothesis. Each gas has the same volume, temperature, and pressure, so each container holds the same number of molecules. Because the molar masses of the three gases are different, the masses of gas in each container are different.

Jacques Alexandre Cesar Charles

1746–1823

The French scientist Jacques Charles was most famous in his lifetime for his experiments in ballooning. The first such flights were made by the Montgolfier brothers in June 1783 using a balloon made of linen and paper and filled with hot air. In August 1783, Charles filled a silk balloon with hydrogen. Inflating the bag to its final diameter took several days and required nearly 500 lb acid and 1000 lb iron to generate the required volume of hydrogen gas. A huge crowd watched the ascent on August 27, 1783. The balloon stayed aloft for almost 45 min and traveled about 15 miles. When it landed in a village, the people there were so terrified that they tore the balloon to shreds.

John Dalton (who devised the atomic theory) strongly opposed Avogadro's ideas and never accepted them. It took about 50 years—long after Avogadro and Dalton had died—for Avogadro's explanation of Gay-Lussac's experiments to be generally accepted.

In 1811 Amadeo Avogadro suggested that Gay-Lussac's observations actually showed that equal volumes of all gases under the same temperature and pressure conditions contain the same number of molecules. Viewed on a molecular scale, if a tiny volume contained only one molecule of a gas, then twice that volume would contain two molecules, and so on (Figure 10.13).

PROBLEM-SOLVING EXAMPLE 10.3 Using Avogadro's Law and the Law of Combining Volumes

Nitrogen and oxygen gases react to form ammonia gas in the reaction

$$N_2(g) + 3\,H_2(g) \longrightarrow 2\,NH_3(g)$$

If 500. mL N_2 at 1 atm and 25 °C were available for reaction, what volume of H_2, at the same temperature and pressure, would be required in the reaction?

Answer 1.50 L H_2

Strategy and Explanation We want to find the volume of H_2, and the information given is the volume of the N_2 at the same temperature and pressure. Therefore, we can solve the problem using the law of combining volumes and the reaction coefficients of 3 for H_2 and 1 for N_2 as the volume ratio.

$$\text{Volume of } H_2 = 500.\text{ mL } N_2 \times \frac{3\text{ mL } H_2}{1\text{ mL } N_2} = 1.50\text{ L } H_2$$

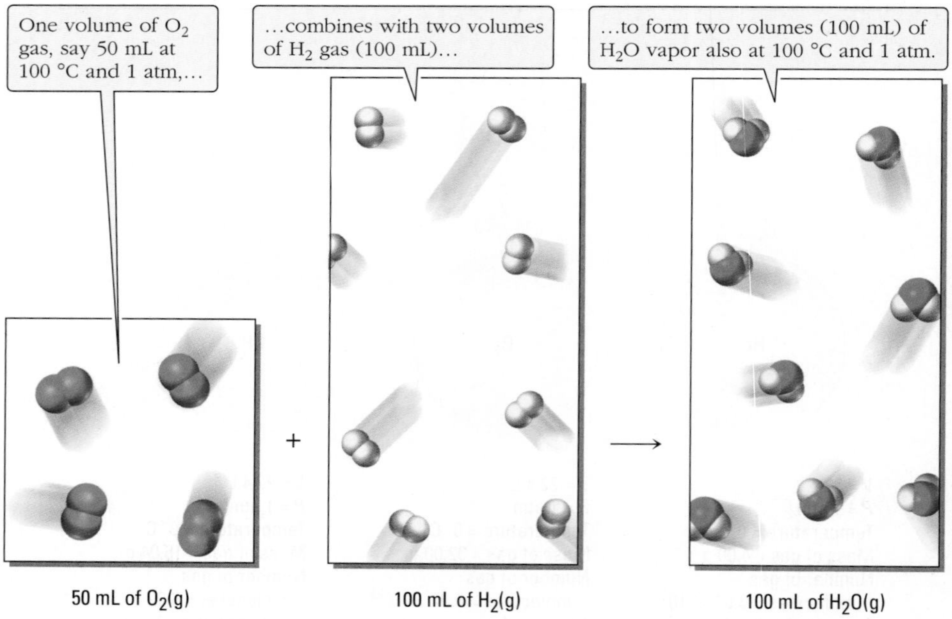

$$O_2(g) \quad + \quad 2\,H_2(g) \quad \longrightarrow \quad 2\,H_2O(g)$$

$$1\text{ vol} \quad + \quad 2\text{ vol} \quad \longrightarrow \quad 2\text{ vol}$$

Figure 10.13 Law of combining volumes. When gases at the same temperature and pressure combine with one another, their volumes are in the ratio of small whole numbers.

PROBLEM-SOLVING PRACTICE 10.3

Nitrogen monoxide (NO) combines with oxygen to form nitrogen dioxide.

$$2\,NO(g) + O_2(g) \longrightarrow 2\,NO_2(g)$$

If 1.0 L oxygen gas at 30.25 °C and 0.975 atm is used and there is an excess of NO, what volume of NO gas at the same temperature and pressure will be converted to NO_2?

CONCEPTUAL EXERCISE 10.9 Gas Burner Design

The gas burner in a stove or furnace admits enough air so that methane gas can react completely with oxygen in the air according to the equation

$$CH_4(g) + 2\,O_2(g) \longrightarrow CO_2(g) + 2\,H_2O(g)$$

Air is one-fifth oxygen by volume. Both air and methane gas are supplied to the flame by passing them through separate small tubes. Compared with the tube for the methane gas, how much bigger does the cross section of the tube for the air need to be? Assume that both gases are at the same T and P.

EXERCISE 10.10 Filling Balloons

One hundred balloons of equal volume are filled with a total of 26.8 g helium at 23 °C and 748 mm Hg. The total volume of these balloons is 168 L. Next, you are given 150 more balloons of the same size and 41.8 g He gas. The temperature and pressure remain the same. Determine by calculation whether you will be able to fill all the balloons with the He you have available.

10.5 The Ideal Gas Law

ThomsonNOW™
Go to the Coached Problems menu for a guided simulation and a tutorial on the **ideal gas law.**

Three gas laws focus on the effects of changes in P, T, or n on gas volume:

- ***Boyle's law and pressure*** $(V \propto 1/P)$; $V_1P_1 = V_2P_2$
- ***Charles's law and temperature*** $(V \propto T)$; $\dfrac{V_1}{T_1} = \dfrac{V_2}{T_2}$
- ***Avogadro's law and amount (mol)*** $(V \propto n)$; $\dfrac{V_1}{n_1} = \dfrac{V_2}{n_2}$

The three gas laws can be combined to give the ideal gas law, which summarizes the relationships among volume, temperature, pressure, and amount.

$$V \propto \frac{nT}{P} \qquad \text{or} \qquad PV \propto nT$$

To make this proportionality into an equation, a proportionality constant, R, named the **ideal gas constant,** is used. The equation becomes

$$V = R\frac{nT}{P}$$

and, on rearranging, gives the equation called the **ideal gas law.**

$$PV = nRT$$

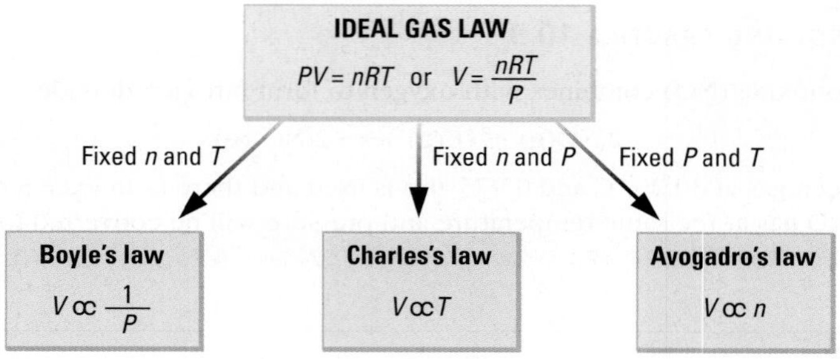

The ideal gas law correctly predicts the amount, pressure, volume, and temperature for samples of most gases at pressures of a few atmospheres or less and at temperatures well above their boiling points. The constant R can be calculated from the experimental fact that at 0 °C and 1 atm the volume of 1 mol gas is 22.414 L. This temperature and pressure are called **standard temperature and pressure (STP),** and the volume is called the **standard molar volume.** Solving the ideal gas law for R, and substituting, gives

$$R = \frac{PV}{nT} = \frac{(22.414\ \text{L})(1\ \text{atm})}{(1\ \text{mol})(273.15\ \text{K})} = 0.082057\ \text{L atm mol}^{-1}\ \text{K}^{-1}$$

which is usually rounded to 0.0821 L atm mol^{-1} K^{-1}. The ideal gas constant has different numerical values in different units, as shown in Table 10.4.

The ideal gas law can be used to calculate P, V, n, or T whenever three of the four variables are known, provided that the conditions of temperature and pressure are not extreme.

Table 10.4 Values of R, in Different Units

$$R = 0.08206\ \frac{\text{L atm}}{\text{mol K}}$$

$$R = 62.36\ \frac{\text{mm Hg L}}{\text{mol K}}$$

$$R = 8.314\ \frac{\text{kPa dm}^3}{\text{mol K}}$$

$$R = 8.314\ \frac{\text{J}}{\text{mol K}}$$

PROBLEM-SOLVING EXAMPLE 10.4 Using the Ideal Gas Law

Calculate the volume that 0.40 g methane, CH_4, occupies at 25 °C and 1.0 atm.

Answer 0.61 L or 6.1 × 10^2 mL CH_4

Strategy and Explanation The given information is the mass of methane and its temperature (T) and pressure (P). We can convert the mass of methane to the number of moles (n) and then use the ideal gas equation to find the volume (V). When we use $PV = nRT$, we must have all the variables in the same units as the gas constant, R = 0.0821 L atm mol^{-1} K^{-1}. That is, temperature must be in kelvins, pressure in atmospheres, volume in liters, and the amount of gas in moles.

We begin by converting the mass of methane to moles.

$$(0.40\ \text{g CH}_4) \times \frac{1\ \text{mol CH}_4}{16.04\ \text{g CH}_4} = 0.0249\ \text{mol CH}_4$$

Next, we convert the temperature to kelvins.

$$(25 + 273.15)\ \text{K} = 298\ \text{K}$$

Now we can solve for V in the ideal gas equation. The result will be in liters.

$$V = \frac{nRT}{P} = \frac{(0.0249\ \text{mol})(0.0821\ \text{L atm mol}^{-1}\ \text{K}^{-1})(298\ \text{K})}{1.0\ \text{atm}}$$
$$= 0.61\ \text{L or } 6.1 \times 10^2\ \text{mL CH}_4$$

Notice how the units cancel. Also, notice that the answer is given with two significant digits because the mass of methane and the pressure had only two significant digits.

✓ **Reasonable Answer Check** The temperature and pressure are close to STP. The mass of methane is about 2.5% of a mole, so the volume should also be about 2.5% of the volume of a mole of gas (22.4 L × 0.025 = 0.56 L). This approximate result is close to our more exact calculation.

PROBLEM-SOLVING PRACTICE 10.4

What volume will 2.64 mol N_2 occupy at 0.640 atm and 31 °C?

For many calculations involving a gas sample under two sets of conditions, it is convenient to use the ideal gas law in the following manner. For two sets of conditions (n_1, P_1, V_1, and T_1; n_2, P_2, V_2, and T_2), the ideal gas law can be written as

$$R = \frac{P_1V_1}{n_1T_1} \quad \text{and} \quad R = \frac{P_2V_2}{n_2T_2}$$

Since in both sets of conditions the quotient is equal to R, we can set the two quotients equal to each other.

$$\frac{P_1V_1}{n_1T_1} = \frac{P_2V_2}{n_2T_2}$$

When the amount of gas, n, is constant, so that $n_1 = n_2$, this equation simplifies to what is known as the **combined gas law:**

$$\frac{P_1V_1}{T_1} = \frac{P_2V_2}{T_2}$$

PROBLEM-SOLVING EXAMPLE 10.5 Pressure and Volume

Consider a gas sample with a volume of 1.00 L at a pressure of 0.500 atm. What volume will this gas sample occupy if the pressure is increased to 2.00 atm? Assume that the temperature remains constant and the gas sample obeys the ideal gas law.

Answer 0.250 L or 250. mL

Strategy and Explanation The temperature (T) and the amount of gas (n) are constant. The given conditions are $P_1 = 0.500$ atm, $P_2 = 2.00$ atm, and $V_1 = 1.00$ L. We must find V_2, which can be calculated by canceling T in the combined gas law and rearranging to solve for V_2.

$$\frac{P_1V_1}{\cancel{T_1}} = \frac{P_2V_2}{\cancel{T_2}}$$

$$V_2 = \frac{P_1V_1}{P_2} = \frac{(0.500 \text{ atm})(1.00 \text{ L})}{2.00 \text{ atm}} = 0.250 \text{ L} = 250. \text{ mL}$$

✓ **Reasonable Answer Check** The inverse relationship between P and V tells us that V_2 will be smaller than V_1 because P_2 is larger than P_1. The answer is reasonable.

PROBLEM-SOLVING PRACTICE 10.5

At a pressure of exactly 1 atm and some temperature, a gas sample occupies 400. mL. What will be the volume of the gas at the same temperature if the pressure is decreased to 0.750 atm?

PROBLEM-SOLVING EXAMPLE 10.6 The Combined Gas Law

Helium-filled balloons are used to carry scientific instruments high into the atmosphere. Suppose that such a balloon is launched on a summer day when the temperature at ground level is 22.5 °C and the barometer reading is 754 mm Hg. If the balloon's volume is 1.00×10^6 L at launch, what will its volume be at a height of 37 km, where the pressure is 76.0 mm Hg and the temperature is 240. K?

Answer 8.05×10^6 L

Strategy and Explanation Assume that no gas escapes from the balloon. Then only T, P, and V change. Using subscript 1 to indicate initial conditions (at launch) and subscript 2 to indicate final conditions (high in the atmosphere) gives

Initial: $P_1 = 754$ mm Hg $T_1 = (22.5 + 273.15)$ K $= 295.6$ K $V_1 = 1.00 \times 10^6$ L
Final: $P_2 = 76.0$ mm Hg $T_2 = 240.$ K

Solving the combined gas law for V_2 gives

$$V_2 = \frac{P_1V_1T_2}{P_2T_1} = \frac{(754 \text{ mm Hg})(1.00 \times 10^6 \text{ L})(240. \text{ K})}{(76.0 \text{ mm Hg})(295.6 \text{ K})} = 8.05 \times 10^6 \text{ L}$$

Thus, the final volume is about eight times larger. The volume has increased because the pressure has dropped. For this reason, weather balloons are never fully inflated at launch. A great deal of room has to be left so that the helium can expand at high altitudes.

✓ **Reasonable Answer Check** The pressure is dropping by a factor of about 10, and T is changing only 20%, so the volume should increase by a factor of about 20% less than 10, that is, 8, and it does.

PROBLEM-SOLVING PRACTICE 10.6

A small sample of a gas is prepared in the laboratory and found to occupy 21 mL at a pressure of 710. mm Hg and a temperature of 22.3 °C. The next morning the temperature has changed to 26.5 °C, and the pressure is found to be 740. mm Hg. No gas has escaped from the container.

(a) What volume does the sample of gas now occupy?
(b) Assume that the pressure does not change. What volume would the gas occupy at the new temperature?

It is important to remember that Boyle's, Charles's, and Avogadro's laws do not depend on the identity of the gas being studied. These laws reflect properties of all gases and therefore depend on the behavior of any gaseous substances, regardless of their identities.

In summary, for problems involving gases, you have your choice of two useful equations:

- ***When three of the variables P, V, n, and T are given, and the value of the fourth variable is needed, use the ideal gas law.***

$$PV = nRT$$

- ***When one set of conditions is given for a single gas sample and one of the variables under a new set of conditions is needed, then use the combined gas law and cancel any of the three variables that do not change.***

$$\frac{P_1V_1}{T_1} = \frac{P_2V_2}{T_2} \qquad (n \text{ constant})$$

CONCEPTUAL EXERCISE **10.11 Predicting Gas Behavior**

Name three ways the volume occupied by a sample of gas can be decreased.

10.6 Quantities of Gases in Chemical Reactions

The law of combining volumes and the ideal gas law make it possible to use volumes as well as masses or molar amounts in calculations based on reaction stoichiometry (⇐ *p. 131*). Consider this balanced equation for the combination reaction of solid carbon and gaseous oxygen to give gaseous carbon dioxide.

$$C(s) + O_2(g) \longrightarrow CO_2(g)$$

Let's look at some of the questions that might be asked about this reaction, which involves one gaseous reactant and one gaseous product. As with any problem to be solved, you have to recognize what information is known and what is needed. Then you can decide which relationship provides the connection between the two.

1. *How many liters of CO_2 are produced from 0.5 L O_2 and excess carbon?* The known and needed information here are both volumes of gases, and the coefficients of the balanced chemical equation represent volumes of gases, so the law of combining volumes leads to the answer.
   Answer: 0.5 L CO_2, because the reaction shows 1 mol CO_2 formed for every mole of O_2 that reacts—a 1:1 ratio.

$$0.5 \text{ L } O_2 \times \frac{1 \text{ vol } CO_2}{1 \text{ vol } O_2} = 0.5 \text{ L } CO_2$$

2. *How many moles of O_2 are required to completely react with 4.00 g C?* Here the known information is the mass of the solid reactant and the needed information is the moles of gaseous product. The answer is provided from the stoichiometric relationships between reactants and products from the balanced reaction, without using any of the gas laws.
   Answer: 0.333 mol O_2, because 4.00 g C is 0.333 mol C, and 1 mol O_2 is required for every 1 mol C.

$$4.00 \text{ g C} \times \frac{1 \text{ mol C}}{12.011 \text{ g C}} \times \frac{1 \text{ mol } O_2}{1 \text{ mol C}} = 0.333 \text{ mol } O_2$$

3. *What volume (in liters) of O_2 at STP is required to react with 12.011 g C?* Because the needed information is the volume of a gaseous reactant, the law of combining volumes can lead to the answer, but first the number of moles of carbon must be found.
   Answer: 22.4 L O_2, because 12.011 g C is 1 mol C, which requires 1 mol O_2, and the standard molar volume of any gas at STP is 22.4 L.

$$12.011 \text{ g C} \times \frac{1 \text{ mol C}}{12.011 \text{ g C}} \times \frac{1 \text{ mol } O_2}{1 \text{ mol C}} \times \frac{22.4 \text{ L } O_2}{1 \text{ mol } O_2} = 22.4 \text{ L } O_2$$

4. *What volume (in liters) of O_2 at 747 mm Hg and 21 °C is required to react with 12.011 g C?* Realizing that 12.011 g C is 1 mol C and that 1 mol O_2 will be required, you then use the ideal gas law to calculate the volume occupied by 1 mol O_2 at the temperature and pressure given.
   Answer: The units must be consistent with those of R. Convert the temperature to kelvins to get 294 K, and convert the given pressure to atmospheres to get 0.983 atm. Finally, use the ideal gas law to calculate the volume of oxygen required.

$$V_{O_2} = \frac{nRT}{P} = \frac{(1 \text{ mol})(0.0821 \text{ L atm mol}^{-1} \text{ K}^{-1})(294 \text{ K})}{0.983 \text{ atm}} = 24.5 \text{ L}$$

© Thomson Learning/Charles D. Winters

Magnesium reacting with hydrochloric acid.

PROBLEM-SOLVING EXAMPLE 10.7 Gases and Stoichiometry

If 13.8 g Mg is reacted with excess HCl, how many liters of H_2 gas are produced at 28.0 °C and 675 torr?

$$Mg(s) + 2\,HCl(aq) \longrightarrow MgCl_2(aq) + H_2(g)$$

Answer 15.8 L H_2

Strategy and Explanation We start to solve this problem by finding the number of moles of H_2 generated, using the coefficients from the balanced equation

$$13.8 \text{ g Mg} \times \frac{1 \text{ mol Mg}}{24.305 \text{ g Mg}} \times \frac{1 \text{ mol } H_2}{1 \text{ mol Mg}} = 0.568 \text{ mol } H_2$$

Once we know the number of moles of H_2 produced, we can find the volume of H_2 from the ideal gas law, $PV = nRT$. We solve the ideal gas law for V and substitute the values for P, T, and n. When we substitute into the rearranged ideal gas equation, the units of V, P, and T must be compatible with the units of R. This means that we must express the pressure in atmospheres and the temperature in kelvins.

$$P = (675 \text{ mm Hg}) \times \frac{1 \text{ atm}}{760 \text{ mm Hg}} = 0.888 \text{ atm}$$

$$V = \frac{nRT}{P} = \frac{(0.568 \text{ mol } H_2)(0.0821 \text{ L atm mol}^{-1} \text{ K}^{-1})(301.2 \text{ K})}{0.888 \text{ atm}} = 15.8 \text{ L } H_2$$

✓ **Reasonable Answer Check** We start with 13.8/24.3 or about 0.6 mol Mg, so about the same amount of H_2 should be produced. Six-tenths of 22.4 L (the volume of one mole of gas at STP) is about 13.4 L, which is comparable to our more exact answer.

PROBLEM-SOLVING PRACTICE 10.7

Ammonium nitrate, NH_4NO_3, is an explosive that undergoes this decomposition.

$$2\,NH_4NO_3(s) \longrightarrow 4\,H_2O(g) + O_2(g) + 2\,N_2(g)$$

If 10.0 g NH_4NO_3 explodes, how many liters of gas are generated at 25 °C and 1 atm?

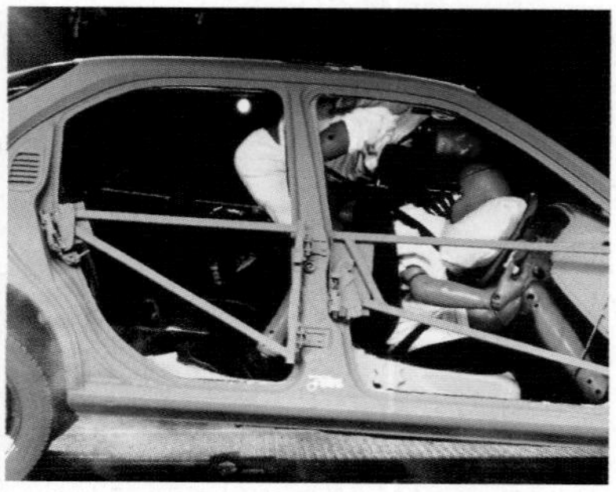

© TRL Ltd./Photo Researchers, Inc.

Air bags deploying on crash test dummies. Air bags have saved numerous lives in automobile collisions.

PROBLEM-SOLVING EXAMPLE 10.8 Stoichiometry with Gases—Air Bags

Automobile air bags are filled with N_2 from the decomposition of sodium azide.

$$2\,NaN_3(s) \longrightarrow 2\,Na(s) + 3\,N_2(g)$$

How many grams of sodium azide are needed to generate 60.0 L N_2 at 1 atm and 26 °C?

Answer 106 g NaN_3

Strategy and Explanation First, we need to calculate the number of moles of N_2 in 60.0 L.

$$n = \frac{PV}{RT} = \frac{(1 \text{ atm})(60.0 \text{ L})}{(0.0821 \text{ L atm mol}^{-1} \text{ K}^{-1})(299.15 \text{ K})} = 2.44 \text{ mol } N_2$$

Now we use the balanced equation to calculate the moles of sodium azide.

$$2.44 \text{ mol } N_2 \times \frac{2 \text{ mol } NaN_3}{3 \text{ mol } N_2} = 1.63 \text{ mol } NaN_3$$

We were asked for the mass of sodium azide, so we convert moles to grams.

$$1.63 \text{ mol } NaN_3 \times \frac{65.01 \text{ g } NaN_3}{1 \text{ mol } NaN_3} = 106 \text{ g } NaN_3$$

Actual air bags use additional reactants because the reaction just described would produce elemental sodium, which is much too hazardous to remain in a consumer product. However, the actual reactions have nearly the same stoichiometric ratio of NaN_3 to N_2 as the simpler reaction used in this example.

✓ **Reasonable Answer Check** Dividing the 106 g NaN_3 by its molar mass of 65 g/mol gives an answer of about 1.6 mol NaN_3. We get $\frac{3}{2}$ as many moles of N_2, or about 2.4 mol N_2, which is about 54 L N_2. This is close to the required volume of N_2.

PROBLEM-SOLVING PRACTICE 10.8

Lithium hydroxide is used in spacecraft to absorb the CO_2 exhaled by astronauts.

$$2\ LiOH(s) + CO_2(g) \longrightarrow Li_2CO_3(s) + H_2O(\ell)$$

What volume of CO_2 at 22 °C and 1 atm is absorbed per gram of LiOH?

ThomsonNOW™
Go to the Coached Problems menu for a tutorial on **stoichiometry of reactions involving gases.**

PROBLEM-SOLVING EXAMPLE 10.9 Gas Law Stoichiometry and Temperature

Benzene, C_6H_6, is one of the hydrocarbons in gasoline that increases its octane rating. In an automobile engine, benzene burns to produce CO_2 and H_2O.

(a) What volume of oxygen, entering the engine at 0.950 atm and 20. °C, is required to burn 1.00 g benzene?

(b) Assuming the pressure remains 0.950 atm, what volume of oxygen would be required on a cold winter day, when the temperature is −20. °C?

Answer (a) 2.43 L O_2 (b) 2.10 L O_2

Strategy and Explanation

(a) First, write the balanced equation for the combustion reaction.

$$2\ C_6H_6(\ell) + 15\ O_2(g) \longrightarrow 12\ CO_2(g) + 6\ H_2O(g)$$

Next, calculate the molar mass of benzene: (6 × 12.011) + (6 × 1.008) = 78.11 g/mol. Then calculate the moles of O_2 required.

$$1.00\text{ g benzene} \times \frac{1\text{ mol benzene}}{78.11\text{ g benzene}} \times \frac{15\text{ mol }O_2}{2\text{ mol benzene}} = 0.0960\text{ mol }O_2$$

Then use the ideal gas law to calculate the volume of O_2.

$$V_{O_2} = \frac{nRT}{P} = \frac{(0.0960\text{ mol }O_2)(0.0821\text{ L atm mol}^{-1}\text{ K}^{-1})(293\text{ K})}{0.950\text{ atm}} = 2.43\text{ L }O_2$$

(b) At −20 °C (253 K), the same type of calculation gives

$$V_{O_2} = 2.10\text{ L }O_2$$

At this colder temperature, less oxygen (and hence less air) is needed by the engine. Modern engines have electronic devices that regulate the volume of fuel injected into the cylinders to maintain the proper ratio of fuel to air whatever the outside air temperature.

✓ **Reasonable Answer Check** We have 1.00 g benzene, which is about 0.0125 mol benzene [1.00 g/(80 g/mol) = 0.0125 mol]. The reaction requires 12/2 = 6 times as much O_2 as benzene, which is about 0.075 mol O_2 or about 1.68 L O_2 at STP. This is close to our more accurate answer.

PROBLEM-SOLVING PRACTICE 10.9

If you carried out the *Chemistry You Can Do* stoichiometry experiment in Chapter 4 (⇐ p. 146), you observed the reaction of vinegar (acetic acid solution) with baking soda (sodium hydrogen carbonate) as it generated carbon dioxide gas which inflated a balloon. The net ionic equation for an acid (p. 168) reacting with hydrogen carbonate ion is

$$H^+(aq) + HCO_3^-(aq) \longrightarrow CO_2(g) + H_2O(\ell)$$

If there is plenty of vinegar, what mass of $NaHCO_3$ is required to inflate a balloon to a diameter of 20. cm at room temperature, 20.°C? Assume that the balloon is a sphere. (The formula for the volume of a sphere is $V = \frac{4}{3}\pi r^3$.) Assume that because the rubber is stretched, the pressure inside the balloon is twice the normal atmospheric pressure.

10.7 Gas Density and Molar Masses

ThomsonNOW

Go to the Coached Problems menu for tutorials and guided simulations on:

- **determining gas density**
- **finding the molecular mass of a gas**

The ideal gas law can be used to relate gas density to molar mass. The definition of density is mass per unit volume (p. 9). The densities of gases are extremely variable because the volume of a gas sample (but not its mass) varies with temperature and pressure. However, once T and P are specified, the density of a gas can be calculated from the ideal gas law. Additionally, because equal volumes of gas at the same T and P contain equal numbers of molecules, the densities of different gases are directly proportional to their molar masses. As a result, experimental gas densities can be used to determine molar masses.

To derive the relationship between gas density and molar mass, start with the ideal gas law, $PV = nRT$. For any substance, the number of moles (n) equals its mass (m) divided by its molar mass (M), so we will substitute m/M for n in the ideal gas equation:

$$PV = \frac{m}{M}RT$$

Density (d) is mass divided by volume (m/V), and we can rearrange the equation so that m/V is on one side:

$$d = \frac{m}{V} = \frac{PM}{RT}$$

Thus, the density of a gas is directly proportional to its molar mass, M.

Consider the densities of the three pure gases He, O_2, and SF_6. If we take 1 mol of each of these gases at 25 °C and 0.750 atm, we can see from the table below that density (at the same conditions) increases with molar mass.

Gas	Molar Mass (g/mol)	Density (25 °C)
He	4.003	0.123 g/L
O_2	31.999	0.981 g/L
SF_6	146.06	4.48 g/L

Let's use the density equation to compute the approximate density of air at STP. The molar mass of air is estimated by the approximate weighted average of the molar masses of N_2 and O_2.

$$\text{Molar mass of air} = (0.80)(\text{molar mass of } N_2) + (0.20)(\text{molar mass of } O_2)$$
$$= (0.80)(28.01) + (0.20)(31.999) = 28.8 \text{ g/mol}$$

$$d = \frac{PM}{RT} = \frac{(1 \text{ atm})(28.8 \text{ g/mol})}{(0.0821 \text{ L atm mol}^{-1}\text{ K}^{-1})(273.15 \text{ K})} = 1.28 \text{ g/L}$$

Air has a density of approximately 1.28 g/L at STP.

ESTIMATION

Helium Balloon Buoyancy

How large a helium balloon is needed to lift a weather-instruments package weighing 500 lb? The buoyancy of He is the difference in density between air and He at the given temperature and pressure.

First, we must estimate the density of helium. Let's assume a temperature of 21 °C and a pressure of 1 atm. Then 1 L He contains

$$n = \frac{(1\text{ atm})(1\text{ L})}{(0.0821\text{ L atm mol}^{-1}\text{ K}^{-1})[(273 + 21)\text{ K}]}$$
$$= 0.0414\text{ mol He}$$

To get helium's density, we need to know the mass of He in 1 L, so

$$0.0414\text{ mol He} \times 4.00\text{ g/mol} = 0.166\text{ g He}$$

The density of He at 21 °C and 1 atm is 0.166 g/L. At these same conditions of temperature and pressure, the density of air (which we computed on p. 452) is approximately 1.20 g/L. The mass difference between 1 L He and 1 L air is 1.20 g/L − 0.166 g/L = 1.03 g/L. This is the buoyant (lifting) force of He per liter.

Now we can tackle the second part of the problem.

$$500\text{ lb} \times 454\text{ g/lb} = 2.27 \times 10^5\text{ g}$$

Since He can lift 1.03 g/L, the total weight can be lifted by

$$2.27 \times 10^5\text{ g} \times \frac{1\text{ L}}{1.03\text{ g}} = 2.20 \times 10^5\text{ L He}$$

Let's change this to cubic meters.

$$2.20 \times 10^5\text{ L He} \times 10^{-3}\text{ m}^3\text{/L} = 220\text{ m}^3\text{ He}$$

The volume and diameter of a spherical balloon are related by

$$V = \tfrac{4}{3}\pi r^3 = \tfrac{1}{6}\pi d^3$$

Rearranging this equation allows us to calculate the diameter of the balloon.

$$d = \left(\frac{6V}{\pi}\right)^{1/3} = \left(\frac{6 \times 220\text{ m}^3}{3.14}\right)^{1/3} = 420^{1/3}\text{ m} = 7.49\text{ m}$$

The diameter of a spherical He balloon that can lift 500 lb is approximately 7.5 m (approximately 25 ft).

ThomsonNOW
Sign in to ThomsonNOW at **www.thomsonedu.com** to work an interactive module based on this material.

EXERCISE 10.12 Calculating Gas Densities

Calculate the densities of Cl_2 and of SO_2 at 25 °C and 0.750 atm. Then calculate the density of Cl_2 at 35 °C and 0.750 atm and the density of SO_2 at 25 °C and 2.60 atm.

CONCEPTUAL EXERCISE 10.13 Comparing Densities

Express the gas density of He (0.123 g/L) in grams per milliliter (g/mL) and compare that value with the density of metallic lithium (0.53 g/mL). The mass of a Li atom (7 amu) is less than twice that of a He atom (4 amu). What do these densities tell you about how closely Li atoms are packed compared with He atoms when each element is in its standard state? To which of the concepts of the kinetic-molecular theory does this comparison apply?

CONCEPTUAL EXERCISE 10.14 Densities of Gas Mixtures

Assume a mixture of equal volumes of the two gases nitrogen and oxygen. Would the density of this gas mixture be higher, lower, or the same as the density of air at the same temperature and pressure? Explain your answer.

PROBLEM-SOLVING EXAMPLE 10.10 Using the Ideal Gas Law to Calculate Molar Mass

Suppose you have a 1.02-g sample of a gas containing C, H, and F atoms, and you suspect that it is $C_2H_2F_4$. The gas sample has a pressure of 750. mm Hg in a 250.-mL vessel at 25.0 °C. From this information, calculate the molar mass of the compound to determine whether your molecular formula is correct.

NASA

A weather balloon filled with helium. As it ascends into the troposphere, does the volume increase or decrease?

Answer 101 g/mol. The molecular formula is correct.

Strategy and Explanation Begin by organizing the data and changing units where necessary.

$$V = 0.250\ \text{L} \quad P = 750.\ \text{mm Hg} \times \frac{1\ \text{atm}}{760\ \text{mm Hg}} = 0.987\ \text{atm} \quad T = 298.1\ \text{K} \quad n = ?$$

Use the ideal gas law equation to find n.

$$n = \frac{PV}{RT} = \frac{(0.987\ \text{atm})(0.250\ \text{L})}{(0.0821\ \text{L atm mol}^{-1}\ \text{K}^{-1})(298.1\ \text{K})} = 0.0101\ \text{mol gas}$$

The mass of the sample is 1.02 g, so the molar mass according to this gas law calculation is

$$\frac{1.02\ \text{g}}{0.0101\ \text{mol}} = 101.\ \text{g/mol}$$

Now sum the atomic weights of the molecular formula, $C_2H_2F_4$. This gives a molar mass of 102.0 g/mol, which is in close agreement with that determined using the ideal gas law.

✓ **Reasonable Answer Check** 250. mL of gas is about 0.250 L/22.4 L = 0.01 mol gas. If 1.0 g of gas is 0.01 mol, then the molar mass is about 1.0 g/0.01 mol = 100 g/mol, which is close to the more accurate answer.

PROBLEM-SOLVING PRACTICE 10.10

A flask contains 1.00 L of a pure gas at 0.850 atm and 20. °C. The mass of the gas is 1.13 g. What is the molar mass of the gas? What is its identity?

10.8 Gas Mixtures and Partial Pressures

ThomsonNOW™
Go to the Coached Problems menu for tutorials on **calculating partial pressures.**

Our atmosphere is a mixture of nitrogen, oxygen, argon, carbon dioxide, water vapor, and small amounts of several other gases (p. 431, Table 10.1). What we call atmospheric pressure is the sum of the pressures exerted by all these individual gases. The same is true of every gas mixture. Consider the mixture of nitrogen and oxygen illustrated in Figure 10.14. The pressure exerted by the mixture is equal to the sum of the pressures that the nitrogen alone and the oxygen alone would exert

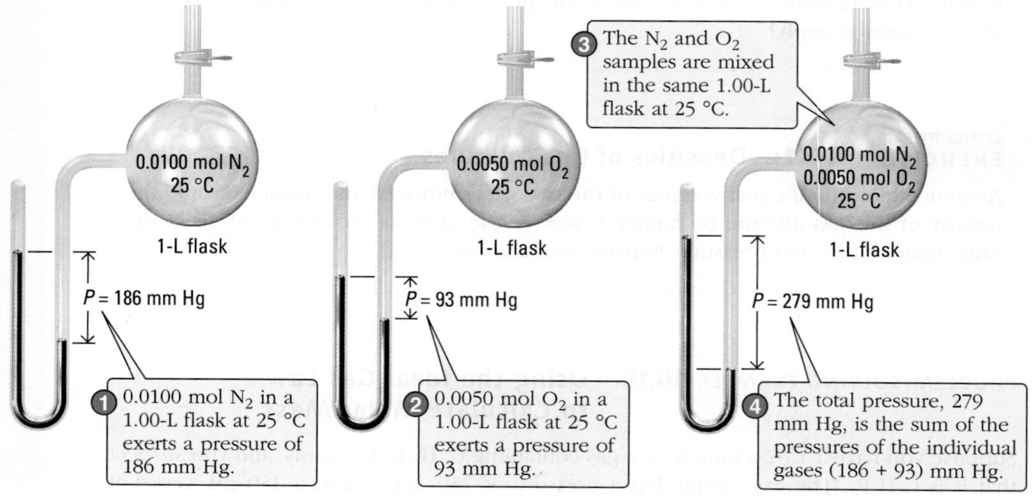

Figure 10.14 **Dalton's law of partial pressures.**

in the same volume at the same temperature and pressure. The pressure of one gas in a mixture of gases is called the **partial pressure** of that gas.

John Dalton was the first to observe that ***the total pressure exerted by a mixture of gases is the sum of the partial pressures of the individual gases in the mixture.*** This statement, known as **Dalton's law of partial pressures,** is a consequence of the fact that gas molecules behave independently of one another. As a demonstration of Dalton's law, consider the main components of our atmosphere, for which the total number of moles is approximately

$$n_{total} = n_{N_2} + n_{O_2} + n_{Ar}$$

If we replace n in the ideal gas law with n_{total}, the summation of the individual numbers of moles of gases, the equation becomes

$$P_{total}V = n_{total}RT$$

$$P_{total} = \frac{n_{total}RT}{V} = \frac{(n_{N_2} + n_{O_2} + n_{Ar})RT}{V}$$

Expanding the right side of this equation and rearranging gives

$$P_{total} = \frac{n_{N_2}RT}{V} + \frac{n_{O_2}RT}{V} + \frac{n_{Ar}RT}{V} = P_{N_2} + P_{O_2} + P_{Ar}$$

The quantities P_{N_2}, P_{O_2}, and P_{Ar} are the partial pressures of the three major components of the atmosphere. Dalton's law means that the pressure exerted by the atmosphere is the sum of the pressures due to nitrogen, oxygen, argon, and the other much less abundant components.

We can write a ratio of the partial pressure of one of the components, A, of a gas mixture over the total pressure,

$$\frac{P_A}{P_{total}} = \frac{n_A(RT/V)}{n_{total}(RT/V)}$$

On canceling terms on the right-hand side of this equation, we get

$$\frac{P_A}{P_{total}} = \frac{n_A}{n_{total}}$$

The ratio of the pressures is the same as the ratio of the number of moles of gas A to the total number of moles. This ratio (n_A/n_{total}) is called the **mole fraction** of A and is given the symbol X_A. Hence, rearranging the equation gives

$$P_A = X_A P_{total}$$

In the gas mixture in Figure 10.14, the mole fractions of nitrogen and oxygen are

$$X_{N_2} = \frac{0.010 \text{ mol } N_2}{0.010 \text{ mol } N_2 + 0.0050 \text{ mol } O_2} = 0.67$$

$$X_{O_2} = \frac{0.0050 \text{ mol } O_2}{0.010 \text{ mol } N_2 + 0.0050 \text{ mol } O_2} = 0.33$$

Because these two gases are the only components of the mixture, the sum of the two mole fractions must equal 1:

$$X_{N_2} + X_{O_2} = 0.67 + 0.33 = 1.00$$

An interesting application of partial pressures is the composition of the breathing atmosphere in deep-sea-diving vessels. If normal air at 1 atm pressure, with an oxygen mole fraction of 0.21, is compressed to 2 atm, the partial pressure of oxygen becomes about 0.42 atm. Such high oxygen partial pressures are toxic, so a

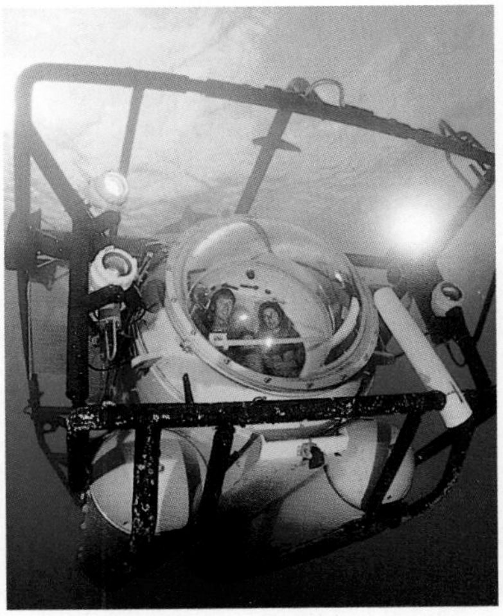
Photo Researchers, Inc.

An undersea explorer. Some deep-sea-diving vessels like this one use an atmosphere of oxygen and helium for their occupants.

diluting gas must be added to lower the oxygen partial pressure to near-normal values. Nitrogen gas might seem the logical choice because it is the diluting gas in the atmosphere. The problem is that nitrogen is fairly soluble in the blood and at high concentrations causes *nitrogen narcosis,* a condition similar to alcohol intoxication.

Helium is much less soluble in the blood and is therefore a good substitute for nitrogen in a deep-sea–diving atmosphere. However, using helium leads to interesting side effects. Because He atoms, on average, move faster than the heavier nitrogen atoms at the same temperature (Figure 10.7), they strike a diver's skin more often than would the nitrogen atoms and are therefore more efficient at transferring away energy. This effect causes divers to complain of feeling chilled while breathing a helium/oxygen mixture.

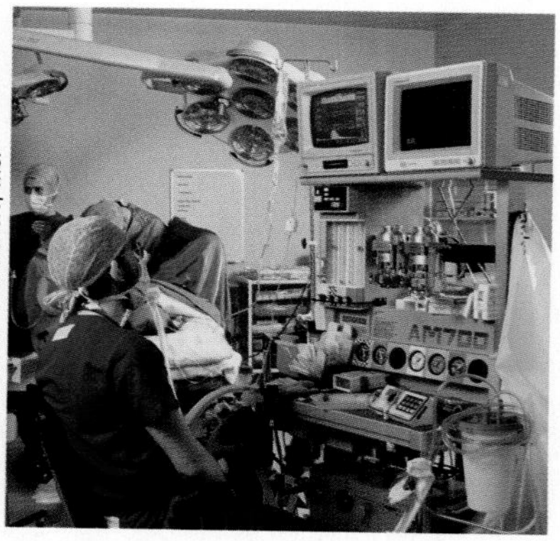

© Chris Priest/Photo Researchers, Inc.

A gas-mixing manifold for anesthesia. An anesthesiologist uses such equipment to prepare a gas mixture to keep a patient unconscious during an operation. By proper mixing, the anesthetic gas can be added slowly to the breathing mixture. Near the end of the operation, the anesthetic gas can be replaced by air of normal composition or by pure oxygen.

PROBLEM-SOLVING EXAMPLE 10.11 Calculating Partial Pressures

Halothane (F_3C—CHBrCl) is a commonly used surgical anesthetic delivered by inhalation. What is the partial pressure of each gas if 15.0 g halothane gas is mixed with 22.6 g oxygen gas and the total pressure is 862 mm Hg?

Answer $P_{\text{halothane}} = 83.8 \text{ mm Hg}$ $P_{O_2} = 778 \text{ mm Hg}$

Strategy and Explanation To find the partial pressures, we need the mole fraction of each gas. We first calculate the number of moles of each gas, and then we calculate the mole fractions.

$$15.0 \text{ g} \times \left(\frac{1 \text{ mol halothane}}{197.4 \text{ g}}\right) = 0.07600 \text{ mol halothane}$$

$$22.6 \text{ g} \times \left(\frac{1 \text{ mol } O_2}{32.00 \text{ g}}\right) = 0.7062 \text{ mol } O_2$$

$$X_{\text{halothane}} = \frac{0.07600 \text{ mol halothane}}{0.7822 \text{ total moles}} = 0.0972$$

Because the sum of the two mole fractions must equal 1.000, the mole fraction of O_2 is 0.903.

$$X_{\text{halothane}} + X_{O_2} = 1.000 = 0.0972 + X_{O_2}$$

$$X_{O_2} = 1.000 - 0.0972 = 0.903$$

Finally, we calculate the partial pressure of each gas.

$$P_{\text{halothane}} = 0.0972 \times P_{\text{total}} = 0.0972 \times (862 \text{ mm Hg}) = 83.8 \text{ mm Hg}$$

$$P_{O_2} = 0.903 \times P_{\text{total}} = 0.903 \times (862 \text{ mm Hg}) = 778 \text{ mm Hg}$$

✓ **Reasonable Answer Check** We have a 10:1 mole ratio of O_2 to halothane, so the ratio of partial pressures should be roughly 10:1, and it is.

PROBLEM-SOLVING PRACTICE 10.11

A mixture of 7.0 g N_2 and 6.0 g H_2 is confined in a 5.0-L reaction vessel at 500. °C. Assume that no reaction occurs and calculate the total pressure. Then calculate the mole fraction and partial pressure of each gas.

CONCEPTUAL EXERCISE 10.15 Pondering Partial Pressures

What happens to the partial pressure of each gas in a mixture when the volume is decreased by (a) lowering the temperature or (b) increasing the total pressure?

EXERCISE 10.16 Partial Pressures

A 355-mL flask contains 0.146 g neon gas, Ne, and an unknown amount of argon gas, Ar, at 35 °C and a total pressure of 626 mm Hg. How many grams of Ar are in the flask?

PROBLEM-SOLVING EXAMPLE 10.12 Partial Pressure

The reaction between nitrogen monoxide, NO, and oxygen gas to form NO_2 is environmentally important.

$$2\ NO(g) + O_2(g) \longrightarrow 2\ NO_2(g)$$

Nitrogen oxides are discussed in Section 10.12, p. 469.

Suppose that the two reactant gases are kept in separate containers, as shown below. Then suppose the valve is opened and the reaction proceeds to completion. Assume a constant temperature of 25 °C.

(a) What gases remain at the end of the reaction, and how much of each of them is present?

(b) What are their partial pressures, and what is the total pressure in the system?

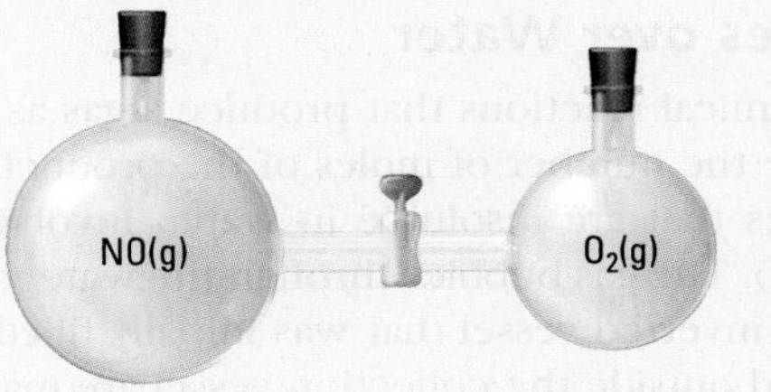

Answer

(a) No NO remains; 0.0427 mol O_2 and 0.0774 mol NO_2 remain

(b) $P_{NO_2} = 0.316$ atm; $P_{O_2} = 0.174$ atm; $P_{total} = 0.490$ atm

Strategy and Explanation

(a) First, we must identify the limiting reactant by finding the number of moles of each gas and comparing these values with the coefficients of the balanced equation (← ***p. 140, Section 4.5***).

$$\frac{(360./760)\ \text{atm}\ (4.0\ \text{L})}{(0.0821\ \text{L atm mol}^{-1}\ \text{K}^{-1})(298\ \text{K})} = 0.0774\ \text{mol NO}$$

$$\frac{(0.996\ \text{atm})(2.0\ \text{L})}{(0.0821\ \text{L atm mol}^{-1}\ \text{K}^{-1})(298\ \text{K})} = 0.0814\ \text{mol}\ O_2$$

NO is the limiting reactant because 0.0744 mol is less than the amount required by the O_2 (2 × 0.0814 mol = 0.163 mol). The NO will be completely consumed by the reaction. The amount of oxygen consumed will be

$$0.0774\ \text{mol NO} \times \frac{1\ \text{mol}\ O_2}{2\ \text{mol NO}} = 0.0387\ \text{mol}\ O_2$$

Subtracting the amount used from the original amount gives 0.0814 − 0.0387 = 0.0427 mol O_2 left when the reaction is complete. The amount of NO_2 formed is

$$0.0774\ \text{mol NO} \times \frac{2\ \text{mol}\ NO_2}{2\ \text{mol NO}} = 0.0774\ \text{mol}\ NO_2\ \text{formed}$$

At the end of the reaction, we have 0.0427 mol O_2, 0.0774 mol NO_2, and no NO gas.

Table 10.5 Vapor Pressure of Water at Different Temperatures

T (°C)	P_{water} (mm Hg)
0	4.6
10	9.2
20	17.5
21	18.6
22	19.8
23	21.1
24	22.4
25	23.8
30	31.8
35	42.2
40	55.3
50	92.5
60	149.4
70	233.7
80	355.1
90	525.8
100	760.0

(b) The pressures of the two gases are

$$P_{NO_2} = \frac{(0.0774\ \text{mol})(0.0821\ \text{L atm mol}^{-1}\ \text{K}^{-1})(298\ \text{K})}{6.0\ \text{L}} = 0.316\ \text{atm NO}_2$$

$$P_{O_2} = \frac{(0.0427\ \text{mol})(0.0821\ \text{L atm mol}^{-1}\ \text{K}^{-1})(298\ \text{K})}{6.0\ \text{L}} = 0.174\ \text{atm O}_2$$

The total pressure of the system is the sum of the partial pressures.

$$P_{total} = 0.316\ \text{atm} + 0.174\ \text{atm} = 0.490\ \text{atm}$$

PROBLEM-SOLVING PRACTICE 10.12

Consider the case with the same reactants in the same vessels as above, but with a NO pressure of 1.00 atm and O_2 pressure of 0.400 atm. What would the final pressure in the system be after the reaction is complete?

Collecting Gases over Water

While studying chemical reactions that produce a gas as a product, it is often necessary to determine the number of moles of the product gas. One convenient way to do this, for gases that are insoluble in water, involves collecting the gas over water (Figure 10.15). The gas bubbles through the water and is collected by displacing the water in an inverted vessel that was initially filled with water. The levels of the water inside and outside the collection vessel are made equal at the end of the experiment. This ensures that the total pressure inside the vessel is equal to the barometric pressure in the laboratory. The volume of gas collected is then determined. Because some of the water evaporates, forming water vapor, the total pressure of the mixture of gases equals the partial pressure of the gas being collected plus the partial pressure of the water vapor. The partial pressure of water in the gaseous mixture is the vapor pressure of water, and it depends on the temperature of the liquid water (Table 10.5).

To calculate the amount of gaseous product, we first subtract the vapor pressure of the water from the total gas pressure (the barometric pressure), which yields the partial pressure of the gaseous product. Substituting this partial pressure and the known volume and temperature into the ideal gas law allows the calculation of the number of moles of the gaseous product.

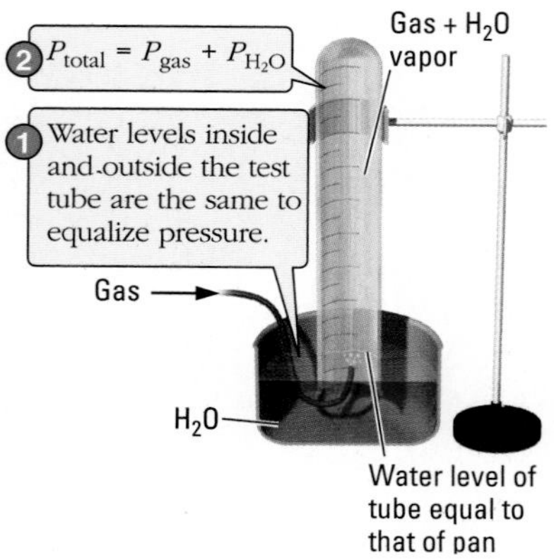

Figure 10.15 Collecting a gas over water.

PROBLEM-SOLVING EXAMPLE 10.13 Collecting a Gas over Water

Before electric lamps were available, the reaction between calcium carbide, CaC_2, and water was used to produce acetylene, C_2H_2, to generate a bright flame in miners' lamps.

$$CaC_2(s) + 2\ H_2O(\ell) \longrightarrow C_2H_2(g) + Ca(OH)_2(aq)$$

At a barometric pressure of 745 mm Hg and a temperature of 24.0 °C, 625 mL of gas was collected over water. How many milligrams of acetylene were produced? The vapor pressure of water at 24.0 °C is 22.4 mm Hg.

Answer 635 mg acetylene

Strategy and Explanation We will need to calculate the number of moles and then milligrams of acetylene, so we must first find the partial pressure of the acetylene. The total pressure is 745 mm Hg, and the vapor pressure of water at 24.0 °C is 22.4 mm Hg, so the partial pressure of acetylene is

$$P_{acetylene} = P_{total} - P_{water} = 745\ \text{mm Hg} - 22.4\ \text{mm Hg} = 723\ \text{mm Hg}$$

Now we calculate the molar amount and mass of acetylene

$$n = \frac{PV}{RT} = \frac{(723/760 \text{ atm})(0.625 \text{ L})}{(0.0821 \text{ L atm mol}^{-1} \text{ K}^{-1})(273.15 + 24.0) \text{ K}}$$

$$= 0.0244 \text{ mol acetylene}$$

$$0.0244 \text{ mol} \times 26.04 \text{ g/mol} = 0.635 \text{ g} = 635 \text{ mg acetylene}$$

$H—C{\equiv}C—H$

acetylene

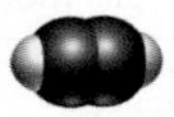

✓ **Reasonable Answer Check** The quantities entered into the ideal gas equation can be approximated as $n = \frac{(1)(0.6)}{(0.082)(300)} = 0.024$ mol, which is close to our more exact answer.

PROBLEM-SOLVING PRACTICE 10.13

Zinc metal reacts with HCl to produce hydrogen gas, H_2.

$$2 \text{ HCl(aq)} + \text{Zn(s)} \longrightarrow \text{ZnCl}_2\text{(aq)} + \text{H}_2\text{(g)}$$

The H_2 can be collected over water. If you collected 260. mL H_2 at 23 °C, and the total pressure was 740. mm Hg, how many milligrams of H_2 were collected?

10.9 The Behavior of Real Gases

The ideal gas law provides accurate predictions for the pressure, volume, temperature, and amount of a gas well above its boiling point. At STP (0 °C and 1 atm), most gases deviate only slightly from ideal behavior. At much higher pressures or much lower temperatures, however, the ideal gas law does not work nearly as well. We can illustrate this departure from ideality by plotting PV/nRT for a gas as a function of pressure (Figure 10.16). For one mole of a gas that follows ideal gas behavior, the ratio PV/nRT must equal 1. But Figure 10.16 shows that for real gases, the ratio PV/nRT deviates from 1, first dipping to values lower than 1 and then rising to values higher than 1 as pressure increases. Thus, the measured volume of the real gas is smaller than expected at medium pressures, and it is higher than expected at high pressures.

To see what causes these deviations, we must revisit two of the fundamental concepts of kinetic-molecular theory (p. 436). The theory assumes that the molecules of a gas occupy no volume themselves and that gas molecules do not attract one another.

At STP, the volume occupied by a single molecule is very small relative to its share of the total gas volume. Recall that there are 6.02×10^{23} molecules in a mole and that 1 mol of a gas occupies about 22.4 L (22.4×10^{-3} m^3) at STP (p. 443). The volume, V, that each molecule has to move around in is given by

$$V = \frac{22.4 \times 10^{-3} \text{ m}^3}{6.02 \times 10^{23} \text{ molecules}} = 3.72 \times 10^{-26} \text{ m}^3/\text{molecule}$$

If this volume is assumed to be a sphere, then the radius, r, of the sphere is about 2000 pm. The radius of the smallest gas molecule, the helium atom, is 31 pm **(⇐ p. 311)**, so a helium atom has a space to move around in that is similar to the room a pea has inside a basketball. Now suppose the pressure is increased significantly, to 1000 atm. The volume available to each molecule is now a sphere only about 200 pm in radius, which means the situation is now like that of a pea inside a sphere a bit larger than a ping-pong ball. The volume occupied by the gas molecules themselves relative to the volume of the sphere is no longer negligible. This violates the first concept of the kinetic-molecular theory. The kinetic-molecular theory and the ideal gas law deal with the volume available for the molecules to move around in,

The volume of a sphere is given by $\frac{4}{3}\pi r^3$. Solving for r gives

$$r = \sqrt[3]{\frac{3V}{4\pi}}$$

$$= \sqrt[3]{\frac{3(3.72 \times 10^{-26} \text{ m}^3)}{4(3.14)}}$$

$$r = 2.07 \times 10^{-9} \text{ m} = 2070 \text{ pm}$$

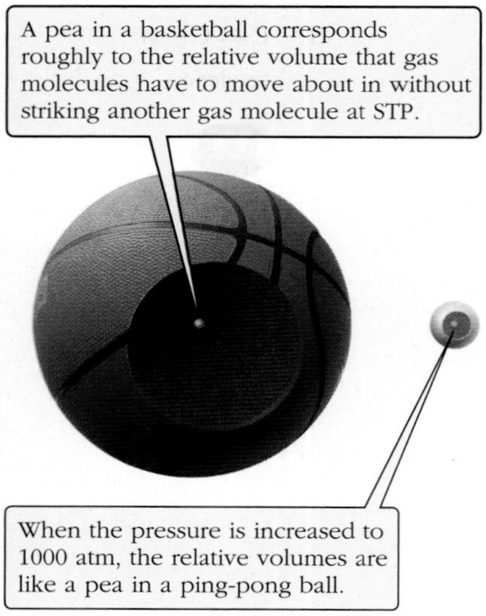

A cut-away view of a pea inside a basketball and inside a ping-pong ball.

not the volume of the molecules themselves. However, the measured volume of the gas must include both. Therefore, at very high pressures, the measured volume will be larger than predicted by the ideal gas law, and the value of PV/nRT will be greater than 1.

At medium pressures, the product PV for a real gas is smaller than the predicted value of nRT for an ideal gas (Figure 10.16). For a given volume of gas, the pressure exerted against the container walls is smaller than expected. Consider a gas molecule that is about to hit the wall of the container, as shown in Figure 10.17. The kinetic-molecular theory assumes that the other molecules exert no forces on the molecule, but in fact such forces do exist (***p. 408***). Their influence increases as higher pressures push gas molecules closer to each other. This means that when a molecule is about to hit the wall of the container, the other molecules tend to pull it *away* from the wall, which causes the molecule to hit the wall with less impact. The collision is softer than if there were no attraction among the molecules. Since all collisions with the walls are softer, the internal pressure is less than that predicted by the ideal gas law, and PV/nRT is less than 1. As the external pressure increases, the gas volume decreases, the molecules are squeezed closer together, and the attraction among the molecules grows stronger, which increases this deviation from ideal behavior. Eventually, the pressure gets so high that the loss of empty space becomes the dominating factor, and PV/nRT becomes larger than 1 (Figure 10.16).

The result of these considerations is that the measured pressure for real gases is less than the ideal pressure due to intermolecular interactions, and the measured volume is larger than the ideal volume due to the volume of the molecules themselves. Thus, the ideal pressure is *larger* than the measured pressure, and the ideal volume is *smaller* than the measured volume.

The **van der Waals equation** predicts the behavior of n moles of a real gas quantitatively by taking these two effects into account. It assumes that $P_{ideal}V_{ideal} = nRT$, but expresses the left-hand side in terms of *measured* P and V.

$$\left(P_{\text{measured}} + \frac{n^2a}{V^2_{\text{measured}}}\right)(V_{\text{measured}} - nb) = nRT$$

Correction for molecular attraction (adjusts measured P up)

Correction for volume of molecules (adjusts measured V down)

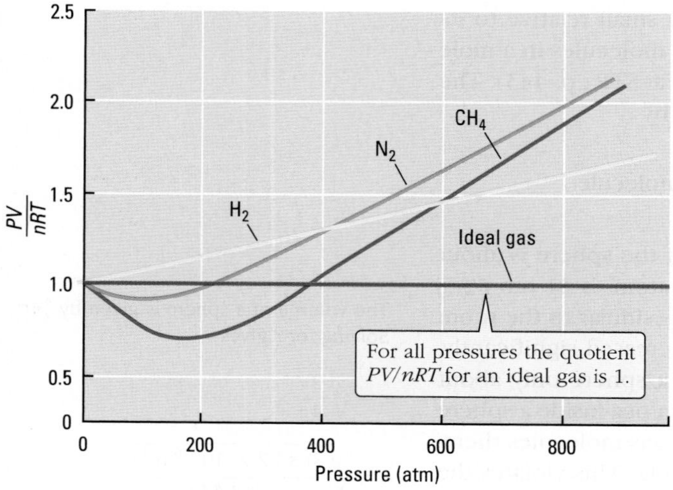

Figure 10.16 The nonideal behavior of real gases compared with that of an ideal gas.

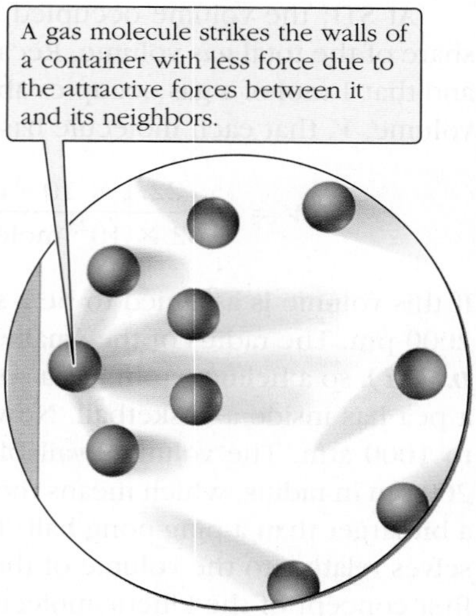

Figure 10.17 Nonideal gas behavior.

The measured volume is decreased by the factor nb, which accounts for the volume occupied by n moles of the gas molecules themselves. The van der Waals constant b has units of L/mol, and it is larger for larger molecules. The measured pressure is increased by the factor n^2a/V^2, which accounts for the attractive forces between molecules. The van der Waals constant a has units of L^2 atm/mol^2. The a pressure correction term has this form because the attractive forces being accounted for depend on interactions between *pairs* of molecules; the a term is therefore proportional to the square of the number of molecules per unit volume, $(n/V)^2$. The value of a shows how strongly the gas molecules attract one another; the stronger the intermolecular interactions, the larger the value of a. The constants a and b are different for each gas (Table 10.6) and must be determined experimentally. In general, the values of a and b increase as the gas molecule's size increases and as the molecule's complexity increases.

Note that for an ideal gas, where the kinetic-molecular theory of gases holds, the attractive forces between molecules are negligible, so $a \approx 0$, and $P_{measured} = P_{ideal}$. The volume of the molecules themselves is negligible compared with the container volume, so $b \approx 0$ and $V_{measured} = V_{ideal}$. Therefore, for ordinary conditions of P and T, the van der Waals equation simplifies to the ideal gas law.

Table 10.6 Van der Waals Constants for Some Common Gases

Gas	$a\left(\frac{L^2\ atm}{mol^2}\right)$	$b\left(\frac{L}{mol}\right)$
He	0.034	0.0237
Ne	0.211	0.0171
Ar	1.35	0.0322
H_2	0.244	0.0266
N_2	1.39	0.0391
O_2	1.36	0.0318
Cl_2	6.49	0.0562
CO_2	3.59	0.0427
CH_4	2.25	0.0428
NH_3	4.17	0.0371
H_2O	5.46	0.0305

PROBLEM-SOLVING EXAMPLE 10.14 Using the van der Waals Equation

What is the pressure of 5.00 mol CH_4 in 2.00 L at 273 K when calculated using the ideal gas law and the van der Waals equation? What is the difference between the two calculated pressures? For CH_4, the values for the van der Waals constants are $a = 2.25\ L^2\ atm/mol^2$ and $b = 0.0428$ L/mol.

Answer Ideal gas law pressure = 56.0 atm and van der Waals equation pressure = 48.7 atm. The difference is a 13.0% lower pressure calculated from the van der Waals equation as compared with the ideal gas law.

Strategy and Explanation First, we use the ideal gas law equation to find the pressure.

$$P = \frac{nRT}{V} = \frac{(5.00\ mol)(0.0821\ L\ atm\ mol^{-1}\ K^{-1})(273\ K)}{2.00\ L} = 56.0\ atm$$

Now we compute the pressure using the van der Waals equation.

$$P = \left(\frac{nRT}{V - nb}\right) - \left(\frac{n^2a}{V^2}\right)$$

$$P = \left(\frac{(5.00\ mol)(0.0821\ L\ atm\ mol^{-1}\ K^{-1})(273\ K)}{(2.00\ L) - (5.00\ mol)(0.0428\ L/mol)}\right) - \left(\frac{(5.00\ mol)^2(2.25\ L^2\ atm/mol^2)}{(2.00\ L)^2}\right) = 48.7\ atm$$

The first term containing the constant b equals 62.75 atm, which differs from the ideal pressure by 6.25 atm, and the second term equals 14.06 atm. Thus, the term with a that accounts for intermolecular forces is more important. The overall percentage difference in pressure is

$$\text{Percentage difference in pressure} = \frac{56.0\ atm - 48.7\ atm}{56.0\ atm} \times 100\% = 13.0\%$$

PROBLEM-SOLVING PRACTICE 10.14

What is the percentage difference between the pressures predicted by the ideal gas law and the van der Waals equation if the volume in Problem-Solving Example 10.14 is increased by a factor of 10 to 20.0 L?

EXERCISE 10.17 Errors Caused by Deviations from Ideal Gas Behavior

In Problem-Solving Example 10.10 (p. 453), the molar mass calculated using the ideal gas law was slightly larger than that calculated using atomic weights. This means that the number of moles, *n*, must have been too small. Look at the Strategy and Explanation for Problem-Solving Example 10.10 and explain why the number of moles is less than it should be.

10.10 Chemical Reactions in the Atmosphere

Molecules in the atmosphere are continually moving and colliding with one another, as described by the kinetic-molecular theory. The atmosphere is also continually illuminated during daylight hours. As a result, absorption of light energy by atmospheric molecules can cause **photochemical reactions,** reactions that would not occur at normal atmospheric temperatures in the absence of light. Such reactions play an important role in determining the composition of the atmosphere itself and the fate of many chemical species that contribute to air pollution.

Nitrogen dioxide, NO_2, is one of the most photochemically active species in the atmosphere. The NO_2 molecule is an example of a *free radical* because it contains an unpaired electron ***(⇐ p. 361),*** represented by a · next to its formula. When an NO_2 molecule absorbs a photon of light with energy $h\nu$, the molecule is raised to a higher energy level; it becomes an **electronically excited molecule,** designated by an asterisk (*).

Recall that some simple molecules, like NO and NO_2, have unpaired electrons ***(⇐ p. 361).***

$$\cdot NO_2(g) \xrightarrow{h\nu} \cdot NO_2^*(g)$$

Recall from Chapter 7 that $E = h\nu$.

The excited molecule, $\cdot NO_2^*$, may quickly re-emit a photon of light, or the energy may break an N—O bond to form a nitrogen monoxide (NO) molecule and an oxygen atom (O).

$$\cdot NO_2^*(g) \longrightarrow \cdot NO(g) + \cdot O \cdot (g)$$

Both NO and O are free radicals, because they have one or more unpaired electrons each denoted by a dot.

Photodissociation is another mechanism of formation of radicals, in which a molecule absorbs an ultraviolet photon and produces two free radicals as products. Molecular oxygen can photodissociate to form two oxygen atoms.

$$O_2(g) \xrightarrow{h\nu} \cdot O \cdot (g) + \cdot O \cdot (g)$$

Some free radicals, such as an oxygen atom, react with another atom or molecule almost immediately. Others, such as an $\cdot NO_2$ molecule, are not quite so reactive and are stable enough to exist for a somewhat longer time. Most radicals are highly reactive and short-lived.

Remember that the oxygen atom has the electron configuration [He] $2s^22p_x^22p_y^12p_z^1$, and it is a free radical with two unpaired electrons.

10.11 Ozone and Stratospheric Ozone Depletion

Ozone, O_3, is an important substance that is currently very much in the news because of its role in the troposphere, where it is a pollutant. It irritates mucous membranes in the nose when it is inhaled. In the stratosphere, however, ozone is essential for life on earth. A hybrid of two resonance structures, ozone has a bent (angular) geometry (⇐ p. 358) with a bond angle of 116.8°. Ozone's ΔH_f° of 142.3 kJ/mol shows that it is less stable than O_2 (which is assigned an enthalpy of formation of zero).

$$\frac{3}{2}O_2(g) \longrightarrow O_3(g) \qquad \Delta H_f^\circ = 142.3 \text{ kJ/mol}$$

Ozone is highly reactive and does not survive long after formation.

In the stratosphere ozone is formed by a natural photodissociation process in which ultraviolet solar radiation with $\lambda < 242$ nm splits an O_2 molecule to produce oxygen atoms. The oxygen atoms then combine with O_2 to form ozone.

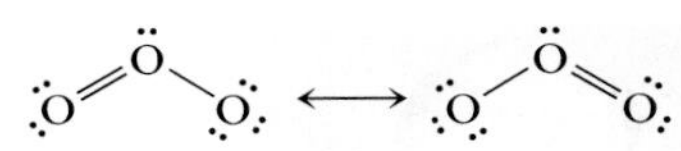

ozone

Ozone resonance structures.

Natural formation of O_3

$$O_2(g) \xrightarrow{h\nu} \cdot O \cdot (g) + \cdot O \cdot (g)$$

$$\cdot O \cdot (g) + O_2(g) \longrightarrow O_3(g)$$

The bond energy of O_2 is 495 kJ/mol, so a calculation using $E = hc/\lambda$ shows that the energy in a photon of $\lambda \leq$ 242 nm is needed to break the O_2 bond.

The region of maximum ozone concentration, known as the **stratospheric ozone layer,** is at an altitude of 25 to 30 km, where the concentration can reach 10 ppm. The ozone concentration in the stratosphere under natural conditions is maintained at a constant level by a reaction that destroys ozone at the same rate at which it is produced.

Natural destruction of O_3

$$O_3 + \cdot O \cdot (g) \longrightarrow 2\,O_2(g)$$

Because ozone molecules and oxygen atoms are at very low concentrations, this reaction is relatively slow. However, it consumes ozone fast enough to maintain a balance with the ozone-forming reaction so that under normal circumstances the concentration of ozone in the stratosphere remains constant. Every day, 3×10^8 tons of stratospheric ozone are formed and destroyed by these two competing natural processes.

Protection of earth's surface

The importance of stratospheric ozone is that by undergoing a photodissociation reaction it prevents damaging ultraviolet radiation from reaching the earth's surface. Wavelengths in the range of 200 to 310 nm are absorbed during the decomposition reaction. The oxygen atoms from the photodissociation of O_3 react with O_2 to regenerate O_3, so this reaction results in no net O_3 loss.

$$O_3(g) \xrightarrow{h\nu} \cdot O \cdot (g) + O_2(g)$$

Absorption of ultraviolet radiation in the stratosphere is essential for living things on earth. Stratospheric ozone prevents 95% to 99% of the sun's ultraviolet radiation from reaching the earth's surface. Photons in this 200- to 310-nm range have enough energy to cause skin cancer in humans and damage to living plants. For every 1% decrease in the stratospheric ozone, an additional 2% of this damaging radiation reaches the earth's surface. Stratospheric ozone depletion therefore has the potential to drastically damage our environment.

This answers the question posed in Chapter 1 (⇐ ***p. 3***): "Why is ozone depletion harmful? I thought too much ozone was bad for your lungs."

Chlorofluorocarbons

Chlorofluorocarbons (CFCs) are small molecules with halogen atoms bonded to central carbons. CFCs play a major role in ozone depletion. Specific examples of CFCs include $CFCl_3$ (CFC-11) and CF_2Cl_2 (CFC-12). These compounds are nonflammable, relatively inert, volatile yet readily liquefied, and nontoxic—an extremely useful set of properties. CFCs have been used as coolants for refrigeration, in foam plastics manufacture, as aerosol propellants, and as industrial solvents. Unfortunately, the same properties that make them useful are also the reason for their destructive effect on the stratospheric ozone. Once gaseous CFCs are released into

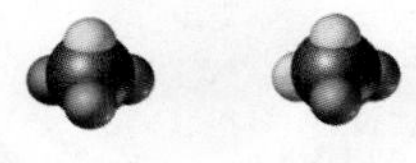

$CFCl_3$ (CFC-11) CF_2Cl_2 (CFC-12)

Hal Garb/AFP/Corbis-Bettmann

F. Sherwood Rowland

1927–

Born in Ohio, Sherwood Rowland entered Ohio Wesleyan University at age 12. He received his Ph.D. from the University of Chicago in 1952. He held faculty appointments at several institutions and joined the newly formed University of California at Irvine in 1964 as Chair of the Chemistry Department. In 1974 he and Mario Molina recognized that CFCs could deplete the ozone layer in the atmosphere. Their work was received skeptically at first, but it was confirmed by others in later experiments, notably in 1985 by satellite data showing an "ozone hole" over Antarctica. Rowland, Molina, and Paul Crutzen shared the 1995 Nobel Prize in chemistry ". . . for their work in atmospheric chemistry, particularly concerning the formation and decomposition of ozone."

Seasons are reversed in the Southern Hemisphere—spring in Antarctica is fall in the Northern Hemisphere.

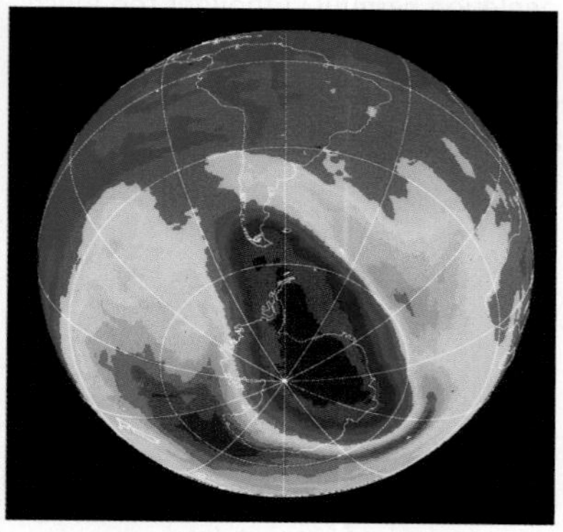

NASA

Figure 10.18 The Antarctic ozone hole. The darker colors indicate where ozone is depleted.

the atmosphere, they persist for a very long time in the troposphere because of their chemical nonreactivity. On average, a CF_2Cl_2 molecule survives roughly 100 years in the troposphere. Eventually, CFCs released into the troposphere rise to the stratosphere through atmospheric mixing, where they are decomposed by high-energy solar radiation. The decomposition products of CFCs participate in reactions in the stratosphere that result in a lowering of the concentration of ozone there.

Destruction of the stratospheric ozone layer by CFCs begins when a photon of high enough energy breaks a carbon-chlorine bond in a CFC molecule. This produces a chlorine atom, as shown here using CFC-12 as an example.

$$CF_2Cl_2(g) \xrightarrow{h\nu} CF_2Cl\cdot(g) + Cl\cdot(g)$$

The chlorine atom, a free radical, then participates in what is called a *chain reaction mechanism.* It first combines with an ozone molecule, producing a chlorine monoxide ($ClO\cdot$) radical and an oxygen molecule.

Step 1: $Cl\cdot(g) + O_3(g) \longrightarrow ClO\cdot(g) + O_2(g)$

Thus, an ozone molecule has been destroyed. If this were the only reaction that particular CFC molecule caused, there would be little danger to the ozone layer. However, once Step 1 has occurred twice, the two ClO radicals produced can react further.

Step 2: $ClO\cdot + ClO\cdot \longrightarrow ClOOCl$

Step 3: $ClOOCl \xrightarrow{h\nu} \cdot ClOO + \cdot Cl$

Step 4: $\cdot ClOO \xrightarrow{h\nu} \cdot Cl + O_2$

The net reaction obtained by adding two Step 1 reactions to Steps 2, 3, and 4 and canceling species that appear as both reactants and products is the conversion of two ozone molecules to three oxygen molecules.

$$\text{Net reaction:} \quad 2\,O_3(g) \longrightarrow 3\,O_2(g)$$

That is, this chain reaction increases the rate at which stratospheric ozone is destroyed, but it does not affect the rate at which ozone is formed. It is called a chain reaction because the reaction steps can repeat over and over. The two chlorine atoms that react when Step 1 occurs twice are regenerated in Steps 3 and 4, so there is no net change in concentration of chlorine atoms. It has been estimated that a single chlorine atom can destroy as many as 100,000 molecules of O_3 before it is inactivated or returned to the troposphere (probably as HCl). This sequence of ozone-destroying reactions upsets the balance in the stratosphere because ozone is being destroyed faster than it is being produced. As a consequence, the concentration of stratospheric ozone decreases.

The most prominent manifestation of stratospheric ozone depletion is the Antarctic **ozone hole.** In 1985 the British Antarctic Survey reported a startlingly large depletion of ozone in September and October, at the end of the Antarctic winter. This ozone hole has reappeared at this time each year (Figure 10.18). Subsequent measurements by several research teams showed that loss of ozone was correlated with high concentrations of ClOOCl, supporting the theory that a chain reaction involving chlorine atoms was responsible. However, the huge depletion of ozone in the Antarctic could not be explained solely by the reaction steps given above. In the dark Antarctic winter, a vortex of intensely cold air containing ice crystals, unique to the region, builds up. On the surfaces of these crystals additional reactions produce hydrogen chloride and chlorine nitrate ($ClONO_2$). They can react with each other to form chlorine molecules.

$$HCl(g) + ClONO_2(g) \longrightarrow Cl_2(g) + HNO_3(g)$$

When sunlight returns in the spring, the Cl_2 molecules are readily photodissociated into chlorine atoms, which can then become involved in the ozone destruction reactions.

$$Cl_2(g) \xrightarrow{h\nu} 2\,Cl\cdot(g)$$

The first direct confirmation of the relationship between stratospheric ozone depletion and increased ultraviolet intensity on the earth was reported in the September 10, 1999, issue of *Science* by scientists from the New Zealand National Institute of Water and Atmospheric Research. They found that ". . . over the past 10 years, peak levels of skin-frying and DNA-damaging ultraviolet (UV) rays have been increasing in New Zealand, just as the concentrations of protective stratospheric ozone have decreased." Figure 10.19 shows a plot of declining stratospheric ozone concentration and increasing UV radiation over a period of 20 years, as reported by the New Zealand scientists.

Dealing with the Problem

Stratospheric ozone depletion is a global problem, and it has led to global cooperation designed to combat the problem. In an effort to reduce the harm done by CFCs and other chemicals to the stratospheric ozone layer, the Montreal Protocol on Substances that Deplete the Ozone Layer (1987) was implemented. The Protocol has been amended four times—London (1990), Copenhagen (1992), Montreal (1997), and Beijing (1999)—and has now been signed by more than 150 countries. This protocol, and its amendments, form the basis of amended Title VI of the Clean Air Act in the United States. CFC production was banned as of 1996 in the developed countries. Other chemicals that deplete the ozone layer were also banned. For example, halons, used as fire-suppression agents, were banned in the developed countries as of 1994, and methyl bromide, used as a pesticide, was banned as of 2001. Developing countries were given extra time to phase out production of CFCs.

The efforts to halt production of ozone-depleting chemicals are beginning to show positive results. The United Nations Environment Programme (UNEP) and the World Meteorological Organization (WMO) periodically issue reports, the latest of

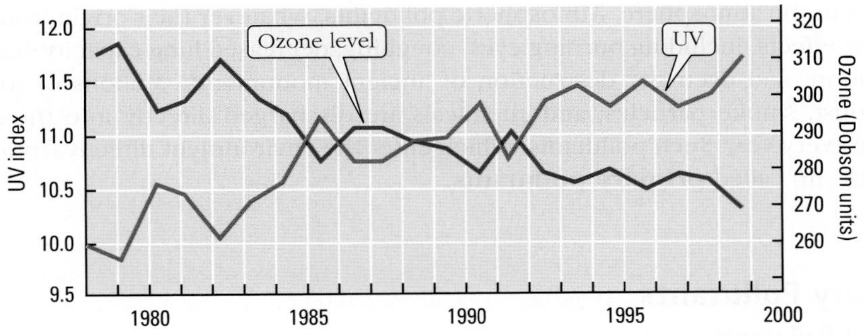

Figure 10.19 The stratospheric ozone level is decreasing, and the UV intensity is increasing. These measurements were made in Lauder, New Zealand. The red line indicates ultraviolet (UV) radiation at noon calculated from measured ozone levels, shown by the blue line. Dobson units: 1 DU = 2.69×10^{16} molecules/cm^2. One Dobson unit refers to a layer of ozone that would be 10 micrometers thick under standard temperature and pressure. The UV index is a standardized way to report UV radiation to the public. The higher the UV index, the more intense the UV radiation. (Source: Reprinted with permission from McKenzie, R., Connor, B., and Bodeker, G. "Increased Summertime UV Radiation in New Zealand in Response to Ozone Loss." *Science,* Vol. 285, September 10, 1999; p. 1709.)

Carlye Calvin. Courtesy of Susan Solomon

Susan Solomon

1956–

A senior scientist at NOAA (National Oceanic and Atmospheric Administration), Susan Solomon was the first to propose a good explanation for the Antarctic ozone hole. Her chemist's intuition told her that the ice crystals that form during the Antarctic winter could provide a surface on which chemical reactions of CFC decomposition products could take place. In 1986, NSF chose Solomon (then 30 years old) to lead a team to Antarctica. Experiments performed during that visit showed that her cloud theory was correct and provided the first solid proof of a connection between CFCs and stratospheric ozone depletion. Solomon was the youngest member of the National Academy of Sciences when elected in 1992. She won a National Medal of Science in March 2000, the 2002 Weizmann Women & Science Award, and the 2004 Blue Planet Prize for ". . . achievements . . . that have contributed to the resolution of global environmental problems." Solomon has said that her winters as a young girl in Chicago prepared her for her visits to Antarctica.

The United Nations Environment Programme Web site reports activities relevant to stratospheric ozone control at **www.unep.org/ozone**.

The U.S. EPA Web site **(www.epa.gov/ozone)** and its many links provide current information about stratospheric ozone depletion.

which is *UNEP/WMO Scientific Assessment of Ozone Depletion: 2002.* Levels of ozone-depleting compounds in the troposphere are slowly declining from the peak that occurred in 1992–1994. However, total chlorine abundance in the stratosphere is now at or near a peak. The latest report predicts that Antarctic ozone levels will be increasing by 2010 because of decreasing amounts of halogens in the atmosphere. The report suggests that it will be about 2050 before the total ozone returns to pre-1980 levels.

Manufacturers began seeking alternatives to CFCs almost immediately after it became clear that CFCs would eventually be phased out. One class of possible CFC substitutes includes molecules called HCFCs in which some C—Cl or C—F bonds are replaced with C—H bonds. An example of such a molecule is CH_2Cl_2. Because they contain C—H bonds, HCFC molecules are more reactive in the troposphere than CFC molecules. Therefore, fewer HCFCs survive long enough to reach the stratosphere, where they could lead to ozone depletion. Even better alternatives are hydrofluorocarbons (HFCs). They contain only carbon, fluorine, and hydrogen, so they have no chlorine atoms to catalyze ozone destruction. In refrigerators, for example, $C_2H_2F_4$ can be substituted for CFC-12. Older car air conditioners used CFC-12, but automakers switched the air-conditioning systems in their new cars to $C_2H_2F_4$ (HFC-134a) by 1995. In the United States, the phaseout of CFCs for auto air conditioners, and the cost associated with switching older cars to new coolants, has led to a substantial amount of smuggling of CFCs into the United States.

10.12 Chemistry and Pollution in the Troposphere

An **air pollutant** is any substance that degrades air quality. Nature pollutes the air on a massive scale with volcanic ash, sulfur oxides, mercury vapor, hydrogen chloride, and hydrogen sulfide from volcanoes and with reactive, odorous organic compounds from coniferous plants such as pine trees. Decaying vegetation, ruminant animals, and even termites add large quantities of methane gas to the atmosphere, and decaying animal carcasses and other protein materials add dinitrogen monoxide (N_2O). But automobiles, electric power plants, smelting and other metallurgic processes, and petroleum refining also add significant quantities of unwanted substances to the atmosphere. Atmospheric pollutants, whatever their origin, can have adverse effects, including burning eyes, coughing, decreased lung capacity, harm to vegetation, and even the destruction of ancient monuments. Millions of tons of soot, dust, smoke particles, and chemicals are discharged directly into the atmosphere every year. Such pollutants, which enter the environment directly from their sources, are called **primary pollutants.**

Primary Pollutants

Particle Pollutants

Pollutant particles range in size from fly ash particles, which are big enough to see, to individual molecules, ions, or atoms. Many pollutants are incorporated into water droplets and form **aerosols,** which are colloids (Section 15.9) consisting of liquid droplets or finely divided solids dispersed in a gas. Fogs and smoke are common examples of aerosols. Larger solid particles in the atmosphere are called **particulates.** The solids in an aerosol or particulate may be metal oxides, soil particles, sea salt, fly ash from electrical generating plants and incinerators, elemental carbon, or even small metal particles. Aerosol particles can range in diameter from about 1 nm to about 10,000 nm (10 μm) and can contain 10^{12} atoms, ions, or small molecules. Particles in the 2000-nm range are largely responsible for the deterioration of visibility often observed in highly populated urban centers such as Houston and Mexico City.

In 1997 the EPA revised its national ambient air quality standards (NAAQS) for particulate matter and set standards for the first time for particles with diameters less than 2.5 μm. The fine-particle rule set an annual limit on the mass per unit volume of particulates with diameters less than 2.5 μm in the air to 15 $\mu g/m^3$. A series of court cases in 1997–2002 ultimately led to the upholding of the U.S. EPA standards by the U.S. Supreme Court, and these standards are now in place.

A table of the current NAAQS for many pollutants, including particulates, can be found at **http://epa.gov/air/criteria.html**.

Aerosols are small enough to remain suspended in the atmosphere for long periods. Such small particles are easily breathable and can cause lung disease. Because of their relatively large surface area, aerosol particles have great capacities to *adsorb* and concentrate chemicals on their surfaces. Liquid aerosols or particles covered with a thin coating of water may also *absorb* air pollutants, thereby concentrating them and providing a medium in which reactions may occur.

To *adsorb* is to attract firmly to a surface. To *absorb* is to draw into the bulk of a solid or liquid.

Sulfur Dioxide

Sulfur dioxide (SO_2), the pollutant that is a major contributor to industrial smog and acid rain, is produced when sulfur or sulfur-containing compounds are burned in air. Most of the coal burned in the United States contains sulfur in the form of the mineral pyrite (FeS_2). The weight percent of sulfur in this coal ranges from 1 to 4%. The pyrite is oxidized as the coal is burned, producing sulfur dioxide.

$$4\ FeS_2(s) + 11\ O_2(g) \longrightarrow 2\ Fe_2O_3(s) + 8\ SO_2(g)$$

Sulfur is also part of some of the organic compounds making up the coal itself.

Oil-burning electrical generation plants produce quantities of SO_2 comparable to coal-burning facilities, since fuel oils can also contain up to 4% sulfur. The sulfur in oil is in the form of smelly organic compounds in which sulfur atoms are bound to carbon and hydrogen atoms (the —SH functional group), such as CH_3CH_2SH. A mixture of such low-molar-mass compounds is used as an odorant in natural gas so that gas leaks can be detected by smell.

EXERCISE 10.18 Calculating SO_2 Emissions from Burning Coal

Large quantities of coal are burned in the United States to generate electricity. A 1000-MW coal-fired generating plant will burn 3.06×10^6 kg of coal per hour. For coal that contains 4% sulfur by weight, calculate the mass of SO_2 released (a) per hour and (b) per year.

CHEMISTRY YOU CAN DO

Particle Size and Visibility

A common feature of all aerosols is that they decrease visibility. This problem can be observed in a city or along a busy highway, for example. Fog is an extreme example of disruption of visibility by aerosol particles. Here is a way to simulate the effect of air pollutants on visibility. You will need a flashlight, a little milk, a transparent container (if possible, with flat, parallel sides) full of water, and something with which to stir the water.

Turn off the room lights and shine the beam of the flashlight through the container perpendicular to the flat sides. What do you observe? Can you see the beam? Now add a couple of drops of milk to the container and stir. Can you see the flashlight beam now? How does the beam's appearance change as the angle of viewing changes? What color is it? What color is the light that passes through the milky water? Keep adding milk dropwise, stirring and observing until the beam of the flashlight is no longer visible from the far side of the container.

1. Which wavelengths of light are scattered more by the particles? Which are scattered less?
2. Based on your observations of the milky water, devise an explanation of the fact that at midday on a sunny day the sun appears to be white or yellow, while at sunset it appears orange or red.

CHEMISTRY IN THE NEWS

Hazy Observations

Haze in the atmosphere can lead to a number of phenomena, both beautiful and unsightly—a polychrome sunset, the smoky bluish color of Tennessee's Great Smoky Mountains, limited visibility in national parks. Such haze forms naturally in many ways. For example, volatile organic compounds released by trees react with gases in the atmosphere to form small particles called aerosols. The largest source of aerosols is the ocean, which sends billions of metric tons of salt spray into the atmosphere each year. Types of aerosol particles include smoke, soot, smog, sea spray, dust, suspended powders, and water droplets with dissolved materials. Whatever their source, aerosol particles are small enough to diffract light, and they cause light scattering, which produces phenomena such as colorful sunsets.

One of the main manmade sources of aerosols is the combination of organic chemicals and sulfur dioxide, which can react in the atmosphere. A recent study[1] focused on aerosol formation chemistry as it could occur where both SO_2 and organic chemicals are released. The most abundant haze was observed when sulfur dioxide levels were elevated. Formation of haze resulted from the combination of acid, such as H_2SO_4 which comes from SO_2, and organic compounds reacting on the surface of aerosol particles in the atmosphere.

The U.S. National Park Service has been studying the air quality in parks for decades, and one component of the study focuses on the decrease in visibility in the parks due to haze. A report of the most recent ten-year study[2] says that the "air quality is generally improving or remaining stable in more than half of the national parks monitored." The national parks with the biggest impairment problems are located in the eastern United States: Mammoth Cave, Shenandoah, Great Smoky Mountains. Sulfate particles ($SO_4^{2-} \cdot x\,H_2O$), a secondary pollutant formed from emitted SO_2, account for 60% to 80% of the visibility impairment in these parks.

Aerosol particles also play a major role in overall atmospheric chemistry. They scatter light back into space. They provide surfaces on which chemical reactions can take place. Droplets of water provide solvent for the dissolution of chemicals that can then undergo reactions in solution. Thousands of reactions can occur in the atmosphere, and sorting through them to find those that are most important is a daunting task. One goal of this area of research is to generate simulations that are realistic enough to be useful while simple enough to be manageable.

Royalty-Free/Corbis

Red sky behind sea stacks at Sunset Beach, Oregon. The red sky results from light scattering due to aerosols in the atmosphere. The stacks are formed as water dissolves rock along lines of weakness, leaving behind a column strong enough to withstand wind and storm.

1. Jang, M., et al. "Heterogeneous Atmospheric Aerosol Production by Acid-Catalyzed Particle-Phase Reactions." *Science*, October 25, 2002; p. 814.
2. National Park Service. "Air Quality in the National Parks." Washington, DC, 2002. Available on the Internet at **http://www2.nature.nps.gov/ard/pubs/aqnps.htm**.

SOURCE: Perkins, S. "Solving Hazy Mysteries." *Science News*, December 7, 2002; p. 360.

Once in the atmosphere, SO_2 can be oxidized by reactions with O_2 or ozone, for example, to form SO_3, which has a strong affinity for water and will dissolve in aqueous aerosol droplets to form sulfuric acid, which contributes to acid rain (Section 17.3).

$$SO_3(g) + H_2O(\ell) \longrightarrow H_2SO_4(aq)$$

Sulfur dioxide can be physiologically harmful to both plants and animals, although most healthy adults can tolerate fairly high levels of SO_2 without apparent lasting ill effects. Exposure to SO_2 levels exceeding 0.2 ppm (p. 431) more than 3% of the time leads to respiratory symptoms in a community of people. Exposure to SO_2 levels exceeding 0.3 ppm for 8 hours can cause vegetation damage. People with chronic respiratory difficulties such as bronchitis or asthma tend to be much more sensitive to SO_2, accounting for many of the deaths during episodes of industrial smog. To reduce the hazards, many facilities have installed equipment that removes SO_2 from emitted gases.

EXERCISE 10.19 Calculations Involving Air Pollutants

Suppose the air on a smoggy day contains 5 ppm SO_2. What volume percent is that?

Nitrogen Oxides

The common oxides of nitrogen found in air, NO and NO_2, are collectively called NO_x.

Most of the nitrogen oxides (**NO_x**) found in the atmosphere originate from nitrogen monoxide, NO, formed whenever nitrogen and oxygen—always present in the atmosphere—are raised to high temperatures, as in an internal combustion engine. This nitrogen monoxide reacts rapidly with atmospheric oxygen to produce NO_2.

Vast quantities of nitrogen oxides are formed each year throughout the world, resulting in a global atmospheric concentration of NO_2 of a few parts per billion or less. In the United States, most oxides of nitrogen are produced during fossil fuel combustion, including that of gasoline in automobile engines, with significantly less coming from natural sources such as the action of lightning. Elsewhere in the world, large amounts are produced by the burning of trees and other biomass. Most NO_2, either from human activities or from natural causes, eventually washes out of the atmosphere in precipitation. This process is one way green plants obtain the nitrogen necessary for their growth. In the troposphere, however, especially around urban centers, excessive NO_2 causes problems.

Normally nitrogen dioxide has a lifetime of about three days in the atmosphere.

In laboratory studies, nitrogen dioxide in concentrations of 25 to 250 ppm inhibits plant growth and causes defoliation. Breathing NO_2 at a concentration of 3 ppm for 1 hour causes bronchial constriction in humans, and short exposures at high levels (150 to 220 ppm) causes changes in the lungs that can be fatal.

As you saw in Section 10.10, during the day nitrogen dioxide photodissociates to form nitrogen monoxide and free oxygen atoms. The oxygen atoms can then react to form ozone and regenerate NO_2. At night, reactions that lead to the formation of dinitrogen pentoxide, N_2O_5, predominate. The N_2O_5 can react with water to form nitric acid, HNO_3, a contributor to acid rain (Section 17.3).

EXERCISE 10.20 Air Pollutant Stoichiometry

If 400 metric tons N_2 is converted to NO and then to HNO_3, what mass (in metric tons) of HNO_3 is produced?

Ozone: A Secondary Pollutant in the Troposphere

In a complex series of reactions involving O_2, NO_2, and oxygen-containing organic compounds, ozone is produced in the troposphere. Ozone is a **secondary pollutant,** one that is formed by reaction of a primary pollutant. Its pungent odor can be detected at concentrations as low as 0.02 ppm. We often smell the ozone produced by sparking electric appliances and photocopiers, or after a thunderstorm when lightning-caused ozone washes out with the rainfall. In the troposphere (the air we breathe), ozone is harmful because it is a component of photochemical smog and because it can damage human health and decompose materials such as plastics and rubber.

The most significant chemical reaction producing ozone in the atmosphere is the combination of molecular oxygen and atomic oxygen. In the troposphere the major source of oxygen atoms is the photodissociation of NO_2 (p. 462).

Ozone photodissociates at any altitude to give an oxygen atom and an oxygen molecule whenever it is struck by photons in the near-ultraviolet range (240 to 310 nm).

$$O_3(g) \xrightarrow{h\nu} O_2(g) + \cdot O \cdot (g)$$

In the troposphere, oxygen atoms react with water to produce hydroxyl radicals (·OH).

$$\cdot O\cdot(g) + H_2O(g) \longrightarrow 2\ \cdot OH(g)$$

In the daytime, when they are produced in large numbers, hydroxyl radicals can react with nitrogen dioxide to produce nitric acid.

$$\cdot NO_2(g) + \cdot OH(g) \longrightarrow HNO_3(g)$$

This three-step process is the primary means of removing NO_2 from the atmosphere. Summing the three steps gives the net reaction

$$O_3(g) + 2\ \cdot NO_2(g) + H_2O(g) \longrightarrow 2\ HNO_3(g) + O_2(g)$$

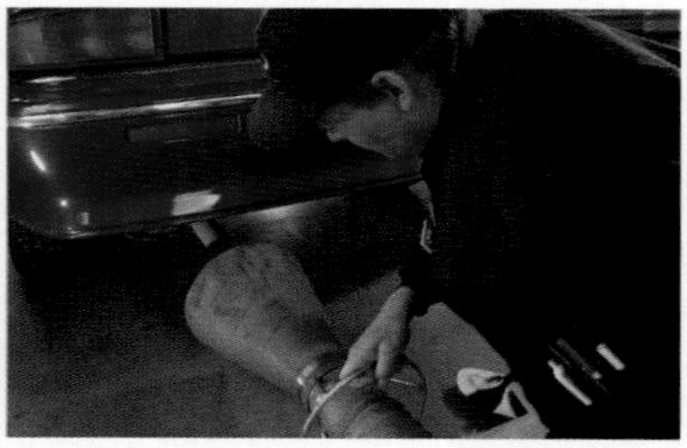

© William Taufic/Corbis

Automobile emissions testing. Such testing is mandated in many cities that have failed to meet EPA's ozone standards. Cars that fail the emissions standards for hydrocarbons and carbon monoxide are required to be repaired. Often the local government will not reissue vehicle registration until satisfactory emissions levels are achieved.

Ozone is a very difficult pollutant to control because its formation depends on sunlight as well as NO_2 and hydrocarbons, which almost every automobile emits to some degree. In cities with high ozone concentrations, the cause is always related to emissions of nitrogen oxides from automobiles, buses, and trucks. Most major urban areas operate vehicle inspection centers for passenger automobiles in an effort to control emissions of nitrogen oxides as well as those of carbon monoxide and unburned hydrocarbons.

As difficult as they are to attain, established ozone standards may not be low enough for good health. Exposure to concentrations of ozone at or near 0.12 ppm has been shown to lower the volume of air a person breathes out per second; studies of children who were exposed to ozone concentrations slightly below the former EPA standard (0.12 ppm) showed a significant decrease in exhaled air volume. In 1997 the EPA lowered the ozone standard to 0.08 ppm for an eight-hour average exposure. No matter what the official standard, ozone concentrations in many urban areas represent health hazards to children at play, joggers, others doing outdoor labor or exercise, and older persons who may have diminished respiratory capabilities.

EXERCISE 10.21 Photodissociation Reactions

Write the equations for the two photodissociation reactions that produce atomic oxygen. Then write the equation for a reaction in which ozone is formed.

Urban Air Pollution—Industrial Smog

The poisonous mixture of smoke (particulate matter), fog (an aerosol), air, and other chemicals was first called **smog** in 1911 by Dr. Harold de Voeux in his report on a London air pollution disaster that caused the deaths of 1150 people. The smog de Voeux identified is the *chemically reducing type* that is derived largely from the combustion of coal and oil and contains sulfur dioxide (a strong reducing agent) mixed with soot, fly ash, smoke, and partially oxidized organic compounds. This industrial smog is common in many cities in the world where heavy industry and power plants are found. Thanks to the U.S. Clean Air Act, industrial smog is becoming less common in the United States as more pollution controls are installed. It is, unfortunately, still a major problem in some cities of the world.

Urban Air Pollution—Photochemical Smog

The other major kind of smog is the *chemically oxidizing type,* which contains strong oxidizing agents such as ozone and oxides of nitrogen, NO_x. It is known as

photochemical smog because light—in this instance sunlight—is important in initiating the reactions that cause it.

Photochemical smog is typical in cities where sunshine is abundant and internal combustion engines exhaust large quantities of pollutants to the atmosphere. Houston and Mexico City are examples (Figure 10.20). This type of smog is practically free of sulfur dioxide but contains substantial amounts of nitrogen oxides, ozone, the products of hydrocarbon oxidation, organic peroxides, and hydrocarbons of varying complexity. The concentrations of these substances vary during the day, building up in the morning hours and dropping off at night (Figure 10.21).

A city's atmosphere is an enormous mixing bowl of interrelated chemical reactions. Identifying the exact chemical reactions that produce photochemical smog was a challenge, but we now know that photochemical reactions are essential to the smog-making process and that aerosols serve to keep the primary pollutants together long enough to form secondary pollutants. Photons in the ultraviolet region of the spectrum are primarily responsible for the formation of photochemical smog.

© AP Images

Figure 10.20 **Photochemical smog over Houston.**

The reaction scheme by which primary pollutants are converted into the secondary pollutants found in photochemical smog (Figure 10.22) is thought to begin with the photodissociation of nitrogen dioxide (Reaction 1). The very reactive atomic oxygen next reacts with molecular oxygen to form ozone, O_3 (Reaction 2), which is then consumed by reacting with nitrogen monoxide to form the original reactant—nitrogen dioxide (Reaction 3).

$$\cdot NO_2(g) \xrightarrow{h\nu} \cdot NO(g) + \cdot O\cdot(g) \quad (1)$$

$$\cdot O\cdot(g) + O_2(g) \longrightarrow O_3(g) \quad (2)$$

$$O_3(g) + \cdot NO(g) \longrightarrow \cdot NO_2(g) + O_2(g) \quad (3)$$

The net effect of these three reactions is absorption of energy without any net chemical change. If this were all that happened there would be no problem. Unfortunately, some of the reactive ozone molecules and oxygen atoms go on to react with other species in the atmosphere, which leads to photochemical smog formation.

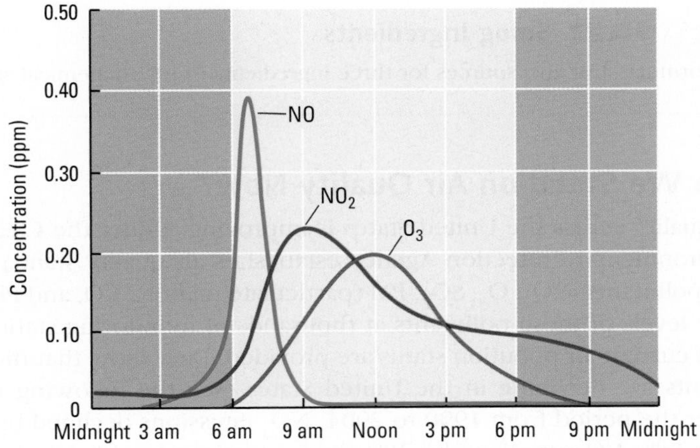

Figure 10.21 **The average concentrations of the pollutants NO, NO_2, and O_3 on a smoggy day in Los Angeles, California.** The NO concentration builds up during the morning rush hour. Later in the day the concentrations of NO_2 and O_3, which are secondary pollutants, build up.

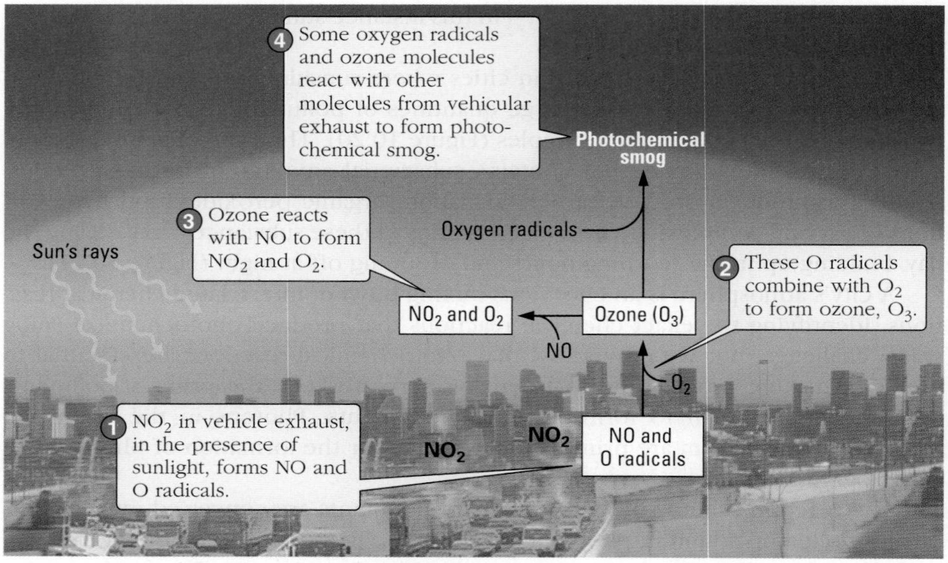

Figure 10.22 **Photochemical smog formation.**

The air in an urban environment contains unburned hydrocarbons released from car exhausts, evaporation, and spillage at filling stations. Atomic oxygen produced in Reaction 1 reacts with the more reactive of these hydrocarbons—unsaturated compounds and aromatics—to form other free radicals. These radicals, in turn, react to form yet other radicals and secondary pollutants such as aldehydes (for example, formaldehyde, HCHO). In addition, reactions of ·OH (hydroxyl radical), ·NO, O_2, and other species can produce other compounds that contribute to the smog. Some of those compounds stabilize NO_2 so that it can be carried over great distances by prevailing winds. Through a variety of chemical reactions coupled with wind, urban pollution in the form of NO_2 can be carried to outlying areas, where it may do additional damage to vegetation, human tissue, and fabrics.

EXERCISE **10.22 Smog Ingredients**

Write the formulas and give sources for three ingredients of photochemical smog.

Where Do We Stand on Air Quality Now?

Average air quality across the United States is improving. Under the Clean Air Act, the U.S. Environmental Protection Agency establishes air quality standards for six principal air pollutants: NO_2, O_3, SO_2, PM (particulate matter), CO, and Pb. The EPA measures the levels of these pollutants at thousands of monitoring stations. Yearly summaries of current air pollution status are provided. Data show that these six primary pollutants are declining in the United States (see the following table). For example, over the period from 1990 to 2004, NO_x emissions declined by 25%, SO_2 emissions by 34%, CO emissions by 39%, lead emissions by 40%, and particulate matter by 17%. The EPA has concluded that "the Clean Air Act has resulted in many improvements in the quality of air in the United States."

Principal Pollutants	Percent Decrease in Emissions (1980–2004)	(1990–2004)
CO	51	39
Pb	96	40
NO_x	31	25
SO_2	41	34
Particulates, < 2.5 μm	—	17

Source: **http://www.epa.gov/airtrends/2005/econ-emissions.html**.

10.13 Atmospheric Carbon Dioxide, the Greenhouse Effect, and Global Warming

Previous sections in this chapter have discussed how earth's atmosphere screens out harmful ultraviolet radiation and makes the surface habitable. The atmosphere also performs another function by moderating the earth's surface temperature.

The Greenhouse Effect

The energy that heats the earth comes from the sun as electromagnetic radiation. Some of the electromagnetic radiation from the sun is reflected by the atmosphere back into space, and some is absorbed by the atmosphere. The remainder reaches the earth, warming its surface and oceans. The warmed surfaces then reradiate this energy into the troposphere as infrared radiation **(⇐ p. 273)**. Carbon dioxide, water vapor, methane, and ozone all absorb radiation in various portions of the infrared region. By absorbing this reradiated energy they warm the atmosphere, creating what is called the **greenhouse effect** (Figure 10.23). Thus, all four are "greenhouse gases." Such gases constitute an absorbing blanket that reduces the quantity of energy radiated back into space. Thanks to the greenhouse effect, the earth's average temperature is a comfortable 15 °C (59 °F). By comparison, the moon, with no moderating atmosphere, has a surface mean daytime temperature of approximately 107 °C and −153 °C at night.

The greenhouse effect derives its name by analogy with a botanical greenhouse. However, the warming in a botanical greenhouse is much more dependent on the glass reducing convection than on blocking infrared radiation from leaving through the glass.

Earth has such a vast reservoir of water in the oceans that human activity has a negligible influence on the concentration of water vapor in the atmosphere. In addition, methane is produced by natural processes in such large quantities that human contributions are negligible. Ozone is present in such small concentrations that its contribution to the greenhouse effect is small. So among the four greenhouse gases, most attention is focused on CO_2.

Radiation from objects on Earth to outer space answers the question, "Why does frost form on top of a parked car in winter, but not on the sides?" that was posed in Chapter 1 **(⇐ p. 2)**.

Carbon dioxide is a greenhouse gas because it absorbs infrared radiation, causing C═O bonds in the molecule to stretch and bend, much like springs attached to balls (Figure 10.24). Stretching and compressing the C═O bonds requires more energy (shorter wavelength) than does bending them. Thus, C═O stretching and compressing occurs when infrared radiation with a wavelength of 4.257 μm is absorbed, whereas the C═O bending vibrations occur at lower energy (longer wavelength) when the molecule absorbs 15.000-μm infrared radiation.

$1\ \mu m = 1 \times 10^{-6}\ m = 1 \times 10^{3}\ nm$

Recall from Section 7.1 that energy and wavelength are inversely related.

Each year fossil fuel combustion worldwide puts about 6.2 billion metric tons of carbon into the atmosphere as CO_2. About 45% is removed from the atmosphere by natural processes—some by plants during photosynthesis and the rest by dissolving in rainwater and the oceans to form hydrogen carbonates and carbonates.

Worldwide, nearly one third of all atmospheric CO_2 is released as a by-product from fossil fuel–burning electric power plants.

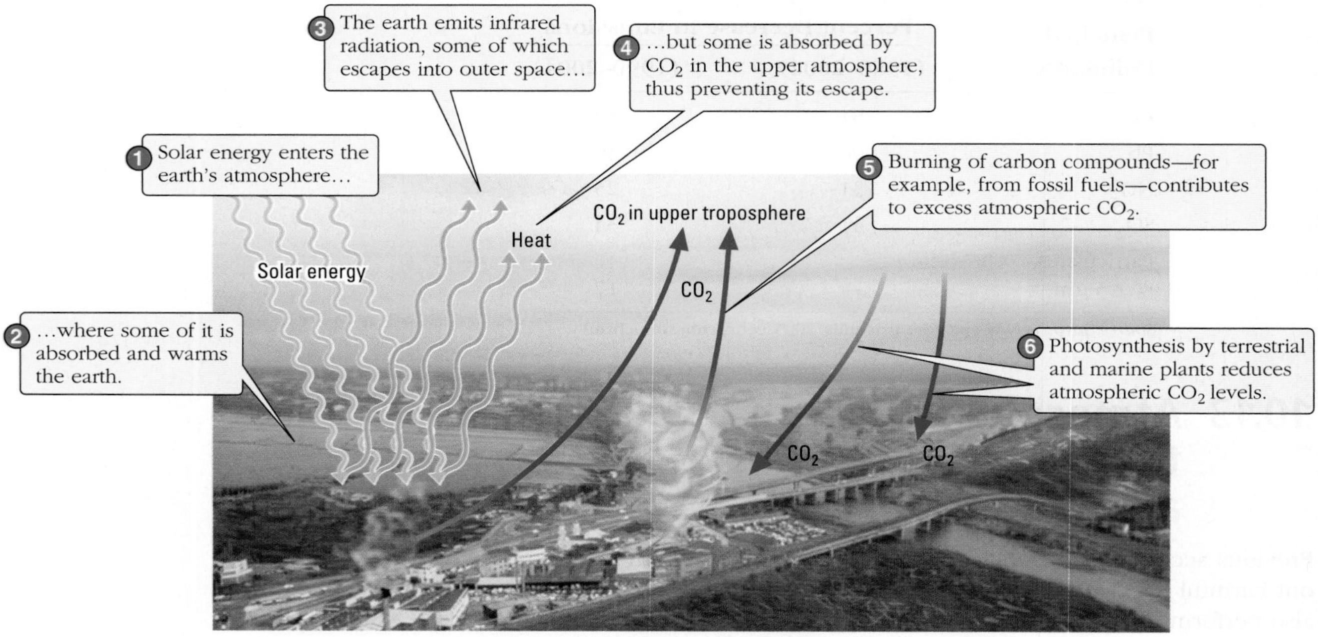

Figure 10.23 The greenhouse effect. Greenhouse gases form an effective barrier that prevents some heat from escaping the earth's surface. Without the greenhouse effect, earth's average temperature would be much lower.

$$CO_2(g) + 2\,H_2O(\ell) \longrightarrow H_3O^+(aq) + HCO_3^-(aq)$$
$$HCO_3^-(aq) + H_2O(\ell) \longrightarrow H_3O^+(aq) + CO_3^{2-}(aq)$$

The other 55% of the carbon dioxide from fossil fuel combustion remains in the atmosphere, increasing the global CO_2 concentration.

CONCEPTUAL EXERCISE 10.23 Sources of CO_2

List as many natural sources of CO_2 as you can. List as many sources of CO_2 from human activities as you can.

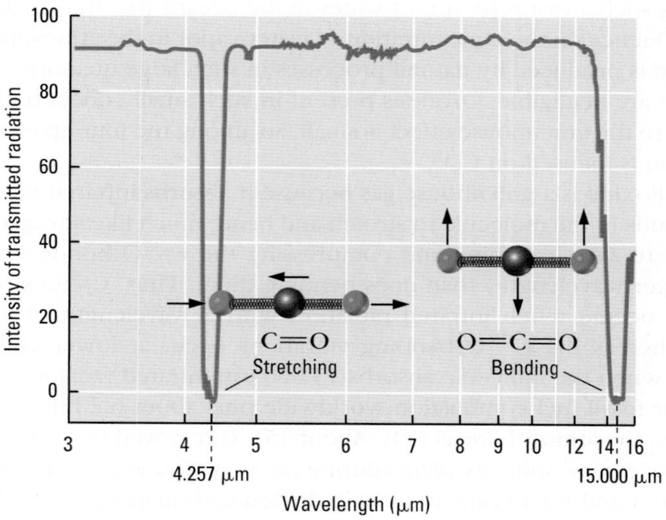

Figure 10.24 Stretching and bending modes in the carbon dioxide gas infrared spectrum. A *Tools of Chemistry* feature describes infrared spectroscopy (← *p. 392*).

Without human influences, the flow of carbon dioxide among the air, plants, animals, and the oceans would be roughly balanced. In 1750, during the preindustrial era, CO_2 concentration in the atmosphere was 277 parts per million (ppm). During the next 130 years, as the Industrial Revolution progressed, the concentration increased to 291 ppm, a 5% increase. Since 1900, however, the rate of increase of CO_2 has reflected the rapid increase in the use of fossil fuel combustion for industrial and domestic purposes, especially for motor vehicle transportation. Between 1958 and 2004, the atmospheric concentration of CO_2 increased from 315 to 377 ppm, an increase of 20% (Figure 10.25). Population pressure is also contributing heavily to increased CO_2 concentrations. In the Amazon region of Brazil, for example, forests are being cut and burned to create cropland. This activity places a tremendous double burden on the natural CO_2 cycle, since there are fewer trees to use the CO_2 in photosynthesis and, at the same time, CO_2 is added to the atmosphere during burning.

Parts per million (ppm) is a convenient way to express low concentrations. One ppm means one part of something in one million parts. A CO_2 concentration of 360 ppm means that for every million molecules of air, 360 are CO_2 molecules.

Stephen Ferry/Liaison/Getty Images

Clearing a Brazilian rain forest.

Expectations are that the atmospheric CO_2 concentration will continue to increase at the current rate of about 1.5 ppm per year, due principally to industrialization, agricultural production, and an expanding global population. As a result, according to sophisticated computer models of climate change, the CO_2 concentration is projected to reach 550 ppm, double its preindustrial value, between 2030 and 2050. The increase may perhaps not be so great if fuel costs increase substantially as fossil fuel supplies get tighter.

The Intergovernmental Panel on Climate Change (IPCC) is a multinational group of climate scientists from around the world. In its 2001 report, *Climate Change 2001,* the IPCC noted that the current concentration of atmospheric carbon dioxide (370 ppm) had not been exceeded during the past 420,000 years and likely not for the past 20 million years. Additionally, nearly 75% of anthropogenic carbon dioxide emissions in the past 20 years are due to the burning of fossil fuels.

To see how easily everyday activities affect the quantity of CO_2 being put into the atmosphere, consider a round-trip flight from New York to Los Angeles. Each passenger pays for about 200 gal jet fuel, which weighs 1400 lb. When burned, each pound of jet fuel produces about 3.14 lb carbon dioxide. So 4400 lb, or 2 metric tons, of carbon dioxide are produced per passenger during that trip.

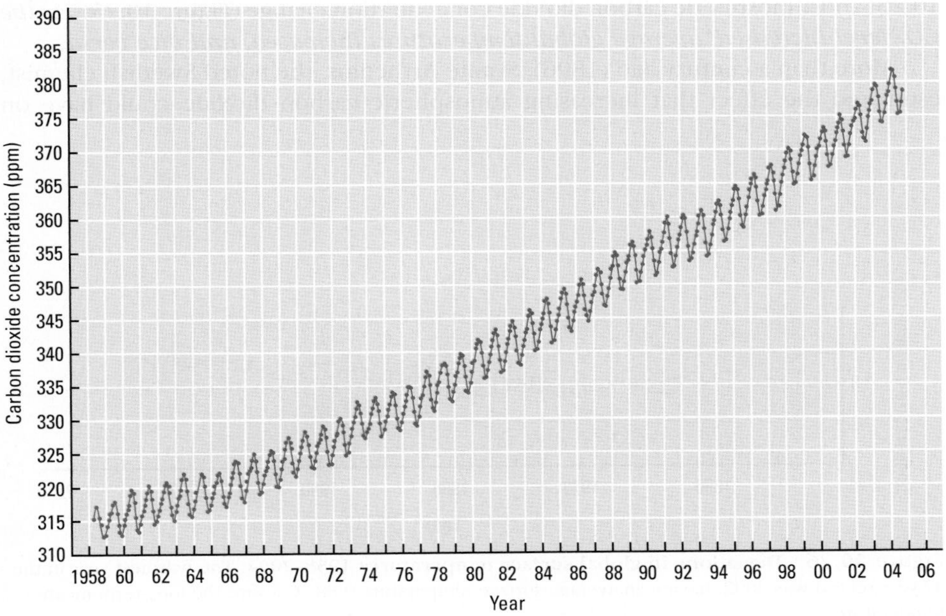

Figure 10.25 **Atmospheric carbon dioxide concentration measured at Mauna Loa, Hawaii.** These data have been carefully collected by a standardized methodology for 47 years, and they are the longest continuous record of atmospheric CO_2 concentrations available. The Mauna Loa record shows a 19.3% increase in CO_2 concentration, from 316 ppm to 377 ppm, over the period 1959 to 2004. *Source:* **http://cdiac.esd.ornl.gov/trends/co2/sio-mlo.htm**.

EXERCISE 10.24 CO_2 Changes

Using data from Figure 10.25, calculate the percent increase in atmospheric CO_2 from
(a) 1900 to 1950
(b) 1950 to 2001
(c) 1990 to 2001
Which period showed the greatest percent increase in CO_2?

CONCEPTUAL EXERCISE 10.25 Annual CO_2 Changes

During a year, atmospheric CO_2 concentration fluctuates, building up to a high value, then dropping to a low value before building up again (Figure 10.25). Explain what causes this fluctuation and when during the year the high and the low occur in the Northern Hemisphere.

CONCEPTUAL EXERCISE 10.26 Carbon Dioxide and Air Travel

Use an Internet search engine to find the annual airline passenger miles for a recent year and calculate how many tons of CO_2 were produced by those flights. Compare this quantity to the quantity of CO_2 produced for the same number of miles traveled in automobiles. (*Hint:* Assume a miles-per-gallon value and an average number of passengers per vehicle. Then use the same numbers for gasoline as were used in the last paragraph on page 475.)

Global Warming

Global warming is the temperature increase due to the greenhouse effect *amplified* by increasing concentrations of CO_2 and other greenhouse gases. Figure 10.26 shows the global surface temperature deviations over the past five decades. Notice the parallel relationship between deviations in global surface temperature (Figure 10.26) and atmospheric carbon dioxide concentration change (Figure 10.25). *As the CO_2 level increased, average global temperatures increased, and vice versa.*

More than a century ago (1896), Svante Arrhenius, the noted Swedish chemist, estimated the effect that increasing atmospheric carbon dioxide could have on

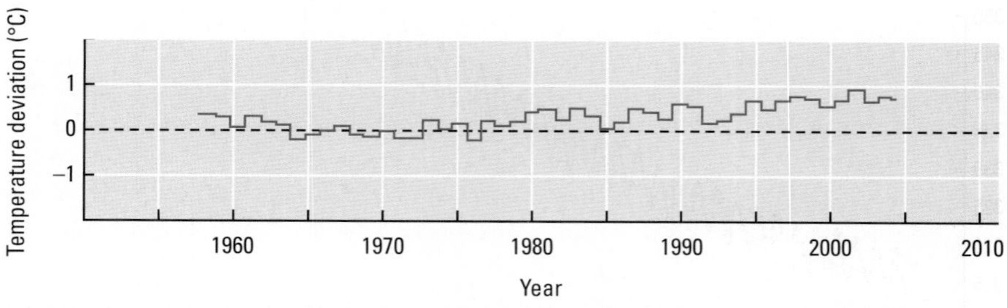

Figure 10.26 Deviations in global surface temperatures 1958–2004. The warmest year in the 47-year record was 2002, having an average surface temperature 0.88 °C above the long-term mean temperature.

Source: Angell, J.K. 2005. Global, hemispheric, and zonal temperature deviations derived from radiosonde records. In Trends Online: A Compendium of Data on Global Change. Carbon Dioxide Information Analysis Center, Oak Ridge National Laboratory, U.S. Department of Energy, Oak Ridge, Tennessee, U.S.A. **http://cdiac.ornl.gov/trends/temp/angell/angell.html.**

global temperature. He calculated that doubling the carbon dioxide concentration would increase the temperature by 5 to 6 °C. Disturbed by the prospects of his prediction, he described the possible scenario in picturesque terms: "We are evaporating our coal mines into the air."

Arrhenius had not foreseen the advent of motor vehicles and their impact on increasing atmospheric carbon dioxide

CONCEPTUAL EXERCISE **10.27 Evaporating Coal Mines**

Explain Arrhenius's quote in terms of global warming.

Many computer models predict that increasing atmospheric CO_2 to 600 ppm will increase average global temperature, and most climate experts who do global warming research agree. What is uncertain is the extent of the temperature increase, with estimates varying from 1.5 to 4.5 °C (2.7 to 8.1 °F). The prestigious United Nations Intergovernmental Panel on Climate Change (IPCC) estimates a 1.0 to 3.5 °C (2 to 6 °F) increase by the year 2100. Warming by as little as 1.5 °C would produce the warmest climate seen on earth in the past 6000 years; an increase of 4.5 °C would produce world temperatures higher than any since the Mesozoic era, the time of the dinosaurs. Recent research suggests that the 2002 average global temperature was the highest in the past 1000 years. In particular, there has been nearly a 0.7 °C increase from the average since the late 1800s, a period of rapid industrial development. In 1996, the IPCC's *Second Assessment Report* concluded, "The balance of evidence suggests a discernible influence on global climate." In its third report (2001), the IPCC declared, "What can be stated in summary regarding the diverse set of impacts reported to date is that there are cases of observed impacts in many diverse environments; that they occur in a wide array of processes, species, and ecosystems; and that the overall patterns and processes reveal a coherent impact of 20th-century climate changes on many physical and biological systems."

A 1.5 °C rise in global temperature is a significant change, requiring a very large input of energy.

Many scientists are concerned that rising temperatures will cause more of the ice caps in Greenland and Antarctica to melt, raising the sea level and flooding coastal cities. In conjunction with this, atmospheric currents will change and produce significant changes in weather and agricultural productivity. Since the 1940s, average summertime temperatures in Antarctica have increased 2.5 °C to just above 0 °C. Ice shelves there lost nearly 13% of their total area during 1998 alone.

Computer models used to predict future global temperature changes have become more sophisticated and accurate over the past decade. When factors in addition to greenhouse gases, such as the presence of aerosols (tiny, suspended particles) and changes in the sun's irradiance are taken into account, the computer models predict temperature changes close to what has been observed since 1860 (Figure 10.27). Such work adds credibility to the predictions of temperature increases of 1.5 to 4.5 °C due to global warming.

Global warming could become a major worldwide problem. Concerns about it prompted nearly 10,000 delegates from 159 countries to convene in Kyoto, Japan, in December 1997. Goals were set there to reduce atmospheric greenhouse gases from 1990 levels. Under these targets, to be met between 2008 and 2012, industrialized nations would decrease their greenhouse gas emissions by about 5% overall. The United States would be expected to lower emissions to 7% below 1990 levels, the European Union nations by 8%, and Japan by 7%. The Kyoto agreement is to take effect 90 days after it is ratified by at least 55 nations that account overall for 55% of the total 1990 CO_2 emissions. In 2002 President George W. Bush announced that the United States will not ratify the treaty because it would be harmful to industrial progress. As of September 2005, 157 nations, accounting for 61% of total CO_2 emissions, have ratified the agreement. The accord became official in February 2005.

The most obvious measure to reduce global warming is to control CO_2 emissions throughout the world. Given our dependence on fossil fuels, however, getting

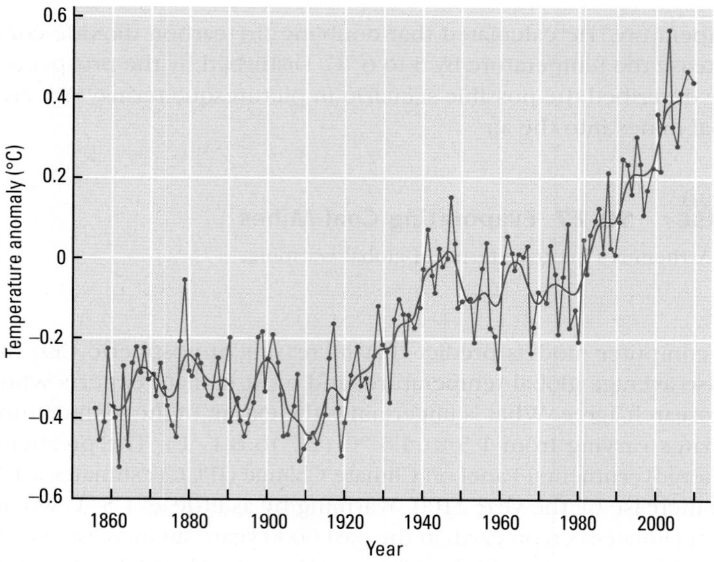

Figure 10.27 **Global temperature change over the past 150 years.** The blue points show the annual average temperatures, and the red line shows the five-year average temperatures. The global average temperature has risen approximately 0.6 to 0.8 °C over the past 150 years.
Source: **http://en.wikipedia.org/wiki/Global_warming.**

and keeping these emissions under control will be very difficult. One direct way to decrease the quantity of atmospheric CO_2 is to plant more trees and to replace those in deforested areas.

The projected extent of global warming remains a thorny issue. The uncertainty in the temperature changes attributable to global warming is related to three fundamental, but difficult, questions:

1. To what levels will CO_2 and other greenhouse gases rise during the next decades?
2. How inherently responsive is the earth's climate to the warming created by the greenhouse effect?
3. Is the current global warming being caused by human activities, or is it part of a natural cycle of global temperature changes?

Credible atmospheric scientists worldwide think that enhanced global warming is already occurring and that anthropogenic sources are contributing to this warming. In 2006, an expert panel convened by the U.S. National Academy of Sciences, the Committee of Surface Temperature Reconstruction for the Last 2,000 Years, produced a report that stated, "It can be said with a high level of confidence that global mean surface temperature was higher during the last few decades of the 20th century than during any comparable period during the preceding four centuries."

SUMMARY PROBLEM

The air that enters an automobile engine contains the oxygen that reacts with the hydrocarbon fuel vapors to provide the energy needed to move the vehicle. Prior to the combustion process the fuel-air mixture is compressed, and then it is ignited with a spark. Most of the fuel is completely burned to CO_2 and H_2O, and some of the nitrogen in air is converted to nitrogen monoxide (NO). For simplicity, assume the fuel has a formula of C_8H_{18} and a density of 0.703 g/mL.

(a) What are the partial pressures of N_2 and O_2 in the air before it goes into the engine if the atmospheric pressure is 734 mm Hg?

(b) If no fuel were added to the air and it was compressed to seven times atmospheric pressure (approximately the compression ratio in a modern engine), what would the partial pressures of N_2 and O_2 become?

(c) Assume the volume of each cylinder in the engine is 485 mL and that the temperature is 150 °C. If 0.050 mL of the fuel is added to the air in each cylinder just prior to compression, and the fuel is completely vaporized, what would be the partial pressure of the mixture in a cylinder due to the fuel molecules?

(d) How many moles of oxygen would be required to burn the fuel completely to CO_2 and H_2O?

(e) If 10.% of the nitrogen in the combustion process is converted to NO, calculate how many grams of NO are produced in a single combustion reaction.

(f) Write an equation that shows the conversion of NO to a more photoreactive compound.

(g) Calculate the mass of the more photoreactive compound that would be formed from the NO produced in part (e).

(h) What additional information would you need to calculate the NO emissions for an entire city for a year?

IN CLOSING

Having studied this chapter, you should be able to . . .

- Describe the components of the atmosphere (Section 10.1). ThomsonNOW homework: Study Question 13
- Describe the properties of gases (Section 10.2). ThomsonNOW homework: Study Questions 16, 120, 121
- State the fundamental concepts of the kinetic-molecular theory and use them to explain gas behavior (Section 10.3). ThomsonNOW homework: Study Question 24
- Solve problems using the appropriate gas laws (Sections 10.4 and 10.5). ThomsonNOW homework: Study Questions 30, 32, 37, 41, 43, 45
- Calculate the quantities of gaseous reactants and products involved in chemical reactions (Section 10.6). ThomsonNOW homework: Study Questions 53, 55, 59
- Apply the ideal gas law to finding gas densities and molar masses (Section 10.7). ThomsonNOW homework: Study Questions 63, 66, 70
- Perform calculations using partial pressures of gases in mixtures (Section 10.8). ThomsonNOW homework: Study Questions 71, 73
- Describe the differences between real and ideal gases (Section 10.9). ThomsonNOW homework: Study Question 84
- Describe the main chemical reactions occurring in the atmosphere (Section 10.10). ThomsonNOW homework: Study Question 92
- Explain the main features of stratospheric ozone depletion and the role of CFCs in it (Section 10.11). ThomsonNOW homework: Study Question 96
- Describe the main chemicals found in industrial pollution and urban pollution and the reactions producing industrial pollution and urban pollution (Section 10.12). ThomsonNOW homework: Study Question 15
- Relate atmospheric CO_2 concentration to the greenhouse effect and to enhanced global warming (Section 10.13). ThomsonNOW homework: Study Question 114

ThomsonNOW™
Sign in to ThomsonNOW at **www.thomsonedu.com** to check your readiness for an exam by taking the Pre-Test and exploring the modules recommended in your Personalized Learning Plan.

KEY TERMS

absolute temperature scale *(10.4)*
absolute zero *(10.4)*
aerosols *(10.12)*
air pollutant *(10.12)*
Avogadro's law *(10.4)*
bar *(10.2)*
barometer *(10.2)*
Boyle's law *(10.4)*
Charles's law *(10.4)*
chlorofluorocarbons (CFCs) *(10.11)*
combined gas law *(10.5)*
Dalton's law of partial pressures *(10.8)*
diffusion *(10.3)*
effusion *(10.3)*
electronically excited molecule *(10.10)*
ideal gas *(10.4)*
ideal gas constant *(10.5)*
ideal gas law *(10.5)*
global warming *(10.13)*
greenhouse effect *(10.13)*
Kelvin temperature scale *(10.4)*
law of combining volumes *(10.4)*
millimeters of mercury (mm Hg) *(10.2)*
mole fraction *(10.8)*
newton (N) *(10.2)*
NO_x *(10.12)*
ozone hole *(10.11)*
partial pressure *(10.8)*
particulates *(10.12)*
pascal (Pa) *(10.2)*
photochemical reactions *(10.10)*
photochemical smog *(10.12)*
photodissociation *(10.10)*
pressure *(10.2)*
primary pollutant *(10.12)*
secondary pollutant *(10.12)*
smog *(10.12)*
standard atmosphere (atm) *(10.2)*
standard molar volume *(10.5)*
standard temperature and pressure (STP) *(10.5)*
stratosphere *(10.1)*
stratospheric ozone layer *(10.11)*
torr *(10.2)*
troposphere *(10.1)*
van der Waals equation *(10.9)*

QUESTIONS FOR REVIEW AND THOUGHT

■ denotes questions available in ThomsonNOW and assignable in OWL.

Blue-numbered questions have short answers at the back of this book and fully worked solutions in the *Student Solutions Manual.*

ThomsonNOW™
Assess your understanding of this chapter's topics with sample tests and other resources found by signing in to ThomsonNOW at **www.thomsonedu.com**.

Review Questions

1. Name the three gas laws and explain how they interrelate *P*, *V*, and *T*. Explain the relationships in words and with equations.
2. What are the conditions represented by STP?
3. What is the volume occupied by 1 mol of an ideal gas at STP?
4. What is the definition of pressure?
5. State Avogadro's law. Explain why two volumes of hydrogen react with one volume of oxygen to form two volumes of steam.
6. State Dalton's law of partial pressures. If the air we breathe is 78% N_2 and 22% O_2 on a mole basis, what is the mole fraction of O_2? What is the partial pressure of O_2 if the total pressure is 720 mm Hg?
7. Explain Boyle's law on the basis of the kinetic-molecular theory.
8. Explain why gases at low temperature and high pressure do not obey the ideal gas equation as well as gases at high temperature and low pressure.
9. Gaseous water and carbon dioxide each absorb infrared radiation. Does either of them absorb ultraviolet radiation? Explain your answer.
10. Describe the difference between primary and secondary air pollutants and give two examples of each.

Topical Questions

The Atmosphere

11. Explain the major roles played by nitrogen in the atmosphere. Do the same for oxygen.
12. Beginning nearest the earth, name the two most important layers or regions of the atmosphere. Describe, in general, the kinds of chemical reactions that occur in each layer.
13. ■ Convert all of the "percentage by volume" figures in Table 10.1 into (a) parts per million and (b) parts per billion. Which atmospheric gases are present at concentrations of less than 1 ppb? Between 1 ppb and 1 ppm? Greater than 1 ppm?
14. The mass of the earth's atmosphere is 5.3×10^{15} metric tons. The atmospheric abundance of helium is 0.7 ppm when expressed as a fraction by *weight* instead of by *volume*, as in Table 10.1. How many metric tons of helium are there in the atmosphere? How many moles of helium is this?
15. ■ Sulfur is about 2.5% of the mass of coal, and when coal is burned the sulfur is all converted to SO_2. In one year, 3.1 ×

10^9 metric tons of coal was burned worldwide. How many tons of SO_2 were added to the atmosphere? How many tons of SO_2 are currently in the atmosphere? (*Note:* The weight fraction of SO_2 in air is 0.4 ppb.)

Properties of Gases

16. ■ Gas pressures can be expressed in units of mm Hg, atm, torr, and kPa. Convert these pressure values.
    (a) 720. mm Hg to atm (b) 1.25 atm to mm Hg
    (c) 542. mm Hg to torr (d) 740. mm Hg to kPa
    (e) 700. kPa to atm
17. Convert these pressure values.
    (a) 120. mm Hg to atm (b) 2.00 atm to mm Hg
    (c) 100. kPa to mm Hg (d) 200. kPa to atm
    (e) 36.0 kPa to atm (f) 600. kPa to mm Hg
18. Mercury has a density of 13.96 g/cm^3. A barometer is constructed using an oil with a density of 0.75 g/cm^3. If the atmospheric pressure is 1.0 atm, what will be the height in meters of the oil column in the barometer?
19. A vacuum pump is connected to the top of an upright tube whose lower end is immersed in a pool of mercury. How high will the mercury rise in the tube when the pump is turned on?
20. Why can't a hand-driven pump on a water well pull underground water from depths more than 33 ft? Would it help to have a motor-driven vacuum pump?
21. A scuba diver taking photos of a coral reef 60 ft below the ocean surface breathes out a stream of bubbles. What is the total gas pressure of these bubbles at the moment they are released? What is the gas pressure in the bubbles when they reach the surface of the ocean?

Kinetic-Molecular Theory

22. List the five basic concepts of the kinetic-molecular theory. Which assumption is incorrect at very high pressures? Which one is incorrect at low temperatures? Which assumption is probably most nearly correct?
23. You are given two flasks of equal volume. Flask A contains H_2 at 0 °C and 1 atm pressure. Flask B contains CO_2 gas at 0 °C and 2 atm pressure. Compare these two samples with respect to each of these properties.
    (a) Average kinetic energy per molecule
    (b) Average molecular velocity
    (c) Number of molecules
24. ■ Place these gases in order of increasing average molecular speed at 25 °C: Kr, CH_4, N_2, CH_2Cl_2.
25. Arrange these four gases in order of increasing average molecular speed at 25 °C: Cl_2, F_2, N_2, O_2.
26. If equal amounts of the four inert gases Ar, Ne, Kr, and Xe are released at the same time at the end of a long tube, which gas will reach the end of the tube first?
27. The reaction of SO_2 with Cl_2 to give dichlorine oxide is

$$SO_2(g) + 2\ Cl_2(g) \longrightarrow SOCl_2(g) + Cl_2O(g)$$

    Place all molecules in the equation in order of increasing average molecular speed.
28. From Table 10.1 list all the gases in the atmosphere in order of *decreasing* average molecular speed. Concern has been expressed about one of these gases escaping into outer space because a fraction of its molecules have velocities large enough to break free from earth's gravitational field. Which gas is it?

Gas Behavior and the Ideal Gas Law

29. How many moles of CO are present in 1.0 L air at STP that contains 950 ppm CO?
30. ■ If 50.75 g of a gas occupies 10.0 L at STP, what volume will 129.3 g of the gas occupy at STP?
31. A sample of gaseous CO exerts a pressure of 45.6 mm Hg in a 56.0-L flask at 22 °C. If the gas is released into a 2.70×10^4-L room, what is the partial pressure of the CO in the room at 22 °C?
32. ■ A sample of a gas has a pressure of 100. mm Hg in a 125-mL flask. If this gas sample is transferred to another flask with a volume of 200. mL, what will be the new pressure? Assume that the temperature remains constant.
33. A sample of a gas is placed in a 256-mL flask, where it exerts a pressure of 75.0 mm Hg. What is the pressure of this gas if it is transferred to a 125-mL flask? (The temperature stays constant.)
34. A sample of gas has a pressure of 62 mm Hg in a 100-mL flask. This sample of gas is transferred to another flask, where its pressure is 29 mm Hg. What is the volume of the new flask? (The temperature does not change.)
35. Some butane, the fuel used in backyard grills, is placed in a 3.50-L container at 25 °C; its pressure is 735 mm Hg. If you transfer the gas to a 15.0-L container, also at 25 °C, what is the pressure of the gas in the larger container?
36. A sample of gas at 30. °C has a pressure of 2.0 atm in a 1.0-L container. What pressure will it exert in a 4.0-L container? The temperature does not change.
37. ■ Suppose you have a sample of CO_2 in a gas-tight syringe with a movable piston. The gas volume is 25.0 mL at a room temperature of 20. °C. What is the final volume of the gas if you hold the syringe in your hand to raise the gas temperature to 37. °C?
38. A balloon is inflated with helium to a volume of 4.5 L at 23 °C. If you take the balloon outside on a cold day (−10. °C), what will be the new volume of the balloon?
39. A sample of gas has a volume of 2.50 L at a pressure of 670. mm Hg and a temperature of 80. °C. If the pressure remains constant but the temperature is decreased, the gas occupies 1.25 L. What is this new temperature, in degrees Celsius?
40. A sample of 9.0 L CO_2 at 20 °C and 1 atm pressure is cooled so that it occupies a volume of 8.0 L at some new temperature. The pressure remains constant. What is the new temperature, in kelvins?
41. ■ A bicycle tire is inflated to a pressure of 3.74 atm at 15 °C. If the tire is heated to 35 °C, what is the pressure in the tire? Assume the tire volume doesn't change.
42. An automobile tire is inflated to a pressure of 3.05 atm on a rather warm day when the temperature is 40. °C. The car is then driven to the mountains and parked overnight. The morning temperature is −5.0 °C. What will be the pressure of the gas in the tire? Assume the volume of the tire doesn't change.

43. ■ A sample of gas occupies 754 mL at 22 °C and a pressure of 165 mm Hg. What is its volume if the temperature is raised to 42 °C and the pressure is raised to 265 mm Hg? (The number of moles does not change.)

44. A balloon is filled with helium to a volume of 1.05×10^3 L on the ground, where the pressure is 745 mm Hg and the temperature is 20. °C. When the balloon ascends to a height of 2 miles, where the pressure is only 600. mm Hg and the temperature is −33 °C, what is the volume of the helium in the balloon?

45. ■ What is the pressure exerted by 1.55 g Xe gas at 20. °C in a 560-mL flask?

46. A 1.00-g sample of water is allowed to vaporize completely inside a 10.0-L container. What is the pressure of the water vapor at a temperature of 150. °C?

47. Which of these gas samples contains the largest number of molecules and which contains the smallest?
   (a) 1.0 L H_2 at STP
   (b) 1.0 L N_2 at STP
   (c) 1.0 L H_2 at 27 °C and 760. mm Hg
   (d) 1.0 L CO_2 at 0 °C and 800. mm Hg

48. Ozone molecules attack rubber and cause cracks to appear. If enough cracks occur in a rubber tire, for example, it will be weakened, and it may burst from the pressure of the air inside. As little as 0.020 ppm O_3 will cause cracks to appear in rubber in about 1 hour. Assume that a 1.0-cm^3 sample of air containing 0.020 ppm O_3 is brought in contact with a sample of rubber that is 1.0 cm^2 in area. Calculate the number of O_3 molecules that are available to collide with the rubber surface. The temperature of the air sample is 25 °C and the pressure is 0.95 atm.

Quantities of Gases in Chemical Reactions

49. When a commercial drain cleaner containing sodium hydroxide and small pieces of aluminum is poured into a clogged drain, this reaction occurs:

$$2\ Al(s) + 2\ NaOH(aq) + 6\ H_2O(\ell) \rightarrow 2\ NaAl(OH)_4(aq) + 2\ H_2(g)$$

If 6.5 g Al and excess NaOH are reacted, what volume of H_2 gas measured at 742 mm Hg and 22.0 °C will be produced?

50. If 2.7 g Al metal is reacted with excess HCl, how many liters of H_2 gas are produced at 25 °C and 1.00 atm pressure?

51. The yeast in rising bread dough converts sugar (sucrose, $C_{12}H_{22}O_{11}$) into carbon dioxide. A popular recipe for two loaves of French bread requires 1 package of yeast and $\frac{1}{4}$ teaspoon (about 2.4 g) of sugar. What volume of CO_2 at STP is produced by the complete conversion of this quantity of sucrose into CO_2 by the yeast? Compare this volume with the typical volume of two loaves of bread.

52. Water can be made by combining gaseous O_2 and H_2. If you begin with 1.5 L H_2(g) at 360. mm Hg and 23 °C, what volume in liters of O_2(g) will you need for complete reaction if the O_2 gas is also measured at 360. mm Hg and 23 °C?

53. ■ Gaseous silane, SiH_4, ignites spontaneously in air according to the equation

$$SiH_4(g) + 2\ O_2(g) \longrightarrow SiO_2(s) + 2\ H_2O(g)$$

If 5.2 L SiH_4 is treated with O_2, what volume in liters of O_2 is required for complete reaction? What volume of H_2O vapor is produced? Assume all gases are measured at the same temperature and pressure.

54. Hydrogen can be made in the "water gas reaction."

$$C(s) + H_2O(g) \longrightarrow H_2(g) + CO(g)$$

If you begin with 250. L gaseous water at 120. °C and 2.00 atm and excess C(s), what mass in grams of H_2 can be prepared?

55. ■ If boron hydride, B_4H_{10}, is treated with pure oxygen, it burns to give B_2O_3 and H_2O.

$$2\ B_4H_{10}(s) + 11\ O_2(g) \longrightarrow 4\ B_2O_3(s) + 10\ H_2O(g)$$

If a 0.050-g sample of the boron hydride burns completely in O_2, what will be the pressure of the gaseous water in a 4.25-L flask at 30. °C?

56. If 1.0×10^3 g uranium metal is converted to gaseous UF_6, what pressure of UF_6 would be observed at 62 °C in a chamber that has a volume of 3.0×10^2 L?

57. Ten liters of F_2 gas at 1.00 atm and 100.0 °C reacts with 99.9 g $CaBr_2$ to form CaF_2 and bromine gas. What volume of Br_2 gas will form at this temperature and pressure?

58. Metal carbonates decompose to the metal oxide and CO_2 on heating according to this general equation.

$$M_x(CO_3)_y(s) \longrightarrow M_xO_y(s) + y\ CO_2(g)$$

You heat 0.158 g of a white, solid carbonate of a Group 2A metal and find that the evolved CO_2 has a pressure of 69.8 mm Hg in a 285-mL flask at 25 °C. What is the molar mass of the metal carbonate?

59. Nickel carbonyl, $Ni(CO)_4$, can be made by the room-temperature reaction of finely divided nickel metal with gaseous CO. This is the basis for purifying nickel on an industrial scale. If you have CO in a 1.50-L flask at a pressure of 418 mm Hg at 25.0 °C, what is the maximum mass in grams of $Ni(CO)_4$ that can be made?

60. Assume that a car burns pure octane, C_8H_{18} (d = 0.703 g/cm^3).
   (a) Write the balanced equation for burning octane in air, forming CO_2 and H_2O.
   (b) If the car has a fuel efficiency of 32 miles per gallon of octane, what volume of CO_2 at 25 °C and 1.0 atm is generated when the car goes on a 10.-mile trip?

61. Follow the directions in the previous question, but use methanol, CH_3OH (d = 0.791 g/cm^3) as the fuel. Assume the fuel efficiency is 20. miles per gallon.

62. Zinc reacts with aqueous sulfuric acid to form hydrogen gas.

$$Zn(s) + H_2SO_4(aq) \longrightarrow ZnSO_4(aq) + H_2(g)$$

In an experiment, 201 mL wet H_2 is collected over water at 27 °C and a barometric pressure of 733 torr. The vapor pressure of water at 27 °C is 26.74 torr. How many grams of H_2 are produced?

Gas Density and Molar Mass

63. ■ What is the molar mass of a gas that has a density of 5.75 g/L at STP?

64. A sample of gaseous SiH_4 weighing 0.425 g is placed in a 580-mL container. The resulting pressure is 0.61 atm. What is the temperature in °C?

65. To find the volume of a flask, it is first evacuated so it contains no gas. Next, 4.4 g CO_2 is introduced into the flask. On warming to 27 °C, the gas exerts a pressure of 730. mm Hg. What is the volume of the flask in milliliters?

66. ■ What mass of helium in grams is required to fill a 5.0-L balloon to a pressure of 1.1 atm at 25 °C?

67. Consider two 5.0-L containers, each filled with gas at 25 °C. One container is filled with helium and the other with N_2. The density of gas in the two containers is the same. What is the relationship between the pressures in the two containers?

68. A hydrocarbon with the general formula C_xH_y is 92.26% carbon. Experiment shows that 0.293 g hydrocarbon fills a 185-mL flask at 23 °C with a pressure of 374 mm Hg. What is the molecular formula for this compound?

69. Forty miles above the earth's surface the temperature is −23 °C, and the pressure is only 0.20 mm Hg. What is the density of air (molar mass = 29.0 g/mol) at this altitude?

70. ■ A newly discovered gas has a density of 2.39 g/L at 23.0 °C and 715 mm Hg. What is the molar mass of the gas?

Partial Pressures of Gases

71. ■ What is the total pressure exerted by a mixture of 1.50 g H_2 and 5.00 g N_2 in a 5.00-L vessel at 25 °C?

72. At 298 K, a 750-mL vessel contains equimolar amounts of O_2, H_2, and He at a total pressure of 3.85 atm. What is the partial pressure of the H_2 gas?

73. ■ A sample of the atmosphere at a total pressure of 740. mm Hg is analyzed to give these partial pressures: $P(N_2) = 575$ mm Hg; $P(Ar) = 6.9$ mm Hg; $P(CO_2) = 0.2$ mm Hg; $P(H_2O) = 4.0$ mm Hg. No other gases except O_2 have appreciable partial pressures.
   (a) What is the partial pressure of O_2?
   (b) What is the mole fraction of each gas?
   (c) What is the composition of each component of this sample in percentage by volume? Compare your results with those of Table 10.1.

74. Gaseous CO exerts a pressure of 45.6 mm Hg in a 56.0-L tank at 22.0 °C. If this gas is released into a room with a volume of 2.70×10^4 L, what is the partial pressure of CO (in mm Hg) in the room at 22 °C?

75. Three flasks are connected as shown in the figure. The starting conditions are shown.
   (a) What is the final pressure inside the system when all the stopcocks are open?
   (b) What is the partial pressure of each of the three gases? Assume that the connecting tube has negligible volume. Assume no change in T.

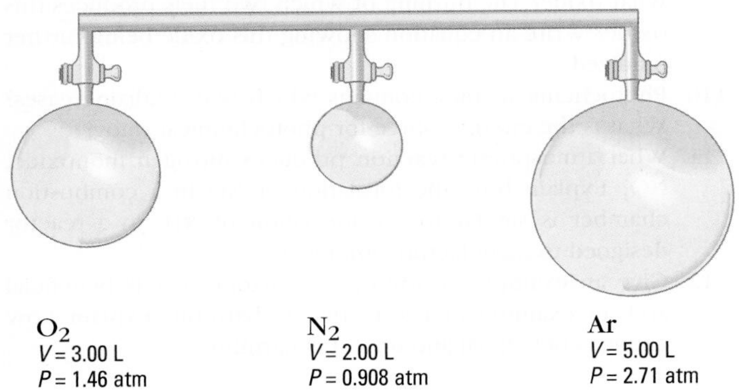

76. The density of air at 20.0 km above the earth's surface is 92 g/m^3. The pressure is 42 mm Hg and the temperature is −63 °C. Assuming the atmosphere contains only O_2 and N_2, calculate
   (a) The average molar mass of the air at 20.0 km.
   (b) The mole fraction of each gas.

77. Benzene has acute health effects. For example, it causes mucous membrane irritation at a concentration of 100 ppm and fatal narcosis at 20,000 ppm (pressure ratios). Calculate the partial pressures in atmospheres at STP corresponding to these concentrations.

78. On a humid, rainy summer day the partial pressure of water vapor in the atmosphere can be as high as 25 mm Hg. What is the mole fraction of water vapor in the atmosphere under these conditions? Compare your results with the composition of dry air given in Table 10.1.

79. The mean fraction *by mass* of water vapor and cloud water in the earth's atmosphere is about 0.0025. Assume that the atmosphere contains two components: "air," with a molar mass of 29.2 g/mol, and water vapor. What is the *mean* mole fraction of water vapor in the earth's atmosphere? What is the *mean* partial pressure of water vapor? Why is this so much smaller than the typical partial pressure of water vapor at the earth's surface on a rainy summer day?

80. Acetylene can be made by reacting calcium carbide with water.

$$CaC_2(s) + 2\,H_2O(\ell) \longrightarrow C_2H_2(g) + Ca(OH)_2(aq)$$

Assume that you place 2.65 g CaC_2 in excess water and collect the acetylene over water. The volume of the acetylene and water vapor is 795 mL at 25.0 °C and a barometric pressure of 735.2 mm Hg. Calculate the percent yield of acetylene. The vapor pressure of water at 25 °C is 23.8 mm Hg.

81. Potassium chlorate, $KClO_3$, can be decomposed by heating.

$$2\,KClO_3(s) \longrightarrow 2\,KCl(s) + 3\,O_2(g)$$

If 465 mL gas was collected over water at a total pressure of 750. mm Hg and a temperature of 23 °C, how many grams of O_2 were collected?

The Behavior of Real Gases

82. From the density of liquid water and its molar mass, calculate the volume that 1 mol liquid water occupies. If water were an ideal gas at STP, what volume would a mole of water vapor occupy? Can we achieve the STP conditions for water vapor? Why or why not?

83. At high temperatures and low pressures, gases behave ideally, but as the pressure is increased the product PV becomes greater than the product nRT. Give a molecular-level explanation of this fact.

84. ■ At low temperatures and very low pressures, gases behave ideally, but as the pressure is increased the product PV becomes less than the product nRT. Give a molecular-level explanation of this fact.

85. The densities of liquid noble gases and their normal boiling points are given in the following table.

Gas	Normal Boiling Point (K)	Liquid Density (g/cm³)
He	4.2	0.125
Ne	27.1	1.20
Ar	87.3	1.40
Kr	120.	2.42
Xe	165	2.95

Calculate the volume occupied by 1 mol of each of these liquids. Comment on any trend that you see. What is the volume occupied by exactly 1 mol of each of these substances as an ideal gas at STP? On the basis of these calculations, which gas would you expect to show the largest deviations from ideality at room temperature?

86. Use the van der Waals constants in Table 10.6 to predict whether N_2 or CO_2 will behave more like an ideal gas at high pressures.

87. Calculate the pressure of 7.0 mol CO_2 in a 2.00-L vessel at 50 °C using
(a) The ideal gas equation.
(b) The van der Waals equation.

Chemical Reactions in the Atmosphere

88. What is a free radical? Give an example of a chemical reaction that occurs in the atmosphere that produces a free radical.

89. What product is formed when two methyl radicals react with each other?

90. For these forms of nitrogen most prevalent in the environment, write chemical formulas and give the oxidation number of the nitrogen.
(a) Ammonia (b) Ammonium ion
(c) Dinitrogen monoxide (d) Gaseous nitrogen
(e) Nitric acid (f) Nitrous acid
(g) Nitrogen dioxide

91. Complete and balance these equations (all reactants and products are gases).
(a) $\cdot O \cdot + O_2 \longrightarrow$ (b) $O_3 \xrightarrow{h\nu}$
(c) $\cdot O \cdot + SO_2 \longrightarrow$ (d) $H_2O \xrightarrow{h\nu}$
(e) $\cdot NO_2 + \cdot NO_2 \longrightarrow$

92. ■ Complete and balance these equations (all reactants and products are gases).
(a) $\cdot O \cdot + H_2O \longrightarrow$ (b) $\cdot NO_2 + \cdot OH \longrightarrow$
(c) $RH + \cdot OH \longrightarrow$

93. Describe and write an equation for a chemical reaction that
(a) Creates a free radical.
(b) Creates a hydroxyl radical.

Ozone and Ozone Depletion

94. Write the products for these reactions that take place in the stratosphere.
(a) $CF_3Cl \xrightarrow{h\nu}$ (b) $\cdot Cl + \cdot O \cdot \longrightarrow$
(c) $ClO \cdot + \cdot O \cdot \longrightarrow$

95. The molecule CF_4 is not implicated as having ozone-depletion potential. Explain why.

96. ■ The molecule CH_3F has much less ozone-depletion potential than the corresponding molecule CH_3Cl. Explain why.

97. Write the chemical formulas of all possible CFCs with one carbon atom.

98. Are CFCs toxic? In considering this question, consider which compounds were used for refrigeration before CFCs were invented. Look up the toxicity of these compounds on the Internet.

99. Can CFCs catalyze the destruction of ozone in the stratosphere at night? Explain.

100. Can ozone form in the stratosphere at night? Explain why or why not.

Chemistry and Pollution in the Troposphere

101. Define air pollution in terms of the kinds of pollutants, their sources, and the ways they are harmful.

102. Explain how particulates can contribute to air pollution.

103. What is adsorption? What is absorption?

104. Assume that limestone ($CaCO_3$) is used to remove 90.% of the sulfur from 4.0 metric tons of coal containing 2.0% S. The product is $CaSO_4$.

$$CaCO_3(s) + SO_3(g) \longrightarrow CaSO_4(s) + CO_2(g)$$

Calculate the mass of limestone required. Express your answer in metric tons.

105. Approximately 65 million metric tons of SO_2 enter the atmosphere every year from the burning of coal. If coal, on average, contains 2.0% S, how many metric tons of coal were burned to produce this much SO_2? A 1000-MW power plant burns about 700. metric tons of coal per hour. Calculate the number of hours the quantity of coal will burn in one of these power plants.

106. What mass of gasoline must be burned according to the reaction

$$C_8H_{18}(\ell) + 8.5\ O_2(g) \longrightarrow 8\ CO(g) + 9\ H_2O(g)$$

to cause a garage with dimensions of 7.00 m × 3.00 m × 3.00 m to contain a CO concentration of 1000. ppm? (Assume STP conditions.)

Urban Air Pollution

107. Give an example of a photochemical reaction. Do all photons of light have sufficient energy to cause photochemical reactions? Explain with examples.

108. What two reactions account for the production of O free radicals in the troposphere?

109. The reducing nature of industrial (London) smog is due to what oxide? The burning of which two fuels produces this oxide? Write an equation showing this oxide being further oxidized.

110. Photochemical smog contains which two oxidizing gases? What is the energy source for photochemical smog?

111. What atmospheric reaction produces nitrogen monoxide, NO? Explain how the formation of NO in a combustion chamber is similar to the formation of NH_3 in a reactor designed to manufacture ammonia.

112. Give an example of atmospheric ozone that is beneficial and an example of ozone that is harmful. Explain how ozone is beneficial and how it is harmful.

113. The air pollutant sulfur dioxide, SO_2, is known to increase mortality in people exposed to it for 24 hours at a concentration of 0.175 ppm.
   (a) What is the partial pressure of SO_2 when its concentration is 0.175 ppm?
   (b) What is the mole fraction of SO_2 at the same concentration?
   (c) Assuming the air is at STP, what mass in micrograms of SO_2 is present in 1 m^3?

Greenhouse Gases and Global Warning

114. ■ What is the difference between the greenhouse effect and global warming? How are they related?
115. What are the four greenhouse gases, and why are they called that?
116. Carbon dioxide is known to be a major contributor to the greenhouse effect. List some of its sources in our atmosphere and some of the processes that remove it. Currently, which predominates—the production of CO_2 or its removal?
117. Name a favorable effect of the global increase of CO_2 in the atmosphere.

General Questions

118. HCl can be made by the direct reaction of H_2 and Cl_2 in the presence of light. Assume that 3.0 g H_2 and 140. g Cl_2 are mixed in a 10-L flask at 28 °C.
   Before the reaction:
   (a) What are the partial pressures of the two reactants?
   (b) What is the total pressure due to the gases in the flask?
   After the reaction:
   (c) What is the total pressure in the flask?
   (d) What reactant remains in the flask? How many moles of it remain?
   (e) What are the partial pressures of the gases in the flask?
   (f) What will be the pressure inside the flask if the temperature is increased to 40. °C?
119. Worldwide, about 100. million metric tons of H_2S are produced annually from sources that include the oceans, bogs, swamps, and tidal flats. One of the major sources of SO_2 in the atmosphere is the oxidation of H_2S, produced by the decay of organic matter. The reaction in which H_2S molecules are oxidized to SO_2 involves O_3. Write an equation showing that one molecule of each reactant combines to form two product molecules, one of them being SO_2. Then calculate the annual production in tons of H_2SO_4, assuming all of this SO_2 is converted to sulfuric acid.

Applying Concepts

120. Consider a sample of N_2 gas under conditions in which it obeys the ideal gas law exactly. Which of these statements are true?
   (a) A sample of Ne(g) under the same conditions must obey the ideal gas law exactly.
   (b) The speed at which one particular N_2 molecule is moving changes from time to time.
   (c) Some N_2 molecules are moving more slowly than some of the molecules in a sample of O_2(g) under the same conditions.
   (d) Some N_2 molecules are moving more slowly than some of the molecules in a sample of Ne(g) under the same conditions.
   (e) When two N_2 molecules collide, it is possible that both may be moving faster after the collision than they were before.
121. Which graph below would best represent the distribution of molecular speeds for the gases acetylene (C_2H_2) and N_2? Both gases are in the same flask with a total pressure of 750. mm Hg. The partial pressure of N_2 is 500. mm Hg.

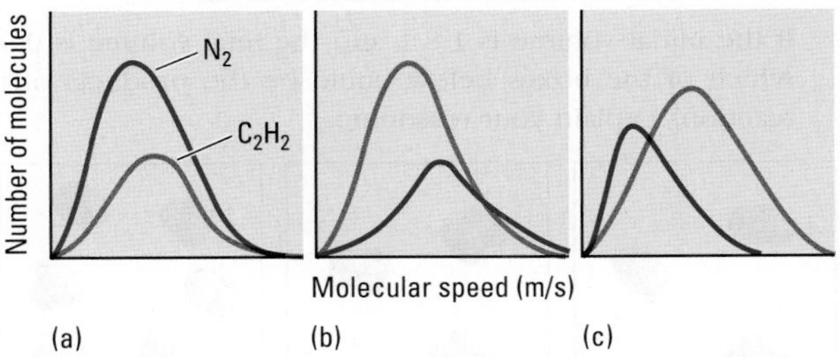

122. Draw a graph representing the distribution of molecular speeds for the gases ethane (C_2H_6) and F_2 when both are in the same flask with a total pressure of 720. mm Hg and a partial pressure of 540. mm Hg for F_2.
123. In this chapter Boyle's, Charles's, and Avogadro's laws were presented as word statements and mathematical relationships. Express each of these laws graphically.
124. The drawing below represents a gas collected in a syringe (the needle end was sealed after collecting) at room temperature and pressure. Redraw the syringe and gas to show what it would look like under the following conditions. Assume that the plunger can move freely but no gas can escape.
   (a) The temperature of the gas is decreased by one half.
   (b) The pressure of the gas is decreased to one half of its initial value.
   (c) The temperature of the gas is tripled and the pressure is doubled.

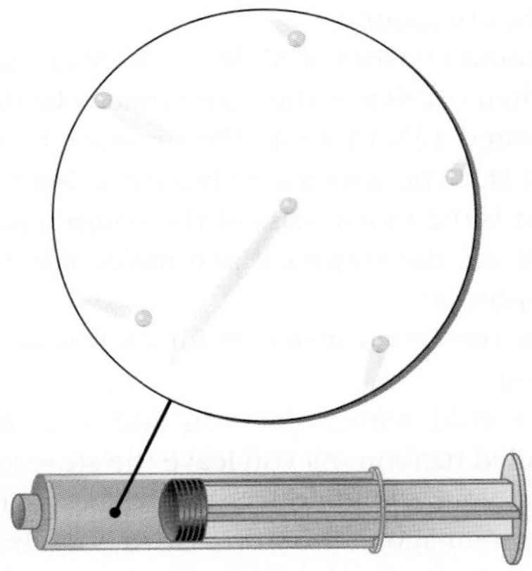

125. A gas phase reaction takes place in a syringe at a constant temperature and pressure. If the initial volume is 40. cm^3 and the final volume is 60. cm^3, which of these general reactions took place? Explain your reasoning.
   (a) $A(g) + B(g) \rightarrow AB(g)$
   (b) $2\ A(g) + B(g) \rightarrow A_2B(g)$
   (c) $2\ AB_2(g) \rightarrow A_2(g) + 2\ B_2(g)$

(d) $2\ AB(g) \rightarrow A_2(g) + B_2(g)$

(e) $2\ A_2(g) + 4\ B(g) \rightarrow 4\ AB(g)$

126. The gas molecules in the box below undergo a reaction at constant temperature and pressure.

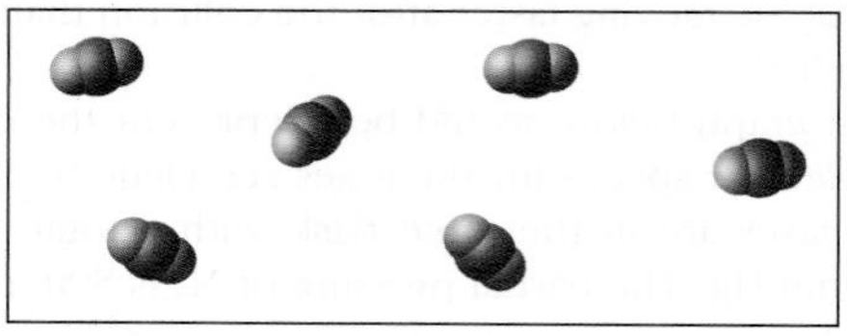

If the initial volume is 1.8 L and the final volume is 0.9 L, which of the boxes below could be the products of the reaction? Explain your reasoning.

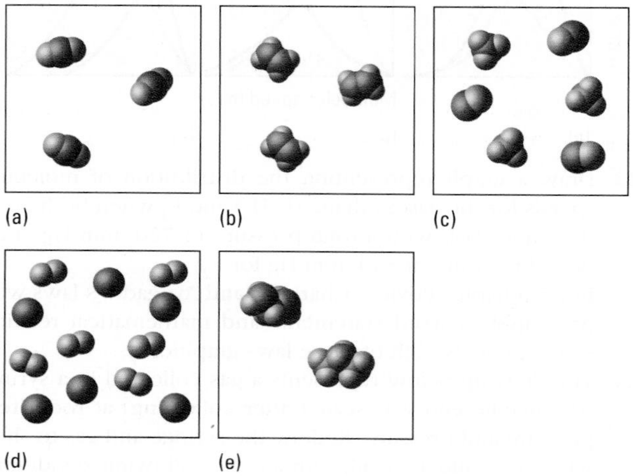

127. A substance is analyzed and found to contain 85.7% carbon and 14.3% hydrogen by mass. A gaseous sample of the substance is found to have a density of 1.87 g/L at STP.
(a) What is the molar mass of the compound?
(b) What are the empirical and molecular formulas of the compound?
(c) What are two possible Lewis structures for molecules of the compound?

128. A compound consists of 37.5% C, 3.15% H, and 59.3% F by mass. When 0.298 g of the compound is heated to 50. °C in an evacuated 125-mL flask, the pressure is observed to be 750. mm Hg. The compound has three isomers.
(a) What is the molar mass of the compound?
(b) What are the empirical and molecular formulas of the compound?
(c) Draw the Lewis structure for each isomer of the compound.

129. One very cold winter day you and a friend purchase a helium-filled balloon. As you leave the store and walk down the street, your friend notices the balloon is not as full as it was a moment ago in the store. He says the balloon is defective and he is taking it back. Do you agree with him? Explain why you do or do not agree.

More Challenging Questions

130. What is the total pressure in an 8.7-L vessel that contains 3.44 g carbon dioxide, 1.88 g methane, and 4.28 g Ar, all at 37 °C?

131. An ideal gas was contained in a glass vessel of unknown volume with a pressure of 0.960 atm. Some of the gas was withdrawn from the vessel and used to fill a 25.0-mL glass bulb to a pressure of 1.00 atm. The pressure of the gas remaining in the vessel of unknown volume was 0.882 atm. All the measurements were done at the same temperature. What is the volume of the vessel?

132. You are holding two balloons, an orange balloon and a blue balloon, both at the same temperature and pressure. The orange balloon is filled with neon gas and the blue balloon is filled with argon gas. The orange balloon has twice the volume of the blue balloon. What is the mass ratio of Ne to Ar in the two balloons?

133. A sealed bulb filled with a gas is immersed in an ice bath, and its pressure is measured as 444 mm Hg. Then the same bulb is placed in a heated oven, and the pressure is measured as 648 mm Hg. What is the temperature of the oven in °C?

134. Nitroglycerine, the explosive ingredient in dynamite, decomposes violently when shocked.

$$4\ C_3H_5(NO_3)_3(\ell) \longrightarrow 12\ CO_2(g) + 10\ H_2O(\ell) + 6\ N_2(g) + O_2(g)$$

(a) How many total moles of gas are produced when 1.00 kg nitroglycerine explodes?
(b) What volume would the gases occupy at 1.0 atm pressure and 25 °C?
(c) At P = 1.00 atm, what would be the partial pressure of each product gas?

135. Liquid oxygen, which has many industrial uses, is produced by cooling dry air to −183 °C. To produce 200. L of liquid oxygen, how many liters of dry air at STP would be needed? (The density of liquid oxygen is 1.14 g/mL.)

136. A container of gas has a pressure of 550. torr. A chemical change then occurs that consumes half of the molecules present at the start and produces two new molecules for each three consumed. What is the new pressure in the container? T and V are unchanged.

137. A balloon filled with helium contains 500. mol He at 1.00 atm and 25 °C.
(a) What is the volume of the balloon?
(b) What is the mass of air that it displaces? (Assume the molar mass of air to be 29.0 g/mol.)
(c) What is the mass of He in the balloon?
(d) What is the buoyancy of the balloon?

138. Imagine a tiny gas bubble with a volume of exactly one cubic millimeter being formed at the bottom of a lake at a pressure of 4.4 atm. When the bubble reaches the surface of the lake, where the pressure is 740. torr, what will its volume be? Assume that the temperature is constant.

139. Propane, $CH_3CH_2CH_3$, is a gaseous fuel that can be liquified when put under modest pressure.
(a) How many moles of propane can be stored in a container with a volume of 150. L at a pressure of 3.00 atm and a temperature of 25 °C?
(b) How many moles of liquid propane can be stored in a vessel of the same volume? (Liquid propane's density is approximately 0.60 g/mL.)

140. The effects of intermolecular interactions on gas properties depend on T and P. Are these effects more and less significant when these changes occur? Why?
(a) A container of gas is compressed to a smaller volume at constant temperature.
(b) A container of gas has more gas added into the same volume at constant temperature.
(c) The gas in a container of variable volume is heated at constant pressure.

141. Formaldehyde, CH_2O, is a volatile organic compound that is sometimes released from insulation used in home construction, and it can be trapped and build up inside the home. When this happens, people exposed to the formaldehyde can suffer adverse health effects. The U.S. federal standard for the maximum allowable concentration of formaldehyde in air is 1.0 ppbv (parts per billion volume) defined as

$$\text{ppbv} = \frac{\text{volume of component X at STP}}{\text{total volume of air at STP}} \times 10^9$$

(a) What is the partial pressure of formaldehyde at the maximum allowable level of 1.0 ppbv?
(b) How many molecules of formaldehyde are present in each cubic centimeter of air when formaldehyde is present at 1.0 ppbv?
(c) How many total molecules of formaldehyde would be present in a room with these dimensions: 15.0 ft long $\times$ 10.0 ft wide $\times$ 8.00 ft high?

Conceptual Challenge Problems

CP10.A (Section 10.1) How would you quickly estimate whether the mass of the earth's atmosphere is 5.3×10^{15} metric tons?

CP10.B (Section 10.4) Under what conditions would you expect to observe that the pressure of a confined gas at constant temperature and volume is *not* constant?

CP10.C (Section 10.5) Suppose that the gas constant, R, were defined as 1.000 L atm mol^{-1} deg^{-1} where the "deg" referred to a newly defined Basic temperature scale. What would be the melting and boiling temperatures of water in degrees Basic (°B)?

11

Liquids, Solids, and Materials

An iceberg floats with about 10% of its mass above the surface of the surrounding water. The hydrogen bonding of water molecules in ice makes the solid less dense than liquid water, which is unusual. This property of water, however, is crucial for life on earth.

© Ralph A. Clevenger/Corbis

The properties of liquids and solids, like those of gases, can be understood on the molecular, nanoscale level. In common liquids and solids—water, salt crystals, metals—the atoms, molecules, or ions are close enough to have strong interactions with each other. The strength of these interactions accounts for the properties of liquids and solids. For example, the strong repulsions when the atoms, molecules, or ions in a liquid or solid are forced very close together account for the fact that solids and liquids can be compressed very little—in contrast to gases. Liquids are like gases in that their atoms, molecules, or ions (in the case of molten ionic compounds) can move freely. Liquids are therefore able to flow and fill a container to a certain level. Solids, on the other hand, are composed of atoms, molecules, or ions in relatively fixed positions, which explains the fact that solids have definite shapes. When the atoms, molecules, or ions making up a solid have enough energy to overcome the attractive forces holding them in place, the solid melts or sublimes.

In molecular liquids and solids, molecules having sufficient energy can leave the surface of the liquid or solid and enter the gaseous state. In the reverse process, as energy is removed, gases condense into liquids, and liquids solidify. All of these properties of solids and liquids have great practical importance.

ThomsonNOW™
Throughout the text, this icon indicates an opportunity to test yourself on key concepts and to explore interactive modules by signing in to ThomsonNOW at **www.thomsonedu.com.**

Sublimation is the direct conversion of a solid to its vapor without becoming a liquid.

11.1 The Liquid State

At low enough temperatures, gases condense to liquids. Condensation occurs when most molecules no longer have enough kinetic energy to overcome their intermolecular attractions ***(← p. 407).*** Most liquids, such as water, alcohol, and gasoline, are substances whose condensation temperatures are above room temperature. Some liquids, such as molten salts and liquid polymers, have no corresponding vapor state, however, so condensation of their vapors has no meaning.

In a liquid, the molecules are much closer together than are those in a gas. Nevertheless, the molecules remain mobile enough that the liquid flows. At the nanoscale, liquids have a regular structure only in very small regions, and most of

© Thomson Learning/Charles D. Winters

The hydraulic lifts are raised and lowered by changes in the pressure on the hydraulic fluid in the cylinders. The lack of compressibility of the fluid makes this application possible.

© Thomson Learning/Charles D. Winters

Figure 11.1 **Viscosity.** Honey is viscous, so it builds up rather than spreading out, as less viscous water would.

the molecules continue to move about randomly. Because confined liquids are difficult to compress and their molecules move in all directions, they can transmit applied pressure equally in all directions. This property has a practical application in the hydraulic fluids that operate mechanical devices such as the hydraulic lifts that raise and lower autos in repair shops.

The resistance of a liquid to flow is called **viscosity.** Water flows smoothly and quickly (low viscosity), while motor oil and honey flow more slowly (higher viscosity; Figure 11.1). The viscosity of a liquid is related to its intermolecular forces, which determine how easily the molecules can move past each other, and also the degree to which the molecules can become entangled. Viscosity decreases as temperature increases because the molecules have more kinetic energy at higher temperature and the attractive intermolecular forces are more easily overcome. Examples of common materials whose viscosity decreases as their temperature rises include motor oil, cooking oil, and honey.

Unlike gases, liquids have *surface properties.* Molecules beneath the surface of the liquid are completely surrounded by other liquid molecules and experience intermolecular attractions in all directions. By contrast, molecules at the liquid surface have intermolecular interactions only with molecules below or beside them, but not above them (Figure 11.2). This unevenness of attractive forces at the liquid surface causes the surface to contract. The energy required to expand a liquid surface is called its **surface tension,** and it is higher for liquids that have stronger intermolecular attractions. For example, water's surface tension is high compared with those of most other liquids (Table 11.1) because extensive hydrogen bonding causes the water molecules to attract each other strongly ***(⟵ p. 411).*** The surface tension of water, 7.29×10^{-2} J/m^2, is the quantity of energy required to increase the surface area of water by 1 m^2 at 20 °C. The very high surface tension of mercury (six times that of water) is due to the much stronger metallic bonding (Section 11.9) that holds Hg atoms together in the liquid.

Even though their densities are greater than that of water, water bugs can walk on the surface of water and small metal objects can float. Surface tension prevents the objects from breaking through the surface and sinking. Surface tension also accounts for the nearly spherical shape of rain droplets, as well as the rounded shape of water droplets that bead up on waxed surfaces. A sphere has less surface area per unit volume than any other shape, so a spherical rain droplet has fewer surface H_2O molecules, minimizing the surface energy.

Surface tension answers the question posed in Chapter 1 ***(⟵ p. 2),*** "Why does rain fall as drops instead of cubes or cylinders?"

The teardrop shape of raindrops you see in illustrations of rain bears little resemblance to actual raindrops, which are spherical. Air pressure begins to distort the sphere into an egg shape for 2- to 3-mm-radius raindrops. Larger raindrops assume other shapes, but they never look like teardrops.

The chemicals known as surfactants (soaps and detergents are examples) can dissolve in water and dramatically lower its surface tension. When this happens, water becomes "wetter" and does a better job of cleaning. You can see the effect of a surfactant by comparing how water alone beads on a surface such as the waxed hood of a car and how a soap solution fails to bead on the same surface. Surfactants are discussed in Section 15.10.

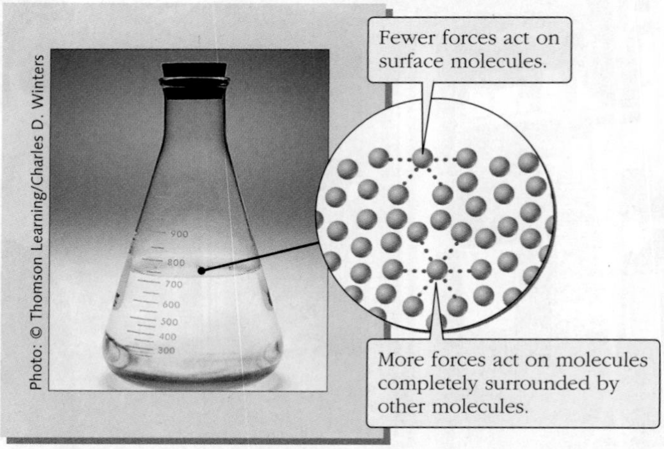

Figure 11.2 **Surface tension.** Surface tension, the energy required to increase the surface area of a liquid, arises from the difference between the forces acting on a molecule within the liquid and those acting on a molecule at the surface of the liquid.

Table 11.1 Surface Tensions of Some Liquids

Substance	Formula	Surface Tension (J/m^2 at 20 °C)
Octane	C_8H_{18}	2.16×10^{-2}
Ethanol	CH_3CH_2OH	2.23×10^{-2}
Chloroform	$CHCl_3$	2.68×10^{-2}
Benzene	C_6H_6	2.85×10^{-2}
Water	H_2O	7.29×10^{-2}
Mercury	Hg	46×10^{-2}

Hermann Elsenbeiss/ Photo Researchers, Inc.

Surface tension of water supports a water bug. This answers the question posed in Chapter 1 (⟸ *p. 2*), "Why can some insects walk on water?"

CONCEPTUAL EXERCISE 11.1 Explaining Differences in Surface Tension

At 20 °C, chloroform ($CHCl_3$) has a surface tension of 2.68×10^{-2} J/m^2, while bromoform ($CHBr_3$) has a higher surface tension of 4.11×10^{-2} J/m^2. Explain this observation in terms of intermolecular forces.

CONCEPTUAL EXERCISE 11.2 Predicting Surface Tension

Predict which substance listed in Table 11.1 has a surface tension most similar to that of

(a) Glycerol, which has three —OH groups in each molecule
(b) Decane, $C_{10}H_{22}$

When a glass tube with a small diameter is put into water, the water rises in the tube due to **capillary action.** The glass walls of the tube are largely silicon dioxide (SiO_2), so the water molecules form hydrogen bonds to the oxygen atoms of the glass. This attractive force is stronger than the attractive forces among water molecules (also hydrogen bonding), so water creeps up the wall of the tube. Simultaneously, the surface tension of the water tries to keep the water's surface area small. The combination of the forces raises the water level in the tube. The liquid surface—concave for water—is called a **meniscus** (Figure 11.3a). The water rises in the tube

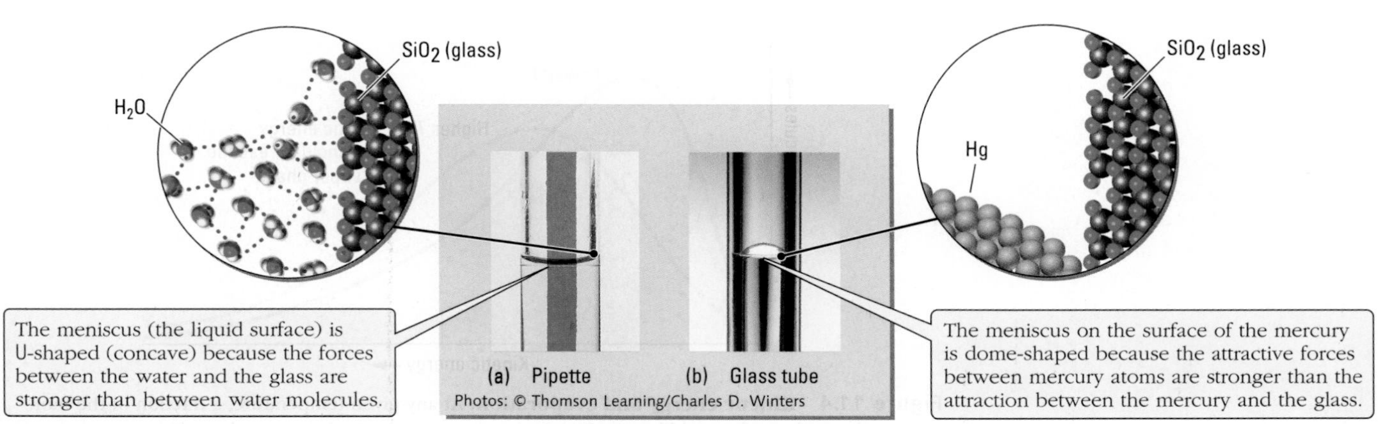

Figure 11.3 Noncovalent forces at surfaces. (a) The meniscus of water in a pipette is concave. (b) The meniscus of mercury in a glass tube is dome-shaped (convex).

until the force of the water-to-wall hydrogen bonds is balanced by the pull of gravity. Capillary action is crucial to plant life because it helps water, with its dissolved nutrients, to move upward through plant tissues against the force of gravity.

Mercury behaves oppositely from water. Mercury in a small-diameter tube has a dome-shaped (convex) meniscus because the attractive forces between mercury atoms are stronger than the attraction between the mercury and the glass wall (Figure 11.3b).

11.2 Vapor Pressure

The tendency of a liquid to vaporize, its **volatility,** increases as temperature increases. Everyday experiences such as heating water or soup in a pan on a stove, or evaporation of rain from hot pavement, demonstrate this phenomenon. Conversely, the volatility of a liquid is lower at lower temperatures.

The change of volatility with temperature can be explained by considering what is happening at the nanoscale. The molecules in a liquid have varying kinetic energies and speeds (Figure 11.4). At any time, some fraction of the molecules have sufficient energy to escape from the liquid into the gas phase. When the temperature of the liquid is raised, a larger number of molecules exceeds the energy threshold, and evaporation proceeds more rapidly. Thus, hot water evaporates more quickly than cold water.

A liquid in an open container will eventually evaporate completely because air currents and diffusion take away most of the gas phase molecules before they can reenter the liquid phase. In a closed container, however, no molecules can escape. If a liquid is injected into an evacuated, closed container, the rate of vaporization (number of molecules vaporizing per unit time) will at first far exceed the rate of condensation. Over time the pressure of the gas above the liquid will increase as the number of gas phase molecules increases. Eventually the system will attain a state of *dynamic equilibrium,* in which molecules are entering and leaving the liquid state at equal rates. At this point the pressure of the gas will no longer increase; this pressure is known as the **equilibrium vapor pressure** (or just the **vapor pressure**) of the liquid.

An evacuated container is specified so that only the pure liquid is present.

As shown in Figure 11.5 for three liquids, the vapor pressure of a liquid increases with increasing temperature. The differences in vapor pressures among the three liquids are due to differences in the strengths of the intermolecular interactions that bind their molecules together in the liquid phase. Consider the vapor

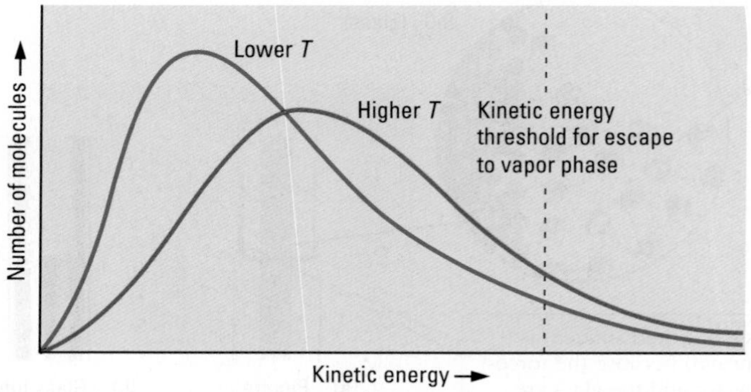

Figure 11.4 **Kinetic energy and evaporation.** At any given temperature, a fraction of the molecules at the surface of a liquid have sufficient energy to escape to the vapor phase. When the temperature of the liquid is raised, a larger fraction of the molecules have energies greater than the kinetic energy threshold, so the vapor pressure increases.

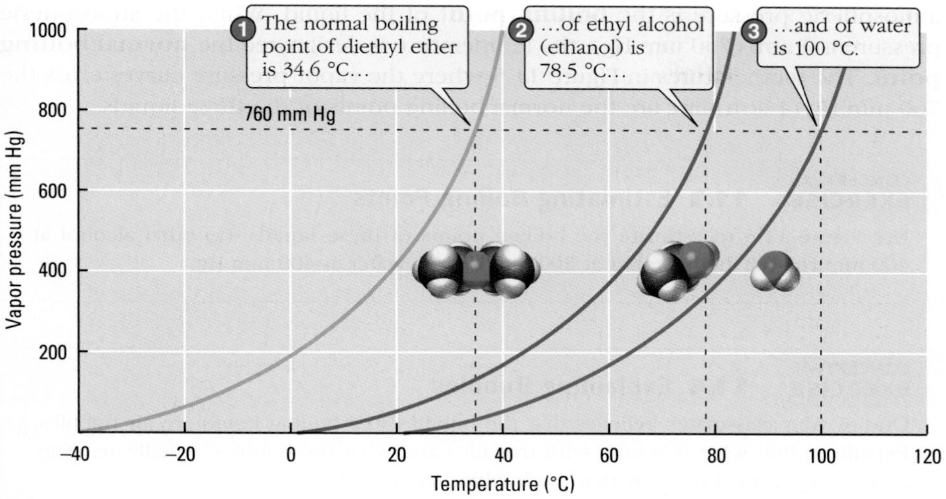

Figure 11.5 Vapor pressure curves for diethyl ether ($C_2H_5OC_2H_5$), ethyl alcohol (C_2H_5OH), and water. Each curve represents the conditions of *T* and *P* where the two phases (pure liquid and its vapor) are in equilibrium. Each compound is a liquid in the temperature and pressure region to the left of its curve, and each compound is a vapor for all temperatures and pressures to the right of its curve.

pressures of ethyl alcohol and water at 60 °C (see Figure 11.5). At that temperature, ethyl alcohol has a higher vapor pressure, which means that it has weaker intermolecular interactions than those in water. Water's stronger intermolecular interactions (due to more hydrogen bonds) require a higher temperature to disrupt them and volatilize liquid water ***(⟸ p. 411)***.

If a liquid is placed in an open container and heated, a temperature eventually is reached at which the vapor pressure of the liquid is equal to the atmospheric pressure. Below this temperature, only molecules at the surface of the liquid can go into the gas phase. But when the vapor pressure equals the atmospheric pressure, the liquid begins vaporizing throughout. Bubbles of vapor form and immediately rise to the surface due to their lower density. The liquid is said to be **boiling** (Figure 11.6). The temperature at which the equilibrium vapor pressure equals the

To shorten cooking times, one can use a pressure cooker, a sealed pot (with a relief valve for safety) that allows water vapor to build up pressures slightly greater than the external atmospheric pressure. At the higher pressure, the boiling point of water is higher, and foods cook faster.

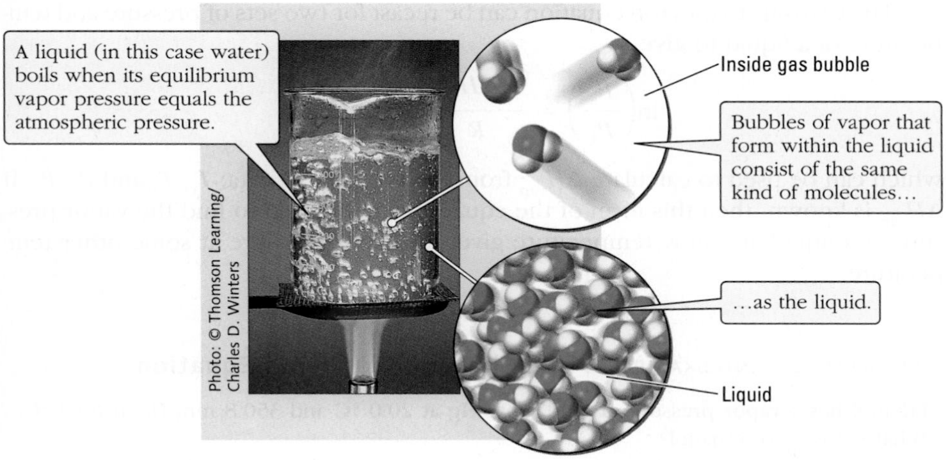

Figure 11.6 Boiling liquid. From Figure 11.5, we see that the lower the atmospheric pressure, the lower the vapor pressure at which boiling can occur. It takes longer to hard-boil an egg high in the mountains, where the atmospheric pressure is lower, than it does at sea level, because water at a higher elevation boils at a lower temperature. In Salt Lake City, Utah (elevation 4390 ft), where the average barometric pressure is about 650 mm Hg, water boils at about 95 °C.

atmospheric pressure is the **boiling point** of the liquid. When the atmospheric pressure is 1 atm (760 mm Hg), the temperature is designated the **normal boiling point.** The temperatures in Figure 11.5 where the vapor pressure curves cross the 760 mm Hg (1 atm) line are the normal boiling points of the three liquids.

CONCEPTUAL EXERCISE 11.3 Estimating Boiling Points

Use Figure 11.5 to estimate the boiling points of these liquids: (a) ethyl alcohol at 400 mm Hg; (b) diethyl ether at 200 mm Hg; (c) water at 400 mm Hg.

CONCEPTUAL EXERCISE 11.4 Explaining Bubbles

One of your classmates believes that the bubbles in a boiling liquid are air bubbles. Explain to him what is wrong with that idea and what the bubbles actually are. Suggest an experiment to show that the bubbles are not air.

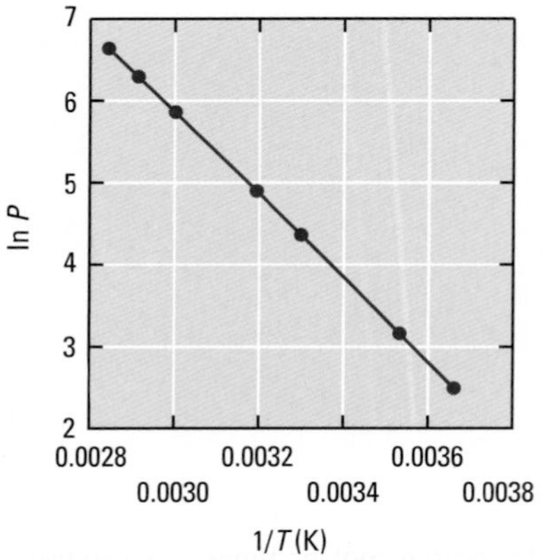

Figure 11.7 Clausius-Clapeyron equation plot for ethanol. Plotting ln P versus $1/T$ yields a straight line whose slope is directly proportional to ΔH_{vap}.

Clausius-Clapeyron Equation

As seen in Figure 11.5, plotting the vapor pressure of a substance versus its temperature results in a curved line. The relationship between vapor pressure and temperature is given by the **Clausius-Clapeyron equation:**

$$\ln P = \frac{-\Delta H_{vap}}{RT} + C$$

which relates the natural logarithm of the vapor pressure P of the liquid to the absolute temperature T, the universal gas constant R (8.31 J mol^{-1} K^{-1}), the molar enthalpy of vaporization ΔH_{vap} (J/mol), and a constant C that is characteristic of the liquid. The form of the Clausius-Clapeyron equation shows that a graph of ln P versus $1/T$ is a straight line with its slope equal to $-\Delta H_{vap}/R$ and a y-axis intercept of C. That is, ln P equals C in the limit when T is very large and $1/T$ tends toward zero. Figure 11.7 shows a plot of ln P versus $1/T$ for ethanol. A comparison of the plots for ethanol in Figures 11.5 and 11.7 illustrates the two different ways of expressing the relationship between T and P.

Note that R is in units of J mol^{-1} K^{-1} here.

The Clausius-Clapeyron equation can be recast for two sets of pressure and temperature of a liquid to give

$$\ln\left(\frac{P_2}{P_1}\right) = \frac{-\Delta H_{vap}}{R}\left[\frac{1}{T_2} - \frac{1}{T_1}\right]$$

which can be used to calculate ΔH_{vap} from the two sets of data: T_1, T_2 and P_1, P_2. If ΔH_{vap} is known, then this form of the equation can be used to find the vapor pressure of a liquid at a new temperature given its vapor pressure at some other temperature.

ThomsonNOW

Go to the Coached Problems menu for simulations and tutorials on:

- **vapor pressures of liquids**
- **vapor pressure and boiling point**
- **calculating enthalpy of vaporization**
- **predicting vapor pressure at a given temperature**

PROBLEM-SOLVING EXAMPLE 11.1 Clausius-Clapeyron Equation

Ethanol has a vapor pressure of 44.22 mm Hg at 20.0 °C and 350.8 mm Hg at 60.0 °C. What is ΔH_{vap} for ethanol?

Answer 42.0 kJ/mol

Strategy and Explanation Use the Clausius-Clapeyron equation in the form that contains the four known quantities: T_1, T_2, P_1, and P_2. The temperatures must be converted to kelvins. Substitute the given values into the equation and solve for ΔH_{vap}.

$$\ln\left(\frac{350.8 \text{ mm Hg}}{44.22 \text{ mm Hg}}\right) = \frac{-\Delta H_{vap}}{8.31 \text{ J mol}^{-1} \text{ K}^{-1}}\left[\frac{1}{333.15 \text{ K}} - \frac{1}{293.15 \text{ K}}\right]$$

$$\ln(7.933) = \frac{-\Delta H_{vap}}{8.31 \text{ J mol}^{-1} \text{ K}^{-1}}(-4.096 \times 10^{-4} \text{ K}^{-1})$$

$$\Delta H_{vap} = \frac{\ln(7.933) \times 8.31 \text{ J mol}^{-1} \text{ K}^{-1}}{4.096 \times 10^{-4} \text{ K}^{-1}} = 42020 \text{ J/mol} = 42.0 \text{ kJ/mol}$$

PROBLEM-SOLVING PRACTICE 11.1

At 30.0 °C the vapor pressure of carbon tetrachloride is 143.0 mm Hg. What is its vapor pressure at 60.0 °C? The ΔH_{vap} of carbon tetrachloride is 32.1 kJ/mol.

Vapor Pressure of Water and Relative Humidity

Water has an appreciable vapor pressure in the temperature range 10 °C to 25 °C, normal outdoor temperatures. Therefore, water vapor is present in the atmosphere at all times. The equilibrium vapor pressure depends on the temperature as shown in Table 10.5 (← ***p. 459***). The vapor pressure of water in the atmosphere is expressed as the **relative humidity,** which is the ratio of the actual partial pressure of the water vapor in the atmosphere, P_{H_2O}, to the equilibrium partial pressure of water vapor at the relevant temperature, $P^{\circ}_{H_2O}$. The factor of 100 changes a fraction into a percentage.

$$\text{Relative humidity} = \frac{P_{H_2O}}{P^{\circ}_{H_2O}} \times 100\%$$

As an example, consider a typical warm day with an outdoor temperature of 25 °C. The equilibrium water vapor pressure at this temperature is 23.8 mm Hg (see Table 10.5). If the actual partial pressure of water vapor were 17.8 mm Hg, then the relative humidity would be

$$\text{Relative humidity} = \frac{17.8 \text{ mm Hg}}{23.8 \text{ mm Hg}} \times 100\% = 75\%$$

If the temperature were lowered (which would lower the equilibrium water vapor pressure) and the partial pressure of water vapor remained constant, the relative humidity would rise. Eventually, it would reach 100%. The temperature at which the actual partial pressure of water vapor equals the equilibrium vapor pressure is the **dew point.** At this temperature, water vapor will condense as water droplets to form fog or dew. When the dew point rises above about 20 °C we consider it to be somewhat muggy; when it rises above about 25 °C we consider the day to be extremely uncomfortable. In desert conditions the relative humidity can fall to less than 10%; this, too, can be uncomfortable for some people.

11.3 Phase Changes: Solids, Liquids, and Gases

Substances in one of the three states of matter—solid, liquid, gas—can change from one state to another. Water evaporates from the street after a rain shower. Ice cubes melt in your cold drink, and water vapor in the air condenses to water droplets on the outside wall of the glass. Each of the three states of matter can be converted to the other two states through six important processes (Figure 11.8).

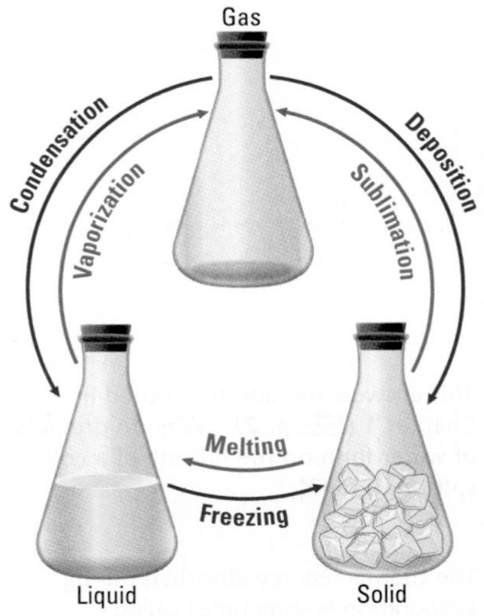

Figure 11.8 The three states of matter and their six interconversions. The red arrows indicate endothermic conversions—processes that require an input of energy. The blue arrows indicate exothermic conversions—processes that require cooling.

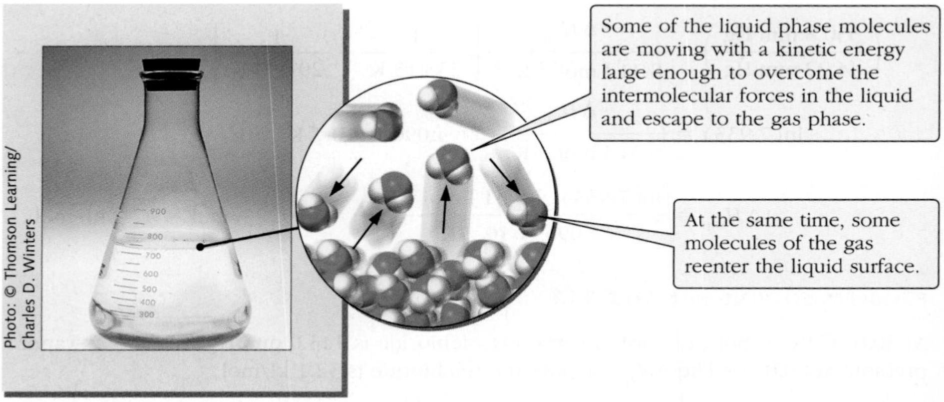

Figure 11.9 **Molecules in the liquid and gas phases.** All the molecules in both phases are moving, although the distances traveled in the liquid before collision with another molecule are much smaller.

ThomsonNOW™
Go to the Chemistry Interactive menu to work a module on **phases of matter: the crushed can experiment.**

Vaporization and Condensation

Like molecules in a gas, molecules in a liquid are in constant motion and have a range of kinetic energies, as shown in Figure 11.4. A fraction of the molecules in the liquid have enough kinetic energy to overcome the intermolecular attractive forces among the liquid molecules. If such a molecule is at the surface of the liquid and moving in the right direction, it will leave the liquid phase and enter the gas phase (Figure 11.9). This process is called **vaporization** or **evaporation.**

As the high-energy molecules leave the liquid, they take some energy with them. Therefore, vaporization is *endothermic;* the enthalpy change is called the enthalpy of vaporization ***(← p. 232).*** Vaporization increases with temperature because an increasingly larger fraction of the molecules have enough energy to vaporize.

Enthalpy of vaporization is also referred to as heat of vaporization.

CONCEPTUAL EXERCISE **11.5 Evaporative Cooling**

In some countries where electric refrigeration is not readily available, drinking water is chilled by placing it in porous clay water pots. Water slowly passes through the clay, and when it reaches the outer surface, it evaporates. Explain how this process cools the water inside.

When a molecule in the gas phase hits the liquid's surface, it can transfer some of its energy to the other liquid particles and remain in the liquid, a process called **condensation.** The overall effect of molecules reentering the liquid phase is a release of thermal energy, making condensation an exothermic process. The heat transferred out of the system upon condensation is equal to the heat transferred into the system upon vaporization.

This answers the question posed in Chapter 1 ***(← p. 2),*** "Why do droplets of water form on the outside of a cold soft-drink can?"

$$\text{Liquid} \underset{\text{heat of condensation}}{\overset{\text{heat of vaporization}}{\rightleftharpoons}} \text{Gas} \qquad \Delta H_{\text{vaporization}} = -\Delta H_{\text{condensation}}$$

For example, the quantity of heat required to completely vaporize 1 mol liquid water once it has reached the boiling point of 100 °C at 1 bar (the *molar enthalpy of vaporization*) and the quantity of heat released when 1 mol water vapor at 100 °C condenses to liquid water at 100 °C (the *molar enthalpy of condensation*) are

The thermal energy absorbed during evaporation is sometimes called the latent heat of vaporization. It is somewhat dependent on the temperature: at 100 °C, ΔH°_{vap} (H_2O) = 40.7 kJ/mol, but at 25 °C the value is 44.0 kJ/mol.

Table 11.2 Molar Enthalpies of Vaporization and Boiling Points for Some Common Substances

Substance	Number of Electrons	ΔH°_{vap} (kJ/mol)*	Boiling Point (°C)†
Polar molecules			
HF	10	25.2	19.7
HCl	18	17.5	−84.8
HBr	36	19.3	−66.5
HI	54	21.2	−35.1
NH_3	10	25.1	−33.4
H_2O	10	40.7	100.0
SO_2	32	26.8	−10.0
Noble gases			
He	2	0.08	−269.0
Ne	10	1.8	−246.0
Ar	18	6.5	−185.9
Xe	54	12.6	−107.1
Nonpolar molecules			
H_2	2	0.90	−252.8
O_2	16	6.8	−183.0
F_2	18	6.54	−188.1
Cl_2	34	20.39	−34.6
Br_2	70	29.54	59.6
CH_4 (methane)	10	8.9	−161.5
$CH_3{-}CH_3$ (ethane)	18	15.7	−88.6
$CH_3{-}CH_2{-}CH_3$ (propane)	26	19.0	−42.1
$CH_3{-}CH_2{-}CH_2{-}CH_3$ (butane)	34	24.3	−0.5

*ΔH°_{vap} is given at the normal boiling point of the liquid.

†Boiling point is the temperature at which vapor pressure = 760 mm Hg.

$$H_2O(\ell) \rightarrow H_2O(g) \qquad \Delta H^\circ = \Delta H_{vap} = +40.7 \text{ kJ/mol}$$

$$H_2O(g) \rightarrow H_2O(\ell) \qquad \Delta H^\circ = \Delta H_{cond} = -40.7 \text{ kJ/mol}$$

Table 11.2 illustrates the influence of noncovalent forces on enthalpies of vaporization and boiling points. In the series of nonpolar molecules and noble gases, the increasing noncovalent forces ***(⇐ p. 408)*** with increasing molecular size and numbers of electrons are shown by the increasing ΔH°_{vap} and boiling point values. Comparison of HF and H_2O with CH_4, which have the same number of electrons, shows the effect of hydrogen bonding.

ThomsonNOW™

Go to the Chemistry Interactive menu to work a module on **boiling point and molecular structure.**

PROBLEM-SOLVING EXAMPLE 11.2 Enthalpy of Vaporization

To vaporize 50.0 g carbon tetrachloride, CCl_4, requires 9.69 kJ at its normal boiling point of 76.7 °C and 1 bar pressure. What is the molar enthalpy of vaporization of CCl_4 under these conditions?

Answer 29.8 kJ/mol

Strategy and Explanation The molar mass of CCl_4 is 153.8 g/mol, so

$$50.0 \text{ g } CCl_4 \times \frac{1 \text{ mol } CCl_4}{153.8 \text{ g } CCl_4} = 0.325 \text{ mol } CCl_4$$

The enthalpy change per mole of CCl_4 is given by

$$\frac{9.69 \text{ kJ}}{0.325 \text{ mol}} = 29.8 \text{ kJ/mol}$$

✓ **Reasonable Answer Check** We have approximately one third mol CCl_4, so the energy required to vaporize this amount of CCl_4 should be approximately one third of the molar enthalpy of vaporization, and it is.

PROBLEM-SOLVING PRACTICE 11.2

Using data from Table 11.2, calculate the thermal energy transfer required to vaporize 0.500 mol Br_2 at its normal boiling point.

PROBLEM-SOLVING EXAMPLE 11.3 Enthalpy of Vaporization

You put 1.00 L water (about 4 cups) in a pan at 100 °C, and the water evaporates. How much thermal energy must have been transferred (at 1 bar) to the water for all of it to vaporize? (The density of liquid water at 100 °C is 0.958 g/mL.)

Answer 2.16×10^3 kJ

Strategy and Explanation You need three pieces of information to solve this problem:

(a) ΔH°_{vap} for water, which is 40.7 kJ/mol at 100 °C (Table 11.2).

(b) The density of water, which is needed because ΔH°_{vap} has units of kJ/mol, so you must first find the mass of water and then the molar amount.

(c) The molar mass of water, 18.02 g/mol, which is needed to convert grams to moles.

From the density of water, a volume of 1.00 L (or 1.00×10^3 cm^3) is equivalent to 958. g. Therefore,

$$\text{Heat required for vaporization} = 958. \text{ g } H_2O \times \frac{1 \text{ mol } H_2O}{18.02 \text{ g } H_2O} \times \frac{40.7 \text{ kJ}}{1 \text{ mol}} = 2164 \text{ kJ}$$

This enthalpy change of 2164 kJ is equivalent to about one third to one half of the caloric energy in the daily food intake of an average person in the United States.

PROBLEM-SOLVING PRACTICE 11.3

A rainstorm deposits 2.5×10^{10} kg of rain. Using the heat of vaporization of water at 25 °C of 44.0 kJ/mol, calculate the quantity of thermal energy, in joules, transferred when this much rain forms. Is this process exothermic or endothermic?

CONCEPTUAL EXERCISE 11.6 Estimating ΔH°_{vap}

Using the data from Table 11.2, estimate the ΔH°_{vap} for Kr and NO_2. (*Hint:* Use the periodic table or choose a substance that has a similar number of electrons.)

CONCEPTUAL EXERCISE 11.7 Understanding Boiling Points

(a) Chlorine and bromine are both diatomic. Explain the difference in their boiling points.

(b) Methane and ammonia have the same number of electrons. Explain the difference in their boiling points.

Melting and Freezing

When a solid is heated, its temperature increases until the solid begins to melt. Unless the solid decomposes first, a temperature is reached at which the kinetic energies of the molecules or ions are sufficiently high that the intermolecular interactions in the solid are no longer strong enough to keep the particles in their fixed positions. The solid's structure collapses, and the solid melts (Figure 11.10). This temperature is the *melting point* of the solid. Melting requires transfer of energy, the *enthalpy of fusion,* from the surroundings into the system, so it is always endothermic. The *molar enthalpy of fusion* **(⇐ p. 231)** is the quantity of energy required to melt 1 mol of a pure solid. Solids with high enthalpies of fusion usually melt at high temperatures, and solids with low enthalpies of fusion usually melt at low temperatures. The reverse of melting—called *solidification, freezing,* or **crystallization**—is always an exothermic process. The *molar enthalpy of crystallization* has the same magnitude as the molar enthalpy of fusion, but the opposite sign.

Some solids do not have measurable melting points, and some liquids do not have measurable boiling points, because increasing temperature causes them to decompose before they melt or boil. Making peanut brittle provides an example: Melted sucrose chars before it boils, but it produces great-tasting candy.

$$\text{Solid} \underset{\text{enthalpy of crystallization}}{\overset{\text{enthalpy of fusion}}{\rightleftharpoons}} \text{Liquid} \qquad \Delta H_{\text{fusion}} = -\Delta H_{\text{crystallization}}$$

Table 11.3 lists melting points and enthalpies of fusion for examples of three classes of compounds: (a) nonpolar molecular solids, (b) polar molecular solids, some capable of hydrogen bonding, and (c) ionic solids. Solids composed of low molecular weight nonpolar molecules have the lowest melting temperatures, because their intermolecular attractions are weakest. These molecules are held together by London forces only **(⇐ p. 408)**, and they form solids with melting points so low that we seldom encounter them in the solid state at normal temperatures. Melting points and enthalpies of fusion of nonpolar molecular solids increase with increasing number of electrons (which corresponds to increasing molar mass) as the London forces become stronger. The ionic compounds in Table 11.3 have the highest melting points and enthalpies of fusion because of the very strong ionic bonding that holds the ions together in the solid. The polar molecular solids have intermediate melting points.

PROBLEM-SOLVING EXAMPLE 11.4 Enthalpy of Fusion

The molar enthalpy of fusion of NaCl is 30.21 kJ/mol at its melting point. How much thermal energy will be absorbed when 10.00 g NaCl melts?

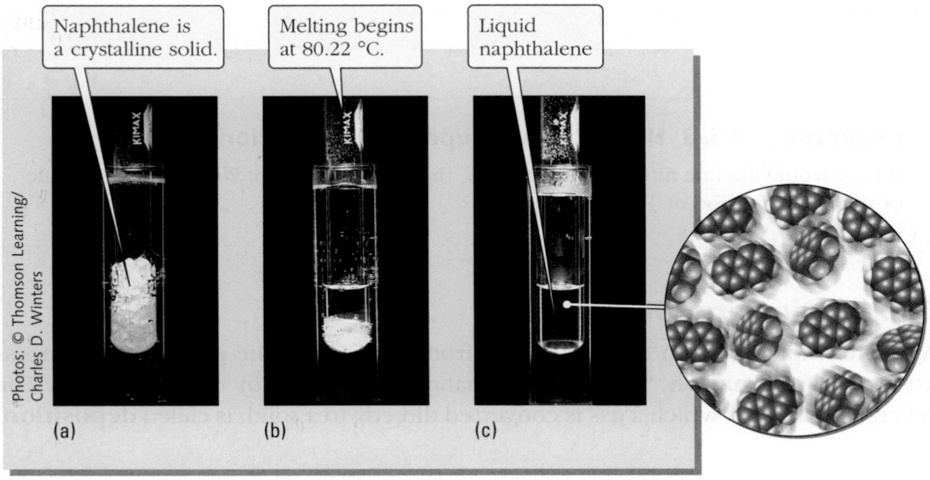

Figure 11.10 The melting of naphthalene, $C_{10}H_8$, at 80.22 °C.

Table 11.3 Melting Points and Enthalpies of Fusion of Some Solids

Solid	Melting Point (°C)	Enthalpy of Fusion (kJ/mol)	Type of Intermolecular Forces
Molecular solids: Nonpolar molecules			
O_2	−248	0.445	These molecules have only London forces (that increase with the number of electrons).
F_2	−220	1.020	
Cl_2	−103	6.406	
Br_2	−7.2	10.794	
Molecular solids: Polar molecules			
HCl	−114	1.990	All of these molecules have London forces enhanced significantly by dipole-dipole forces. H_2O also has significant hydrogen bonding.
HBr	−87	2.406	
HI	−51	2.870	
H_2O	0	6.020	
H_2S	−86	2.395	
Ionic solids			
NaCl	800	30.21	All ionic solids have strong attractions between oppositely charged ions.
NaBr	747	25.69	
NaI	662	21.95	

Answer 5.169 kJ

Strategy and Explanation The molar mass of NaCl is 58.443 g/mol, so

$$10.00 \text{ g NaCl} \times \frac{1 \text{ mol NaCl}}{58.443 \text{ g NaCl}} = 0.1711 \text{ mol NaCl}$$

Now we can use the molar enthalpy of fusion to calculate the thermal energy needed to melt this sample of NaCl.

$$0.1711 \text{ mol NaCl} \times \frac{30.21 \text{ kJ}}{\text{mol NaCl}} = 5.169 \text{ kJ}$$

✓ **Reasonable Answer Check** We have approximately one sixth mol NaCl, so the energy required to melt this amount of NaCl should be approximately one sixth of the molar enthalpy of fusion, and it is.

PROBLEM-SOLVING PRACTICE **11.4**

Calculate the thermal energy transfer required to melt 0.500 mol NaI at its normal melting point.

EXERCISE 11.8 Heat Liberated upon Crystallization

Which would liberate more thermal energy, the crystallization of 2 mol liquid bromine or the crystallization of 1 mol liquid water?

Sublimation and Deposition

Atoms or molecules can escape directly from the solid to the gas phase, a process known as **sublimation.** The enthalpy change is the *enthalpy of sublimation.* The reverse process, in which a gas is converted directly to a solid, is called **deposition.**

The enthalpy change for this exothermic process (the enthalpy of deposition) has the same magnitude as the enthalpy of sublimation, but the opposite sign.

$$\text{Solid} \underset{\text{enthalpy of deposition}}{\overset{\text{enthalpy of sublimation}}{\rightleftharpoons}} \text{Gas} \qquad \Delta H_{\text{sublimation}} = -\Delta H_{\text{deposition}}$$

One common substance that sublimes at normal atmospheric pressure is solid carbon dioxide (Dry Ice), which has a vapor pressure of 1 atm at −78 °C (Figure 11.11). Having such a high vapor pressure below its melting point causes solid carbon dioxide to sublime rather than melt. Because of the high vapor pressure of the solid, liquid carbon dioxide can exist only at pressures much higher than 1 atm.

© Thomson Learning/Charles D. Winters

Figure 11.11 **Dry Ice.** In this photo the cold vapors of CO_2 cause moisture, which is seen as wispy white clouds, to condense. Being more dense than air at room temperature, the CO_2 vapors glide slowly downward toward the table top.

Have you noticed that snow outdoors and ice cubes in a frost-free refrigerator slowly disappear even if the temperature never gets above freezing? The enthalpy of sublimation of ice is 51 kJ/mol, and its vapor pressure at 0 °C is 4.60 mm Hg. Therefore, ice sublimes readily in dry air when the partial pressure of water vapor is below 4.60 mm Hg (Figure 11.12). Given enough air passing over it, a sample of ice will sublime completely, leaving no trace behind. In a frost-free refrigerator, a current of dry air periodically blows across any ice formed in the freezer compartment, taking away water vapor (and hence the ice) without warming the freezer enough to thaw the food.

In the reverse of sublimation, atoms or molecules in the gas phase can deposit (solidify directly) on the surface of a solid. Deposition is used to form thin coatings of metal atoms on surfaces. Audio CD discs and CD-ROM discs, for example, have shiny metallic surfaces of deposited aluminum or gold atoms. To make such discs, a metal filament is heated in a vacuum to a temperature at which metal atoms begin to sublime rapidly off the surface. The plastic compact disc is cooler than the filament, so the metal atoms in the gas phase quickly deposit on the cool surface. The purpose of the metal coating is to provide a reflective surface for the laser beam that reads the pits and lands (unpitted areas) containing the digital audio or data information ***(⇐ p. 286)***.

CONCEPTUAL EXERCISE **11.9 Frost-Free Refrigeration**

Sometimes, because of humidity, a frost-free refrigerator doesn't work as efficiently as it should. Explain why.

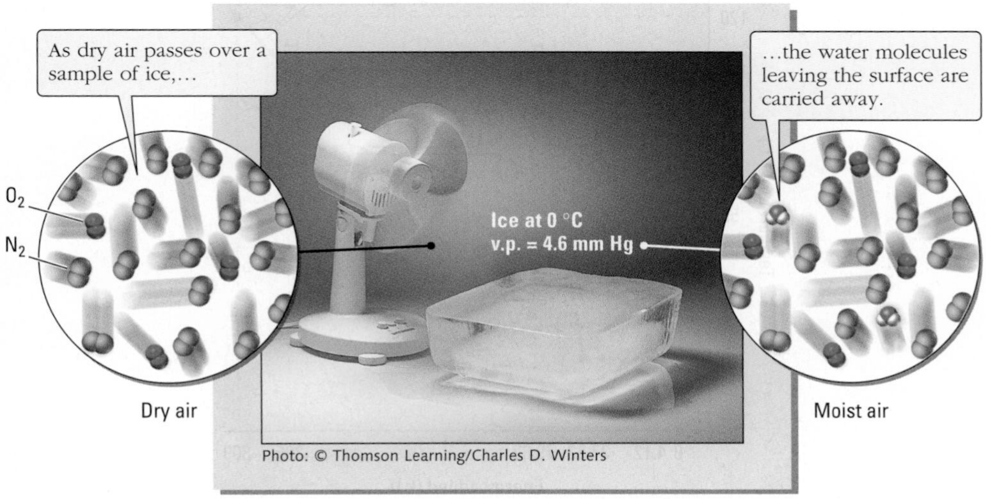

Figure 11.12 **Ice subliming.**

CONCEPTUAL EXERCISE 11.10 Purification by Sublimation

Sublimation is an excellent means of purification for compounds that will readily sublime. Explain how purification by sublimation works at the nanoscale.

Heating Curve

Heating a solid or liquid increases its temperature as long as its phase does not change. The size of this temperature increase is governed by the quantity of energy added (in joules), the mass of the substance (in grams), and its specific heat capacity (J g^{-1} $°C^{-1}$) (⇐ *p. 223*). The temperature rises until a phase-transition temperature is reached—for example, 100 °C for water. At this point, the temperature no longer rises. Instead, the energy goes into changing the phase of the substance. Once all of the substance has changed phase, then the addition of still more energy causes the temperature to rise. A plot of the temperature of a substance versus the energy added is called a **heating curve** (Figure 11.13).

For example, consider how much energy is required to heat 100. g water from −20 °C to 120 °C, as illustrated in Figure 11.13. The constants used to construct the heating curve are as follows: specific heat capacity of liquid water = 4.184 J g^{-1} $°C^{-1}$; specific heat capacity of solid water = 2.06 J g^{-1} $°C^{-1}$; specific heat capacity of water vapor = 1.84 J g^{-1} $°C^{-1}$; $\Delta H^\circ_{\text{fusion}}$ = 6.020 kJ/mol; $\Delta H^\circ_{\text{vaporization}}$ = 40.7 kJ/mol.

The heating curve has five distinct parts. Three parts relate to heating the water in its three states (red lines). Two parts relate to phase changes (horizontal blue lines).

1. *Heat the ice from −20 °C to 0 °C (A → B).*

$$H_2O(s) \text{ at } -20\ °C \rightarrow H_2O(s) \text{ at } 0\ °C$$

$$\Delta H^\circ = (100.\ g)(2.06\ J\ g^{-1}\ °C^{-1})(20\ °C) = 4120\ J = 4.12\ kJ$$

2. *Melt the ice at 0 °C (B → C).*

$$H_2O(s) \text{ at } 0\ °C \rightarrow H_2O(\ell) \text{ at } 0\ °C$$

$$\Delta H^\circ = 100.\ g \times \frac{1\ mol}{18.015\ g} \times \frac{6.020\ kJ}{1\ mol} = 33.4\ kJ$$

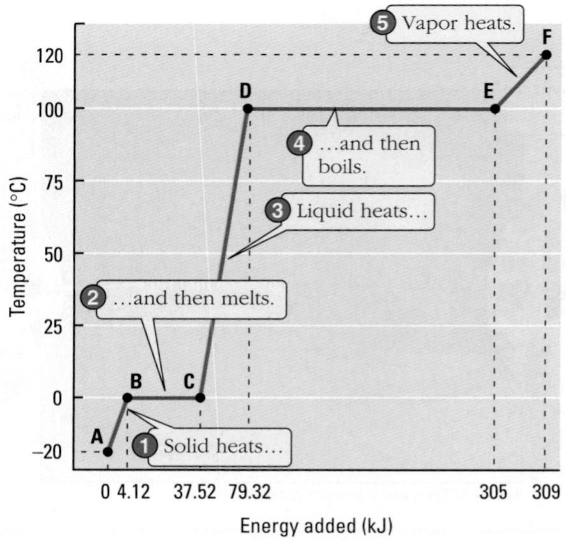

Figure 11.13 **Heating curve for water.**

Notice that there is no temperature change during a phase change.

3. *Heat the water from 0 °C to 100 °C (C → D).*

$$H_2O(\ell) \text{ at } 0\ °C \rightarrow H_2O(\ell) \text{ at } 100\ °C$$

$$\Delta H° = (100.\ g)(4.184\ J\ g^{-1}\ °C^{-1})(100\ °C) = 41800\ J = 41.8\ kJ$$

4. *Boil the water at 100 °C (D → E).*

$$H_2O(\ell) \text{ at } 100\ °C \rightarrow H_2O(g) \text{ at } 100\ °C$$

$$\Delta H° = 100.\ g \times \frac{1\ mol}{18.015\ g} \times \frac{40.7\ kJ}{1\ mol} = 226.\ kJ$$

5. *Heat the water vapor from 100 °C to 120 °C (E → F).*

$$H_2O(g) \text{ at } 100\ °C \rightarrow H_2O(g) \text{ at } 120\ °C$$

$$\Delta H° = (100.\ g)(1.84\ J\ g^{-1}\ °C^{-1})(20\ °C) = 3680\ J = 3.68\ kJ$$

The total energy required to complete the transformation is 309. kJ, the sum of the five steps. Notice that the largest portion of the energy, 226. kJ (73%), goes into vaporizing water at 100 °C to steam at 100 °C.

Phase Diagrams

All three phases and the six interconversions among them shown in Figure 11.8 (p. 495) can be represented in a **phase diagram** (Figure 11.14). The pressure-temperature values at which each phase exists are also shown on the phase diagram. Each of the three phases—solid, liquid, gas—is represented. Each solid line in the diagram represents the conditions of temperature and pressure at which equilibrium exists between the two phases on either side of the line. The point at which all three phases are in equilibrium is the **triple point.** Every pure substance that exists in all three phases has a characteristic phase diagram.

The phase diagram for water is shown in Figure 11.15 (p. 504). The three shaded regions represent the three phases—solid, liquid, and gas. The temperature scale has been exaggerated to better illustrate some of the features of water's phase diagram. The temperatures and pressures along the line *AD* represent conditions at which liquid water and gaseous water are in equilibrium. This line, the *vapor pressure curve,* is the same one shown in Figure 11.5 (p. 493). The line *AC*, the *melting point curve,* represents the solid/liquid (ice/water) equilibrium, and the line *BA*

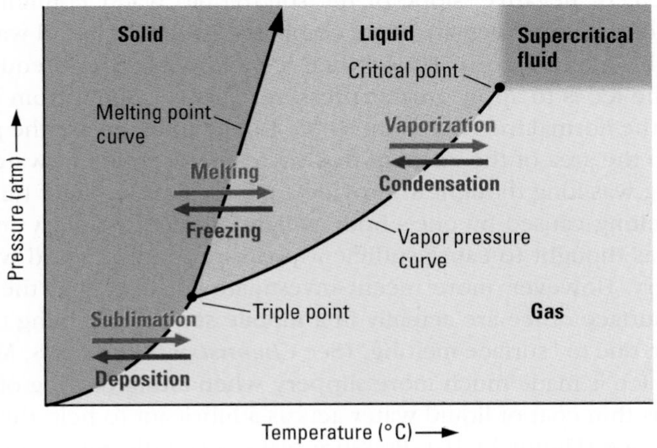

Figure 11.14 Generic phase diagram. The phase diagram shows the pressure-temperature regions in which the substance is solid, liquid, or vapor (gas). It also shows the melting point curve, the vapor pressure curve, and the six interconversions among the three phases.

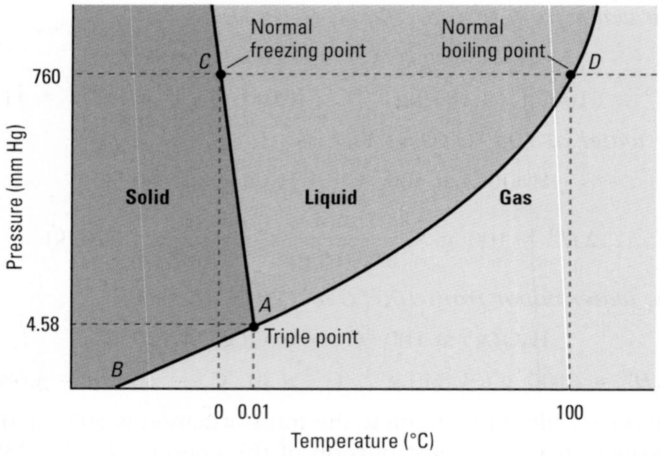

Figure 11.15 The phase diagram for water. The temperature and pressure scales are nonlinear for emphasis. Line *AD* is the vapor pressure curve, and line *AC* is the melting point curve.

ThomsonNOW

Go to the Coached Problems menu for an exercise on **phase diagrams and phase changes** and the Chemistry Interactive menu to work a module on **phase diagrams.**

represents the solid/gaseous (ice/water vapor) equilibrium. The triple point for water occurs at P = 4.58 mm Hg and T = 0.01 °C.

You are most likely familiar with the common situation in which ice and liquid water are in equilibrium because of keeping food cool in an ice chest. If you fill an ice chest with ice, some of the ice melts to produce liquid. (Thermal energy is slowly transferred into the ice chest, no matter how well it is insulated.) The ice-liquid water mixture remains at approximately 0 °C until all of the ice has melted. This equilibrium between solid water and liquid water is represented in the phase diagram (Figure 11.15) by point *C*, at which P = 760 mm Hg and T = 0 °C.

On a very cold day, ice can have a temperature well below 0 °C. Look along the temperature axis of the phase diagram for water and notice that below 1 atm and 0 °C the only equilibrium possible is between ice and water vapor. As a result, if the partial pressure of water in the air is low enough, ice will sublime on a cold day. Sublimation, which is endothermic, takes place more readily when solar energy warms the ice. The sublimation of ice allows snow or ice to gradually disappear even though the temperature does not climb above freezing.

The phase diagram for water is unusual in that the melting point curve *AC* slopes in the opposite direction from that seen for almost every other substance. The right-to-left, or negative, slope of the solid/liquid water equilibrium line is a consequence of the lower density of ice compared to that of liquid water (which is discussed in the next section). Thus, when ice and water are in equilibrium, one way to melt the ice is to apply greater pressure. This is evident from Figure 11.15. If you start at the normal freezing point (0 °C, 1 atm) and increase the pressure, you will move into the area of the diagram that corresponds to liquid water.

Ice skating was long thought to provide a practical example of this property of water. The melting caused by one's body weight applied to a very small area of a skate blade was thought to cause sufficient pressure to form liquid water to make the ice slippery. However, more recent investigations show that the water molecules on the surface of ice are actually in a mobile state, resembling their mobility in liquid water, due to "surface melting." (See *Chemistry in the News,* Melting Below Zero, p. 509.) Ice is made much more slippery when a thin coating of liquid water is present. This thin coat of liquid water acts as a lubricant to help the skates move easily over the ice (Figure 11.16). Pressure plays very little role in making the ice slippery for skating. Although increasing the pressure on ice does cause it to melt, the effect is too small to contribute significantly in the context of ice skating.

© Rhyan McVay/Photodisc Red/Getty Images

Figure 11.16 Ice skating.

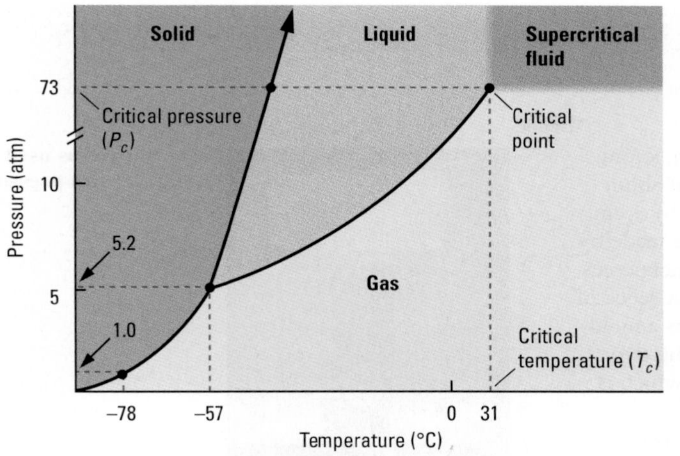

Figure 11.17 **The phase diagram for carbon dioxide.**

The phase diagram for CO_2 (Figure 11.17) is similar to that of water, except for one very important difference—the solid/liquid equilibrium line has a positive slope, as it does for most substances. Solid CO_2 is more dense than liquid CO_2. Notice also that the values of the pressure and temperature axes in the phase diagram for CO_2 are much different from those in the diagram for water. For pressures below about 5 atm, the only equilibrium that can exist is between solid and gaseous CO_2. This means solid CO_2 sublimes when heated. Liquid CO_2 can be produced only at pressures above 5 atm. The temperature range for liquid CO_2 is narrower than that for water. Tanker trucks marked "liquid carbonic" carry liquid CO_2, a convenient source of CO_2 gas for making carbonated beverages.

PROBLEM-SOLVING EXAMPLE 11.5 Phase Diagrams

Use the phase diagram for CO_2 (Figure 11.17) to answer these questions.

(a) What is the temperature and pressure at the triple point?

(b) Starting at the triple point, what phase exists when the pressure is held constant and the temperature is increased to 65 °C?

(c) Starting at $T = -70$ °C and $P = 4$ atm, what phase change occurs when the pressure is held constant and the temperature is increased to -30 °C?

(d) Starting at $T = -30$ °C and $P = 5$ atm, what phase change occurs when the temperature is held constant and the pressure is increased to 10 atm?

Answer (a) $T = -57$ °C, $P = 5.2$ atm (b) Gas (c) Solid to gas (sublimation) (d) Gas to liquid (condensation)

Strategy and Explanation In each case, consult the location on the phase diagram that corresponds to the given temperature and pressure conditions.

(a) The phase diagram shows that the triple point occurs at a temperature of -57 °C and a pressure of 5.2 atm.

(b) Increasing the temperature and holding the pressure constant means moving somewhat to the right from the triple point. This is the gas region of the phase diagram.

(c) At the starting temperature and pressure, the CO_2 is a solid. Increasing the temperature while holding the pressure constant causes the solid to sublime and change directly to the gas phase.

(d) At the starting temperature and pressure, the CO_2 is a liquid. Increasing the pressure while holding the temperature constant causes the gas to condense to the liquid phase.

CHEMISTRY YOU CAN DO

Melting Ice with Pressure

Do this experiment in a sink. Obtain a piece of thin, strong, single-strand wire about 50 cm long, two weights of about 1 kg each, and a piece of ice about 25 cm by 3 cm by 3 cm. The ice can be either a cylinder or a bar and can be made by pouring some water into a mold made of several thicknesses of aluminum foil and then placing it into a freezer. A piece of plastic pipe, not tightly sealed, will also work fine as a mold. You can use metal weights or make weights by filling two 1-qt milk jugs with water. (One quart is about 1 L, which is 1 kg of water.)

Fasten one weight to each end of the wire. Support the bar of ice so that, without breaking the ice, you can hang the wire over it with one weight on each side. Observe the bar of ice and the wire every minute or so and record what happens. Suggest an explanation for what you have observed. The effect of pressure on the melting of ice and the enthalpy of fusion of ice are good ideas to consider when thinking about your explanation.

© Thomson Learning/Charles D. Winters

The apparatus used to melt ice with pressure.

1. Explain how the ice froze once again after the wire had passed through it.
2. What would be the effect of using a thinner piece of wire? Of using heavier weights?

PROBLEM-SOLVING PRACTICE **11.5**

On the phase diagram for CO_2 (Figure 11.17), the point that corresponds to a temperature of −13 °C and a pressure of 7.5 atm is on the vapor pressure curve where liquid phase and gas phase are in equilibrium. What phase of CO_2 exists when the pressure remains the same and the temperature is increased by several degrees?

EXERCISE 11.11 Using a Phase Diagram

Consider the phase diagram for CO_2 (Figure 11.17). A curve connects the triple point and the critical point; what is the name of this curve? What phase transition occurs when you traverse this curve at its midpoint going upward, that is, increasing the pressure at constant temperature? Downward? What phase transition occurs when you traverse this curve at its midpoint going from left to right, that is, increasing the temperature at constant pressure? Right to left?

Critical Temperature and Pressure

On the phase diagram for CO_2, notice the upper point where the liquid/gas equilibrium line terminates (Figure 11.17). For CO_2 the conditions at this critical point are 73 atm and 31 °C. For water the termination of the solid/liquid curve occurs at a pressure of 217.7 atm and a temperature of 374.0 °C (Figure 11.15). These conditions at the critical point are called the **critical pressure** (P_c) and **critical temperature** (T_c). At any temperature above T_c the molecules of a substance have sufficient kinetic energy to overcome any attractive forces, and no amount of pressure can cause the substance to act like a liquid again. Above T_c and P_c the substance becomes a **supercritical fluid,** which has a density characteristic of a liquid but the flow properties of a gas, thereby enabling it to diffuse through many substances easily.

The term "fluid" describes a substance that will flow. It is used for both liquids and gases.

Supercritical CO_2 is present in a fire extinguisher under certain conditions. As the phase diagram shows, at any temperature below 31 °C, the pressurized CO_2 (usually at about 73 atm) is a liquid that can slosh around in the container. On a hot day, however, the CO_2 becomes a supercritical fluid and cannot be heard sloshing. In fact, under these conditions the only way to know whether CO_2 is in the extinguisher—without discharging it—is to weigh it and compare its mass with the mass of the empty container, which is usually indicated on a tag attached to the fire extinguisher.

Supercritical fluids are excellent solvents. Because supercritical CO_2 is nonpolar and is therefore a good solvent for nonpolar substances, it is used for dry cleaning. Supercritical CO_2 is also used to extract caffeine from coffee beans and for extracting toxic components from hazardous industrial wastes.

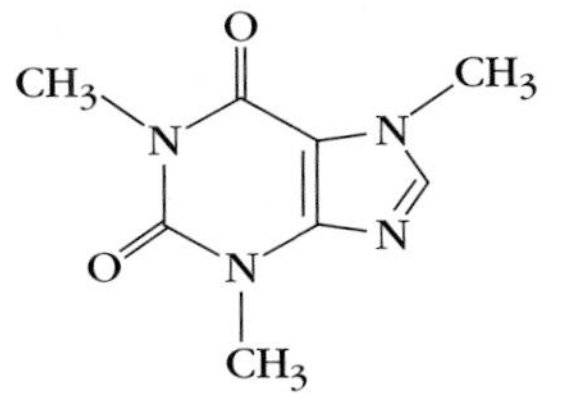

caffeine

© Thomson Learning/Charles D. Winters

Coffee beans and the molecular structure of caffeine.

CONCEPTUAL EXERCISE 11.12 The Behavior of CO_2

If liquid CO_2 is slowly released to the atmosphere from a cylinder, what state will the CO_2 be in? If the liquid is suddenly released, as in the discharge of a CO_2 fire extinguisher, why is solid CO_2 seen? Can you explain this phenomenon on the basis of the phase diagram alone, or do you need to consider other factors?

11.4 Water: An Important Liquid with Unusual Properties

Earth is sometimes called the blue planet because the large quantities of water on its surface make it look blue from outer space. Three quarters of the globe is covered by oceans, and vast ice sheets cover the poles. Large quantities of water are present in soils and rocks on the surface. Water is essential to almost every form of life, has played a key role in human history, and is a significant factor in weather and climate. Water's importance is linked to its unique properties (Table 11.4). Ice floats on water; in contrast, when most substances freeze, the solid sinks in its liquid. More thermal energy must be transferred to melt ice, heat water, and vaporize water than to accomplish these changes for the same mass of almost any other substance. Water has the largest thermal conductivity and the highest surface tension of any molecular substance in the liquid state. In other words, this most common of substances in our daily lives has properties that are highly unusual. These properties are crucial for the welfare of our planet and our species.

Most of water's unusual properties can be attributed to its molecules' unique capacity for hydrogen bonding. As seen from Figure 9.22 (⇐ ***p. 413***), one water molecule can participate in four hydrogen bonds to other water molecules. When liquid water freezes, a three-dimensional network of water molecules forms to accommodate the maximum hydrogen bonding. In the crystal lattice of ice, the oxygen atoms lie at the corners of puckered, six-sided rings. Considerable open space is left within the rings, forming empty channels that run through the entire crystal lattice.

"If there is magic on this planet, it is contained in water . . . Its substance reaches everywhere."
—Loren Eiseley

The six-sided symmetry of snowflakes corresponds to the symmetry of these hexagonal rings.

When ice melts to form liquid water, approximately 15% of the hydrogen bonds are broken and the rigid ice lattice collapses. This makes the density of liquid water greater than that of ice at the melting point. The density of ice at 0 °C is 0.917 g/mL, and that of liquid water at 0 °C is 0.998 g/mL. The density difference is not large, but it is enough so that ice floats on the surface of the liquid. This explains why about 90% of an iceberg is submerged and about 10% is above water.

As the liquid water is warmed further, more hydrogen bonds break, and more empty space is filled by water molecules. The density continues to increase until a temperature of 3.98 °C and a density of 1.000 g/mL are reached. As the temperature rises beyond 3.98 °C, increased molecular motion causes the molecules to push

Table 11.4 Unusual Properties of Water

Property	Comparison with Other Substances	Importance in Physical and Biological Environment
Specific heat capacity ($4.18\ J\ g^{-1}\ °C^{-1}$)	Highest of all liquids and solids except NH_3	Moderates temperature in the environment and in organisms; climate affected by movement of water (e.g., Gulf Stream)
Heat of fusion (333 J/g)	Highest of all molecular solids except NH_3	Freezing water releases large quantity of thermal energy; used to save crops from freezing by spraying them with liquid water
Heat of vaporization (2250 J/g)	Highest of all molecular substances	Condensation of water vapor in clouds releases large quantities of thermal energy, fueling storms
Surface tension ($7.3 \times 10^{-2}\ J/m^2$)	Highest of all molecular liquids	Contributes to capillary action in plants; causes formation of spherical droplets; supports insects on water surfaces
Thermal conductivity ($0.6\ J\ s^{-1}\ m^{-1}\ °C^{-1}$)	Highest of all molecular liquids	Provides for transfer of thermal energy within organisms; rapidly cools organisms immersed in cold water, causing hypothermia

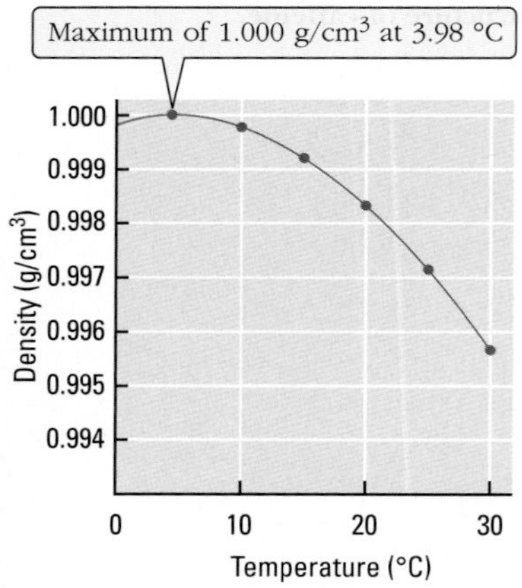

Figure 11.18 The density of liquid water between 0 °C and 30 °C. The density is largest at 1.000 g/cm³ at 3.98 °C. The density of ice at 0 °C is 0.917 g/cm³.

each other aside more vigorously, the empty space between molecules increases, and the density decreases by about 0.0001 g/mL for every 1 °C temperature rise above 3.98 °C (Figure 11.18).

Because of this unusual variation of density with temperature, when water in a lake is cooled to 3.98 °C, the higher density causes the cold water to sink to the bottom. Water cooled below 3.98 °C is less dense and stays on the surface, where it can be cooled even further. Consequently, the water at the bottom of the lake remains at 3.98 °C, while that on the surface freezes. Ice on the surface insulates the remaining liquid water from the cold air, and, unless the lake is quite shallow, not all of the water freezes. This allows fish and other organisms to survive without being frozen in the winter. When water at 3.98 °C sinks to the bottom of a lake in

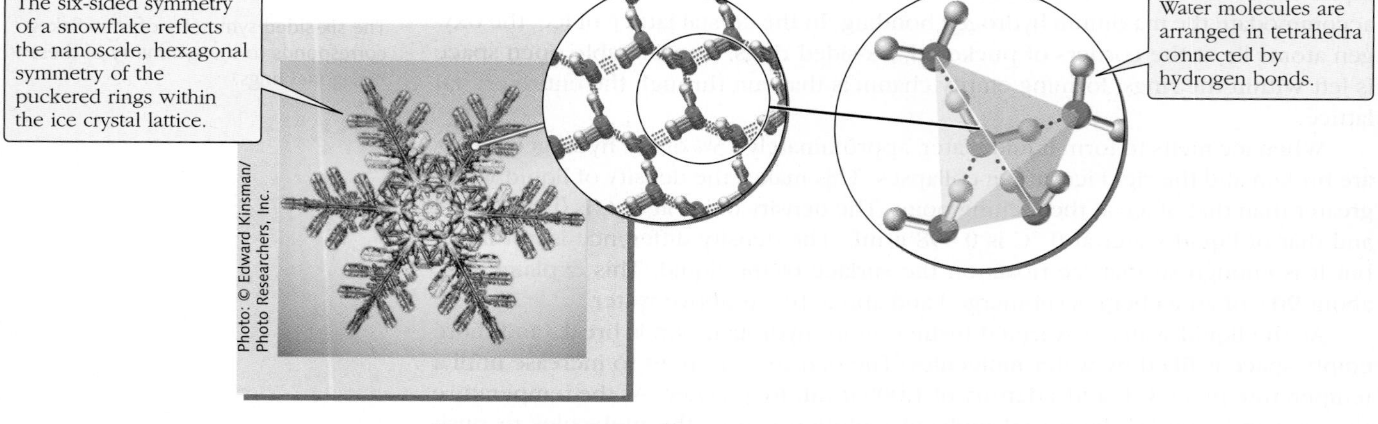

Open-cage structure of ice.

CHEMISTRY IN THE NEWS

Melting Below Zero

Details on how the freezing of water and the thawing of ice proceed at the molecular level are being revealed by new research. The key lies in a very thin layer of water, only a few molecules thick, created by a process termed "surface melting." This thin layer is very similar to the ice beneath it, but it has the mobility of the liquid state. Effects due to its presence include the sliding of ice skates over ice, the eruption of boulders from the ground during freeze-thaw cycles (frost heave), and the electrification of thunderclouds.

Surface melting is an intrinsic property of the ice surface, even at tens of degrees Celsius below the usual melting point. It arises due to the fact that the surface water molecules have interactions with fewer neighbors than do those molecules deeper in the solid. The ice lattice becomes less and less ordered closer to the surface because the surface molecules have the fewest hydrogen bonds holding them in place. That is, these molecules vibrate around their lattice positions more than the molecules deeper in the solid. At temperatures well below the melting point, the surface molecules begin to take on the characteristics of a liquid. Surface melting was first described by Michael Faraday in 1842, and scientists are even now refining their understanding of this phenomenon.

The presence of the surface liquid phase permits you to develop a snowball. The liquid on the surface of ice particles refreezes and joins them together into a snowball. Truly dry snow does not permit the formation of a snowball.

While the ice-water system is best known in the everyday world, this surface melting phenomenon occurs for virtually all solids.

SOURCE: Wettlaufer, J. S., and Dash, J. G. "Melting Below Zero." *Scientific American*, February 2000, pp. 50–53.

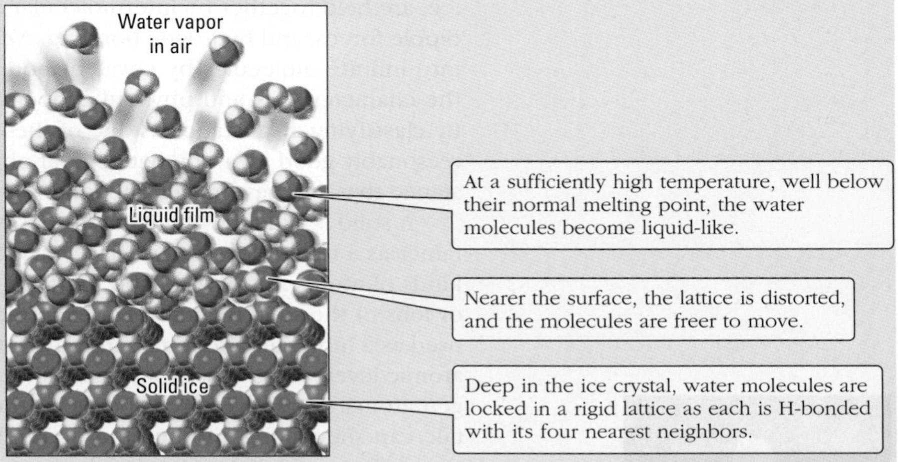

The surface of ice is slick due to a liquid-like film of water.

the fall, it carries with it dissolved oxygen. Nutrients from the bottom are brought to the surface by the water it displaces. This is called "turnover" of the lake. The same thing happens in the spring, when the ice melts and water on the surface warms to 3.98 °C. Spring and fall turnovers are essential to maintain nutrient and oxygen levels required by fish and other lake-dwelling organisms.

When water is heated, the increased molecular motion breaks additional hydrogen bonds. The strength of these intermolecular forces requires that considerable energy be transferred to raise the temperature of 1 g of water by 1 °C. That is, water's specific heat capacity is quite large. Many hydrogen bonds are broken when liquid water vaporizes, because the molecules are completely separated. This gives rise to water's very large enthalpy of vaporization, which is a factor in humans' ability to regulate their body temperature by evaporation of sweat. As we have already described, hydrogen bonds are broken when ice melts, and this requires a large enthalpy of fusion. Its larger-than-normal enthalpy changes upon vaporization and freezing, together with its large specific heat capacity, allow water to moderate climate and influence weather by a much larger factor than other liquids could. In the vicinity of a large body of water, summer temperatures do not get as high and winter temperatures do not get as low (at least until the water freezes over) as they do far away from water ***(⇐ p. 223).*** Seattle is farther north than Minneapolis, for example, but Seattle has a much more moderate climate because it borders the Pacific Ocean and Puget Sound.

11.5 Types of Solids

The relationship of nanoscale structure to macroscale properties is a central theme of this text. Nowhere is the influence of the nanoscale arrangement of atoms, molecules, or ions on properties more evident than in the study of solids. Practicing chemists, in collaboration with physicists, engineers, and other scientists, explore such relationships as they work to create new and useful materials. The nature of solid substances is determined by the type of forces holding them together. *Ionic solids,* such as common table salt (NaCl), are held together by electrostatic interactions between cations and anions. *Molecular solids,* such as water in the form of ice, are held together by intermolecular interactions such as London forces, dipole-dipole forces, and hydrogen bonding. *Network solids,* such as diamond, are bonded into infinite molecules by covalent bonds between atoms. Table 11.5 summarizes the characteristics and physical properties of the major types of solid substances. By classifying a substance as one of these types of solid, you will be able to form a reasonably good idea of what general physical properties to expect, even for a substance that you have never encountered before.

A solid is rigid, having its own shape rather than assuming the shape of its container as a liquid does. Solids have varying degrees of hardness that depend on the kinds of atoms in the solid and the types of forces that hold the atoms, molecules, or ions of the solid together. For example, talc (soapstone, Figure 11.19a), which is used as a lubricant and in talcum powder, is one of the softest solids known. At the atomic level, talc consists of layered sheets containing silicon, magnesium, and oxygen atoms. Attractive forces between these sheets are very weak, so one sheet of talc can slide along another and be removed easily from the rest. In contrast, diamond (Figure 11.19b) is one of the hardest solids known. In diamond, each carbon atom is strongly bonded to four neighbors. Each of those neighbor atoms is in turn

© Thomson Learning/Charles D. Winters

(a)

© Thomson Learning/Charles D. Winters

(b)

Figure 11.19 **(a) Talc.** Although they do not appear to be soft, these talc crystals are so soft that they can be crushed between one's fingers. **(b) Diamond.** One of the hardest substances known.

Table 11.5 Structures and Properties of Various Types of Solid Substances

Type	Examples	Structural Units
Ionic ***(⇐ p. 89)***	NaCl, K_2SO_4, $CaCl_2$, $(NH_4)_3PO_4$	Positive and negative ions (some polyatomic); no discrete molecules
Metallic (Section 11.9)	Iron, silver, copper, other metals and alloys	Metal atoms (positive metal ions surrounded by an electron sea)
Molecular ***(⇐ p. 79)***	H_2, O_2, I_2, H_2O, CO_2, CH_4, CH_3OH, CH_3COOH	Molecules with covalent bonds
Network (Section 11.7)	Graphite, diamond, quartz, feldspars, mica	Atoms held in an infinite one-, two-, or three-dimensional network
Amorphous (glassy)	Glass, polyethylene, nylon	Covalently bonded networks of atoms or collections of large molecules with short-range order only

strongly bonded to four other carbon atoms, and so on throughout the solid (a network solid, Section 11.7). Because of the number and strength of the bonds holding each carbon atom to its neighbors, diamond is so hard that it can scratch or cut almost any other solid. For this reason diamonds are used in cutting tools and abrasives, which are more important commercially than diamonds used as gemstones.

Although all solids consist of atoms, molecules, or ions in relatively immobile positions, some solids exhibit a greater degree of regularity than others. In **crystalline solids,** the ordered arrangement of the individual particles is reflected in the planar faces and sharp angles of the crystals. Salt crystals, minerals, gemstones, and ice are examples of crystalline solids. **Amorphous solids** are somewhat like liquids in that they exhibit very little long-range order, yet they are hard and have definite shapes. Ordinary glass is an amorphous solid, as are organic polymers such as polyethylene and polystyrene. The remainder of this chapter is devoted to explaining the nanoscale structures that give rise to the properties of solids summarized in Table 11.5.

PROBLEM-SOLVING EXAMPLE 11.6 Types of Solids

What types of solids are these substances?

(a) Sucrose, $C_{12}H_{22}O_{11}$ (table sugar), has a melting point of about 185 °C. It has poor electrical conductance both as a solid and as a liquid.

(b) Solid Na_2SO_4 has a melting point of 884 °C and has low electrical conductivity that increases dramatically when the solid melts.

Answer (a) Molecular solid (b) Ionic solid

Strategy and Explanation

(a) Sucrose molecules contain covalently bonded atoms. Sucrose's properties correspond to those of a molecular solid since it has poor electrical conductance both as a solid and as a liquid.

(b) Sodium sulfate is composed of Na^+ and SO_4^{2-} ions. The given properties are consistent with those of ionic solids. Ionic solids have high melting points and are poor conductors as solids but good conductors as liquids.

Forces Holding Units Together	Typical Properties
Ionic bonding; attractions among charges on positive and negative ions	Hard; brittle; high melting point; poor electrical conductor as solid, good as molten liquid; often water-soluble
Metallic bonding; electrostatic attraction among metal ions and electrons	Malleable; ductile; good electrical conductor in solid and liquid; good heat conductor; wide range of hardness and melting point
London forces, dipole-dipole forces, hydrogen bonds	Low to moderate melting point and boiling point; soft; poor electrical conductor in solid and liquid
Covalent bonds; directional electron-pair bonds	Wide range of hardness and melting point (three-dimensional bonding > two-dimensional bonding > one-dimensional bonding); poor electrical conductor with some exceptions
Covalent bonds; directional electron-pair bonds	Noncrystalline; wide temperature range for melting; poor electrical conductor, with some exceptions

PROBLEM-SOLVING PRACTICE 11.6

What types of solids are these substances?

(a) The hydrocarbon decane, $C_{10}H_{22}$, has a melting point of −31 °C and is a poor electrical conductor.

(b) Solid $MgCl_2$ has a melting point of 780 °C and conducts electricity only when melted.

CONCEPTUAL EXERCISE 11.13 Lead into Gold?

Imagine a sample of gold and a sample of lead, each with a smoothly polished surface. The surfaces of these two samples are placed in contact with one another and held in place, under pressure, for about one year. After that time the two surfaces are analyzed. The gold surface is tested for the presence of lead, and the lead surface is tested for the presence of gold. Predict what the outcome of these two tests will be and explain what has happened, if anything.

11.6 Crystalline Solids

The beautiful regularity of ice crystals, crystalline salts, and gemstones suggests that they must have some *internal* regularity. Toward the end of the eighteenth century, scientists found that shapes of crystals can be used to identify minerals. The angles at which crystal faces meet are characteristic of a crystal's composition. The shape of each crystalline solid reflects the shape of its **crystal lattice**—the orderly, repeating arrangement of ions, molecules, or atoms that shows the position of each individual particle. In such a lattice each ion, molecule, or atom is surrounded by neighbors in exactly the same arrangement. Each crystal is built up from a three-dimensional repetition of the same pattern, which gives the crystal long-range order throughout.

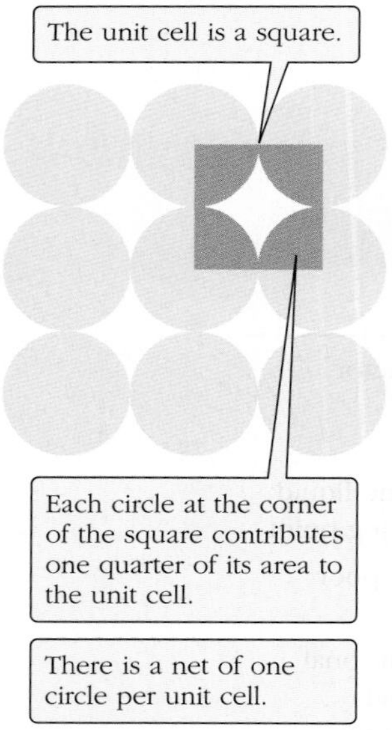

Figure 11.20 Unit cell for a two-dimensional solid made from flat, circular objects, such as coins.

Unit Cells

A convenient way to describe and classify the repeating pattern of atoms, molecules, or ions in a crystal is to define a small segment of a crystal lattice as a **unit cell**—a small part of the lattice that, when repeated along the directions defined by its edges, reproduces the entire crystal structure. To help understand the idea of the unit cell, look at the simple two-dimensional array of circles shown in Figure 11.20. The same size circle is repeated over and over, but a circle is not a proper unit cell because it gives no indication of its relationship to all the other circles. A better choice is to recognize that the centers of four adjacent circles lie at the corners of a square and to draw four lines connecting those centers. A square unit cell results. Figure 11.20 shows this simple unit cell superimposed on the circles. As you look at the unit cell drawn in darker blue, notice that each of four circles contributes one quarter of itself to the unit cell, so a net of one circle is located within the unit cell. When this unit cell is repeated by moving the square parallel to its edges (that is, when unit cells are placed next to and above and below the first one), the two-dimensional lattice results. Notice that the corners of a unit cell are equivalent to each other and that collectively they define the crystal lattice.

The three-dimensional unit cells from which all known crystal lattices can be constructed fall into only seven categories. These seven types of unit cells have edges of different relative lengths that meet at different angles. We will limit our discussion here to one of these types—cubic unit cells composed of atoms or monatomic ions. Such unit cells are quite common in nature and are simpler and easier to visualize than the other types of unit cells. The principles illustrated, however, apply to all unit cells and all crystal structures, including those composed of polyatomic ions and large molecules.

Cubic unit cells have edges of equal length that meet at 90° angles. There are three types: *primitive cubic* or *simple cubic (sc), body-centered cubic (bcc), and face-centered cubic (fcc)* (Figure 11.21). Many metals and ionic compounds crystallize in cubic unit cells.

In metals, all three types of cubic unit cells have identical atoms centered at each corner of the cube. When the cubes pack into three-dimensional space, an atom at a corner is shared among eight cubes (Figure 11.21); thus only one eighth of each corner atom is actually within the unit cell. Since a cube has eight corners and since one eighth of the atom at each corner belongs to the unit cell, the net result is $8 \times \frac{1}{8} = 1$ *atom per primitive (simple) cubic unit cell.*

In the bcc unit cell an additional atom is at the center of the cube and lies entirely within the unit cell. This atom, combined with the net of one atom from the corners, gives a total of *two atoms per body-centered cubic unit cell.*

In the face-centered cubic unit cell six atoms or ions lie in the centers of the faces of the cube. One half of each of these atoms or ions belongs to the unit cell (Figure 11.21). In this case there is a net result of $6 \times \frac{1}{2} = 3$ atoms per unit cell, plus the net of one atom contributed by the corners, for a total of *four atoms per face-centered cubic unit cell.* The number of atoms per unit cell helps to determine the density of a solid.

Examples of metals with cubic unit cells:

Primitive (simple) cubic: Po

Body-centered cubic: alkali metals, V, Cr, Mo, W, Fe

Face-centered cubic: Ni, Cu, Ag, Au, Al, Pb

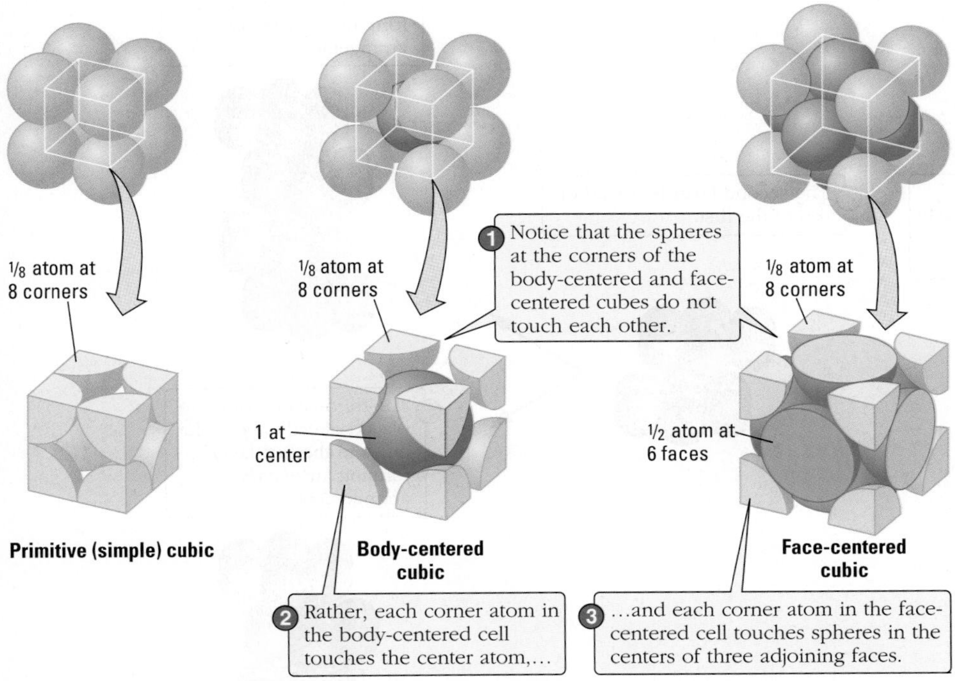

Figure 11.21 The three different types of cubic unit cells. The top row shows the lattice points of the three cells superimposed on space-filling spheres centered on the lattice points. The bottom row shows the three cubic unit cells with only those atoms included that belong to the unit cell.

ThomsonNOW

Go to the Chemistry Interactive menu to work modules on:

- **crystal lattice formed from unit cells**
- **formation of a molecular solid from fullerene molecules**

sc: 1 atom/unit cell
bcc: 2 atoms/unit cell
fcc: 4 atoms/unit cell

EXERCISE 11.14 Counting Atoms in Unit Cells of Metals

Crystalline polonium has a primitive (simple) cubic unit cell, lithium has a body-centered cubic unit cell, and calcium has a face-centered cubic unit cell. How many Po atoms belong to one unit cell? How many Li atoms belong to one unit cell? How many Ca atoms belong to one unit cell? Draw each unit cell. Indicate on your drawing what fraction of each atom lies within the unit cell.

Closest Packing of Spheres

In crystalline solids, the atoms, molecules, or ions are usually arranged as closely as possible so that their interactions are maximized, which results in a stable structure. This arrangement is most easily illustrated for metals, in which the individual particles are identical atoms that can be represented as spheres. The arrangement known as **closest packing** can be built up as a series of layers of atoms. In each layer of equal-sized spheres, as shown in Figure 11.22, part 1, each sphere is surrounded by six neighbors. A second layer can be put on top of the first layer so the spheres nestle into the depressions of the first layer (Figure 11.22, part 2). Then a third layer can be added. There are two ways to add the third layer, each of which yields a different structure, as shown in Figure 11.22, parts 3 and 4. If the third layer is directly above the first layer, an *ababab* arrangement results, called a **hexagonal close-packed** structure. In this *ababab* structure, the centers of the spheres of the

In *ababab* packing, the repeat occurs every third layer; in *abcabc* packing, it is every fourth layer.

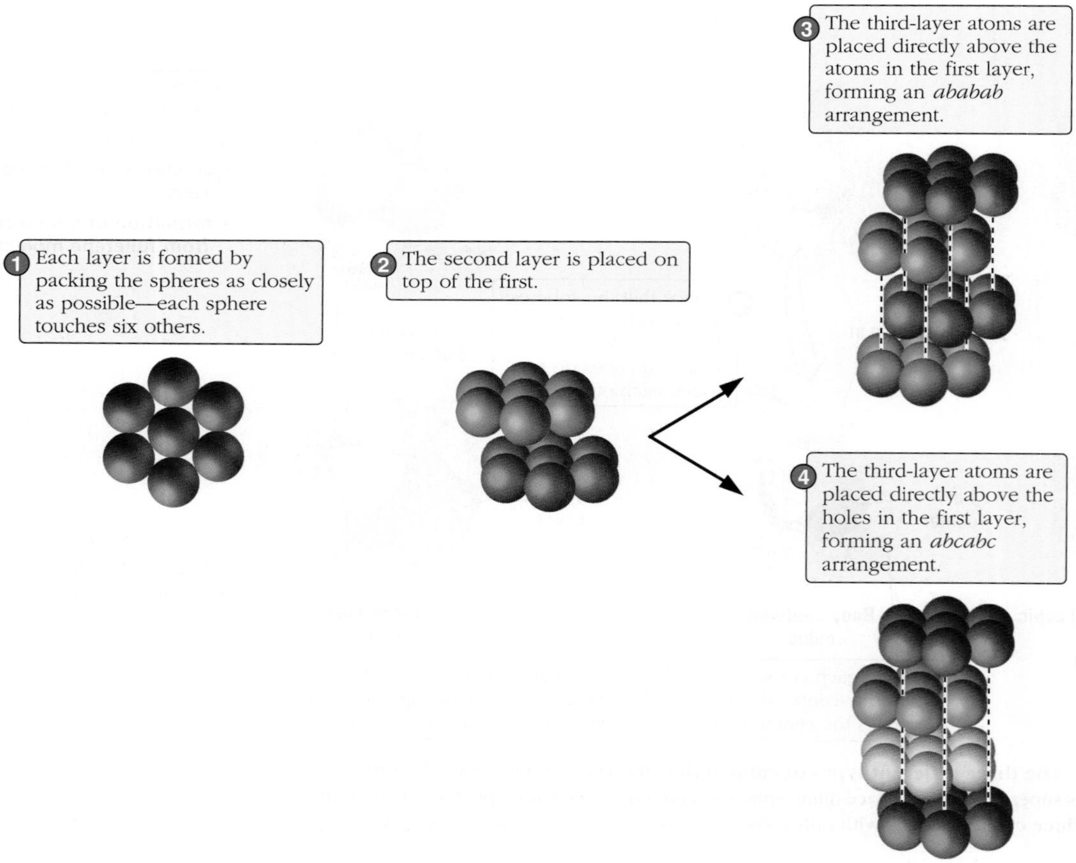

Figure 11.22 Closest packing of spheres. Hexagonal close-packed structure (part 3) and cubic close-packed structure (part 4).

third layer are directly above the centers of the spheres of the first layer. If the third layer is *not* directly above the first layer, an *abcabc* arrangement results, giving a **cubic close-packed** structure. In the *abcabc* structure, the centers of the spheres of the third layer are directly above the holes between the spheres of the first layer. In the *abcabc* structure, the centers of the spheres of the fourth layer are directly above the centers of the spheres of the first layer. The unit cell for a cubic close-packed structure is face-centered cubic (fcc).

In each of these two close-packed structures, each sphere has 12 nearest-neighbor spheres that are equidistant. In each of these arrangements, 74% of the total volume of the structure is occupied by spheres and 26% is empty. Compare these percentages with those for the body-centered cubic structure, which is 68% occupied, and for the simple cubic structure, which is only 52% occupied.

Recently, a rigorous mathematical proof was developed that showed the impossibility of packing spheres to get a packing fraction greater than 74%.

© Stockbyte Platinum/Getty Images

The stacked fruits in markets are placed in closest packed arrangements for efficiency.

Unit Cells and Density

The information given so far about unit cells allows us to check whether a proposed unit cell is reasonable. Because a unit cell can be replicated to give the entire crystal lattice, the unit cell should have the same density as the crystal. As an example, we will consider platinum.

PROBLEM-SOLVING EXAMPLE 11.7 Unit Cell Dimension, Type, and Density

Platinum crystals are fcc, with a density of 21.45 g/cm^3. Platinum has a molar mass of 195.08 g/mol, and platinum atoms have a 139-pm radius. What is the length of a unit cell edge? Is this consistent with Pt being fcc?

Answer 392 pm. Yes, it is consistent with fcc.

Strategy and Explanation Starting with the radius of a Pt atom, we can calculate the diagonal length of the unit cell, the length of an edge of the unit cell, and the unit cell's volume. From the mass of Pt atoms per unit cell and the unit cell's volume we can calculate the density and compare this to the known density.

The mass of one Pt atom is

$$\frac{195.08 \text{ g Pt}}{1 \text{ mol Pt}} \times \frac{1 \text{ mol Pt}}{6.022 \times 10^{23} \text{ atoms Pt}} = 3.239 \times 10^{-22} \text{ g}$$

In an fcc unit cell there are four atoms per unit cell, so the mass of Pt atoms per unit cell is

$$4 \times 3.239 \times 10^{-22} \text{ g} = 1.296 \times 10^{-21} \text{ g Pt per unit cell}$$

Now we calculate the volume of the unit cell. To start we calculate the face diagonal length (see figure in margin).

$$\text{Face diagonal length} = 4 \times \text{Pt atom radius} = 4 \times 139 \text{ pm} = 556 \text{ pm}$$

For an fcc unit cell, the relationship between the edge length of the unit cell and its face diagonal length is (see figure in margin)

$$(\text{Diagonal length})^2 = \text{edge}^2 + \text{edge}^2 = 2(\text{edge})^2$$

so

$$\text{Edge} = \frac{\text{diagonal length}}{\sqrt{2}} = \frac{556 \text{ pm}}{1.414} = 393 \text{ pm}$$

The volume of the unit cell is

$$V = \ell^3 = (393 \text{ pm})^3 = 6.07 \times 10^{-23} \text{ cm}^3$$
$$(1 \text{ pm} = 10^{-12} \text{ m} = 10^{-10} \text{ cm})$$

The density is the mass of Pt atoms per unit cell divided by the unit cell's volume.

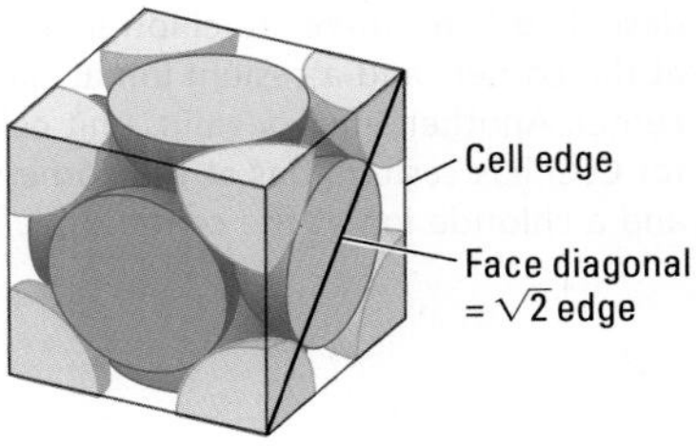

A face-centered cubic unit crystal.

ThomsonNOW™
Go to the Coached Problems menu for an exercise on **calculating density from ion radii and structure.**

$$d = \frac{m}{V} = \frac{1.296 \times 10^{-21}\ \text{g Pt}}{6.07 \times 10^{-23}\ \text{cm}^3} = 21.4\ \text{g/cm}^3$$

This density value compares well with the given value, and the calculation shows that the data are consistent with an fcc unit cell for the Pt crystal.

✓ **Reasonable Answer Check** The density, atomic weight, unit cell edge length and diagonal length, and Pt atom radius are all in agreement.

PROBLEM-SOLVING PRACTICE 11.7

Gold crystals have a bcc structure. The radius of a gold atom is 144 pm, and the atomic weight of gold is 196.97 amu. Calculate the density of gold.

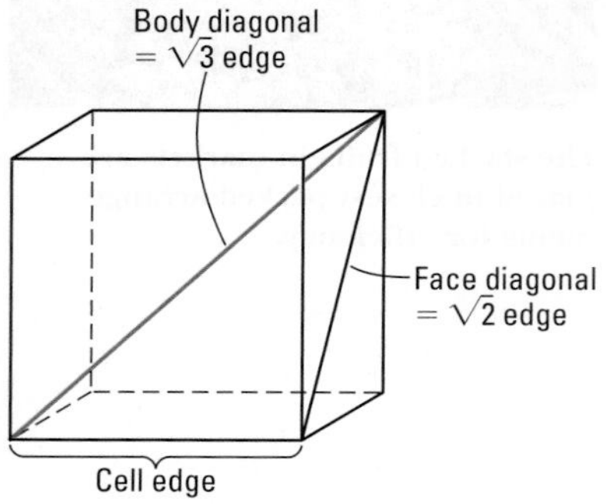

Dimensions of a cubic unit cell.

For each of the three cubic unit cells, there is a close relationship between the radius of the atom forming the unit cell and the unit cell size. For the simple cubic unit cell, halves of two atoms form the edge of the unit cell. For the face-centered cubic unit cell, one complete atom and halves of two other atoms form the face diagonal of the unit cell. For the body-centered cubic unit cell, one complete atom and halves of two other atoms form the body diagonal of the unit cell. To summarize:

Simple cubic: 2 × (atomic radius) = edge
Face-centered cubic: 4 × (atomic radius) = edge × $\sqrt{2}$
Body-centered cubic: 4 × (atomic radius) = edge × $\sqrt{3}$

Ionic Crystal Structures

Remember that negative ions are usually larger than positive ions. Therefore, building an ionic crystal is a lot like placing marbles (positive ions) in the spaces among larger ping-pong balls (negative ions).

It is not appropriate to describe the CsCl structure as bcc. In a bcc lattice, the species at the center of the unit cell must be the same as the species at the corner of the cell. In the CsCl unit cell described here, there are chloride ions at the corners and a cesium ion at the center. Another, equally valid, unit cell for CsCl has cesium ions at the corners and a chloride ion at the center.

The crystal structures of many ionic compounds can be described as simple cubic or face-centered cubic lattices of spherical negative ions, with positive ions occupying spaces (called holes) among the negative ions. The number and locations of the occupied holes are the keys to understanding the relation between the lattice structure and the formula of an ionic compound. The simplest example is an ionic compound in which the hole in a primitive (simple) cubic unit cell (Figure 11.21) is occupied. The ionic compound cesium chloride, CsCl, has such a structure. In it, each simple cube of Cl^- ions has a Cs^+ ion at its center (Figure 11.23). The spaces occupied by the Cs^+ ions are called cubic holes, and each Cs^+ has eight nearest-neighbor Cl^- ions.

The structure of sodium chloride, NaCl, is one of the most common ionic crystal lattices (Figures 11.24 and 11.25). If you look carefully at Figure 11.24, it is possible to determine the number of Na^+ and Cl^- ions in the NaCl unit cell. There is

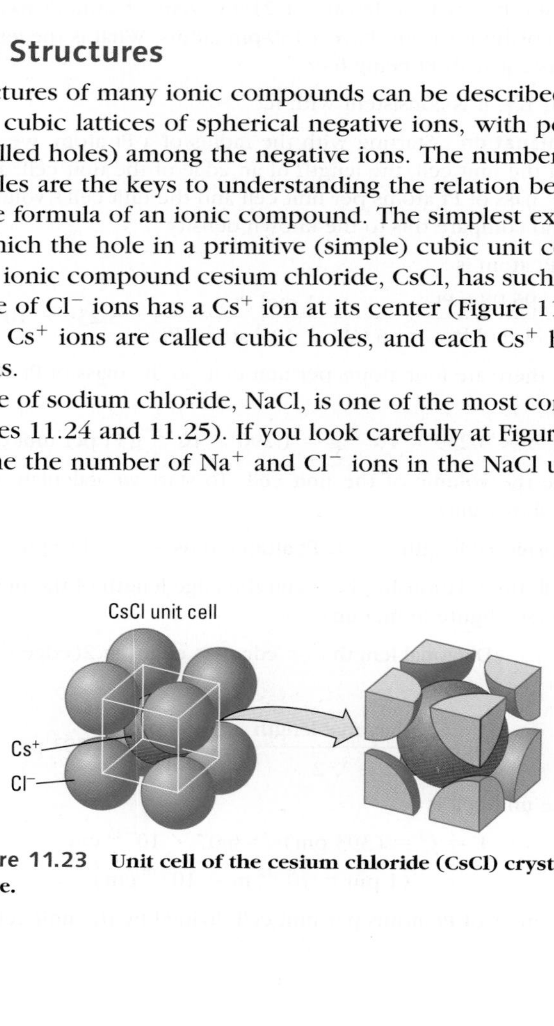

Figure 11.23 Unit cell of the cesium chloride (CsCl) crystal lattice.

one eighth of a Cl^- ion at each corner of the unit cell and one half of a Cl^- ion in the middle of each face. The total number of Cl^- ions within the unit cell is

$\frac{1}{8}\ Cl^-$ per corner $\times$ 8 corners $=$ 1 Cl^-

$\frac{1}{2}\ Cl^-$ per face $\times$ 6 faces $=$ 3 Cl^-

Total of 4 Cl^- in a unit cell

There is one fourth of a Na^+ at the midpoint of each edge and a whole Na^+ in the center of the unit cell. For Na^+ ions, the total is

$\frac{1}{4}\ Na^+$ per edge $\times$ 12 edges $=$ 3 Na^+

1 Na^+ per center $\times$ 1 center $=$ 1 Na^+

Total of 4 Na^+ in a unit cell

Thus, the unit cell contains four Na^+ and four Cl^- ions. This result agrees with the formula of NaCl for sodium chloride.

As shown in Figure 11.25, the NaCl crystal lattice consists of an fcc lattice of the larger Cl^- ions, in which Na^+ ions occupy so-called *octahedral* holes—octahedral because each Na^+ ion is surrounded by six Cl^- ions at the corners of an octahedron. Likewise, each Cl^- ion is surrounded by six Na^+ ions. Figure 11.25 also shows a space-filling model of the NaCl lattice, in which each ion is drawn to scale based on its ionic radius.

EXERCISE 11.15 Formulas and Unit Cells

Cesium chloride has a cubic unit cell, as seen in Figure 11.23. Show that the formula for the salt must be CsCl.

Since the edge of a cube in a cubic lattice is surrounded by four cubes, one fourth of a spherical ion at the midpoint of an edge is within any one of the cubes.

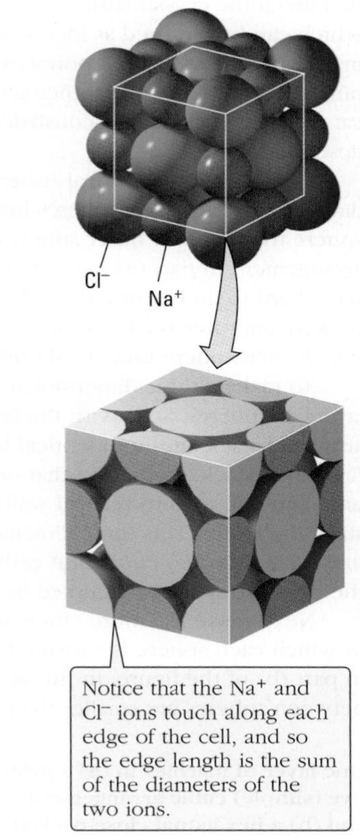

Figure 11.24 An NaCl unit cell.

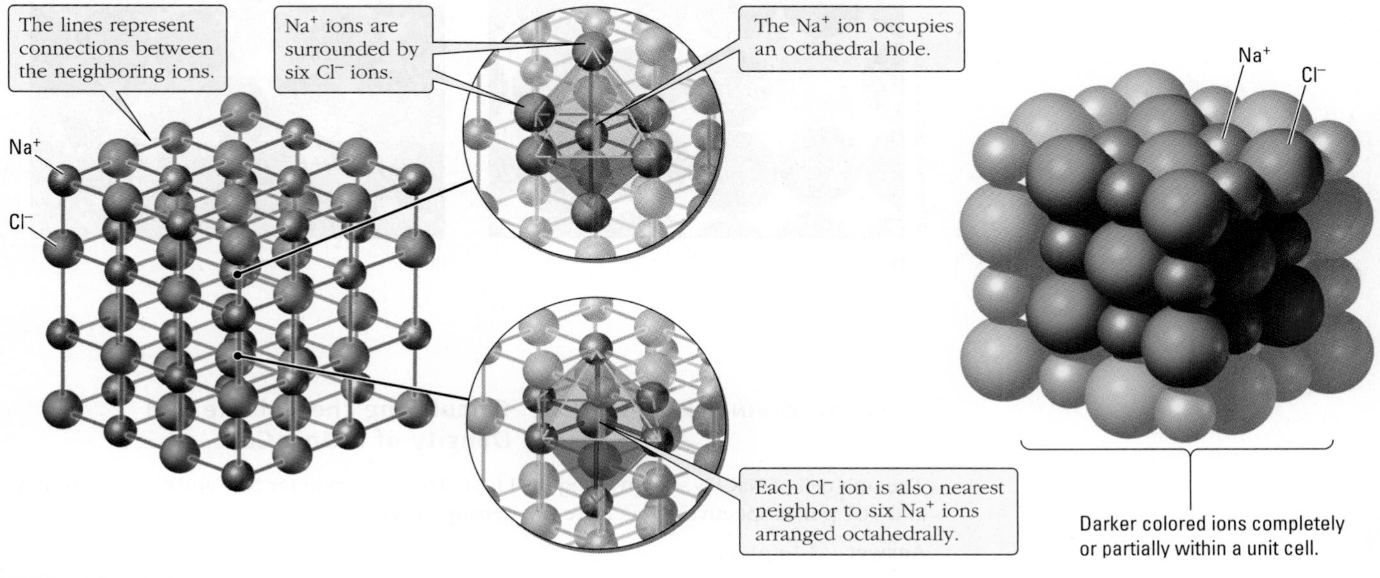

Active Figure 11.25 The NaCl crystal lattice. Go to the Active Figures menu at ThomsonNOW to test your understanding of the concepts in this figure.

CHEMISTRY YOU CAN DO

Closest Packing of Spheres

In a metal the crystal lattice is occupied by identical atoms, which can be pictured as identical spheres. Obtain a bag of marbles, some expanded polystyrene foam spheres, some ping-pong balls, or some other set of reasonably small, identical spheres. Use them to construct models of each situation described here.

Consider how identical spheres can be arranged in two dimensions. Pack your spheres into a layer so that each sphere touches four other spheres; this should resemble the arrangement in part (a) of the figure. You will find this somewhat hard to do because the spheres are rather inefficiently packed, and they readily adopt a more efficient packing in which each sphere touches six other spheres, part (b).

To make a three-dimensional lattice requires stacking layers of spheres. Start with the layer of spheres in a square array and stack another identical layer directly on top of the first; then stack another on that one, and so on. This is really hard and will require vertical walls to hold the spheres as you stack the layers. This three-dimensional lattice will consist of *primitive (simple) cubic* unit cells; in such a lattice 52.4% of the available space is occupied by the spheres.

Next, make the more efficiently packed hexagonal layer, in which each sphere is surrounded by six others, as shown in part (b) of the figure. In this arrangement, the holes between spheres are smaller than they were in the square array; in fact, they are as small as possible. For this reason the layer you have made is called a close-packed layer. Now add a second layer, and let the spheres nestle into the holes in the first layer. Now add a third layer. If you look carefully, you will see that there are two ways to put down the third layer. One of these places spheres directly above *holes* in the first layer. This is called *cubic close packing,* and the unit cell is face-centered cubic (fcc) (Figure 11.22). The other arrangement, also found for many metals, places third-layer spheres directly above *spheres* in the first layer. This is *hexagonal close packing,* and its unit cell is *not* cubic. Cubic and hexagonal close packing are the most efficient ways possible for filling space with spheres; 74% of the available space is occupied. The atoms in most metals are arranged in cubic close packing, in hexagonal close packing, or in lattices composed of body-centered cubic unit cells. Efficient packing of the atoms or ions in the crystal lattice allows stronger bonding, which gives greater stability to the crystal.

1. In either the cubic close-packed or the hexagonal close-packed arrangement, each atom has six neighbors in the same plane. How many closest neighbors does each atom have, considering all three dimensions?
2. How many closest neighbors does each atom have in the primitive (simple) cubic structure?

One layer of marbles in (a) a primitive (simple) cubic arrangement and (b) a hexagonal close-packed arrangement.

(a)

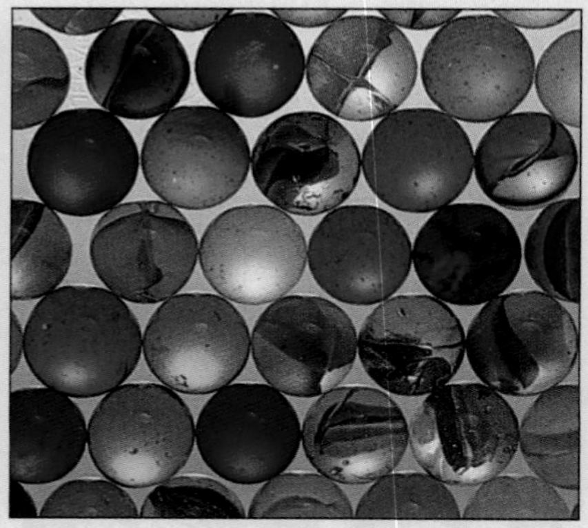
(b)

© Thomson Learning/Charles D. Winters

PROBLEM-SOLVING EXAMPLE **11.8** **Calculating the Volume and Density of a Unit Cell**

The unit cell of NaCl is shown in Figure 11.24. The ionic radii for Na^+ and Cl^- are 116 pm and 167 pm, respectively. Calculate the density of NaCl.

Answer 2.14 g/cm^3

Strategy and Explanation To calculate the density, we need to determine the mass and the volume of the unit cell. The mass can be found from the number of formula units in a unit cell and the molar mass of NaCl. The volume can be found from the length of an edge of the cubic unit cell. As seen in Figure 11.24, the Na^+ and Cl^- ions touch along the edge of the unit cell. Thus, the edge length is equal to two Cl^- radii plus two Na^+ radii.

$$\text{Edge} = 167\text{ pm} + (2 \times 116\text{ pm}) + 167\text{ pm} = 566\text{ pm}$$

The volume of the cubic unit cell is the cube of the edge length.

$$\text{Volume of unit cell} = (\text{edge})^3 = (566\text{ pm})^3 = 1.81 \times 10^8\text{ pm}^3$$

Converting this to cm^3 gives

$$1.81 \times 10^8\text{ pm}^3 \times \left(\frac{10^{-10}\text{ cm}}{\text{pm}}\right)^3 = 1.81 \times 10^{-22}\text{ cm}^3$$

Next we can calculate the mass of a unit cell and divide it by the volume to get the density. With four NaCl formula units per unit cell,

$$4\text{ NaCl formula units} \times \frac{58.44\text{ g}}{\text{mol NaCl}} \times \frac{1\text{ mol}}{6.022 \times 10^{23}\text{ formula units}} = 3.88 \times 10^{-22}\text{ g}$$

This means the density of a NaCl unit cell is

$$\frac{3.88 \times 10^{-22}\text{ g}}{1.81 \times 10^{-22}\text{ cm}^3} = 2.14\text{ g/cm}^3$$

✓ **Reasonable Answer Check** The experimental density is 2.164 g/cm^3, which is in reasonable agreement with the calculated value. Remember, however, that all experiments have uncertainties associated with them. The density of NaCl calculated from unit cell dimensions could easily have given a value closer to the experimental density if the tabulated radii for the Na^+ and Cl^- ions were slightly smaller. There is, of course, a slight uncertainty in the published radii of all ions.

The general relationships among the unit cell type, ion or atom size, and solid density for most metallic or ionic solids are as follows:

Mass of 1 formula unit (e.g., NaCl) × number of formula units per unit cell (4) = mass of unit cell

Mass of unit cell ÷ unit cell volume (= edge^3 for NaCl) = density

PROBLEM-SOLVING PRACTICE 11.8

KCl has the same crystal structure as NaCl. Calculate the volume of the unit cell for KCl, given that the ionic radii are $K^+ = 152$ pm and $Cl^- = 167$ pm. Compute the density of KCl. Which has the larger unit cell, NaCl or KCl?

11.7 Network Solids

A number of solids are composed of nonmetal atoms connected by a network of covalent bonds. Such **network solids** really consist of one huge molecule in which all the atoms are connected to all the others via such a network. Separate small molecules do not exist in a network solid.

The most important network solids are the *silicates*. Many bonding patterns exist among the silicates, but extended arrays of covalently bonded silicon and oxygen atoms are common, such as quartz, SiO_2. Silicates will be discussed in depth in Chapter 21.

Graphite, Diamond, and Fullerenes

Graphite, diamond, and fullerenes are allotropes of carbon (⇐ ***p. 27***). Graphite's name comes from the Greek *graphein,* meaning "to write," because one of its earliest uses was for writing on parchment. Artists today still draw with charcoal, an impure form of graphite, and we write with graphite pencil leads. Graphite is an example of a *planar network solid* (Figure 11.26). Each carbon atom is covalently bonded to three other carbon atoms. The planes consist of six-membered rings of carbon atoms (like those in benzene) (⇐ ***p. 364***). Each hexagon shares all six of its sides with other hexagons around it, forming a *two-dimensional network* resembling chicken wire. Some of the bonding electrons are able to move freely around this network, so graphite readily conducts electricity. Within a plane, there are strong

The distance between graphite planes is more than twice the distance between the nearest carbon atoms within a plane.

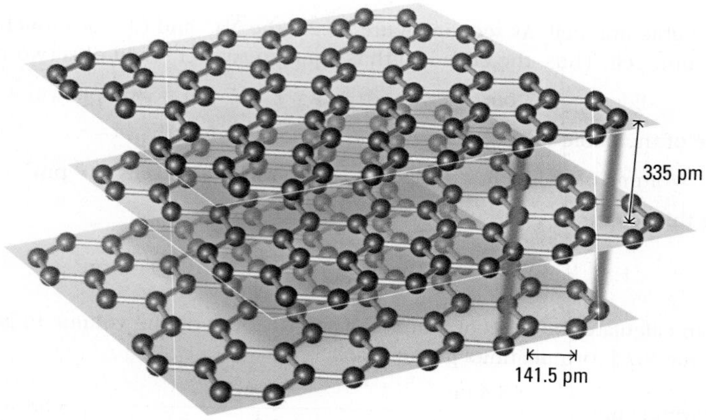

Figure 11.26 The structure of graphite. Three of the many layers of six-membered carbon rings are shown. These layers can slide past one another relatively easily, making graphite a good lubricant. In addition, some of the carbon valence electrons in the layers are delocalized, allowing graphite to be a good conductor of electricity parallel to the layers.

covalent bonds between carbon atoms, but attractions between the planes are caused by London forces and hence are weaker. Because of this, the planes can easily slip across one another, which makes graphite an excellent solid lubricant for uses such as in locks, where greases and oils are undesirable.

Diamonds are also built of six-membered carbon rings, with each carbon atom bonded to four others by single covalent bonds. This structure forms a *three-dimensional network* (Figure 11.27). Because of the tetrahedral arrangement of bonds around each carbon atom, the six-membered rings in the diamond structure are puckered. As a result, diamond (3.51 g/cm^3) is much denser than graphite (2.22 g/cm^3). Also, because its valence electrons are localized in covalent bonds between carbon atoms, diamond does not conduct electricity. Diamond is one of the hardest materials and also one of the best conductors of heat known. It is also transparent to visible, infrared, and ultraviolet radiation.

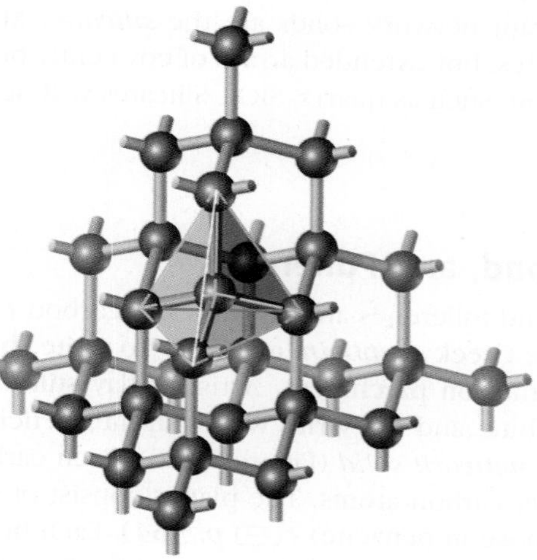

Figure 11.27 The structure of diamond. Each carbon atom is covalently bonded to four other carbon atoms in an extended tetrahedral arrangement.

In the 1950s, scientists at General Electric in Schenectady, New York, first produced man-made diamonds. Their technique, still in use today, was to heat graphite to a temperature of 1500 °C in the presence of a metal catalyst, such as nickel or iron, and under a pressure of 50,000 to 65,000 atm. Under these conditions, the carbon dissolves in the metal and recrystallizes in its higher-density form, slowly becoming diamond. Today a $500 million worldwide market exists for diamonds made this way, many of which are used for abrasives and diamond-coated cutting tools for drilling.

Buckyballs, the prototype of the third allotrope of carbon, were discovered in the 1980s. Since then, a variety of carbon structures have been developed, all classified as **fullerenes.** The prototype structure, C_{60}, is a sphere composed of pentagons and hexagons of carbon atoms similar to a soccer ball (*Figure 1.22c, p. 27*). Larger cage-like structures have also been synthesized. In fullerenes, each carbon atom has three carbon atom neighbors. Each carbon atom has sp^2 hybridization, and has one unhybridized *p* orbital. Electrons can be delocalized over these *p* orbitals, just as they can in graphite. Unlike graphite, each carbon atom and its three bonds are not quite planar, resulting in the curved fullerene structures. Another fullerene geometry is elongated tubes of carbon atoms, called **nanotubes** because of their small size. Nanotubes have been formed with a single wall of carbon atoms similar to graphite rolled into a tube, resembling rolled-up chicken wire. The nanotube is capped at each end with a truncated buckyball (Figure 11.28). Nanoscale materials such as nanotubes have physical and chemical properties different from bulk materials. Scientists are now exploring the possible useful properties of nanotubes and other similar materials.

Dorothy Crowfoot Hodgkin

1910–1994

Dorothy Crowfoot Hodgkin was born in Egypt, where her father was a supervisor of schools and ancient monuments. Schooled in England, she graduated from Oxford University in 1931. She was fascinated by the study of crystals and went to Cambridge University, where she eventually joined the faculty.

Hodgkin's first major achievement in crystallography was the determination of the structure of penicillin in 1945. In 1964 she received the Nobel Prize in chemistry for determining the molecular structure of vitamin B-12. Much of her work required pioneering and painstaking experimental techniques that, as one biographer put it, "transformed crystallography from a black art into an indispensable scientific tool."

11.8 Materials Science

Humans have long adapted or altered naturally occurring materials for use in clothing, structures, and devices. The tanning of leather and firing of clay pots predate recorded history. Operations such as these alter the nanoscale structure of the material to improve its resulting properties. The names of the periods of early civilization reflect the defining materials of the time—Stone Age, Bronze Age, Iron Age. This same close relationship between the nature of societies and their materials continues to hold in the modern world. The critical role played by materials is a cornerstone of life today. Only recently has the *scientific* understanding of the relationships among the processing, structure, and properties of materials been developed and exploited; the creation of new materials has accelerated as a consequence. Furthermore, new phenomena have been discovered that permit the invention of new

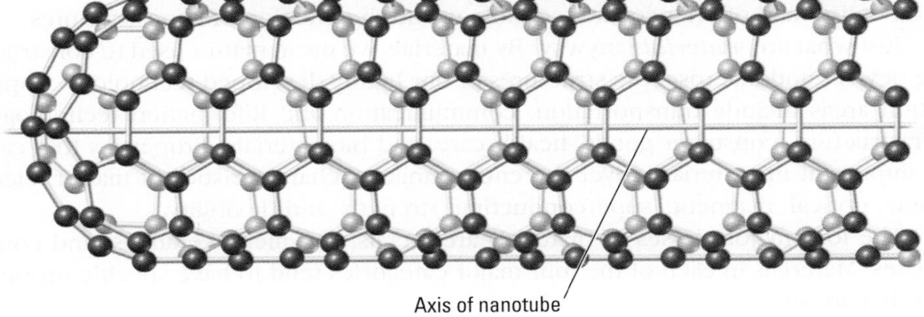

Figure 11.28 **A single-walled carbon nanotube composed of hexagons of carbon atoms.**

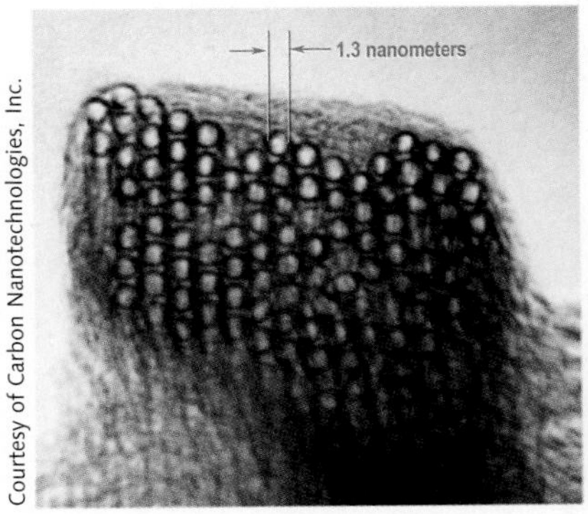

High-resolution transmission electron micrograph image of a cross section of a bundle of single-walled and double-walled nanotubes.
Source: Chemical Heritage, Fall 2005; p. 16.

TOOLS OF CHEMISTRY

X-Ray Crystallography

X-ray crystallography is used to determine the absolute atomic arrangement of the atoms in solid samples. One of the most powerful tools of solid-state chemistry, it is routinely applied to solids as varied as crystalline minerals, proteins, and semiconductors. When X-rays strike crystals, the X-rays are scattered in different directions and with different intensities due to interference effects. X-rays have wavelengths on the order of 1 nm, the same scale as atomic dimensions. When an X-ray beam strikes a crystal, the X-rays are scattered. When the interference is *constructive,* the waves combine to produce X-rays that can be observed indirectly because they expose a spot on photographic film. When the interference is *destructive,* the waves partly or entirely cancel each other, so little or no X-ray intensity is recorded.

Interference effects among the scattered X-rays from the different atoms cause the intensity of the scattered radiation to show maxima and minima in various directions, creating a diffraction pattern. The particular diffraction pattern obtained depends on the X-ray wavelength and the distances between the planes of atoms in the crystal. The Bragg equation relates the X-ray wavelength (λ), the spacing between atomic layers in the crystal (d), the angle of scattering (θ), and an integer (n, usually considered as 1):

$$n\lambda = 2d \sin \theta$$

Waves *a* and *b* reinforce each other when the Bragg equation is satisfied—that is, when the additional distance traveled by wave *b* to reach the detector is an integer multiple of the X-ray wavelength. Therefore, the X-ray diffraction pattern can be related back to the nanoscale arrangement of the atoms in the crystal. The intensity of the scattered X-ray beam depends on the electron density of the atoms in the crystal. Therefore, a hydrogen atom is least effective in causing X-rays to scatter, while heavy atoms such as lead or mercury are quite effective.

Photographic film was used to record the diffraction patterns in early instruments. Today, crystallographers use computer-controlled instruments, highly sensitive solid-state detectors, and other advanced instrumentation to measure the angles of reflection and the intensities of X-ray beams diffracted by crystals. Sophisticated software allows the atomic arrangements in crystalline materials to be determined quickly enough that X-ray crystallography is used routinely.

In one of the most famous uses of X-ray crystallography, James Watson and Francis Crick in 1953 interpreted X-ray data obtained by Maurice Wilkins and Rosalind Franklin to discover the double helix structure of DNA, the biological macromolecule that carries genetic information (***p. 416***). Watson, Crick, and Wilkins were awarded the Nobel Prize in medicine and physiology in 1962 for this discovery (Franklin was deceased and therefore could not share the prize).

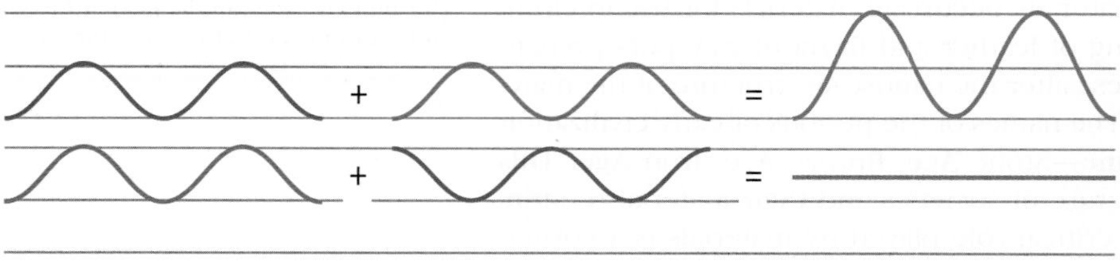

Constructive interference occurs when two in-phase waves combine to produce a wave of greater amplitude.

Destructive interference results from the combination of two waves of equal magnitude that are exactly out of phase. The result is zero amplitude.

materials. For example, superconducting ceramic oxides that conduct electricity without resistance at critical temperatures greater than the boiling point of liquid nitrogen may pave the way to astounding advances in information technology and computing in the coming decades. The study of materials on the nanoscale has led to an entire field of science and technology and the creation of nanostructures.

Just what are *materials* anyway? By materials we mean matter used to construct the devices and macroscopic structures of our highly developed technology. Application areas include transportation, communication and information technology, infrastructure, consumer goods, health care, and biomaterials. Properties that can be important in materials cover the entire range of characteristics of matter: electronic, optical, magnetic, superconducting, strength, and flexibility.

The four major classes of materials are metals, polymers, ceramics, and composites. Materials in each of the four major categories tend to have specific properties that are similar:

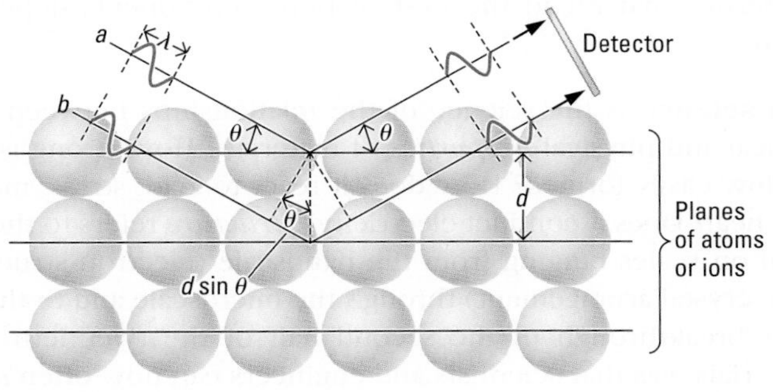

X-ray diffraction from a solid. The relationships among the variables in the Bragg equation are shown. For wave *b* to reach the detector in phase with wave *a*, *b* must travel farther by $2d \sin \theta$, and this distance must be an integral multiple of the X-ray wavelength.

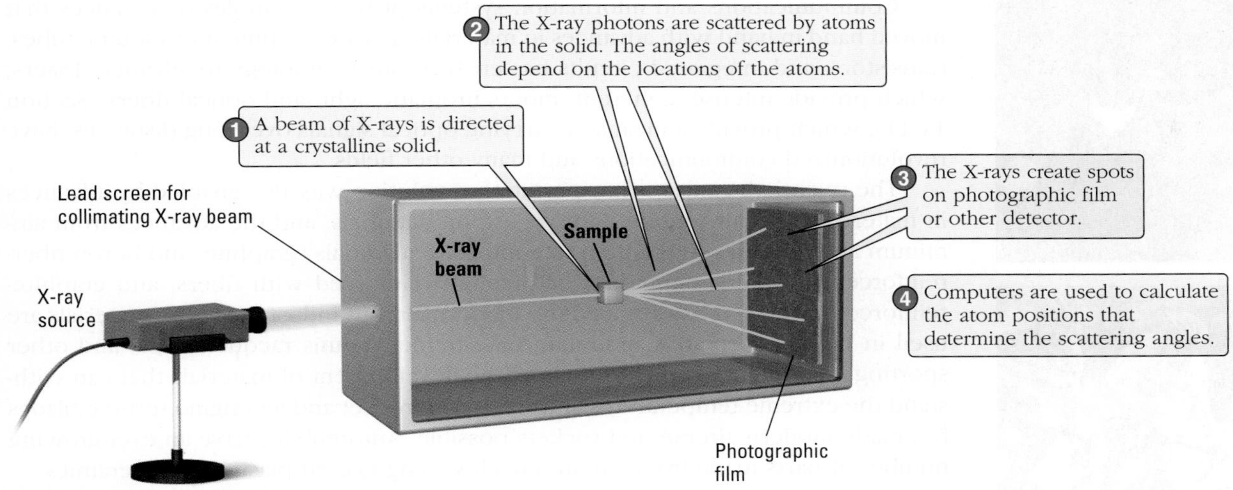

An X-ray diffraction experiment.

- **Metals** Opaque with shiny surface (unless covered by an oxidized coating, as in rusted iron). Usually crystalline. Generally ductile—can be drawn into wires (copper). Strong and stiff (steel). Most are not magnetic, except Fe, Ni, and Co or alloys. Usually conduct heat and electricity well (Cu). Form alloys such as stainless steel, bronze, and brass.
- **Polymers** Both natural (wool, cotton, rubber) and synthetic (polyethylene, polystyrene). Most are flexible and can be bent, but some are brittle. Thermoplastics become more flexible when heated; thermoset polymers become hard and brittle when heated. Usually thermal and electrical insulators. Not magnetic.
- **Ceramics** Nonmetallic materials, often based on clays. Porcelain, bricks, glass, and cement are examples. Usually brittle and cannot be bent. Poor thermal conductors and good thermal insulators; can withstand high temperatures. Usually poor electrical conductors and good electrical insulators. Some ceramics are

magnetic. Usually crystalline. Many are transparent (glass). Semiconductors are ceramics with special electrical properties. Glasses, a special class of ceramics, are brittle yet often strong and are amorphous.

- **Composites** Materials combining components from the other three categories with properties that blend the best of both components depending on the application.

Materials science is the science of the relationships between the structure and the chemical and physical *properties* of materials. How strong is the material? How dense? How easily formed? How does it react to acid, stress, magnetic fields, high pressure, heat? Does it conduct electricity? *Structure* refers to the organization of the material on scales ranging from the nanoscale (electron structure, arrangement of atoms, crystal arrangement) through the microscale and to the macroscale.

The major breakthrough of the second half of the twentieth century with respect to materials was that scientists and engineers can now often *design* a material for a specific application. That is, scientific understanding at the nanoscale permits synthesis and fabrication of new materials with precise properties desired for a particular application. Coupling this capability with inventiveness and technological know-how results in cost-effective manufacture of materials and devices.

Communications and information systems provide examples of advances that moved hand in hand with advances in materials. The development of vacuum tubes, transistors, and integrated circuits has enabled our technology to advance. Lasers, which provide intense, coherent, monochromatic light, and optical fibers (Section 11.11), which provide a means of carrying optical signals over long distances, have revolutionized communications and many other fields.

The twentieth-century transportation revolution was also enabled by advances in materials. Aircraft require light yet strong materials, and the advances from aluminum and its alloys to titanium to composite materials (graphite- and boron fiber-reinforced polymers, aluminum or titanium reinforced with fibers, and graphite-reinforced epoxy) have advanced the modern aircraft industry. Similar materials are used in high-performance mountain bike frames, tennis racquets, skis, and other sporting equipment. At the same time, the development of materials that can withstand the extreme temperatures and stresses in rocket and jet engine turbine blades has made modern aircraft and rockets possible. Automobiles have an ever-growing number of parts made from aluminum alloys, engineered plastics, and ceramics.

© Royalty-Free/Corbis

© Thomson Learning/Charles D. Winters

© Tim de Waele/Corbis

Modern materials in action. Modern materials are employed in many ways to improve our lives—for example, in hip replacements, fleece garments, and bicycle parts.

11.9 Metals, Semiconductors, and Insulators

All metals are solids except mercury (m.p. −38.8 °C) at room temperature, and exhibit common properties that we call metallic.

- **High electrical conductivity** Metal wires are used to carry electricity from power plants to homes and offices because electrons in metals are highly mobile.
- **High thermal conductivity** We learn early in life not to touch any part of a hot metal pot because it will transfer heat rapidly and painfully.
- **Ductility and malleability** Most metals are easily drawn into wire (ductility) or hammered into thin sheets (malleability); some metals (gold, for example) are more easily formed into shapes than others.
- **Luster** Polished metal surfaces reflect light. Most metals have a silvery-white color because they reflect all wavelengths equally well.

- **Insolubility in water and other common solvents** No metal dissolves in water, but a few (mainly from Groups 1A and 2A) react with water to form hydrogen gas and solutions of metal hydroxides.

As you will see, these properties are explained by the kinds of bonding that hold atoms together in metals.

The enthalpies of fusion and melting points of metals vary greatly. Low melting points correlate with low enthalpies of fusion, which implies weaker attractive forces holding the metal atoms together. Mercury, which is a liquid at room temperature, has an enthalpy of fusion of only 2.3 kJ/mol. The alkali metals and gallium also have very low enthalpies of fusion and notably low melting points (Table 11.6). Compare these values with those in Table 11.3 for nonmetals (p. 500).

Figure 11.29 shows the relative enthalpies of fusion of the metals related to their positions in the periodic table. The transition metals, especially those in the third transition series, have very high melting points and extraordinarily high enthalpies of fusion. Tungsten (W) has the highest melting point (3410 °C) of all the metals, and among all the elements it is second only to carbon as graphite, which has a melting point of 3550 °C. Pure tungsten is used in incandescent light bulbs as the filament, the wire that glows white-hot. No other material has been found to be better since the invention of commercially successful, long-lived light bulbs in 1908 by Thomas Edison and his co-workers.

Table 11.6 Enthalpies of Fusion and Melting Points of Some Metals

Metal	ΔH°_{fusion} (kJ/mol)	Melting Point (°C)
Hg	2.3	−38.8
Ga	7.5	29.78*
Na	2.59	97.9
Li	3.0	180.5
Al	10.7	660.4
U	12.6	1132.1
Fe	13.8	1535.0
Ti	20.9	1660.1
Cr	16.9	1857.0
W	35.2	3410.1

*This means that gallium metal will melt in the palm of your hand from the warmth of your body (37 °C). It happens that gallium is a liquid over the largest range of temperature of any metal. Its boiling point is approximately 2250 °C.

PROBLEM-SOLVING EXAMPLE 11.9 Calculating Enthalpies of Fusion

Use data from Table 11.6 to calculate the thermal energy transfer required to melt 10.0 g chromium at its melting point.

Answer 3.25 kJ

Strategy and Explanation First, we determine how many moles of chromium are present. Then we calculate the energy required from the ΔH°_{fusion} value in Table 11.6.

$$10.0 \text{ g Cr} \times \frac{1 \text{ mol Cr}}{52.00 \text{ g Cr}} = 0.192 \text{ mol Cr}$$

$$0.192 \text{ mol Cr} \times \frac{16.9 \text{ kJ}}{1 \text{ mol Cr}} = 3.25 \text{ kJ}$$

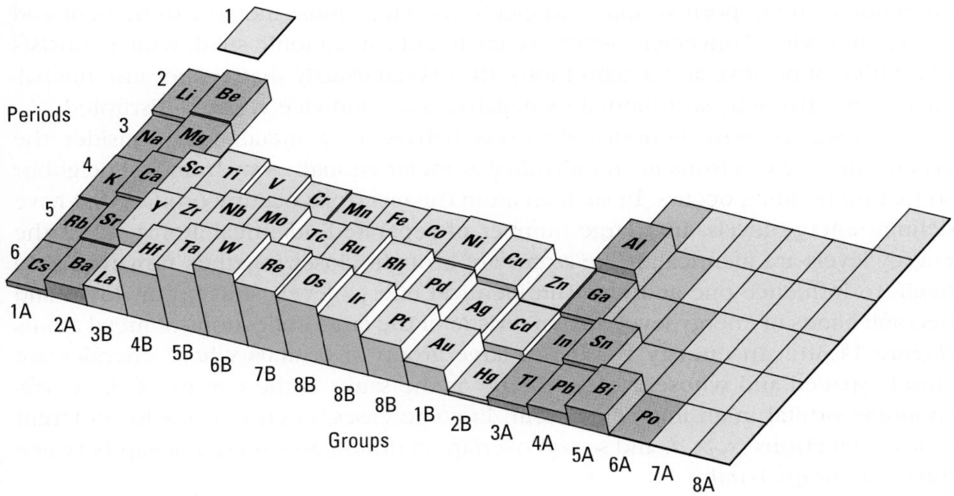

Figure 11.29 Relative enthalpies of fusion for the metals in the periodic table. See Table 11.6 for some numerical values of enthalpies of fusion.

✓ **Reasonable Answer Check** We have about two tenths of a mole of chromium, so the energy required should be about two tenths of the molar enthalpy of fusion, about 17 kJ/mol, or about 3.4 kJ, which compares well with our more accurate answer.

PROBLEM-SOLVING PRACTICE 11.9

Use data from Table 11.6 to calculate the heat transfer required to melt 1.45 g aluminum.

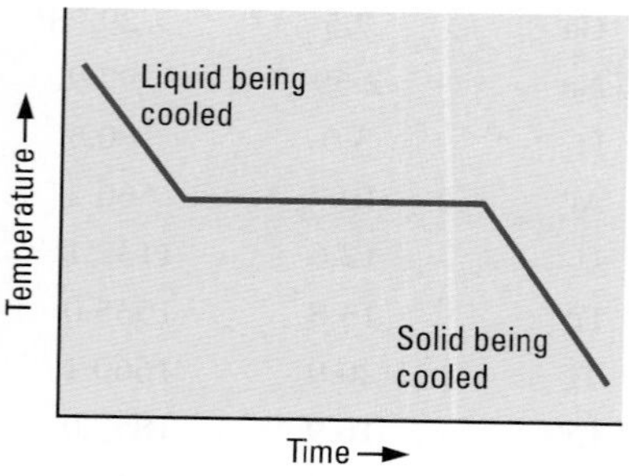

CONCEPTUAL EXERCISE 11.16 Cooling a Liquid Metal Until It Solidifies

When a liquid metal is cooled at a constant rate to the temperature at which it solidifies, and the solid is then cooled to an even lower temperature, the "cooling curve"—a plot of temperature against time—looks like the chart to the left. Account for the shape of this curve. Would all substances exhibit similar curves?

CONCEPTUAL EXERCISE 11.17 Heats of Fusion and Electronic Configuration

Look in Appendix D and compare the electron configurations shown there with the heats of fusion for the metals shown in Table 11.6. Is there any correlation between these configurations and this property? Does strength of attraction among metal atoms correlate with number of valence electrons? Explain.

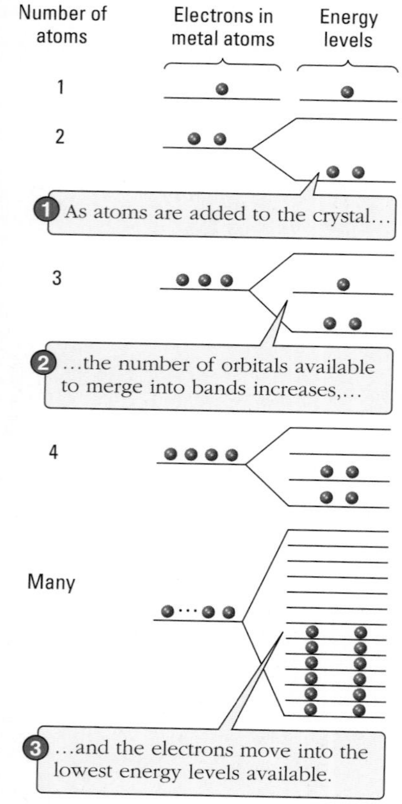

Figure 11.30 Formation of bands of electron orbitals in a metal crystal.

Electrons in Metals, Semiconductors, and Insulators

Metals behave as though metal cations exist in a "sea" of mobile electrons—the valence electrons of all the metal atoms. **Metallic bonding** is the nondirectional attraction between positive metal ions and the surrounding sea of negative charge (valence electrons). Each metal ion has a large number of near neighbors. The valence electrons are spread throughout the metal's crystal lattice, holding the positive metal ions together. When an electric field is applied to a metal, these valence electrons move toward the positive end of the field, and the metal conducts electricity.

The mobile valence electrons provide a uniform charge distribution in a metal lattice, so the positions of the positive ions can be changed without destroying the attractions among positive ions and electrons. Thus, most metals can be bent and drawn into wire. Conversely, when we try to deform an ionic solid, which consists of a lattice of positive and negative ions, the crystal usually shatters because the balance of positive ions surrounded by negative ions, and vice versa, is disrupted.

To visualize how bonding electrons behave in a metal, first consider the arrangement of electrons in an individual atom far enough away from any neighbor so that no bonding occurs. In such an atom the electrons occupy orbitals that have definite energy levels. In a large number of separated, identical atoms, all of the energy levels are identical. If the atoms are brought closer together, however, they begin to influence one another. The identical energy levels shift up or down and become bands of energy levels characteristic of the large collections of metal atoms (Figure 11.30). An **energy band** is a large group of orbitals whose energies are closely spaced and whose average energy is the same as the energy of the corresponding orbital in an individual atom. In some cases, energy bands for different types of electrons (*s*, *p*, *d*, and so on) overlap; in other cases there is a gap between different energy bands.

Within each band, electrons fill the lowest energy orbitals much as electrons fill orbitals in atoms or molecules. The number of electrons in a given energy band depends on the number of metal atoms in the crystal. In considering conductivity and other metallic properties, it is usually necessary to consider only valence electrons, as other electrons all occupy completely filled bands in which two electrons occupy every orbital. In these bands, no electron can move from one orbital to another, because there is no empty spot for it.

A band containing the valence electrons is called the **valence band**. If the valence band is partially filled it requires little added energy to excite a valence electron to a slightly higher energy orbital. Such a small increment of energy can be provided by applying an electric field, for example. The presence of low-energy, empty orbitals into which electrons can move allows the electrons to be mobile and to conduct an electric current (Figure 11.31).

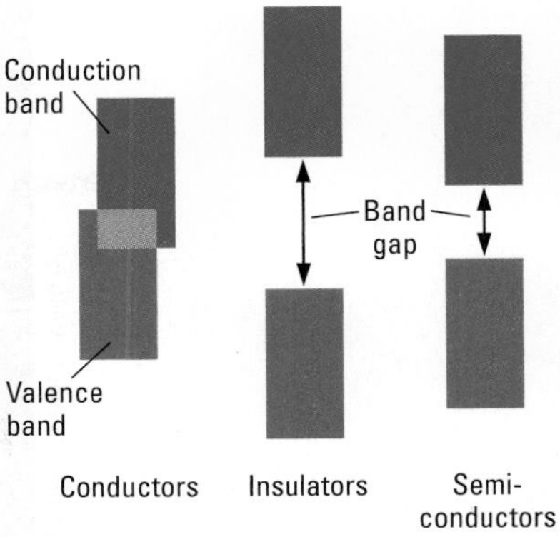

Figure 11.31 **Differences in the energy bands of available orbitals in conductors, insulators, and semiconductors.**

Another band containing higher energy orbitals (the **conduction band**) exists at an average energy above the valence band. In a metal, the valence band and the conduction band overlap, so electrons can move from the valence band to the conduction band freely; this ability explains metals' electrical conductivity. Such a metal with overlapping valence and conduction bands is a **conductor.**

When the conduction band is close in energy to the valence band, the electrons can absorb a wide range of wavelengths in the visible region of the spectrum. As the excited electrons fall back to their lower energy states, they emit their extra energy as visible light, producing the luster characteristic of metals.

The energy band theory also explains why some solids are **insulators,** which do not conduct electricity. In an insulator the valence band and conduction band do not overlap. Rather, there is a large band gap between them (Figure 11.31). Very few electrons have enough energy to move across the large gap from a filled lower energy band to an empty higher energy band, so no current flows through an insulator when an external electric field is applied.

In a **semiconductor** a very *narrow* energy gap separates the valence band and the conduction band (Figure 11.31). At quite low temperatures, electrons remain in the filled lower energy valence band, and semiconductors are not good conductors. At higher temperatures, or when an electric field is applied, some electrons have enough energy to jump across the band gap into the conduction band. This allows an electric current to flow. This property of semiconductors—to switch from insulator to conductor with the application of an external electric field—is the basis for the operation of transistors, the cornerstone of modern electronics.

ThomsonNOW™
Go to the Coached Problems menu for a simulation and an exercise on:
- **metallic bonding—band theory**
- **doped silicon semiconductors**

© Roger Ressmeyer/Corbis

Ceramic insulators are used on high-voltage electrical transmission lines.

Superconductors

One interesting property of metals is that their electrical conductivity *decreases* with increasing temperature. In Figure 11.32b a metal in a burner flame shows higher resistance (lower conductivity) than the same metal at room temperature (Figure 11.32a). The lower conductivity of metals at higher temperatures can be explained by considering valence electrons in the lattice of metal ions as waves. As an electron wave moves through the metal crystal under the influence of an electrical voltage, the wave encounters lattice positions where the metal ions are close enough together to scatter it. This scattering is analogous to the scattering of X-rays caused by atoms in crystals. The scattered electron wave moves off in another direction, only to be scattered again when it encounters some other occupied lattice position. All of this scattering *lowers* the conductivity of the metal. At higher temperatures, the metal ions vibrate more, and the distances between lattice positions change more from their average values. This effect causes more scattering of electron waves as they move through the crystal, because there are now more possibilities of unfavorable lattice spacings. Hence electrical conductivity is lower.

Recall from Section 7.4 that electrons have wave-like properties as well as particle-like properties.

From this picture of electrical conductivity, it might be expected that the conductivity of a metal crystal at absolute zero (0 K or -273.15 °C) might be very large.

ThomsonNOW™
Go to the Chemistry interactive menu to work a module on **formation of a band of molecular orbitals for Li.**

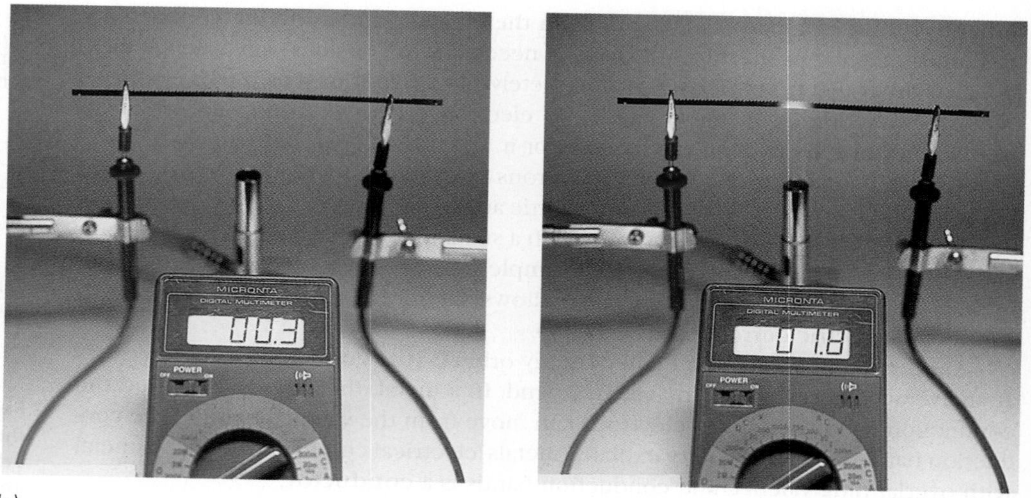

© Thomson Learning/Charles D. Winters

(a) (b)

Figure 11.32 Resistance, temperature, and electrical conductivity. (a) A piece of metal at room temperature exhibits a small resistance (high electrical conductivity). (b) While being heated, this same piece of metal exhibits a higher resistance value, indicating a lower conductivity.

Superconductivity was discovered in 1911 by the Dutch physicist Kamerlingh Onnes, who won a Nobel Prize for his work.

Information about superconductors is available at this Web site: **http://superconductors.org**.

In fact, the conductivity of a pure metal crystal approaches infinity as absolute zero is approached. In some metals, however, a more interesting phenomenon occurs. At a critical temperature (T_c) that is low but finite, the conductivity abruptly increases to infinity, which means that the resistance drops to zero (Figure 11.33). As a result, the metal becomes a **superconductor** of electricity. A superconductor offers no resistance whatsoever to electric current. Once a current has been started in a superconducting circuit, it continues to flow indefinitely. No clear theory explaining superconductivity has yet emerged, but it appears that the scattering of electron waves by vibrating atoms is replaced in a superconductor by some cooperative action that allows the electrons to move through the crystal unhindered.

If a material could be made superconducting at a high enough temperature, the material would find uses in the transmission of electrical energy, in high-efficiency motors, and in computers and other devices. Table 11.7 lists some metals that have superconducting critical temperatures. While some useful devices can be fabricated

Table 11.7 Superconducting Transition Temperatures of Some Metals*

Metal	Superconducting Transition Temperature (K)
Gallium	1.10
Aluminum	1.15
Tin	3.72
Mercury	4.15
Lanthanum	4.9
Lead	7.2

*Not all metals have superconducting properties. Those that can become superconductors at atmospheric pressure are Al, Ti, Zn, Ga, Zr, Mo, Tc, Ru, Cd, In, Sn, La, Hf, Ta, W, Re, Os, Ir, Hg, Tl, Pb, Th, Pa, and U.

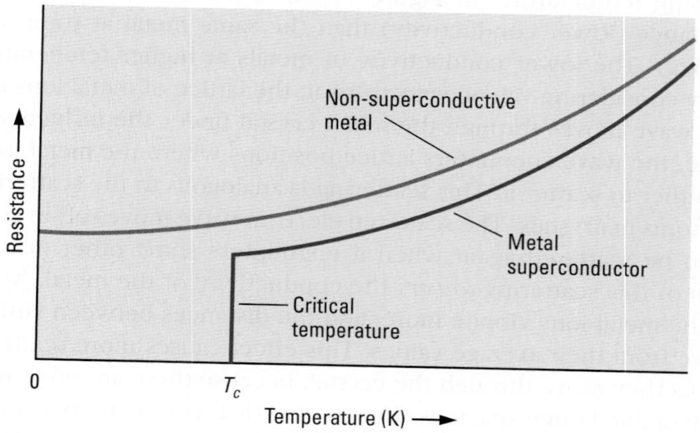

Figure 11.33 The resistance of a superconducting metal and a non-superconducting metal as a function of temperature.

from these metals, the very low temperatures at which they become superconductors make them impractical for most applications. Shortly after superconductivity of metals was discovered, alloys were prepared that had higher transition temperatures. Niobium alloys were the best, but still required cooling to below 23 K (−250 °C) to exhibit superconductivity. Maintenance of such a low temperature requires liquid helium, which is expensive.

This picture abruptly changed in January 1986, when Alex Müller and Georg Bednorz, IBM scientists in Switzerland, discovered that a lanthanum-barium-copper oxide became superconducting at 35 K (−238 °C). This type of mixed metal oxide is a ceramic with the same structure as the mineral perovskite ($CaTiO_3$) and, therefore, would be expected to have insulating properties. The announcement of the superconducting properties of $LaBa_2Cu_3O_x$ (x means that varying amounts of oxygen are incorporated) rocked the world of science and provoked a flurry of activity to prepare related compounds in the hope that even higher critical temperatures could be found. Within four months, a material ($YBa_2Cu_3O_7$) that became superconducting at 90 K (−183 °C) was announced. Its identification was a major breakthrough because 90 K exceeds the boiling point of liquid nitrogen (bp = 77 K or −196 °C), which is easily obtainable and cheap. The current record critical temperature of 138 K (−135 °C) at atmospheric pressure is for a thallium-doped mercuric-cuprate ceramic with the composition $Hg_{0.8}Tl_{0.2}Ba_2Ca_2Cu_3O_{8.23}$.

Why the great excitement over the potential of superconductivity? Superconducting materials would allow the building of more powerful electromagnets such as those used in nuclear particle accelerators and in magnetic resonance imaging (MRI) machines for medical diagnosis (**⇐ *p. 308***). Such electromagnets would permit higher energies to be maintained for longer periods of time (and at lower cost) in the case of the particle accelerators, and support better imaging of problem areas in a patient's body. Currently, the main barrier to their wider application is the cost of cooling the magnets used in these devices.

Many scientists say that the discovery of high-temperature superconducting materials is more important than the discovery of the transistor because of its potential effect on electrical and electronic technology. For example, the use of superconducting materials for transmission of electric power could save as much as 30% of the energy now lost because of the resistance of the wire. Superchips for computers could be as much as 1000 times faster than existing silicon chips. Since a superconductor repels magnetic materials (Figure 11.34), trains can be levitated above a track and move with no friction other than air resistance to slow them down. When a maglev (magnetic levitation) rail line in Japan was tested on April 4, 1999, the test train attained a speed of 343 mi/h (552 km/h). On December 2, 2003, a Japanese three-car test train attained a maximum speed of 581 km/h. On December 31, 2002, the world's first commercial maglev train service ran at 430 km/h over a 30-km link from Pudong airport to Pudong (adjacent to Shanghai). The German government is now engaged in the Transrapid Project, which will connect Berlin to Hamburg, a distance of 292 km, with a maglev train traveling at about 300 km/h.

Müller and Bednorz received the 1987 Nobel Prize in physics for their discovery of the superconducting properties of $LaBa_2Cu_3O_x$.

IBM Research/Peter Arnold, Inc.

Figure 11.34 Levitation of a magnet above a superconductor. A magnet moving toward a superconductor induces a current in the superconductor, which induces a magnetic field. This magnetic field and that of the magnet oppose one another. The magnet remains at that height above the superconductor surface where the repulsive magnetic field strength is balanced by the force of gravity. The magnet remains in place as long as the current continues in the superconductor.

© Transrapid International GmbH & Co. KG

Shanghai maglev train.

11.10 Silicon and the Chip

Silicon is known as an "intrinsic" semiconductor because the element itself is a semiconductor. Silicon of about 98% purity can be obtained by heating silica (purified sand) and coke (an impure form of carbon) at 3000 °C in an electric arc furnace.

$$SiO_2(s) + 2\ C(s) \xrightarrow{\text{heat}} Si(s) + 2\ CO(g)$$

Silicon of this purity can be alloyed with aluminum and magnesium to increase the hardness and durability of the metals and is used for making silicone polymers. For use in electronic devices, however, a much higher degree of purification is needed. High-purity silicon can be prepared by reducing $SiCl_4$ with magnesium.

$$SiCl_4(\ell) + 2\ Mg(s) \longrightarrow Si(s) + 2\ MgCl_2(s)$$

Magnesium chloride, which is water-soluble, is washed from the silicon. The final purification of the silicon takes place by a melting process called **zone refining** (Figure 11.35), which produces silicon containing less than one part per billion of impurities such as boron, aluminum, and arsenic. Zone refining takes advantage of the fact that impurities are often more soluble in the liquid phase than in the solid phase. As a hot molten zone is moved through a sample being purified, the impurities move along in the liquefied portion of the sample. As the heated zone cools, the sample that resolidifies is purer than it was. Multiple passes of the hot molten zone are usually necessary to achieve the degree of purity necessary to fabricate semiconducting devices.

Like all semiconductors, high-purity silicon fails to conduct an electric current until a certain electrical voltage is applied, but at higher voltages it conducts moderately well. Silicon's semiconducting properties can be improved dramatically by a process known as doping. **Doping** is the addition of a tiny amount of some other element (a *dopant*) to the silicon.

For example, consider what happens when a few atoms of a Group 5A element such as arsenic are added to silicon. Arsenic has five valence electrons, whereas silicon has four. Thus, only four of the five valence electrons of As are used for bonding with four Si atoms, leaving one electron relatively free to move. This type of doped silicon is referred to as negative-type or *n-type silicon* because it has extra (negative) valence electrons. In ***n*-type semiconductors**, electrons are the charge carriers.

A positive hole in an energy band of a semiconductor is a place where there is one less electron than normal and hence extra positive charge.

On the other hand, consider what happens when a small number of boron atoms (or atoms of some other Group 3A element) replace silicon atoms (Group 4A) in solid silicon. Boron has only three valence electrons. This leaves a deficiency of one electron around the B atom, creating what is called a *hole* for every B atom added. Hence silicon doped in this manner is referred to as positive-type or *p-type silicon* (Figure 11.36). In ***p*-type semiconductors**, holes are the charge carriers. It is important to remember that such holes in semiconductors are the absence of electrons. Thus, the flow of holes in one direction is in reality the flow of electrons in the opposite direction.

When *p*-type and *n*-type semiconductors are brought together, a ***p-n* junction** results. Such a junction can act as a rectifier; that is, it allows current to flow in one direction but not the other. When the two materials are joined, some of the excess

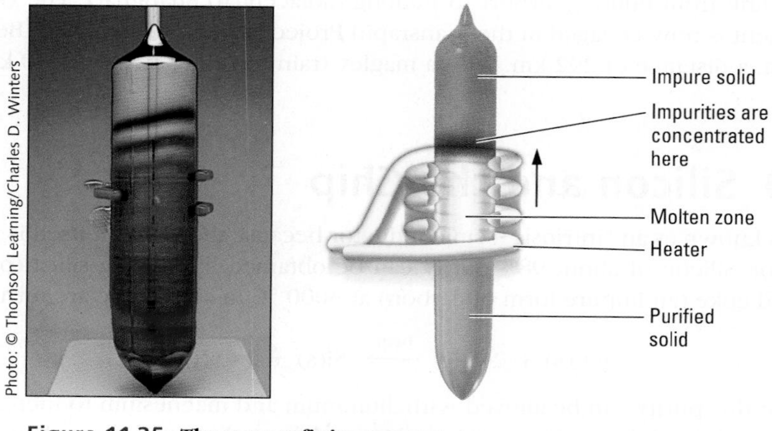

Figure 11.35 The zone refining process.

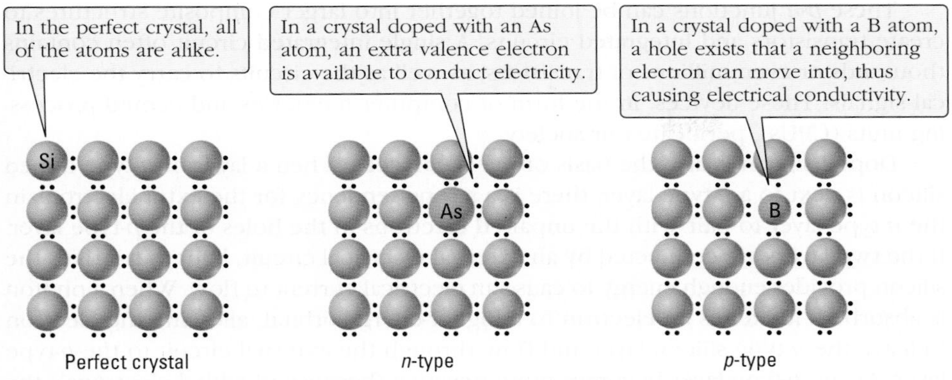

Figure 11.36 Schematic drawing of semiconductor crystals derived from silicon.

electrons in the *n*-type material migrate across the junction and some of the holes in the *p*-type material migrate in the opposite direction. The result is the buildup of a negative charge on the *p*-type region and a positive charge on the *n*-type region. This charge buildup is called the *junction potential,* and it prevents the further migration of electrons or holes. However, if an external potential is applied to the *p-n* junction, one of two effects can result. If a negative charge is connected to the *p*-type side and a positive charge to the *n*-type side, then the electrons and holes migrate away from the junction, and no current flows through the junction (Figure 11.37, *bottom*). If a negative charge is connected to the *n*-type side and a positive charge to the *p*-type side, then both electrons and holes flow across the junction, and current flows through the device (Figure 11.37, *top*). Thus, the *p-n* junction acts to pass current one way but not the other.

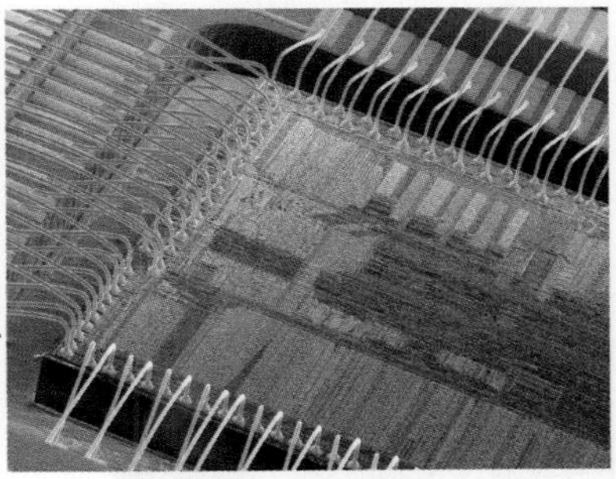

© Andrew Syred/Photo Researchers, Inc.

Intel Pentium III microprocessor at 200× magnification.

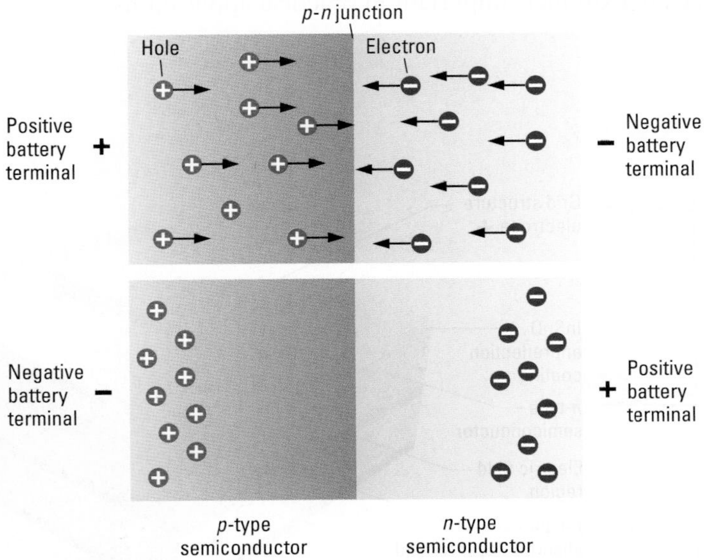

Figure 11.37 A *p-n* junction. Placing a *p*-type semiconductor next to an *n*-type semiconductor creates a *p-n* junction. The charge carriers in the *p*-type region are holes, and the charge carriers in the *n*-type region are electrons. *Top:* The negative battery terminal is connected to the *n*-type region, and the positive battery terminal is connected to the *p*-type region. The holes and electrons move as indicated by the arrows. Electric current flows through the junction and the overall device. *Bottom:* If the battery terminals are reversed, the holes and electrons are attracted to the edges of the regions, charge depletion occurs near the junction, and no current flows through the junction or the overall device.

National Renewable Energy Laboratory

© Thomson Learning/Charles D. Winters

Solar power can provide electricity in remote areas. These Brazilian houses and this water pump are powered by solar-generated electricity.

These *p-n* junctions can be joined together into larger composite structures to create transistors and integrated circuits. A single integrated circuit often contains thousands or even millions of transistors, as well as the circuits to carry the electrical signals. These devices, in the form of computer memories and central processing units (CPUs), permeate our society.

Doped silicon is also the basis of the **solar cell.** When a layer of *n*-type doped silicon is next to a *p*-type layer, there is a strong tendency for the extra electrons in the *n*-type layer to pair with the unpaired electrons in the holes of the *p*-type layer. If the two layers are connected by an external electrical circuit, light that strikes the silicon provides enough energy to cause an electrical current to flow. When a photon is absorbed, it excites an electron to a higher-energy orbital, allowing the electron to leave the *n*-type silicon layer and flow through the external circuit to the *p*-type layer. As the *p*-type layer becomes more negative (because of added electrons), the extra electrons are repelled *internally* back into the *n*-type layer (which has become positive because of the loss of electrons via the circuit). This process can continue as long as the silicon layers are exposed to sunlight and the circuit remains closed. Figure 11.38 shows a schematic diagram of a typical solar cell.

Solar cells are on the threshold of a major technological breakthrough, perhaps comparable to the computer chip. Although experimental solar-powered automobiles are now available and many novel applications of solar cells exist, the real breakthrough will come from the general use of banks of solar cells at utility power plants to produce huge quantities of electricity. One plant operating in California uses banks of solar cells to produce 20 megawatts (MW) of power—enough to supply the daily electricity needs of a city the size of Tampa, Florida.

11.11 Cement, Ceramics, and Glass

Cement, ceramics, and glass are examples of amorphous solids; that is, they lack crystalline structures with easily defined unit cells. Thanks to their useful properties, all three are extremely important in practical applications.

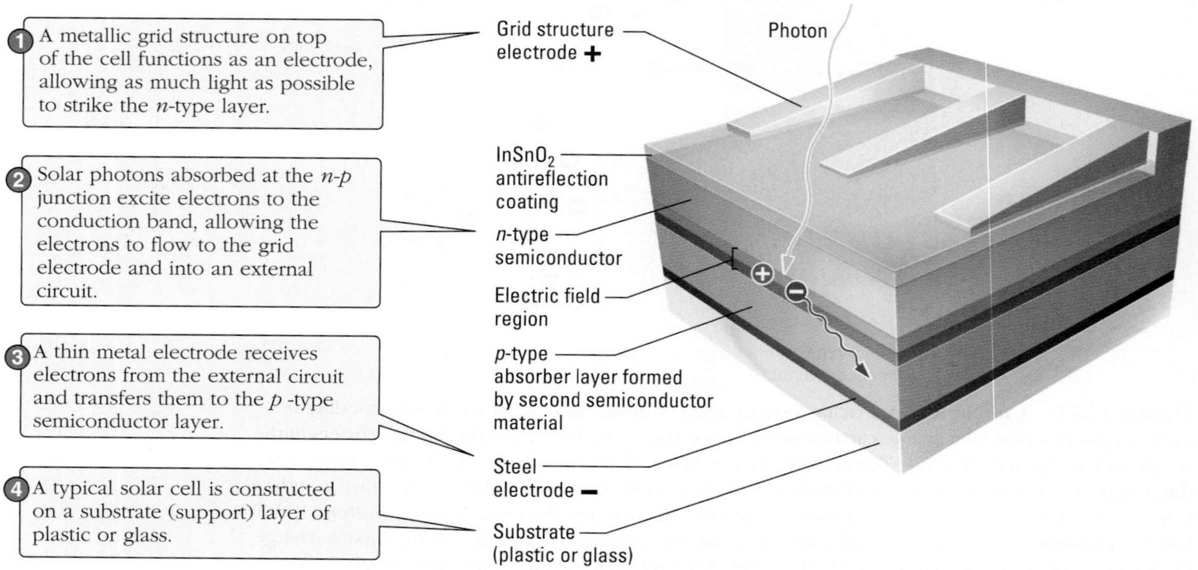

Figure 11.38 **Typical photovoltaic cell using layers of doped silicon.**

Cement

Cement consists of microscopic particles containing compounds of calcium, iron, aluminum, silicon, and oxygen in varying proportions. In the presence of water, cement forms hydrated particles with large surface areas, which subsequently undergo recrystallization and reaction to bond to themselves as well as to the surfaces of bricks, stone, or other silicate materials.

Cement is made by roasting a powdered mixture of calcium carbonate (limestone or chalk), silica (sand), aluminosilicate mineral (kaolin, clay, or shale), and iron oxide at a temperature of up to 870 °C in a rotating kiln. As the materials pass through the kiln, they lose water and carbon dioxide and ultimately form a "clinker," in which the materials are partially fused. A small amount of calcium sulfate is added, and the cooled clinker is then ground to a very fine powder. A typical composition of cement is 60% to 67% CaO, 17% to 25% SiO_2, 3% to 8% Al_2O_3, up to 6% Fe_2O_3, and small amounts of magnesium oxide, magnesium sulfate, and oxides of potassium and sodium.

Figure 11.39 **Pouring concrete.** After the concrete has been formed and exposed surfaces smoothed, it is allowed to set, a process hastened by moisture, in which strong bonds are formed between many of the tiny particles originally present in the dry concrete.

Cement is usually mixed with other substances. *Mortar* is a mixture of cement, sand, water, and lime. **Concrete** is a mixture of cement, sand, and aggregate (crushed stone or pebbles) in proportions that vary according to the application and the strength required.

In cement, the oxides are not isolated into ionic crystals, but an entire nanoscale structure forms that is a complex network of ions, each satisfying its charge requirements with ions of opposite charge. Many different reactions occur during the setting of cement. Various constituents react with water and with carbon dioxide in the air. The initial reaction of cement with water involves the hydrolysis of the calcium silicates, which forms a gel that sticks to itself and to the other particles (sand, crushed stone, or gravel). This gel has a very large surface area and ultimately is responsible for the great strength of concrete once it has set. The setting process involves formation of small, densely interlocked crystals. Their formation continues after the initial setting and increases the compressive strength of the cement (Figure 11.39). For this reason, freshly poured concrete is kept moist for several days.

Concrete, like many other materials containing Si—O bonds, is highly noncompressible but lacks tensile strength. When concrete is to be used where it will be subject to tension, as in a bridge or building, it must be reinforced with steel.

An informative overview of cement chemistry is found in *Journal of Chemical Education,* Vol. 80, 2003; pp. 623–635.

An article describing new uses for concrete is found in *Science News*, January 1, 2005; p. 7.

Compressive strength refers to a solid's resistance to shattering under compression.

Tensile strength refers to a substance's resistance to stretching.

Ceramics

Ceramics are generally fashioned from clay or other natural earths at room temperature and then permanently hardened by heat in a baking ("firing") process that binds the particles together.

Silicate ceramics include objects made from clays (aluminosilicates), such as pottery, bricks, and table china. China clay, or kaolin, is primarily kaolinite that is practically free of iron, which otherwise imparts a red color to the clay. As a result, china clay is white and particularly valuable in making fine pottery. Clays mixed with water form a moldable paste consisting of tiny silicate sheets that can easily slide past one another. When heated, the water is driven off, and new Si—O—Si bonds form so that the mass becomes permanently rigid.

Oxide ceramics are produced from powdered metal oxides such as alumina Al_2O_3) and magnesia (MgO) by heating the solids under pressure, causing the particles to bind to one another and thereby form a rigid solid. Because it has a high electrical resistivity, alumina is used in spark plug insulators. High-density alumina has very high mechanical strength, so it is also used in armor plating and in high-speed cutting tools for machining metals. Magnesia is an insulator with a high melting point (2800 °C), so it is often used as insulation in electric heaters and electric stoves.

A third class of ceramics includes the *nonoxide ceramics* such as silicon nitride (Si_3N_4), silicon carbide (SiC), and boron nitride (BN). Heating the solids under pressure forms ceramics that are hard and strong, but brittle. Boron nitride has the same average number of electrons per atom as does elemental carbon and exists in the graphite structure or the diamond structure, making it comparable in hardness with diamond and more resistant to oxidation. For this reason, boron nitride cups and tubes are used to contain molten metals that are being evaporated. Silicon carbide (trade name Carborundum) is a widely used abrasive that can be regarded as the diamond structure with half of the C atoms replaced by Si atoms.

The one severely limiting problem in using ceramics is their brittleness. Ceramics deform very little before they fail catastrophically, with the failure resulting from a weak point in the bonding within the ceramic matrix. Such weak points are not consistent from sample to sample, so the failure is not readily predicted. Stress failure of ceramic composites occurs due to nanoscale irregularities resulting from impurities or disorder in the atomic arrangements, so much attention is now being given to using purer starting materials and more strictly controlling the processing steps. Adding fibers to ceramic composites makes them less susceptible to brittleness and sudden fracture.

Glasses

One of the more common **glasses** is soda-lime glass, which is clear and colorless if the purity of the ingredients is carefully controlled. Various substances give color to the glass (Table 11.8).

"Lead glass," as the name implies, contains lead as PbO. It is highly prized for its massive feel, acoustic properties, and high index of refraction.

The simplest glass is probably amorphous silica, SiO_2 (known as *vitreous silica*); it is prepared by melting and quickly cooling either quartz or cristobalite. Such glass is built up of corner-sharing SiO_4 tetrahedra linked into a three-dimensional network that lacks symmetry or long-range order. Another common glass is *borosilicate glass* or Pyrex, which contains SiO_2, B_2O_3, and Al_2O_3. It is made from melting boric acid (H_3BO_3), soda ash (Na_2CO_3), silica sand (SiO_2), alumina (Al_2O_3), and borax ($Na_2B_4O_7 \cdot 10\ H_2O$) and is valuable because of its low expansion with temperature and high chemical durability.

Mole percent is just another way of expressing concentration. If 0.75 mol SiO_2 and 0.25 mol Na_2O are mixed, 1.00 mol matter is present. The mole percent of SiO_2 is 75%, and the mole percent of Na_2O is 25%.

If another oxide is added to SiO_2, the melting point of the SiO_2 mixture is lowered considerably (from 1800 °C for quartz to about 800 °C if about 25 mole percent of Na_2O is added). The resulting melt cools to form a glass that is somewhat water-soluble and definitely soluble in strongly basic solutions. It is also prone to convert back to a crystalline solid. If other metal oxides such as CaO, MgO, or Al_2O_3

© Fulvio Roiter/Corbis

Colored glass. Adding small amounts of metal oxides to colorless glass creates various colors.

Table 11.8 Substances Used to Color Glass

Substance	Color
Calcium fluoride	Milky white
Cobalt(II) oxide	Blue
Copper(I) oxide	Red, green, blue
Finely divided gold	Red, purple, blue
Iron(II) compounds	Green
Iron(III) compounds	Yellow
Manganese(IV) oxide	Violet
Tin(IV) oxide	Opaque
Uranium compounds	Yellow, green

CHEMISTRY IN THE NEWS

Brilliant Colors in Paintings

Recent investigations of archives in Venice have uncovered important details about fifteenth- and sixteenth-century Italian Renaissance paintings. Art historians have long puzzled over how Renaissance painters managed to make the colors in their works so strong, clear, and bright that they seemed to glow. The findings of art historian sleuths, including Barbara Berrie, a conservation scientist at the National Gallery of Art in Washington, DC, show that ". . . Italian Renaissance artists weren't merely painters. They were also experimental chemists who mixed and matched unconventional ingredients." The artists mixed their paint with small (4–8 micron) glass particles made from ground silica obtained from quartzite pebbles, which is extremely pure silica. These glass particles made the paint layers somewhat transparent, and the overall effect is to make the pigments appear to glow. The painters also used various types of glass to expand the range of colors available. The Venetian artists borrowed materials from other crafts and trades to expand and enhance their art, and they created art that has inspired for centuries.

SOURCE: Goho, A. "Venetian Grinds." *Science News*, March 12, 2005; p. 168.

© Art Resource

Lorenzo Lotto's 1522 painting *Saint Catherine*. This painting contains glass particles mixed with the paint, which leads to especially vibrant colors. The image can be seen at the web site of the National Gallery of Art, Washington, DC.

are added, the mixture still melts at a fairly low temperature, but it becomes resistant to chemical attack. Common glass like that used for windows, bottles, and lamps contains these metal oxides in addition to SiO_2.

It is important that glass be *annealed* properly during the manufacturing process. Annealing means cooling the glass slowly as it passes from a viscous liquid state to a solid at room temperature. If a glass is cooled too quickly, bonding forces become uneven because small regions of crystallinity develop. Poorly annealed glass may crack or shatter when subjected to mechanical shocks or sudden temperature changes. High-quality glass, such as that used in optics, must be annealed very carefully. For example, the 200-in mirror for the telescope at Mt. Palomar, California, was annealed from 500 °C to 300 °C over a period of nine months.

Optical Fibers

Our technological culture's dependence on instantaneous communication relies on the properties of many materials, but none more so than optical fibers. These fibers have rapidly replaced copper wire for the transmission of data such as telephone conversations as well as Internet-based digital data.

The refractive index of a material expresses the angle at which light is diffracted upon entering the material from a vacuum.

An **optical fiber** has three parts: core glass, which carries the light; cladding glass, which surrounds the core; and a polymer on the outside for physical protection and strength (Figure 11.40). The cladding glass has a slightly lower refractive index than the core glass, so there is total internal reflection of light traveling through the fiber as long as the light hits the surface of the core at a sufficiently small angle.

A good optical fiber must have two properties: (1) It must contain the light—that is, it must produce total internal reflection and have no defects on the surface that would let light out of the fiber; and (2) it must pass light over long distances without significant loss of intensity. To pass light with no attenuation, the core glass must be pure—in fact, ultrapure. Before 1965, when light was put into the best

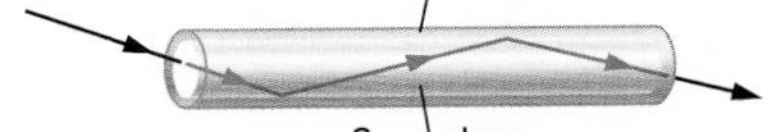

Figure 11.40 **Total internal reflection in an optical fiber.**

Novastock/Photo Researchers, Inc.

A bundle of optical fibers. Optical fibers carry information in the form of light waves.

available optical fiber 1000 m long, no light came out, because it was all absorbed. In the decades that followed, sophisticated manufacturing methods were developed that allowed the generation of core glass appropriate for optical fiber. Pure silica, SiO_2, is evaporated into a rod that can be heated and pulled (like taffy) to make a tiny optical fiber. The attenuation of the light signals was decreased by as much as 100 orders of magnitude by the materials scientists working on this problem. At present, optical fibers carrying signals over long distances need to have optical amplifiers only every 50 km or so to keep the signals from becoming too weak. Using such methodology, very long fiber optic cables are now in routine use.

The two main advantages of optical fibers for transmission of voice and electronic information are the capability of the fibers to carry many more streams of data than copper wire can and the decreased interference when fibers rather than wires are used. In addition, optical fibers are made from cheap, abundant materials.

SUMMARY PROBLEM

Part 1

Use the vapor pressure curves shown in Figure 11.5 to answer these questions.

(a) What is the vapor pressure of diethyl ether at 0 °C?

(b) Does diethyl ether have stronger or weaker intermolecular attractions than ethanol?

(c) At what temperature does diethyl ether have a vapor pressure of 600 mm Hg?

(d) If the normal boiling point of diethyl ether is 34.6 °C and it has a vapor pressure of 410 mm Hg at 20 °C, calculate ΔH°_{vap} for diethyl ether.

Part 2

Consider the phase diagram for xenon shown below. Answer these questions.

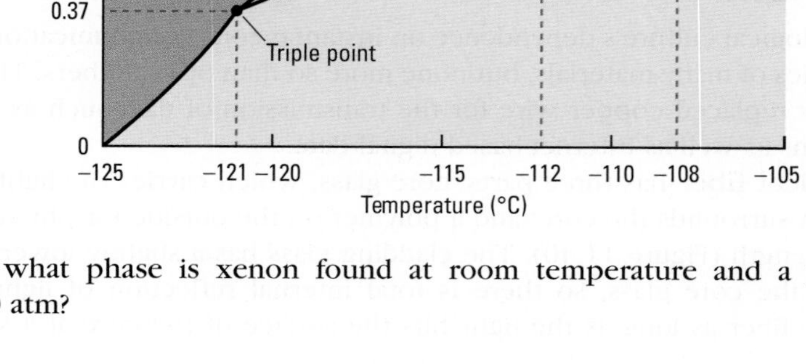

(a) In what phase is xenon found at room temperature and a pressure of 1.0 atm?

(b) If the pressure exerted on a sample of xenon is 0.75 atm and the temperature is −114 °C, in what phase does xenon exist?

(c) If the vapor pressure of a sample of liquid xenon is 375 mm Hg, what is the temperature of the liquid phase?

(d) What is the vapor pressure of solid xenon at −122 °C?

(e) Which is the denser phase, solid or liquid? Explain.

Part 3

Consider the CsCl unit cell shown in Figure 11.23.

(a) How many Cs^+ ions are there per unit cell?

(b) How many Cl^- ions are there per unit cell?

(c) How many Cl^- ions share each face of the unit cell?

IN CLOSING

Having studied this chapter, you should be able to . . .

- Explain the properties of surface tension, capillary action, vapor pressure, and boiling point, and describe how these properties are influenced by intermolecular forces (Sections 11.1 and 11.2). ThomsonNOW homework: Study Questions 25, 28, 46, 109
- Calculate the energy transfers associated with vaporization and fusion (Section 11.3). ThomsonNOW homework: Study Questions 21, 32, 34, 94
- Describe the phase changes that occur among solids, liquids, and gases (Section 11.3). ThomsonNOW homework: Study Questions 40, 42, 44
- Use phase diagrams to predict what happens when temperature and pressure are changed for a sample of matter (Section 11.3). ThomsonNOW homework: Study Questions 49, 51, 101
- Understand critical temperature and critical pressure (Section 11.3).
- Describe and explain the unusual properties of water (Section 11.4).
- Differentiate among the major types of solids (Section 11.5). ThomsonNOW homework: Study Questions 56, 58
- Do calculations based on knowledge of simple unit cells and the dimensions of atoms and ions that occupy positions in those unit cells (Section 11.6). ThomsonNOW homework: Study Questions 62, 67
- Explain the bonding in network solids and how it results in their properties (Section 11.7). ThomsonNOW homework: Study Question 71
- Explain the basis of materials science (Section 11.8).
- Explain metallic bonding and how it results in the properties of metals and semiconductors (Section 11.9). ThomsonNOW homework: Study Question 79
- Describe the phenomenon of superconductivity (Section 11.9).
- Describe *n*-type and *p*-type semiconductors and the use of *p-n* junctions as rectifiers (Section 11.10).
- Explain how the lack of regular structure in amorphous solids affects their properties (Section 11.11). ThomsonNOW homework: Study Question 90

ThomsonNOW™
Sign in to ThomsonNOW at **www.thomsonedu.com** to check your readiness for an exam by taking the Pre-Test and exploring the modules recommended in your Personalized Learning Plan.

KEY TERMS

amorphous solids *(11.5)*

boiling *(11.2)*

boiling point *(11.2)*

capillary action *(11.1)*

cement *(11.11)*

ceramics *(11.11)*

Clausius-Clapeyron equation *(11.2)*

closest packing *(11.6)*

concrete *(11.11)*

condensation *(11.3)*

conduction band *(11.9)*

conductor *(11.9)*

critical pressure (P_c) *(11.3)*

critical temperature (T_c) *(11.3)*

crystal lattice *(11.6)*

crystalline solids *(11.5)*

crystallization *(11.3)*

cubic close packing *(11.6)*

cubic unit cell *(11.6)*

deposition *(11.3)*

dew point *(11.2)*

doping *(11.10)*

energy band *(11.9)*

equilibrium vapor pressure *(11.2)*

evaporation *(11.3)*

fullerenes *(11.7)*

glass *(11.11)*

heating curve *(11.3)*

hexagonal close packing *(11.6)*

insulator *(11.9)*

materials science *(11.8)*

meniscus *(11.1)*

metallic bonding *(11.9)*

***n*-type semiconductor** *(11.10)*

nanotube *(11.7)*

network solids *(11.7)*

normal boiling point *(11.2)*

optical fiber *(11.11)*

***p-n* junction** *(11.10)*

***p*-type semiconductor** *(11.10)*

phase diagram *(11.3)*

relative humidity *(11.2)*

semiconductor *(11.9)*

solar cell *(11.10)*

sublimation *(11.3)*

superconductor *(11.9)*

supercritical fluid *(11.3)*

surface tension *(11.1)*

triple point *(11.3)*

unit cell *(11.6)*

valence band *(11.9)*

vapor pressure *(11.2)*

vaporization *(11.3)*

viscosity *(11.1)*

volatility *(11.2)*

X-ray crystallography (*Tools of Chemistry,* p. 522)

zone refining *(11.10)*

QUESTIONS FOR REVIEW AND THOUGHT

■ denotes questions available in ThomsonNOW and assignable in OWL.

Blue-numbered questions have short answers at the back of this book and fully worked solutions in the *Student Solutions Manual.*

ThomsonNOW™

Assess your understanding of this chapter's topics with sample tests and other resources found by signing in to ThomsonNOW at **www.thomsonedu.com**.

Review Questions

1. Name three properties of solids that are different from those of liquids. Explain the differences for each.
2. List the concepts of the kinetic-molecular theory that apply to liquids.
3. What causes surface tension in liquids? Name a substance that has a very high surface tension. What kinds of intermolecular forces account for the high value?
4. Explain how the equilibrium vapor pressure of a liquid might be measured.
5. Define boiling point and normal boiling point.
6. What is the heat of crystallization of a substance, and how is it related to the substance's heat of fusion?
7. What is sublimation?
8. Which of these processes are endothermic?
   (a) Condensation (b) Melting (c) Evaporation
   (d) Sublimation (e) Deposition (f) Freezing
9. What is the unit cell of a crystal?
10. Assuming the same substance could form crystals with its atoms or ions in either simple cubic packing or hexagonal closest packing, which form would have the higher density? Explain.
11. How does conductivity vary with temperature for (a) a conductor, (b) a nonconductor, (c) a semiconductor, and (d) a superconductor? In your answer, begin at high temperatures and come down to low temperatures.

Topical Questions

The Liquid State

12. Predict which substance in Table 11.1 has a surface tension most similar to that of each liquid:
    (a) Ethylene glycol, $HOCH_2—CH_2OH$
    (b) Hexane, C_6H_{14}
    (c) Gallium metal at 40 °C

13. The surface tension of a liquid decreases with increasing temperature. Using the idea of intermolecular attractions, explain why this is so.
14. Explain on the molecular scale the processes of condensation and vaporization.
15. How would you convert a sample of liquid to vapor without changing the temperature?
16. What is the heat of vaporization of a liquid? How is it related to the heat of condensation of that liquid? Using the idea of intermolecular attractions, explain why the process of vaporization is endothermic.
17. After exercising on a hot summer day and working up a sweat, you often become cool when you stop. What is the molecular-level explanation of this phenomenon?
18. The substances Ne, HF, H_2O, NH_3, and CH_4 all have the same number of electrons. In a thought experiment, you can make HF from Ne by removing a single proton a short distance from the nucleus and having the electrons follow the new arrangement of nuclei so as to make a new chemical bond. You can do the same for each of the other compounds. (Of course, none of these thought experiments can actually be done because of the enormous energies required to remove protons from nuclei.) For all of these substances, make a plot of (a) the boiling point in kelvins versus the number of hydrogen atoms and (b) the molar heat of vaporization versus the number of hydrogen atoms. Explain any trend that you see in terms of intermolecular forces.
19. How much heat energy transfer is required to vaporize 1.0 metric ton of ammonia? (1 metric ton = 10^3 kg.) The ΔH_{vap} for ammonia is 25.1 kJ/mol.
20. The chlorofluorocarbon CCl_3F has an enthalpy of vaporization of 24.8 kJ/mol. To vaporize 1.00 kg of the compound, how much heat energy transfer is required?
21. ■ The molar enthalpy of vaporization of methanol is 38.0 kJ/mol at 25 °C. How much heat energy transfer is required to convert 250. mL of the alcohol from liquid to vapor? The density of CH_3OH is 0.787 g/mL at 25 °C.
22. Some camping stoves contain liquid butane (C_4H_{10}). They work only when the outside temperature is warm enough to allow the butane to have a reasonable vapor pressure (so they are not very good for camping in temperatures below about 0 °C). Assume the enthalpy of vaporization of butane is 24.3 kJ/mol. If the camp stove fuel tank contains 190. g liquid C_4H_{10}, how much heat energy transfer is required to vaporize all of the butane?
23. Mercury is a highly toxic metal. Although it is a liquid at room temperature, it has a high vapor pressure and a low enthalpy of vaporization (294 J/g). What quantity of heat energy transfer is required to vaporize 0.500 mL of mercury at 357 °C, its normal boiling point? The density of Hg (ℓ) is 13.6 g/mL. Compare this heat energy transfer with the amount needed to vaporize 0.500 mL water. See Table 11.2 for the molar enthalpy of vaporization of H_2O.
24. Rationalize the observation that 1-propanol ($CH_3CH_2CH_2OH$) has a boiling point of 97.2 °C, whereas a compound with the same empirical formula, ethyl methyl ether ($CH_3CH_2OCH_3$), boils at 7.4 °C.
25. ■ Briefly explain the variations in the boiling points in the table following. In your discussion be sure to mention the types of intermolecular forces involved.

Compound	Boiling Point (°C)
NH_3	−33.4
PH_3	−87.5
AsH_3	−62.4
SbH_3	−18.4

Vapor Pressure

26. Give a molecular-level explanation of why the vapor pressure of a liquid increases with temperature.
27. Methanol, CH_3OH, has a normal boiling point of 64.7 °C and a vapor pressure of 100 mm Hg at 21.2 °C. Formaldehyde, $H_2C{=}O$, has a normal boiling point of −19.5 °C and a vapor pressure of 100 mm Hg at −57.3 °C. Explain why these two compounds have different boiling points and require different temperatures to achieve the same vapor pressure.
28. ■ The vapor pressure curves for four substances are shown in the plot. Which one of these four substances will have the greatest intermolecular attractive forces at 25 °C? Explain your answer.

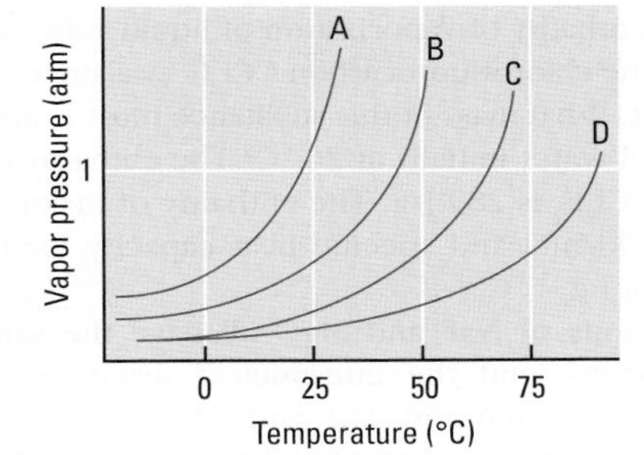

29. The lowest sea-level barometric pressure ever recorded was 25.90 in mercury, recorded in a typhoon in the South Pacific. Suppose you were in this typhoon and, to calm yourself, boiled water to make yourself a cup of tea. At what temperature would the water boil? Remember that 1 atm is 760 mm (29.92 in) Hg, and use Figure 11.5.
30. The highest mountain in the western hemisphere is Mt. Aconcagua, in the central Andes of Argentina (22,834 ft). If atmospheric pressure decreases at a rate of 3.5 millibar every 100 ft, estimate the atmospheric pressure at the top of Mt. Aconcagua, and then estimate from Figure 11.5 the temperature at which water would boil at the top of the mountain.
31. A liquid has a ΔH_{vap} of 38.7 kJ/mol and a boiling point of 110 °C at 1 atm pressure. What is the vapor pressure of the liquid at 97 °C?
32. ■ A liquid has a ΔH_{vap} of 44.0 kJ/mol and a vapor pressure of 370 mm Hg at 90 °C. What is the vapor pressure of the liquid at 130 °C?
33. The vapor pressure of ethanol, C_2H_5OH, at 50.0 °C is 233 mm Hg, and its normal boiling point at 1 atm is 78.3 °C. What is the ΔH_{vap} of ethanol?
34. ■ What would the ΔH_{vap} be for a substance whose vapor pressure doubled when its temperature was raised from 70.0 °C to 80.0 °C?

Phase Changes: Solids, Liquids, and Gases

35. What does a low enthalpy of fusion for a solid tell you about the solid (its bonding or type)?
36. What does a high melting point and a high enthalpy of fusion tell you about a solid (its bonding or type)?
37. Which would you expect to have the higher enthalpy of fusion, N_2 or I_2? Explain your choice.
38. The enthalpy of fusion for H_2O is about 2.5 times larger than the enthalpy of fusion for H_2S. What does this say about the relative strengths of the forces between the molecules in these two solids? Explain.
39. Benzene is an organic liquid that freezes at 5.5 °C and forms beautiful, feather-like crystals. How much heat is evolved when 15.5 g benzene freezes at 5.5 °C? The enthalpy of fusion of benzene is 127 J/g. If the 15.5-g sample is remelted, again at 5.5 °C, what quantity of heat transfer is required to convert it to a liquid?
40. ■ What is the total quantity of heat energy transfer required to change 0.50 mol ice at −5 °C to 0.50 mol steam at 100 °C?
41. How much thermal energy is needed to melt a 36.00-g ice cube that is initially at −10 °C and bring it to room temperature (20 °C)? The solid ice and liquid water have heat capacities of 2.06 J g^{-1} °C^{-1} and 4.184 J g^{-1} °C^{-1}, respectively. The enthalpy of fusion for solid ice is 6.02 kJ/mol and the enthalpy of vaporization of liquid water is 40.7 kJ/mol.
42. ■ The chlorofluorocarbon CCl_2F_2 was once used as a refrigerant. What mass of this substance must evaporate to freeze 2 mol water initially at 20 °C? The enthalpy of vaporization for CCl_2F_2 is 289 J/g. The enthalpy of fusion for solid ice is 6.02 kJ/mol and specific heat capacity for liquid water is 4.184 J g^{-1} °C^{-1}.
43. The ions of NaF and MgO all have the same number of electrons, and the internuclear distances are about the same (235 pm and 212 pm). Why, then, are the melting points of NaF and MgO so different (992 °C and 2642 °C, respectively)?
44. ■ For the pair of compounds LiF and CsI, tell which compound is expected to have the higher melting point, and briefly explain why.
45. Which of these substances has the highest melting point? The lowest melting point? Explain your choice briefly.
    (a) LiBr (b) CaO
    (c) CO (d) CH_3OH
46. ■ Which of these substances has the highest melting point? The lowest melting point? Explain your choice briefly.
    (a) SiC (b) I_2
    (c) Rb (d) $CH_3CH_2CH_2CH_3$
47. Why is solid CO_2 called Dry Ice?
48. During thunderstorms, very large hailstones can fall from the sky. To preserve some of these stones, you place them in the freezer compartment of your frost-free refrigerator. A friend, who is a chemistry student, tells you to put the hailstones in a tightly sealed plastic bag. Why?
49. ■ In this phase diagram, make the following identifications:

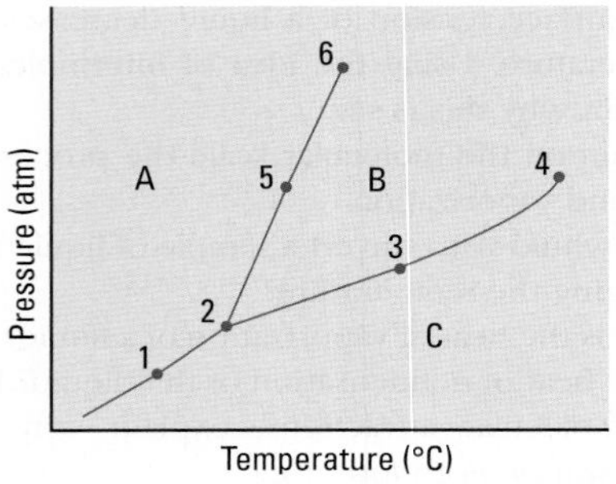

(a) What phase is present in region A? Region B? Region C?
(b) What phases are in equilibrium at point 1? Point 2? Point 3? Point 5?

50. From memory, sketch the phase diagram of water. Label all the regions as to the physical state of water. Draw either horizontal (constant pressure) or vertical (constant temperature) paths (i.e., lines with arrows indicating a direction) for these changes of state:
    (a) Sublimation (b) Condensation to a liquid
    (c) Melting (d) Vaporization
    (e) Crystallization
51. ■ Consult the phase diagram of CO_2 in Figure 11.17. What phase or phases are present under these conditions:
    (a) $T = -70$ °C and $P = 1.0$ atm
    (b) $T = -40$ °C and $P = 15.5$ atm
    (c) $T = -80$ °C and $P = 4.7$ atm
52. At the critical point for carbon dioxide, the substance is very far from being an ideal gas. Prove this statement by calculating the density of an ideal gas in g/cm^3 at the conditions of the critical point and comparing it with the experimental value. Compute the experimental value from the fact that a mole of CO_2 at its critical point occupies 94 cm^3.

Types of Solids

53. Classify each of these solids as ionic, metallic, molecular, network, or amorphous.
    (a) KF (b) I_2
    (c) SiO_2 (d) BN
54. Classify each of these solids as ionic, metallic, molecular, network, or amorphous.
    (a) Tetraphosphorus decaoxide
    (b) Brass
    (c) Graphite
    (d) Ammonium phosphate
55. On the basis of the description given, classify each of these solids as molecular, metallic, ionic, network, or amorphous, and explain your reasoning.
    (a) A brittle, yellow solid that melts at 113 °C; neither its solid nor its liquid conducts electricity
    (b) A soft, silvery solid that melts at 40 °C; both its solid and its liquid conduct electricity
    (c) A hard, colorless, crystalline solid that melts at 1713 °C; neither its solid nor its liquid conducts electricity
    (d) A soft, slippery solid that melts at 63 °C; neither its solid nor its liquid conducts electricity
56. ■ On the basis of the description given, classify each of these solids as molecular, metallic, ionic, network, or amorphous, and explain your reasoning.

(a) A soft, slippery solid that has no definite melting point but decomposes at temperatures above 250 °C; the solid does not conduct electricity
(b) Violet crystals that melt at 114 °C and whose vapor irritates the nose; neither the solid nor the liquid conducts electricity
(c) Hard, colorless crystals that melt at 2800 °C; the liquid conducts electricity, but the solid does not
(d) A hard solid that melts at 3410 °C; both the solid and the liquid conduct electricity

57. Describe how each of these materials would behave if it were deformed by a hammer strike. Explain why the materials behave as they do.
(a) A metal, such as gold
(b) A nonmetal, such as sulfur
(c) An ionic compound, such as NaCl

58. ■ What type of solid exhibits each of these sets of properties?
(a) Melts below 100 °C and is insoluble in water
(b) Conducts electricity only when melted
(c) Insoluble in water and conducts electricity
(d) Noncrystalline and melts over a wide temperature range

Crystalline Solids

59. Each diagram below represents an array of like atoms that would extend indefinitely in two dimensions. Draw a two-dimensional unit cell for each array. How many atoms are in each unit cell?

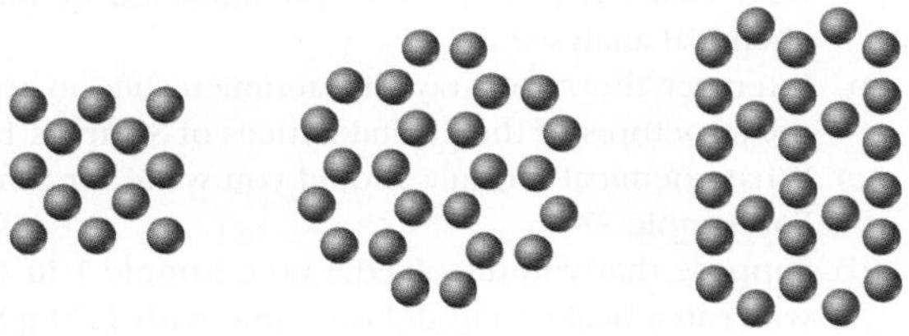

60. Name and draw the three cubic unit cells. Describe their similarities and differences.

61. Explain how the volume of a simple cubic unit cell is related to the radius of the atoms in the cell.

62. ■ Solid xenon forms crystals with a face-centered unit cell that has an edge of 620 pm. Calculate the atomic radius of xenon.

63. Gold (atomic radius = 144 pm) crystallizes in an fcc unit cell. What is the length of a side of the cell?

64. Using the NaCl structure shown in Figure 11.24, how many unit cells share each of the Na^+ ions in the front face of the unit cell? How many unit cells share each of the Cl^- ions in this face?

65. The ionic radii of Cs^+ and Cl^- are 181 and 167 pm, respectively. What is the length of the body diagonal in the CsCl unit cell? What is the length of the side of this unit cell? (See Figure 11.23.)

66. You know that thallium chloride, TlCl, crystallizes in either a simple cubic or a face-centered cubic lattice of Cl^- ions with Tl^+ ions in the holes. If the density of the solid is 7.00 g/cm^3 and the edge of the unit cell is 3.85×10^{-8} cm, what is the unit cell geometry?

67. ■ Could $CaCl_2$ possibly have the NaCl structure? Explain your answer briefly.

68. A simple cubic unit cell is formed so that the spherical atoms or ions just touch one another along the edge. Prove mathematically that the percentage of empty space within the unit cell is 47.6%. (The volume of a sphere is $\frac{4}{3}\pi r^3$, where r is the radius of the sphere.)

69. Metallic lithium has a body-centered cubic structure, and its unit cell is 351 pm along an edge. Lithium iodide has the same crystal lattice structure as sodium chloride. The cubic unit cell is 600 pm along an edge.
(a) Assume that the metal atoms in lithium touch along the body diagonal of the cubic unit cell, and estimate the radius of a lithium atom.
(b) Assume that in lithium iodide the I^- ions touch along the face diagonal of the cubic unit cell and that the Li^+ and I^- ions touch along the edge of the cube; calculate the radius of an I^- ion and of an Li^+ ion.
(c) Compare your results in parts (a) and (b) for the radius of a lithium atom and a lithium ion. Are your results reasonable? If not, how could you account for the unexpected result? Could any of the assumptions that were made be in error?

Network Solids

70. Explain why diamond is denser than graphite.

71. ■ Determine, by looking up data in a reference such as the *Handbook of Chemistry and Physics,* whether the examples of network solids given in the text are soluble in water or other common solvents. Explain your answer in terms of the chemical bonding in network solids.

72. Explain why diamond is an electrical insulator and graphite is an electrical conductor.

Tools of Chemistry: X-Ray Crystallography

73. The surface of a CD-ROM disc contains narrowly separated lines that diffract light into its component colors. The lines are spaced at distances approximately the same as the wavelength of the light. Taking the middle of the visible spectrum to be green light with a wavelength of 550 nm, calculate how many aluminum atoms (radius = 143 pm) touching its neighbors would make a straight line 550 nm long. Using this result, explain why an optical microscope using visible radiation will never be able to detect an individual aluminum atom (or any other atom, for that matter).

74. For a clear diffraction pattern to be seen from a regularly spaced lattice, the radiation falling on the lattice must have a wavelength less than the lattice spacing. From the unit cell size of the NaCl crystal, estimate the maximum wavelength of the radiation that would be diffracted by this crystal. Calculate the frequency of the radiation and the energy associated with (a) one photon and (b) one mole of photons of the radiation. In what region of the spectrum is this radiation?

75. The first-order Bragg reflection ($n = 1$) from an aluminum crystal for X-rays with a wavelength of 154 pm is 19.3°. What is the spacing between the planes of aluminum atoms?

76. The second-order Bragg reflection ($n = 2$) from a copper crystal for X-rays with a wavelength of 166 pm is 27.35°. What is the spacing between the planes of copper atoms?

77. If the first-order Bragg reflection ($n = 1$) from a NaCl crystal with a spacing of 282 pm is seen at 23.0°, what is the wavelength of the X-ray radiation used?

Metals, Semiconductors, and Insulators

78. What is the principal difference between the orbitals that electrons occupy in individual, isolated atoms and the orbitals they occupy in solids?
79. ■ In terms of band theory, what is the difference between a conductor and an insulator? Between a conductor and a semiconductor?
80. Name three properties of metals, and explain them by using a theory of metallic bonding.
81. Which substance has the greatest electrical conductivity? The smallest electrical conductivity? Explain your choice briefly.
    (a) Si (b) Ge
    (c) Ag (d) P_4
82. Which substance has the greatest electrical conductivity? The smallest electrical conductivity? Explain your choices briefly.
    (a) $RbCl(\ell)$ (b) NaBr(s)
    (c) Rb (d) Diamond
83. Define the term "superconductor." Give the chemical formulas of two kinds of superconductors and their associated transition temperatures.
84. What is the main technological or economic barrier to the widespread use of superconductors?

Silicon and the Chip

85. What are the two main chemical reactions involved in the production of electronic-grade silicon? Identify the elements being reduced and being oxidized.
86. Extremely high-purity silicon is required to manufacture semiconductors such as the memory chips found in calculators and computers. If a silicon wafer is 99.99999999% pure, approximately how many silicon atoms per gram have been replaced by impurity atoms of some other element?
87. What is the process of doping, as applied to semiconductors? Why are Group 3A and Group 5A elements used to dope silicon?
88. Explain the difference between *n*-type semiconductors and *p*-type semiconductors.

Cement, Ceramics, and Glass

89. Define the term "amorphous."
90. ■ What makes a glass different from a solid such as NaCl? Under what conditions could NaCl become glass-like?
91. A typical cement contains, by weight, 65% CaO, 20% SiO_2, 5% Al_2O_3, 6% Fe_2O_3, and 4% MgO. Determine the mass percent of each element present. Then determine an empirical formula of the material from the percent composition, setting the coefficient of the least abundant element to 1.00.
92. Give two examples of (a) oxide ceramics and (b) nonoxide ceramics.

General Questions

93. The chlorofluorocarbon CCl_2F_2 was once used in air conditioners as the heat transfer fluid. Its normal boiling point is −30 °C, and its enthalpy of vaporization is 165 J g^{-1}. The gas and the liquid have specific heat capacities of 0.61 J g^{-1} $°C^{-1}$ and 0.97 J g^{-1} $°C^{-1}$, respectively. How much heat is evolved when 10.0 g CCl_2F_2 is cooled from 40 °C to −40 °C?
94. ■ Liquid ammonia, $NH_3(\ell)$, was used as a refrigerant fluid before the discovery of the chlorofluorocarbons and is still widely used today. Its normal boiling point is −33.4 °C, and its enthalpy of vaporization is 23.5 kJ/mol. The gas and liquid have specific heat capacities of 2.2 J g^{-1} K^{-1} and 4.7 J g^{-1} K^{-1}, respectively. How much heat transfer is required to 10.0 kg liquid ammonia to raise its temperature from −50.0 °C to −33.4 °C, and then to 0.0 °C?
95. Potassium chloride and rubidium chloride both have the sodium chloride structure. X-ray diffraction experiments indicate that their cubic unit cell dimensions are 629 pm and 658 pm, respectively.
    (i) One mol KCl and 1 mol RbCl are ground together in a mortar and pestle to a very fine powder, and the X-ray diffraction pattern of the pulverized solid is measured. Two patterns are observed, each corresponding to a cubic unit cell—one with an edge length of 629 pm and one with an edge length of 658 pm. Call this Sample 1.
    (ii) One mol KCl and 1 mol RbCl are heated until the entire mixture is molten and then cooled to room temperature. A single X-ray diffraction pattern indicates a cubic unit cell with an edge length of roughly 640 pm. Call this Sample 2.
    (a) Suppose that Samples 1 and 2 were analyzed for their chloride content. What fraction of each sample is chloride? Could the samples be distinguished by means of chemical analysis?
    (b) Interpret the two X-ray diffraction results in terms of the structures of the crystal lattices of Samples 1 and 2.
    (c) What chemical formula should you write for Sample 1? For Sample 2?
    (d) Suppose that you dissolved 1.00 g Sample 1 in 100 mL water in a beaker and did the same with 1.00 g Sample 2. Which sample would conduct electricity better, or would both be the same? What ions would be present in each solution at what concentrations?
96. Sulfur dioxide, SO_2, is found in polluted air.
    (a) What type of forces are responsible for binding SO_2 molecules to one another in the solid or liquid phase?
    (b) Using the information below, place the compounds listed in order of increasing intermolecular attractions.

Compound	Normal Boiling Point (°C)
SO_2	−10
NH_3	−33.4
CH_4	−161.5
H_2O	100

Applying Concepts

97. Refer to Figure 11.5 when answering these questions.
    (a) What is the equilibrium vapor pressure for ethyl alcohol at room temperature?

(b) At what temperature does diethyl ether have an equilibrium vapor pressure of 400 mm Hg?

(c) If a pot of water were boiling at a temperature of 95 °C, what would be the atmospheric pressure?

(d) At 200 mm Hg and 60 °C, which of the three substances are gases?

(e) If you put a couple of drops of each substance on your hand, which would immediately evaporate, and which would remain as a liquid?

(f) Which of the three substances has the greatest intermolecular attractions?

98. The normal boiling point of SO_2 is 263.1 K and that of NH_3 is 239.7 K. At −40 °C, would you predict that ammonia has a vapor pressure greater than, less than, or equal to that of sulfur dioxide? Explain.

99. Butane is a gas at room temperature; however, if you look closely at a butane lighter you see it contains liquid butane. How is this possible?

100. While camping with a friend in the Rocky Mountains, you decide to cook macaroni for dinner. Your friend says the macaroni will cook faster in the Rockies because the lower atmospheric pressure will cause the water to boil at a lower temperature. Do you agree with your friend? Explain your reasoning.

101. ■ Examine the nanoscale diagrams and the phase diagram below. Match each particulate diagram (1 through 7) to its corresponding point (A through H) on the phase diagram.

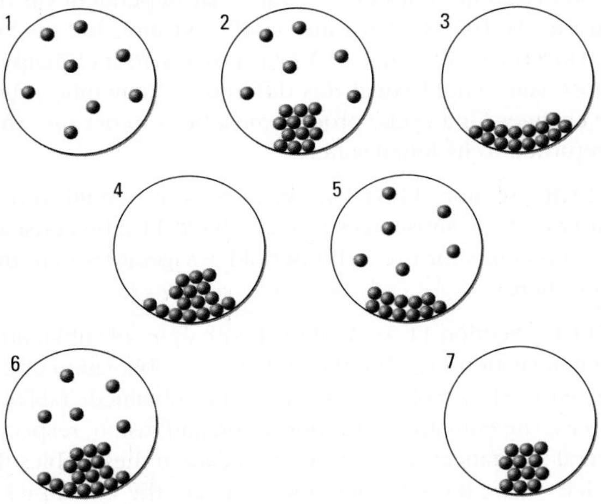

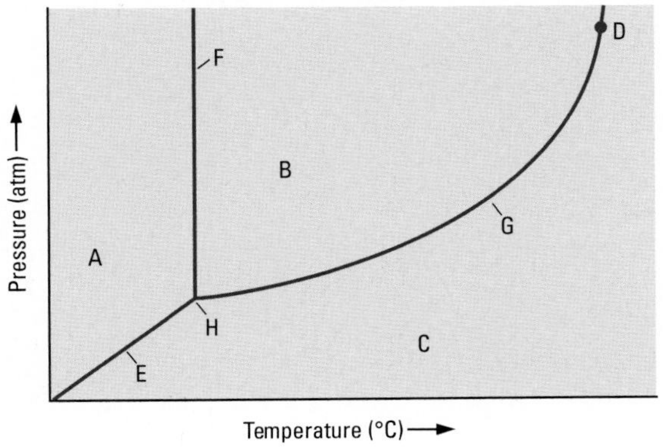

102. Consider the phase diagram below. Draw corresponding heating curves for T_1 to T_2 at pressures P_1 and P_2. Label each phase and phase change on your heating curves.

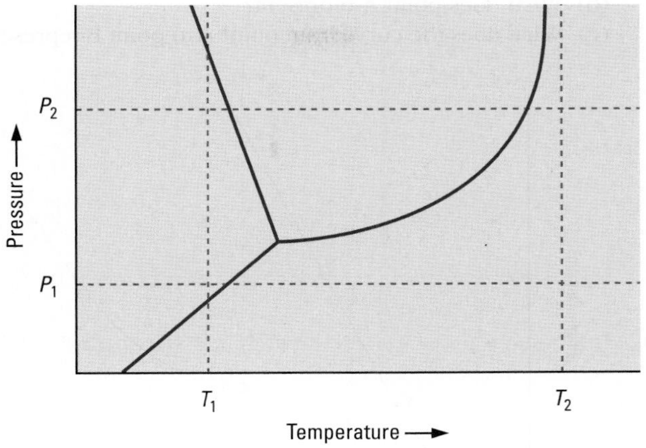

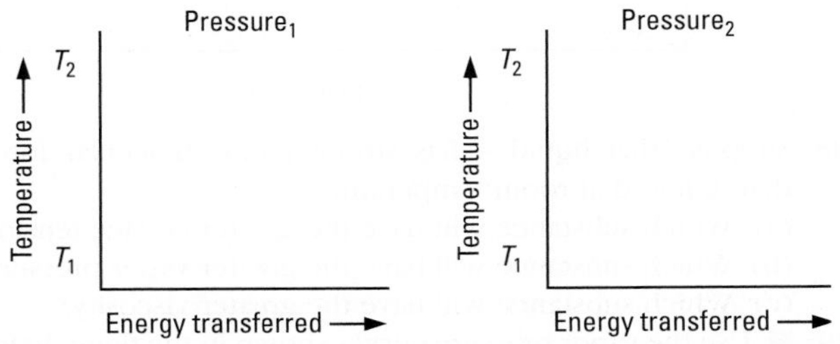

103. Consider three boxes of equal volume. One is filled with tennis balls, another with golf balls, and the third with marbles. If a closest-packing arrangement is used in each box, which one has the most occupied space? Which one has the least occupied space? (Disregard the difference in filling space at the walls, bottom, and top of the box.)

More Challenging Questions

104. If you get boiling water at 100 °C on your skin, it burns. If you get 100 °C steam on your skin, it burns much more severely. Explain why this is so.

105. If water at room temperature is placed in a flask that is connected to a vacuum pump and the vacuum pump then lowers the pressure in the flask, we observe that the volume of the water has decreased and the remaining water has turned into ice. Explain what has happened.

106. We hear reports from weather forecasters of "relative humidity," the ratio of the partial pressure of water in the air to the equilibrium vapor pressure of water at the same temperature. (The vapor pressure of water at 32.2 °C is 36 mm Hg.)

(a) On a sticky, humid day, the relative humidity may reach 90% with a temperature of 90. °F (32.2 °C). What is the partial pressure of water under these conditions? How many moles per liter are present in the air? How many water molecules per cm^3 are present in such air?

(b) On a day in a desert, the relative humidity may be 5.% with the same temperature of 90. °F. How many water molecules per cm^3 are present in such air?

107. (a) In the diagram below, for a substance going from point F (initial state) to point G (final state), what changes in phase occur?
(b) What does point A represent?
(c) What does the curve from point A to point B represent?

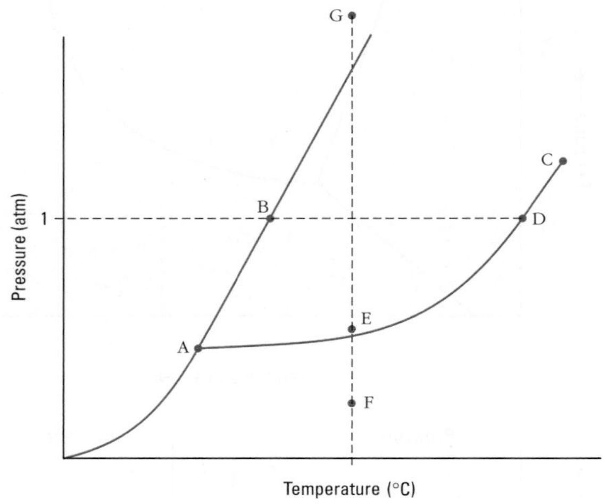

108. Suppose that liquid A has stronger intermolecular forces than liquid B at room temperature.
(a) Which substance will have the greater surface tension?
(b) Which substance will have the greater vapor pressure?
(c) Which substance will have the greater viscosity?

109. ■ Use the vapor pressure curves shown in the figure below for methyl ethyl ether ($CH_3OCH_2CH_3$), carbon disulfide (CS_2), and benzene (C_6H_6) to answer the following questions.
(a) What is the vapor pressure of methyl ethyl ether at 0 °C?
(b) Which of these three liquids has the strongest intermolecular attractions?
(c) At what temperature does benzene have a vapor pressure of 600 mm Hg?
(d) What are the normal boiling points of these three liquids?

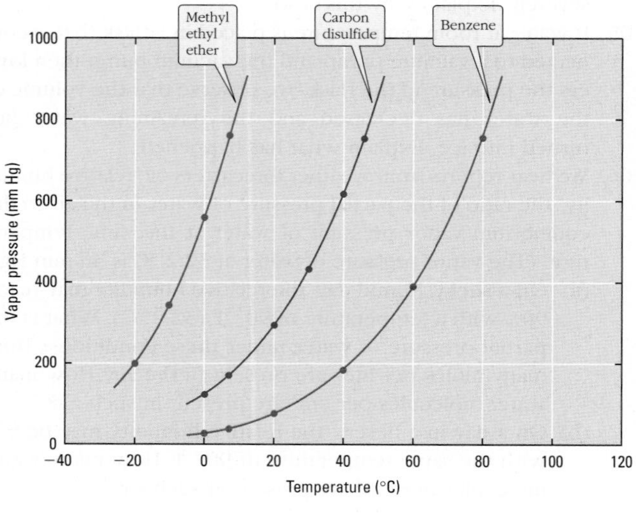

110. Will a closed container of water at 70 °C or an open container of water at the same temperature cool faster? Explain why.

111. Calculate the boiling point of water at 24 mm Hg. (The ΔH_{vap} of water is 40.7 kJ/mol.)

112. What is the concentration in mol/L of water vapor in air at 25 °C at saturation?

113. Solid lithium has a body-centered cubic unit cell with the length of the edge of 351 pm at 20 °C. What is the density of lithium at this temperature?

114. Tungsten has a body-centered cubic unit cell and an atomic radius of 139 pm. What is the density of solid tungsten?

115. Copper is an important metal in the U.S. economy. Most of it is mined in the form of the mineral chalcopyrite, $CuFeS_2$.
(a) To obtain one metric ton (1000. kilograms) of copper metal, how many metric tons of chalcopyrite would you have to mine?
(b) If the sulfur in chalcopyrite is converted to SO_2, how many metric tons of the gas would you get from one metric ton of chalcopyrite?
(c) Copper crystallizes as a face-centered cubic lattice. Knowing that the density of copper is 8.95 g/cm^3, calculate the radius of the copper atom.

Conceptual Challenge Problems

CP11.A (Section 11.2) In Section 11.2 you read that the enthalpy of vaporization of water "is somewhat dependent on the temperature." At 100 °C this value is 40.7 kJ/mol, but at 25 °C it is 44.0 kJ/mol, a difference of 3.3 kJ/mol. List four enthalpy changes whose sum would equal this difference. Remember, the sum of the changes for a cyclic process must be zero because the system is returned to its initial state.

CP11.B (Section 11.3) For what reasons would you propose that two of the substances listed in Table 11.2 be considered better refrigerants for use in household refrigerators than the others listed there?

CP11.C (Section 11.3) A table of enthalpies of sublimation is not given in Section 11.3, but the enthalpy of sublimation of ice at 0 °C is given as 51 kJ/mol. How was this value obtained? Tables 11.2 and 11.3 list the enthalpies of vaporization and fusion, respectively, for several substances. Determine from data in these tables the ΔH_{sub} for ice. Using the same method, estimate the enthalpies of sublimation of HBr and HI at their melting points.

12 Fuels, Organic Chemicals, and Polymers

The snowboard in this picture is made from several synthetic polymers, as are the clothing and protective gear worn by its rider. Polymers such as Kevlar and laminated polyethylene used in the snowboard make it lighter and more durable than wood.

© Dylan Martinez/Reuters/Corbis

ThomsonNOW™
Throughout the text, this icon indicates an opportunity to test yourself on key concepts and to explore interactive modules by signing in to ThomsonNOW at **www.thomsonedu.com**.

The law of supply and demand dictates cost.

The great Russian chemist Dimitri Mendeleev recognized the importance of petroleum as a source from which to make valuable carbon compounds and not merely to be used as a fuel. On visiting the oil fields of Pennsylvania and Azerbaijan, he supposedly remarked that burning petroleum as a fuel "would be akin to firing up a kitchen stove with bank notes."

The combustion of fossil fuels—coal, natural gas, and petroleum—provides nearly 85% of all the energy used in the world. When these substances burn, the carbon they contain is released into the atmosphere as CO_2. Photosynthesis converts CO_2 back into other carbon-containing compounds. Many of the carbon compounds produced by photosynthesis are directly or indirectly very useful as energy sources for humans and animals. But such carbon compounds are not as convenient to use in power plants or automobiles as are fossil fuels, which are burned in prodigious quantities daily. As fossil fuel becomes more scarce, and if stringent conservation measures are not taken, conventional petroleum reserves could last for no more than into the last half of the 21st century. If this occurs, fuel costs will inevitably rise due to the increasing scarcity of petroleum.

Fossil fuels are also, by far, the largest source of hydrocarbons and their derivatives. Only about 3% of the petroleum refined today is the source of most of the organic chemicals used to make consumer products such as plastics, pharmaceuticals, synthetic rubber, synthetic fibers, and hundreds of other products we rely on. For this reason, the organic chemical industry is often referred to as the petrochemical industry. In this chapter we will discuss a few of the major classes of organic compounds and some of their reactions, especially those used to furnish energy and to make polymers, synthetic as well as natural ones.

12.1 Petroleum

Petroleum is a complex mixture. There are at least 20,000 different compounds in petroleum, about the same number as genes in the human body.

Petroleum is a complex mixture of alkanes, cycloalkanes, alkenes, and aromatic hydrocarbons formed from the remains of plants and animals from millions of years ago. Thousands of compounds, almost all of them hydrocarbons, are present in *crude oil,* the form of petroleum that is pumped from the ground. Crude oil's composition and color vary with the location in which it is found. Pennsylvania crude oils are primarily straight-chain hydrocarbons, whereas California crude oil contains a larger portion of aromatic hydrocarbons.

The different classes of hydrocarbons (compounds of hydrogen and carbon) were introduced earlier ***(⇐ p. 339).*** Alkanes have C—C bonds; alkenes have one or more C═C bonds; aromatics include benzene-like rings.

The early uses for petroleum components were mainly for lubrication and as kerosene burned in lamps. The development of automobiles with internal combustion engines created the need for liquid fuels that would burn efficiently in these engines. To meet our need for gasoline and other petroleum products, it is necessary to refine crude oil—that is, to separate the various useful components from the complex mixture and to modify their properties.

Petroleum Refining

Distillation can separate substances that have different boiling points from liquid mixtures and solutions. For example, simple distillation can separate a mixture of the liquids cyclohexane (b.p. 80.7 °C) and toluene (b.p. 110.6 °C). The mixture is heated to slightly above 80.7 °C, at which point cyclohexane vaporizes from the mixture. The cyclohexane vapor is condensed as a pure liquid and collected in a separate container (Figure 12.1).

The difference between simple distillation and fractional distillation is the degree of separation achieved.

Petroleum fractions are each mixtures of hundreds of hydrocarbons with boiling points within a certain range.

Petroleum is a much more complex mixture. Petroleum contains thousands of different hydrocarbons and their separation as individual pure compounds is neither economically feasible nor necessary. Instead, petroleum refining uses *fractional distillation* to separate petroleum into **petroleum fractions.** Each petroleum fraction is a mixture of hundreds of hydrocarbons that have boiling points within certain ranges. Such separation is possible because the boiling point increases as the number of carbon atoms increases: Larger hydrocarbon molecules (larger number of electrons and greater polarizability) have greater noncovalent intermolecular forces and higher boiling points than smaller ones ***(⇐ p. 409).***

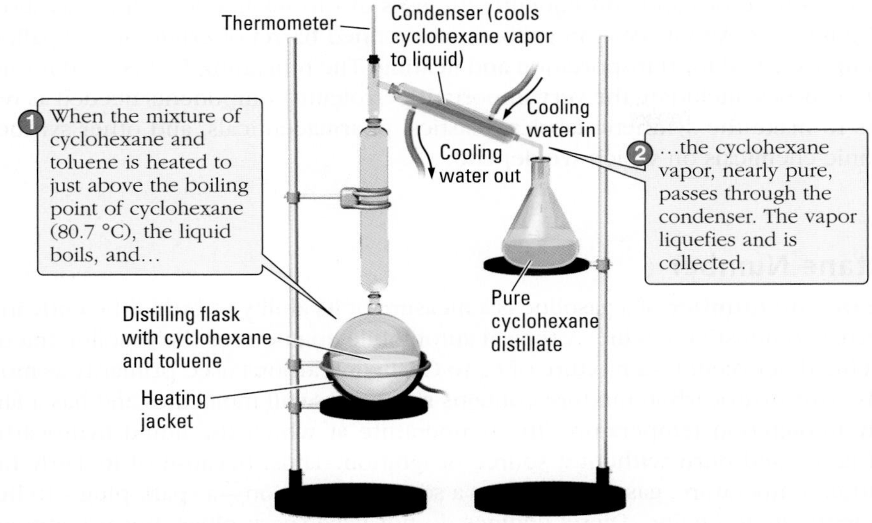

Figure 12.1 **Distillation apparatus.**

A petroleum fractional distillation tower.

In fractional distillation, the crude oil is first heated to about 400 °C to produce a hot vapor mixture that enters the bottom of the fractionating tower (Figure 12.2). The temperature decreases as the vapor rises up the tower. Consequently, different gaseous components condense at various points in the tower. The more volatile, lower-boiling petroleum fractions remain in the vapor state longer than the less volatile, higher-boiling fractions. The smallest hydrocarbon molecules do not condense and are drawn off the top of the tower as gases. The largest hydrocarbon molecules do not vaporize even at 400 °C and are collected at the bottom of the tower as liquids and dissolved solids.

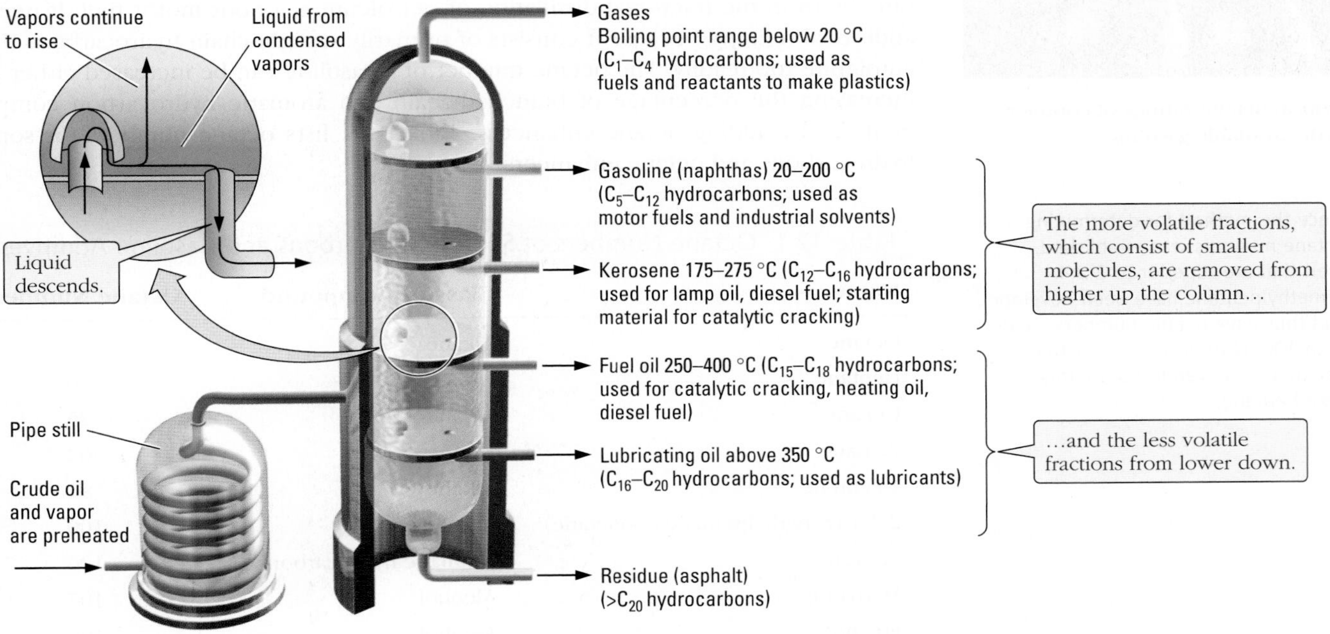

Figure 12.2 **Petroleum fractional distillation.** Crude oil is first heated to 400 °C in the pipe still. The vapors then enter the fractionation tower. As they rise, the vapors cool and condense so that different fractions can be removed at different heights in the tower.

Many years ago, petroleum was shipped in barrels. Today it seldom is seen in barrels, but rather is shipped in pipelines and ocean-going tankers. Nevertheless, the barrel remains as the common unit of volume measure for petroleum. A petroleum barrel contains 42 U.S. gallons.

The properties and consequently the uses of various fractions differ, as shown in Figure 12.2. About 83% (35 gallons) of a refined barrel of crude oil (42 gallons) is simply burned for transportation and heating. The remaining 17% is used for nonfuel purposes, including the very important petroleum components needed as reactants to make the synthetic fabrics, plastics, pharmaceuticals, and other synthetic organic chemicals on which we depend.

Octane Number

The **octane number** of a gasoline is a measure of its ability to burn efficiently in an internal combustion engine. A typical automobile engine uses the gasoline fraction of refined petroleum—a mixture of C_5 to C_{12} hydrocarbons used primarily as motor fuels. This hydrocarbon mixture contains relatively small molecules and has a fairly high autoignition temperature, the temperature at which the liquid hydrocarbon will ignite and burn without a source of ignition. Thus, because of its fairly high ignition temperature, gasoline requires a source of ignition—a spark plug—to burn efficiently in an engine. Diesel engines do not have spark plugs, but use autoignition to ignite the fuel, so diesel fuel consists of larger hydrocarbon molecules.

The octane-number rating of a gasoline is determined by comparing the burning characteristics when the gasoline burns in a one-cylinder test engine with those obtained for mixtures of heptane and 2,2,4-trimethylpentane (often called isooctane). Heptane does not burn smoothly and is arbitrarily assigned an octane number of 0, whereas 2,2,4-trimethylpentane burns smoothly and is assigned an octane number of 100 (Table 12.1). A gasoline assigned an octane number of 87 has the same premature autoignition characteristics as a mixture of 13% heptane and 87% 2,2,4-trimethylpentane. This octane rating corresponds to the octane number of regular unleaded gasoline currently available in the United States. Other, higher grades of gasoline available at gas stations have octane numbers of 89 (regular plus) and 92 (premium).

© Thomson Learning/ Charles D. Winters

Typical octane ratings of commercially available gasoline.

Straight-chain alkanes are less thermally stable and burn less smoothly than branched-chain alkanes. For example, the "straight-run" gasoline fraction obtained directly from the fractional distillation of petroleum is a poor motor fuel. It needs additional refining because it consists of primarily straight-chain hydrocarbons that autoignite too readily. The octane number of a gasoline can be increased either by increasing the percentage of branched-chain and aromatic hydrocarbon components or by adding octane enhancers. Table 12.1 lists octane numbers for some hydrocarbons and octane enhancers.

Since the method for determining octane numbers was established, fuels that are superior to 2,2,4-trimethylpentane have been developed and thus have octane numbers greater than 100. Note in Table 12.1 that octane burns even less smoothly than heptane.

Table 12.1 Octane Numbers of Some Hydrocarbons and Gasoline Additives

Name	Class of Compound	Octane Number
Octane	Alkane	−20
Heptane	Alkane	0
Hexane	Alkane	25
Pentane	Alkane	62
1-Pentene	Alkene	91
2,2,4-Trimethylpentane (isooctane)	Alkane	100
Benzene	Aromatic hydrocarbon	106
Methanol	Alcohol	107
Ethanol	Alcohol	108
Tertiary-butyl alcohol	Alcohol	113
Toluene	Aromatic hydrocarbon	118

In addition to fractional distillation, petroleum refining also includes converting the components of various fractions into more economically important products through catalytic cracking and catalytic reforming. Among these products are compounds that can be added to gasoline to increase its octane rating.

Catalytic Cracking

During petroleum refining, the percentage of each fraction collected is adjusted to match the market demand. For example, there is greater demand for gasoline than for kerosene and diesel fuel. Demands also vary seasonally. In winter, the need for home heating oil is high; in summer, when more people take vacations, demand for gasoline is higher. In summer, refiners use chemical reactions in a process called "cracking" to convert some of the larger, kerosene-fraction molecules (C_{12} to C_{16}) into smaller molecules in the gasoline range (C_5 to C_{12}). **Catalytic cracking** uses a catalyst, high temperatures, and pressure to break long-chain hydrocarbons into shorter-chain hydrocarbons that include alkanes and alkenes, many in the gasoline range. A **catalyst** is a substance that increases the rate of a chemical reaction without being consumed as a reactant would be. (The role of catalysts in chemical reactions is further discussed in Section 13.8.)

$$\underset{\text{An alkane}}{C_{16}H_{34}} \xrightarrow{\text{catalyst, pressure, and heat}} \underset{\text{An alkene}}{C_8H_{16}} + \underset{\text{An alkane}}{C_8H_{18}}$$

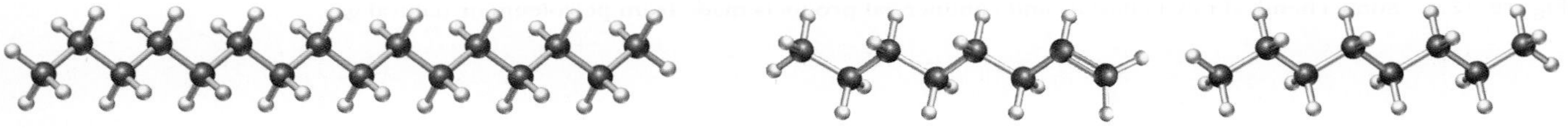

Since alkenes have higher octane numbers than alkanes, catalytic cracking also increases the octane number of the mixture. Catalytic cracking is beneficial in another way. Unlike alkanes, alkenes have C=C bonds, which makes them much more reactive than alkanes. Thus, as seen in Figure 12.3, alkenes such as ethylene and propylene can be used as starting materials to make other organic compounds, many of which are the raw materials for making plastics (Section 12.8).

Catalytic Reforming

After its separation from crude oil by fractional distillation, the gasoline fraction (straight-run gasoline) has an octane number of only 50, unsatisfactory for a motor vehicle fuel. The octane rating of gasoline can be increased by using **catalytic reforming** to convert straight-chain hydrocarbons to branched-chain hydrocarbons and aromatics. In catalytic reforming, certain catalysts, such as finely divided platinum on a support of Al_2O_3, reform straight-chain hydrocarbons with low octane numbers into their branched-chain isomers, which have higher octane numbers.

$$CH_3CH_2CH_2CH_2CH_3 \xrightarrow{\text{catalyst}} CH_3\overset{\overset{\displaystyle CH_3}{|}}{C}HCH_2CH_3$$

pentane
62 octane
(C_5H_{12})

2-methylbutane
94 octane
(C_5H_{12})

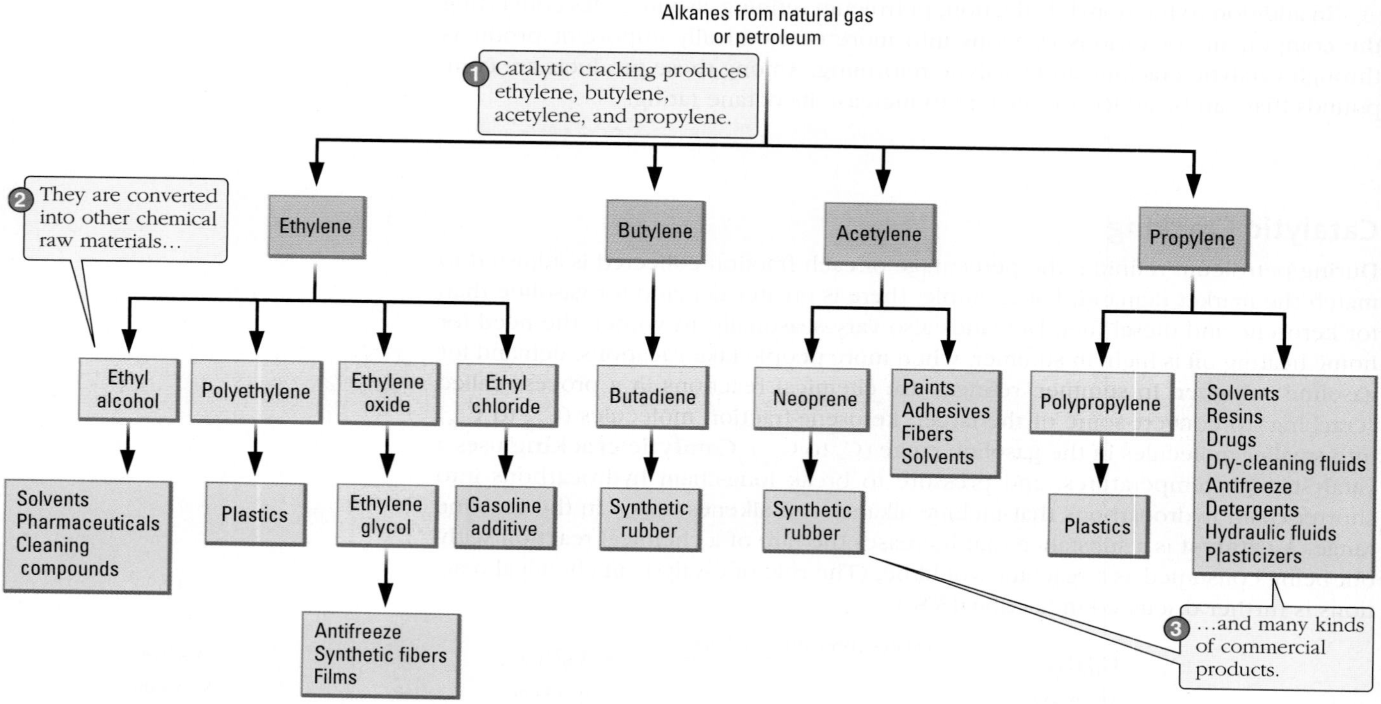

Figure 12.3 **Some chemical raw materials and commercial products made from petroleum or natural gas.**

The additional cost of higher-octane gasoline is due to the extra processing required to make higher-octane compounds.

By using different catalysts and petroleum mixtures, catalytic reforming also produces aromatic hydrocarbons, which have high octane numbers. For example, catalytic reforming converts a high percentage of straight-run gasoline, kerosene, and light oil fractions into a mixture of aromatic hydrocarbons including benzene, toluene, and xylenes. This process can be represented by the equation for converting hexane into benzene.

$$CH_3CH_2CH_2CH_2CH_2CH_3 \xrightarrow{\text{catalyst}} C_6H_6 + 4\,H_2$$

hexane, 25 octane (C_6H_{14}) — benzene, 106 octane (C_6H_6)

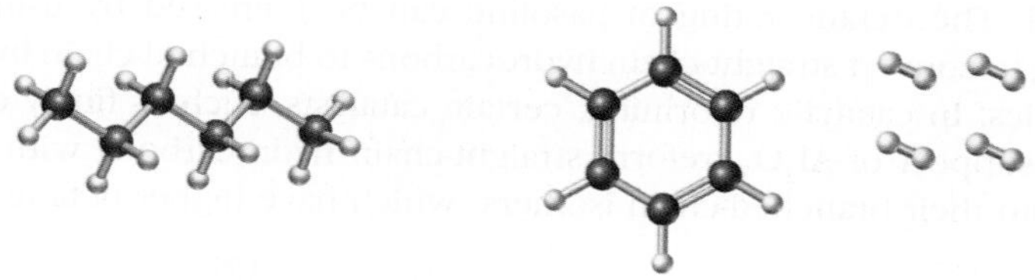

It is no exaggeration to state that our economy relies on the hydrocarbons present in petroleum or derived from it. In addition to being the source of our fuels for transportation, petroleum provides raw materials to make an impressive array of consumer products, as shown in Figure 12.3.

CONCEPTUAL EXERCISE 12.1 Rearranging Hydrocarbons

Heptane (C_7H_{16}) can be catalytically reformed to make toluene ($C_6H_5CH_3$), another seven-carbon molecule.

(a) How many hydrogen molecules are produced for every toluene molecule derived from heptane?

(b) Write a balanced chemical equation for this reaction.

(c) Why would it be profitable to convert heptane into toluene?

© Document General Motors/Reuter R/Corbis Sygma

A catalytic converter. Semiprecious metals, like platinum and rhodium, coat the surface of ceramic beads in the catalytic converter. The metals catalyze the complete combustion of CO to carbon dioxide in the exhaust. Other metal catalysts in the converter speed up the rate at which nitrogen oxides in the exhaust are decomposed to nitrogen and oxygen.

Octane Enhancers

The octane number of a given blend of gasoline is increased by adding octane enhancers to prevent premature autoignition. In the United States, prior to 1975, the most widely used anti-knock agent was tetraethyllead, $(C_2H_5)_4Pb$.

The exhaust emissions of internal combustion engines contain carbon monoxide, nitrogen oxides, and unburned hydrocarbons, all of which contribute to air pollution. As urban air pollution worsened, Congress passed the Clean Air Act of 1970, which required that 1975-model-year cars emit no more than 10% of the carbon monoxide and hydrocarbons emitted by 1970 models. The solution to lowering these emissions was a platinum-based catalytic converter, which accelerates the conversion of carbon monoxide to carbon dioxide and the more complete burning of hydrocarbons. The only problem was that the catalyic converter required lead-free gasolines, since lead deactivates the platinum catalyst by coating its surface. As a result, automobiles manufactured since 1975 have been required to use lead-free gasoline to protect the catalytic converter. Because tetraethyllead can no longer be used in the United States and a few other countries, other octane enhancers are now added to gasoline. These include toluene, 2-methyl-2-propanol (also called *tertiary*-butyl alcohol), methanol, and ethanol.

Premature autoignition is also known as "knocking."

As little as two tanks of leaded gasoline can destroy the activity of a catalytic converter.

Regrettably, most countries of the world still allow the use of leaded gasoline, putting millions of children at risk for lead poisoning from automobile exhaust fumes.

Oxygenated and Reformulated Gasolines

The 1990 amendments to the Clean Air Act of 1970 require cities with excessive carbon monoxide pollution to use oxygenated gasoline during the winter. *Oxygenated gasoline* is a blend of gasoline to which organic compounds that contain oxygen, such as methanol, ethanol, and *tertiary*-butyl alcohol, have been added. Tests conducted by the Environmental Protection Agency (EPA) indicate that in cold weather oxygenated gasoline burns more completely than nonoxygenated gasoline, thus potentially reducing carbon monoxide emissions in urban areas by up to 17%.

Reformulated gasoline (RFG) is oxygenated gasoline that contains a lower percentage of aromatic hydrocarbons and has a lower volatility than ordinary (nonoxygenated) gasoline. Reformulated gasoline is now used in 17 states and the District of Columbia. The 1990 regulations require RFG to contain a minimum of 2.7% oxygen by mass. Ethanol is the only gasoline oxygenate additive now used in RFG by U.S. refineries.

Oxygenated gasoline is produced by adding oxygen-containing organic compounds to refined gasoline. Reformulated gasoline, which contains such oxygenates, also requires changes in the refining process to alter its percentages of various hydrocarbons, particularly alkenes and aromatics.

All gasolines are highly volatile and have vapors that can be ignited, allowing you to start your car even in the coldest of weather. However, this volatility means that some hydrocarbons get into the atmosphere as a result of accidental spills and evaporation during normal filling operations at the gas station, especially so during warm weather. Recent federal regulations require that the vapor pressure of RFG meet a limit of 9.0 psi from June 1 to September 15, the summer ozone season. More stringent requirements (7.8 psi) may apply in areas not meeting federal guidelines for air quality. Because atmospheric hydrocarbons play an important role in a series of reactions that contribute to urban air pollution (⇐ *p. 470*) including tropospheric ozone formation (especially in heavy-traffic metropolitan areas), reduction of hydrocarbon emissions improves air quality. The EPA estimates that RPG use has reduced smog-forming emissions by 105 million tons, the equivalent of such emissions from 16 million vehicles.

EXERCISE 12.2 Percent Oxygen in Ethanol

Calculate the percent oxygen by mass in ethanol, CH_3CH_2OH. Is it less than 3%? How can ethanol help to meet the 2.7% oxygen requirement for RFG?

Engineering improvements such as emission control systems have succeeded in decreasing the emissions of ozone-forming nitrogen oxides and hydrocarbons from automobiles per mile traveled. Today's cars typically emit 70% less nitrogen oxides and 80–90% less hydrocarbons over their lifetimes compared with automobiles produced 30 to 40 years ago. Nevertheless, tropospheric ozone levels remain high for two reasons: (1) Since 1970 the number of vehicles in the United States has doubled, as has the number of miles they travel (Figure 12.4), and (2) The EPA attributes a major portion (approximately 25%) of ozone-forming hydrocarbons to a relatively small percentage of "super-dirty" vehicles with faulty emission control systems.

PROBLEM-SOLVING EXAMPLE 12.1 The Enthalpy of Combustion of Ethanol Compared to That of Octane

Calculate the enthalpy of combustion of ethanol in kilojoules per mole (kJ/mol) and compare the value with that of octane. Then, using the densities of the liquids, calculate the thermal energy liberated on burning a liter of each liquid fuel. The densities of octane and ethanol are 0.703 g/mL and 0.789 g/mL, respectively. The enthalpy of formation of octane(g) is −208.0 kJ/mol.

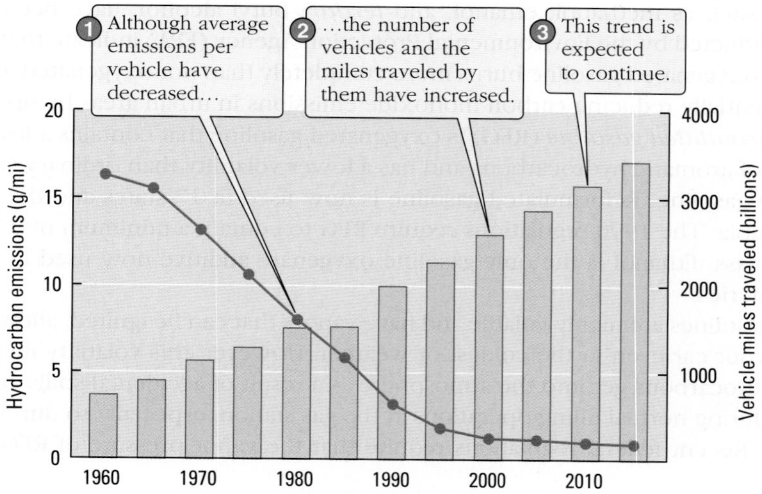

Figure 12.4 **Average per-vehicle emissions (grams of hydrocarbons/mile) and mileage increases since 1960.**

Answer

Ethanol: $\Delta H_{comb} = -1277.37$ kJ/mol $= -2.19 \times 10^4$ kJ/L

Octane: $\Delta H_{comb} = -5116.4$ kJ/mol $= -3.15 \times 10^4$ kJ/L

Strategy and Explanation All internal combustion engines burn fuel vapors. The balanced equation for the combustion of ethanol vapor is

$$C_2H_5OH(g) + 3\,O_2(g) \longrightarrow 2\,CO_2(g) + 3\,H_2O(g)$$

Using the standard molar enthalpies of formation from Appendix J and Hess's law (← ***p. 246***) for both the products and the reactants, we find that the enthalpy of combustion, ΔH_{comb}, for ethanol is

$$\Delta H_{comb} = 2[\Delta H_f^\circ\ CO_2(g)] + 3[\Delta H_f^\circ H_2O(g)] - 1[\Delta H_f^\circ\ C_2H_5OH(g)]$$
$$= 2(-393.509\ \text{kJ/mol}) + 3(-241.818\ \text{kJ/mol}) - (-235.10\ \text{kJ/mol})$$
$$= -1277.37\ \text{kJ/mol}$$

The balanced combustion reaction for octane vapor is

$$C_8H_{18}(g) + \tfrac{25}{2}\,O_2(g) \longrightarrow 8\,CO_2(g) + 9\,H_2O(g)$$

Using Hess's law, the heat of combustion of octane is

$$\Delta H_{comb} = 8[\Delta H_f^\circ\ CO_2(g)] + 9[\Delta H_f^\circ\ H_2O(g)] - 1[\Delta H_f^\circ\ C_8H_{18}(g)]$$
$$= 8(-393.509\ \text{kJ/mol}) + 9(-241.818\ \text{kJ/mol}) - (-208.0\ \text{kJ/mol})$$
$$= -5116.4\ \text{kJ/mol}$$

The molar masses of ethanol and octane are 46.069 g/mol and 114.23 g/mol, respectively. The thermal energy liberated per liter for each is calculated as follows:

$$\text{Ethanol:}\quad -1277.37\ \text{kJ/mol} \times \frac{1\ \text{mol}}{46.069\ \text{g}} \times \frac{0.789\ \text{g}}{\text{mL}} \times \frac{1000\ \text{mL}}{\text{L}} = -2.19 \times 10^4\ \text{kJ/L}$$

$$\text{Octane:}\quad -5116.4\ \text{kJ/mol} \times \frac{1\ \text{mol}}{114.23\ \text{g}} \times \frac{0.703\ \text{g}}{\text{mL}} \times \frac{1000\ \text{mL}}{\text{L}} = -3.15 \times 10^4\ \text{kJ/L}$$

✓ **Reasonable Answer Check** There are about 17 mol ethanol in a liter of ethanol [(789 g ethanol/L ethanol)(1 mol ethanol/46 g ethanol) = 17 mol] and about 6 mol octane in a liter of octane [(703 g octane/L octane)(1 mol octane/114 g octane) = 6 mol]. But nearly four times as much energy is liberated by burning a mole of octane. Applying this factor on a liter-to-liter basis:

$$\frac{5000\ \text{kJ/mol octane}}{1200\ \text{kJ/mol ethanol}} \times \frac{6\ \text{mol octane/L}}{17\ \text{mol ethanol/L}} = \frac{1.5\ \text{kJ/L octane}}{1.0\ \text{kJ/L ethanol}} = 1.5$$

The 1.5 indicates that about 50% more energy is released by combustion of 1 L octane than from 1 L ethanol. This is close to the 44% difference in the energy per liter calculated for the two fuels, $(3.15 \times 10^4/2.19 \times 10^4) \times 100\% = 1.44\%$.

PROBLEM-SOLVING PRACTICE 12.1

Calculate the enthalpy of combustion of methanol and the energy released per liter using data from Appendix J. The density of methanol is 0.791 g/mL.

EXERCISE 12.3 Carbon Monoxide from Ethanol and from Toluene

(a) The combustion of C_2H_5OH can produce carbon monoxide and water. Use the balanced chemical equation for this reaction as the basis to calculate the mass in grams of CO produced per gram of ethanol burned.

(b) Repeat balancing the equation and the calculation this time using toluene, $C_6H_5CH_3$, instead of ethanol.

(c) What conclusions can you draw from your answers about using ethanol to reduce carbon monoxide emissions?

© AP Images

© David R. Frazier Photolibrary, Inc./Alamy

Using ethanol as an automotive fuel. The ethanol is mixed with gasoline.

© Peter McGahey

A natural gas–powered bus. Natural gas powers this bus, which can refuel at a natural gas pump.

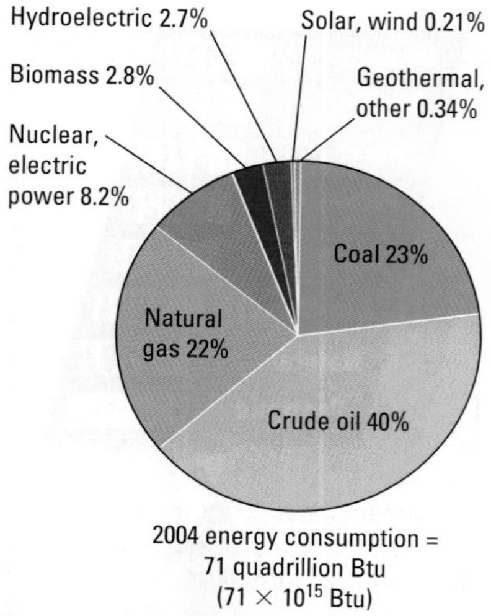

Figure 12.5 Fossil fuels predominate as sources of U.S. energy. *Source:* **EIA.DOE.GOV** Energy Information Administration

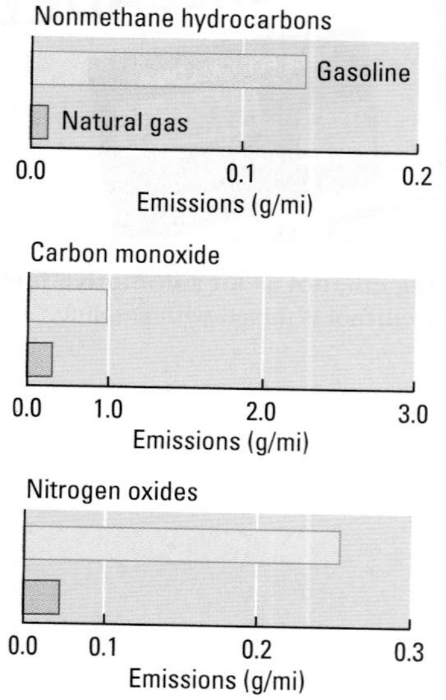

Figure 12.6 Comparisons of tailpipe emissions (grams per mile) from natural gas—and from gasoline-powered vehicles.

The mass percent of carbon in coal varies from about 40% to more than 80%, depending on the type of coal.

The usefulness of coal tar to make other materials is summed up in this bit of doggerel from a 1905 organic chemistry textbook:

You can make anything
From a salve to a star
If you only know how
From black coal tar*

*Cornish, *Organic Chemistry,* 1905.

12.2 Natural Gas and Coal

Natural Gas

Natural gas is a mixture of low-molar-mass hydrocarbons and other gases trapped with petroleum in the earth's crust. It can be recovered from oil wells or from gas wells to which the gases have migrated through the surrounding rock. The natural gas found in North America is a mixture of C_1 to C_4 alkanes [methane, CH_4 (60–90%); ethane, C_2H_6 (5–9%); propane, C_3H_8 (3–18%); and butane, C_4H_{10} (1–2%)] with small and varying amounts of other gases, such as CO_2, N_2, H_2S, and the noble gases, mainly helium. In Europe and Japan, natural gas is essentially only methane. The widespread use of natural gas as a fuel did not occur until a vast underground network of pipelines was built to distribute it from natural gas wells to consumers. Before then, most of it was simply burned at the wellheads. Oil, natural gas, and coal predominate as U.S. energy sources (Figure 12.5).

For more than three decades, the U.S. production of natural gas has exceeded that of U.S.-produced oil. Of all the natural gas produced, nearly half is used in industrial applications, 22% for home heating and cooling, 14% in commercial applications, and about 11% as a fuel to generate electricity. About half of the homes in the United States are heated by natural gas.

Natural gas is now also used as a vehicle fuel. Worldwide, nearly one million vehicles are powered by natural gas, including 30,000 in the United States. The U.S. Postal Service is the largest user of natural gas vehicles, with a fleet of more than 3000 such vehicles. California and several other states are encouraging the use of natural gas vehicles to help meet new air quality regulations. It has been shown that vehicles powered by natural gas emit significantly less carbon monoxide, hydrocarbons, and nitrogen oxides per mile compared to gasoline-powered cars and trucks (Figure 12.6). The main disadvantages of natural gas vehicles include the need for a pressurized gas tank and the lack of service stations that sell the gas in liquefied form.

CONCEPTUAL EXERCISE 12.4 Natural Gas as a CO Source

It has been asserted that burning natural gas produces 30% less carbon monoxide than the burning of gasoline. Assume that natural gas is only methane and that gasoline is only octane, C_8H_{18}. Based on the assumption that the same fraction of the carbon in each fuel is converted to CO, do calculations that either confirm or refute the assertion.

Coal

Known world coal reserves are far greater than petroleum reserves. About 90% of our annual coal production is burned to produce electricity. The use of coal as the fuel for commercial power plants is on the rise. But the burning of coal for home heating has declined because it is a relatively dirty fuel and bulky to handle. Burning coal is a major cause of air pollution because of coal's 3–4% sulfur content.

Coal consists of a complex and irregular array of partially hydrogenated six-membered carbon rings and other structures, some of which contain oxygen, nitrogen, and sulfur atoms. Like petroleum, coal supplies raw materials to the chemical industry. Most of the useful compounds obtained from coal are aromatic hydrocarbons. Heating coal at high temperatures in the absence of air, a process called *pyrolysis,* produces a mixture of coke (mostly carbon), coal tar, and coal gas. Fractional distillation of coal tar produces aromatic hydrocarbons such as benzene, toluene, and xylene. They serve as the starting materials for a large variety of important commercial products such as paints, solvents, pharmaceuticals, plastics, dyes, and synthetic detergents.

TOOLS OF CHEMISTRY

Gas Chromatography

Gas chromatography (GC) is an important method to separate, identify, and quantify chemical compounds in complex mixtures. Widely used in chemistry, biochemistry, environmental analysis, and forensic science, GC is applicable to compounds that have appreciable volatility and are thermally stable at temperatures up to several hundred degrees Celsius. We focus here on capillary column gas chromatography.

An analysis begins by injecting the sample into an inlet at the head of the GC column, where the sample is vaporized. A flow of inert carrier gas, generally helium, sweeps the vaporized sample along the column where the components are separated. The carrier gas stream containing the separated components passes through a detector, which allows identification of individual compounds in the gas stream. The resulting signal produces a *chromatogram*—a plot of concentration of each component versus time.

For capillary GC, the carrier gas usually flows at a rate in the range of 0.5 to 15 mL/min. A measured volume of sample (0.1 to 10 μL) is injected using a microsyringe. Capillary GC columns are made from specially purified silica tubes, typically 10 to 100 m long, that are drawn to have an inside diameter of 0.1 to 0.5 mm. The column is flexible, coiled, and put inside an oven for temperature control. The inside of the column tube is coated with an immobilized liquid, the *stationary phase.* Many factors determine the coating used to separate a particular mixture, but ultimately the choice is dictated by the molecular structure of the stationary liquid phase material in relation to that of the components being separated.

The detector must respond to very low concentrations of separated compounds in the flowing carrier gas. Two widely used detectors are (a) flame-ionization detectors, which atomize and ionize the sample and measure the flow of current that results, and (b) thermal conductivity detectors, which measure the thermal conductivity of the gas stream. Mass spectrometers *(⇐ p. 56)* are also used as detectors. The resulting chromatogram, a series of peaks, is a plot of the concentration of each component as a function of time. The position of each peak on the time (x) axis qualitatively identifies the components in the sample; the area under each peak provides a quantitative measure of the amount of each compound.

Compounds in a mixture are separated by GC due to their interactions with the stationary liquid phase on the column. Molecular structure dictates how quickly each component moves along the column to the detector. This depends on the magnitude of intermolecular interactions—polar interactions and London forces ***(⇐ p. 408)***—between components of the mixture and the stationary phase. Components having strong attractions for the stationary phase are retained longer on the column; those with weaker interactions reach the detector sooner. Thus, as the sample moves along the column, the components are progressively separated before they reach the detector.

If polar compounds are to be separated from a mixture, then a polar stationary phase works best, one that contains polar functional groups such as —CN, > C=O, and —OH. A nonpolar stationary phase contains hydrocarbon groups only. When the polarity of the stationary phase is matched well with that of the sample, the components exit from the column in order of their boiling points.

Capillary column GC can readily identify and measure components in gasoline. In the chromatogram below, thirty-one compounds ranging in size and complexity from butane and pentane to larger, ring compounds such as xylenes and toluene are separated from a gasoline sample.

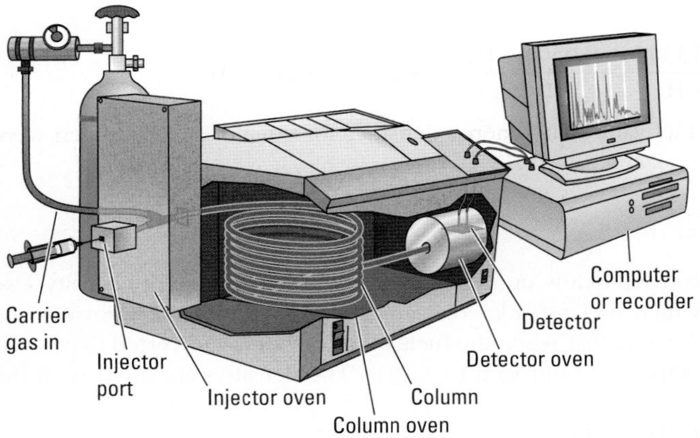

An illustration of a gas chromatograph.

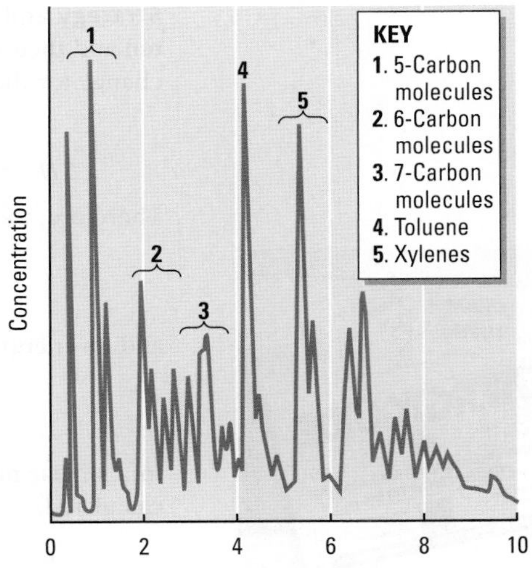

The chromatogram for a gasoline analysis. (Column: Petrocol A; Carrier: helium, 2.5 mL/min; Detector: flame ionization.) Peaks 1 are for components with five-carbon molecules, peaks 2 for six-carbon components, and peaks 3 for seven-carbon components. The last two peaks are for aromatic compounds—peak 4 indicates the presence of toluene, $C_6H_5CH_3$, and peak 5 the various xylenes, $C_6H_4(CH_3)_2$. These more complex aromatic hydrocarbons are held on the column longer than the nonaromatic hydrocarbons.

12.3 Energy Conversions

By now it should be apparent that our energy comes from a variety of sources. When you drive your car, the gasoline that moves it may have come from the United States or a foreign country. Some people are already driving cars powered by natural gas, electricity, or a combination of electricity and gasoline, as in hybrid vehicles. The natural gas may be imported and the electricity may have come from burning coal, natural gas, fuel oil, or even from a nuclear reactor (Section 20.6).

The convenience of use and the quantity of energy derived from different fuels vary depending on their chemical composition and properties. Two important measures of a fuel are its *fuel value* (quantity of energy released per gram of fuel burned) and its *energy density* (quantity of energy released per unit volume of fuel burned) (**⇐ *p. 255***). Problem-Solving Example 12.2 gives you the opportunity to investigate the relationship between these two criteria.

© Thomson Learning/Charles D. Winters

Energy efficiency comparison guide. Cost per kilowatt-hour of a refrigerator-freezer, fully self-defrosting.

PROBLEM-SOLVING EXAMPLE 12.2 Comparing Fuels

Evaluate each of the fuels listed below on the basis of fuel value and energy density. Use data from Table 6.2 or Appendix J. Which fuel provides the largest fuel value? Which provides the greatest energy density? Assume that when the fuels burn, carbon is converted to gaseous CO_2 and hydrogen to water vapor. The densities are given with the substances.

(a) Methane, $CH_4(g)$ (0.656 g/L)
(b) Ethanol, $C_8H_{18}(\ell)$ (0.789 g/mL)
(c) Hydrogen, $H_2(g)$ (0.082 g/L)

Answer

(a) 50.013 kJ/g CH_4, 3.28×10^1 kJ/L CH_4
(b) 26.807 kJ/g C_2H_5OH, 2.19×10^4 kJ/L C_2H_5OH
(c) 119.96 kJ/g H_2, 9.84 kJ/L H_2

Hydrogen has the highest fuel value; ethanol has the highest energy density.

Strategy and Explanation In each case, the balanced chemical equation must be written and then used in conjunction with the thermodynamic data to calculate the enthalpy change for the reaction. For methane:

$$CH_4(g) + 2\,O_2(g) \longrightarrow CO_2(g) + 2\,H_2O(g)$$

$$\Delta H^\circ = [(-393.509\text{ kJ}) + 2(-241.818\text{ kJ}) - (-74.81\text{ kJ})] = -802.34\text{ kJ}$$

Therefore, the fuel value of methane is

$$\frac{802.34\text{ kJ}}{1\text{ mol }CH_4} \times \frac{1\text{ mol }CH_4}{16.0426\text{ g }CH_4} = 50.013\text{ kJ/g }CH_4$$

and its energy density is

$$\frac{50.013\text{ kJ}}{1\text{ g }CH_4} \times \frac{0.656\text{ g }CH_4}{1\text{ L }CH_4} = 3.28 \times 10^1\text{ kJ/L }CH_4$$

In a similar manner the fuel values and energy densities for ethanol and hydrogen were calculated.

PROBLEM-SOLVING PRACTICE 12.2

Evaluate each of the fuels listed below on the basis of fuel value and energy density. Use data from Appendix J. Which fuel provides the largest fuel value? Which provides the greatest energy density? Assume that when the fuels burn, carbon is converted to gaseous CO_2, hydrogen to water vapor, and nitrogen to N_2 gas. The densities are given with the substances.

(a) Octane, $C_8H_{18}(\ell)$ (0.703 g/mL)
(b) Hydrazine, $N_2H_4(\ell)$ (1.004 g/mL)
(c) Glucose, $C_6H_{12}O_6(s)$ (1.56 g/mL)

Table 12.2 A Chart of Energy Units*

Cubic Feet of Natural Gas	Barrels of Oil	Tons of Bituminous Coal	Kilowatt Hours of Electricity	Joules	Btu
1	0.00018	0.00004	0.293	1.055×10^6	1.00×10^3
1000	0.18	0.04	293	1.055×10^9	1.00×10^6
5556	1	0.22	1628	5.9×10^9	5.6×10^6
25,000	4.50	1	7326	26.4×10^9	25.0×10^7
1×10^6	180	40	293,000	1.055×10^{12}	1.00×10^9
3.41×10^6	614	137	1×10^6	3.6×10^{12}	3.4×10^9
1×10^9	180,000	40,000	293×10^6	1.055×10^{15}	1.00×10^{12}
1×10^{12}	180×10^6	40×10^6	293×10^9	1.055×10^{18}	1.00×10^{15}

*Based on normal fuel-heating values. 10^6 = 1 million; 10^9 = 1 billion; 10^{12} = 1 trillion; 10^{15} = quadrillion (quad).

1 Btu (British thermal unit) is the quantity of energy required to raise the temperature of 1 lb water from 63 °F to 64 °F; 1 Btu = 252 cal = 1.05×10^3 J.

All forms of energy are, in principle, interchangeable. The work a given quantity of energy can do is the same, no matter what the energy source. The energy contents of natural gas, fuel oil, and coal in terms of their equivalents in various units are compared in Table 12.2. As a consumer, it doesn't matter to you whether you travel using energy from a fossil fuel in the form of gasoline or whether you use electricity created by burning coal, although the energy is measured in different units. A trip might require 1 gal gasoline for the regular automobile. An electric automobile would require about 39 kilowatt-hours (kWh) of electricity to travel the same distance.

All fuel-burning engines, including automobile engines and electrical power plants, are less than 100% efficient; there is always wasted thermal energy. For example, the generation and distribution of electricity is only about 33% efficient overall. This means that for every 100 J energy produced by burning a fossil fuel such as coal, only 33 J electrical energy reaches the consumer.

One watt (W) of power is 1 J/s, so a 100-W electric lamp uses energy at the rate of 100 J every second. Using data from Table 12.2 we find that one cubic foot of natural gas supplies sufficient energy (1.055×10^6 J) to light a 100-W bulb for about 3 hours; a barrel of oil has enough energy (5.9×10^9 J) to light 1000 100-W light bulbs for almost 16 hours.

PROBLEM-SOLVING EXAMPLE 12.3 Energy Conversions

A large ocean-going tanker holds 1.5 million barrels (bbl) of crude oil.
(a) What is the energy equivalent of this oil in joules?
(b) How many tons of coal is this oil equivalent to?

Answer

(a) 8.9×10^{15} J
(b) 3.3×10^5 ton coal

Strategy and Explanation

(a) Table 12.2 gives the thermal energy equivalent to 1 barrel of oil as 5.9×10^9 J. Use this information as a conversion factor to calculate the first answer.

$$1.5 \times 10^6 \text{ bbl} \times \frac{5.9 \times 10^9 \text{ J}}{1 \text{ bbl}} = 8.9 \times 10^{15} \text{ J}$$

(b) Look in Table 12.2 and find the conversion between barrels of oil and tons of coal. One barrel of oil is equivalent to 0.22 ton coal. Use this conversion factor to calculate the answer.

$$1.5 \times 10^6 \text{ bbl} \times \frac{0.22 \text{ ton coal}}{1 \text{ bbl}} = 3.3 \times 10^5 \text{ ton coal}$$

✓ **Reasonable Answer Check** It takes only 0.22 ton coal (approximately one-fourth ton) to furnish the energy equivalent of a barrel of oil. Therefore, the coal equivalent of 1.5×10^6 barrels of oil should be about one fourth that number of barrels of oil, or about $(0.25)(1.5 \times 10^6) = 4 \times 10^5$, which is close to the calculated value.

PROBLEM-SOLVING PRACTICE 12.3

How much energy, in joules, can be obtained by burning 4.2×10^9 ton coal? This is equivalent to how many cubic feet of natural gas?

EXERCISE 12.5 Energy from Burning Oil

A large ocean-going oil tanker holds 1.5×10^6 barrels of crude oil. How many BTUs of energy are released by burning this oil? How many kilowatt-hours of electricity would be delivered to the consumer by burning this much oil, assuming a 33% overall efficiency?

CONCEPTUAL EXERCISE 12.6 The Energy Value of CO_2

Explain why CO_2 has no fuel energy value.

12.4 Organic Chemicals

Organic chemicals were once obtained only from plants, animals, and fossil fuels. A few living organisms are still direct sources of useful hydrocarbons. Rubber trees produce latex that contains rubber, a familiar hydrocarbon, and other plants produce an oil that burns almost as well in a diesel engine as diesel fuel. As important

ESTIMATION

Burning Coal

A coal-fired electric power plant burns about 1.5 million tons of coal a year. Coal has an approximate composition of $C_{135}H_{96}O_9NS$. When coal burns, it releases about 30 kJ/g. We can approximate how much energy (kJ) is released by this plant in a year and the mass of CO_2 released in that year by burning 1.5 million tons of coal.

The mass of coal is

$$1.5 \times 10^6 \text{ ton} \times \frac{2000 \text{ lb}}{1 \text{ ton}} \times \frac{1 \text{ kg}}{2.2 \text{ lb}} \approx 1 \times 10^9 \text{ kg}$$

This is approximately 1×10^9 kg, or 1×10^{12} g. Burning the coal at 30 kJ/g yields about 3×10^{13} kJ per year.

$$1 \times 10^{12} \text{ g} \times \frac{30 \text{ kJ}}{1 \text{ g}} = 3 \times 10^{13} \text{ kJ}$$

There are 135 mol carbon (1620 g C) in 1 mol coal (1906 g coal/mol). Thus, the ratio of grams of carbon to grams of coal is roughly 0.9 and so in 1×10^{12} g coal there is approximately $0.9 \times 1 \times 10^{12}$ g carbon, which is roughly 1×10^{12} g of carbon. When burned, each gram of carbon produces about 4 g CO_2 because there are 44 g CO_2 formed per 12 g C.

$$\frac{44 \text{ g CO}_2}{12 \text{ g C}} \approx 4 \text{ g CO}_2/\text{g C}$$

Thus, in one year the plant generates

$$(1 \times 10^{12} \text{ g C})\left(\frac{4 \text{ g CO}_2}{1 \text{ g C}}\right) = 4 \times 10^{12} \text{ g CO}_2$$

This is approximately the mass of 2 million SUVs.

ThomsonNOW

Sign in to ThomsonNOW at **www.thomsonedu.com** to work an interactive module based on this material.

as these examples are, the development of synthetic organic chemistry has led to cheaper methods of making copies of naturally occurring substances and to many substances that have no counterpart in nature.

Prior to 1828, it was widely believed that chemical compounds found in living matter could not be made without living matter—a "vital force" was thought to be necessary for their synthesis. In 1828 a young German chemist, Friedrich Wöhler, dispelled the vital force theory when he prepared the organic compound urea, a major product in urine, by heating an aqueous solution of ammonium cyanate, a compound obtained from mineral sources.

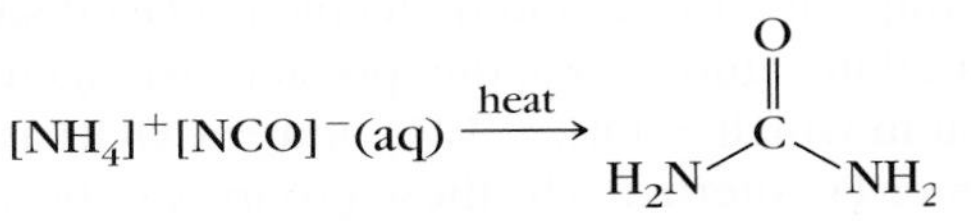

ammonium cyanate urea

Soon thereafter, other chemists began to prepare more and more organic chemicals without using a living system. Catalytic cracking of petroleum is very important for the production of small, unsaturated hydrocarbons such as ethylene ($CH_2{=}CH_2$), propylene ($CH_3CH{=}CH_2$), butylene ($CH_3CH_2CH{=}CH_2$), and acetylene ($HC{\equiv}CH$) **(⇐ *p. 344*).** These reactive molecules are starting materials in the organic chemical industry for the production of a substantial variety of substances we use daily. Aromatic compounds—such as benzene, toluene, and xylene—derived from coal tar and catalytic reforming are also important compounds from which a vast array of commercial products are produced.

Because about 85% of all known compounds are organic compounds, it is natural to ask: Why are there so many organic compounds, almost all of which contain carbon and hydrogen atoms (and commonly other kinds of atoms as well)? As discussed in earlier sections on bonding and isomerism **(⇐ *p. 339, p. 345*),** two reasons are (1) the ability of as many as thousands of carbon atoms to be linked to each other in a single molecule by stable C—C bonds, and (2) the occurrence of structural isomers. A third reason—the variety of functional groups that bond to carbon atoms—is further illustrated in this chapter. A **functional group** is a distinctive grouping of atoms that, as part of an organic molecule, imparts specific properties to the molecule. In addition to these three reasons, many molecules also display a very subtle type of molecular isomerism related to "handedness."

A table of functional groups and further information on how organic compounds are named is given in Appendix E.

The alcohol, aldehyde, ketone, carboxylic acid, ester, amine, and amide functional groups are discussed in Sections 12.5–12.8.

Chiral Molecules

Are you right-handed or left-handed? Regardless of the preference, we learn at a very early age that a right-handed glove doesn't fit the left hand, and vice versa. Our hands are mirror images of one another and are not superimposable (Figure 12.7). *An object that cannot be superimposed on its mirror image is called* **chiral.** Objects that are superimposable on their mirror images are **achiral.** Stop and think about the extent to which chirality is a part of our everyday life. We've already discussed the chirality of hands (and feet). Helical seashells are chiral (most spiral to the right like a right-handed screw), and many creeping vines show a chirality when they wind around a tree or post.

What is not as well known is that a large number of the molecules in plants and animals are chiral, and usually only one form (left-handed or right-handed) of the chiral molecule is found in nature. For example, all but one of the 20 amino acids from which proteins are made are chiral, and the left-handed amino acids predominate in nature! Most natural sugars are right-handed, including glucose and sucrose and deoxyribose, the sugar found in DNA.

A chiral molecule and its *nonsuperimposable* mirror image are called **enantiomers;** they are two different molecules, just as your left and right hands are

© Thomson Learning/Charles D. Winters

Figure 12.7 Nonsuperimposable mirror images. Right- and left-handed seashells are mirror images, as are the hands holding them.

In *A Midsummer Night's Dream*, Shakespeare wrote of the chirality of honeysuckle and woodbine plants. Queen Titania says to Bottom, ". . . Sleep thou, and I will wind thee in my arms . . . So doth the woodbine the sweet honeysuckle gently entwist. . . ." Woodbine spirals clockwise and honeysuckle twists in a counterclockwise direction.

In *Through the Looking Glass* (the companion volume to *Alice in Wonderland*), Alice speculates to her cat that ". . . perhaps looking glass milk is not good to drink."

different. The simplest case of chirality is a tetrahedral carbon atom that is bonded to four *different* atoms or groups of atoms. Such a carbon atom is said to be a *chiral center,* and a molecule with just one chiral center is always a chiral molecule.

Lactic acid is one of the compounds found in nature in both enantiomeric forms under different circumstances. During the contraction of muscles, the body produces only one enantiomer of lactic acid. The other enantiomer is produced when milk sours. Lactic acid has its central C atom bonded to four different groups: —CH_3, —OH, —H, and —COOH (Figure 12.8a). As a result of the tetrahedral geometry around the central carbon atom, it is possible to have two different arrangements of the four groups. If a lactic acid molecule is placed so that the C—H bond is vertical, as illustrated in Figure 12.8a, one possible arrangement of the remaining groups would be that in which —OH, —CH_3, and —COOH are attached in a clockwise sequence (Isomer I). Alternatively, these groups can be attached in a counterclockwise sequence (Isomer II), as in Figure 12.8b.

To illustrate further that the arrangements are different, we place Isomer I in front of a mirror (Figure 12.8c). Now you see that Isomer II is the mirror image of Isomer I. What is important, however, is that these mirror image molecules *cannot be superimposed* on one another. *These two nonsuperimposable, mirror image chiral molecules are enantiomers.*

The "handedness" of enantiomers is sometimes represented by D for right-handed (D stands for "dextro" from the Latin *dexter,* meaning "right") and L for left-handed (L stands for "levo" from the Latin *laevus,* meaning "left"). Nature's preference for one enantiomer of amino acids (the L form) has provoked much discussion and speculation among scientists since Louis Pasteur's discovery of molecular chirality in 1848. However, there is still no widely accepted explanation of this preference.

Large organic molecules may have a number of chiral carbon atoms within the same molecule. At each such carbon atom (a chiral center), two arrangements of the molecule are possible. The maximum number of possible isomers increases exponentially with the number of different chiral carbon atoms; with n different chiral carbon atoms there are a maximum of 2^n possible isomers. (The word "maximum" is used because in some cases a mirror image may not be different from the mirrored structure.) The widely used artificial sweetener aspartame (NutraSweet) has two chiral centers and two pairs of enantiomers. One enantiomer has a sweet taste, while another enantiomer is bitter, indicating that the receptor sites on our taste buds must be chiral, because they respond differently to the "handedness" of aspartame enantiomers! In another example, D-glucose is sweet and nutritious, while L-glucose is tasteless and cannot be metabolized by the body.

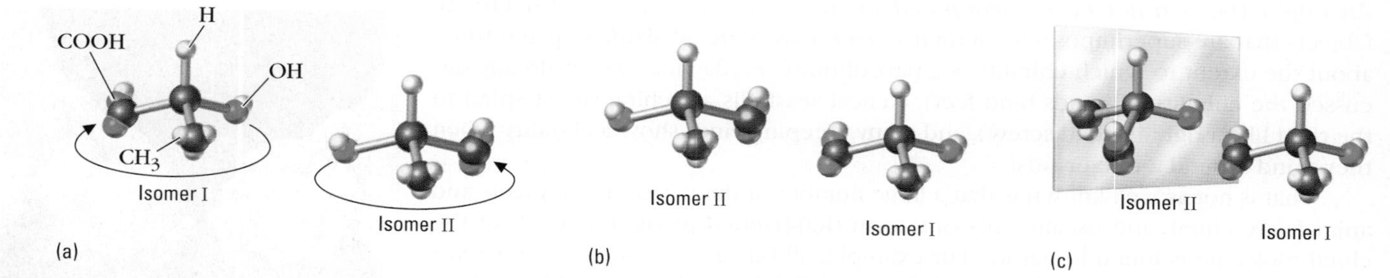

Figure 12.8 The enantiomers of lactic acid. (a) Isomer I: —OH, —CH_3, and —COOH, are attached in a clockwise manner. Isomer II: —OH, —CH_3, and —COOH are attached in a counterclockwise manner. (b) The isomers are nonsuperimposable. (c) Isomer I is placed in front of a mirror, and its mirror image is Isomer II. You could superimpose C, H, and CH_3, but then OH and COOH would not superimpose.

PROBLEM-SOLVING EXAMPLE 12.4 Handedness in Asparagine

Asparagine is a naturally occurring amino acid first isolated as a bitter-tasting white powder from asparagus juice. Later, a sweet-tasting second form of asparagine was isolated from a sprouting vetch plant. D-Asparagine is bitter; the L isomer is sweet. The Lewis structure of asparagine is

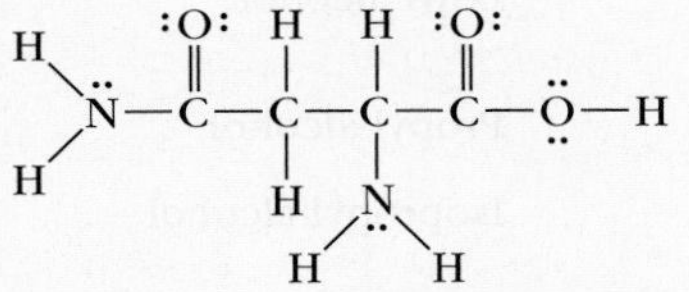

Identify which carbon atom in asparagine is the chiral center (chiral carbon).

Answer

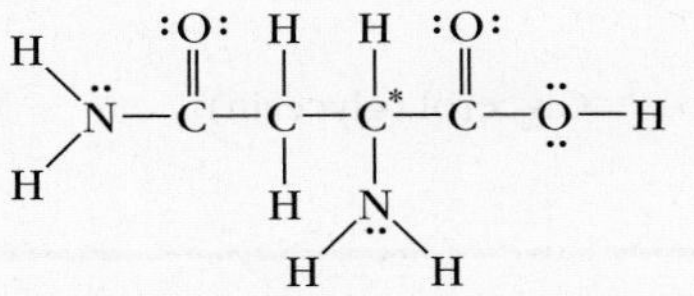

Strategy and Explanation Carefully examine the Lewis structure to identify a carbon atom with four different atoms or groups attached to it; that carbon is the chiral center. The carbon next to the —COOH group is the chiral center. It has four different atoms or groups of atoms attached to it: (1) a hydrogen atom, (2) a —COOH group, (3) an $—NH_2$ group, and (4) the rest of the molecule, starting with the $—CH_2—$ group.

PROBLEM-SOLVING PRACTICE 12.4

Aspartame, a widely used sugar substitute, is a chiral molecule with the structural formula

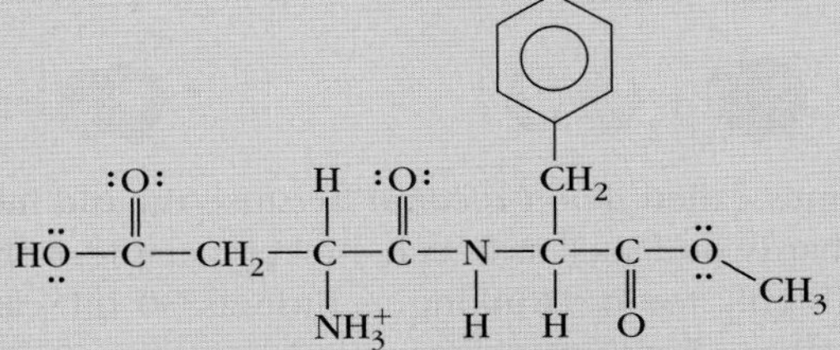

Identify the asymmetric (chiral) carbon atoms.

We turn next to compounds containing particular functional groups. Some of these very useful compounds are alcohols, acids, esters, and the natural and synthetic polymers made from them. These are discussed in Sections 12.5 through 12.8.

12.5 Alcohols and Their Oxidation Products

Alcohols are a major class of organic compounds. All alcohols, both natural and synthetic, contain the characteristic —OH functional group bonded directly to a carbon atom. Some alcohols contain more than one —OH group. Examples of commercially important alcohols and their uses are listed in Table 12.3.

ThomsonNOW™
Sign in to ThomsonNOW at **www.thomsonedu.com** to access a set of interactive molecular models including over 200 models of organic compounds organized by **functional group.**

Methanol and Ethanol

Methanol, CH_3OH, the simplest of all alcohols, has just one carbon atom. Because methanol is so useful in making other products, more than 8 billion pounds of it are

Table 12.3 Some Important Alcohols

Condensed Formula	b.p. (°C)	Systematic Name	Common Name	Use
CH_3OH	65.0	Methanol	Methyl alcohol	Fuel, gasoline additive, making formaldehyde
CH_3CH_2OH	78.5	Ethanol	Ethyl alcohol	Beverages, gasoline additive, solvent
$CH_3CH_2CH_2OH$	97.4	1-propanol	Propyl alcohol	Industrial solvent
$CH_3CH(OH)CH_3$	82.4	2-propanol	Isopropyl alcohol	Rubbing alcohol
$CH_2(OH)CH_2(OH)$	198	1,2-ethanediol	Ethylene glycol	Antifreeze
$CH_2(OH)—CH(OH)—CH_2(OH)$	290	1,2,3-propanetriol	Glycerol (glycerin)	Moisturizer in foods

produced annually in the United States by the reaction of carbon monoxide with hydrogen in the presence of a catalyst at 300 °C.

$$CO(g) + 2\,H_2(g) \xrightarrow{\text{catalyst, 300 °C}} CH_3OH(g)$$

Methanol is sometimes called *wood alcohol* because the old method of producing it was by heating a hardwood such as beech, hickory, maple, or birch in the absence of air. Methanol is highly toxic. Drinking as little as 30 mL can cause death, and smaller quantities (10 to 15 mL) can cause blindness.

About 50% of methanol is used in the production of formaldehyde (HCHO), which is used to make plastics, embalming fluid, germicides, and fungicides; 30% is used in the production of other chemicals; and the remaining 20% is used for jet fuels, antifreeze solvent mixtures, and gasoline additives.

Because it can be made from coal, methanol will likely increase in importance as petroleum and natural gas become too expensive as sources of both energy and chemicals. Since methanol is relatively cheap, its potential as a fuel and as a starting material for the synthesis of other chemicals is receiving more attention. The technology for methanol-powered vehicles has existed for many years, particularly for racing cars that burn methanol because of its high octane rating (107). Methanol has both advantages and disadvantages as a replacement for gasoline. As a motor fuel, methanol burns more cleanly than gasoline, thus reducing levels of troublesome pollutants. Also, burning methanol emits no unburned hydrocarbons, which contribute significantly to air pollution. However, methanol has only about half the energy density of the same volume of gasoline. Therefore, twice as much methanol must be burned to give the same distance per tankful as gasoline. This disadvantage is partially compensated for by the fact that methanol costs about half as much to produce as gasoline. Another disadvantage is the tendency for methanol to corrode ordinary steel. Therefore, it is necessary to use stainless steel or a methanol-resistant coating for the fuel system.

ThomsonNOW™
Go to the Coached Problems menu for simulations and tutorials on **naming alcohols.**

© Bernard Asset/Photo Researchers, Inc.

Some racing cars burn methanol.

PROBLEM-SOLVING EXAMPLE 12.5 Methanol and MTBE

Methanol reacts with 2-methylpropene to yield methyl *tert*-butyl ether (MTBE), which was used as an octane enhancer and in reformulated gasolines.

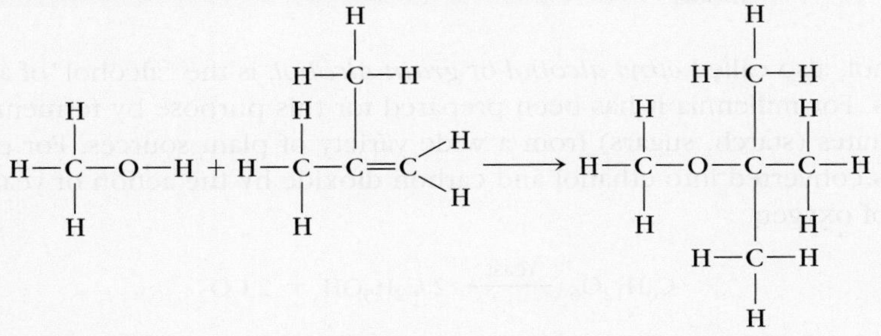

methanol 2-methylpropene methyl *tert*-butyl ether (MTBE)

Given these bond enthalpy data, estimate the enthalpy change, ΔH, for the synthesis of MTBE. Is the reaction endothermic or exothermic?

Bond	Bond Enthalpy (kJ/mol)
C—H	416
C—O	336
O—H	467
C—C	356
C=C	598

Answer −43.0 kJ; the reaction is exothermic.

Strategy and Explanation We can think of the reaction as being one in which bonds in the reactants are broken (endothermic process) and then bonds are formed in the products (exothermic). The balanced chemical equation for the reaction is given using Lewis structures, so we can directly count the number of moles of each kind of bond to be broken in the reactants and to be formed in the product. We then multiply these amounts by their respective bond enthalpies, D, to estimate the enthalpy change for the reaction (← *Section 8.6*).

$$\begin{aligned}\Delta H^\circ &= \sum[(\text{moles of bonds}) \times D(\text{bonds broken})] \\ &\quad - \sum[(\text{moles of bonds}) \times D(\text{bonds formed})] \\ &= \{[(3\text{ mol C—H})(416\text{ kJ/mol}) + (1\text{ mol C—O})(336\text{ kJ/mol}) \\ &\quad + (1\text{ mol O—H})(467\text{ kJ/mol})] + [(8\text{ mol C—H})(416\text{ kJ/mol}) \\ &\quad + (2\text{ mol C—C})(356\text{ kJ/mol}) + (1\text{ mol C=C})(598\text{ kJ/mol})]\} \\ &\quad - [(12\text{ C—H})(416\text{ kJ/mol}) + (2\text{ mol C—O})(336\text{ kJ/mol}) \\ &\quad + (3\text{ mol C—C})(356\text{ kJ/mol})] \\ &= (6689\text{ kJ}) - (6732) = -43.0\text{ kJ}\end{aligned}$$

The negative sign indicates that the reaction is exothermic.

✓ Reasonable Answer Check The net change in the reaction is the conversion of 1 mol C=C bonds and 1 mol O—H bonds into 1 mol C—H bonds, 1 mol C—C bonds, and 1 mol C—O bonds. The other bonds are unchanged. The enthalpy change for the conversions is

$$\begin{aligned}\Delta H^\circ &= [(1\text{ mol C=C})(598\text{ kJ/mol}) + (1\text{ mol O—H})(467\text{ kJ/mol})] \\ &\quad - [(1\text{ mol C—H})(416\text{ kJ/mol}) + (1\text{ mol C—C})(356\text{ kJ/mol}) \\ &\quad + (1\text{ mol (C—O})(336\text{ kJ/mol})]\end{aligned}$$

which equals −43.0 kJ, the correct answer.

PROBLEM-SOLVING PRACTICE 12.5

Using Table 8.2 of Average Bond Enthalpies, estimate the enthalpy change for the industrial synthesis of methanol by the catalyzed reaction of carbon monoxide with hydrogen.

Ethanol, also called *ethyl alcohol* or *grain alcohol,* is the "alcohol" of alcoholic beverages. For millennia it has been prepared for this purpose by fermentation of carbohydrates (starch, sugars) from a wide variety of plant sources. For example, glucose is converted into ethanol and carbon dioxide by the action of yeast in the absence of oxygen.

$$C_6H_{12}O_6 \xrightarrow{\text{Yeast}} 2\ C_2H_5OH + 2\ CO_2$$

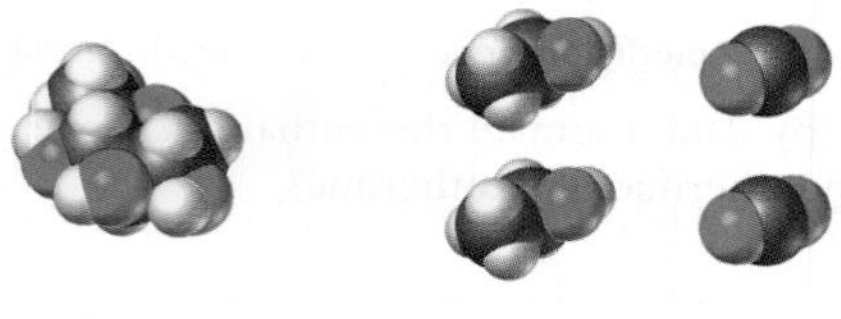

glucose ethanol

© Thomson Learning/ Charles D. Winters

Alcohol concentration in wine.

Ninety-five percent ethanol is the maximum ethanol concentration that can be obtained by distillation of alcohol/water mixtures because ethanol and water form a mixture that boils without changing composition.

Ethanol as a vehicle fuel is also available as Ethanol85, a mixture of 85% ethanol and 15% gasoline. There are now more than four million FlexFuel vehicles in the United States using gasohol and Ethanol85 in conjunction with regular gasoline.

Table 12.4 Blood Alcohol Levels and Their Effects

% by Volume	Effect
0.05–0.15	Lack of coordination
0.08	Commonly defined point for "driving while intoxicated"
0.15–0.20	Obvious intoxication
0.30–0.40	Unconsciousness
0.50	Possible death

Fermentation eventually stops when the alcohol concentration reaches a level sufficient to inhibit the yeast cells. The "proof" of an alcoholic beverage is twice the volume percent of ethanol; 80-proof vodka, for example, contains 40% ethanol by volume. Although ethanol is not as toxic as methanol, one pint of pure ethanol, rapidly ingested, will kill most people. Ethanol is a depressant; the effects of various blood levels of alcohol are shown in Table 12.4. Rapid consumption of two 1-oz "shots" of 90-proof whiskey, two 12-oz beers, or two 4-oz glasses of wine can cause one's blood alcohol level to reach 0.05%.

In the United States, the federal tax on alcoholic beverages is about $13 per gallon, which is about 20 cents per ounce of ethanol in the beverage. Since the cost of producing ethanol is only about $1 per gallon, ethanol intended for industrial use must be *denatured* to avoid the beverage tax and to prevent people from drinking the alcohol. Ethanol is denatured by adding to it small amounts of a toxic substance, such as methanol or gasoline, that cannot be removed easily by chemical or physical means.

Ethanol, like methanol, is receiving increased attention as an alternative fuel. At present, most of it is used in a blend of 90% gasoline and 10% ethanol (known as *gasohol* when introduced in the 1970s). Ethanol is also used as an oxygenated fuel to add to gasoline. The fermentation of corn, an abundant (but not limitless) source of carbohydrate, is used to produce ethanol for fuel use.

Hydrogen Bonding in Alcohols

The physical properties of liquid alcohols are a direct result of the effects of hydrogen bonding among alcohol molecules. Alcohols can be considered as compounds in which alkyl groups such as CH_3— and CH_3CH_2— are substituted for one of the hydrogens of water. The change from the hydrogen in water to the alkyl group in an alcohol reduces the influence of hydrogen bonding in the progression from water (HOH) to methanol (CH_3OH) to ethanol (CH_3CH_2OH) and higher-molar-mass alcohols. The boiling points of methanol (32 g/mol; 65 °C) and ethanol (46 g/mol; 78.5 °C) are lower than that of water (18 g/mol; 100 °C) because methanol and ethanol have only one —OH hydrogen atom available for hydrogen bonding; water has two. The higher boiling point of ethylene glycol (198 °C) can be attributed to the presence of two —OH groups per molecule. Glycerol, with three —OH groups, has an even higher boiling point (290 °C). Hydrogen bonding among ethanol molecules explains why it is a liquid, while propane, which has a similar number of electrons (and molar mass) but no hydrogen bonding, is a gas at the same temperature. The alcohols listed in Table 12.3 are very water-soluble because of hydrogen bonding between water molecules and the —OH alcohol group.

See Table 12.3 (p. 562) for the structural formulas of these compounds.

CONCEPTUAL EXERCISE 12.7 Water Solubility of Alcohols

What would you expect concerning the water solubility of an alcohol containing ten carbon atoms and one —OH group? Recall that hydrocarbons such as octane are not water-soluble.

CONCEPTUAL EXERCISE 12.8 One Alcohol in Another

Methanol dissolves in glycerol. Use Lewis structures to illustrate the hydrogen bonding between methanol and glycerol molecules.

Oxidation of Alcohols

Alcohols are classified according to the number of carbon atoms *directly* bonded to the —C—OH carbon. If no carbon atom or one carbon atom is bonded directly, the compound is a *primary* alcohol. If two are bonded directly, it is a *secondary* alcohol; with three it is a *tertiary* alcohol, as illustrated below. The use of R, R′, and R″ to represent alkyl groups indicates that the alkyl groups can be different.

ThomsonNOW
Go to the Coached Problems menu for a simulation on **reactivity of alcohols.**

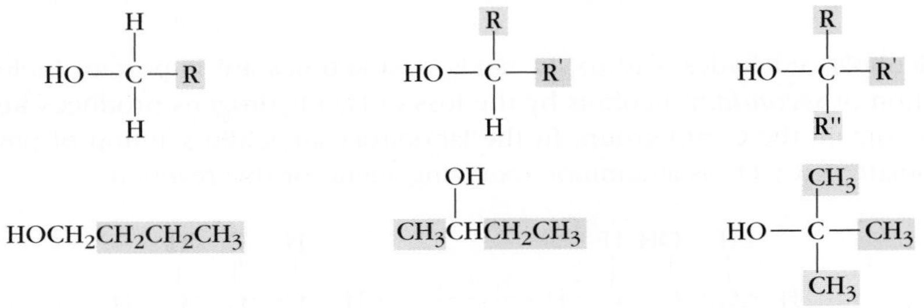

1-butanol, a primary alcohol | 2-butanol, a secondary alcohol | 2-methyl-2-propanol, a tertiary alcohol

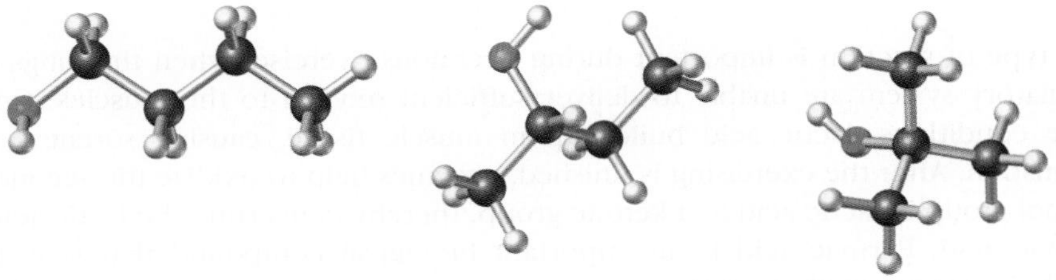

In naming alcohols, the longest chain of carbon atoms is numbered so that the carbon with the —OH attached has the lowest possible number. A table of functional groups and further information on how organic compounds are named is given in Appendix E.

Stepwise oxidation of primary alcohols produces compounds called aldehydes, which are then oxidized to carboxylic acids.

$$\text{Primary alcohol} \longrightarrow \text{aldehyde} \longrightarrow \text{carboxylic acid}$$

Oxidation of organic compounds generally results from either the loss of two hydrogen atoms or the gain of one oxygen atom. For example, the stepwise oxidation of

© Thomson Learning/Charles D. Winters

Vinegar is a 5% solution of acetic acid in water.

Oxidation of organic compounds is usually the removal of two hydrogens or the addition of one oxygen; reduction is usually the addition of two hydrogens or the removal of one oxygen.

Functional Group Class	Functional Group	Example
Aldehyde	$-\overset{O}{\overset{\|}{C}}H$	Formaldehyde $H-\overset{O}{\overset{\|}{C}}H$
Carboxylic acid	$-\overset{O}{\overset{\|}{C}}-OH$	Acetic acid $CH_3-\overset{O}{\overset{\|}{C}}-OH$
Ketone	$-\overset{O}{\overset{\|}{C}}-$	Acetone $CH_3-\overset{O}{\overset{\|}{C}}-CH_3$

ethanol with aqueous potassium permanganate as the oxidizing agent first produces acetaldehyde, a member of the **aldehyde** functional group class, which contains a —CHO group.

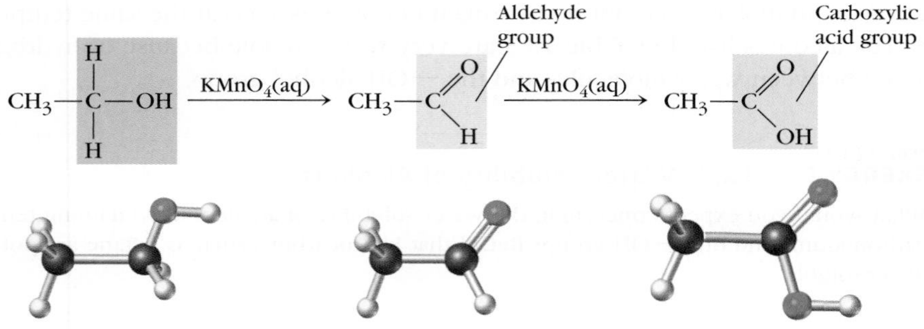

ethanol (a primary alcohol) — acetaldehyde — acetic acid

The acetaldehyde is then oxidized to acetic acid, a member of the **carboxylic acid** functional group class, which contains the —COOH group (also represented as $-CO_2H$). When ethanol is ingested, enzymes in the liver produce the same products. Acetaldehyde, the intermediate product, contributes to the toxic effects of alcoholism. In the presence of oxygen in air, ethanol in wine is oxidized naturally to acetic acid, converting the wine from a beverage into something more suitable for a salad dressing.

> **CONCEPTUAL EXERCISE 12.9 Looking at the Oxidation of Primary Alcohols**
>
> Look carefully at the formulas for ethanol and acetaldehyde. Explain the change in structure when ethanol is oxidized to acetaldehyde. Do the same for the oxidation of acetaldehyde to acetic acid. How do your explanations differ for the different products?

Alcohols, aldehydes, carboxylic acids, and ketones are important biologically. Oxidation of *secondary* alcohols by the loss of two hydrogens produces **ketones,** which contain the C=O group. In the laboratory an acidic solution of potassium dichromate, $K_2Cr_2O_7$, is a common oxidizing agent for this reaction.

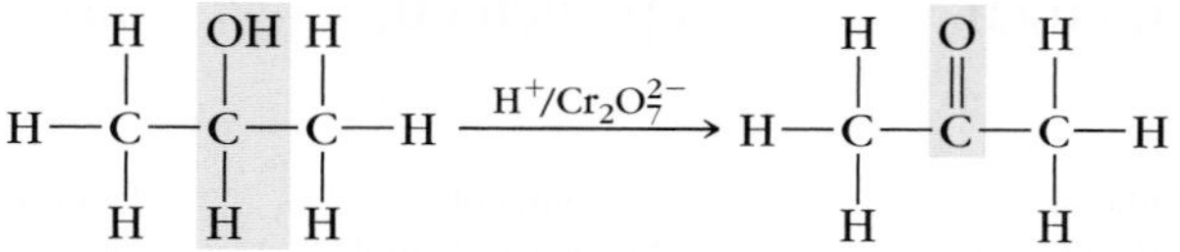

Secondary alcohol ⟶ ketone

This type of reaction is important during strenuous exercise, when the lungs and circulatory system are unable to deliver sufficient oxygen to the muscles. Under these conditions, lactic acid builds up in muscle tissue, causing soreness and exhaustion. After the exercising is finished, enzymes help to oxidize the secondary alcohol group in lactic acid to a ketone group, thereby converting the lactic acid to pyruvic acid. Pyruvic acid is an important biological compound that is further metabolized to provide energy.

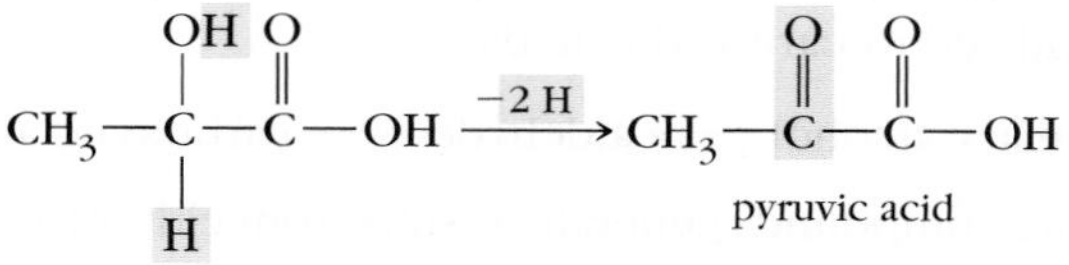

lactic acid

Tertiary alcohols, having no hydrogen atoms directly bonded to the carbon bearing the —OH group, are not oxidized easily.

PROBLEM-SOLVING EXAMPLE 12.6 Oxidation of Alcohols

Write the condensed structural formulas of the alcohols that can be oxidized to make these compounds:

(a) $CH_3CH_2CH_2C(=O)—H$ (b) $CH_3CH_2C(=O)—CH_3$ (c) $CH_3CH_2CH_2CH_2C(=O)—OH$

Answer

(a) $CH_3CH_2CH_2CH_2OH$ (b) $CH_3CH_2CH(OH)CH_3$ (c) $CH_3CH_2CH_2CH_2CH_2OH$

Strategy and Explanation An aldehyde or carboxylic acid group is formed by the oxidation of a primary alcohol in which the —OH group is at the end of the molecule. A ketone group is made by the oxidation of a secondary alcohol, a compound in which the —OH group is not on a terminal (end) carbon atom.

(a) The oxidation of the four-carbon primary alcohol, 1-butanol, will produce this aldehyde.
(b) To produce this ketone, choose the secondary alcohol, 2-butanol, which has two carbons to the left and one carbon to the right of the C—OH group.
(c) The oxidation of the five-carbon primary alcohol, 1-pentanol, will produce this carboxylic acid.

PROBLEM-SOLVING PRACTICE 12.6

Draw the structural formulas of the expected oxidation products of these compounds.

(a) $CH_3CH_2CH_2OH$ (b) $CH_3CH(OH)CH_2CH_3$

CONCEPTUAL EXERCISE 12.10 Aldehydes and Combustion Products

Write the equation for the formation of an aldehyde by the oxidation of methanol. Critics of the use of methanol as a fuel or fuel oxygenate have cited the formation of this aldehyde as a major health threat. Use the Internet to find some of the toxic properties of the aldehyde.

CONCEPTUAL EXERCISE 12.11 Working Backward

When oxidized, a certain alcohol yields an aldehyde containing three carbon atoms. Further oxidation forms a three-carbon acid with the acid functional group located on the number one carbon of the chain. What are the structural formula and the name of the alcohol?

Biologically Important Compounds Containing Alcohol Groups

Many natural organic compounds are cyclic. They can be considered to be derivatives of hydrocarbons that consist of aromatic rings (⇐ *p. 363*), cycloalkane (⇐ *p. 340*), or fused cycloalkene rings. In many of these compounds, two or more rings are fused, that is, the rings share carbon atoms. Steroids, all of which have the four-ring structure shown next, are an example of these fused-ring structures.

Cycloalkenes are nonaromatic ring compounds that contain at least one C=C double bond.

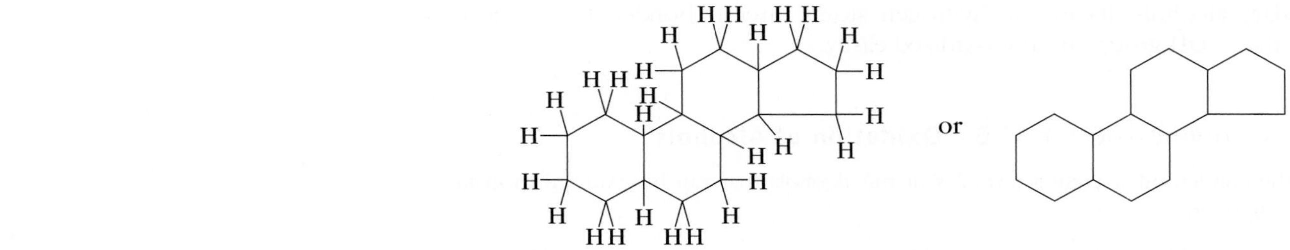

Many steroids—including cholesterol, the female sex hormones estradiol and estrone, and the male sex hormone testosterone—contain alcohol functional groups. Cholesterol is the most abundant steroid in the human body, where it serves as a major component of cell membranes and as the starting point for the production of the steroid hormones. The elongated, flat, rigid structure of cholesterol helps to make cell membranes sturdier. However, elevated levels of cholesterol in the blood are associated with *atherosclerosis,* a thickening of arterial walls that can lead to medical problems such as strokes and heart attacks.

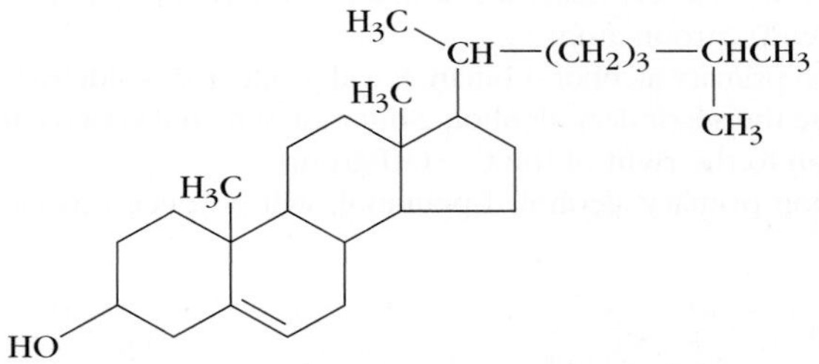

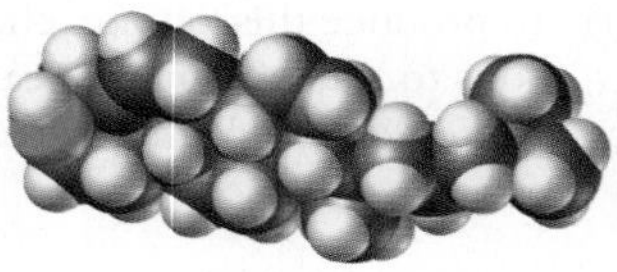

cholesterol

The presence and position of the C=C bond and the presence of the aromatic ring differ among steroids, as seen from the structural formulas of cholesterol, estradiol, and testosterone. Estradiol and estrone are female sex hormones responsible for the development of secondary sexual characteristics during puberty; testosterone is the male counterpart. From their structural formulas you can see that steroids are large molecules made up predominantly of carbon and hydrogen. Thus, steroids are not soluble in water.

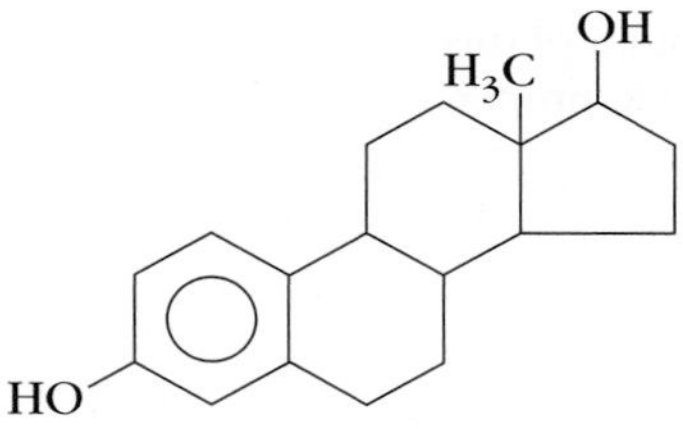

estradiol
(female hormone,
an estrogen)

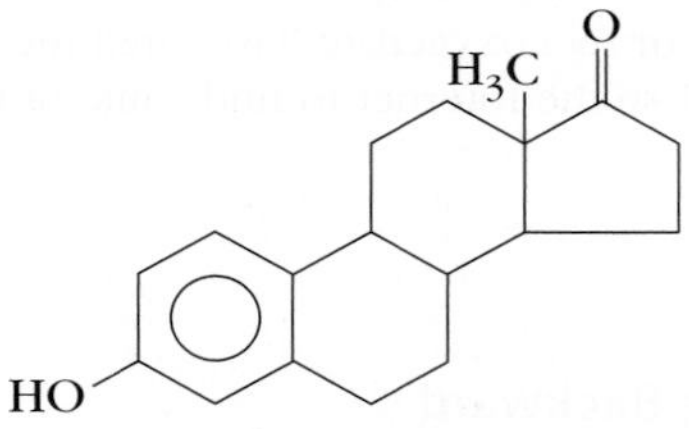

estrone
(female hormone,
an estrogen)

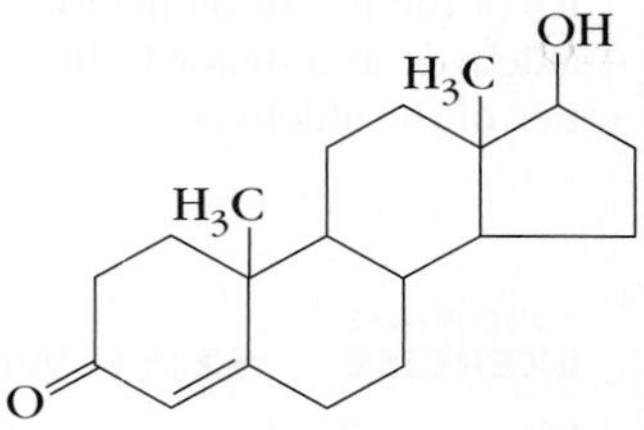

testosterone
(male hormone)

CONCEPTUAL EXERCISE **12.12 A Closer Look**

Look carefully at the structures for estradiol and estrone.

(a) What does the *-diol* suffix indicate in estradiol?
(b) What kind of alcohol group is on the five-membered ring in estradiol?
(c) What process converts the alcohol group of the five-membered ring in estradiol to the functional group present in that same ring in estrone?
(d) Write a description of the differences in the molecular structures between the male and female sex hormones, testosterone and estradiol, respectively.

EXERCISE 12.13 Take Me Out to the Ball Game

Home run slugger Barry Bonds and other athletes have been accused of using synthetic anabolic steroids to enhance their athletic performance. Androstenedione is such a steroid; its molecular structure is

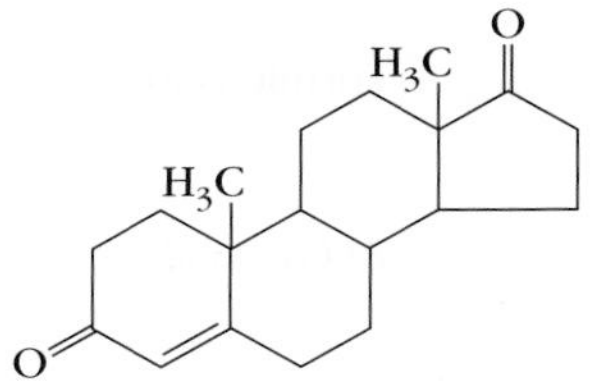

androstenedione

Compare it with the molecular structure of testosterone. In the body, what simple chemical process converts androstenedione to testosterone?

12.6 Carboxylic Acids and Esters

Carboxylic Acids

Carboxylic acids contain the —C(=O)—OH (—COOH or —CO_2H) functional group and are prepared by the oxidation of aldehydes or the complete oxidation of primary alcohols (p. 565). All carboxylic acids react with bases to form salts; for example, sodium lactate is formed by the neutralization reaction of lactic acid and sodium hydroxide.

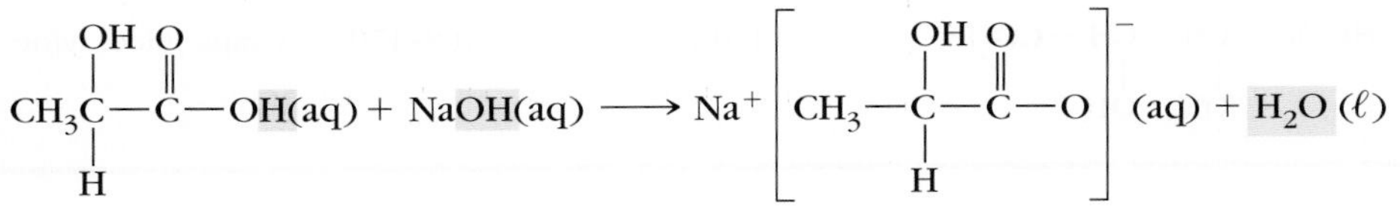

lactic acid

sodium lactate

Carboxylic acid molecules are polar and form hydrogen bonds with each other. This hydrogen bonding results in relatively high boiling points for the acids—even higher than those of alcohols of comparable molecular size. For example, formic acid (46 g/mol) has a boiling point of 101 °C, while ethanol (46 g/mol) has a boiling point of only 78.5 °C. Both formic acid and ethanol form hydrogen bonds, but those in formic acid are stronger.

EXERCISE 12.14 Hydrogen Bonding in Formic Acid

Use the structural formula of formic acid given in Table 12.5 to illustrate hydrogen bonding in formic acid.

A large number of carboxylic acids are found in nature and have been known for many years. As a result, some of the familiar carboxylic acids are almost always referred to by their common names (Table 12.5).

Three commercially important carboxylic acids—adipic acid, terephthalic acid, and phthalic acid—have two acid groups per molecule and are known as *dicarboxylic acids.* These three acids are used as starting materials to make vast quantities of synthetic polymers (Section 12.8).

Percy Lavon Julian
1899–1975

After receiving a doctorate in chemistry in Vienna in 1931, Percy Julian spent 18 years as a research director in the chemical industry, and then directed his own research institute. He was granted more than 100 patents and was the first to synthesize hydrocortisone (a steroid) and to isolate from soybean oil the compounds used to make the first synthetic sex hormone (progesterone). These amazing accomplishments came from a person who had to leave his home in Montgomery, Alabama, after eighth grade for further studies—no more public education was available there for an African American man. Julian enrolled as a "subfreshman" at DePauw University in Indiana. On his first day, a white student welcomed him with a handshake. Julian later related his reaction: "In the shake of a hand my life was changed. I soon learned to smile and act like I believed they all liked me, whether they wanted to or not."

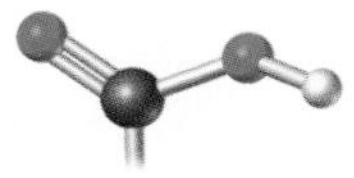

carboxylic acid group

The carboxylic acid group is present in all organic acids. Acids of all kinds are an important class of compounds, as discussed in Chapter 16.

Acids in foods such as citrus fruits, strawberries, and vinegar cause them to have a sour taste.

In *Les Miserables,* Victor Hugo comments about naturally occurring acids when he writes, "Comrades, we will overthrow the government, as sure as there are fifteen acids intermediate between margaric acid and formic acid." Formic acid, the simplest organic acid, has just one carbon atom. Margaric acid, from which margarine is derived, has seventeen carbon atoms.

Table 12.5 Some Naturally Occurring Carboxylic Acids

Structure	Common Name	b.p. (°C)	Natural Source
$H\overset{O}{\overset{\|\|}{C}}OH$	Formic acid	101	Ants
$CH_3\overset{O}{\overset{\|\|}{C}}OH$	Acetic acid	118	Fermented fruit
$CH_3CH_2\overset{O}{\overset{\|\|}{C}}OH$	Propionic acid	141	Dairy products
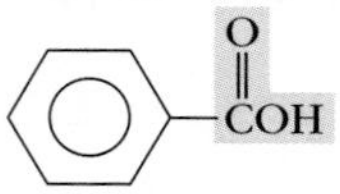	Benzoic acid	250	Berries
		m.p. (°C)	
$HOOC{-}CH_2{-}\overset{OH}{\overset{\|}{\underset{COOH}{\underset{\|}{C}}}}{-}CH_2{-}COOH$	Citric acid	153	Citrus fruits
$HOOC{-}CH_2{-}\underset{OH}{\underset{\|}{CH}}{-}COOH$	Malic acid	131	Apples
$HOOC{-}\underset{OH}{\underset{\|}{CH}}{-}\underset{OH}{\underset{\|}{CH}}{-}COOH$	Tartaric acid	168–170	Grape juice, wine

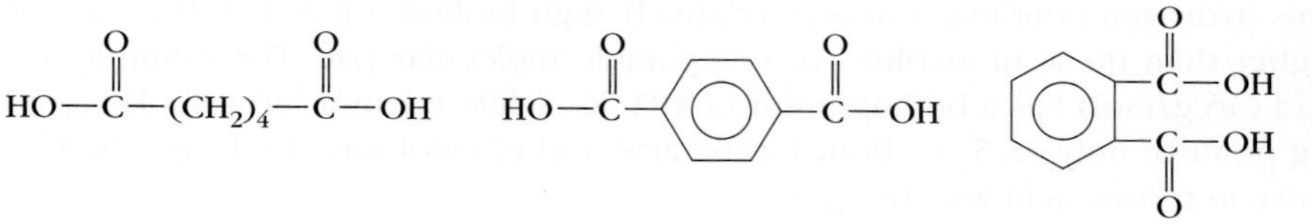

adipic acid   terephthalic acid   phthalic acid

Esters

Carboxylic acids react with alcohols in the presence of strong acids (such as sulfuric acid) to produce **esters,** which contain the

$$-\overset{O}{\overset{\|\|}{C}}-O-R$$

functional group. In an ester, the —OH of the carboxylic acid is replaced by the —OR group from the alcohol. The general equation for ester formation (esterification) is

$$\underset{\text{alcohol}}{R{-}OH} + \underset{\text{organic acid}}{H{-}O{-}\overset{O}{\overset{\|\|}{C}}{-}R'} \xrightarrow{H^+} \underset{\text{ester}}{R{-}O{-}\overset{O}{\overset{\|\|}{C}}{-}R'} + \underset{\text{water}}{H_2O}$$

© Royalty-Free/Corbis

Carboxylic acids in foods. These citrus fruits contain citric acid as well as other naturally occurring acids.

Esterification is an example of a condensation reaction. In a **condensation reaction,** two molecules combine to form a larger molecule (in esterification it is the ester) while simultaneously splitting out a small molecule (such as water). For example, just over a century ago, Felix Hoffmann, a chemist at the Bayer Chemical Company in Germany, synthesized aspirin, the world's most common pain reliever, by esterifying an alcohol group on salicylic acid with acetic acid in strong acid solution to form acetylsalicylic acid, which is aspirin. The ester group makes aspirin less irritating to the stomach lining than salicylic acid. The carboxylic acid group originally in salicylic acid remains intact in aspirin.

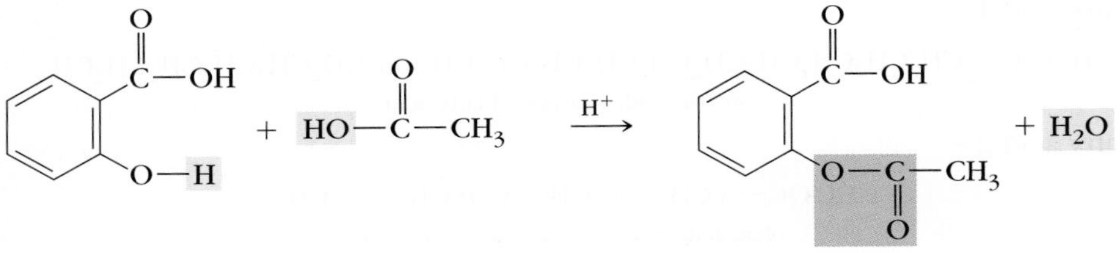

salicylic acid — acetic acid — aspirin (acetylsalicyclic acid) — water

The systematic name for asprin (acetylsalicylic acid) is 2-(acetyloxy)-benzoic acid.

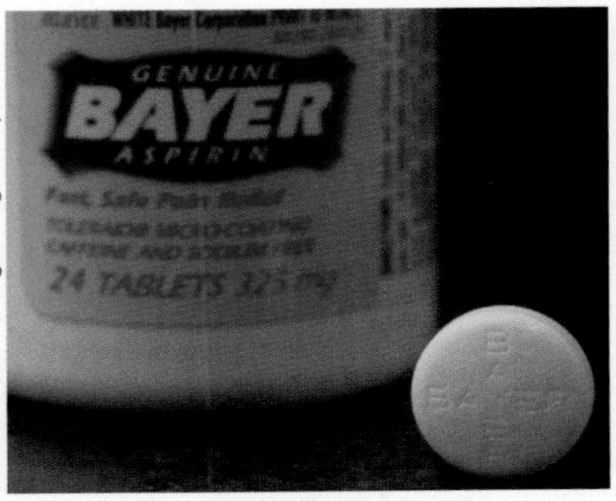

© Thomson Learning/George Semple

Aspirin (acetylsalicylic acid).

Triglycerides: Biologically Important Esters

One benefit of understanding organic molecules is in applying this understanding to the molecules involved in life—organic molecules that we eat, that provide the structure of our bodies, and that allow our bodies to function. Fats and oils are such molecules. *Fats* are solids at room temperature; *oils* are liquids at this temperature. Edible fats and oils are all **triglycerides** because they share the common structural feature of a three-carbon backbone from glycerol to which three long-chain fatty acids are bonded. Fatty acids generally have an even number of carbon atoms, ranging from 4 to 20. Triglycerides are formed by the esterification reaction of three moles of fatty acids with one mole of glycerol.

$$3 \text{ Fatty acid} + \text{glycerol} \longrightarrow \text{triglyceride} + 3\ H_2O$$

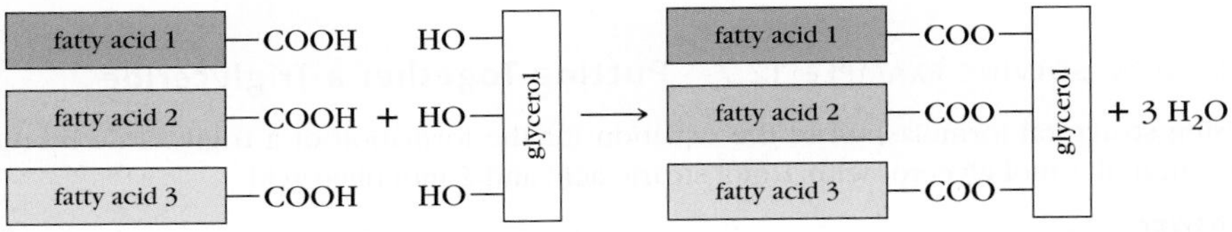

To illustrate this process, consider the reaction of a glycerol molecule with three molecules of stearic acid to produce tristearin, a very common animal fat. Stearic acid is representative of fatty acids, all of which are molecules with long chains of carbon atoms with their attached hydrogens and, at the end of the carbon chain, a —COOH *carboxylic acid* group characteristic of all organic acids. In tristearin formation, the carboxylic acid group in each of three molecules of stearic acid reacts with an —OH group (hydroxyl group) of a glycerol molecule. A water molecule is formed and released as each stearic acid molecule is joined to the glycerol molecule:

$$\text{Glycerol} + 3 \text{ stearic acid} \longrightarrow \text{tristearin} + 3 \text{ water}$$

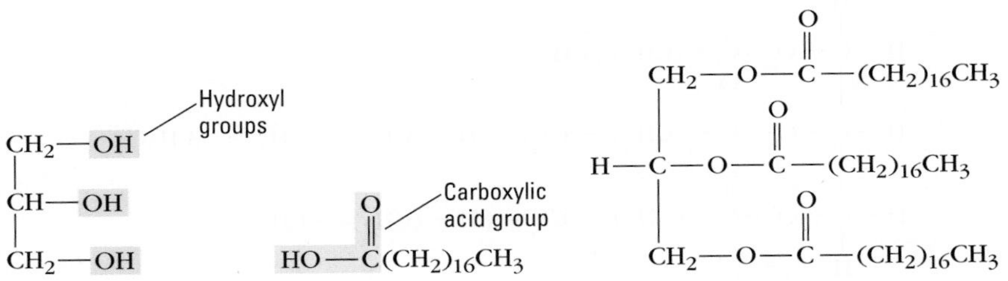

glycerol — stearic acid — tristearin

© Thomson Learning/Charles D. Winters

Cooking oils are liquids at room temperature. Liquid oils and solid fats differ in the connections among the carbon atoms within their molecular structures.

Linoleic and linolenic acids are essential fatty acids; we must have them in our diet. The body cannot manufacture them.

Animal and vegetable fats and oils vary considerably because their fatty acids differ in the length of the hydrocarbon chain and the number of double bonds in the chain. **Saturated fats,** such as stearic acid, contain only C—C single bonds in their hydrocarbon chains along with C—H bonds; **unsaturated fats** contain one or more C=C double bonds in their hydrocarbon chains. Oleic acid, with one C=C bond per molecule, is classified as a *monounsaturated* fatty acid, whereas fatty acids such as linoleic acid, with two or more C=C double bonds per molecule, are termed *polyunsaturated.*

The three fatty acids in a triglyceride can be the same (stearic acid in tristearin) or can be different such as stearic acid, oleic acid, and linoleic acid.

Fatty acid 1

$$HOOC{-}CH_2CH_2CH_2CH_2CH_2CH_2CH_2CH_2CH_2CH_2CH_2CH_2CH_2CH_2CH_2CH_2CH_3$$

stearic acid, a saturated fatty acid

Fatty acid 2

$$HOOC{-}(CH_2)_7{-}CH{=}CH(CH_2)_7{-}CH_3$$

oleic acid, a monounsaturated fatty acid

Fatty acid 3

$$HOOC{-}(CH_2)_7{-}CH{=}CH{-}CH_2{-}CH{=}CH{-}(CH_2)_4{-}CH_3$$

linoleic acid, a polyunsaturated fatty acid

The resulting triglyceride is

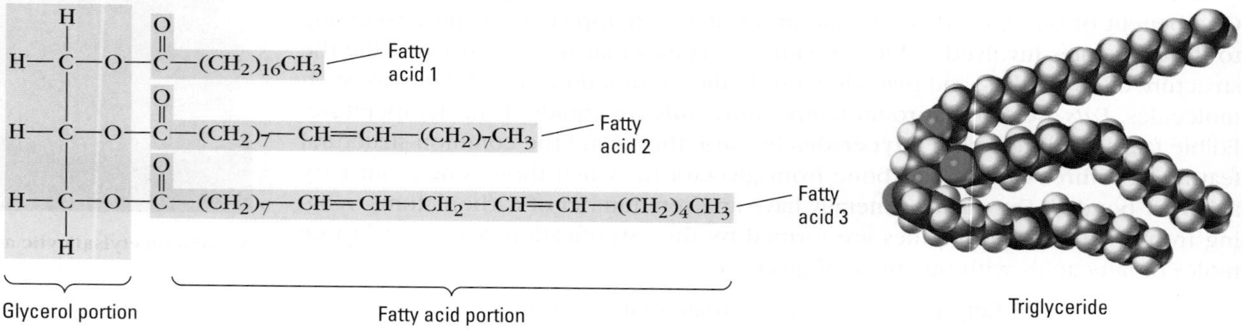

PROBLEM-SOLVING EXAMPLE 12.7 Putting Together a Triglyceride

Using structural formulas, write the equation for the formation of a triglyceride by the reaction of 1 mol glycerol with 1 mol stearic acid and 2 mol oleic acid.

Answer

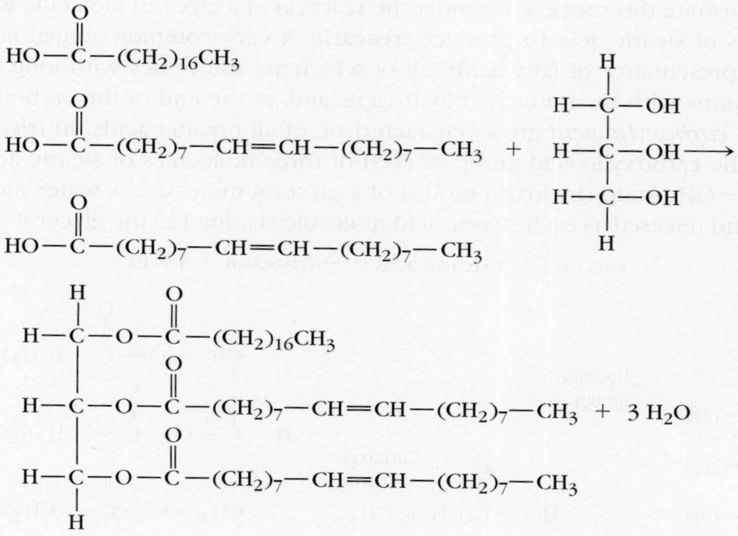

Strategy and Explanation Use the structural formulas given previously for the acids and glycerol and combine them through an esterification reaction. A water molecule is eliminated for each ester bond formed. Several different triglycerides are possible in this case depending on the position of the component fatty acids in the glycerol carbon chain. In the example shown in the answer, stearic acid is attached to the "first" (top) carbon in glycerol, with oleic acid attached to carbons 2 and 3. See Answer above.

PROBLEM-SOLVING PRACTICE 12.7

Use structural formulas to write the equation for the formation of a triglyceride by the reaction of 1 mol glycerol with 1 mol stearic acid and 2 mol oleic acid other than the triglyceride given in Problem-Solving Example 12.7.

Diets consisting of moderate amounts of fats and oils containing mono- and polyunsaturated fatty acids are considered better for good health than diets containing only saturated fats. In spite of this fact, there is a demand for solid or semisolid fats because of their texture and spreadability. The figure below indicates the relative proportions of saturated, monounsaturated, and polyunsaturated fats in some familiar cooking oils and solids.

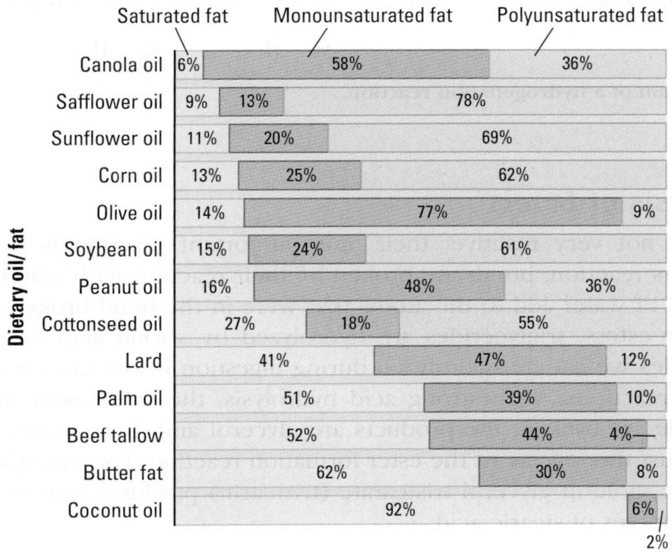

Saturated fats: No C=C

Monounsaturated fats: One C=C bond per molecule

Polyunsaturated fats: Several C=C bonds per molecule

The American Heart Association recommends that no more than 30% of dietary calories come from fat. Fats account for almost 40% of the calories in the average American's diet.

As seen from the diagram above, most dietary vegetable oils are high in unsaturated fatty acids, while most dietary animal fats contain mainly saturated fatty acids. In general, the greater the percentage of unsaturated fatty acids in a triglyceride, the lower its melting point. Thus, highly unsaturated fats are liquids at room temperature (oils); animal fats high in saturated fats are solids at that temperature. The melting points of fats reflect the shape of the molecules. The C—C single bonds in the hydrocarbon portion of saturated fats are all the same, and they allow the molecule to adopt a rather linear shape, which fits nicely into a solid packing arrangement. The C=C double bonds in unsaturated fats create a different shape. Most natural unsaturated fats are in the *cis* configuration at the C=C double bond (***← Section 8.5***), which puts a "kink" into the molecule, preventing unsaturated fat molecules from packing regularly into a solid. *Trans* fatty acid molecules are more linear, similar to those of saturated fats, which has raised health concerns about the widespread dietary use of foods containing *trans* fatty acids.

Vegetable oils can be converted to semisolids by *hydrogenation*—reaction of the oil with H_2 in the presence of a metal such as palladium, which accelerates the

Hydrogenation converts

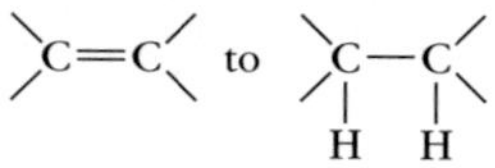

© Thomson Learning/George Semple

Partially hydrogenated fats. Most snack foods contain partially hydrogenated fats.

reaction. The hydrogen reacts by addition to some of the C=C double bonds converting them to C—C single bonds as shown to the left. The degree of saturation in the partially hydrogenated product is limited by carefully controlling reaction conditions so that the product has the proper softness and spreadability. Margarine, shortening (for example, Crisco), and many snack foods contain partially hydrogenated fats, noted on the label as "partially hydrogenated soybean oil" (or cottonseed or other vegetable oils).

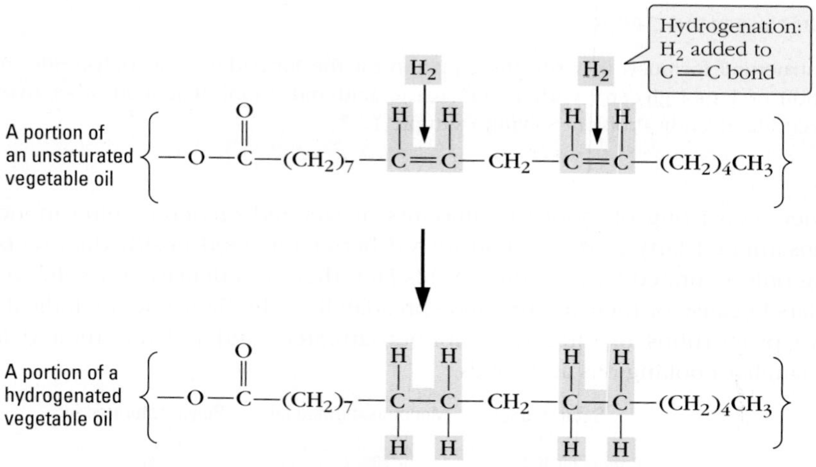

Diagram of a hydrogenation reaction.

Hydrolysis of Esters

Esters are not very reactive; their most important reaction is hydrolysis. In a **hydrolysis** reaction, bonds are broken by their reaction with water, and the H— and —OH of water add to the atoms that were in the bond broken by hydrolysis. Like other esters, triglycerides are hydrolyzed by strong acid or aqueous base. Triglycerides we eat are hydrolyzed during digestion in the same way by enzyme-catalyzed reactions. With strong acid hydrolysis, the three ester linkages in the triglyceride are broken; the products are glycerol and three moles of fatty acids, which is just the reverse of the ester formation reaction. For example, acid hydrolysis of one mole of glycerol tristearate (tristearin) produces one mole of glycerol and three moles of stearic acid.

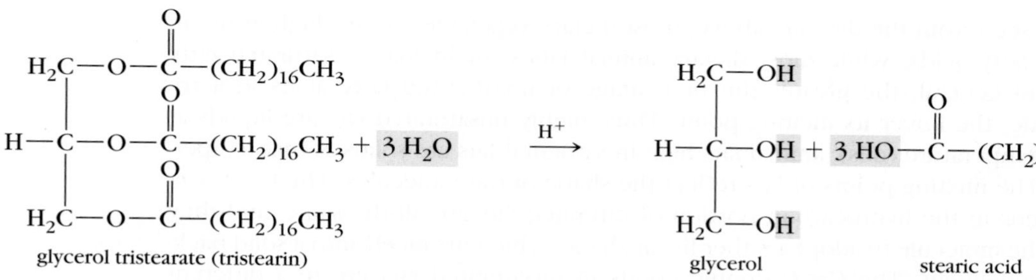

During hydrolysis of a triglyceride with an aqueous base such as NaOH, glycerol is formed and the fatty acids released then react with the base, converting the fatty acids to their salts. In aqueous base, the hydrolysis process is called **saponification,** and the salts formed are called soaps. In biological systems, enzymes assist with saponification reactions that digest fats and oils. The saponification of one mole of glycerol tristearate forms one mole of glycerol and three moles of sodium stearate, a soap.

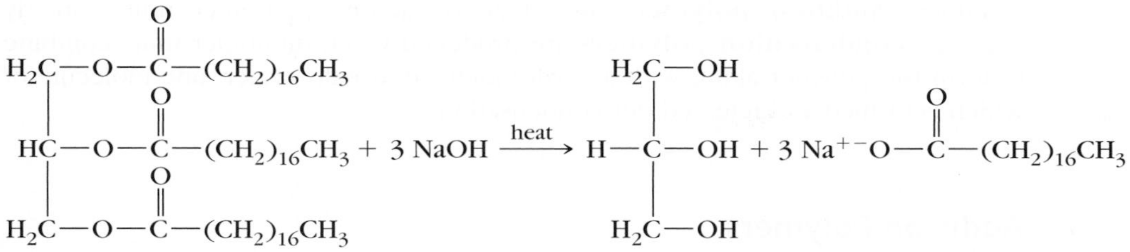

glycerol tristearate, a fat NaOH glycerol sodium stearate, a soap

Note that the saponification reaction requires three moles of base per mole of triglyceride.

EXERCISE 12.15 Triglyceride Structures

(a) Draw the structural formula for the triglyceride formed when glycerol reacts with linoleic acid. Circle the ester linkages in this triester molecule.
(b) Using structural formulas, write the equation for the hydrolysis in aqueous NaOH of the triglyceride formed in part (a).

12.7 Synthetic Organic Polymers

As important as simple organic molecules are, they are also used as starting materials to make an important class of compounds called polymers. **Polymers** (*poly,* "many"; *mer,* "part") are large molecules composed of smaller repeating units, usually arranged in a chain-like structure. For example, polyethylene consists of long chains of $—CH_2—CH_2—$ groups made from repeating ethylene units, $CH_2{=}CH_2$. Polymers occur in nature and are synthesized by chemists as well. It is virtually impossible for us to get through a day without using a dozen or more synthetic organic polymers. Today, synthetic polymers are used to make our clothes, package our foods, and build our computers, phones, and cars. You, a friend, or a family member may be alive because of a medical application of synthetic polymers. Synthetic polymers are so important that approximately 80% of the organic chemical industry is devoted to their production.

Nature makes many different polymers, including cellulose and starch in plants and proteins in both plants and animals.

The discussion in this section answers the question posed in Chapter 1 (← *p. 3*), "How are plastics made and why are there so many different kinds?"

There are two broad categories of the synthetic polymers commonly known as "plastics." One type, called **thermoplastics,** softens and flows when heated; when it is cooled, it hardens again. Common plastic materials that undergo such reversible changes when heated and cooled are polyethylene (milk jugs), polystyrene (inexpensive sunglasses and toys), and polycarbonates (CD audio discs). The other general type is **thermosetting plastics.** When first heated, a thermosetting plastic flows like a thermoplastic. When heated further, however, it forms a rigid structure that will not remelt. Bowling balls, football helmets, and some kitchen countertops are examples of thermosetting plastics.

© Thomson Learning/ Charles D. Winters

Common household items made from plastic.

Some of the most useful synthetic polymers have resulted from copying natural polymers. Synthetic rubber, used in almost every automobile tire, is a copy of the molecule found in natural rubber. Many other useful synthetic polymers, such as polystyrene, nylon, Teflon, and Dacron, have no natural analogs.

Both synthetic and natural polymers are made by chemically joining many small molecules, called **monomers,** into giant polymer molecules known as **macromolecules,** which have molar masses ranging from thousands to millions. In nature, polymerization reactions usually are controlled by enzymes, and in animal cells biopolymer synthesis takes place rapidly at body temperature. Making synthetic polymers often requires high temperatures and pressures and lengthy reaction times. Synthetic and natural polymers are formed by addition or condensation

A macromolecule is a molecule with a very high molar mass.

reactions. **Addition polymers** are made by adding monomer units directly together; **condensation polymers** are produced when monomer units combine to form the polymer along with a small molecule, usually water, one molecule of which is formed and released per condensation.

Addition Polymers

ThomsonNOW™
Go to the Chemistry Interactive menu for a module on **addition polymerization.**

In addition polymerization, the monomer units are added *directly* to each other, hooking together like boxcars on a train to form the polymer; no other products are formed. The monomers for making addition polymers usually contain one or more C═C double bonds.

Polyethylene

The simplest monomer for addition polymerization is ethylene, $CH_2{=}CH_2$, which polymerizes to form *polyethylene*. When heated to 100 to 250 °C at a pressure of 1000 to 3000 atm in the presence of a catalyst, ethylene forms polyethylene chains with molar masses of up to many thousands. Polymerization involves three steps: initiation, propagation, and chain termination.

An organic peroxide, RO—OR, produces two free radicals, RO·, each with an unpaired electron.

Initiation. The first step, *initiation* of the polymerization, involves chemicals such as organic peroxides (R—O—O—R) that are unstable and easily break apart into free radicals, ·OR, each with an unpaired electron (*p. 361*). The free radicals react readily with molecules containing carbon-carbon double bonds to produce new free radicals.

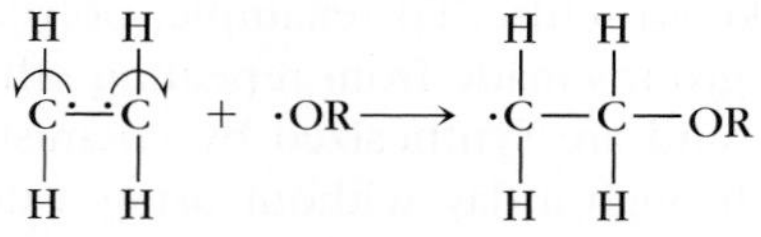

Propagation. The polyethylene chain begins to grow as the unpaired electron radical formed in the initiation step bonds to a double-bond electron in another ethylene molecule.

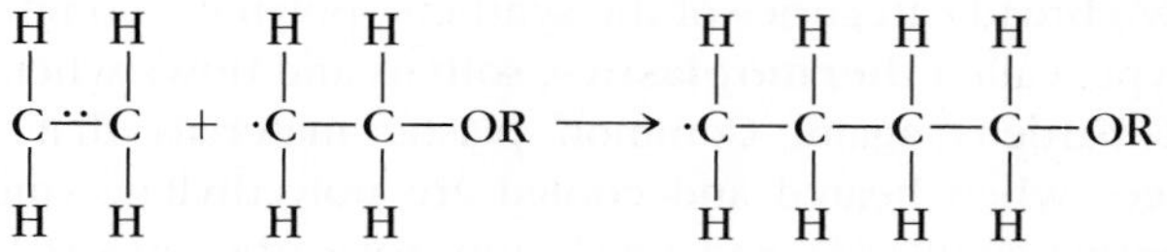

This forms another radical containing an unpaired electron that can bond with yet another ethylene molecule. The process continues, with the chain growing to form a huge polymer molecule.

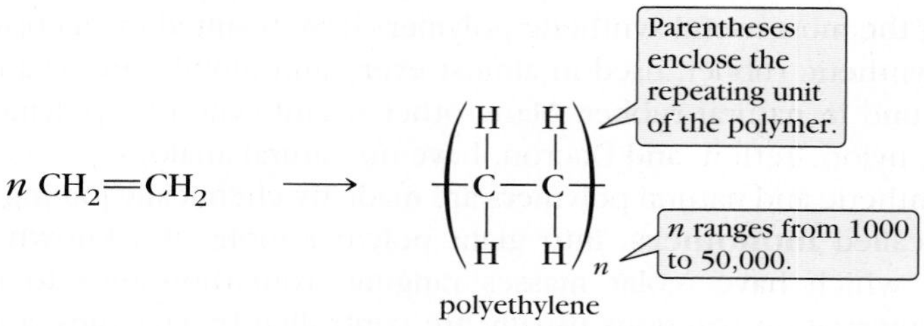

The C═C double bonds in the ethylene monomer have been changed to C—C single bonds in the polyethylene chain.

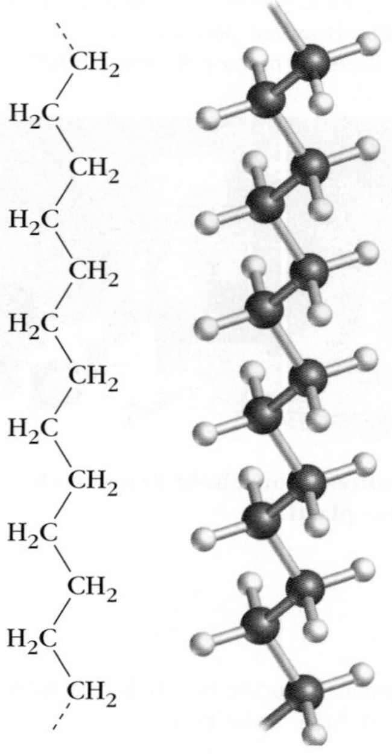

A portion of a polyethylene molecule.

Chain Termination. Eventually, production of the polymer chain stops. This occurs when the supply of monomer is consumed or when no more free radicals are produced, such as when two chains containing free radicals combine. The value of n is called the **degree of polymerization,** the number of repeating units in the polymer chain.

$$R{-}(CH_2)_n{-}CH_2\cdot \; + \; \cdot CH_2{-}(CH_2)_{n^*}{-}R' \longrightarrow R{-}(CH_2)_n{-}CH_2CH_2{-}(CH_2)_{n^*}{-}R'$$

n and n^* represent different numbers of CH_2 groups.

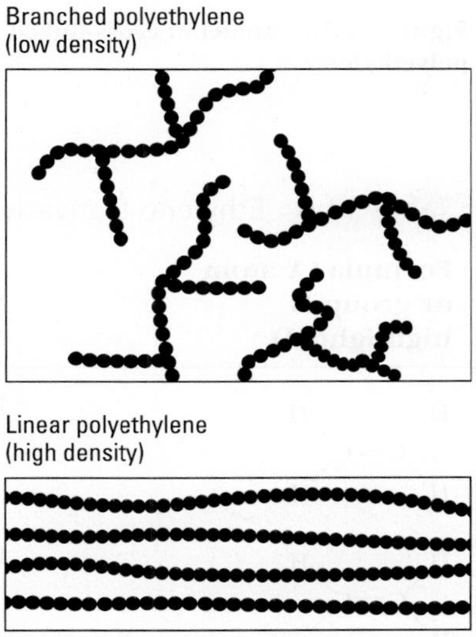

Linear and branched polyethylene.

> **CONCEPTUAL EXERCISE 12.16 What Is at the Ends of the Polymer Chains?**
>
> What do you think is attached at the ends of the polymer chains when all of the ethylene monomer molecules have been polymerized to form polyethylene?

Changing pressures and catalytic conditions produces polyethylenes of different molecular structures and hence different physical properties. For example, chromium oxide as a catalyst yields almost exclusively the linear polyethylene shown in the margin—a polymer with no branches on the carbon chain. Because the bonds around each carbon in the saturated polyethylene chain are in a tetrahedral arrangement, the zigzag structure (shown on page 576) more closely represents the shape of the chain than does a linear drawing. When ethylene is heated to 230 °C at a pressure of 200 atm without the chromium oxide catalyst, free radicals attack the chain at random positions, causing irregular branching.

Polyethylene is the world's most widely used polymer (Figure 12.9). Long linear chains of polyethylene can pack closely together to give a material with high density (0.97 g/mL) and high molar mass, referred to as high-density polyethylene (HDPE). This material is hard, tough, and semirigid; it is used in plastic milk jugs. Branched chains of polyethylene cannot pack as closely together as the linear chains in HDPE,

Chris Springmann/The Stock Market/Corbis

© Thomson Learning/Charles D. Winters

(a) (b)

Figure 12.9 Polyethylene. (a) Production of polyethylene film. The film is manufactured by forcing the polymer through a thin space and inflating it with air. (b) The wide range of properties of different structural types of polyethylene leads to a wide variety of applications.

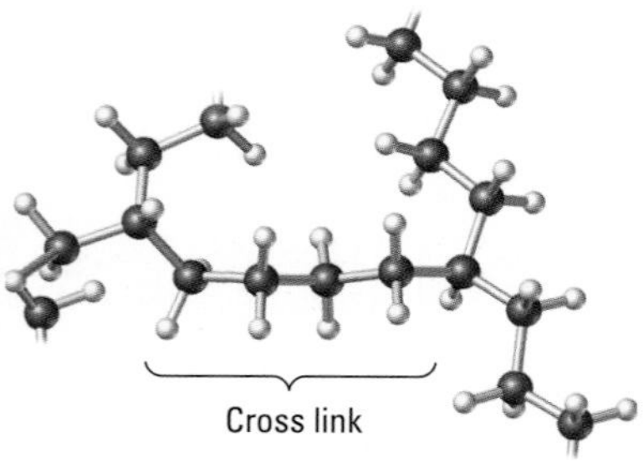

Figure 12.10 **Model of cross-linked polyethylene.**

so the resulting material has a lower density (0.92 g/mL) and is called low-density polyethylene (LDPE). This material is soft and flexible because of its weaker intermolecular forces. It is used to make sandwich bags, for example. If the linear chains of polyethylene are treated in a way that causes short chains of $—CH_2—$ groups to connect adjacent chains, the result is cross-linked polyethylene (CLPE), a very tough material, used for synthetic ice rinks and soft-drink bottle caps (Figure 12.10).

Other Addition Polymers

Many different kinds of addition polymers are made from monomers in which one or more of the hydrogen atoms in ethylene have been replaced with a halogen atom or an organic group. Table 12.6 gives information on some of these monomers and their

Table 12.6 Ethylene Derivatives That Undergo Addition Polymerization

Formula (*X* atom or group is highlighted)	Monomer Common Name	Polymer Name (trade names)	Uses
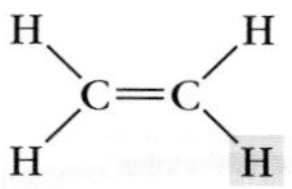	Ethylene	Polyethylene (Polythene)	Squeeze bottles, bags, films, toys and molded objects, electrical insulation
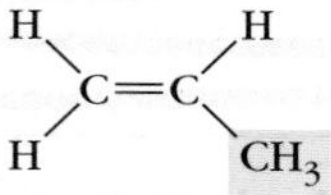	Propylene	Polypropylene (Vectra, Herculon)	Bottles, films, indoor-outdoor carpets
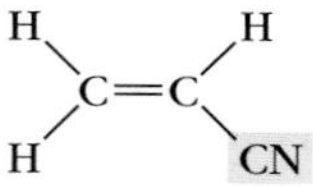	Vinyl chloride	Poly(vinyl chloride) (PVC)	Floor tile, raincoats, pipe
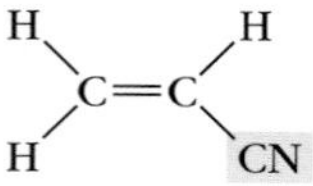	Acrylonitrile	Polyacrylonitrile (Orlon, Acrilan)	Rugs, fabrics
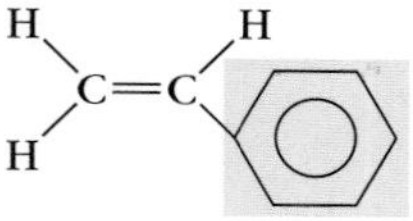	Styrene	Polystyrene (Styrene, Styrofoam, Styron)	Food and drink coolers, building material insulation
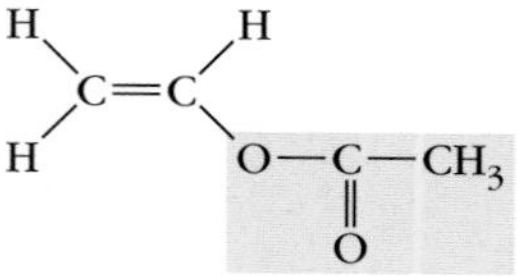	Vinyl acetate	Poly(vinyl acetate) (PVA)	Latex paint, adhesives, textile coatings
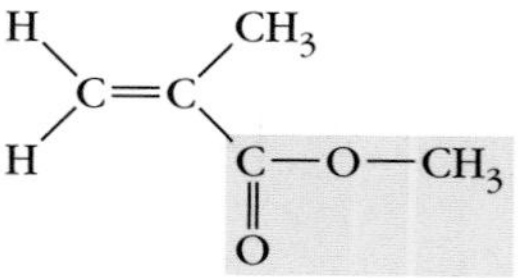	Methyl methacrylate	Poly(methyl methacrylate) (Plexiglas, Lucite)	High-quality transparent objects, latex paints, contact lenses
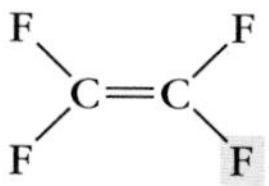	Tetrafluoroethylene	Polytetrafluoroethylene (Teflon)	Gaskets, insulation, bearings, cooking pan coatings

addition polymers. In each case, the replacement atom or group is represented by X in the equation below.

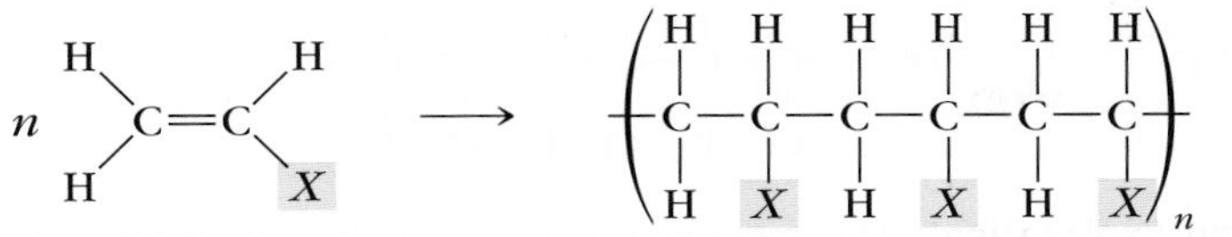

The growing chain

X is an aromatic ring in styrene, the monomer for making polystyrene.

X can be an atom, such as Cl in vinyl chloride, or a group of atoms, such as $-CH_3$ in propylene or $-CN$ in acrylonitrile. For example, vinyl chloride units combine to form poly(vinyl chloride). Each monomer is incorporated directly into the growing polymer chain.

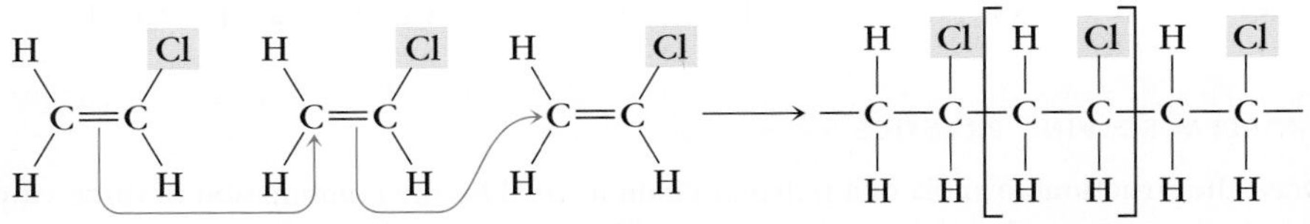

vinyl chloride

Repeating unit poly(vinyl chloride)

In polystyrene, n is typically about 5700. Polystyrene is a clear, hard, colorless, solid thermoplastic that can be molded easily at 250 °C. Nearly seven billion pounds of polystyrene are used annually in the United States alone to make food containers, toys, electrical parts, and many other items. The variation in properties shown by polystyrene products is typical of synthetic polymers. For example, a clear polystyrene drinking glass that is brittle and breaks into sharp pieces somewhat like glass is quite different from an expanded polystyrene coffee cup that is soft and pliable (Figure 12.11).

© Thomson Learning/Charles D. Winters

Figure 12.11 **Polystyrene.** Expanded polystyrene coffee cup (*left*) is soft. Clear polystyrene cup (*right*) is brittle.

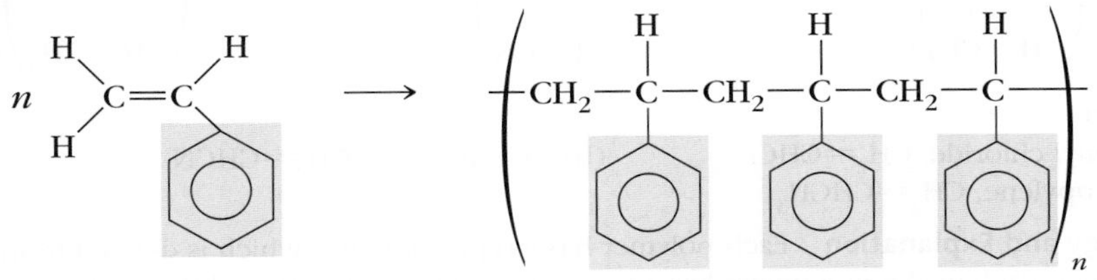

Styrene

The growing chain

A major use of polystyrene is in the production of Styrofoam by "expansion molding." In this process, polystyrene beads are placed in a mold and heated with steam or hot air. The tiny beads contain 4–7% by weight of a low-boiling liquid such as pentane. The steam causes the low-boiling liquid to vaporize and expand the beads. As the foamed particles expand, they are molded into the shape of the mold cavity. Styrofoam is used for meat trays, coffee cups, and many kinds of packing material.

The numerous variations in chain length, branching, and crosslinking make it possible to produce a variety of properties for each type of addition polymer. Chemists and chemical engineers can fine-tune the properties of the polymer to match the desired properties by appropriate selection of monomer and reaction conditions, thus accounting for the widespread and growing use of synthetic polymers.

PROBLEM-SOLVING EXAMPLE 12.8 Adding Up the Monomers

Kel-F is an addition polymer made from the monomer $FClC{=}CF_2$.

(a) Write the Lewis structure of this monomer.

(b) Write the Lewis structure of a portion of the Kel-F polymer containing three monomer units.

Answer

(a) 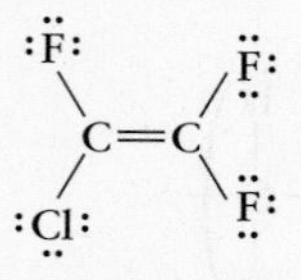 (b) 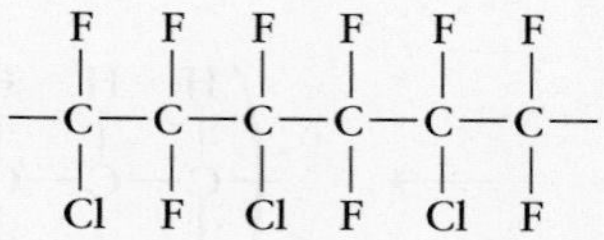

Strategy and Explanation This monomer, which is derived from ethylene, forms an addition polymer. Three monomer units combine to form the beginning of a long polymer chain with each monomer unit coupled directly to the others. No other products form.

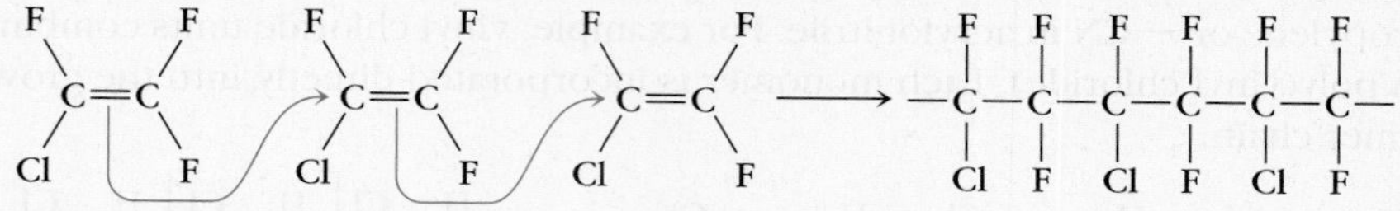

PROBLEM-SOLVING PRACTICE 12.8

Draw the structural formula of a polymer chain formed by the combination of three vinyl acetate monomers. The structural formula of vinyl acetate is in Table 12.6.

PROBLEM-SOLVING EXAMPLE 12.9 Identify the Monomer

Use Table 12.6 to identify the monomer used to make each of the addition polymers, a portion of whose molecule is represented by the structures below.

PVC

(a) 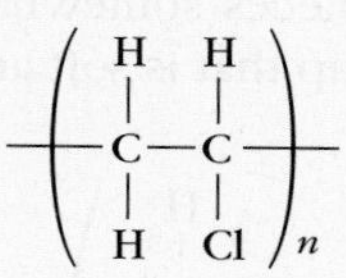

Acrilan

(b) 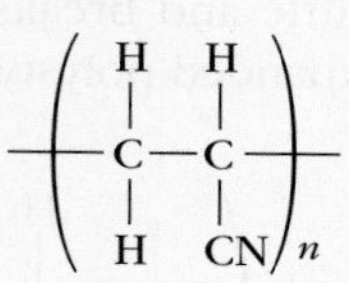

Polypropylene

(c) 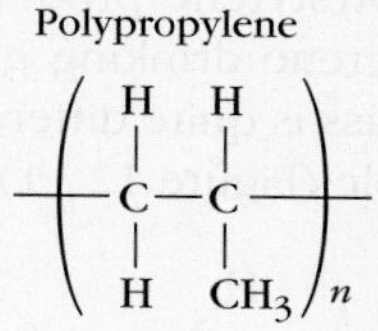

Answer

(a) Vinyl chloride, $CH_2{=}CHCl$ (b) Acrylonitrile, $CH_2{=}CHCN$
(c) Propylene, $CH_2{=}CHCH_3$

Strategy and Explanation Each polymer has a repeating unit, which is derived from its monomer. Each of the monomers has a C=C double bond, but they differ in the nonhydrogen atom or group attached to the carbon atom.

(a) $CH_2{=}CHCl$ (b) $CH_2{=}CHCN$
(c) $CH_2{=}CHCH_3$

PROBLEM-SOLVING PRACTICE 12.9

Draw the structural formula of the repeating unit for each of these addition polymers.
(a) Polypropylene (b) Poly(vinyl acetate) (c) Poly(vinyl alcohol)

© GRANDADAM/Photo Researchers, Inc.

Natural latex coming from a rubber tree.

Natural and Synthetic Rubbers

Natural rubber is a hydrocarbon whose monomer unit has the empirical formula C_5H_8. When rubber is decomposed in the absence of oxygen, the monomer 2-methyl-1,3-butadiene (isoprene) is obtained.

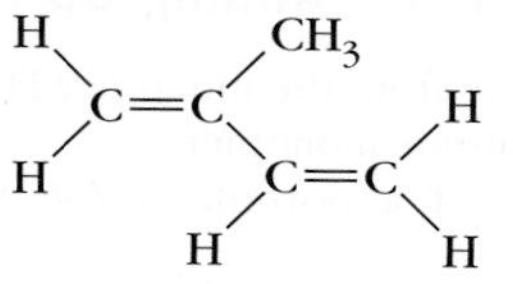

2-methyl-1,3-butadiene (isoprene)

CHEMISTRY YOU CAN DO

Making "Gluep"

White school glue, such as Elmer's glue, contains poly(vinyl acetate) and other ingredients. A "gluep" similar to Silly Putty can be made by mixing $\frac{1}{2}$ cup of glue with $\frac{1}{2}$ cup of water and then adding $\frac{1}{2}$ cup of liquid starch and stirring the mixture. After stirring it, work the mixture in your hands until it has a putty consistency. Roll it into a ball and let it sit on a flat surface. Shape a piece into a ball and drop it on a hard surface.

The "gluep" can be stored in a sealed plastic bag for several weeks. Although "gluep" does not readily stick to clothes, it leaves a water mark on wooden furniture, so be careful where you set it. Mold will form on the "gluep" after a few weeks, but adding a few drops of Lysol to it will retard mold formation.

1. What did you observe about "gluep" when it was left sitting on a flat surface?
2. Did the ball of "gluep" bounce when it was dropped?

Natural rubber occurs as *latex* (an emulsion of rubber particles in water) that oozes from rubber trees when the bark is cut. Precipitation of the rubber particles yields a gummy mass that is not only elastic and water-repellent but also very sticky, especially when warm. In 1839, after five years' work on natural rubber, Charles Goodyear (1800–1860) discovered that heating gum rubber with sulfur produces a material that is no longer sticky but is still elastic, water-repellent, and resilient.

Vulcanized rubber, as the type of rubber Goodyear discovered is now known, contains short chains of sulfur atoms that bond together the polymer chains of the natural rubber and reduce its unsaturation. The sulfur chains help to align the polymer chains, so the material does not undergo a permanent change when stretched, but springs back to its original shape and size when the stress is removed. Substances that behave this way are called *elastomers.*

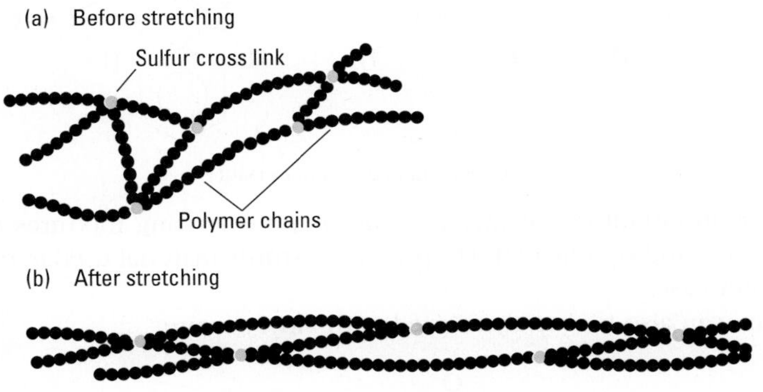

The behavior of natural rubber (polyisoprene) is due to the specific molecular geometry within the polymer chain. We can write the formula for polyisoprene with the $—CH_2CH_2—$ groups on opposite sides of the double bond (the *trans* arrangement)

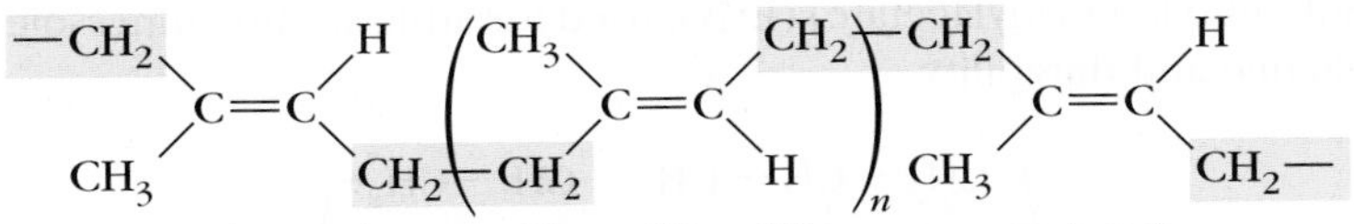

poly-*trans*-isoprene (the $—CH_2—CH_2—$ groups are *trans*)

or with the $—CH_2CH_2—$ groups on the same side of the double bond in a *cis* arrangement (p. 344),

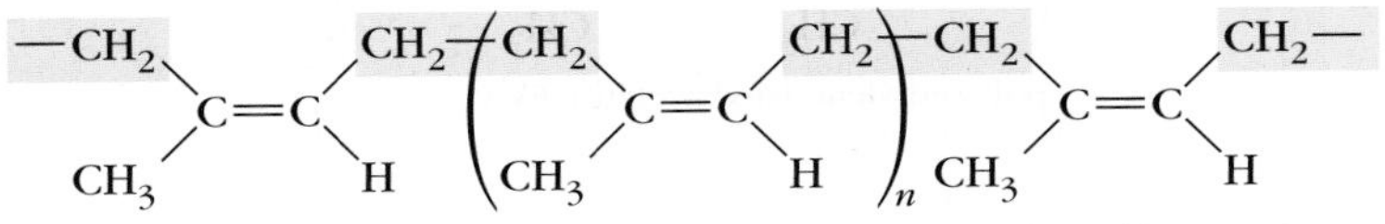

poly-*cis*-isoprene (the $—CH_2—CH_2—$ groups are *cis*)

Natural rubber is poly-*cis*-isoprene. However, the *trans* material also occurs in nature in the leaves and bark of the sapotacea tree and is known as *gutta-percha.* It is brittle and hard and is used for golf ball cores and electrical insulation.

In 1955, chemists at the Goodyear and Firestone companies almost simultaneously discovered how to prepare synthetic poly-*cis*-isoprene. This material is structurally identical to natural rubber. Today, synthetic poly-*cis*-isoprene can be manufactured cheaply and is used when natural rubber is in short supply.

Copolymers

Saran Wrap is an example of a copolymer of vinyl chloride with 1,1-dichloroethylene.

Many commercially important addition polymers are **copolymers,** polymers obtained by polymerizing a mixture of two or more different monomers. A copolymer of styrene with butadiene is the most important synthetic rubber produced in the United States. More than 1.5 million tons of styrene-butadiene rubber (SBR) are produced each year in the United States for making tires. A 3:1 mole ratio of butadiene to styrene is used to make SBR.

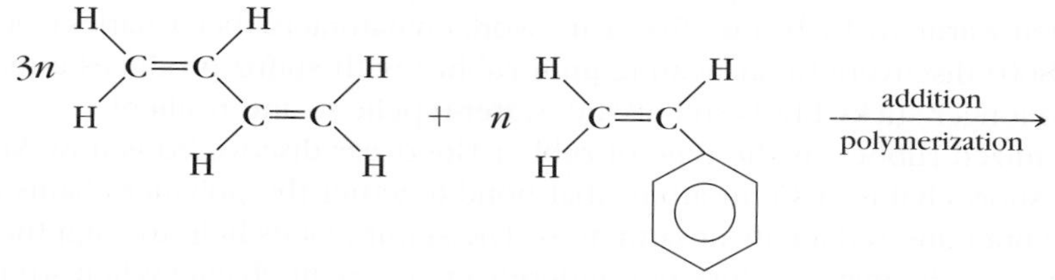

1,3-butadiene styrene

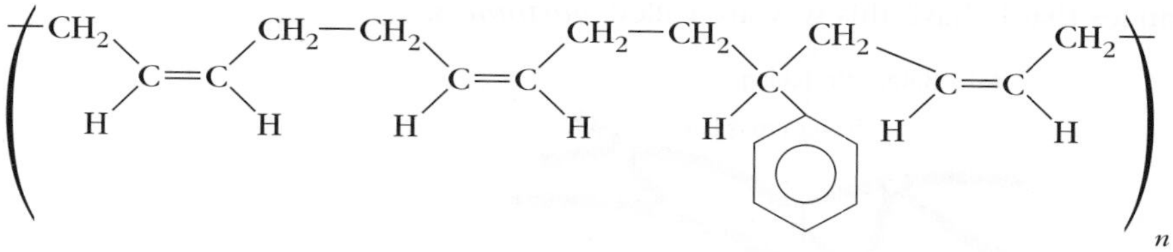

styrene-butadiene rubber (SBR)

Another important copolymer is made by polymerizing mixtures of acrylonitrile, butadiene, and styrene (ABS) to produce a sturdy material used in car bumpers and computer cases.

Ethylene can also be copolymerized with vinyl acetate

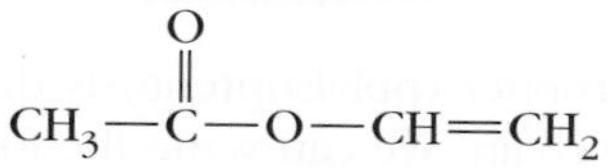

vinyl acetate

to form poly(ethylene vinylacetate) (EVA), used for athletic shoe innersoles because of its resilience and durability.

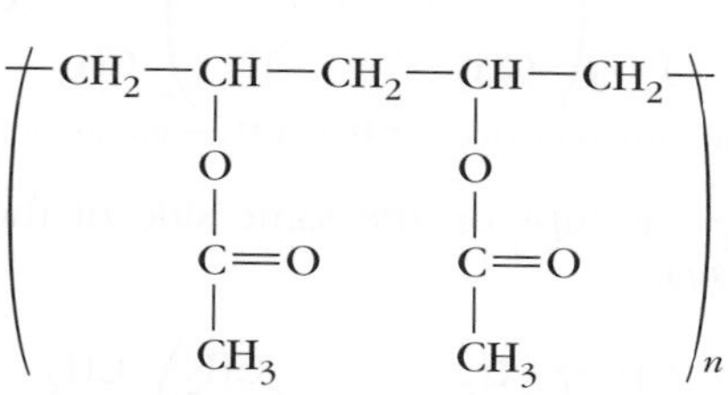

poly (ethylene vinyl acetate), EVA

© Thomson Learning/George Semple

EVA innersole.

PROBLEM-SOLVING EXAMPLE 12.10 Macromolecular Masses

Polytetrafluoroethylene (Teflon) is an addition polymer made of chains of $CF_2{=}CF_2$ monomer units. This polymer has a molar mass of 1.0×10^6 g/mol. Calculate the number of such units in the polymer—that is, the degree of polymerization.

Answer 10,000 monomer units

Strategy and Explanation Each $CF_2{=}CF_2$ monomer unit has a molar mass of 100.0 g/mol. Therefore, the number of monomer units can be calculated using the molar mass of the polymer.

$$1 \times 10^6 \text{ g} \times \frac{1 \text{ monomer unit}}{100 \text{ g}} = 1 \times 10^4 \text{ monomer units}$$

PROBLEM-SOLVING PRACTICE 12.10

Calculate the degree of polymerization of poly(vinyl chloride) that has a molar mass of 150,000 g/mol.

Condensation Polymers

The reactions of alcohols with carboxylic acids to give esters (p. 570) are examples of condensation reactions. Condensation polymers are formed by condensation polymerization reactions between monomers. Unlike addition polymerization reactions, condensation polymerization reactions do not depend on the presence of a double bond in the reacting molecules. Rather, condensation polymerization reactions generally require two different functional groups present in the same monomer or in two different monomers. Each of the two monomers has a functional group at each end of the monomer. As the functional groups at each end of one monomer react with the groups of the other monomer, long-chain condensation polymers are produced.

For example, molecules with two carboxylic acid groups (—COOH), such as terephthalic acid, and other molecules with two alcohol groups, such as ethylene glycol, can react with each other at both ends to form ester linkages (shaded part of the structure). Water is the other product of this condensation polymerization reaction; it is produced during the formation of each ester linkage in the polymer.

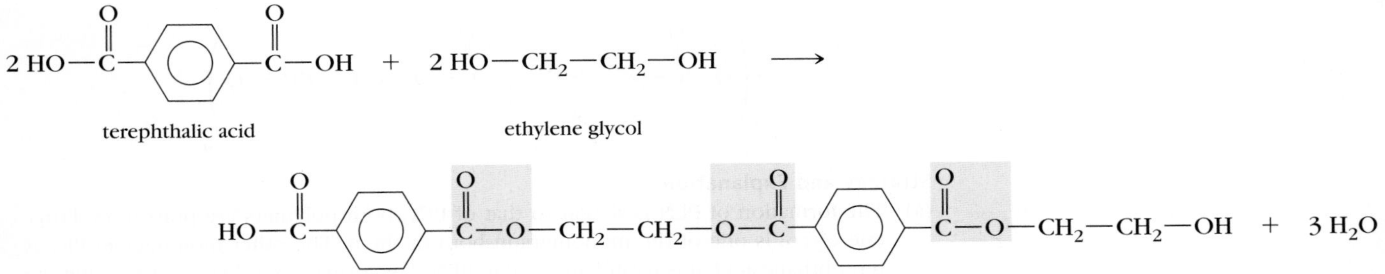

terephthalic acid

ethylene glycol

terephthalic acid-ethylene glycol ester

Because this ester has a —COOH group on one end and an —OH group on the other end, the —COOH group can react with an —OH group of another ethylene glycol molecule. Similarly, the remaining alcohol group on the ester can react with another terephthalic acid molecule. This process continues, forming long chains of poly(ethylene terephthalate), a **polyester** commonly known as PET.

ThomsonNOW™
Go to the Chemistry Interactive menu for a module on **polyester formation.**

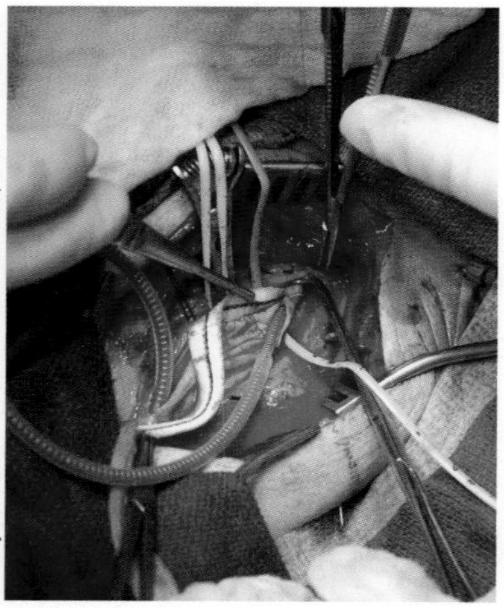

© Barry Slaven/The Medical File/Peter Arnold, Inc.

Medical uses of Dacron. A Dacron patch is used to close an atrial septal defect in a heart patient.

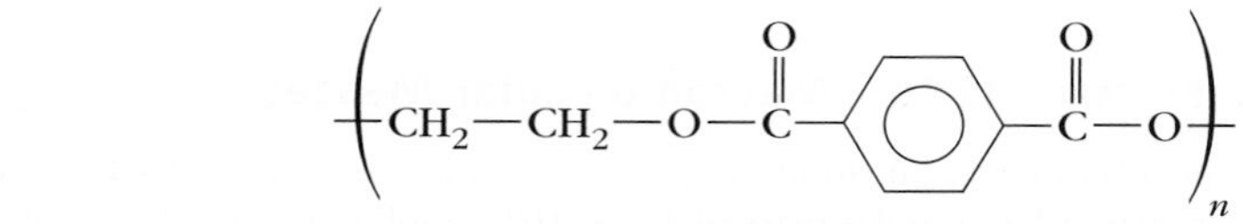

the repeating unit poly(ethylene terephthalate), PET

Each year more than one billion pounds of PET are produced in the United States for making beverage bottles, apparel, tire cord, film for photography and magnetic recording, food packaging, coatings for microwave and conventional ovens, and home furnishings. A variety of trade names is associated with these applications. PET textile fibers are marketed under such names as Dacron and Terylene. Films of the same polyester, when magnetically coated, are used to make audio and TV tapes. This film, Mylar, has unusual strength and can be rolled into sheets one thirtieth the thickness of a human hair. The inert, nontoxic, noninflammatory, and non-blood-clotting characteristics of PET polymers make Dacron tubing an excellent substitute for human blood vessels in heart bypass operations. Dacron sheets are also used as a skin substitute for burn victims.

PROBLEM-SOLVING EXAMPLE 12.11 Condensation Polymerization

Poly(ethylene naphthalate) (PEN) is used for bar code labels. This condensation polymer is made by the reaction between naphthalic acid and ethylene glycol,

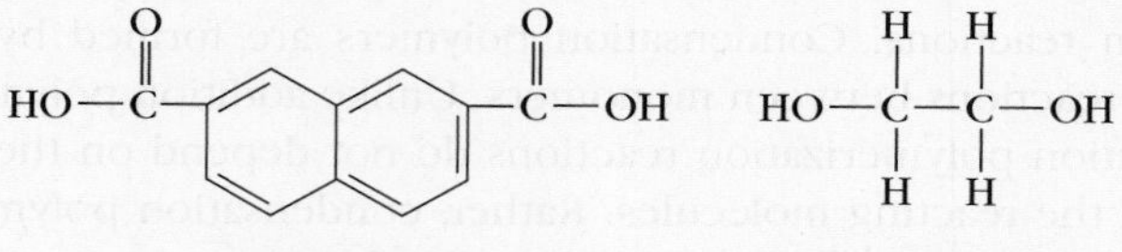

naphthalic acid ethylene glycol

(a) Write the structural formula of the molecule formed after two ethylene glycol molecules have polymerized with two naphthalic acid molecules.

(b) Write the structural formula of the repeating unit of the polymer.

Answer

(a)

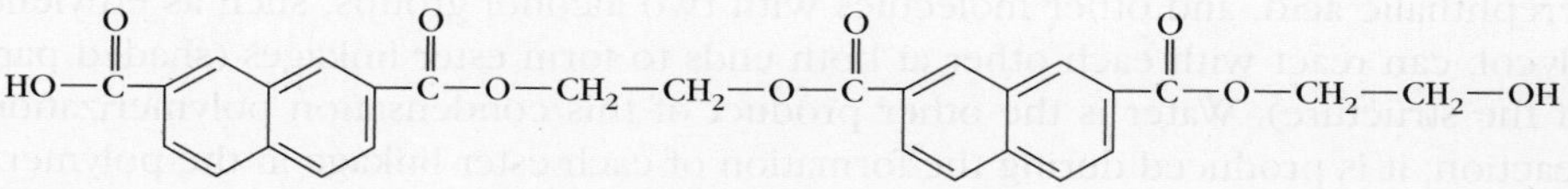

(b)

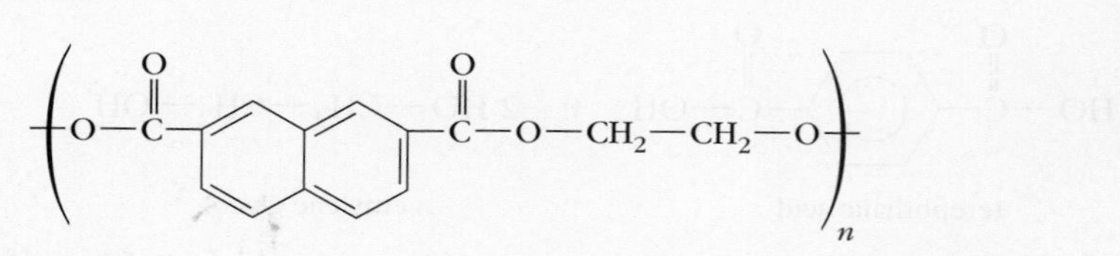

Strategy and Explanation

(a) The formation of PEN is similar to that of PET; both polymers are polyesters. Ethylene glycol is one of the monomers in both of them. The other monomer in PET is terephthalic acid; it is naphthalic acid in PEN. The formation of PEN occurs when the carboxylic acid groups of naphthalic acid react with the alcohol groups of ethylene glycol to form ester linkages.

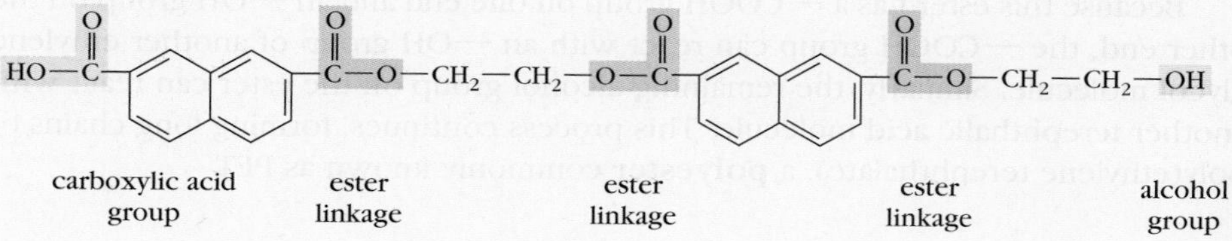

Notice that there are unreacted carboxylic acid and alcohol groups at each end of the molecule. These react with other ethylene glycol and naphthalic acid groups, respectively. The growing polymer chain continues reacting at each end until it becomes very long.

(b) The repeating unit is the smallest unit that contains both monomers. In this case, the repeating unit is formed by combining one naphthalic acid molecule with one ethylene glycol molecule.

PROBLEM-SOLVING PRACTICE 12.11

A condensation polymer can be made from the single monomer glycolic acid. A portion of the polymer is given below.

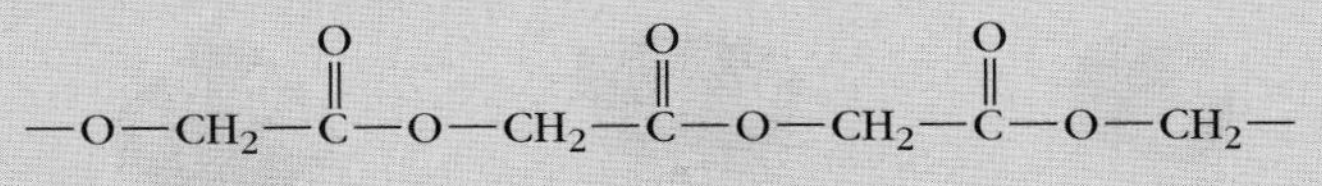

Write the structural formula of glycolic acid.

CHEMISTRY IN THE NEWS

Superabsorbent Polymers

Disposable diapers, a common commodity, have been greatly improved because of the development of superabsorbent polymers (SAPs), which absorb up to 1000 times their weight in liquid, making them an ideal absorbent for urine in diapers. Disposable diapers using SAPs came on the market in the mid-1980s and were an immediate success. Today approximately 95% of all diapers sold in the United States are SAP-based.

Although the exact formulation of the SAPs used in disposable diapers is proprietary, some general details are known about their composition and production. Modern SAPs are made from partially neutralized, cross-linked poly(acrylic acid). Their ionic nature and interconnected structures allow them to absorb large quantities of liquids without dissolving. Most SAPs are manufactured by a solution polymerization process that involves joining acrylic acid with a cross-linking material. Manufacturing is a four-step process. In the first step, monomers and an initiator are dissolved in water. The monomers undergo condensation polymerization to form the polymer, a rubbery, colorless gel. In subsequent steps, the wet gel is dried and then ground into its final form, a granular, amorphous powder. The fine powder particles are further cross-linked by the addition of small amounts of a cross-linking agent to form the final product. The amount of cross linker used determines the extent of absorbency.

When wetted, the SAPs form a solid, rubbery gel that prevents urine leaking from it. Superabsorbent diapers generally contain 10 to 15 g of SAPs, enough to retain 30 times their weight in urine while remaining soft and pliable. In 2003, more than 22 billion SAP-based diapers were sold in the United States and Canada. Quite a remarkable development for SAPs, developed nearly 70 years ago, that remained a curiosity until applied to disposable diapers.

SAPs can also be used by firefighters to form a watery gel that prevents or retards the spread of flames. Underground cables and wires coated with SAPs prevent the penetration of water into areas where the wires or cables are spliced or cut.

SOURCE: American Chemical Society, *Chemistry*, Spring 2005; pp. 19–22.

Courtesy of BASF

Superabsorbent polymers (SAPs) can absorb prodigious amounts of liquid per gram of SAP.
Source: American Chemical Society, *Chemistry*, Spring 2005; p. 20.

Amines, Amides, and Polyamides

Amines are organic compounds containing an $-NH_2$ functional group and are classified as primary, secondary, or tertiary amines according to how many of the H atoms in the $-NH_2$ group are replaced by alkyl groups. There can be one, two, or three alkyl groups covalently bonded to the nitrogen atom, for example as in methylamine, dimethylamine, and trimethylamine:

RNH_2 is primary; R_2NH is secondary; and R_3N is tertiary.

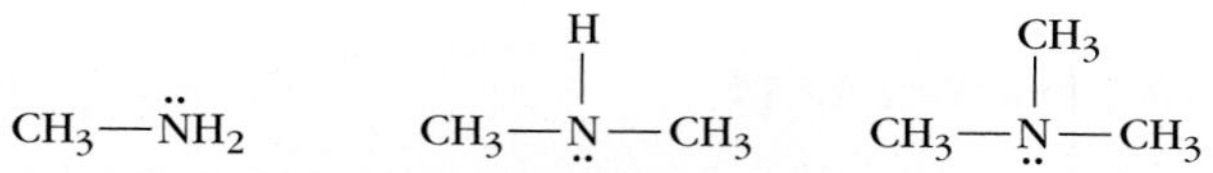

methylamine dimethylamine trimethylamine

An important condensation reaction occurs when an amine reacts with a carboxylic acid at high temperature to split out a water molecule and form an **amide:**

Amides contain the $-\overset{\overset{O}{\|}}{C}-\overset{\overset{H}{|}}{N}-$ functional group.

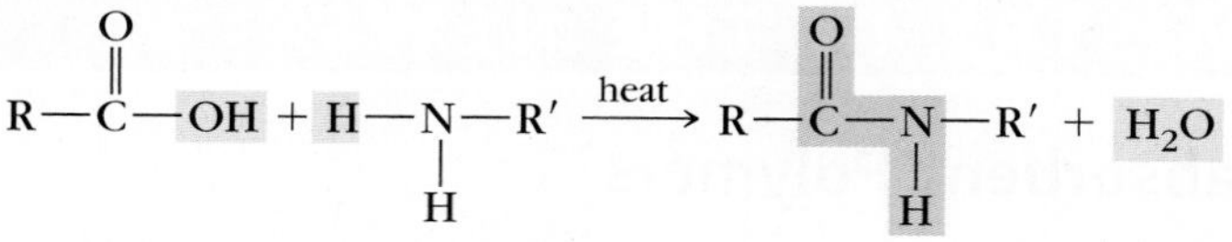

carboxylic acid amine amide water

Dr. Wallace Carothers of the DuPont Company discovered a useful and important type of condensation polymerization reaction that occurs when diamines (compounds containing two $-NH_2$ groups) react with dicarboxylic acids (compounds containing two $-COOH$ groups) to form polymers called **polyamides** or nylons. In February 1935 his research yielded a product known as nylon-66 prepared from adipic acid (a dicarboxylic acid) and hexamethylenediamine (a diamine). Adipoyl chloride, a derivative of adipic acid, is also used in place of adipic acid (Figure 12.12).

The name of nylon-66 is based on the number of carbon atoms in the diamine and diacid, respectively, that are used to make the polymer. Since hexamethylenediamine and adipic acid each have six carbon atoms, the product is called nylon-66.

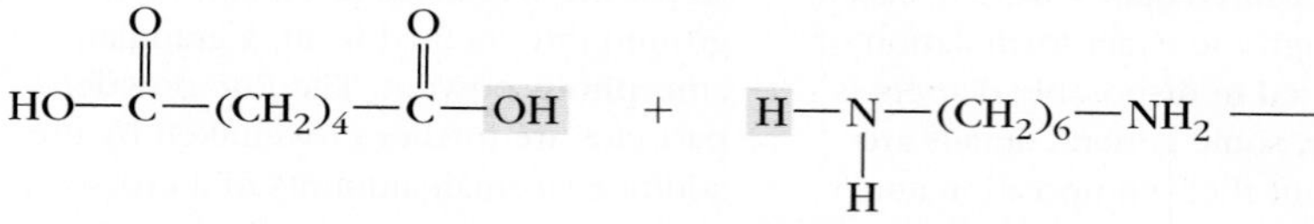

adipic acid hexamethylenediamine

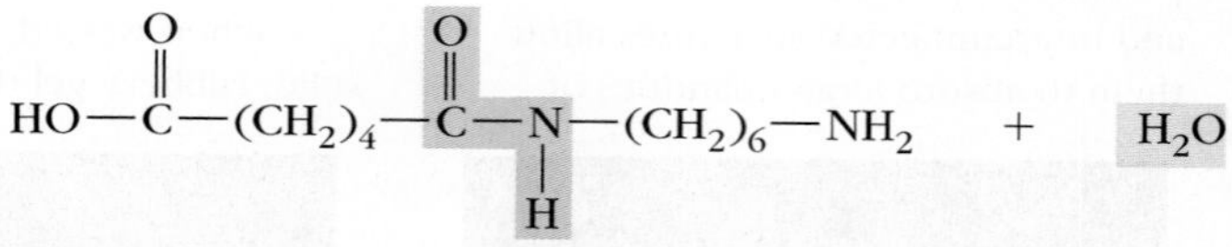

The reactions continue, extending the polymer chain, which consists of alternating adipic acid and hexamethylenediamine units. The overall equation is

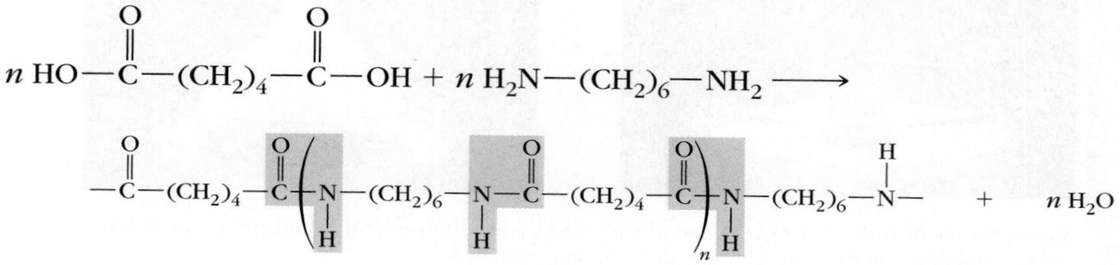

nylon

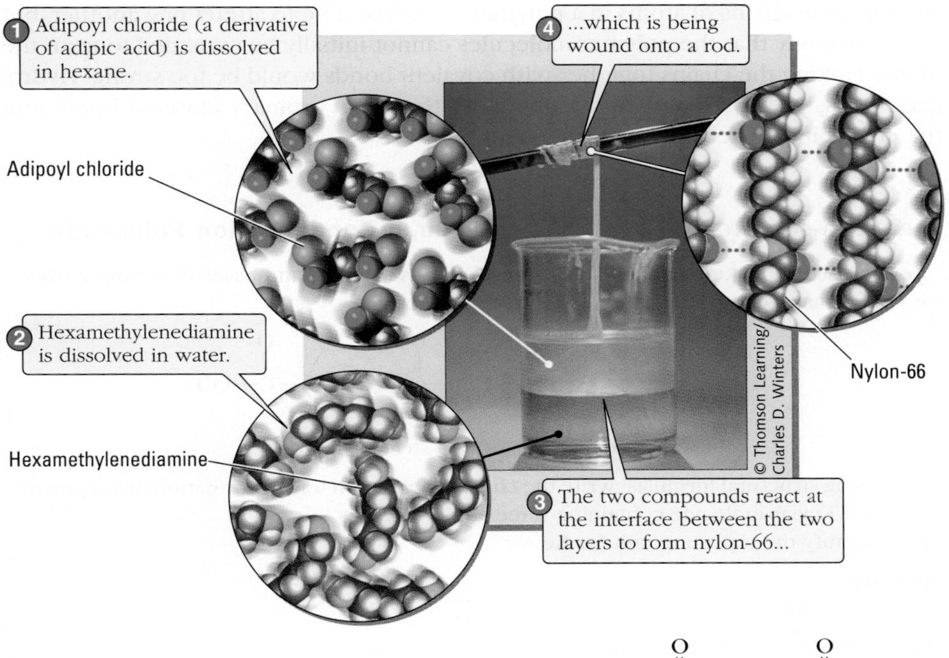

Active Figure 12.12 **Making nylon-66.** Adipoyl chloride is $\mathrm{Cl{-}\overset{O}{\overset{\|}{C}}{-}(CH_2)_4{-}\overset{O}{\overset{\|}{C}}{-}Cl}$. Go to the Active Figures menu at ThomsonNOW to test your understanding of the concepts in this figure.

The functional group $\mathrm{{-}\overset{O}{\overset{\|}{C}}{-}\overset{H}{\overset{|}{N}}{-}}$ between the monomers is the **amide linkage;** hence, the polymers are known as polyamides.

Figure 12.13 illustrates another facet of the structure of nylon—hydrogen bonding—that explains why nylon makes such good fibers. To have good tensile

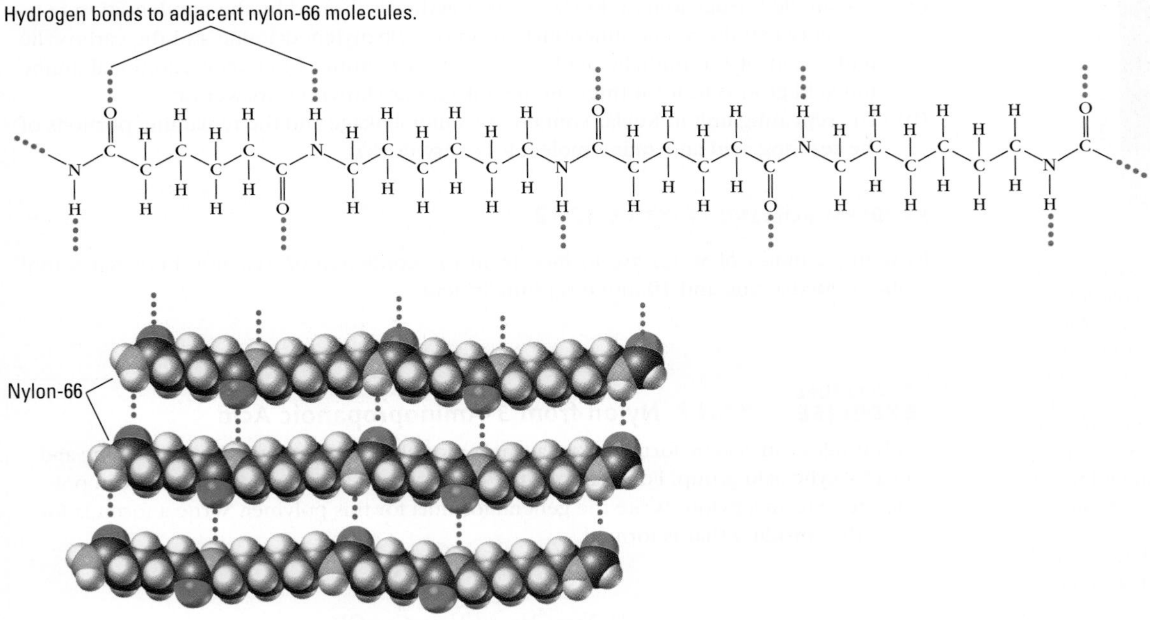

Figure 12.13 **Hydrogen bonding in nylon-66.**

© Reuters/Corbis

A Kevlar helmet. A bullet creased, but did not penetrate, the helmet.

strength, the chains of atoms in a polymer should be able to attract one another, but not so strongly that the polymer molecules cannot initially be extended to form the fibers. Linking the chains together with covalent bonds would be too strong. Hydrogen bonds, with a strength about one tenth that of an ordinary covalent bond, join the chains in the desired manner.

PROBLEM-SOLVING EXAMPLE 12.12 Kevlar, a Condensation Polyamide

Kevlar, used to make bulletproof vests and helmets, canoes, and baseball batting gloves, is made from *p*-phenylenediamine and terephthalic acid.

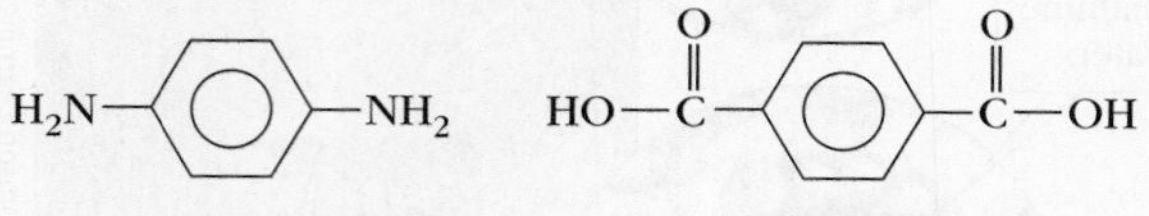

p-phenylenediamine terephthalic acid

(a) Using structural formulas, write the chemical equation for the formation of a segment of a Kevlar molecule containing three amide linkages.

(b) Identify the repeating unit for Kevlar.

Answer

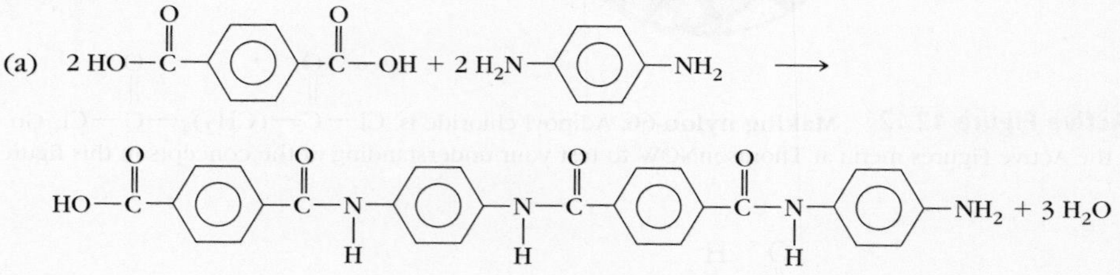

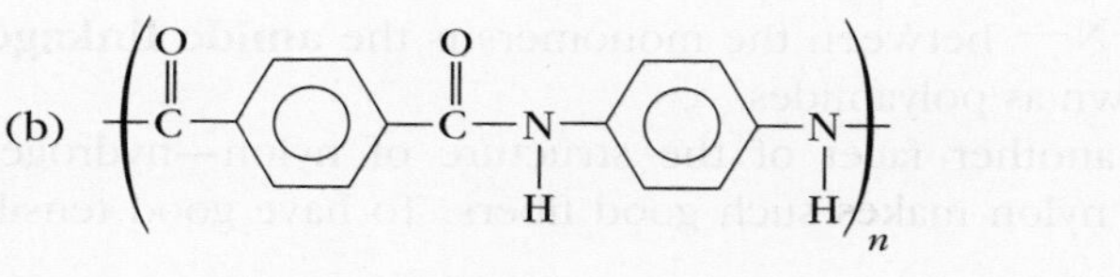

Strategy and Explanation

(a) The amide linkage joining Kevlar units together is formed by the condensation reaction between the amine functional group of *p*-phenylenediamine and the carboxylic acid group of terephthalic acid. The reaction continues between additional amine and acid groups to form three amide linkages as shown in Answer (a).

(b) The repeating unit in Kevlar contains an amide linkage and the remaining portions of the reacting acid and amine molecules (Answer (b)).

PROBLEM-SOLVING PRACTICE 12.12

How many moles of water are formed from the condensation reaction between 6 mol *p*-phenylenediamine and 10 mol terephthalic acid?

Courtesy DuPont Company

Stephanie Louise Kwolek

1923–

In 1946, Stephanie Kwolek received a Bachelor of Science degree from Carnegie Tech (now Carnegie Mellon University). Although wanting to study medicine, she couldn't afford it and decided to take a temporary job at DuPont. She liked her work so well that she stayed for 40 years, retiring in 1986. Kwolek is best known for the development of Kevlar fiber, which is five times stronger than steel on an equal weight basis. She has received many awards, including the Perkin Medal in 1997, considered one of the most prestigious awards a chemist can receive in the United States.

CONCEPTUAL EXERCISE 12.17 Nylon from 3-Aminopropanoic Acid

Polyamides can also be formed from a single monomer that contains both an amine and a carboxylic acid group. For example, the compound 3-aminopropanoic acid can polymerize to form a nylon. Write the general formula for this polymer. Write a formula for the other product that is formed.

$$H_2N-CH_2-CH_2-\overset{\displaystyle O}{\overset{\|}{C}}-OH$$

3-aminopropanoic acid

EXERCISE 12.18 Functional Groups

We have discussed several functional groups. Shown below is the structural formula of aspartame, an artificial sweetener. Identify each of the numbered functional groups.

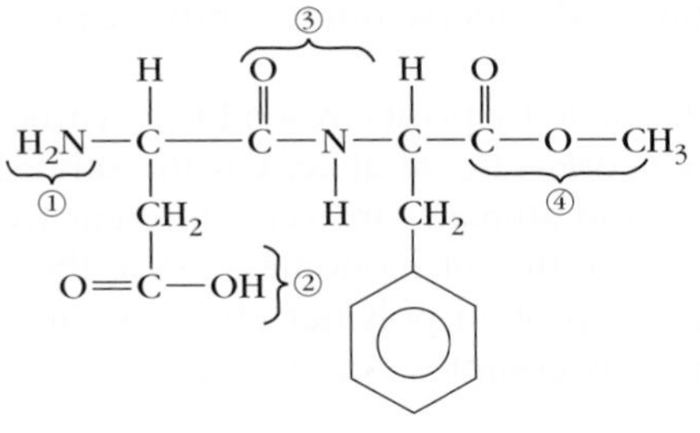

aspartame

Recycling Plastics

Polyethylene terephthalate (PET), widely used for soft-drink bottles, and high-density polyethylene (HDPE) are the most commonly recycled plastics. Major end uses for recycled PET include fiberfill for ski jackets and sleeping bags, carpet fibers, and tennis balls. It takes just five recycled 2-L PET soft-drink bottles to make a T-shirt and only three for the insulation in a ski jacket. High-density polyethylene (HDPE) is the second most widely recycled plastic; principal sources are milk, juice, and water jugs. In the United States, more than 200 million recycled HDPE milk and water jugs have been converted into a fiber to make Tyvek, which is used for sportswear, insulating wrap for new buildings, and very durable shipping envelopes.

Codes are stamped on plastic containers to help consumers identify and sort their recyclable plastics (Table 12.7). There has been a dramatic increase in the recycling of plastics in recent years. Still further increases require a sufficient demand for products made partially or completely from recycled materials. The use of some recycled, postconsumer plastics has been mandated by law in some places. Since 1995 in California, for example, all HDPE packaging must contain 25% recycled material. A real challenge lies ahead in finding economically viable methods to recycle the plastics from the growing, massive numbers of obsolete personal computers, CD players, and cellular phones.

Through recycling, more than 850,000 tons of PET did not end up in landfills in 2005.

© Thomson Learning/Charles D. Winters

These jackets are made from recycled PET soda bottles.

Table 12.7 Plastic Container Codes

Code	Material	Code	Material
1 PETE	Polyethylene terephthalate (PET)*	5 PP	Polypropylene
2 HDPE	High-density polyethylene	6 PS	Polystyrene
3 V	Poly(vinyl chloride) (PVC)*	7 OTHER	All other resins and layered multimaterial
4 LDPE	Low-density polyethylene		

*Bottle codes are different from standard industrial identification to avoid confusion with registered trademarks.

John Sohlden/Visuals Unlimited, Inc.

A Tyvek-wrapped house under construction.

ThomsonNOW
Sign in to ThomsonNOW at **www.thomsonedu.com** to access a set of interactive molecular models of **biologically important molecules.**

12.8 Biopolymers: Proteins and Polysaccharides

Biopolymers—naturally occurring polymers—are an integral part of living things. Many advances in creating and understanding synthetic polymers came from studying biopolymers.

Cellulose and starch, made by plants, resemble a synthetic polymer in that the monomer molecules—glucose—are all alike. On the other hand, proteins, which are made by both plants and animals, are very different from synthetic polymers because they include many different monomers. Also, the occurrences of the different monomers along the protein polymer chain are anything but regular. As a result, proteins are extremely complex copolymers.

Amino Acids to Proteins

Amino acids, the monomer units in proteins, each contain a carboxylic acid group and an amine group. The 20 amino acids from which proteins are made have the general formula

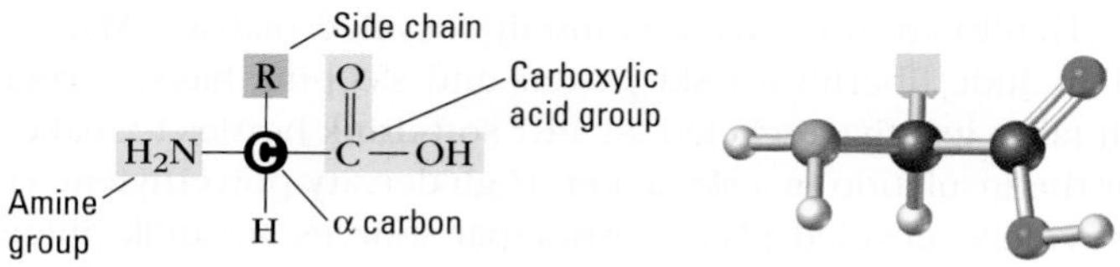

and are described as α-amino acids because the amine ($-NH_2$) group is attached to the **alpha carbon,** the first carbon next to the carboxylic acid ($-COOH$) group. Each amino acid has a different R group, called a side chain (Table 12.8, p. 591). Glycine, the simplest amino acid, has just hydrogen as its R group. Note from the table that some amino acid R groups contain only carbon and hydrogen, while others contain carboxylic acid, amine, or other functional groups. The amino acids are grouped in Table 12.8 according to whether the R group is nonpolar, polar, acidic, or basic. Each amino acid has a three-letter abbreviation for its name.

CONCEPTUAL EXERCISE 12.19 Hydrogen Bonding Between Amino Acids in Proteins

Pick two amino acids from Table 12.8 whose R groups could hydrogen-bond with one another if they were close together in a protein chain or in two adjacent protein chains. Then pick two whose R groups would not hydrogen-bond under similar circumstances.

Like nylon, proteins are polyamides. The amide bond in a protein is formed by the condensation polymerization reaction between the amine group of one amino acid and the carboxylic acid group of another. In proteins, the amide linkage is called a **peptide linkage.** Relatively small amino acid polymers (up to about 50 amino acids) are known as **polypeptides.** Proteins are polypeptides containing hundreds to thousands of amino acids bonded together.

Peptide linkages are also referred to as peptide bonds.

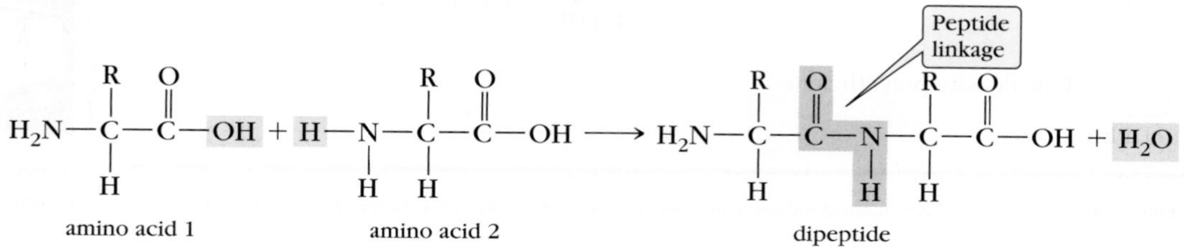

Table 12.8 Common L-Amino Acids Found in Proteins†

Amino Acid	Abbreviation	Structure	Amino Acid	Abbreviation	Structure
Nonpolar R groups					
Glycine	Gly	$H-CH(NH_2)-COOH$	*Isoleucine	Ile	$CH_3-CH_2-CH(CH_3)-CH(NH_2)-COOH$
Alanine	Ala	$CH_3-CH(NH_2)-COOH$	Proline	Pro	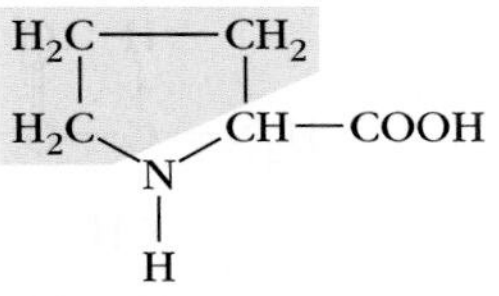
*Valine	Val	$CH_3-CH(CH_3)-CH(NH_2)-COOH$	*Phenylalanine	Phe	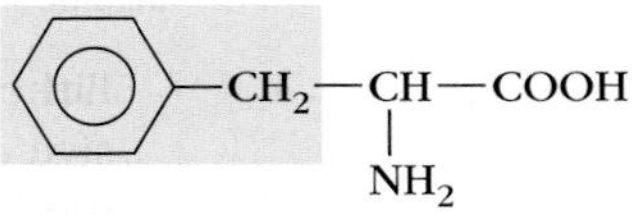
*Leucine	Leu	$CH_3-CH(CH_3)-CH_2-CH(NH_2)-COOH$	*Methionine	Met	$CH_3-S-CH_2CH_2-CH(NH_2)-COOH$
			*Tryptophan	Trp	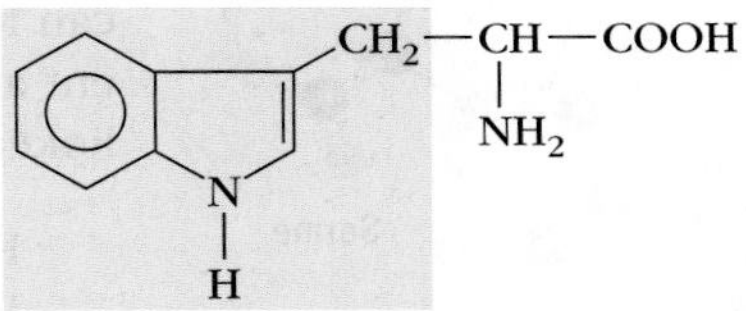
Polar but neutral R groups					
Serine	Ser	$HO-CH_2-CH(NH_2)-COOH$	Asparagine	Asn	$H_2N-C(=O)-CH_2-CH(NH_2)-COOH$
*Threonine	Thr	$CH_3-CH(OH)-CH(NH_2)-COOH$	Glutamine	Gln	$H_2N-C(=O)-CH_2CH_2-CH(NH_2)-COOH$
Cysteine	Cys	$HS-CH_2-CH(NH_2)-COOH$	Tyrosine	Tyr	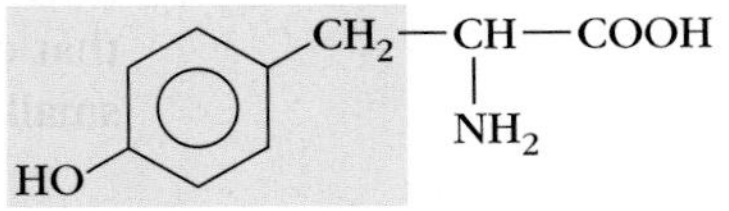
Acidic R groups			**Basic R groups**		
Glutamic acid	Glu	$HO-C(=O)-CH_2CH_2-CH(NH_2)-COOH$	*Lysine	Lys	$H_2N-CH_2CH_2CH_2CH_2-CH(NH_2)-COOH$
Aspartic acid	Asp	$HO-C(=O)-CH_2-CH(NH_2)-COOH$	‡Arginine	Arg	$H_2N-C(=NH)-NH-CH_2CH_2CH_2-CH(NH_2)-COOH$
			Histidine	His	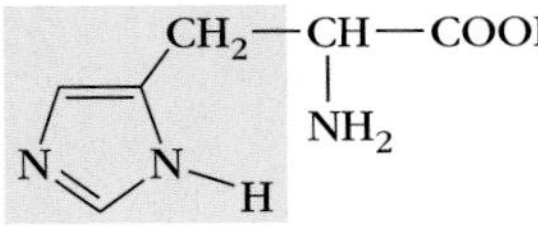

*Essential amino acids that must be part of the human diet. The other amino acids can be synthesized by the body.

†The R group in each amino acid is highlighted.

‡Growing children also require arginine in their diet.

Note that in glycylalanine the amine group of glycine is unreacted as is the carboxylic acid group of alanine. This differs from alanylglycine, which is formed by the condensation reaction of the amine group of glycine (its carboxylic acid group is unreacted) and the carboxylic acid group of alanine (its amine group is unreacted).

Any two amino acids can react to form two different dipeptides, depending on which amine and acid groups react from each amino acid. For example, glycine and alanine can react in either of the following two ways:

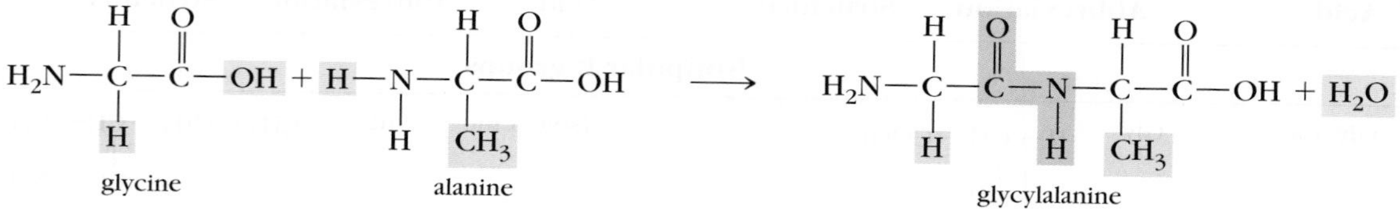

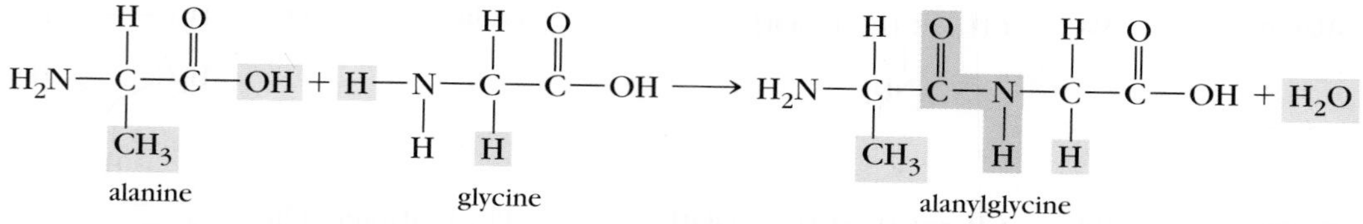

Either of these dipeptides can react with other amino acids at both ends. The extensive chains of amino acid units in proteins are built up by such condensation polymerization reactions.

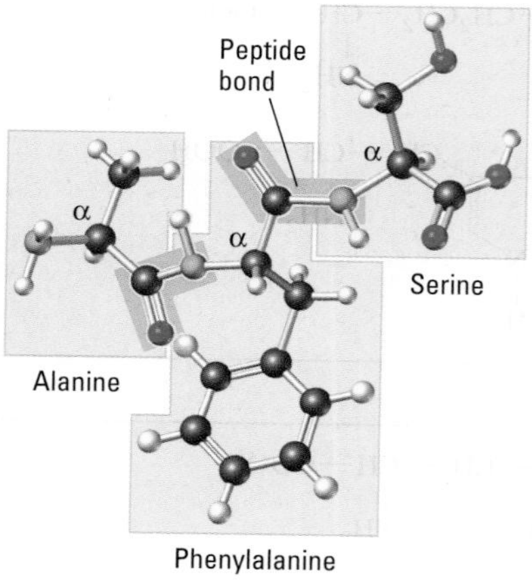

The Ala-Phe-Ser tripeptide

As the number of amino acids in the chain increases and the polypeptide chain lengthens, the number of variations quickly increases to a degree of complexity not generally found in synthetic polymers. As we have just seen, two different dipeptides can form from two different amino acids. Six *tri*peptides are possible if three different amino acids (for example, phenylalanine, Phe; alanine, Ala; and serine, Ser) are linked in combinations that contain all three amino acids, if each is used only once:

Phe-Ala-Ser	Ser-Ala-Phe	Ala-Ser-Phe
Phe-Ser-Ala	Ser-Phe-Ala	Ala-Phe-Ser

If n different amino acids are present, the number of arrangements is $n!$ (n factorial). For four different amino acids, the number of different tetrapeptides is 4!, or $4 \times 3 \times 2 \times 1 = 24$. With five different amino acids, the number of different arrangements is 5!, or 120. If all 20 different naturally occurring amino acids were bonded in one polypeptide, the sequences would make $20! = 2.43 \times 10^{18}$ (2.43 quintillion) unique 20-monomer molecules. *Because proteins can also include more than one molecule of a given amino acid, the number of possible combinations is astronomical.* It is truly remarkable that of the many different proteins that could be made from a set of amino acids, a living cell makes only the relatively small number of proteins it needs.

PROBLEM-SOLVING EXAMPLE 12.13 Peptides

Using information from Table 12.8, draw the structural formula of the tripeptide represented by Ala-Ser-Gly. Explain why it is a different compound from the tripeptide with the amino acids joined in the order Gly-Ala-Ser.

Answer

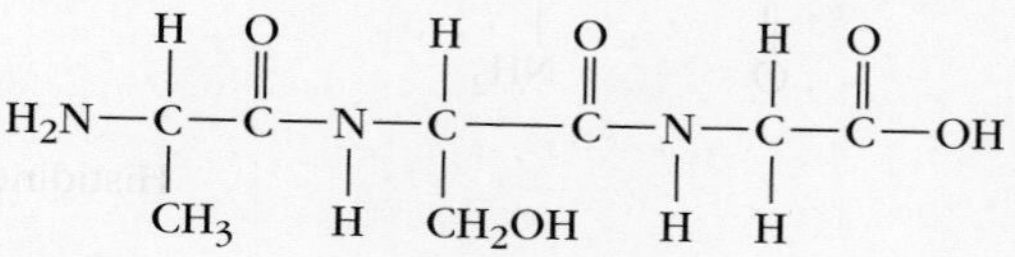

Ala-Ser-Gly

The structure Gly-Ala-Ser differs because the free $—NH_2$ group is on the glycine part of the molecule and the free $—COOH$ group is on the serine part of the molecule.

Strategy and Explanation The amino acid sequence in the abbreviated name shows that alanine should be written at the left with a free $H_2N—$ group, glycine should be written at the right with a free —COOH group, and both should be connected to serine by peptide bonds. Writing the structure of Gly-Ala-Ser shows how the two tripeptides are different.

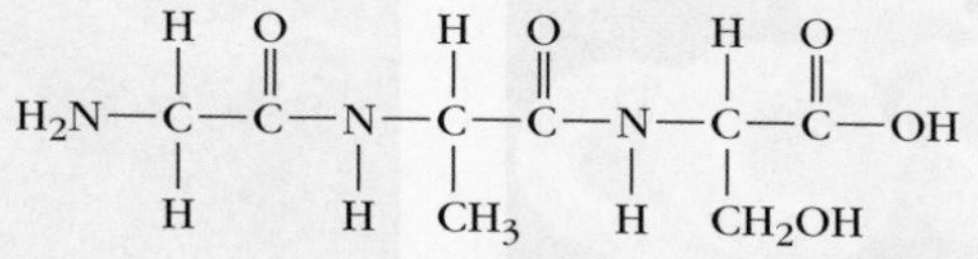

Gly-Ala-Ser

PROBLEM-SOLVING PRACTICE 12.13

Draw the structural formula of the tetrapeptide Cys-Phe-Ser-Ala.

EXERCISE 12.20 Peptide Sequences

Draw the structural formula of the tetrapeptide Ala-Ser-Phe-Cys.

Primary, Secondary, and Tertiary Structure of a Protein

The shape of a protein, and consequently its function, is determined by the sequence of amino acids along the chain, known as the **primary structure** of the protein. All proteins, no matter how large, have a peptide backbone of amino acid units covalently bonded to each other through peptide linkages.

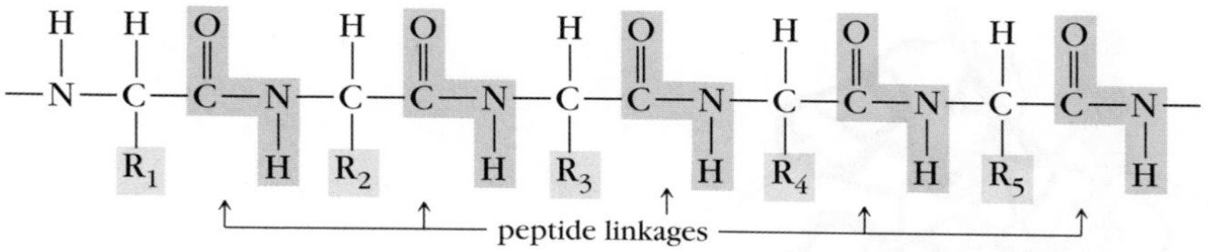

The distinctions that determine the shape and function of a protein lie in the sequence of amino acids and the order of the R groups along the backbone. Even one amino acid out of place can create dramatic changes in the shape of a protein, which can lead to serious medical conditions. For example, sickle cell anemia results from an alteration in the primary structure of hemoglobin, the molecule that carries oxygen in red blood cells. Glutamic acid, the seventh amino acid in a 146-amino acid chain in hemoglobin, is replaced by valine. Replacement of the carboxylic acid side chain of glutamic acid with the nonpolar side chain of valine (Table 12.8) disturbs the intramolecular attractions in hemoglobin and changes its shape. As a result, hemoglobin molecules gather into fibrous chains that distort the red blood cells into a sickle shape.

The change in structure of hemoglobin that causes sickle-cell anemia answers the question, "How can a disease be caused or cured by a tiny change in a molecule?" that was posed in Chapter 1 (*p. 2*).

Protein chains are not long and floppy, as you might imagine. Instead, regular patterns of **secondary structure** are created by hydrogen bonding. There are two major types of secondary protein structure: (1) the alpha (α)-helix, which occurs within a protein molecule, and (2) the beta (β)-pleated sheet, which occurs between adjacent protein chains. In the alpha-helix, hydrogen bonding occurs between the N—H hydrogen of an amine group in a peptide bond with a lone electron pair on a C=O oxygen of a peptide bond four amino acid units farther down the peptide backbone (Figure 12.14). In effect, the hydrogen in the hydrogen bond "looks over its shoulder," causing the protein to curl into a helix, much like the coiling of a

Wool is primarily the protein keratin, which has an alpha-helix secondary structure. Fibroin, the principal protein in silk, is largely beta-pleated sheets.

CNRI/Science Photo Library/Photo Researchers, Inc.
Omikron/Science Source/Photo Researchers, Inc.

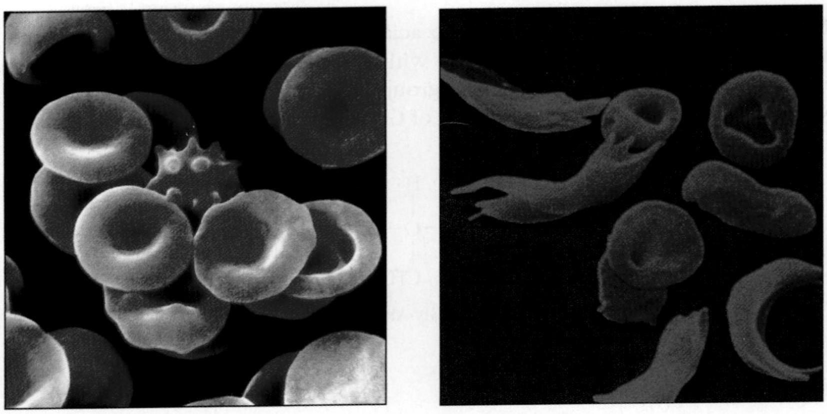

(a) (b)

Red blood cells. (a) Normal cells; (b) sickled cells.

telephone cord. In the alpha-helix, the R groups on the amino acid units are on the outside of the helix. In contrast, hydrogen bonding in the beta-pleated sheet occurs between the peptide backbones of neighboring protein chains, creating a zigzag pattern resembling a pleated sheet with the R groups above and below the sheet (Figure 12.14b).

The overall three-dimensional arrangement that accounts for all the twists and turns and folding of a protein is called its **tertiary structure.** The twists and turns of the tertiary structure result in a protein molecule of maximum stability. Tertiary

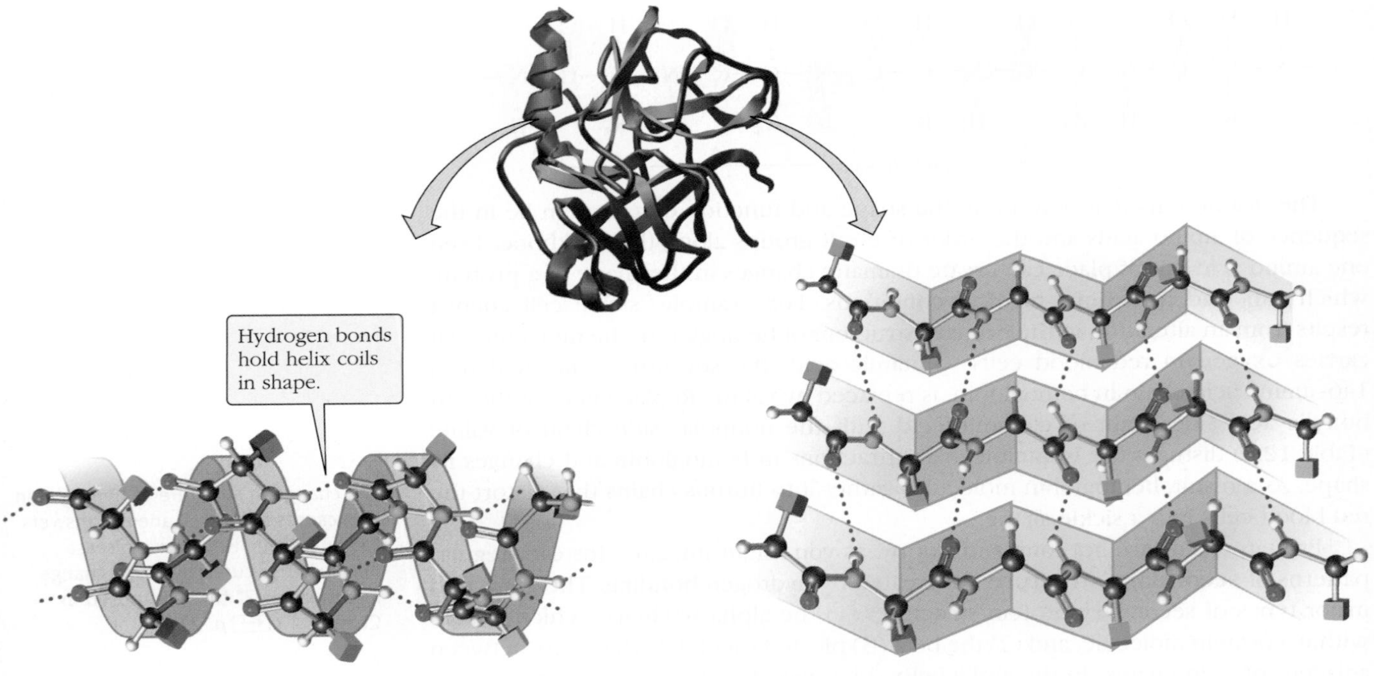

(a) Alpha-helix

(b) Beta-pleated-sheet

Figure 12.14 Alpha-helix (a) and beta-pleated sheet (b) structures of proteins. The enzyme molecule has regions of both alpha-helix and beta-pleated sheet protein structures. R groups are represented by green blocks.

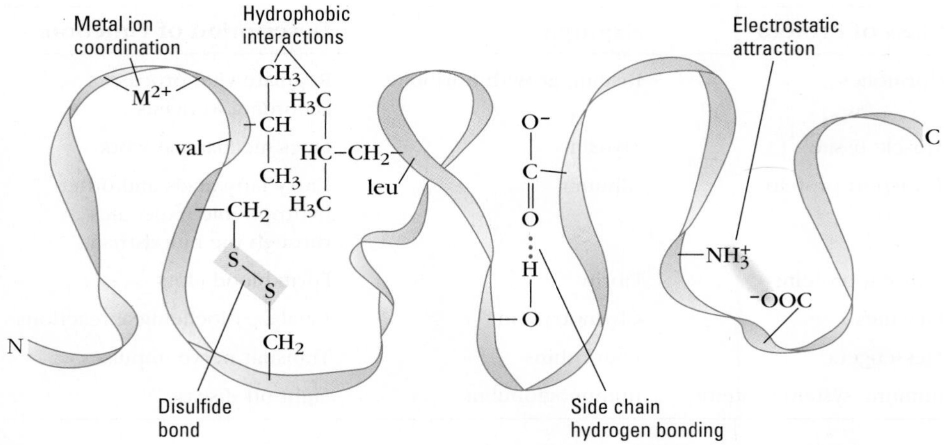

Figure 12.15 **Noncovalent forces and bonds that stabilize protein tertiary structure.** The tertiary structure of a protein is stabilized by several different forces.

structure is determined by interactions among the side chains strategically placed along the backbone of the chain. These interactions include noncovalent forces of attraction and covalent bonding, as illustrated in Figure 12.15.

Noncovalent Attractions	Covalent Bonds
Hydrogen bonding between side-chain groups	Disulfide bonds (—S—S—)
Hydrophobic (water-hating) interactions between nonpolar side-chain hydrocarbon groups	Coordinate covalent bonding between metal ions and electron pairs of side-chain N and O atoms
Electrostatic attractions between $—NH_3^+$ and $—COO^-$ side-chain groups	

The hydrogen bonding, hydrophobic interactions, and electrostatic attractions bring the groups closer together. Metal ions, such as Fe^{2+} in hemoglobin, are incorporated into a protein by the donation of lone pair electrons from oxygen or nitrogen atoms in side-chain groups to form coordinate covalent bonds to the metal ions. By loss of H, the —SH groups in proximate cysteine units form disulfide (—S—S—) covalent bonds that cross-link regions of the peptide backbone. The number and proximity of disulfide bonds help to limit the flexibility of a protein.

Proteins can be divided into two broad categories—fibrous proteins and globular proteins—that reflect differences in their tertiary structures. *Fibrous proteins,* such as hair, muscle fibers, and fingernails, are rod-like, with the coils or sheets of protein aligned into parallel bundles, making for tough, water-insoluble materials. In contrast, *globular proteins* are highly folded, with hydrophilic (water-loving) side chains on the outside, making these proteins water-soluble. Hemoglobin and chymotrypsin (Figure 12.16) are globular proteins, as are most enzymes.

Because of the complexity and the variety of properties provided by the different R groups and associated molecules or ions, proteins are able to perform widely diverse functions in the body. Consider some of them.

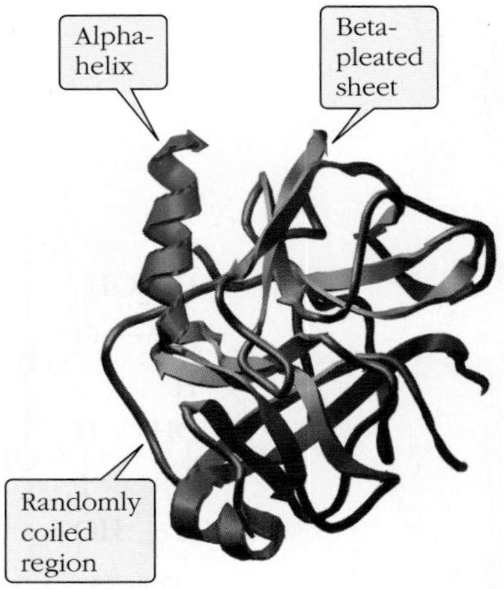

Figure 12.16 **Protein folding.** The protein chymotrypsin is shown in a ribbon structure that illustrates only the polypeptide backbone. Alpha-helix regions are shown in blue, beta-pleated sheet regions are shown in green, and randomly coiled regions are shown in copper.

Class of Protein	Example	Description of Function
Hormones	Insulin, growth hormone	Regulate vital processes according to needs
Muscle tissue	Myosin	Does mechanical work
Transport proteins	Albumin	Carry fatty acids and other hydrophobic molecules through the bloodstream
Clotting proteins	Fibrin	Form blood clots
Enzymes	Chymotrypsin	Catalyze biochemical reactions
Messengers	Endorphins	Transmit nerve impulses
Immune system proteins	Immunoglobulins	Fight off disease

Monosaccharides to Polysaccharides

Nature makes an abundance of compounds with the general formula $C_x(H_2O)_y$, in which x and y are whole numbers, such as in glucose, $C_6H_{12}O_6$, where $x = 6$, $y = 6$. These compounds are variously known as sugars, carbohydrates, and mono-, di-, or polysaccharides (from the Latin *saccharum,* "sugar"—because they taste sweet). As noted in Figure 12.17, the simplest carbohydrates, such as glucose, are **monosaccharides,** also called simple sugars, because they contain only one type of saccharide molecule. **Disaccharides** consist of two monosaccharide units joined together, such as glucose and fructose linked to form sucrose (table sugar) or two glucose units to form maltose. **Polysaccharides** are polymers containing many monosaccharide units, up to several thousand.

1,6-glycosidic linkages are also possible.

The monomer units of disaccharides and polysaccharides are joined by a C—O—C arrangement called a **glycosidic linkage** between carbons 1 and 4 of adjacent monosaccharide units. Polysaccharides contain many monosaccharide monomers joined together via glycosidic linkages into a very large polymer. The glycosidic linkages in disaccharides and polysaccharides are formed by a condensation reaction like the condensation reactions by which synthetic polymers are formed. A water molecule is released during the formation of each glycosidic bond from the reaction between the —OH groups of the monosaccharide monomers.

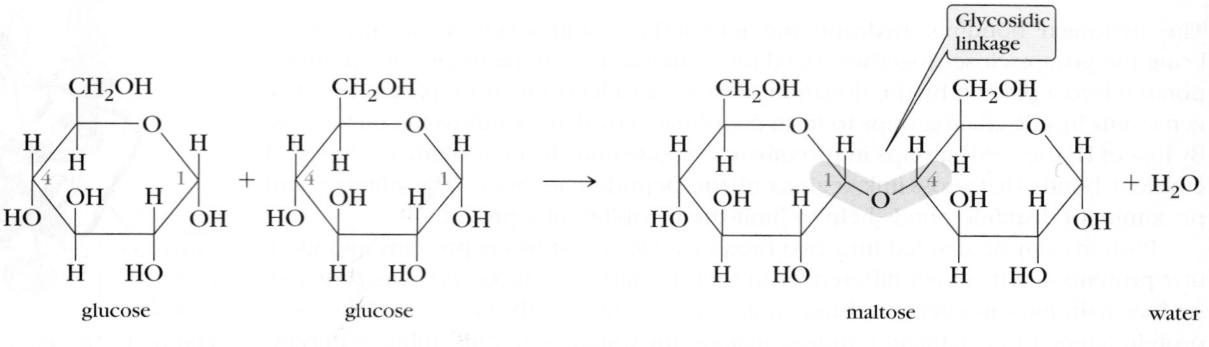

Notice that maltose has two fewer hydrogen atoms and one less oxygen atom than the combined formulas of two glucose molecules. This difference arises because a water molecule is eliminated as a product of the condensation reaction.

Starches and cellulose are the most abundant natural polysaccharides. D-glucose is the monomer in each of these polymers, which can contain as many as 5000 glucose units.

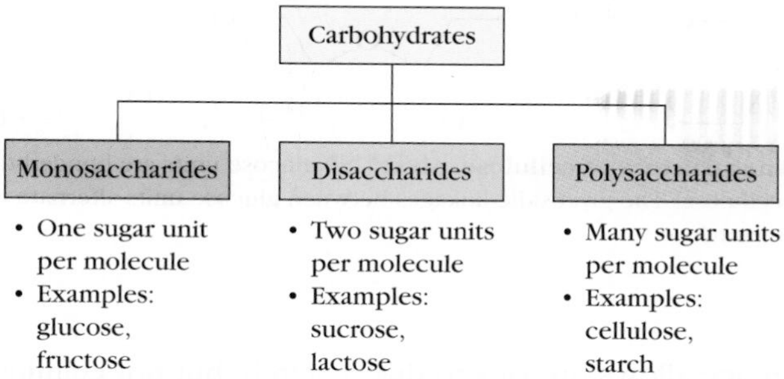

Figure 12.17 **The classes of carbohydrates.**

> **CONCEPTUAL EXERCISE** **12.21 Sucrose Solubility**
>
> On a chemical basis, explain why table sugar (sucrose) is soluble in water.

Polysaccharides: Starches and Glycogen

Plant starch is stored in protein-covered granules until glucose is needed for synthesis of new molecules or for energy production. If these granules are ruptured by heat, they yield two starches—*amylose* and *amylopectin.* Natural starches contain about 75% amylopectin and 25% amylose, both of which are polymers of glucose units joined by glycosidic linkages. Structurally, amylose is a condensation polymer with an average of about 200 glucose monomers per molecule arranged in a straight chain, like pearls on a necklace. Amylopectin is a branched-chain polymer analogous to the branched-chain synthetic polymers discussed earlier. A typical amylopectin molecule has about 1000 glucose monomers arranged into branched chains. The branched chains of glucose units give amylopectin properties different from those of the unbranched amylose. The main difference is their water solubilities. A family of enzymes called amylases helps to break down starches sequentially into a mixture of small branched-chain polysaccharides called dextrins and ultimately into glucose. Dextrins are used as food additives and in mucilage, paste, and finishes for paper and fabrics.

Amylose turns blue-black when tested with iodine solution, whereas amylopectin turns red.

In animals, *glycogen* serves the same storage function as starch does in plants. Glycogen, the reserve carbohydrate in the body, is stored in the liver and muscle tissues and provides glucose for "instant" energy until the process of fat metabolism can take over and serve as the energy source (⇐ ***p. 256***). The chains of D-glucose units in glycogen are more highly branched than those in amylopectin.

Animals store energy as fats rather than carbohydrates because fats have more energy per gram.

Cellulose, a Polysaccharide

Cellulose is the most abundant organic compound on earth, found as the woody part of trees and the supporting material in plants and leaves. Cotton is the purest natural form of cellulose. Like amylose, cellulose is composed of D-glucose units. The difference between the structures of cellulose and amylose lies in the orientation of the glycosidic linkages between the glucose units. In cellulose, the —OH groups at carbons 1 and 4 are in the *trans* position, so the glycosidic linkages between glucose units alternate in direction; thus, every other glucose unit is turned over (Figure 12.18). In amylose, the —OH groups at carbons 1 and 4 are in the *cis* position, so all the glycosidic linkages are in the same direction. This subtle

Paper and cotton are essentially cellulose.

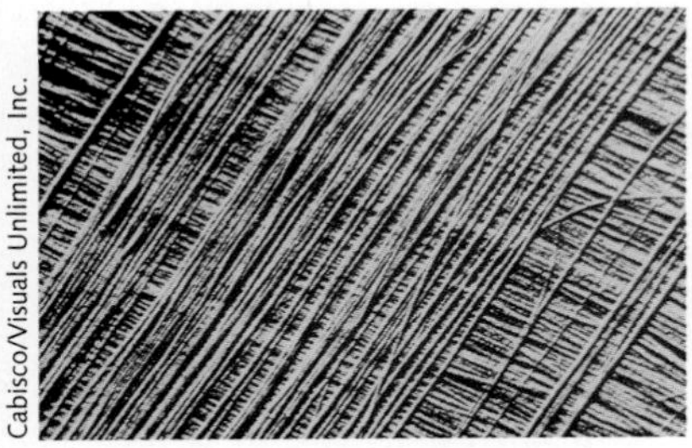

Parallel strands of cellulose in a plant fiber.

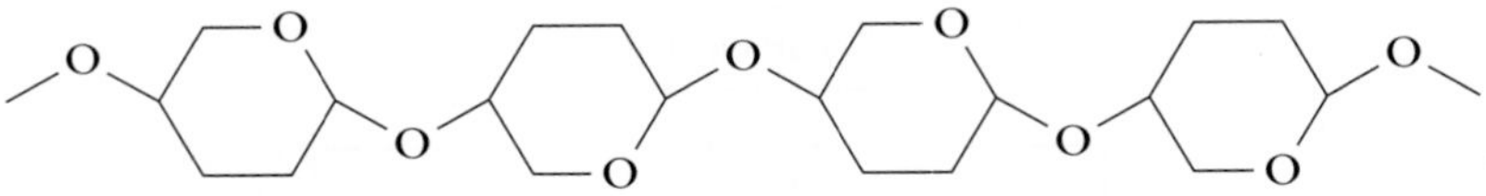

Figure 12.18 The structure of cellulose. About 280 glucose units are bonded together to form a chain structure in cellulose. The glycosidic linkages between glucose units alternate in their orientation, unlike those in amylose.

structural difference allows humans to digest starch, but not cellulose; we lack the enzyme necessary to break the *trans* glycosidic linkages in cellulose. However, termites, a few species of cockroaches, and ruminant mammals such as cows, sheep, goats, and camels do have the proper internal chemistry for this purpose. Because cellulose is so abundant, it would be advantageous if humans could use it, as well as starch, for food.

CONCEPTUAL EXERCISE 12.22 Digestion of Cellulose

Explain why humans cannot digest cellulose. Consult a reference on the Internet and explain why ruminant animals can digest cellulose.

CONCEPTUAL EXERCISE 12.23 What If Humans Could Digest Cellulose?

Think of some of the implications if humans could digest cellulose. What would be some desirable consequences? What would be some undesirable ones?

SUMMARY PROBLEM

Part 1

This chapter has described many kinds of carbon-containing compounds from a variety of sources. Several classes of carbon compounds have molecules with a carbon-to-oxygen bond, which gives the compound certain chemical properties. Use the information in the chapter to complete the sequence of chemical changes for the compound

$$CH_3(CH_2)_8CH_2OH$$

(a) Suppose this compound reacts with aqueous $KMnO_4$. Write the structural formulas of the initial and final oxidation products of this compound.

(b) Use structural formulas to write the equation for the reaction of the initial reactant in Question (a) with the final oxidation product in Question (a).

(c) Into what class of compounds does the product of the reaction in Question (b) fall?

(d) The final product in Question (b) reacts with aqueous sodium hydroxide. Write the equation for this reaction. What types of compounds are formed by this reaction? What would the products be if the reaction took place under acidic conditions instead of with aqueous base?

(e) The final oxidation product in Question (a) reacts with dimethylamine, $(CH_3)_2NH$. Write the structural formula of the product of this reaction. What class of compound is formed?

(f) Can the two reactants in Question (b) form a polymer? Explain.

Part 2

The citric acid cycle is a series of steps involving the degradation and reformation of oxaloacetic acid. Two steps in the cycle involve a reaction studied in this chapter. One step converts isocitric acid into oxalosuccinic acid.

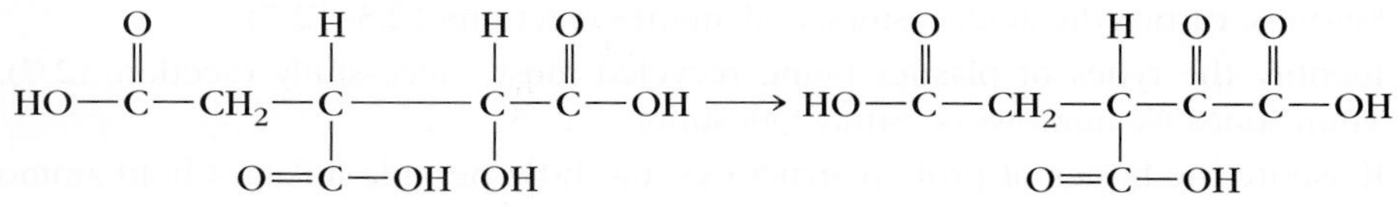

isocitric acid — oxalosuccinic acid

In the last step of the cycle, L-malic acid is converted into oxaloacetic acid.

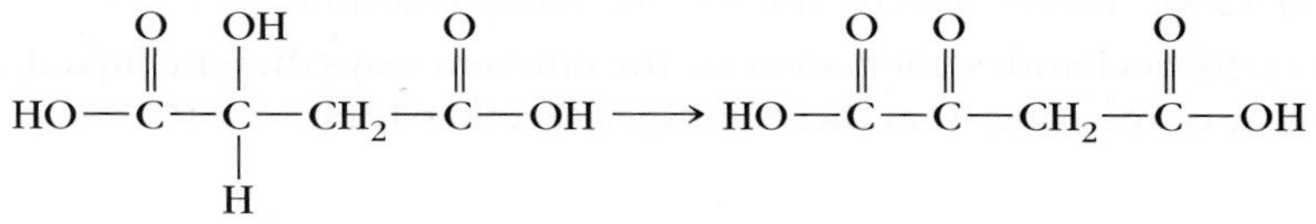

L-malic acid — oxaloacetic acid

(a) Identify the general type of reaction in each step.

(b) What do the two steps have in common?

(c) Identify any chiral carbon atoms in the structures above in Part 2.

Part 3

Select any four amino acids from Table 12.8. Write the structural formulas of four different tetrapeptides that could be formed from these four amino acids.

IN CLOSING

Having studied this chapter, you should be able to . . .

- Describe petroleum refining and methods used to improve the gasoline fraction (Section 12.1).
- Identify the major components of natural gas (Section 12.2).
- Identify processes used to obtain organic chemicals from coal, and name some of their products (Section 12.2).
- Convert equivalent energy units (Section 12.3). ThomsonNOW homework: Study Question 103
- Identify major organic chemicals of industrial and economic importance (Section 12.4).
- Define and describe the nature of chiral molecules and enantiomers (Section 12.4). ThomsonNOW homework: Study Question 26
- Name and draw the structures of three functional groups produced by the oxidation of alcohols (Section 12.5). ThomsonNOW homework: Study Question 39
- Name and give examples of the uses of some important alcohols (Section 12.5). ThomsonNOW homework: Study Question 35
- List some properties of carboxylic acids, and write equations for the formation of esters from carboxylic acids and alcohols (Section 12.6). ThomsonNOW homework: Study Question 45

ThomsonNOW™
Sign in to ThomsonNOW at **www.thomsonedu.com** to check your readiness for an exam by taking the Pre-Test and exploring the modules recommended in your Personalized Learning Plan.

- Use Lewis structures to illustrate triglyceride formation (12.6).
- Differentiate among saturated, monounsaturated, and polyunsaturated fats (Section 12.6). ThomsonNOW homework: Study Question 54
- Explain the formation of polymers by addition or condensation polymerization; give examples of synthetic polymers formed by each type of reaction (Section 12.7). ThomsonNOW homework: Study Questions 56, 69, 98
- Draw the structures of the repeating units in some common types of synthetic polymers and identify the monomers that form them (Section 12.7).
- Identify or write the structures of the functional groups in alcohols, aldehydes, ketones, carboxylic acids, esters, and amines (Sections 12.5–12.7).
- Identify the types of plastics being recycled most successfully (Section 12.7). ThomsonNOW homework: Study Questions 74, 75
- Illustrate the basics of protein structures and how peptide linkages hold amino acids together in proteins (Section 12.8). ThomsonNOW homework: Study Question 65
- Differentiate among the primary, secondary, and tertiary structures of proteins (Section 12.8). ThomsonNOW homework: Study Question 78
- Identify polysaccharides, their sources, the different ways they are linked, and the different uses resulting from these linkages (Section 12.8).

KEY TERMS

achiral *(12.4)*
addition polymer *(12.7)*
aldehyde *(12.5)*
alpha carbon *(12.8)*
amide *(12.7)*
amide linkage *(12.7)*
amine *(12.7)*
amino acid *(12.8)*
carboxylic acid *(12.6)*
catalyst *(12.1)*
catalytic cracking *(12.1)*
catalytic reforming *(12.1)*
chiral *(12.4)*
condensation polymer *(12.7)*
condensation reaction *(12.6)*
copolymer *(12.7)*
degree of polymerization, *n* *(12.7)*
disaccharide *(12.8)*
enantiomers *(12.4)*
ester *(12.6)*
functional group *(12.4)*
glycosidic linkage *(12.8)*
hydrolysis *(12.6)*
ketone *(12.5)*
macromolecule *(12.7)*
monomer *(12.7)*
monosaccharide *(12.8)*
octane number *(12.1)*
peptide linkage *(12.8)*
petroleum fractions *(12.1)*
polyamides *(12.7)*
polyester *(12.7)*
polymer *(12.7)*
polypeptide *(12.8)*
polysaccharide *(12.8)*
primary structure (proteins) *(12.8)*
saponification *(12.6)*
saturated fats *(12.6)*
secondary structure (proteins) *(12.8)*
tertiary structure (proteins) *(12.8)*
thermoplastics *(12.7)*
thermosetting plastics *(12.7)*
triglycerides *(12.6)*
unsaturated fats *(12.6)*

QUESTIONS FOR REVIEW AND THOUGHT

■ denotes questions available in ThomsonNOW and assignable in OWL.

Blue-numbered questions have short answers at the back of this book and fully worked solutions in the *Student Solutions Manual.*

ThomsonNOW
Assess your understanding of this chapter's topics with sample tests and other resources found by signing in to ThomsonNOW at **www.thomsonedu.com**.

Review Questions

1. Why is the organic chemical industry referred to as the petrochemical industry?
2. What products are produced by the petrochemical industry?
3. What is the difference between catalytic cracking and catalytic reforming?
4. Explain how the octane number of a gasoline is determined.
5. Why is coal receiving increased attention as a source of organic compounds?
6. What is the difference between oxygenated gasoline and reformulated gasoline? Why are they being produced?
7. Explain why world use of natural gas is predicted to double between 1990 and 2010.
8. Table 12.1 lists several compounds with octane numbers above 100 and one compound with an octane number below zero. Explain why such values are possible.
9. Explain why methanol has a lower boiling point (65.0 °C) than water (100 °C).
10. Explain why ethylene glycol has a higher boiling point than ethanol.
11. Outline the steps necessary to obtain 89-octane gasoline, starting with a barrel of crude oil.
12. What is the major difference between crude oil and coal as a source of hydrocarbons?
13. Write the structural formula of a representative compound for each of these classes of organic compounds: alcohols, aldehydes, ketones, carboxylic acids, esters, and amines.
14. Explain why esters have lower boiling points than carboxylic acids with the same number of electrons.
15. What structural feature must a molecule have to undergo addition polymerization?
16. What feature do all condensation polymerization reactions have in common?
17. Give examples of (a) a synthetic addition polymer, (b) a synthetic condensation polymer, and (c) a natural addition polymer.
18. How does *cis-trans* isomerism affect the properties of rubber?
19. Discuss which two plastics are currently being recycled the most successfully, and give examples of some products being made from these recycled plastics.
20. What is the difference between the formation of an addition polymer and a condensation polymer?

Topical Questions

Petroleum and Fuels

21. What are petroleum fractions? What process is used to produce them?
22. (a) What is the boiling point range for the petroleum fraction containing the hydrocarbons that will provide fuel for your car?
    (b) Would you expect the octane rating from the "straight-run" gasoline obtained by fractional distillation of petroleum to be greater than 87 octane? Explain your answer.
    (c) Would you use this fraction to fuel your car? Why or why not?
23. (a) Draw the Lewis structure for the hydrocarbon that is assigned an octane rating of 0.
    (b) Draw the Lewis structure for the hydrocarbon that is assigned an octane rating of 100.
    (c) What is the boiling point for each of these hydrocarbons?
24. Explain what is meant by this statement: "All gasolines are highly volatile."
25. What would be the advantage of removing the higher-octane components such as aromatics and alkenes from oxygenated gasolines?

Chirality in Organic Compounds

26. ■ Circle the chiral centers, if any, in these molecules.

(a) 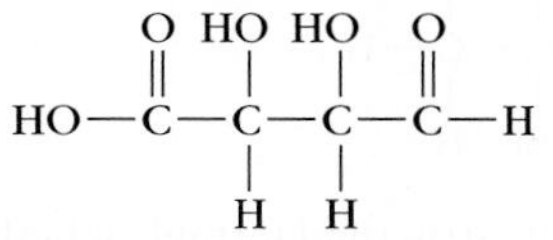

(b) 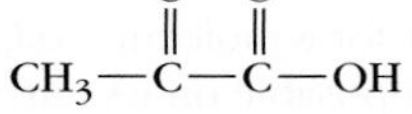

(c) 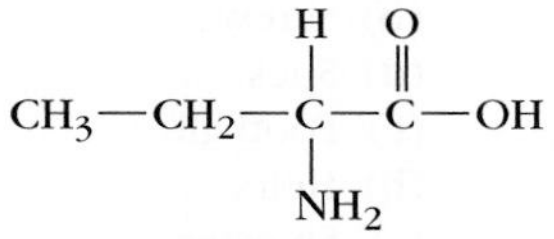

27. Circle the chiral centers, if any, in these molecules.

(a) 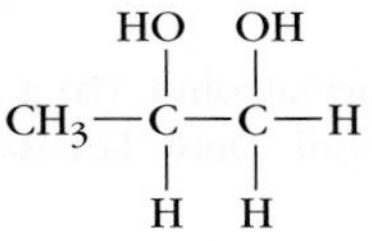

(b) 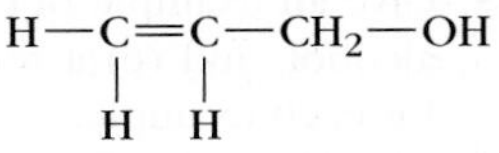

(c) 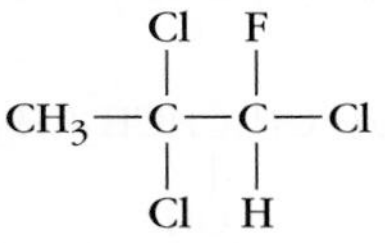

28. ■ Circle the chiral centers, if any, in these compounds.

(a) 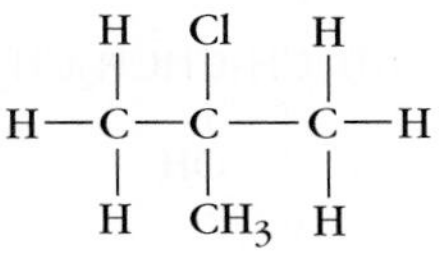

(b) 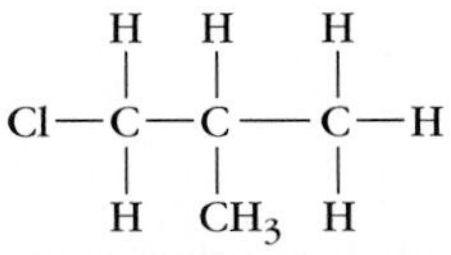

(c) 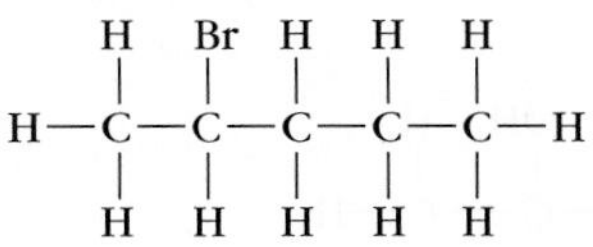

(d) 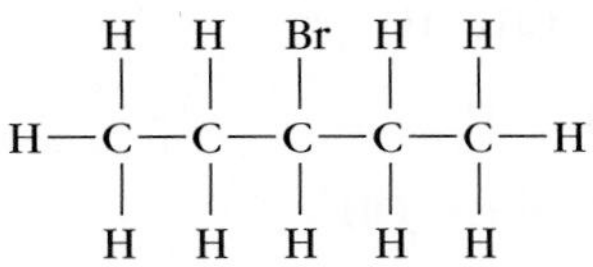

29. Circle the chiral centers, if any, in these compounds.

(a) 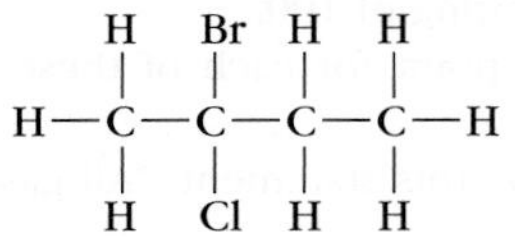

(b) 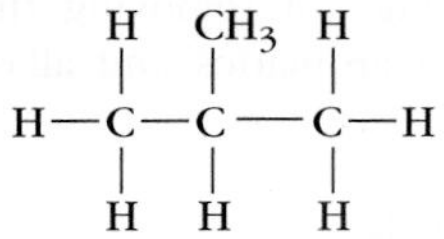

(c) 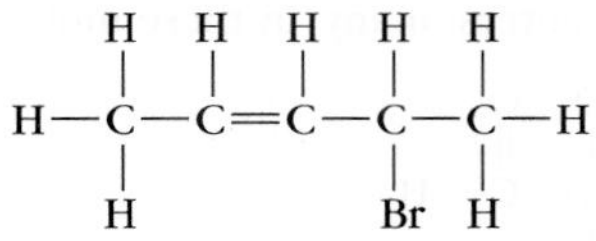

30. How can you tell from its structural formula whether a compound can exist as a pair of enantiomers?
31. What conditions must be met for a molecule to be chiral?
32. Which of these is not superimposable on its mirror image?
    (a) Nail (b) Screw
    (c) Shoe (d) Sock
    (e) Golf club (f) Football
    (g) Your ear (h) Helix
    (i) Baseball bat (j) Sweater

Alcohols

33. Give an example of (a) a primary alcohol, (b) a secondary alcohol, and (c) a tertiary alcohol. Draw Lewis structures for each example.
34. Classify each of these alcohols as primary, secondary, or tertiary.
    (a) $CH_3CH_2CH_2CH_2OH$ (b) 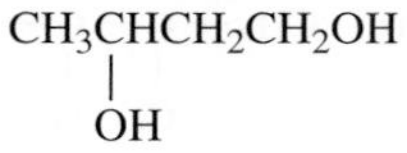
    (c) 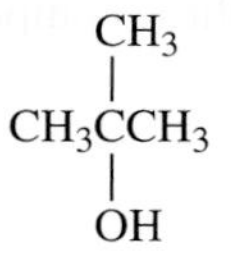 (d) 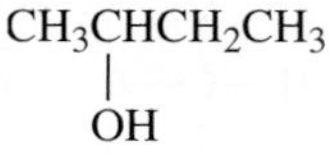
    (e) 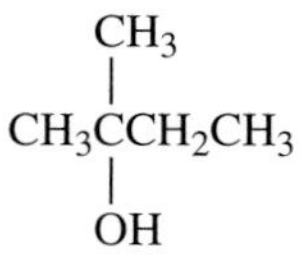
35. ■ Classify each of these alcohols as primary, secondary, or tertiary.

(a) 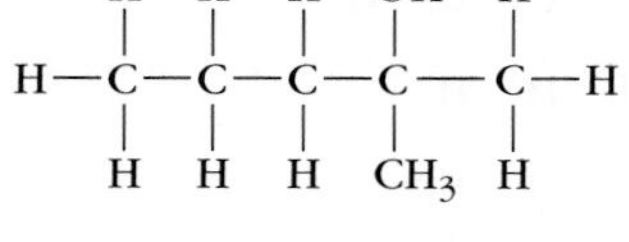

(b) 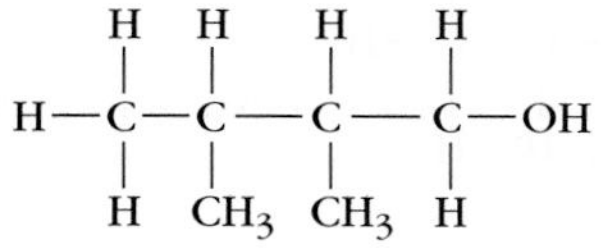

(c) 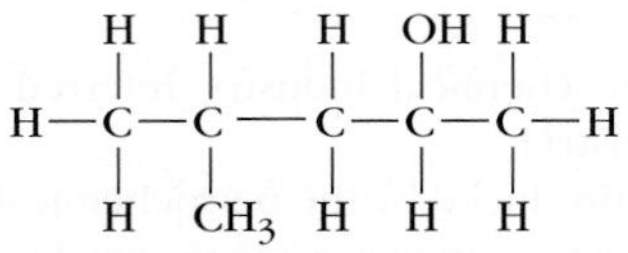

(d) 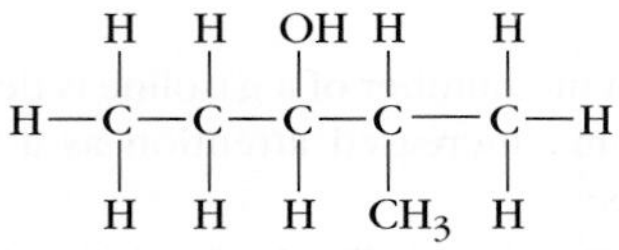

(e) 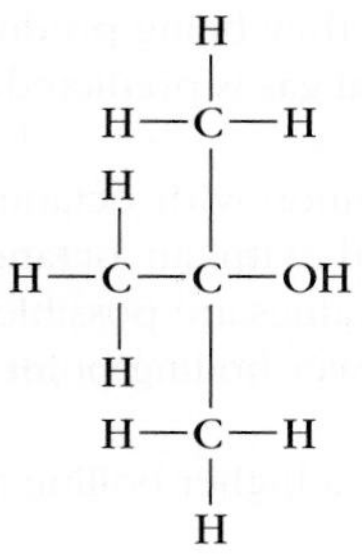

(f) 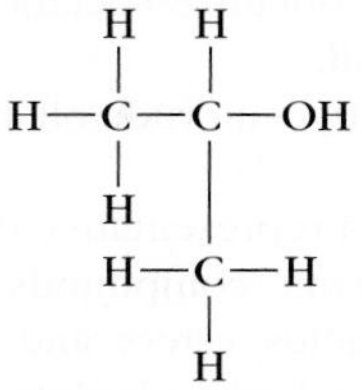

36. Explain what *oxidation* of organic compounds usually involves. What is meant by *reduction* of organic compounds?
37. ■ Draw the structures of the first two oxidation products of each of these alcohols.
    (a) CH_3CH_2OH (b) $CH_3CH_2CH_2CH_2OH$
38. Draw the structures of the oxidation products of each of these alcohols.

(a) 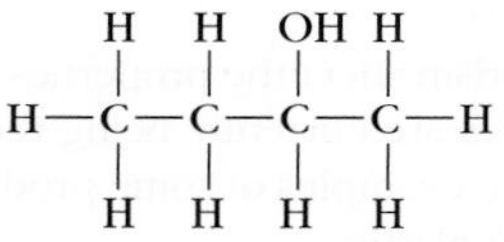

(b) 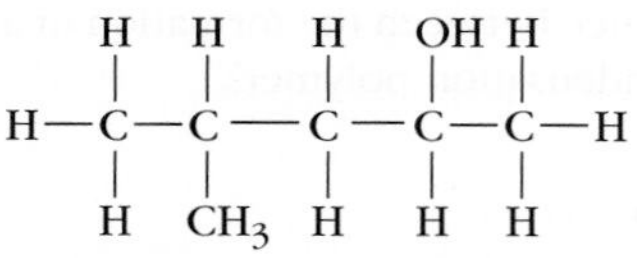

39. ■ Write the condensed structural formula of the alcohols that can be oxidized to make these compounds.

(a) 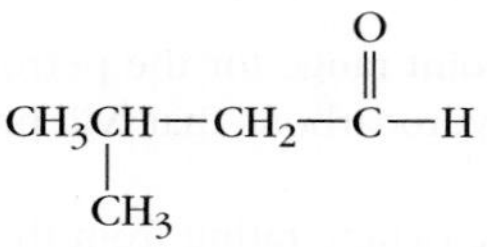

(b) 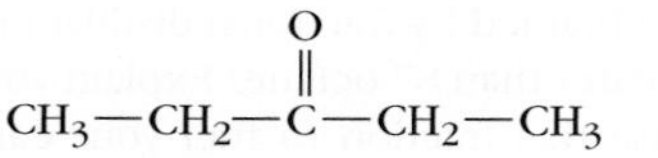

(c) 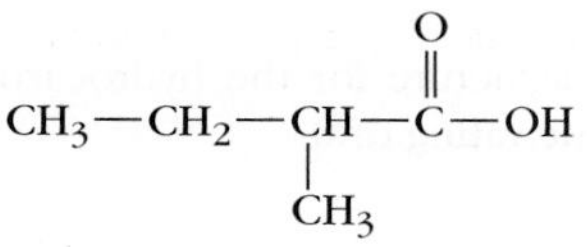

40. What is the percentage of ethanol in 90-proof vodka?
41. Explain how the common names *wood alcohol* for methanol and *grain alcohol* for ethanol came about.
42. What is denatured alcohol? Why is it made?
43. Many biological molecules, including steroids and carbohydrates, contain many —OH groups. What need might biological systems have for this particular functional group?

Carboxylic Acids and Esters

44. Explain why the boiling points for carboxylic acids are higher than those for alcohols with comparable molar masses.
45. ■ Write the structural formula of the esters that can be formed from these reactions.
   (a) $CH_3COOH + CH_3CH_2OH$
   (b) $CH_3CH_2COOH + CH_3CH_2CH_2OH$
   (c) $CH_3CH_2COOH + CH_3OH$
46. Write the structural formula for the esters that can be produced by these reactions.
   (a) Formic acid + methanol
   (b) Butyric acid + ethanol
   (c) Acetic acid + 1-butanol
   (d) Propanoic acid + 2-propanol
47. Write the condensed formula of the alcohol and acid that will react to form each of these esters.
   (a) 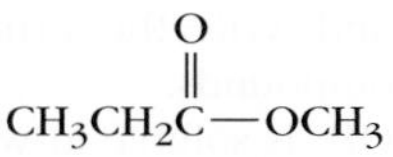
   (b) 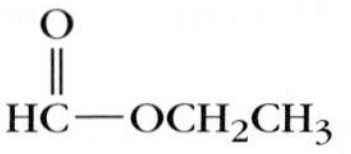
   (c) 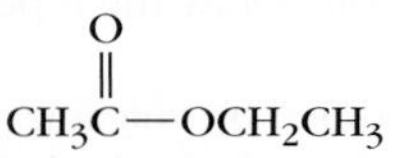
48. Explain why carboxylic acids are more soluble in water than are esters with the same molar mass.

Organic Polymers

49. What are some examples of thermoplastics? What are the properties of thermoplastics when heated and cooled?
50. What are some examples of thermosetting plastics? What are the properties of thermosetting plastics when heated and cooled?
51. Draw the structure of the repeating unit in a polymer in which the monomer is
   (a) 1-butene
   (b) 1,1-dichloroethylene
   (c) Vinyl acetate
52. What is the principal structural difference between low-density and high-density polyethylene? Is polyethylene an addition or a condensation polymer?
53. Methyl methacrylate has the structural formula shown in Table 12.6. When polymerized, it is very transparent, and it is sold in the United States under the trade names Lucite and Plexiglas.
   (a) Use structural formulas to write the chemical equation for the formation of a segment of poly(methyl methacrylate) having four monomer units.
   (b) Identify the repeating unit in the polymer.
54. ■ Use structural formulas and data from Table 12.6 to write the chemical equation for the formation of a polymer of five monomer units from these monomers.
   (a) Acrylonitrile
   (b) Propylene
55. Use structural formulas and data from Table 12.6 to write the chemical equation for the formation of a polymer of five monomer units from these monomers.
   (a) Vinylidene chloride, $H_2C{=}CCl_2$
   (b) Tetrafluoroethylene
56. ■ What monomers are used to prepare these polymers?
   (a) $—CH_2CH_2CH_2CH_2CH_2CH_2CH_2CH_2CH_2—$
   (b) 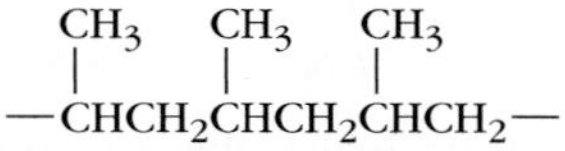
   (c) 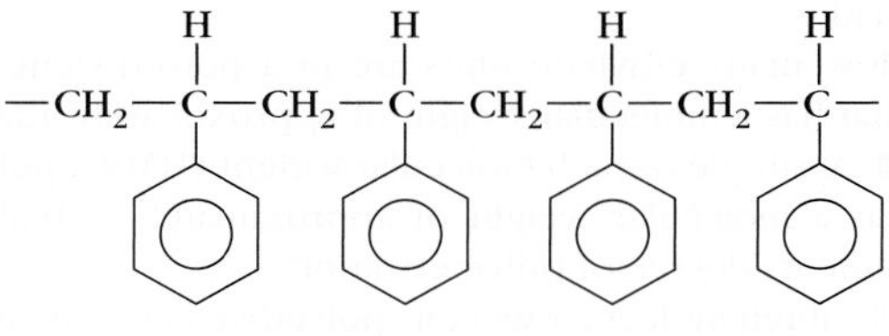
   (d) 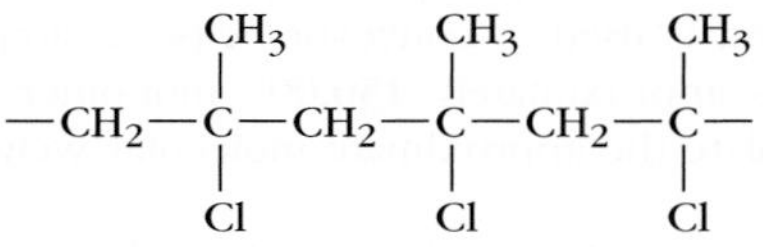
   (e) 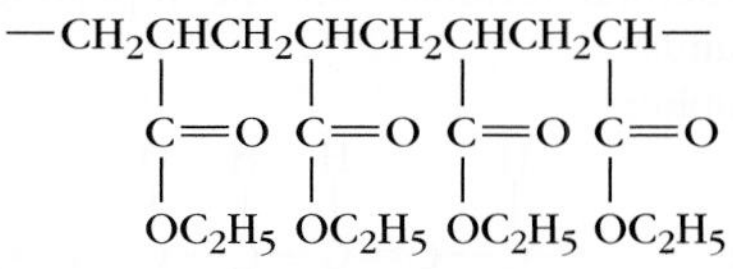
57. What is the monomer in *natural rubber*? Which isomer is present in natural rubber, *cis* or *trans?*
58. Write the structural formula of four units of the polymer made from the reaction of $H_2N—(CH_2)_4—NH_2$ and HOOCCOOH. Indicate the repeating unit of the polymer.
59. ■ 4-hydroxybenzoic acid can form a condensation polymer. Use structural formulas to write the chemical equation for the formation of four units of the polymer. Indicate the repeating unit of the polymer.

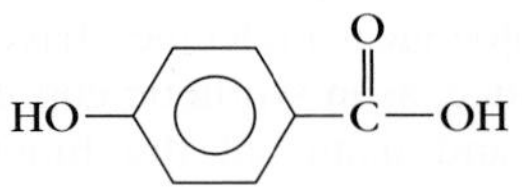

4-hydroxybenzoic acid

60. What are the two monomers used to make SBR?
61. The formation of polyesters involves which two functional groups?
62. Name one important polyester polymer and its uses.
63. Polyamides are made by condensing which functional groups? Name the most common example of this class of synthetic polymers.
64. How are amide linkages and peptide linkages similar? How are they different?
65. ■ State one major difference between proteins and unstructured polyamides.

66. Draw structures of monomers that could form each of these condensation polymers.

(a) 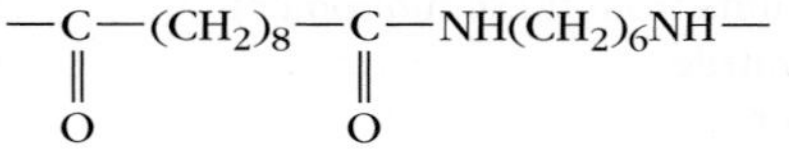

(b) 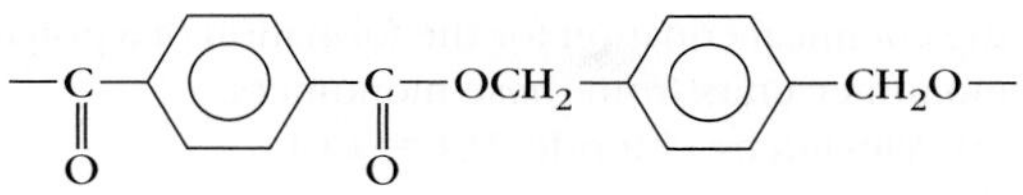

67. Orlon has this polymeric chain structure:

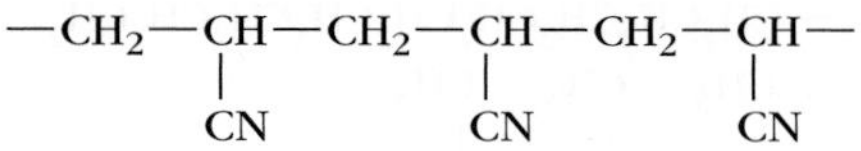

What is the monomer from which this structure can be made?

68. How many ethylene units are in a polyethylene molecule that has a molecular weight of approximately 42,000?

69. ■ A sample of high-molecular-weight (HMW) polyethylene has a molecular weight of approximately 450,000. Determine its degree of polymerization.

70. Ultrahigh-molecular-weight polyethyelene has high wear resistance and is used in conveyor belts. A sample of the polymer has approximately 150,000 monomer units per chain. Calculate the approximate molecular weight of this polymer.

71. Write the structural formulas for the repeating units of these compounds.

(a) Natural rubber

(b) Neoprene 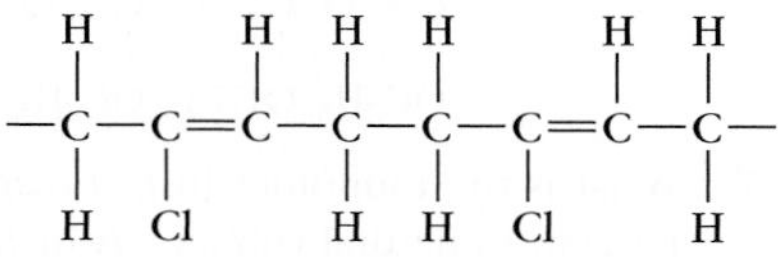

(c) Polybutadiene

72. What are some major end uses for recycled PET and HDPE polymers?

Proteins and Polysaccharides

73. Which biological molecules have monomer units that are all alike, as in synthetic polymers?

74. ■ Which biological molecules have monomer units that are not all alike, as in synthetic copolymers?

75. ■ Identify and name all the functional groups in this tripeptide.

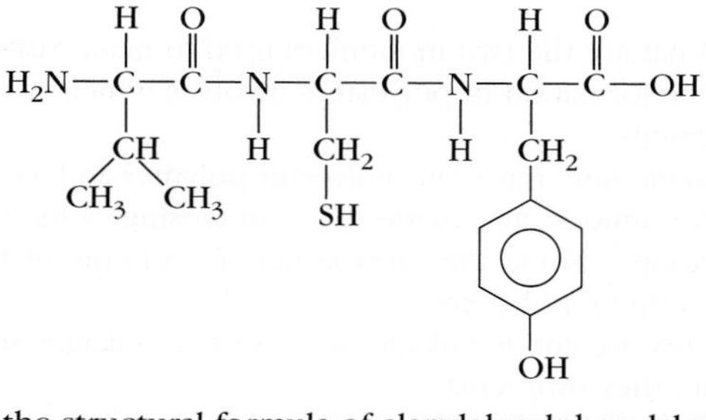

76. Draw the structural formula of alanylglycylphenylalanine.

77. Draw the structural formula of leucylmethionylalanylserine.

78. ■ Explain the difference between (a) monosaccharides and disaccharides, and (b) disaccharides and polysaccharides.

79. What is the chief function of glycogen in animal tissue?

80. What polysaccharides yield only D-glucose upon complete hydrolysis?

81. (a) How do amylose and amylopectin differ?
(b) How are they similar?
(c) Are amylose and glycogen similar?

82. (a) Explain why humans can use glycogen but not cellulose for energy.
(b) Why can cows digest cellulose?

Tools of Chemistry: Gas Chromatography

83. If you were to analyze an oxygenated gasoline using GC, would you use a less polar or more polar stationary phase than the one used for unoxygenated gasoline?

84. Would polar compounds appear earlier or later on a chromatogram if a nonpolar stationary phase were used? Explain your answer.

General Questions

85. Compounds A and B both have the molecular formula C_2H_6O. The boiling points of compounds A and B are 78.5 °C and −23.7 °C, respectively. Use the table of functional groups in Appendix E and write the structural formulas and names of the two compounds.

86. Explain why ethanol, CH_3CH_2OH, is soluble in water in all proportions, but decanol, $CH_3(CH_2)_9OH$, is almost insoluble in water.

87. Nitrile rubber (Buna N) is a copolymer of two parts 1,3-butadiene to one part acrylonitrile. Draw the repeating unit of this polymer.

88. How are rubber molecules modified by vulcanization?

89. Write the condensed structural formula for 3-ethyl-5-methyl-3-hexanol. Is this a primary, secondary, or tertiary alcohol?

90. Using structural formulas, write a reaction for the hydrolysis of a triglyceride that contains fatty acid chains, each consisting of 16 total carbon atoms.

91. Is the plastic wrap used in covering food a thermoplastic or thermosetting plastic? Explain.

92. ■ Assume that a car burns pure octane,

$$C_8H_{18}\ (d = 0.703\ g/cm^3)$$

(a) Write the balanced equation for burning octane in air, forming CO_2 and H_2O.
(b) If the car has a fuel efficiency of 32 miles per gallon of octane, what volume of CO_2 at 25 °C and 1.0 atm is generated when the car goes on a 10.0-mile trip? (The volume of 1 mol $CO_2(g)$ at 25 °C and 1 atm is 24.5 L.)

93. Perform the same calculations as in Question 92, but use methanol, CH_3OH (d = 0.791 g/cm³) as the fuel. Assume the fuel efficiency is 20.0 miles per gallon.

94. Show structurally why glycogen forms granules when stored in the liver, but cellulose is found in cell walls as sheets.

95. Polytetrafluoroethylene (Teflon) is made by first treating HF with chloroform, then cracking the resultant difluorochloromethane.

$$CHCl_3 + 2\ HF \longrightarrow CHClF_2 + 2\ HCl$$

$$2\ CHClF_2 + \text{heat} \longrightarrow F_2C{=}CF_2 + 2\ HCl$$

$$F_2C{=}CF_2 \xrightarrow{\text{peroxide catalyst}} \text{Teflon}$$

If you wish to make 1.0 kg Teflon, what mass of chloroform and HF must you use to make the starting material, $CHClF_2$? (Although it is not realistic, assume that each reaction step proceeds to a 100% yield.)

Applying Concepts

96. Hydrogen bonds can form between propanoic acid molecules and between 1-butanol molecules. Draw all the propanoic acid molecules that can hydrogen-bond to the one shown below. Draw all the 1-butanol molecules that can hydrogen-bond to the one shown below. Use dotted lines to represent the hydrogen bonds.

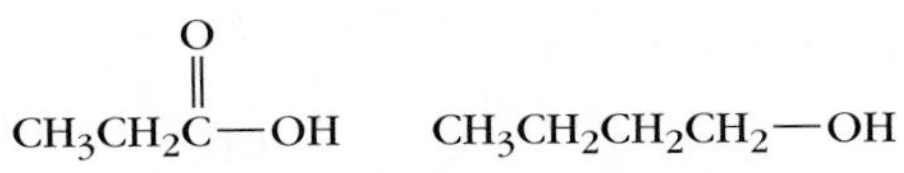

propanoic acid 1-butanol

Based on your drawings, which should have the higher boiling point, propanoic acid or 1-butanol? Explain your reasoning.

97. Both propanoic acid and ethyl methanoate form hydrogen bonds with water. Draw all the water molecules that can hydrogen-bond to these molecules. Use dotted lines to represent the hydrogen bonds.

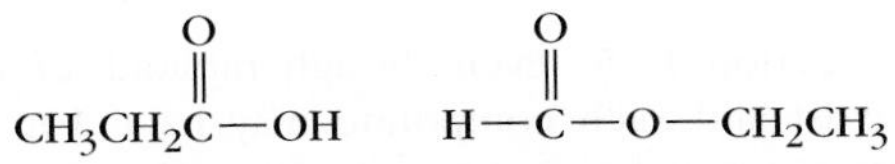

propanoic acid ethyl methanoate

Based on your drawings, which should be more soluble in water: propanoic acid or ethyl methanoate? Explain your reasoning.

98. ■ What monomer formed this polymer?

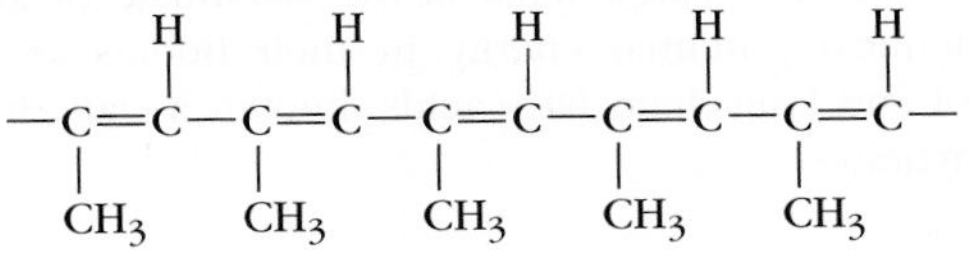

99. The illustrations below represent two different samples of polyethylene, each with the same number of monomer units. Based on the concept of density and not structure, which one is high-density polyethylene and which is low-density polyethylene? Write a brief explanation.

(a)

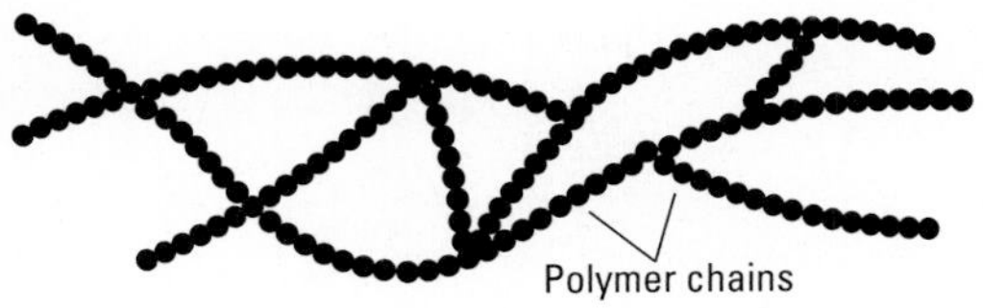

(b)

100. The backbone of a DNA molecule is a polymer of alternating sugar (deoxyribose) and phosphoric acid units held together by a phosphate ester bond. Draw a segment of the polymer consisting of at least two sugar and two phosphate units. Circle the phosphate ester bonds.

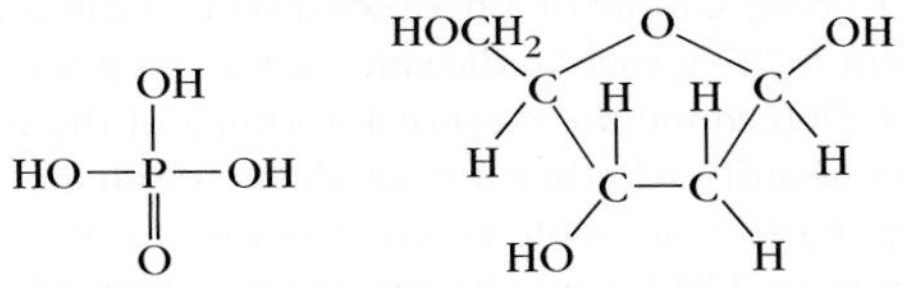

phosphoric acid deoxyribose

101. Draw the structure of a molecule that could undergo a condensation reaction with itself to form a polyester. Draw a segment of the polymer consisting of at least five monomer units.

102. It has been asserted that the photosynthesis of the trees in a forest the size of Australia would be needed to compensate for the additional CO_2 put into the atmosphere each year from burning fossil fuels. Identify the data that would be required to check whether this assertion is valid.

103. ■ A large oil refinery runs 400,000 barrels of crude oil per day through fractional distillation. Assume that all the crude oil was simply burned to produce energy. Use data from Table 12.2 to answer the following.
   (a) How many 100-W light bulbs could be lighted for one year by this amount of energy? (Assume that the energy can be converted to electrical energy with 100% efficiency.)
   (b) The average toaster uses about 39 kWh per year. How many toasters would this amount of energy operate for a year?

More Challenging Questions

104. The total mass of carbon in living systems on earth is estimated to be 7.5×10^{17} g. Given that the total mass of carbon on the earth is estimated as 7.5×10^{22} g, what is the concentration of carbon atoms on earth expressed in percent and in parts per million (ppm)?

105. In the laboratory, a student was given three bottles labeled X, Y, and Z. One of the bottles contained acetic acid, the second acetaldehyde, and the third ethanol. The student ran a series of experiments to determine the contents of each bottle. Substance X reacted with substance Y to form an ester under certain conditions and substance Y formed an acidic solution when dissolved in water. (a) Identify which compound is in which bottle, and write the Lewis structural formula for each compound. (b) Using structural formulas, write a chemical equation for the ester formation reaction and for the ionization of the acid. (c) The student confirmed the identifications by treating each compound with a strong oxidizing agent and found that compound X required roughly twice the amount of oxidizing agent as compound Z. Explain why this was the case.

106. In his 1989 essay "The End of Nature," William McKibben states that ". . . a clean burning automobile engine will emit 5.5 lb of carbon in the form of carbon dioxide for every gallon of gasoline it consumes." Assume that the gasoline is C_8H_{18} and its density is 0.703 g/mL.

(a) Write a balanced equation for the complete combustion of gasoline.
(b) Do calculations that either corroborate or refute McKibben's assertion. Is his assertion refuted or corroborated?

107. A 1.685-g sample of a hydrocarbon is burned completely to form 5.287 g carbon dioxide and 2.164 g water.
(a) Determine the empirical formula of the hydrocarbon.
(b) Identify whether it is an alkane or an alkene.
(c) Write a plausible Lewis structure for it.

108. Suppose 2.511 g of a hydrocarbon is burned completely to form 7.720 g carbon dioxide and 3.612 g water.
(a) Determine the empirical formula of the hydrocarbon.
(b) Identify whether it is an alkane or an alkene.
(c) Write a plausible Lewis structure for it.

109. Consider these data:

Hydrocarbon	Formula	Enthalpy of Combustion (kJ/mol)
Butane	C_4H_{10}	2853.9
Pentane	C_5H_{12}	3505.8
Hexane	C_6H_{14}	4159.5
Heptane	C_7H_{16}	4812.8
Octane	C_8H_{18}	5465.7

Graph these data with enthalpy of combustion (kJ/mol C) on the *y*-axis and number of carbon atoms on the *x*-axis. Use the graph to estimate the enthalpy of combustion of propane (C_3H_8), nonane (C_9H_{20}), and hexadecane ($C_{16}H_{34}$).

110. Two different compounds each have the formula $C_5H_{10}O_2$. Each contains a C=O group. Write the Lewis structure of each compound and identify the functional group in each one.

111. Using structural formulas, show how vinyl chloride can polymerize to form three types of PVC polymers.

112. Explain why an amino acid has a higher boiling point than an amine with the same number of electrons.

113. Silicones are Si-containing polymers used in waterproof caulking. They do not contain carbon-to-carbon bonds.
(a) Silly Putty is a polymer made from the monomer dimethylsilanol, $(CH_3)_2Si(OH)_2$. Use structural formulas to write the structure of four units of this polymer.
(b) Identify the type of polymerization that occurs.

114. Polyacetylene is an electrically conducting polymer of acetylene, HC≡CH. Now used in batteries, the polymer was discovered accidentally in 1970 when far too much catalyst was used in an experimental attempt to polymerize acetylene into synthetic rubber. Write a plausible Lewis structure for a portion of a polyacetylene molecule.

115. Glycolic acid, $HOCH_2COOH$, and lactic acid form a copolymer used as absorbable stitches in surgery. Use structural formulas to write a chemical equation showing the formation of four units of the copolymer.

116. A particular condensation copolymer forms a silk-like synthetic fabric. A portion of the polymer's structure is shown below.

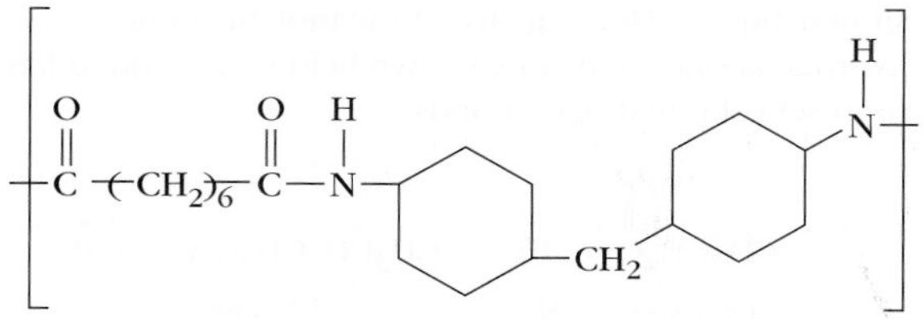

Write the structural formulas of the two monomers used to synthesize the polymer.

Conceptual Challenge Problems

CP12.A (Section 12.1) How are the boiling points of hydrocarbons during the distillation of petroleum related to their molecular size?

CP12.B (Section 12.5) Even though millions of organic compounds exist and each compound may have 10, 100, or even thousands of atoms bonded together to make one molecule, the reactions of organic compounds can be studied and even predicted for compounds yet to be discovered. What characteristic of organic compounds allows their reactions to be studied and predicted?

CP12.C (Section 12.6) What is the advantage of animals storing chemical potential energy in their bodies as triesters of glycerol and long-chain fatty acids, known as fats, instead of as carbohydrates?

APPENDIX

A Problem Solving and Mathematical Operations

In this book we have provided many illustrations of problem solving and many problems for practice. Some are numerical problems that must be solved by mathematical calculations. Others are conceptual problems that must be solved by applying an understanding of the principles of chemistry. Often, it is necessary to use chemical concepts to relate what we know about matter at the nanoscale to the properties of matter at the macroscale. The problems throughout this book are representative of the kinds of problems that chemists and other scientists must regularly solve to pursue their goals, although our problems are often not as difficult as those encountered in the real world.

Problem solving is not a simple skill that can be mastered with a few hours of study or practice. Because there are many different kinds of problems and many different kinds of people who are problem solvers, no hard and fast rules are available that are guaranteed to lead you to solutions. The general guidelines presented in this appendix are, however, helpful in getting you started on any kind of problem and in checking whether your answers are correct. The problem-solving skills you develop in a chemistry course can later be applied to difficult and important problems that may arise in your profession, your personal life, or the society in which you live.

In getting a clear picture of a problem and asking appropriate questions regarding the problem, you need to keep in mind all the principles of chemistry and other subjects that you think may apply. In many real-life problems, not enough information is available for you to arrive at an unambiguous solution; in such cases, try to look up or estimate what is needed and then forge ahead, noting assumptions you have made. Often the hardest part is deciding which principle or idea is most likely to help solve the problem and what information is needed. To some degree this can be a matter of luck or chance. Nevertheless, in the words of Louis Pasteur, "In the field of observation chance only favors those minds which have been prepared." The more practice you have had, and the more principles and facts you can keep in mind, the more likely you are to be able to solve the problems that you face.

A.1 General Problem-Solving Strategies

"The mere formulation of a problem is often far more essential than its solution. To raise new questions, new possibilities, to regard old problems from a new angle, requires creative imagination and marks real advances in science."
—Albert Einstein

1. **Define the problem.** Carefully review the information contained in the problem. What is the problem asking you to find? What key principles are involved? What known information is necessary for solving the problem and what information is there just to place the question in context? Organize the information to see what is necessary and to see the relationships among the known data. Try writing the information in an organized way. If the information is numerical, be sure to include proper units. Can you picture the situation under consideration? Try sketching it and including any relevant dimensions in the sketch.
2. **Develop a plan.** Have you solved a problem of this type before? If you recognize the new problem as similar to ones you know how to solve, you can use the same method that worked before. Try reasoning backward from the units of what is being sought. What data are needed to find an answer in those units?

Can the problem be broken down into smaller pieces, each of which can be solved separately to produce information that can be assembled to solve the entire problem? When a problem can be divided into simpler problems, it often helps to write down a plan that lists the simpler problems and the order in which those problems must be put together to arrive at an overall solution. Many major problems in chemical research have to be solved in this way. In problems in this book we have mostly provided the needed numerical data, but in the laboratory, the first aspect of solving a problem is often devising experiments to gather the data or searching databases to find needed information.

If you are still unsure about what to do, do something anyway. It may not be the right thing to do, but as you work on it, the way to solve the problem may become apparent, or you may see what is wrong with your initial approach, thereby making clearer what a good plan would be.

3. **Execute the plan.** Carefully write down each step of a mathematical problem, being sure to keep track of the units. Do the units cancel to give you the answer in the desired units? Don't skip steps. Don't do any except the simplest steps in your head. Once you've written down the steps for a mathematical problem, check what you've written—is it all correct? Students often say they got a problem wrong because they "made a stupid mistake." Teachers—and textbook authors—make mistakes, too. These errors usually arise because they don't take the time to write down the steps of a problem clearly and correctly. In solving a mathematical problem, remember to apply the principles of dimensional analysis and significant figures. Dimensional analysis is introduced in Sections 1.4 (⇐ ***p. 7***) and 2.3 (⇐ ***p. 46***); it is reviewed below. Section 2.4 (⇐ ***p. 52***) and Appendix A.3 ***(p. A.5)*** introduce significant figures.

4. ✓ **Check the answer to see whether it is reasonable.** As a final check of your solution to any problem, ask yourself whether the answer is reasonable: Are the units of a numerical answer correct? Is a numerical answer of about the right size? Don't just copy a result from your calculator without thinking about whether it makes sense.

Suppose you have been asked to convert 100. yards to a distance in meters. Using dimensional analysis and some well-known factors for converting from the English system to the metric system, you could write

$$100.\ \text{yd} \times \frac{3\ \text{ft}}{1\ \text{yd}} \times \frac{12\ \text{in.}}{1\ \text{ft}} \times \frac{2.54\ \text{cm}}{1\ \text{in.}} \times \frac{1\ \text{m}}{100\ \text{cm}} = 91.4\ \text{m}$$

To check that a distance of 91.4 m is about right, recall that a yard is a little shorter than a meter. Therefore 100 yd should be a little less than 100 m. If you had mistakenly divided instead of multiplied by 3 ft/yd in the first step, your final answer would have been a little more than 10 m. This is equivalent to only about 30 ft, and you probably know a 100-yd football field is longer than that.

A.2 Numbers, Units, and Quantities

Many scientific problems require you to use mathematics to calculate a result or draw a conclusion. Therefore, knowledge of mathematics and its application to problem solving is important. However, one aspect of scientific calculations is often absent from pure mathematical work: Science deals with *measurements* in which an unknown quantity is compared with a standard or unit of measure. For example, using a balance to determine the mass of an object involves comparing the object's mass with standard masses, usually in multiples or fractions of one gram; the result is reported as some number of grams, say 4.357 g. *Both the number and the unit are important.* If the result had been 123.5 g, this would clearly be different, but a result of 4.357 oz (ounces) would also be different, because the unit "ounce" is different from the unit "gram." A *result that describes the quantitative measurement of a property,* such as 4.357 g, is called a *quantity* (or physical quantity), and it consists of a number and a unit. Chemical problem solving requires calculating with quantities. Notice that whether a quantity is large or small depends on the units as well as the number; the two quantities 123.5 g and 4.357 oz, for example, represent the *same* mass.

A quantity is always treated as though the number and the units are multiplied together; that is, 4.357 g can be handled mathematically as $4.357 \times \text{g}$. Using this simple rule, you will see that calculations involving quantities follow the normal rules of algebra and arithmetic: $5\ \text{g} + 7\ \text{g} = 5 \times \text{g} + 7 \times \text{g} = (5 + 7) \times \text{g} = 12\ \text{g}$; or $6\ \text{g} \div 2\ \text{g} = (6\ \cancel{\text{g}})/(2\ \cancel{\text{g}}) = 3$.

(Notice that in the second calculation the unit g appears in both the numerator and the denominator and cancels out, leaving a pure number, 3.) Treating units as algebraic entities has the advantage that *if a calculation is set up correctly, the units will cancel or multiply together so that the final result has appropriate units.* For example, if you measured the size of a sheet of paper and found it to be 8.5 in. by 11 in., the area A of the sheet could be calculated as area = length × width = 11 in. × 8.5 in. = 94 in.^{2}, or 94 square inches. If a calculation is set up incorrectly, the units of the result will be inappropriate. Using units to check whether a calculation has been properly set up is called *dimensional analysis* **(⇐ p. 10)**.

This idea of using algebra on units as well as numbers is useful in all kinds of situations. For example, suppose you are having a party for some friends who like pizza. A large pizza consists of 12 slices and costs \$10.75. You expect to need 36 slices of pizza and want to know how much you will have to spend. A strategy for solving the problem is first to figure out how many pizzas you need and then to figure out the cost in dollars. This solution could be diagrammed as

$$\text{Slices} \xrightarrow[\text{step 1}]{\text{slices per pizza}} \text{pizzas} \xrightarrow[\text{step 2}]{\text{dollars per pizza}} \text{dollars}$$

Step 1: Find the number of pizzas required by dividing the number of slices per pizza into the number of slices, thus converting "units" of slices to "units" of pizzas:

$$\text{Number of pizzas} = 36 \text{ slices}\left(\frac{1 \text{ pizza}}{12 \text{ slices}}\right) = 3 \text{ pizzas}$$

If you had multiplied the number of slices times the number of slices per pizza, the result would have been labeled pizzas × slices^2, which does not make sense. In other words, the labels indicate whether multiplication or division is appropriate.

Strictly speaking, slices and pizzas are not units in the same sense that a gram is a unit. Nevertheless, labeling things this way will often help you keep in mind what a number refers to—pizzas, slices, or dollars in this case.

Step 2: Find the total cost by multiplying the cost per pizza by the number of pizzas needed, thus converting "units" of pizzas to "units" of dollars:

$$\text{Total price} = 3 \text{ pizzas}\left(\frac{\$10.75}{1 \text{ pizza}}\right) = \$32.25$$

Notice that in each step you have multiplied by a factor that allowed the initial units to cancel algebraically, giving the answer in the desired units. A factor such as (1 pizza/12 slices) or (\$10.75/pizza) is referred to as a *proportionality factor* **(⇐ p. 10)**. This name indicates that it comes from a proportion. For instance, in the pizza problem you could set up the proportion

$$\frac{x \text{ pizzas}}{36 \text{ slices}} = \frac{1 \text{ pizza}}{12 \text{ slices}} \quad \text{or} \quad x \text{ pizzas} = 36 \text{ slices}\left(\frac{1 \text{ pizza}}{12 \text{ slices}}\right) = 3 \text{ pizzas}$$

A proportionality factor such as (1 pizza/12 slices) is also called a *conversion factor,* which indicates that it converts one kind of unit or label to another; in this case the label "slices" is converted to the label "pizzas."

Many everyday scientific problems involve proportionality. For example, the bigger the volume of a solid or liquid substance, the bigger its mass. When the volume is zero, the mass is also zero. These facts indicate that mass, m, is directly proportional to volume, V, or, symbolically,

$$m \propto V$$

where the symbol $\propto$ means "is proportional to." Whenever a proportion is expressed this way, it can also be expressed as an equality by using a proportionality constant—for example,

$$m = d \times V$$

In this case the proportionality constant, d, is called the density of the substance. This equation embodies the definition of density as mass per unit volume, since it can be rearranged algebraically to

$$d = \frac{m}{V}$$

As with any algebraic equation involving three variables, it is possible to calculate any one of the three quantities *m, V,* or *d,* provided the other two are known. If density is wanted, simply use the definition of mass per unit volume; if mass or volume is to be calculated, the density can be used as a proportionality factor.

Suppose that you are going to buy a ton of gravel and want to know how big a bin you will need to store it. You know the mass of gravel and want to find the volume of the bin; this implies that density will be useful. If the gravel is primarily limestone, you can assume that its density is about the same as for limestone and look it up. Limestone has the chemical formula $CaCO_3$, and its density is 2.7 kg/L. However, these mass units are different from the units for mass of gravel—namely, tons. Therefore you need to recall or look up the mass of 1 ton (exactly 2000 pounds [lb]) and the fact that there are 2.20 lb per kilogram. This provides enough information to calculate the volume needed. Here is a "roadmap" plan for the calculation:

$$\text{Mass of gravel in tons} \xrightarrow[\text{step1}]{\text{change units}} \text{mass of gravel in kilograms} \xrightarrow[\text{step 2}]{\text{density}} \text{volume of bin}$$

Step 1: Figure out how many kilograms of gravel are in a ton.

$$m_{\text{gravel}} = 1 \text{ ton} = 2000 \text{ lb} = 2000 \text{ lb} \left(\frac{1 \text{ kg}}{2.20 \text{ lb}}\right) = 909 \text{ kg}$$

The fact that there are 2.20 pounds per kilogram implies two proportionality factors: (2.20 lb/1 kg) and (1 kg/2.20 lb). The latter was used because it results in appropriate cancellation of units.

Step 2: Use the density to calculate the volume of 909 kg of gravel.

$$V_{\text{gravel}} = \frac{m_{\text{gravel}}}{d_{\text{gravel}}} = \frac{909 \text{ kg}}{2.7 \text{ kg/L}} = 909 \text{ kg} \left(\frac{1 \text{ L}}{2.7 \text{ kg}}\right) = 340 \text{ L}$$

In this step we used the definition of density, solved algebraically for volume, substituted the two known quantities into the equation, and calculated the result. However, it is quicker simply to remember that mass and volume are related by a proportionality factor called density and to use the units of the quantities to decide whether to multiply or divide by that factor. In this case we divided mass by density because the units kilograms canceled, leaving a result in liters, which is a unit of volume.

Also, it is quicker and more accurate to solve a problem like this one by using a single setup. Then all the calculations can be done at once, and no intermediate results need to be written down. The "roadmap" plan given above can serve as a guide to the single-setup solution, which looks like this:

$$V_{\text{gravel}} = 1 \text{ ton} \left(\frac{2000 \text{ lb}}{1 \text{ ton}}\right)\left(\frac{1 \text{ kg}}{2.20 \text{ lb}}\right)\left(\frac{1 \text{ L}}{2.7 \text{ kg}}\right) = 340 \text{ L}$$

To calculate the result, then, you would enter 2000 on your calculator, divide by 2.20, and divide by 2.7. Such a setup makes it easy to see what to multiply and divide by, and the calculation goes more quickly when it can be entered into a calculator all at once.

The liter is not the most convenient volume unit for this problem, however, because it does not relate well to what we want to find out—how big a bin to make. A liter is about the same volume as a quart, but whether you are familiar with liters, quarts, or both, 300 of them is not easy to visualize. Let's convert liters to something we can understand better. A liter is a volume equal to a cube one tenth of a meter (1 dm) on a side; that is, $1\text{L} = 1 \text{ dm}^3$. Consequently,

$$340 \text{ L} = 340 \text{ L} \left(\frac{1 \text{ dm}^3}{1 \text{ L}}\right)\left(\frac{1 \text{ m}}{10 \text{ dm}}\right)^3 = 340 \text{ dm}^3 \left(\frac{1 \text{ m}^3}{1000 \text{ dm}^3}\right) = 0.34 \text{ m}^3$$

Thus, the bin would need to have a volume of about one third of a cubic meter; that is, it could be a meter wide, a meter long, and about a third of a meter high and it would hold the ton of gravel.

One more thing should be noted about this example. We don't need to know the volume of the bin very precisely, because being off a bit will make very little difference; it might mean getting a little too much wood to build the bin, or not making the bin quite big enough and having a little gravel spill out, but this isn't a big deal. In other cases, such as calculating the quantity of fuel needed to get a space shuttle into orbit, being off by a few percent could be a life-or-death matter. Because it is important to know how precise data are and to be able to evaluate how important precision is, scientific results usually indicate their precision. The simplest way to do so is by means of significant figures.

A.3 Precision, Accuracy, and Significant Figures

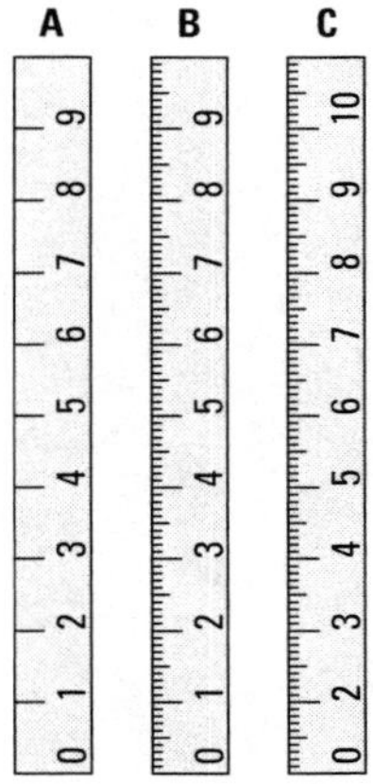

Three rulers.

The **precision** of a measurement indicates how well several determinations of the same quantity agree. Some devices can make more precise measurements than others. Consider rulers A and B shown in the margin. Ruler A is marked every centimeter and ruler B is marked every millimeter. Clearly you could measure at least to the nearest millimeter with ruler B, and probably you could estimate to the nearest 0.2 mm or so. However, using ruler A you could probably estimate only to the nearest millimeter or so. We say that ruler B allows more precise measurement than ruler A. If several different people used ruler B to measure the length of an iron bar, their measurements would probably agree more closely than if they used ruler A.

Precision is also illustrated by the results of throwing darts at a bull's-eye (Figure A.1). In part (a), the darts are scattered all over the board; the dart thrower was apparently not very skillful (or threw the darts from a long distance away from the board), and the precision of their placement on the board is low. This is analogous to the results that would be obtained by several people using ruler A. In part (b), the darts are all clustered together, indicating much better reproducibility on the part of the thrower—that is, greater precision. This is analogous to measurements that might be made using ruler B.

Notice also that in Figure A.1b every dart has come very close to the bull's-eye; we describe this result by saying that the thrower has been quite **accurate**—the average of all throws is very close to the accepted position, the bull's-eye. Figure A.1c illustrates that it is possible to be precise without being accurate—the dart thrower has consistently missed the bull's-eye, but all darts are clustered very precisely around the wrong point on the board. This third case is like an experiment with some flaw (either in its design or in a measuring device) that causes all results to differ from the correct value by the same quantity. An example is measuring length with ruler C, on which the scale is incorrectly labeled. The precision (reproducibility) of measurements with ruler C might be quite good, but the accuracy would be poor because all items longer than 1 cm would be off by a centimeter.

In the laboratory we attempt to set up experiments so that the greatest possible accuracy can be obtained. As a further check on accuracy, results may be compared among different laboratories so that any flaw in experimental design or measurement can be detected. For each individual experiment, several measurements are usually made and their precision determined. In most cases, better precision is taken as an indication of better experimental work, and it is necessary to know the precision to compare results among different experimenters. If two different experimenters both had results like those in Figure A.1a, for example, their average values could differ quite a lot before they would say that their results did not agree within experimental error.

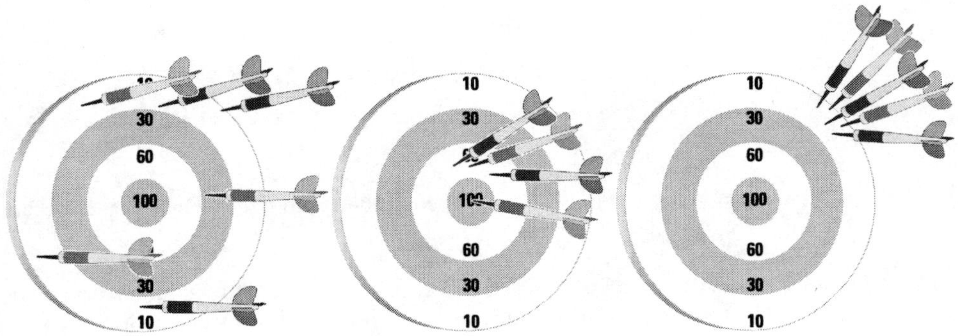

Figure A.1 Precision and accuracy. (a) Poor precision. (b) Good precision and good accuracy. (c) Good precision and poor accuracy.

In most experiments several different kinds of measurements must be made, and some can be done more precisely than others. It is common sense that *a calculated result can be no more precise than the least precise piece of information that went into the calculation.* This is where the rules for significant figures come in. In the last example in the preceding section, the quantity of gravel was described as "a ton." Usually gravel is measured by weighing an empty truck, putting some gravel in the truck, weighing the truck again, and subtracting the weight of the truck from the weight of the truck plus gravel. The quantity of gravel is not adjusted if there is a bit too much or a bit too little, because that would be a lot of trouble. You might end up with as much as 2200 pounds or as little as 1800 pounds, even though you asked for a ton. In terms of significant figures this would be expressed as 2.0×10^3 lb.

The quantity 2.0×10^3 lb is said to have two significant figures; it designates a quantity in which the 2 is taken to be exactly right but the 0 is not known precisely. (In this case, the number could be as large as 2.2 or as small as 1.8, so the 0 obviously is not exactly right.) In general, in a number that represents a scientific measurement, the last digit on the right is taken to be inexact, but all digits farther to the left are assumed to be exact. When you do calculations using such numbers, you must follow some simple rules so that your results will reflect the precision of all the measurements that go into the calculations. Here are the rules:

Rule 1: To determine the number of significant figures in a measurement, read the number from left to right and count all digits, starting with the first digit that is *not* zero.

For a number written in scientific notation, all digits are significant.

Example	Number of Significant Figures
1.23 g	3
0.00123 g	3; the zeros to the left of the 1 simply locate the decimal point. The number of significant figures is more obvious if you write numbers in scientific notation; thus, $0.00123 = 1.23 \times 10^{-3}$.
2.0 g and 0.020 g	2; both have two significant digits. When a number is greater than 1, *all zeros to the right of the decimal point are significant.* For a number less than 1, only zeros to the right of the first significant digit are significant.
100 g	1; in numbers that do not contain a decimal point, "trailing" zeros may or may not be significant. To eliminate possible confusion, the practice followed in this book is to include a decimal point if the zeros are significant. Thus, 100. has three significant digits, while 100 has only one. Alternatively, we write in scientific notation 1.00×10^2 (three significant digits) or 1×10^2 (one significant digit). For a number written in scientific notation, all digits preceding the 10^x term are significant.
100 cm/m	Infinite number of significant figures, because this is a defined quantity. There are *exactly* 100 centimeters in one meter.
$\pi = 3.1415926\ldots$	The value of π is known to a greater number of significant figures than any data you will ever use in a calculation.

The number π is now known to 1,011,196,691 digits. It is doubtful that you will need that much precision in this course—or ever.

Rule 2: When adding or subtracting, the number of decimal places in the answer should be equal to the number of decimal places in the number with the *fewest* places. Suppose you add three numbers:

0.12	2 significant figures	2 decimal places
1.6	2 significant figures	1 decimal place
+ 10.976	5 significant figures	3 decimal places
12.696		

This sum should be reported as 12.7, a number with one decimal place, because 1.6 has only one decimal place.

Rule 3: In multiplication or division, the number of significant figures in the answer should be the same as that in the quantity with the fewest significant figures.

$$\frac{0.1208}{0.0236} = 0.512 \text{ or, in scientific notation, } 5.12 \times 10^{-1}$$

Since 0.0236 has only three significant figures, while 0.01208 has four, the answer is limited to three significant figures.

Rule 4: When a number is rounded (the number of digits is reduced), the last digit retained is increased by 1 only if the following digit is 5 or greater. If the following digit is exactly 5 (or 5 followed by zeros), then increase the last retained digit by 1 if it is *odd* or leave the last digit unchanged if it is *even*. Thus, both 18.35 and 18.45 are rounded to 18.4.

Full Number	Number Rounded to Three Significant Figures
12.696	12.7
16.249	16.2
18.350	18.4
18.351	18.4

One last word regarding significant figures and calculations. In working problems on a pocket calculator, you should do the calculation using all the digits allowed by the calculator and round only at the end of the problem. Rounding in the middle can introduce small errors (called *rounding errors* or *round-off errors*). If your answers do not quite agree with those in the Appendices of this book, rounding errors may be the source of the disagreement.

Now let us consider a problem that is of practical importance and that makes use of all the rules. Suppose you discover that young children are eating chips of paint that flake off a wall in an old house. The paint contains 200. ppm lead (200. milligrams of Pb per kilogram of paint). Suppose that a child eats five such chips. How much lead has the child gotten from the paint?

The ppm unit stands for "parts per million." If a substance is present with a concentration of 1 ppm, there is 1 gram of the substance in 1 million grams of the sample.

As stated, this problem does not include enough information for a solution to be obtained; however, some reasonable assumptions can be made, and they can lead to experiments that could be used to obtain the necessary information. The statement does not say how big the paint chips are. Let's assume that they are 1.0 cm by 1.0 cm so that the area is 1.0 cm^2. Then eating five chips means eating 5.0 cm^2 of paint. (This assumption could be improved by measuring similar chips from the same place.) Since the concentration of lead is reported in units of mass of lead per mass of paint, we need to know the mass of 5.0 cm^2 of paint. This could be determined by measuring the areas of several paint chips and determining the mass of each. Suppose that the results of such measurements were those given in the table.

Mass of Chip (mg)	Area of Chip (cm^2)	Mass per Unit Area (mg/cm^2)
29.6	2.34	12.65
21.9	1.73	12.66
23.6	1.86	12.69

$$\text{Average mass per unit area} = \frac{(12.65 + 12.66 + 12.69)\ \text{mg/cm}^2}{3}$$

$$= 12.67\ \text{mg/cm}^2 = 12.7\ \text{mg/cm}^2$$

The average has been rounded to three significant figures because each experimentally measured mass and area has three significant figures. (Notice that more than three significant figures were kept in the intermediate calculations so as not to lose precision.) Now we can use this information to calculate how much lead the child has consumed.

$$m_{\text{paint}} = 5.0\ \text{cm}^2\ \text{paint}\left(\frac{12.7\ \text{mg paint}}{1\ \text{cm}^2\ \text{paint}}\right)\left(\frac{1\ \text{g}}{1000\ \text{mg}}\right)\left(\frac{1\ \text{kg}}{1000\ \text{g}}\right)$$

$$= 6.35 \times 10^{-5}\ \text{kg paint}$$

$$m_{\text{Pb}} = 6.35 \times 10^{-5}\ \text{kg paint}\left(\frac{200.\ \text{mg Pb}}{1\ \text{kg paint}}\right) = 1.27 \times 10^{-2}\ \text{mg Pb}$$

$$= 1.3 \times 10^{-2}\ \text{mg Pb} = 0.013\ \text{mg Pb}$$

The final result was rounded to two significant figures because there were only two significant figures in the initial 5.0 cm^2 area of the paint chip. This is quite adequate precision, however, for you to determine whether this quantity of lead is likely to harm the child.

The methods of problem solving presented here have been developed over time and represent a good way of keeping track of the precision of results, the units in which those results were obtained, and the correctness of calculations. These methods are not the only way that such goals can be achieved, but they do work well. We recommend that you include units in all calculations and check that they cancel appropriately. It is also important not to overstate the precision of results by keeping too many significant figures. By solving many problems, you should be able to develop your problem-solving skills so that they become second nature and you can use them without thinking about the mechanics. You can then devote all your thought to the logic of a problem solution.

A.4 Electronic Calculators

The directions for calculator use in this section are given for calculators using "algebraic" logic. Such calculators are the most common type used by students in introductory courses. For calculators using RPN logic (such as those made by Hewlett-Packard), the procedure will differ slightly.

The advent of inexpensive electronic calculators has made calculations in introductory chemistry much more straightforward. You are well advised to purchase a calculator that has the capability of performing calculations in scientific notation, has both base 10 and natural logarithms, and is capable of raising any number to any power and of finding any root of any number. In the discussion below, we will point out in general how these functions of your calculator can be used. You should practice using your calculator to carry out arithmetic operations and make certain that you are able to use all of its functions correctly.

Although electronic calculators have greatly simplified calculations, they have also forced us to focus again on significant figures. A calculator easily handles eight or more significant figures, but real laboratory data are rarely known to this precision. Therefore, if you have not already done so, review Appendix A.3 on significant figures, precision, and rounding numbers.

The mathematical skills required to read and study this textbook successfully involve algebra, some geometry, scientific notation, logarithms, and solving quadratic equations. The next three sections review the last three of these topics.

A.5 Exponential or Scientific Notation

In exponential or scientific notation, a number is expressed as a product of two numbers: $N \times 10^n$. The first number, N, is called the digit term and is a number between 1 and 10. The second number, 10^n, the exponential term, is some integer power of 10. For example, 1234 would be written in scientific notation as 1.234×10^3 or 1.234 multiplied by 10 three times.

$$1234 = 1.234 \times 10^1 \times 10^1 \times 10^1 = 1.234 \times 10^3$$

Conversely, a number less than 1, such as 0.01234, would be written as 1.234×10^{-2}. This notation tells us that 1.234 should be divided twice by 10 to obtain 0.01234.

$$0.01234 = \frac{1.234}{10^1 \times 10^1} = 1.234 \times 10^{-1} \times 10^{-1} = 1.234 \times 10^{-2}$$

Some other examples of scientific notation follow:

$10{,}000 = 1 \times 10^4$	$12{,}345 = 1.2345 \times 10^4$
$1000 = 1 \times 10^3$	$1234 = 1.234 \times 10^3$
$100 = 1 \times 10^2$	$123 = 1.23 \times 10^2$
$10 = 1 \times 10^1$	$12 = 1.2 \times 10^1$
$1 = 1 \times 10^0$	(any number to the zeroth power = 1)
$1/10 = 1 \times 10^{-1}$	$0.12 = 1.2 \times 10^{-1}$
$1/100 = 1 \times 10^{-2}$	$0.012 = 1.2 \times 10^{-2}$
$1/1000 = 1 \times 10^{-3}$	$0.0012 = 1.2 \times 10^{-3}$
$1/10{,}000 = 1 \times 10^{-4}$	$0.00012 = 1.2 \times 10^{-4}$

When converting a number to scientific notation, notice that the exponent n is positive if the number is greater than 1 and negative if the number is less than 1. The value of n is the number of places by which the decimal was shifted to obtain the number in scientific notation.

$$12345. = 1.2345 \times 10^4$$

Decimal shifted 4 places to the left. Therefore, n is positive and equal to 4.

$$0.0012 = 1.2 \times 10^{-3}$$

Decimal shifted 3 places to the right. Therefore, n is negative and equal to 3.

If you wish to convert a number in scientific notation to the usual form, the procedure above is simply reversed.

$$6.273 \times 10^2 = 627.3$$

Decimal point shifted 2 places to the right, because n is positive and equal to 2.

$$006.273 \times 10^{-3} = 0.006273$$

Decimal point shifted 3 places to the left, because n is negative and equal to 3.

To enter a number in scientific notation into a calculator, first enter the number itself. Then press the EE (Enter Exponent) key followed by n, the power of 10. For example, to enter 6.022×10^{23}, you press these keys in succession:

6 . 0 2 2 EE 2 3 .

(Do not enter the number using the multiplication key, the number 10, and the EE key. This will result in a number that is 10 times bigger than you want. For example, pressing these keys

6 . 0 2 2 × 1 0 EE 2 3

enters the number $6.022 \times 10 \times 10^{23} = 6.022 \times 10^{24}$, because EE 2 3 means 10^{23}.)

There are two final points concerning scientific notation. First, if you are used to working on a computer you may be in the habit of writing a number such as 1.23×10^3 as 1.23E3, or 6.45×10^{-5} as 6.45E−5. Second, some electronic calculators allow you to convert numbers readily to scientific notation. If you have such a calculator, you can change a number shown in the usual form to scientific notation by pressing an appropriate key or keys.

Usually you will handle numbers in scientific notation with a calculator. In case you need to work without a calculator, however, the next few sections describe pencil-and-paper calculations as well as calculator methods.

1. Adding and Subtracting

When adding or subtracting numbers in scientific notation without using a calculator, first convert the numbers to the same powers of 10. Then add or subtract the digit terms.

$$(1.234 \times 10^{-3}) + (5.623 \times 10^{-2}) = (0.1234 \times 10^{-2}) + (5.623 \times 10^{-2})$$
$$= 5.746 \times 10^{-2}$$

$$(6.52 \times 10^2) - (1.56 \times 10^3) = (6.52 \times 10^2) - (15.6 \times 10^2)$$
$$= -9.1 \times 10^2$$

In this calculation, the result has only two significant figures, although each of the original numbers had three. Subtracting two numbers that are nearly the same can reduce the number of significant figures appreciably.

2. Multiplying

The digit terms are multiplied in the usual manner, and the exponents are added algebraically. The result is expressed with a digit term with only one nonzero digit to the left of the decimal.

$$(1.23 \times 10^3)(7.60 \times 10^2) = (1.23 \times 7.60)(10^3 \times 10^2) = (1.23)(7.60) \times 10^{3+2}$$
$$= 9.35 \times 10^5$$
$$(6.02 \times 10^{23})(2.32 \times 10^{-2}) = (6.02)(2.32) \times 10^{23-2}$$
$$= 13.966 \times 10^{21} = 1.3966 \times 10^{22}$$
$$= 1.40 \times 10^{22} \quad \text{(rounded to 3 significant figures)}$$

3. Dividing

The digit terms are divided in the usual manner, and the exponents are subtracted algebraically. The quotient is written with one nonzero digit to the left of the decimal in the digit term.

$$\frac{7.60 \times 10^3}{1.23 \times 10^2} = \frac{7.60}{1.23} \times 10^{3-2} = 6.18 \times 10^1$$
$$\frac{6.02 \times 10^{23}}{9.10 \times 10^{-2}} = \frac{6.02}{9.10} \times 10^{(23)-(-2)} = 0.662 \times 10^{25} = 6.62 \times 10^{24}$$

4. Raising Numbers in Scientific Notation to Powers

When raising a number in scientific notation to a power, treat the digit term in the usual manner. The exponent is then multiplied by the number indicating the power.

$$(1.25 \times 10^3)^2 = (1.25)^2 \times (10^3)^2 = (1.25)^2 \times 10^{3\times 2} = 1.5625 \times 10^6 = 1.56 \times 10^6$$
$$(5.6 \times 10^{-10})^3 = (5.6)^3 \times 10^{(-10)\times 3} = 175.6 \times 10^{-30} = 1.8 \times 10^{-28}$$

Electronic calculators usually have two methods of raising a number to a power. To square a number, enter the number and then press the "x^2" key. To raise a number to any power, use the "y^x" key. For example, to raise 1.42×10^2 to the 4th power, that is, to find $(1.42 \times 10^2)^4$,

(a) Enter 1.42×10^2.
(b) Press "y^x."
(c) Enter 4 (this should appear on the display).
(d) Press "=" and $4.0658689\ldots \times 10^8$ will appear on the display. (The number of digits depends on the calculator.)

As a final step, express the number in the correct number of significant figures (4.07×10^8 in this case).

5. Taking Roots of Numbers in Scientific Notation

Unless you use an electronic calculator, the number must first be put into a form in which the exponential is exactly divisible by the root. The root of the digit term is found in the usual way, and the exponent is divided by the desired root.

$$\sqrt{3.6 \times 10^7} = \sqrt{36 \times 10^6} = \sqrt{36} \times \sqrt{10^6} = 6.0 \times 10^3$$
$$\sqrt[3]{2.1 \times 10^{-7}} = \sqrt[3]{210 \times 10^{-9}} = \sqrt[3]{210} \times \sqrt[3]{10^{-9}} = 5.9 \times 10^{-3}$$

To take a square root on an electronic calculator, enter the number and then press the "$\sqrt{x}$" key. To find a higher root of a number, such as the fourth root of 5.6×10^{-10},

On some calculators, Steps (a) and (c) may be interchanged.

(a) Enter the number, 5.6×10^{-10} in this case.
(b) Press the "$\sqrt[x]{y}$" key. (On most calculators, the sequence you actually use is to press "2ndF" and then "$\sqrt[x]{y}$." Alternatively, you may have to press "INV" and then "y^x".)
(c) Enter the desired root, 4 in this case.
(d) Press "=". The answer here is 4.8646×10^{-3} or 4.9×10^{-3}.

A general procedure for finding any root is to use the "y^x" key. For a square root, x is 0.5 (or $\frac{1}{2}$), whereas it is 0.33 (or $\frac{1}{3}$) for a cube root, 0.25 (or $\frac{1}{4}$) for a fourth root, and so on.

A.6 Logarithms

There are two types of logarithms used in this text: common logarithms (abbreviated log), whose base is 10, and natural logarithms (abbreviated ln), whose base is e (=2.7182818284).

Logarithms to the base 10 are needed when dealing with pH.

$$\log x = n \qquad \text{where } x = 10^n$$

$$\ln x = m \qquad \text{where } x = e^m$$

Most equations in chemistry and physics were developed in natural or base e logarithms, and this practice is followed in this text. The relation between log and ln is

$$\ln x = 2.303 \log x$$

Aside from the different bases of the two logarithms, they are used in the same manner. What follows is largely a description of the use of common logarithms.

A common logarithm is the power to which you must raise 10 to obtain the number. For example, the log of 100 is 2, since you must raise 10 to the power 2 to obtain 100. Other examples are

$$\log 1000 = \log (10^3) = 3$$

$$\log 10 = \log (10^1) = 1$$

$$\log 1 = \log (10^0) = 0$$

$$\log 1/10 = \log (10^{-1}) = -1$$

$$\log 1/10{,}000 = \log (10^{-4}) = -4$$

To obtain the common logarithm of a number other than a simple power of 10, use an electronic calculator. For example,

$$\log 2.10 = 0.3222, \text{ which means that } 10^{0.3222} = 2.10$$

$$\log 5.16 = 0.7126, \text{ which means that } 10^{0.7126} = 5.16$$

$$\log 3.125 = 0.49485, \text{ which means that } 10^{0.49485} = 3.125$$

To check this result on your calculator, enter the number and then press the "log" key.

To obtain the natural logarithm of the numbers above, use a calculator having this function. Enter each number and press "ln".

$$\ln 2.10 = 0.7419, \text{ which means that } e^{0.7419} = 2.10$$

$$\ln 5.16 = 1.6409, \text{ which means that } e^{1.6409} = 5.16$$

To find the common logarithm of a number greater than 10 or less than 1 with a log table, first express the number in scientific notation. Then find the log of each part of the number and add the logs. For example,

Nomenclature of Logarithms: The number to the left of the decimal in a logarithm is called the *characteristic*, and the number to the right of the decimal is called the *mantissa*.

$$\log 241 = \log (2.41 \times 10^2) = \log 2.4 + \log 10^2$$
$$= 0.382 + 2 = 2.382$$

$$\log 0.00573 = \log (5.73 \times 10^{-3}) = \log 5.73 + \log 10^{-3}$$
$$= 0.758 + (-3) = -2.242$$

Significant Figures and Logarithms

The mantissa (digits to the right of the decimal point in the logarithm) should have as many significant figures as the number whose log was found. (So that you could more clearly see the result obtained with a calculator or a table, this rule was not strictly followed until the last two examples.)

Obtaining Antilogarithms

If you are given the logarithm of a number and need to find the number from it, you need to obtain the "antilogarithm" or "antilog" of the number. There are two common procedures used by electronic calculators to do this:

Procedure A	Procedure B
(a) Enter the log or ln (a number).	(a) Enter the log or ln (a number).
(b) Press 2ndF.	(b) Press INV.
(c) Press 10^x or e^x.	(c) Press log or ln x.

Test one or the other of these procedures with the following examples.

EXAMPLE 1 Find the number whose log is 5.234.

Recall that $\log x = n$, where $x = 10^n$. In this case $n = 5.234$. Enter that number in your calculator and find the value of 10^n, the antilog. In this case,

$$10^{5.234} = 10^{0.234} \times 10^5 = 1.71 \times 10^5$$

Notice that the characteristic (5) sets the decimal point; it is the power of 10 in the exponential form. The mantissa (0.234) gives the value of the number x. Thus, if you use a log table to find x, you need only look up 0.234 in the table and see that it corresponds to 1.71.

EXAMPLE 2 Find the number whose log is −3.456.

$$10^{-3.456} = 10^{0.544} \times 10^{-4} = 3.50 \times 10^{-4}$$

Notice here that -3.456 must be expressed as the sum of -4 and $+0.544$.

Mathematical Operations Using Logarithms

Because logarithms are exponents, operations involving them follow the same rules as the use of exponents. Thus, multiplying two numbers can be done by adding logarithms.

$$\log xy = \log x + \log y$$

For example, we multiply 563 by 125 by adding their logarithms and finding the antilogarithm of the result.

$$\log 563 = 2.751$$

$$\log 125 = 2.097$$

$$\log (563 \times 125) = 2.751 + 2.097 = 4.848$$

$$563 \times 125 = 10^{4.848} = 10^4 \times 10^{0.848} = 7.05 \times 10^4$$

One number (x) can be divided by another (y) by subtraction of their logarithms.

$$\log \frac{x}{y} = \log x - \log y$$

For example, to divide 125 by 742,

$$\log 125 = 2.097$$

$$\log 742 = 2.870$$

$$\log (125/742) = 2.097 - 2.870 = -0.773$$

$$125/742 = 10^{-0.773} = 10^{0.227} \times 10^{-1} = 1.69 \times 10^{-1}$$

Similarly, powers and roots of numbers can be found using logarithms.

$$\log x^y = y(\log x)$$

$$\log \sqrt[y]{x} = \log x^{1/y} = \frac{1}{y} \log x$$

As an example, find the fourth power of 5.23. First find the log of 5.23 and then multiply it by 4. The result, 2.874, is the log of the answer. Therefore, find the antilog of 2.874.

$$(5.23)^4 = ?$$

$$\log (5.23)^4 = 4 \log 5.23 = 4(0.719) = 2.874$$

$$(5.23)^4 = 10^{2.874} = 748$$

As another example, find the fifth root of 1.89×10^{-9}.

$$\sqrt[5]{1.89 \times 10^{-9}} = (1.89 \times 10^{9})^{1/5} = ?$$

$$\log (1.89 \times 10^{-9})^{1/5} = \frac{1}{5} \log (1.89 \times 10^{-9}) = \frac{1}{5}(-8.724) = -1.745$$

The answer is the antilog of -1.745.

$$(1.89 \times 10^{-9})^{1/5} = 10^{-1.745} = 1.80 \times 10^{-2}$$

A.7 Quadratic Equations

Algebraic equations of the form $ax^2 + bx + c = 0$ are called **quadratic equations.** The coefficients a, b, and c may be either positive or negative. The two roots of the equation may be found using the *quadratic formula.*

$$x = \frac{-b \pm \sqrt{b^2 - 4ac}}{2a}$$

As an example, solve the equation $5x^2 - 3x - 2 = 0$. Here $a = 5$, $b = -3$, and $c = -2$. Therefore,

$$x = \frac{3 \pm \sqrt{(-3^2) - 4(5)(-2)}}{2(5)}$$

$$= \frac{3 \pm \sqrt{9 - (-40)}}{10} = \frac{3 \pm \sqrt{49}}{10} = \frac{3 \pm 7}{10}$$

$$x = 1 \text{ and } -0.4$$

How do you know which of the two roots is the correct answer? You have to decide in each case which root has physical significance. However, it is usually true in this course that negative values are not significant.

Many calculators have a built-in quadratic-equation solver. If your calculator offers this capability, it will be convenient to use it, and you should study the manual until you know how to use your calculator to obtain the roots of a quadratic equation.

When you have solved a quadratic expression, you should always check your values by substituting them into the original equation. In the example above, we find that $5(1)^2 - 3(1) - 2 = 0$ and that $5(-0.4)^2 - 3(-0.4) - 2 = 0$.

You will encounter quadratic equations in the chapters on chemical equilibria, particularly in Chapters 14, 16, and 17. Here you may be faced with solving an equation such as

$$1.8 \times 10^{-4} = \frac{x^2}{0.0010 - x}$$

This equation can certainly be solved by using the quadratic formula or your calculator (to give $x = 3.4 \times 10^{-4}$). However, you may find the method of successive approximations to be especially convenient. Here you begin by making a reasonable approximation of x. This approximate value is substituted into the original equation, and this expression is solved to give what is hoped to be a more correct value of x. This process is repeated until the answer converges on a particular value of x—that is, until the value of x derived from two successive approximations is the same.

Step 1: Assume that x is so small that $(0.0010 - x) \approx 0.0010$. This means that

$$x^2 = 1.8 \times 10^{-4}(0.0010)$$

$$x = 4.2 \times 10^{-4} \text{ (to 2 significant figures)}$$

Step 2: Substitute the value of x from Step 1 into the denominator (but not the numerator) of the original equation and again solve for x.

$$x^2 = (1.8 \times 10^{-4})(0.0010 - 0.00042)$$

$$x = 3.2 \times 10^{-4}$$

Step 3: Repeat Step 2 using the value of x found in that step.

$$x = \sqrt{1.8 \times 10^{-4}(0.0010 - 0.00032)} = 3.5 \times 10^{-4}$$

Step 4: Continue by repeating the calculation, using the value of x found in the previous step.

Step 5. $x = \sqrt{1.8 \times 10^{-4}(0.0010 - 0.00034)} = 3.4 \times 10^{-4}$

Here we find that iterations after the fourth step give the same value for x, indicating that we have arrived at a valid answer (and the same one obtained from the quadratic formula).

Some final thoughts on using the method of successive approximations: First, in some cases this method does not work. Successive steps may give answers that are random or that diverge from the correct value. For quadratic equations of the form $K = x^2/(C - x)$, the method of approximations will work only as long as $K < 4C$ (assuming one begins with $x = 0$ as the first guess; that is, $K \approx x^2/C$). This will always be true for weak acids and bases.

Second, values of K in the equation $K = x^2/(C - x)$ are usually known only to two significant figures. Therefore, we are justified in carrying out successive steps until two answers are the same to two significant figures.

Finally, if your calculator does not automatically obtain roots of quadratic equations, we highly recommend this method. If your calculator has a memory function, successive approximations can be carried out easily and very rapidly. Even without a memory function, the method of successive approximations is much quicker than solving a quadratic equation by hand.

A.8 Graphing

When analyzing experimental data, chemists and other scientists often graph the data to see whether the data agree with a mathematical equation. If the equation does fit the data (often indicated by a linear graph), then the graph can be used to obtain numerical values (parameters) that can be used in the equation to predict information not specifically included in the data set. For example, suppose that you measured the masses and the volumes of several samples of aluminum. Your data set might look like the table in the margin. When these data are plotted with volume along the horizontal (x) axis and mass on the vertical (y) axis, a graph like this one can be obtained.

Mass (g)	Volume (mL)
2.03	0.76
5.27	1.95
9.57	3.54
11.46	4.25
14.96	5.55
18.02	6.68
21.83	8.10
25.17	9.32
30.08	11.14
32.84	12.17
36.27	13.43
36.77	13.62
39.36	14.58

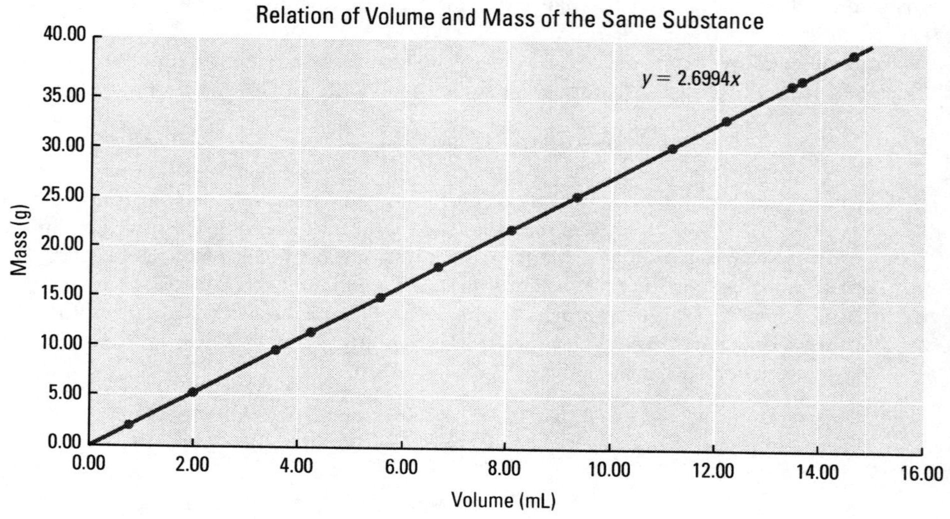

Notice the features of this graph. It has a title that describes its contents, it has a label for each axis that specifies the quantity plotted and the units used, it has equally spaced grid lines in the vertical and horizontal directions, and the numbers associated with those grid lines have the same difference between successive grid lines. (The differences are 2.00 mL on the horizontal axis and 5.00 g on the vertical axis.) The experimental points are indicated by circular markers, and a straight line has been drawn through the points. Because the line passes through all of the points and through the origin (point 0, 0), the data can be represented by the equation $y = 2.70x$, where 2.70 is the slope of the line. (On the graph, the slope is indicated by 2.6994; in the equation, it has been rounded to 2.70 because some of the data have only three significant figures.)

The slope of a graph such as this one can be obtained by choosing two points on the straight line (not two data points). The points should be far apart to obtain the most precise result. The slope is then given by the change in the y-axis variable divided by the change in the x-axis variable from the first point to the second. An example is shown on the graph below. From the calculation of the slope, it is more obvious that the slope has only three significant figures. For this graph, the slope represents mass divided by volume—that is, density. A good way to measure density is to measure the mass and volume of several samples of the same substance and then plot the data. The resulting graph should be linear and should pass very nearly through the origin. The density can be obtained from its slope. When a graph passes through the origin, we say that the y-axis variable is directly proportional to the x-axis variable.

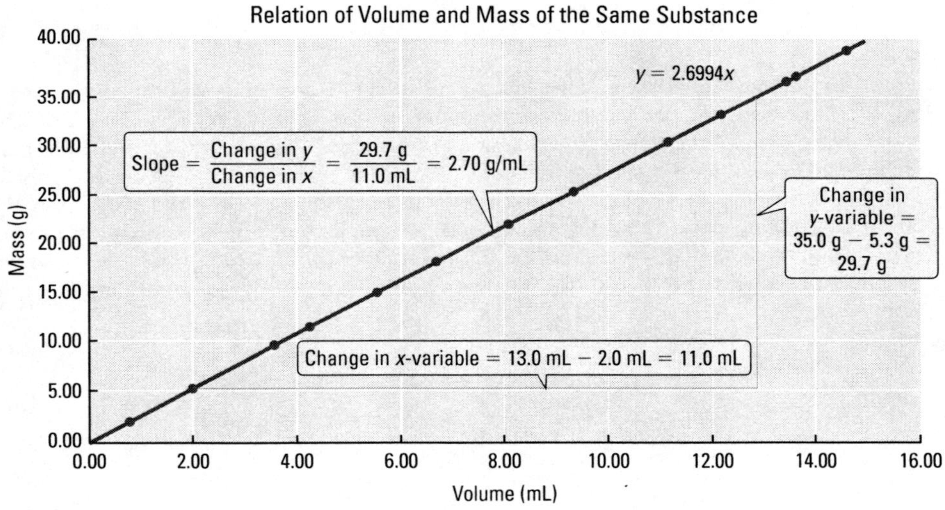

When a graph does not pass through the origin, there is an intercept as well as a slope. The intercept is the value of the y-axis variable when the x-axis variable is zero. A good example is the relation between Celsius and Fahrenheit temperatures. Suppose you have measured a series of temperatures using both a Celsius thermometer and a Fahrenheit thermometer. Your data set might look something like this table.

Temperature (°C)	**Temperature (°F)**
−5.23	22.586
13.54	56.372
32.96	91.328
48.34	119.012
63.59	146.462
74.89	166.802
88.02	190.436
105.34	221.612

When graphed, these data look like this.

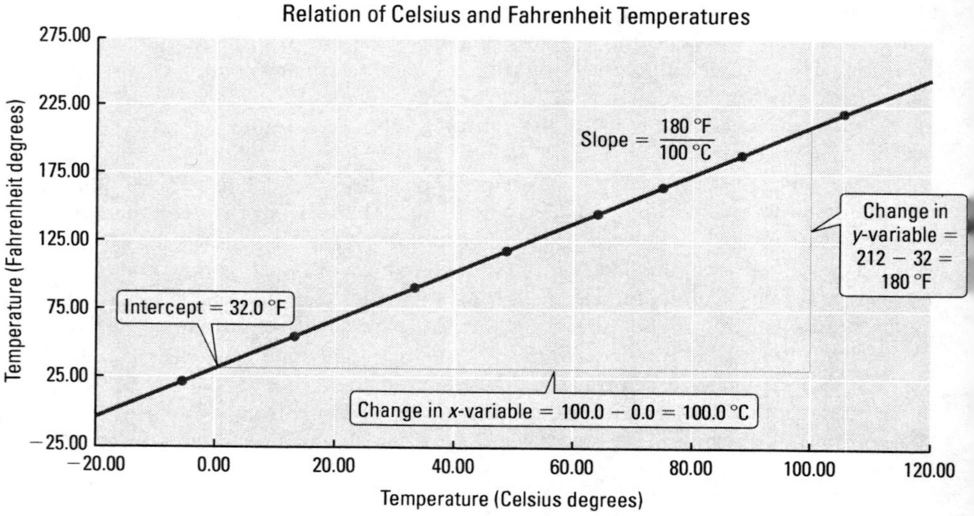

In this case, although the data are on a straight line, that line does not pass through the origin. Instead, it intersects the vertical line corresponding to $x = 0$ (0 °C) at a value of 32 °F. This makes sense, because the normal freezing point of water is 0 °C, which is the same temperature as 32 °F. This value, 32 °F, is the intercept.

If we determine the slope by starting at the intercept value of 32 °F and going to 212° F, the normal boiling point of water, the change in temperature on the Fahrenheit scale is 180 °F. The corresponding change on the Celsius scale is 100 °C, from which we can determine that the slope is 180 °F/100 °C. Thus the equation relating Celsius and Fahrenheit temperatures is

$$y \quad = \quad m \quad x \quad + \quad b$$

$$\text{temperature }^\circ\text{F} = \frac{180\ ^\circ\text{F}}{100\ ^\circ\text{C}} \times \text{temperature }^\circ\text{C} + 32\ ^\circ\text{F}$$

QUESTIONS FOR APPENDIX A

Blue-numbered questions have short answers at the end of this book and fully worked solutions in the *Student Solutions Manual.*

General Problem-Solving Strategies

1. List four steps that can be used for guidance in solving problems. Choose a problem that you are interested in solving, and apply the four steps to that problem.
2. You are asked to study a lake in which fish are dying and determine the cause of their deaths. Suggest three things you might do to define this problem.
3. You have calculated the area in square yards of a carpet whose dimensions were originally given to you as 96 in by 72 in. Suggest at least one way to check that the results of your calculation are reasonable. (12 in. = 1 ft; 3 ft = 1 yd.)

Numbers, Units, and Quantities

4. When a calculation is done and the units for the answer do not make sense, what can you conclude about the solution to the problem? What would you do if you were faced with a situation like this?
5. The term "quantity" (or "physical quantity") has a specific meaning in science. What is that meaning, and why is it important?
6. To measure the length of a pencil, you use a tape measure calibrated in inches with marks every sixteenth of an inch. Which of these results would be a suitable record of your observation? Why would the other results be unsuitable? (1/16 in = 0.0625 in)
   (a) 8.38 ft (b) 8.38 m (c) 8.38 in
   (d) 8.38 (e) 0.698 ft

7. To measure the inseam length of a pair of slacks, you use a tape measure calibrated in centimeters with marks every tenth of a centimeter. Which of these results would be a suitable record of your observation? Why would the other results be unsuitable?
   (a) 75.0 cm (b) 75.0 m (c) 75.0
   (d) 75.0 in (e) 750 mm
8. What is wrong with each calculation? How would you carry out each calculation correctly? What is the correct result for each calculation?
   (a) $4.32\text{ g} + 5.63\text{ g} = 9.95\text{ g}^2$
   (b) $5.23\text{ g} \times \dfrac{4.87\text{ g}}{1.00\text{ mL}} = 25.5\text{ g}$
   (c) $3.57\text{ cm}^3 \times \left(\dfrac{1\text{ m}}{100\text{ cm}}\right) = 3.57 \times 10^{-2}\text{ m}^3$
9. What is wrong with each calculation? How would you carry out each calculation correctly? What is the correct result for each calculation?
   (a) $7.86\text{ g} - 5.63\text{ g} = 2.23\text{ g}^2$
   (b) $7.37\text{ mL} \times \dfrac{1.00\text{ mL}}{2.23\text{ g}} = 3.30\text{ mL}$
   (c) $9.26\text{ m}^3 \times \left(\dfrac{100\text{ cm}}{1\text{ m}}\right) = 9.26 \times 10^2\text{ m}^3$

Precision, Accuracy, and Significant Figures

10. These measurements were reported for the length of an eight-foot pole: 95.31 in; 96.44 in; 96.02 in; 95.78 in; 95.94 in (1 ft = 12 in).
   (a) Based on these measurements, what would you report as the length of the pole?
   (b) How many significant figures should appear in your result?
   (c) Assuming that the pole is exactly eight feet long, is the result accurate?
11. These measurements were reported for the mass of a sample in the laboratory: 32.54 g; 32.67 g; 31.98 g; 31.76 g; 32.05 g.
   (a) Based on these measurements, what would you report as the mass of the sample?
   (b) How many significant figures should appear in your result?
   (c) The sample is exactly balanced by a weight known to have a mass of 35.0 g. Is the result accurate?
12. How many significant figures are in each quantity?
   (a) 3.274 g (b) 0.0034 L
   (c) 43,000 m (d) 6200. ft
13. How many significant figures are in each quantity?
   (a) 0.2730 g (b) 8.3 g/mL
   (c) 300 m (d) 2030.0 dm^3
14. Round each number to four significant figures.
   (a) 43.3250 (b) 43.3165 (c) 43.3237
   (d) 43.32499 (e) 43.3150 (f) 43.32501
15. Round each number to three significant figures.
   (a) 88.3520 (b) 88.365 (c) 88.45
   (d) 88.5500 (e) 88.2490 (f) 88.4501
16. Evaluate each expression and report the result to the appropriate number of significant figures.
   (a) $\dfrac{4.47}{0.3260}$ (b) $\dfrac{4.03 + 3.325}{29.75}$
   (c) $\dfrac{8.234}{5.673 - 4.987}$
17. Evaluate each expression and report the result to the appropriate number of significant figures.
   (a) $\dfrac{4.47}{0.3260}$ (b) $\dfrac{4.03 + 3.325}{29.75}$
   (c) $\dfrac{8.234}{5.673 - 4.987}$

Exponential or Scientific Notation

18. Without using a calculator, express each number in scientific notation and with the appropriate number of significant figures.
   (a) 76,003 (b) 0.00037 (c) 34,000
19. Without using a calculator, express each number in scientific notation and with the appropriate number of significant figures.
   (a) 49,002 (b) 0.0234 (c) 23,400
20. Evaluate each expression using your calculator and report the result to the appropriate number of significant figures with appropriate units.
   (a) $\dfrac{0.7346}{304.2}$
   (b) $\dfrac{(3.45 \times 10^{-3})(1.83 \times 10^{12})}{23.4}$
   (c) $3.240 - 4.33 \times 10^{-3}$
   (d) $(4.87\text{ cm})^3$
21. Evaluate each expression using your calculator and report the result to the appropriate number of significant figures with appropriate units.
   (a) $\dfrac{893.0}{0.2032}$
   (b) $\dfrac{(5.4 \times 10^3)(8.36 \times 10^{-12})}{5.317 \times 10^{-3}}$
   (c) $3.240 \times 10^5 - 8.33 \times 10^3$
   (d) $(4.87\text{ cm} + 7.33 \times 10^{-1}\text{ cm})^3$

Logarithms

22. Use your calculator to find the logarithm of each number and report the logarithm to the appropriate number of significant figures.
   (a) log(0.7327) (b) ln(34.5)
   (c) $\log(6.022 \times 10^{23})$ (d) $\ln(6.022 \times 10^{23})$
   (e) $\log\left(\dfrac{8.34 \times 10^{-5}}{2.38 \times 10^3}\right)$
23. Use your calculator to find the logarithm of each number and report the logarithm to the appropriate number of significant figures.
   (a) log(54.3) (b) ln(0.0345)
   (c) $\log(4.344 \times 10^{-3})$ (d) $\ln(8.64 \times 10^4)$
   (e) $\ln\left(\dfrac{4.33 \times 10^{24}}{8.32 \times 10^{-2}}\right)$
24. Use your calculator to evaluate each expression and report the result to the appropriate number of significant figures.
   (a) antilog(0.7327) (b) antiln(34.5)
   (c) $10^{2.043}$ (d) $e^{3.20 \times 10^{-4}}$
   (e) exp(4.333/3.275)
25. Use your calculator to evaluate each expression and report the result to the appropriate number of significant figures.
   (a) antilog(87.2) (b) antiln(0.0034)
   (c) $e^{2.043}$ (d) $10^{(3.20 \times 10^{-4})}$
   (e) $\exp(4.3 \times 10^3/8.314)$

Quadratic Equations

26. Find the roots of each quadratic equation.
   (a) $3.27x^2 + 4.32x - 2.83 = 0$
   (b) $x^2 + 4.32 = 4.57x$
27. Find the roots of each quadratic equation.
   (a) $8.33x^2 - 2.32x - 7.53 = 0$
   (b) $4.3x^2 - 8.37 = -2.22x$

Graphing

28. Graph these data involving mass and volume, label the graph appropriately, and determine whether m is directly proportional to V.

V (mL)	m (g)
0.347	0.756
1.210	2.638
2.443	5.326
7.234	15.76
11.43	24.90

29. Graph these data for heat transfers during a reaction, label the graph appropriately, and determine whether the heat evolved is directly proportional to the amount of reactant consumed.

Amount of Reactant (mol)	Heat Evolved (J)
94.2	43.2
70.7	32.5
65.7	30.1
34.2	15.7
54.3	24.9

APPENDIX

B Units, Equivalences, and Conversion Factors

B.1 Units of the International System (SI)

The metric system was begun by the French National Assembly in 1790 and has undergone many modifications since its inception. The International System of Units, or *Système International* (SI), which represents an extension of the metric system, was adopted by the 11th General Conference on Weights and Measures in 1960. It is constructed from seven base units, each of which represents a particular physical quantity (Table B.1). More information about the SI is available at **http://physics.nist.gov/cuu/Units/index.html**.

The first five units listed in Table B.1 are particularly useful in chemistry. They are defined as follows:

1. The *meter* is the length of the path traveled by light in a vacuum during a time interval of 1/299,792,458 of a second.
2. The *kilogram* represents the mass of a platinum-iridium block kept at the International Bureau of Weights and Measures in Sevres, France.
3. The *second* is the duration of 9,192,631,770 periods of a certain line in the microwave spectrum of cesium-133.
4. The *kelvin* is 1/273.16 of the temperature interval between absolute zero and the triple point of water (the temperature at which liquid water, ice, and water vapor coexist).
5. The *mole* is the amount of substance that contains as many elementary entities (atoms, molecules, ions, or other particles) as there are atoms in exactly 0.012 kg of carbon-12 (12 g of ^{12}C atoms).

Decimal fractions and multiples of metric and SI units are designated by using the **prefixes** listed in Table B.2. The prefix *kilo-*, for example, means that a unit is multiplied by 10^3.

$$1 \text{ kilogram} = 1 \times 10^3 \text{ grams} = 1000 \text{ grams}$$

The prefix *centi-* means that the unit is multiplied by the factor 10^{-2}.

$$1 \text{ centigram} = 1 \times 10^{-2} \text{ gram} = 0.01 \text{ gram}$$

Table B.1 SI Fundamental Units

Physical Quantity	Name of Unit	Symbol
Length	Meter	m
Mass	Kilogram	kg
Time	Second	s
Temperature	Kelvin	K
Amount of substance	Mole	mol
Electric current	Ampere	A
Luminous intensity	Candela	cd

The prefixes are added to give units of a magnitude appropriate to what is being measured. The distance from New York to London (5.6×10^3 km = 5600 km) is much easier to comprehend measured in kilometers than in meters (5.6×10^6 m = 5,600,000 m). Following Table B.2 is a list of units for measuring very small and very large distances.

Table B.2 Prefixes for Metric and SI Units*

Factor	Prefix	Symbol	Factor	Prefix	Symbol
10^{18}	exa-	E	10^{-1}	*deci-*	d
10^{15}	peta-	P	10^{-2}	*centi-*	c
10^{12}	tera-	T	10^{-3}	*milli-*	m
10^{9}	giga-	G	10^{-6}	*micro-*	μ
10^{6}	mega-	M	10^{-9}	*nano-*	n
10^{3}	*kilo-*	k	10^{-12}	*pico-*	p
10^{2}	hecto-	h	10^{-15}	femto-	f
10^{1}	deka-	da	10^{-18}	atto-	a

*The prefixes most commonly used in chemistry are shown in italics.

attometer (am)	0.000000000000000001 meter
femtometer (fm)	0.000000000000001 meter
picometer (pm)	0.000000000001 meter
nanometer (nm)	0.000000001 meter
micrometer (μm)	0.000001 meter
millimeter (mm)	0.001 meter
centimeter (cm)	0.01 meter
decimeter (dm)	0.1 meter
meter (m)	1 meter
dekameter (dam)	10 meters
hectometer (hm)	100 meters
kilometer (km)	1000 meters
megameter (Mm)	1,000,000 meters
gigameter (Gm)	1,000,000,000 meters
terameter (Tm)	1,000,000,000,000 meters
petameter (Pm)	1,000,000,000,000,000 meters
exameter (Em)	1,000,000,000,000,000,000 meters

In the International System of Units, all physical quantities are represented by appropriate combinations of the base units listed in Table B.1. The result is a derived unit for each kind of measured quantity. The most common derived units are listed in Table B.3. It is easy

Table B.3 Derived SI Units

Physical Quantity	Name of Unit	Symbol	Definition	Expressed in Fundamental Units
Area	Square meter	m^2	—	
Volume	Cubic meter	m^3	—	
Density	Kilogram per cubic meter	kg/m	—	
Force	Newton	N	$\frac{\text{(kilogram)(meter)}}{\text{(second)}^2}$	kg m/s^2
Pressure	Pascal	Pa	$\frac{\text{(newton)}}{\text{(meter)}^2}$	$\text{N/m}^2 = \text{kg m}^{-1}\text{ s}^{-2}$
Energy	Joule	J	$\frac{\text{(kilogram)(meter)}^2}{\text{(second)}^2}$	$\text{kg m}^2\text{ s}^{-2}$
Electric charge	Coulomb	C	(ampere)(second)	A s
Electric potential difference	Volt	V	$\frac{\text{(joule)}}{\text{(ampere)(second)}}$	$\text{J A}^{-1}\text{ s}^{-1} = \text{kg m}^2\text{ s}^{-3}\text{ A}^{-1}$

to see that the derived unit for area is length × length = meter × meter = square meter, m^2, or that the derived unit for volume is length × length × length = meter × meter × meter = cubic meter, m^3. More complex derived units are arrived at by a similar kind of combination of units. Units such as the joule, which measures energy, have been given simple names that represent the combination of fundamental units by which they are defined.

B.2 Conversion of Units for Physical Quantities

The result of a measurement is a physical quantity, which consists of a number and a unit. Algebraically, a physical quantity can be treated as if the number is multiplied by the unit. To convert a physical quantity from one unit of measure to another requires a conversion factor (proportionality factor) based on equivalences between units of measure such as those given in Table B.4. (See Appendix A.2 for more about physical quantities and proportionality factors.) Each equivalence provides two conversion factors that are the reciprocals of each other. For example, the equivalence between a quart and a liter, 1 quart = 0.9463 liter, gives

$$\frac{1 \text{ quart}}{0.9463 \text{ liter}} \quad \text{There is 1 quart per 0.9463 liter.}$$

$$\frac{0.9463 \text{ liter}}{1 \text{ quart}} \quad \text{There is 0.9463 liter per 1 quart.}$$

The method of canceling units described in Appendix A.2 provides the basis for choosing which conversion factor is needed: It is always the one that allows the unit being converted to be canceled and leaves the new unit uncanceled.

To convert 2 quarts to liters:

$$2 \text{ quarts} \times \frac{0.9463 \text{ liter}}{1 \text{ quart}} = 1.893 \text{ liters}$$

To convert 2 liters to quarts:

$$2 \text{ liters} \times \frac{1 \text{ quart}}{0.9463 \text{ liter}} = 2.113 \text{ quarts}$$

Because of the definitions of Celsius degrees and Fahrenheit degrees, conversions between these temperature scales are a bit more complicated. Both units are based on the properties of water. The Celsius unit is defined by assigning 0 °C as the freezing point of pure water and 100 °C as its boiling point, when the pressure is exactly 1 atm. The size of the Fahrenheit degree is equally arbitrary. Fahrenheit defined 0 °F as the freezing point of a solution in which he had dissolved the maximum quantity of ammonium chloride (because this was the lowest temperature he could reproduce reliably), and he intended 100 °F to be the normal human body temperature (but this value turned out to be 98.6 °F). Today, the reference points are set at exactly 32 °F and 212 °F (the freezing and boiling points of pure water, at 1 atm). The number of units between these two Fahrenheit temperatures is 180 °F. Thus, the Celsius degree is almost twice as large as the Fahrenheit degree; it takes only 5 Celsius degrees to cover the same temperature range as 9 Fahrenheit degrees.

To be entirely correct, we must specify that pure water boils at 100 °C and freezes at 0 °C only when the pressure of the surrounding atmosphere is 1 atm.

$$\frac{100 \text{ °C}}{180 \text{ °F}} = \frac{5 \text{ °C}}{9 \text{ °F}}$$

This relationship is the basis for converting a temperature on one scale to a temperature on the other. If t_C is the numerical value of the temperature in °C and t_F is the numerical value of the temperature in °F, then

$$t_C = \left(\tfrac{5}{9}\right)(t_F - 32)$$

$$t_F = \left(\tfrac{9}{5}\right)t_C + 32$$

Table B.4 Common Units of Measure

Mass and Weight

1 pound = 453.59 grams = 0.45359 kilogram
1 kilogram = 1000 grams = 2.205 pounds
1 gram = 10 decigrams = 100 centigrams = 1000 milligrams
1 gram = 6.022×10^{23} atomic mass units
1 atomic mass unit = 1.6605×10^{-24} grams
1 short ton = 2000 pounds = 907.2 kilograms
1 long ton = 2240 pounds
1 metric tonne = 1000 kilograms = 2205 pounds

Length

1 inch = 2.54 centimeters (exactly)
1 mile = 5280 feet = 1.609 kilometers
1 yard = 36 inches = 0.9144 meter
1 meter = 100 centimeters = 39.37 inches = 3.281 feet = 1.094 yards
1 kilometer = 1000 meters = 1094 yards = 0.6215 miles
1 Angstrom = 1.0×10^{-8} centimeters = 0.10 nanometers = 100 picometers
= 1.0×10^{-10} meters = 3.937×10^{-9} inches

Volume

1 quart = 0.9463 liters
1 liter = 1.0567 quarts
1 liter = 1 cubic decimeter = 10^3 cubic centimeters = 10^{-3} cubic meters
1 milliliter = 1 cubic centimeters = 0.001 liters = 1.056×10^{-3} quarts
1 cubic foot = 28.316 liters = 29.924 quarts = 7.481 gallons

Force and Pressure

1 atmosphere = 760.0 millimeters of mercury = 1.01325×10^5 pascals
= 14.70 pounds per square inch
1 bar = 10^5 pascals = 0.98692 atmospheres
1 torr = 1 millimeter of mercury
1 pascal = 1 kg m^{-1} s^{-2} = 1 N/m^2

Energy

1 joule = 1×10^7 ergs
1 thermochemical calorie = 4.184 joules = 4.184×10^7 ergs
= 4.129×10^{-2} liter-atmospheres
= 2.612×10^{19} electron volts
1 erg = 1×10^{-7} joules = 2.3901×10^{-8} calories
1 electron volt = 1.6022×10^{-19} joules = 1.6022×10^{-12} ergs = 96.85 kJ/mol*
1 liter-atmosphere = 24.217 calories = 101.32 joules = 1.0132×10^9 ergs
1 British thermal unit = 1055.06 joules = 1.05506×10^{10} ergs = 252.2 calories

Temperature

0 K = −273.15 °C

If T_K is the numerical value of the temperature in kelvins, t_C is the numerical value of the temperature in °C, and t_F is the numerical value of the temperature in °F, then

$$T_K = t_C + 273.15$$
$$t_C = \left(\tfrac{5}{9}\right)(t_F - 32)$$
$$t_F = \left(\tfrac{9}{5}\right)t_C + 32$$

*The other units in this line are per particle and must be multiplied by 6.022×10^{23} to be strictly comparable.

For example, to show that your normal body temperature of 98.6 °F corresponds to 37.0 °C, use the first equation.

$$t_C = \left(\tfrac{5}{9}\right)(t_F - 32) = \left(\tfrac{5}{9}\right)(98.6 - 32) = \left(\tfrac{9}{5}\right)(66.6) = 37.0$$

Thus, body temperature in °C = 37.0 °C.

Laboratory work is almost always done using Celsius units, and we rarely need to make conversions to and from Fahrenheit degrees. It is best to try to calibrate your senses to Celsius units; to help you do so, it is useful to know that water freezes at 0 °C, a comfortable room temperature is about 22 °C, your body temperature is 37 °C, and the hottest water you could leave your hand in for some time is about 60 °C.

QUESTIONS FOR APPENDIX B

Blue-numbered questions have short answers at the end of this book and fully worked solutions in the *Student Solutions Manual.*

Units of the International System

1. Which SI unit accompanied by which prefix would be most convenient for describing each quantity?
   (a) Mass of this book
   (b) Volume of a glass of water
   (c) Thickness of this page
2. Which SI unit accompanied by which prefix would be most convenient for describing each quantity?
   (a) Distance from New York to San Francisco
   (b) Mass of a glass of water
   (c) Area of this page
3. Explain the difference between an SI base (fundamental) unit and a derived SI unit.
4. What is the official SI definition of the mole? Describe in your own words each part of the definition and explain why each part of the definition is important.

Conversion of Units for Physical Quantities

5. Express each quantity in SI base (fundamental) units. Use exponential (scientific) notation whenever it is needed.
   (a) 475 pm (b) 56 Gg (c) 4.28 μA
6. Express each quantity in SI base (fundamental) units. Use exponential (scientific) notation whenever it is needed.
   (a) 32.5 ng (b) 56 Mm (c) 439 pm
7. Express each quantity in SI base (fundamental) units. Use exponential (scientific) notation whenever it is needed.
   (a) 8.7 nm^2 (b) 27.3 aJ (c) 27.3 μN
8. Express each quantity in SI base (fundamental) units. Use exponential (scientific) notation whenever it is needed.
   (a) 56.3 cm^3 (b) 5.62 MJ (c) 33.4 kV
9. Express each quantity in the units indicated. Use scientific notation.
   (a) 1.00 kg in pound
   (b) 2.45 ton in kilograms
   (c) 1 L in cubic inches (in^3)
   (d) 1 atm in pascals and in bars
10. Express each quantity in the units indicated. Use scientific notation.
   (a) 24.3 amu in grams
   (b) 87.3 mL in cubic feet (ft^3)
   (c) 24.7 dg in ounces
   (d) 1.02 bar in millimeters of mercury (mm Hg) and in torrs
11. Express each temperature in Fahrenheit degrees.
   (a) 37 °C (b) −23.6 °C (c) −40.0 °C
12. Express each temperature in Celsius degrees.
   (a) 180. °F (b) −40.0 °F (c) 28.3 °F

APPENDIX C

Physical Constants* and Sources of Data

Quantity	Symbol	Traditional Units	SI Units
Acceleration of gravity	g_n	980.665 cm/s^2	9.806 65 m/s^2
Atomic mass unit ($\frac{1}{12}$ the mass of ^{12}C atom)	amu or u	$1.660\ 54 \times 10^{-24}$ g	$1.660\ 54 \times 10^{-27}$ kg
Avogadro constant	N_A, L	$6.022\ 142 \times 10^{23}$ particles/mol	$6.022\ 142 \times 10^{23}$ particles/mol
Bohr radius	a_o	0.529 177 2108 Å	$5.291\ 772\ 108 \times 10^{-11}$ m
Boltzmann constant	k	$1.380\ 650\ 5 \times 10^{-16}$ erg/K	$1.380\ 650\ 5 \times 10^{-23}$ J/K
Charge-to-mass ratio of electron	e/m	$-1.758\ 820\ 12 \times 10^{8}$ C/g	$-1.758\ 820\ 12 \times 10^{11}$ C/kg
Elementary charge (electron or proton charge)	e	$1.602\ 176\ 53 \times 10^{-19}$ C	$1.602\ 176\ 53 \times 10^{-19}$ C
Electron rest mass	m_e	$9.109\ 3826 \times 10^{-28}$ g	$9.109\ 3826 \times 10^{-31}$ kg
Faraday constant	F	96 485.3383 C/mol e$^-$ 23.06 kcal V^{-1} mol^{-1}	96 485.3383 C/mol e$^-$ 96 485 J V^{-1} mol^{-1}
Gas constant	R	0.082 057 L atm mol^{-1} K^{-1} 1.987 cal mol^{-1} K^{-1}	8.314 472 dm^3 Pa mol^{-1} K^{-1} 8.314 472 J mol^{-1} K^{-1}
Molar volume (STP)	V_m	22.414 L/mol	22.414×10^{-3} m^3/mol 22.414 dm^3/mol
Neutron rest mass	m_n	$1.674\ 927\ 28 \times 10^{-24}$ g 1.008 664 amu	$1.674\ 927\ 28 \times 10^{-27}$ kg
Planck's constant	h	$6.626\ 0693 \times 10^{-27}$ erg s	$6.626\ 0693 \times 10^{-34}$ J s
Proton rest mass	m_p	$1.672\ 621\ 71 \times 10^{-24}$ g 1.007 276 amu	$1.672\ 621\ 71 \times 10^{-27}$ kg
Rydberg constant	R_∞	$3.289\ 841\ 960 \times 10^{15}$ s^{-1} $2.179\ 871\ 90 \times 10^{-11}$ erg	$1.097\ 373\ 156\ 8525 \times 10^{7}$ m^{-1} $2.179\ 871\ 90 \times 10^{-18}$ J
Velocity of light (in a vacuum)	c, c_0	$2.997\ 924\ 58 \times 10^{10}$ cm/s 186 282 mile/s	$2.997\ 924\ 58 \times 10^{8}$ m/s

*Data from the National Institute for Standards and Technology reference on constants, units, and uncertainty, **http://physics.nist.gov/cuu/Constants/index.html.**

Online Sources

- Finding Chemical Data in Web and Library Sources. University of Adelaide Library.
  http://www.library.adelaide.edu.au/guide/sci/Chemistry/propindex.html
- SIRCh: Selected Internet Resources for Chemistry
  http://www.indiana.edu/~cheminfo/cis_ca.html
  SIRCh: Physical Property Information
  http://www.indiana.edu/~cheminfo/ca_ppi.html
- Thermodex. University of Texas at Austin.
  http://thermodex.lib.utexas.edu/
- How Many? A Dictionary of Units of Measurement.
  http://www.unc.edu/~rowlett/units/index.html

Print Sources

- Lide, David R., ed. *CRC Handbook of Chemistry and Physics,* 87th edition, Boca Raton, FL: CRC Press, 2006.
- Budavari, Susan; O'Neil, Maryadele J.; Smith, Ann; Heckelman, Patricia E., eds. *The Merck Index: An Encyclopedia of Chemicals, Drugs, and Biologicals,* 13th edition, Rahway, NJ: Merck & Co., 2001.
- Speight, James, ed. *Lange's Handbook of Chemistry,* 16th edition, New York: McGraw-Hill, 2004.
- Perry, Robert H., Green, Don W., eds. *Perry's Chemical Engineer's Handbook,* 7th edition, New York: McGraw-Hill, 1997.
- Zwillinger, Daniel, ed. *CRC Standard Mathematical Tables and Formulae,* 30th edition, Boca Raton, FL: CRC Press, 1991.
- Lewis, Richard J., Jr. *Hawley's Condensed Chemical Dictionary* (with CD-ROM), 14th edition, New York: Wiley, 2002.

APPENDIX D

Ground-State Electron Configurations of Atoms

Z	Element	Configuration	Z	Element	Configuration	Z	Element	Configuration
1	H	$1s^1$	40	Zr	[Kr] $4d^2 5s^2$	78	Pt	[Xe] $4f^{14} 5d^9 6s^1$
2	He	$1s^2$	41	Nb	[Kr] $4d^4 5s^1$	79	Au	[Xe] $4f^{14} 5d^{10} 6s^1$
3	Li	[He] $2s^1$	42	Mo	[Kr] $4d^5 5s^1$	80	Hg	[Xe] $4f^{14} 5d^{10} 6s^2$
4	Be	[He] $2s^2$	43	Tc	[Kr] $4d^5 5s^2$	81	Tl	[Xe] $4f^{14} 5d^{10} 6s^2 6p^1$
5	B	[He] $2s^2 2p^1$	44	Ru	[Kr] $4d^7 5s^1$	82	Pb	[Xe] $4f^{14} 5d^{10} 6s^2 6p^2$
6	C	[He] $2s^2 2p^2$	45	Rh	[Kr] $4d^8 5s^1$	83	Bi	[Xe] $4f^{14} 5d^{10} 6s^2 6p^3$
7	N	[He] $2s^2 2p^3$	46	Pd	[Kr] $4d^{10}$	84	Po	[Xe] $4f^{14} 5d^{10} 6s^2 6p^4$
8	O	[He] $2s^2 2p^4$	47	Ag	[Kr] $4d^{10} 5s^1$	85	At	[Xe] $4f^{14} 5d^{10} 6s^2 6p^5$
9	F	[He] $2s^2 2p^5$	48	Cd	[Kr] $4d^{10} 5s^2$	86	Rn	[Xe] $4f^{14} 5d^{10} 6s^2 6p^6$
10	Ne	[He] $2s^2 2p^6$	49	In	[Kr] $4d^{10} 5s^2 5p^1$	87	Fr	[Rn] $7s^1$
11	Na	[Ne] $3s^1$	50	Sn	[Kr] $4d^{10} 5s^2 5p^2$	88	Ra	[Rn] $7s^2$
12	Mg	[Ne] $3s^2$	51	Sb	[Kr] $4d^{10} 5s^2 5p^3$	89	Ac	[Rn] $6d^1 7s^2$
13	Al	[Ne] $3s^2 3p^1$	52	Te	[Kr] $4d^{10} 5s^2 5p^4$	90	Th	[Rn] $6d^2 7s^2$
14	Si	[Ne] $3s^2 3p^2$	53	I	[Kr] $4d^{10} 5s^2 5p^5$	91	Pa	[Rn] $5f^2 6d^1 7s^2$
15	P	[Ne] $3s^2 3p^3$	54	Xe	[Kr] $4d^{10} 5s^2 5p^6$	92	U	[Rn] $5f^3 6d^1 7s^2$
16	S	[Ne] $3s^2 3p^4$	55	Cs	[Xe] $6s^1$	93	Np	[Rn] $5f^4 6d^1 7s^2$
17	Cl	[Ne] $3s^2 3p^5$	56	Ba	[Xe] $6s^2$	94	Pu	[Rn] $5f^6 7s^2$
18	Ar	[Ne] $3s^2 3p^6$	57	La	[Xe] $5d^1 6s^2$	95	Am	[Rn] $5f^7 7s^2$
19	K	[Ar] $4s^1$	58	Ce	[Xe] $4f^1 5d^1 6s^2$	96	Cm	[Rn] $5f^7 6d^1 7s^2$
20	Ca	[Ar] $4s^2$	59	Pr	[Xe] $4f^3 6s^2$	97	Bk	[Rn] $5f^9 7s^2$
21	Sc	[Ar] $3d^1 4s^2$	60	Nd	[Xe] $4f^4 6s^2$	98	Cf	[Rn] $5f^{10} 7s^2$
22	Ti	[Ar] $3d^2 4s^2$	61	Pm	[Xe] $4f^5 6s^2$	99	Es	[Rn] $5f^{11} 7s^2$
23	V	[Ar] $3d^3 4s^2$	62	Sm	[Xe] $4f^6 6s^2$	100	Fm	[Rn] $5f^{12} 7s^2$
24	Cr	[Ar] $3d^5 4s^1$	63	Eu	[Xe] $4f^7 6s^2$	101	Md	[Rn] $5f^{13} 7s^2$
25	Mn	[Ar] $3d^5 4s^2$	64	Gd	[Xe] $4f^7 5d^1 6s^2$	102	No	[Rn] $5f^{14} 7s^2$
26	Fe	[Ar] $3d^6 4s^2$	65	Tb	[Xe] $4f^9 6s^2$	103	Lr	[Rn] $5f^{14} 6d^1 7s^2$
27	Co	[Ar] $3d^7 4s^2$	66	Dy	[Xe] $4f^{10} 6s^2$	104	Rf	[Rn] $5f^{14} 6d^2 7s^2$
28	Ni	[Ar] $3d^8 4s^2$	67	Ho	[Xe] $4f^{11} 6s^2$	105	Db	[Rn] $5f^{14} 6d^3 7s^2$
29	Cu	[Ar] $3d^{10} 4s^1$	68	Er	[Xe] $4f^{12} 6s^2$	106	Sg	[Rn] $5f^{14} 6d^4 7s^2$
30	Zn	[Ar] $3d^{10} 4s^2$	69	Tm	[Xe] $4f^{13} 6s^2$	107	Bh	[Rn] $5f^{14} 6d^5 7s^2$
31	Ga	[Ar] $3d^{10} 4s^2 4p^1$	70	Yb	[Xe] $4f^{14} 6s^2$	108	Hs	[Rn] $5f^{14} 6d^6 7s^2$
32	Ge	[Ar] $3d^{10} 4s^2 4p^2$	71	Lu	[Xe] $4f^{14} 5d^1 6s^2$	109	Mt	[Rn] $5f^{14} 6d^7 7s^2$
33	As	[Ar] $3d^{10} 4s^2 4p^3$	72	Hf	[Xe] $4f^{14} 5d^2 6s^2$	110	Ds	[Rn] $5f^{14} 6d^8 7s^2$
34	Se	[Ar] $3d^{10} 4s^2 4p^4$	73	Ta	[Xe] $4f^{14} 5d^3 6s^2$	111	Rg	[Rn] $5f^{14} 6d^9 7s^2$
35	Br	[Ar] $3d^{10} 4s^2 4p^5$	74	W	[Xe] $4f^{14} 5d^4 6s^2$	112	—	[Rn] $5f^{14} 6d^{10} 7s^2$
36	Kr	[Ar] $3d^{10} 4s^2 4p^6$	75	Re	[Xe] $4f^{14} 5d^5 6s^2$	113	—	[Rn] $5f^{14} 6d^{10} 7s^2 7p^1$
37	Rb	[Kr] $5s^1$	76	Os	[Xe] $4f^{14} 5d^6 6s^2$	114	—	[Rn] $5f^{14} 6d^{10} 7s^2 7p^2$
38	Sr	[Kr] $5s^2$	77	Ir	[Xe] $4f^{14} 5d^7 6s^2$	115	—	[Rn] $5f^{14} 6d^{10} 7s^2 7p^3$
39	Y	[Kr] $4d^1 5s^2$						

E Naming Simple Organic Compounds

The systematic nomenclature for organic compounds was proposed by the International Union of Pure and Applied Chemistry (IUPAC). The IUPAC set of rules provides different names for the more than 10 million known organic compounds, and allows names to be assigned to new compounds as they are synthesized. Many organic compounds also have *common* names. Usually the common name came first and is widely known. Many consumer products are labeled with the common name, and when only a few isomers are possible, the common name adequately identifies the product for the consumer. However, as illustrated in Section 3.4 (⇐ ***p. 86***), a system of common names quickly fails when several structural isomers are possible.

E.1 Hydrocarbons

The name of each member of the hydrocarbon classes has two parts. The first part, called the prefix (*meth-*, *eth-*, *prop-*, *but-*, and so on), reflects the number of carbon atoms. When more than four carbons are present, the Greek or Latin number prefixes are used: *pent-*, *hex-*, *hept-*, *oct-*, *non-*, and *dec-*. The second part of the name, called the suffix, tells the class of hydrocarbon. Alkanes have carbon-carbon single bonds, alkenes have carbon-carbon double bonds, and alkynes have carbon-carbon triple bonds.

Unbranched Alkanes and Alkyl Groups

The names of the first 20 unbranched (straight-chain) alkanes are given in Table E.1.

Alkyl groups are named by dropping *-ane* from the parent alkane and adding *-yl* (see Table 3.5 for examples).

Branched-Chain Alkanes

The rules for naming branched-chain alkanes are as follows:

1. *Find the longest continuous chain of carbon atoms; it determines the parent name for the compound.* For example, the following compound has two methyl groups attached to a *heptane* parent; the longest continuous chain contains seven carbon atoms.

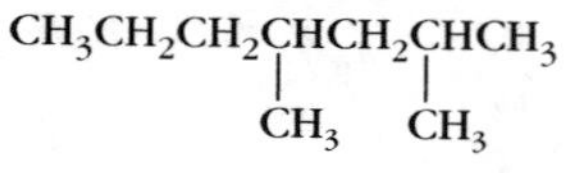

Table E.1 Names of Unbranched Alkanes

CH_4	Methane	$C_{11}H_{24}$	Undecane
C_2H_6	Ethane	$C_{12}H_{26}$	Dodecane
C_3H_8	Propane	$C_{13}H_{28}$	Tridecane
C_4H_{10}	Butane	$C_{14}H_{30}$	Tetradecane
C_5H_{12}	Pentane	$C_{15}H_{32}$	Pentadecane
C_6H_{14}	Hexane	$C_{16}H_{34}$	Hexadecane
C_7H_{16}	Heptane	$C_{17}H_{36}$	Heptadecane
C_8H_{18}	Octane	$C_{18}H_{38}$	Octadecane
C_9H_{20}	Nonane	$C_{19}H_{40}$	Nonadecane
$C_{10}H_{22}$	Decane	$C_{20}H_{42}$	Eicosane

The longest continuous chain may not be obvious from the way the formula is written, especially for the straight-line format that is commonly used. For example, the longest continuous chain of carbon atoms in the following chain is *eight,* not *four* or *six.*

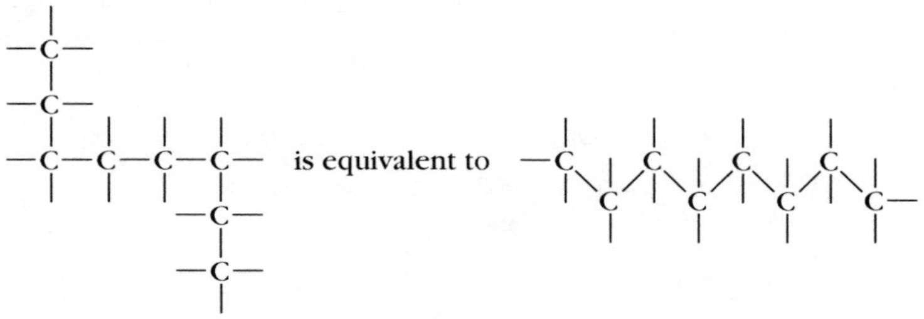

2. *Number the longest chain beginning with the end of the chain nearest the branching. Use these numbers to designate the location of the attached group. When two or more groups are attached to the parent, give each group a number corresponding to its location on the parent chain.* For example, the name of

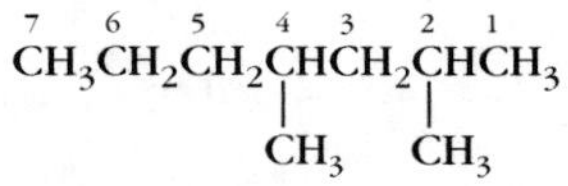

is 2,4-dimethylheptane. The name of the compound below is 3-methylheptane, not 5-methylheptane or 2-ethylhexane.

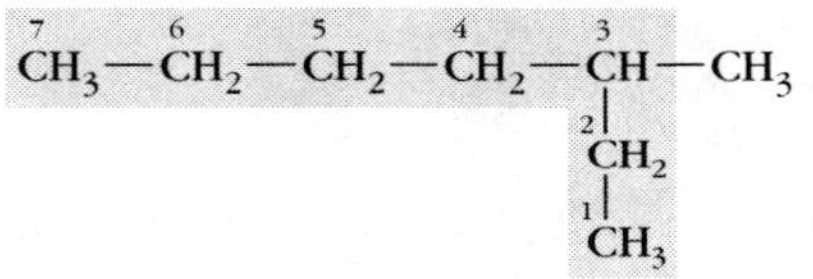

3. *When two or more substituents are identical, indicate this by the use of the prefixes* di-, tri-, tetra., *and so on. Positional numbers of the substituents should have the smallest possible sum.*

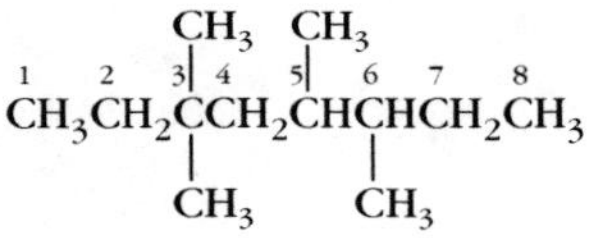

The correct name of this compound is 3,3,5,6-tetramethyloctane.

4. *If there are two or more different groups, the groups are listed alphabetically.*

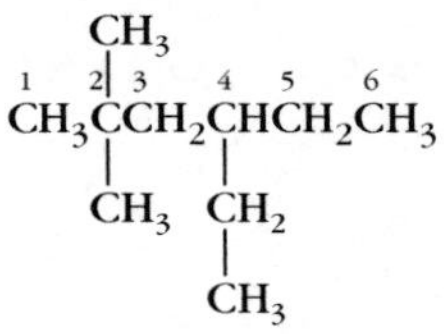

The correct name of this compound is 4-ethyl-2,2-dimethylhexane. Note that the prefix *di-* is ignored in determining alphabetical order.

Alkenes

Alkenes are named by using the prefix to indicate the number of carbon atoms and the suffix *-ene* to indicate one or more double bonds. The systematic names for the first two members of the alkene series are *ethene* and *propene.*

$$CH_2{=}CH_2 \qquad CH_3CH{=}CH_2$$

When groups, such as methyl or ethyl, are attached to carbon atoms in an alkene, the longest hydrocarbon chain is numbered from the end that will give the double bond the lowest number, and then numbers are assigned to the attached groups. For example, the name of

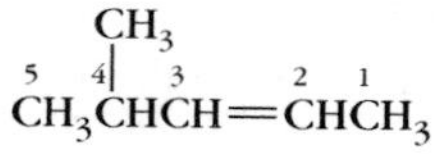

is 4-methyl-2-pentene. See Section 8.5 for a discussion of *cis-trans* isomers of alkenes.

Alkynes

The naming of alkynes is similar to that of alkenes, with the lowest number possible being used to locate the triple bond. For example, the name of

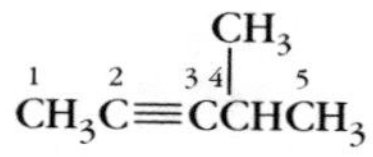

is 4-methyl-2-pentyne.

Benzene Derivatives

Monosubstituted benzene derivatives are named by using a prefix for the substituent. Some examples are

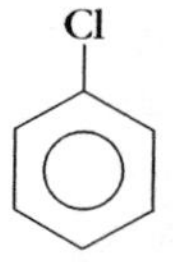

chlorobenzene

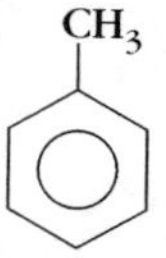

methylbenzene (toluene)

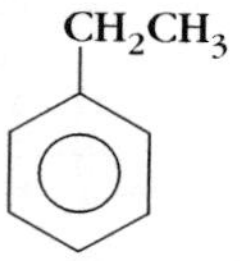

ethylbenzene

Three isomers are possible when two groups are substituted for hydrogen atoms on the benzene ring. The relative positions of the substituents are indicated either by the prefixes *ortho-*, *meta-*, and *para-* (abbreviated *o-*, *m-*, and *p-*, respectively) or by numbers. For example,

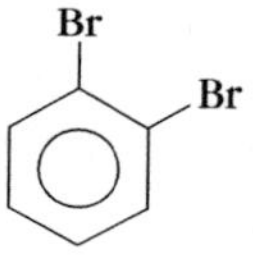

1,2-dibromobenzene (*o*-dibromobenzene)

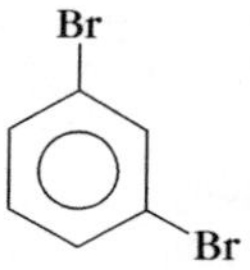

1,3-dibromobenzene (*m*-dibromobenzene)

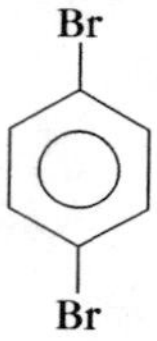

1,4-dibromobenzene (*p*-dibromobenzene)

The dimethylbenzenes are called *xylenes.*

If more than two groups are attached to the benzene ring, numbers must be used to identify the positions. The benzene ring is numbered to give the lowest possible numbers to the substituents.

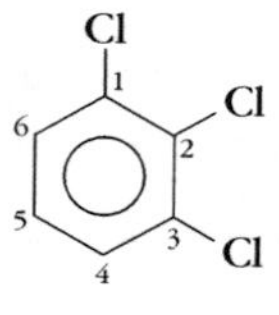

1,2,3-trichlorobenzene

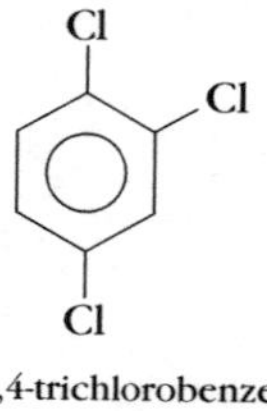

1,2,4-trichlorobenzene

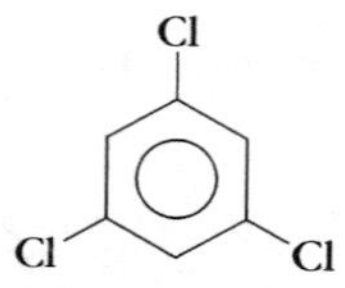

1,3,5-trichlorobenzene

E.2 Functional Groups

An atom or group of atoms that defines the structure of a specific class of organic compounds and determines their properties is called a *functional group* **(****p. 80****).** The millions of organic compounds include classes of compounds that are obtained by replacing hydrogen atoms of hydrocarbons with functional groups (Sections 3.1, 12.5, 12.6, and 12.7). The important functional groups are shown in Table E.2.

The "R" attached to the functional group represents the hydrocarbon framework with one hydrogen removed for each functional group added. The IUPAC system provides a systematic method for naming all members of a given class. For example, alcohols end in *-ol* (methan*ol*); aldehydes end in *-al* (methan*al*); carboxylic acids end in *-oic* (ethan*oic* acid); and ketones end in *-one* (propan*one*).

Alcohols

Isomers are also possible for molecules containing functional groups. For example, three different alcohols are obtained when a hydrogen atom in pentane is replaced by —OH, depending on which hydrogen atom is replaced. The rules for naming the "R" or hydrocarbon framework are the same as those for hydrocarbon compounds.

$CH_3CH_2CH_2CH_2CH_2OH$ 1-pentanol

$CH_3CH_2CH_2CHCH_3$ (OH on C-2) 2-pentanol

$CH_3CH_2CHCH_2CH_3$ (OH on C-3) 3-pentanol

Compounds with one or more functional groups (Table E.2) and alkyl substituents are named so as to give the functional groups the lowest numbers. For example, the correct name of

$\overset{1}{C}H_3\overset{2}{C}H\overset{3}{C}H_2\overset{4}{C}\overset{5}{C}H_3$ (OH on C-2; two CH_3 on C-4)

is 4,4-dimethyl-2-pentanol.

Aldehydes and Ketones

The systematic names of the first three aldehydes are methanal, ethanal, and propanal.

HCH(=O)	CH_3CH(=O)	CH_3CH_2CH(=O)
methanal (formaldehyde)	ethanal (acetaldehyde)	propanol (propionaldehyde)

For ketones, a number is used to designate the position of the carbonyl group, and the chain is numbered in a way that gives the carbonyl carbon the smallest number.

CH_3CCH_3 (C=O)	$CH_3CH_2CCH_3$ (C=O)	$CH_3CCH_2CH{=}CH_2$ (C=O)
2-propanone (acetone)	2-butanone (methyl ethyl ketone)	4-penten-2-one

Carboxylic Acids

The systematic names of carboxylic acids are obtained by dropping the final *e* of the name of the corresponding alkane and adding *-oic acid.* For example, the name of

$$CH_3CH_2CH_2CH_2CH_2COOH$$

is hexanoic acid. Other examples are

$\overset{4}{C}H_3\overset{3}{C}H_2\overset{2}{C}H\overset{1}{C}OOH$ (CH_3 on C-2)	$\overset{4}{C}H_3\overset{3}{C}H{=}\overset{2}{C}H\overset{1}{C}OOH$
2-methylbutanoic acid	2-butenoic acid

Table E.2 Classes of Organic Compounds Based on Functional Groups*

General formulas of class members	Class name	Typical compound	Compound name	Common use of sample compound
R—X	Halide	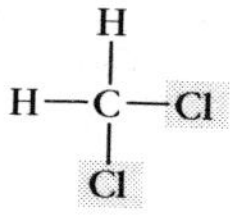	Dichloromethane (methylene chloride)	Solvent
R—OH	Alcohol	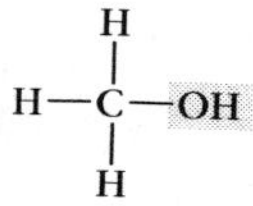	Methanol (wood alcohol)	Solvent
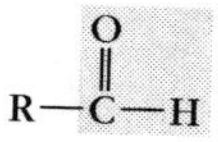	Aldehyde	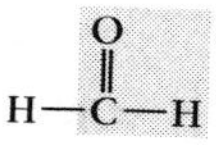	Methanal (formaldehyde)	Preservative
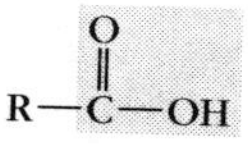	Carboxylic acid	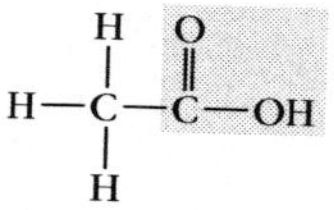	Ethanoic acid (acetic acid)	Vinegar
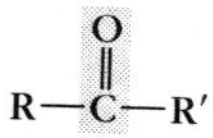	Ketone	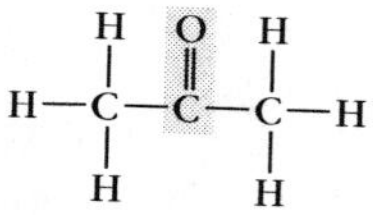	Propanone (acetone)	Solvent
R—O—R′	Ether	$C_2H_5—O—C_2H_5$	Diethyl ether (ethyl ether)	Anesthetic
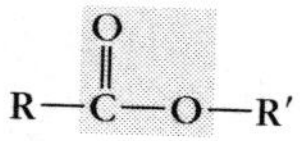	Ester	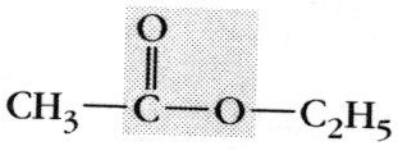	Ethyl ethanoate (ethyl acetate)	Solvent in fingernail polish
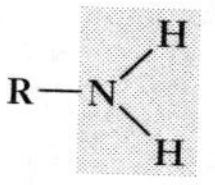	Amine	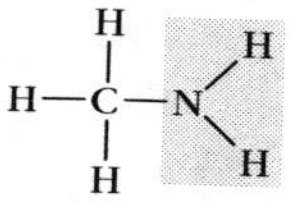	Methylamine	Tanning hides (foul odor)
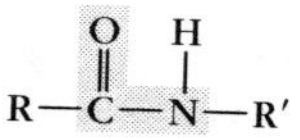	Amide	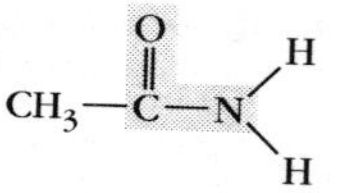	Acetamide	Plasticizer

*R stands for an H or a hydrocarbon group such as $—CH_3$ or $—C_2H_5$. R′ could be a different group from R.

Esters

The systematic names of esters are derived from the names of the alcohol and the acid used to prepare the ester. The general formula for esters is

$$R—\overset{\overset{\large O}{\|}}{C}—OR'$$

As shown in Section 12.4, the $R—\overset{\overset{O}{\|}}{C}$ comes from the acid and the R′O comes from the alcohol. The alcohol part is named first, followed by the name of the acid changed to end in *-ate*. For example,

$$CH_3CH_2\overset{\overset{O}{\|}}{C}—OCH_3$$

is named methyl propanoate and

$$CH_3\overset{\overset{O}{\|}}{C}—OCH{=}CH_2$$

is named ethenyl ethanoate.

APPENDIX F

Ionization Constants for Weak Acids at 25 °C

Acid	Formula and Ionization Equation	K_a
Acetic	$CH_3COOH + H_2O \rightleftharpoons H_3O^+ + CH_3COO^-$	1.8×10^{-5}
Arsenic	$H_3AsO_4 + H_2O \rightleftharpoons H_3O^+ + H_2AsO_4^-$	$K_1 = 2.5 \times 10^{-4}$
	$H_2AsO_4^- + H_2O \rightleftharpoons H_3O^+ + HAsO_4^{2-}$	$K_2 = 5.6 \times 10^{-8}$
	$HAsO_4^{2-} + H_2O \rightleftharpoons H_3O^+ + AsO_4^{3-}$	$K_3 = 3.0 \times 10^{-13}$
Arsenous	$H_3AsO_3 + H_2O \rightleftharpoons H_3O^+ + H_2AsO_3^-$	$K_1 = 6.0 \times 10^{-10}$
	$H_2AsO_3^- + H_2O \rightleftharpoons H_3O^+ + HAsO_3^{2-}$	$K_2 = 3.0 \times 10^{-14}$
Benzoic	$C_6H_5COOH + H_2O \rightleftharpoons H_3O^+ + C_6H_5COO^-$	6.3×10^{-5}
Boric	$B(OH)_3(H_2O) + H_2O \rightleftharpoons H_3O^+ + B(OH)_4^-$	7.3×10^{-10}
Carbonic	$H_2CO_3 + H_2O \rightleftharpoons H_3O^+ + HCO_3^-$	$K_1 = 4.2 \times 10^{-7}$
	$HCO_3^- + H_2O \rightleftharpoons H_3O^+ + CO_3^{2-}$	$K_2 = 4.8 \times 10^{-11}$
Citric	$H_3C_6H_5O_7 + H_2O \rightleftharpoons H_3O^+ + H_2C_6H_5O_7^-$	$K_1 = 7.4 \times 10^{-3}$
	$H_2C_6H_5O_7^- + H_2O \rightleftharpoons H_3O^+ + HC_6H_5O_7^{2-}$	$K_2 = 1.7 \times 10^{-5}$
	$HC_6H_5O_7^{2-} + H_2O \rightleftharpoons H_3O^+ + C_6H_5O_7^{3-}$	$K_3 = 4.0 \times 10^{-7}$
Cyanic	$HOCN + H_2O \rightleftharpoons H_3O^+ + OCN^-$	3.5×10^{-4}
Formic	$HCOOH + H_2O \rightleftharpoons H_3O^+ + HCOO^-$	1.8×10^{-4}
Hydrazoic	$HN_3 + H_2O \rightleftharpoons H_3O^+ + N_3^-$	1.9×10^{-5}
Hydrocyanic	$HCN + H_2O \rightleftharpoons H_3O^+ + CN^-$	4.0×10^{-10}
Hydrofluoric	$HF + H_2O \rightleftharpoons H_3O^+ + F^-$	7.2×10^{-4}
Hydrogen peroxide	$H_2O_2 + H_2O \rightleftharpoons H_3O^+ + HO_2^-$	2.4×10^{-12}
Hydrosulfuric	$H_2S + H_2O \rightleftharpoons H_3O^+ + HS^-$	$K_1 = 1 \times 10^{-7}$
	$HS^- + H_2O \rightleftharpoons H_3O^+ + S^{2-}$	$K_2 = 1 \times 10^{-19}$
Hypobromous	$HOBr + H_2O \rightleftharpoons H_3O^+ + OBr^-$	2.5×10^{-9}
Hypochlorous	$HOCl + H_2O \rightleftharpoons H_3O^+ + OCl^-$	3.5×10^{-8}
Nitrous	$HNO_2 + H_2O \rightleftharpoons H_3O^+ + NO_2^- H_3O^+$	4.5×10^{-4}
Oxalic	$H_2C_2O_4 + H_2O \rightleftharpoons H_3O^+ + HC_2O_4^-$	$K_1 = 5.9 \times 10^{-2}$
	$HC_2O_4^- + H_2O \rightleftharpoons H_3O^+ + C_2O_4^{2-}$	$K_2 = 6.4 \times 10^{-5}$
Phenol	$HC_6H_5O + H_2O \rightleftharpoons H_3O^+ + C_6H_5O^-$	1.3×10^{-10}
Phosphoric	$H_3PO_4 + H_2O \rightleftharpoons H_3O^+ + H_2PO_4^-$	$K_1 = 7.5 \times 10^{-3}$
	$H_2PO_4^- + H_2O \rightleftharpoons H_3O^+ + HPO_4^{2-}$	$K_2 = 6.2 \times 10^{-8}$
	$HPO_4^{2-} + H_2O \rightleftharpoons H_3O^+ + PO_4^{3-}$	$K_3 = 3.6 \times 10^{-13}$
Phosphorous	$H_3PO_3 + H_2O \rightleftharpoons H_3O^+ + H_2PO_3^-$	$K_1 = 1.6 \times 10^{-2}$
	$H_2PO_3^- + H_2O \rightleftharpoons H_3O^+ + HPO_3^{2-}$	$K_2 = 7.0 \times 10^{-7}$
Selenic	$H_2SeO_4 + H_2O \rightleftharpoons H_3O^+ + HSeO_4^-$	K_1 = very large
	$HSeO_4^- + H_2O \rightleftharpoons H_3O^+ + SeO_4^{2-}$	$K_2 = 1.2 \times 10^{-2}$
Selenous	$H_2SeO_3 + H_2O \rightleftharpoons H_3O^+ + HSeO_3^-$	$K_1 = 2.7 \times 10^{-3}$
	$HSeO_3^- + H_2O \rightleftharpoons H_3O^+ + SeO_3^{2-}$	$K_2 = 2.5 \times 10^{-7}$
Sulfuric	$H_2SO_4 + H_2O \rightleftharpoons H_3O^+ + HSO_4^-$	K_1 = very large
	$HSO_4^- + H_2O \rightleftharpoons H_3O^+ + SO_4^{2-}$	$K_2 = 1.2 \times 10^{-2}$
Sulfurous	$H_2SO_3 + H_2O \rightleftharpoons H_3O^+ + HSO_3^-$	$K_1 = 1.7 \times 10^{-2}$
	$HSO_3^- + H_2O \rightleftharpoons H_3O^+ + SO_3^{2-}$	$K_2 = 6.4 \times 10^{-8}$
Tellurous	$H_2TeO_3 + H_2O \rightleftharpoons H_3O^+ + HTeO_3^-$	$K_1 = 2 \times 10^{-3}$
	$HTeO_3^- + H_2O \rightleftharpoons H_3O^+ + TeO_3^{2-}$	$K_2 = 1 \times 10^{-8}$

APPENDIX

G Ionization Constants for Weak Bases at 25 °C

Base	Formula and Ionization Equation	K_b
Ammonia	$NH_3 + H_2O \rightleftharpoons NH_4^+ + OH^-$	1.8×10^{-5}
Aniline	$C_6H_5NH_2 + H_2O \rightleftharpoons C_6H_5NH_3^+ + OH^-$	4.2×10^{-10}
Dimethylamine	$(CH_3)_2NH + H_2O \rightleftharpoons (CH_3)_2NH_2^+ + OH^-$	7.4×10^{-4}
Ethylenediamine	$(CH_2)_2(NH_2)_2 + H_2O \rightleftharpoons (CH_2)_2(NH_2)_2H^+ + OH^-$	$K_1 = 8.5 \times 10^{-5}$
	$(CH_2)_2(NH_2)_2H^+ + H_2O \rightleftharpoons (CH_2)_2(NH_2)_2H_2^{2+} + OH^-$	$K_2 = 2.7 \times 10^{-8}$
Hydrazine	$N_2H_4 + H_2O \rightleftharpoons N_2H_5^+ + OH^-$	$K_1 = 8.5 \times 10^{-7}$
	$N_2H_5^+ + H_2O \rightleftharpoons N_2H_6^{2+} + OH^-$	$K_2 = 8.9 \times 10^{-16}$
Hydroxylamine	$NH_2OH + H_2O \rightleftharpoons NH_3OH^+ + OH^-$	6.6×10^{-9}
Methylamine	$CH_3NH_2 + H_2O \rightleftharpoons CH_3NH_3^+ + OH^-$	5.0×10^{-4}
Pyridine	$C_5H_5N + H_2O \rightleftharpoons C_5H_5NH^+ + OH^-$	1.5×10^{-9}
Trimethylamine	$(CH_3)_3N + H_2O \rightleftharpoons (CH_3)_3NH^+ + OH^-$	7.4×10^{-5}

APPENDIX H

Solubility Product Constants for Some Inorganic Compounds at 25 °C*

Substance	K_{sp}
Aluminum Compounds	
$AlAsO_4$	1.6×10^{-16}
$Al(OH)_3$	1.9×10^{-33}
$AlPO_4$	1.3×10^{-20}
Barium Compounds	
$Ba_3(AsO_4)_2$	1.1×10^{-13}
$BaCO_3$	8.1×10^{-9}
$BaC_2O_4 \cdot 2\,H_2O$†	1.1×10^{-7}
$BaCrO_4$	2.0×10^{-10}
BaF_2	1.7×10^{-6}
$Ba(OH)_2 \cdot 8\,H_2O$†	5.0×10^{-3}
$Ba_3(PO_4)_2$	1.3×10^{-29}
$BaSeO_4$	2.8×10^{-11}
$BaSO_3$	8.0×10^{-7}
$BaSO_4$	1.1×10^{-10}
Bismuth Compounds	
$BiOCl$	7.0×10^{-9}
$BiO(OH)$	1.0×10^{-12}
$Bi(OH)_3$	3.2×10^{-40}
BiI_3	8.1×10^{-19}
$BiPO_4$	1.3×10^{-23}
Cadmium Compounds	
$Cd_3(AsO_4)_2$	2.2×10^{-32}
$CdCO_3$	2.5×10^{-14}
$Cd(CN)_2$	1.0×10^{-8}
$Cd_2[Fe(CN)_6]$	3.2×10^{-17}
$Cd(OH)_2$	1.2×10^{-14}
Calcium Compounds	
$Ca_3(AsO_4)_2$	6.8×10^{-19}
$CaCO_3$	3.8×10^{-9}
$CaCrO_4$	7.1×10^{-4}
$CaC_2O_4 \cdot H_2O$†	2.3×10^{-9}
CaF_2	3.9×10^{-11}
$Ca(OH)_2$	7.9×10^{-6}
$CaHPO_4$	2.7×10^{-7}
$Ca(H_2PO_4)_2$	1.0×10^{-3}
$Ca_3(PO_4)_2$	1.0×10^{-25}
$CaSO_3 \cdot 2\,H_2O$†	1.3×10^{-8}
$CaSO_4 \cdot 2\,H_2O$†	2.4×10^{-5}
Chromium Compounds	
$CrAsO_4$	7.8×10^{-21}
$Cr(OH)_3$	6.7×10^{-31}
$CrPO_4$	2.4×10^{-23}
Cobalt Compounds	
$Co_3(AsO_4)_2$	7.6×10^{-29}
$CoCO_3$	8.0×10^{-13}
$Co(OH)_2$	2.5×10^{-16}
$Co(OH)_3$	4.0×10^{-45}
Copper Compounds	
$CuBr$	5.3×10^{-9}
$CuCl$	1.9×10^{-7}
$CuCN$	3.2×10^{-20}
$Cu_2O(Cu^+ + OH^-)$‡	1.0×10^{-14}
CuI	5.1×10^{-12}
$CuSCN$	1.6×10^{-11}
$Cu_3(AsO_4)_2$	7.6×10^{-36}
$CuCO_3$	2.5×10^{-10}
$Cu_2[Fe(CN)_6]$	1.3×10^{-16}
$Cu(OH)_2$	1.6×10^{-19}
Gold Compounds	
$AuBr$	5.0×10^{-17}
$AuCl$	2.0×10^{-13}
AuI	1.6×10^{-23}
$AuBr_3$	4.0×10^{-36}
$AuCl_3$	3.2×10^{-25}
$Au(OH)_3$	1×10^{-53}
AuI_3	1.0×10^{-46}
Iron Compounds	
$FeCO_3$	3.5×10^{-11}
$Fe(OH)_2$	7.9×10^{-15}
FeS	4.9×10^{-18}
$Fe_4[Fe(CN)_6]_3$	3.0×10^{-41}
$Fe(OH)_3$	6.3×10^{-38}

Substance	K_{sp}
Lead Compounds	
$Pb_3(AsO_4)_2$	4.1×10^{-36}
$PbBr_2$	6.3×10^{-6}
$PbCO_3$	1.5×10^{-13}
$PbCl_2$	1.7×10^{-5}
$PbCrO_4$	1.8×10^{-14}
PbF_2	3.7×10^{-8}
$Pb(OH)_2$	2.8×10^{-16}
PbI_2	8.7×10^{-9}
$Pb_3(PO_4)_2$	3.0×10^{-44}
$PbSeO_4$	1.5×10^{-7}
$PbSO_4$	1.8×10^{-8}
Magnesium Compounds	
$Mg_3(AsO_4)_2$	2.1×10^{-20}
$MgCO_3 \cdot 3\ H_2O$†	4.0×10^{-5}
MgC_2O_4	8.6×10^{-5}
MgF_2	6.4×10^{-9}
$MgNH_4PO_4$	2.5×10^{-12}
Manganese Compounds	
$Mn_3(AsO_4)_2$	1.9×10^{-11}
$MnCO_3$	1.8×10^{-11}
$Mn(OH)_2$	4.6×10^{-14}
$Mn(OH)_3$	$\sim 1 \times 10^{-36}$
Mercury Compounds	
Hg_2Br_2	1.3×10^{-22}
Hg_2CO_3	8.9×10^{-17}
Hg_2Cl_2	1.1×10^{-18}
Hg_2CrO_4	5.0×10^{-9}
Hg_2I_2	4.5×10^{-29}
$Hg_2O \cdot H_2O\ (Hg_2^{2+} + 2\ OH^-)$†‡	1.6×10^{-23}
Hg_2SO_4	6.8×10^{-7}
$Hg(CN)_2$	3.0×10^{-23}
$Hg(OH)_2$	2.5×10^{-26}
HgI_2	4.0×10^{-29}
Nickel Compounds	
$Ni_3(AsO_4)_2$	1.9×10^{-26}
$NiCO_3$	6.6×10^{-9}
$Ni(CN)_2$	3.0×10^{-23}
$Ni(OH)_2$	2.8×10^{-16}
Silver Compounds	
Ag_3AsO_4	1.1×10^{-20}
$AgBr$	3.3×10^{-13}
Ag_2CO_3	8.1×10^{-12}
$AgCl$	1.8×10^{-10}
Ag_2CrO_4	9.0×10^{-12}
$AgCN$	1.2×10^{-16}
$Ag_4[Fe(CN)_6]$	1.6×10^{-41}
$Ag_2O\ (Ag^+ + OH^-)$‡	2.0×10^{-8}
AgI	1.5×10^{-16}
Ag_3PO_4	8.9×10^{-17}
Ag_2SO_3	1.5×10^{-14}
Ag_2SO_4	1.7×10^{-5}
$AgSCN$	1.0×10^{-12}
Strontium Compounds	
$Sr_3(AsO_4)_2$	1.3×10^{-18}
$SrCO_3$	9.4×10^{-10}
$SrC_2O_4 \cdot 2\ H_2O$†	5.6×10^{-8}
$SrCrO_4$	3.6×10^{-5}
$Sr(OH)_2 \cdot 8\ H_2O$†	3.2×10^{-4}
$Sr_3(PO_4)_2$	1.0×10^{-31}
$SrSO_3$	4.0×10^{-8}
$SrSO_4$	2.8×10^{-7}
Tin Compounds	
$Sn(OH)_2$	2.0×10^{-26}
SnI_2	1.0×10^{-4}
$Sn(OH)_4$	1×10^{-57}
Zinc Compounds	
$Zn_3(AsO_4)_2$	1.1×10^{-27}
$ZnCO_3$	1.5×10^{-11}
$Zn(CN)_2$	8.0×10^{-12}
$Zn_3[Fe(CN)_6]$	4.1×10^{-16}
$Zn(OH)_2$	4.5×10^{-17}
$Zn_3(PO_4)_2$	9.1×10^{-33}

*No metallic sulfides are listed in this table because sulfide ion is such a strong base that the usual solubility product equilibrium equation does not apply. See Myers, R. J. *Journal of Chemical Education,* Vol. 63, 1986; pp. 687–690.

†Since $[H_2O]$ does not appear in equilibrium constants for equilibria in aqueous solution in general, it does *not* appear in the K_{sp} expressions for hydrated solids.

‡Very small amounts of these oxides dissolve in water to give the ions indicated in parentheses. Solid hydroxides of these metal ions are unstable and decompose to oxides as rapidly as they are formed.

APPENDIX I

Standard Reduction Potentials in Aqueous Solution at 25 °C

Acidic Solution	Standard Reduction Potential, $E°$ (volts)
$F_2(g) + 2e^- \longrightarrow 2\,F^-(aq)$	2.87
$Co^{3+}(aq) + e^- \longrightarrow Co^{2+}(aq)$	1.82
$Pb^{4+}(aq) + 2\,e^- \longrightarrow Pb^{2+}(aq)$	1.8
$H_2O_2(aq) + 2\,H_3O^+(aq) + 2\,e^- \longrightarrow 4\,H_2O(\ell)$	1.77
$NiO_2(s) + 4\,H_3O^+(aq) + 2\,e^- \longrightarrow Ni^{2+}(aq) + 6\,H_2O(\ell)$	1.7
$PbO_2(s) + SO_4^{2-}(aq) + 4\,H_3O^+(aq) + 2\,e^- \longrightarrow PbSO_4(s) + 6\,H_2O(\ell)$	1.685
$Au^+(aq) + e^- \longrightarrow Au(s)$	1.68
$2\,HClO(aq) + 2\,H_3O^+(aq) + 2\,e^- \longrightarrow Cl_2(g) + 4\,H_2O(\ell)$	1.63
$Ce^{4+}(aq) + e^- \longrightarrow Ce^{3+}(aq)$	1.61
$NaBiO_3(s) + 6\,H_3O^+(aq) + 2\,e^- \longrightarrow Bi^{3+}(aq) + Na^+(aq) + 9\,H_2O(\ell)$	~ 1.6
$MnO_4^-(aq) + 8\,H_3O^+(aq) + 5\,e^- \longrightarrow Mn^{2+}(aq) + 12\,H_2O(\ell)$	1.51
$Au^{3+}(aq) + 3\,e^- \longrightarrow Au(s)$	1.50
$2\,ClO_3^-(aq) + 12\,H_3O^+(aq) + 10\,e^- \longrightarrow Cl_2(g) + 18\,H_2O(\ell)$	1.47
$BrO_3^-(aq) + 6\,H_3O^+(aq) + 6\,e^- \longrightarrow Br^-(aq) + 9\,H_2O(\ell)$	1.44
$Cl_2(g) + 2\,e^- \longrightarrow 2\,Cl^-(aq)$	1.358
$Cr_2O_7^{2-}(aq) + 14\,H_3O^+(aq) + 6\,e^- \longrightarrow 2\,Cr^{3+}(aq) + 21\,H_2O(\ell)$	1.33
$N_2H_5^+(aq) + 3\,H_3O^+(aq) + 2\,e^- \longrightarrow 2\,NH_4^+(aq) + 3\,H_2O(\ell)$	1.24
$MnO_2(s) + 4\,H_3O^+(aq) + 2\,e^- \longrightarrow Mn^{2+}(aq) + 6\,H_2O(\ell)$	1.23
$O_2(g) + 4\,H_3O^+(aq) + 4\,e^- \longrightarrow 6\,H_2O(\ell)$	1.229
$Pt^{2+}(aq) + 2\,e^- \longrightarrow Pt(s)$	1.2
$IO_3^-(aq) + 6\,H_3O^+(aq) + 5\,e^- \longrightarrow \frac{1}{2}\,I_2(aq) + 9\,H_2O(\ell)$	1.195
$ClO_4^-(aq) + 2\,H_3O^+(aq) + 2\,e^- \longrightarrow ClO_3^-(aq) + 3\,H_2O(\ell)$	1.19
$Br_2(\ell) + 2\,e^- \longrightarrow 2\,Br^-(aq)$	1.066
$AuCl_4^-(aq) + 3\,e^- \longrightarrow Au(s) + 4\,Cl^-(aq)$	1.00
$Pd^{2+}(aq) + 2\,e^- \longrightarrow Pd(s)$	0.987
$NO_3^-(aq) + 4\,H_3O^+(aq) + 3\,e^- \longrightarrow NO(g) + 6\,H_2O(\ell)$	0.96
$NO_3^-(aq) + 3\,H_3O^+(aq) + 2\,e^- \longrightarrow HNO_2(aq) + 4\,H_2O(\ell)$	0.94
$2\,Hg^{2+}(aq) + 2\,e^- \longrightarrow Hg_2^{2+}(aq)$	0.920
$Hg^{2+}(aq) + 2\,e^- \longrightarrow Hg(\ell)$	0.855
$Ag^+(aq) + e^- \longrightarrow Ag(s)$	0.7994
$Hg_2^{2+}(aq) + 2\,e^- \longrightarrow 2\,Hg(\ell)$	0.789
$Fe^{3+}(aq) + e^- \longrightarrow Fe^{2+}(aq)$	0.771
$SbCl_6^-(aq) + 2\,e^- \longrightarrow SbCl_4^-(aq) + 2\,Cl^-(aq)$	0.75
$[PtCl_4]^{2-}(aq) + 2\,e^- \longrightarrow Pt(s) + 4\,Cl^-(aq)$	0.73
$O_2(g) + 2\,H_3O^+(aq) + 2\,e^- \longrightarrow H_2O_2(aq) + 2\,H_2O(\ell)$	0.682
$[PtCl_6]^{2-}(aq) + 2\,e^- \longrightarrow [PtCl_4]^{2-}(aq) + 2\,Cl^-(aq)$	0.68
$H_3AsO_4(aq) + 2\,H_3O^+(aq) + 2\,e^- \longrightarrow H_3AsO_3(aq) + 3\,H_2O(\ell)$	0.58
$I_2(s) + 2\,e^- \longrightarrow 2\,I^-(aq)$	0.535

Acidic Solution	Standard Reduction Potential, $E°$ (volts)
$TeO_2(s) + 4\,H_3O^+(aq) + 4\,e^- \longrightarrow Te(s) + 6\,H_2O(\ell)$	0.529
$Cu^+(aq) + e^- \longrightarrow Cu(s)$	0.521
$[RhCl_6]^{3-}(aq) + 3\,e^- \longrightarrow Rh(s) + 6\,Cl^-(aq)$	0.44
$Cu^{2+}(aq) + 2\,e^- \longrightarrow Cu(s)$	0.337
$Hg_2Cl_2(s) + 2\,e^- \longrightarrow 2\,Hg(\ell) + 2\,Cl^-(aq)$	0.27
$AgCl(s) + e^- \longrightarrow Ag(s) + Cl^-(aq)$	0.222
$SO_4^{2-}(aq) + 4\,H_3O^+(aq) + 2\,e^- \longrightarrow SO_2(g) + 6\,H_2O(\ell)$	0.20
$SO_4^{2-}(aq) + 4\,H_3O^+(aq) + 2\,e^- \longrightarrow H_2SO_3(aq) + 5\,H_2O(\ell)$	0.17
$Cu^{2+}(aq) + e^- \longrightarrow Cu^+(aq)$	0.153
$Sn^{4+}(aq) + 2\,e^- \longrightarrow Sn^{2+}(aq)$	0.15
$S(s) + 2\,H_3O^+(aq) + 2\,e^- \longrightarrow H_2S(aq) + 2\,H_2O(\ell)$	0.14
$AgBr(s) + e^- \longrightarrow Ag(s) + Br^-(aq)$	0.0713
$2\,H_3O^+(aq) + 2\,e^- \longrightarrow H_2(g) + 2\,H_2O(\ell)$ (reference electrode)	0.0000
$N_2O(g) + 6\,H_3O^+(aq) + 4\,e^- \longrightarrow 2\,NH_3OH^+(aq) + 5\,H_2O(\ell)$	−0.05
$Pb^{2+}(aq) + 2\,e^- \longrightarrow Pb(s)$	−0.126
$Sn^{2+}(aq) + 2\,e^- \longrightarrow Sn(s)$	−0.14
$AgI(s) + e^- \longrightarrow Ag(s) + I^-(aq)$	−0.15
$[SnF_6]^{2-}(aq) + 4\,e^- \longrightarrow Sn(s) + 6\,F^-(aq)$	−0.25
$Ni^{2+}(aq) + 2\,e^- \longrightarrow Ni(s)$	−0.25
$Co^{2+}(aq) + 2\,e^- \longrightarrow Co(s)$	−0.28
$Tl^+(aq) + e^- \longrightarrow Tl(s)$	−0.34
$PbSO_4(s) + 2\,e^- \longrightarrow Pb(s) + SO_4^{2-}(aq)$	−0.356
$Se(s) + 2\,H_3O^+(aq) + 2\,e^- \longrightarrow H_2Se(aq) + 2\,H_2O(\ell)$	−0.40
$Cd^{2+}(aq) + 2\,e^- \longrightarrow Cd(s)$	−0.403
$Cr^{3+}(aq) + e^- \longrightarrow Cr^{2+}(aq)$	−0.41
$Fe^{2+}(aq) + 2\,e^- \longrightarrow Fe(s)$	−0.44
$2\,CO_2(g) + 2\,H_3O^+(aq) + 2\,e^- \longrightarrow (COOH)_2(aq) + 2\,H_2O(\ell)$	−0.49
$Ga^{3+}(aq) + 3\,e^- \longrightarrow Ga(s)$	−0.53
$HgS(s) + 2\,H_3O^+(aq) + 2\,e^- \longrightarrow Hg(\ell) + H_2S(g) + 2\,H_2O(\ell)$	−0.72
$Cr^{3+}(aq) + 3\,e^- \longrightarrow Cr(s)$	−0.74
$Zn^{2+}(aq) + 2\,e^- \longrightarrow Zn(s)$	−0.763
$Cr^{2+}(aq) + 2\,e^- \longrightarrow Cr(s)$	−0.91
$Mn^{2+}(aq) + 2\,e^- \longrightarrow Mn(s)$	−1.18
$V^{2+}(aq) + 2\,e^- \longrightarrow V(s)$	−1.18
$Zr^{4+}(aq) + 4\,e^- \longrightarrow Zr(s)$	−1.53
$Al^{3+}(aq) + 3\,e^- \longrightarrow Al(s)$	−1.66
$H_2(g) + 2\,e^- \longrightarrow 2\,H^-(aq)$	−2.25
$Mg^{2+}(aq) + 2\,e^- \longrightarrow Mg(s)$	−2.37
$Na^+(aq) + e^- \longrightarrow Na(s)$	−2.714
$Ca^{2+}(aq) + 2\,e^- \longrightarrow Ca(s)$	−2.87
$Sr^{2+}(aq) + 2\,e^- \longrightarrow Sr(s)$	−2.89
$Ba^{2+}(aq) + 2\,e^- \longrightarrow Ba(s)$	−2.90
$Rb^+(aq) + e^- \longrightarrow Rb(s)$	−2.925
$K^+(aq) + e^- \longrightarrow K(s)$	−2.925
$Li^+(aq) + e^- \longrightarrow Li(s)$	−3.045

Basic Solution	Standard Reduction Potential, $E°$ (volts)
$ClO^-(aq) + H_2O(\ell) + 2\,e^- \longrightarrow Cl^-(aq) + 2\,OH^-(aq)$	0.89
$OOH^-(aq) + H_2O(\ell) + 2\,e^- \longrightarrow 3\,OH^-(aq)$	0.88
$2\,NH_2OH(aq) + 2\,e^- \longrightarrow N_2H_4(aq) + 2\,OH^-(aq)$	0.74
$ClO_3^-(aq) + 3\,H_2O(\ell) + 6\,e^- \longrightarrow Cl^-(aq) + 6\,OH^-(aq)$	0.62
$MnO_4^-(aq) + 2\,H_2O(\ell) + 3\,e^- \longrightarrow MnO_2(s) + 4\,OH^-(aq)$	0.588
$MnO_4^-(aq) + e^- \longrightarrow MnO_4^{2-}(aq)$	0.564
$NiO_2(s) + 2\,H_2O(\ell) + 2\,e^- \longrightarrow Ni(OH)_2(s) + 2\,OH^-(aq)$	0.49
$Ag_2CrO_4(s) + 2\,e^- \longrightarrow 2\,Ag(s) + CrO_4^{2-}(aq)$	0.446
$O_2(g) + 2\,H_2O(\ell) + 4\,e^- \longrightarrow 4\,OH^-(aq)$	0.40
$ClO_4^-(aq) + H_2O(\ell) + 2\,e^- \longrightarrow ClO_3^-(aq) + 2\,OH^-(aq)$	0.36
$Ag_2O(s) + H_2O(\ell) + 2\,e^- \longrightarrow 2\,Ag(s) + 2\,OH^-(aq)$	0.34
$2\,NO_2^-(aq) + 3\,H_2O(\ell) + 4\,e^- \longrightarrow N_2O(g) + 6\,OH^-(aq)$	0.15
$N_2H_4(aq) + 2\,H_2O(\ell) + 2\,e^- \longrightarrow 2\,NH_3(aq) + 2\,OH^-(aq)$	0.10
$[Co(NH_3)_6]^{3+}(aq) + e^- \longrightarrow [Co(NH_3)_6]^{2+}(aq)$	0.10
$HgO(s) + H_2O(\ell) + 2\,e^- \longrightarrow Hg(\ell) + 2\,OH^-(aq)$	0.0984
$O_2(g) + H_2O(\ell) + 2\,e^- \longrightarrow OOH^-(aq) + OH^-(aq)$	0.076
$NO_3^-(aq) + H_2O(\ell) + 2\,e^- \longrightarrow NO_2^-(aq) + 2\,OH^-(aq)$	0.01
$MnO_2(s) + 2\,H_2O(\ell) + 2\,e^- \longrightarrow Mn(OH)_2(s) + 2\,OH^-(aq)$	−0.05
$CrO_4^{2-}(aq) + 4\,H_2O(\ell) + 3\,e^- \longrightarrow Cr(OH)_3(s) + 5\,OH^-(aq)$	−0.12
$Cu(OH)_2(s) + 2\,e^- \longrightarrow Cu(s) + 2\,OH^-(aq)$	−0.36
$Fe(OH)_3(s) + e^- \longrightarrow Fe(OH)_2(s) + OH^-(aq)$	−0.56
$2\,H_2O(\ell) + 2\,e^- \longrightarrow H_2(g) + 2\,OH^-(aq)$	−0.8277
$2\,NO_3^-(aq) + 2\,H_2O(\ell) + 2\,e^- \longrightarrow N_2O_4(g) + 4\,OH^-(aq)$	−0.85
$Fe(OH)_2(s) + 2\,e^- \longrightarrow Fe(s) + 2\,OH^-(aq)$	−0.877
$SO_4^{2-}(aq) + H_2O(\ell) + 2\,e^- \longrightarrow SO_3^{2-}(aq) + 2\,OH^-(aq)$	−0.93
$N_2(g) + 4\,H_2O(\ell) + 4\,e^- \longrightarrow N_2H_4(aq) + 4\,OH^-(aq)$	−1.15
$[Zn(OH)_4]^{2-}(aq) + 2\,e^- \longrightarrow Zn(s) + 4\,OH^-(aq)$	−1.22
$Zn(OH)_2(s) + 2\,e^- \longrightarrow Zn(s) + 2\,OH^-(aq)$	−1.245
$[Zn(CN)_4]^{2-}(aq) + 2\,e^- \longrightarrow Zn(s) + 4\,CN^-(aq)$	−1.26
$Cr(OH)_3(s) + 3\,e^- \longrightarrow Cr(s) + 3\,OH^-(aq)$	−1.30
$SiO_3^{2-}(aq) + 3\,H_2O(\ell) + 4\,e^- \longrightarrow Si(s) + 6\,OH^-(aq)$	−1.70

APPENDIX

J Selected Thermodynamic Values*

Species	ΔH_f° (298.15 K) (kJ/mol)	S° (298.15 K) (J K^{-1} mol^{-1})	ΔG_f° (298.15 K) (kJ/mol)
Aluminum			
Al(s)	0	28.275	0
Al^{3+}(aq)	−531	−321.7	−485
$AlCl_3$(s)	−704.2	110.67	−628.8
Al_2O_3(s, corundum)	−1675.7	50.92	−1582.3
Argon			
Ar(g)	0	154.843	0
Ar(aq)	−12.1	59.4	16.4
Barium			
$BaCl_2$(s)	−858.6	123.68	−810.4
BaO(s)	−553.5	70.42	−525.1
$BaSO_4$(s)	−1473.2	132.2	−1362.2
$BaCO_3$(s)	−1216.3	112.1	85.35
Beryllium			
Be(s)	0	9.5	0
$Be(OH)_2$(s)	−902.5	51.9	−815
Bromine			
Br(g)	111.884	175.022	82.396
Br_2(ℓ)	0	152.231	0
Br_2(g)	30.907	245.463	3.110
Br_2(aq)	−2.59	130.5	3.93
Br^-(aq)	−121.55	82.4	−103.96
BrCl(g)	14.64	240.10	−0.98
BrF_3(g)	−255.6	292.53	−229.43
HBr(g)	−36.40	198.695	−53.45
Calcium			
Ca(s)	0	41.42	0
Ca(g)	178.2	158.884	144.3
Ca^{2+}(g)	1925.9	—	—
Ca^{2+}(aq)	−542.83	−53.1	−553.58
CaC_2(s)	−59.8	69.96	−64.9
$CaCO_3$(s, calcite)	−1206.92	92.9	−1128.79
$CaCl_2$(s)	−795.8	104.6	−748.1
CaF_2(s)	−1219.6	68.87	−1167.3
CaH_2(s)	−186.2	42	−147.2
CaO(s)	−635.09	39.75	−604.03
CaS(s)	−482.4	56.5	−477.4
$Ca(OH)_2$(s)	−986.09	83.39	−898.49
$Ca(OH)_2$(aq)	−1002.82	−74.5	−868.07
$CaSO_4$(s)	−1434.11	106.7	−1321.79

*Taken from Wagman, D. D., Evans, W. H., Parker, V. B., Schumm, R. H., Halow, I., Bailey, S. M., Churney, K. L., and Nuttall, R. The NBS Tables of Chemical Thermodynamic Properties. *Journal of Physical and Chemical Reference Data,* Vol. 11, Suppl. 2, 1982.

Species	ΔH_f° (298.15 K) (kJ/mol)	S° (298.15 K) (J K^{-1} mol^{-1})	ΔG_f° (298.15 K) (kJ/mol)
Carbon			
C(s, graphite)	0	5.74	0
C(s, diamond)	1.895	2.377	2.9
C(g)	716.682	158.096	671.257
CCl_4(ℓ)	−135.44	216.4	−65.21
CCl_4(g)	−102.9	309.85	−60.59
$CHCl_3$(ℓ)	−134.47	201.7	−73.66
$CHCl_3$(g)	−103.14	295.71	−70.34
CH_4 (g, methane)	−74.81	186.264	−50.72
C_2H_2 (g, ethyne)	226.73	200.94	209.2
C_2H_4 (g, ethene)	52.26	219.56	68.15
C_2H_6 (g, ethane)	−84.68	229.6	−32.82
C_3H_8 (g, propane)	−103.8	269.9	−23.49
C_4H_{10} (g, butane)	−126.148	310.227	−16.985
C_6H_6(ℓ, benzene)	49.03	172.8	124.5
C_6H_{14}(ℓ, hexane)	−198.782	296.018	−4.035
C_8H_{18} (g, octane)	−208.447	466.835	16.718
C_8H_{18}(ℓ, octane)	−249.952	361.205	6.707
CH_3OH(ℓ, methanol)	−238.66	126.8	−166.27
CH_3OH(g, methanol)	−200.66	239.81	−161.96
CH_3OH(aq, methanol)	−245.931	133.1	−175.31
C_2H_5OH(ℓ, ethanol)	−277.69	160.7	−174.78
C_2H_5OH(g, ethanol)	−235.1	282.7	−168.49
C_2H_5OH(aq, ethanol)	−288.3	148.5	−181.64
$C_6H_{12}O_6$ (s, glucose)	−1274.4	235.9	−917.2
CH_3COO^-(aq)	−486.01	86.6	−369.31
CH_3COOH(aq)	−485.76	178.7	−396.46
CH_3COOH(ℓ)	−484.5	159.8	−389.9
CO(g)	−110.525	197.674	−137.168
CO_2(g)	−393.509	213.74	−394.359
H_2CO_3(aq)	−699.65	187.4	−623.08
HCO_3^-(aq)	−691.99	91.2	−586.77
CO_3^{2-}(aq)	−677.14	−56.9	−527.81
$HCOO^-$(aq)	−425.55	92.0	−351.0
HCOOH(aq)	−425.43	163	−372.3
HCOOH(ℓ)	−424.72	128.95	−361.35
CS_2(g)	117.36	237.84	67.12
CS_2(ℓ)	89.70	151.34	65.27
$COCl_2$(g)	−218.8	283.53	−204.6
Cesium			
Cs(s)	0	85.23	0
Cs^+(g)	457.964	—	—
CsCl(s)	−443.04	101.17	−414.53
Chlorine			
Cl(g)	121.679	165.198	105.68
Cl^-(g)	−233.13	—	—
Cl^-(aq)	−167.159	56.5	−131.228
Cl_2(g)	0	223.066	0

Species	ΔH_f° (298.15 K) (kJ/mol)	S° (298.15 K) (J K^{-1} mol^{-1})	ΔG_f° (298.15 K) (kJ/mol)
$Cl_2(aq)$	−23.4	121	6.94
$HCl(g)$	−92.307	186.908	−95.299
$HCl(aq)$	−167.159	56.5	−131.228
$ClO_2(g)$	102.5	256.84	120.5
$Cl_2O(g)$	80.3	266.21	97.9
$ClO^-(aq)$	−107.1	42.0	−36.8
$HClO(aq)$	−120.9	142.	−79.9
$ClF_3(g)$	−163.2	281.61	−123.0
Chromium			
$Cr(s)$	0	23.77	0
$Cr_2O_3(s)$	−1139.7	81.2	−1058.1
$CrCl_3(s)$	−556.5	123	−486.1
Copper			
$Cu(s)$	0	33.15	0
$CuO(s)$	−157.3	42.63	−129.7
$CuCl_2(s)$	−220.1	108.07	−175.7
$CuSO_4(s)$	−771.36	109.	−661.8
Fluorine			
$F_2(g)$	0	202.78	0
$F(g)$	78.99	158.754	61.91
$F^-(g)$	−255.39	—	—
$F^-(aq)$	−332.63	−13.8	−278.79
$HF(g)$	−271.1	173.779	−273.2
HF(aq, un-ionized)	−320.08	88.7	−296.82
HF(aq, ionized)	−332.63	−13.8	−278.79
Hydrogen†			
$H_2(g)$	0	130.684	0
$H_2(aq)$	−4.2	57.7	17.6
$HD(g)$	0.318	143.801	−1.464
$D_2(g)$	0	144.960	0
$H(g)$	217.965	114.713	203.247
$H^+(g)$	1536.202	—	—
$H^+(aq)$	0	0	0
$OH^-(aq)$	−229.994	−10.75	−157.244
$H_2O(\ell)$	−285.83	69.91	−237.129
$H_2O(g)$	−241.818	188.825	−228.572
$H_2O_2(\ell)$	−187.78	109.6	−120.35
$H_2O_2(aq)$	−191.17	143.9	−134.03
$HO_2^-(aq)$	−160.33	23.8	−67.3
$HDO(\ell)$	−289.888	79.29	−241.857
$D_2O(\ell)$	−294.600	75.94	−243.439
Iodine			
$I_2(s)$	0	116.135	0
$I_2(g)$	62.438	260.69	19.327
$I_2(aq)$	22.6	137.2	16.40
$I(g)$	106.838	180.791	70.25

Species	ΔH_f° (298.15 K) (kJ/mol)	S° (298.15 K) (J K^{-1} mol^{-1})	ΔG_f° (298.15 K) (kJ/mol)
I^-(g)	−197	—	—
I^-(aq)	−55.19	111.3	−51.57
I_3^-(aq)	−51.5	239.3	−51.4
HI(g)	26.48	206.594	1.70
HI(aq, ionized)	−55.19	111.3	−51.57
IF(g)	−95.65	236.17	−118.51
ICl(g)	17.78	247.551	−5.46
ICl_3(s)	−89.5	167.4	−22.29
ICl(ℓ)	−23.89	135.1	−13.58
IBr(g)	40.84	258.773	3.69
Iron			
Fe(s)	0	27.78	0
FeO(s, wustite)	−266.27	57.9	−245.12
Fe_2O_3(s, hematite)	−824.2	87.4	−742.2
Fe_3O_4(s, magnetite)	−1118.4	146.4	−1015.4
$FeCl_2$(s)	−341.79	117.95	−302.3
$FeCl_3$(s)	−399.49	142.3	−344
FeS_2 (s, pyrite)	−178.2	52.93	−166.9
$Fe(CO)_5$(ℓ)	−774	338.1	−705.3
Lead			
Pb(s)	0	64.81	0
$PbCl_2$(s)	−359.41	136	−314.1
PbO(s, yellow)	−217.32	68.7	−187.89
PbS(s)	−100.4	91.2	−98.7
Lithium			
Li(s)	0	29.12	0
Li^+(g)	685.783	—	—
LiOH(s)	−484.93	42.8	−438.95
LiOH(aq)	−508.48	2.8	−450.58
LiCl(s)	−408.701	59.33	−384.37
Magnesium			
Mg(s)	0	32.68	0
Mg^{2+}(aq)	−466.85	−138.1	−454.8
$MgCl_2$(g)	−400.4	—	—
$MgCl_2$(s)	−641.32	89.62	−591.79
$MgCl_2$(aq)	−801.15	−25.1	−717.1
MgO(s)	−601.70	26.94	−569.43
$Mg(OH)_2$(s)	−924.54	63.18	−833.51
MgS(s)	−346	50.33	−341.8
$MgSO_4$(s)	−1284.9	91.6	−1170.6
$MgCO_3$(s)	−1095.8	65.7	−1012.1
Mercury			
Hg(ℓ)	0	76.02	0
$HgCl_2$(s)	−224.3	146	−178.6
HgO(s, red)	−90.83	70.29	−58.539
HgS(s, red)	−58.2	82.4	−50.6

Species	ΔH_f° (298.15 K) (kJ/mol)	S° (298.15 K) (J K^{-1} mol^{-1})	ΔG_f° (298.15 K) (kJ/mol)
Nickel			
Ni(s)	0	29.87	0
NiO(s)	−239.7	37.99	−211.7
$NiCl_2$(s)	−305.332	97.65	−259.032
Nitrogen			
N_2(g)	0	191.61	0
N_2(aq)	−10.8	—	—
N(g)	472.704	153.298	455.563
NH_3(g)	−46.11	192.45	−16.45
NH_3(aq)	−80.29	111.3	−26.50
NH_4^+(aq)	−132.51	113.4	−79.31
N_2H_4(ℓ)	50.63	121.21	149.34
NH_4Cl(s)	−314.43	94.6	−202.87
NH_4Cl(aq)	−299.66	169.9	−210.52
NH_4NO_3(s)	−365.56	151.08	−183.87
NH_4NO_3(aq)	−339.87	259.8	−190.56
NO(g)	90.25	210.761	86.55
NO_2(g)	33.18	240.06	51.31
N_2O(g)	82.05	219.85	104.20
N_2O_4(g)	9.16	304.29	97.89
N_2O_4(ℓ)	−19.50	209.2	97.54
NOCl(g)	51.71	261.69	66.08
HNO_3(ℓ)	−174.10	155.60	−80.71
HNO_3(g)	−135.06	266.38	−74.72
HNO_3(aq)	−207.36	146.4	−111.25
NO_3^-(aq)	−205.0	146.4	−108.74
NF_3(g)	−124.7	260.73	−83.2
Oxygen†			
O_2(g)	0	205.138	0
O_2(aq)	−11.7	110.9	16.4
O(g)	249.170	161.055	231.731
O_3(g)	142.7	238.93	163.2
OH^-(aq)	−229.994	−10.75	−157.244
Phosphorus			
P_4(s, white)	0	164.36	0
P_4(s, red)	−70.4	91.2	−48.4
P(g)	314.64	163.193	278.25
PH_3(g)	5.4	310.23	13.4
PCl_3(g)	−287	311.78	−267.8
PCl_3(ℓ)	−319.7	217.1	−272.3
PCl_5(s)	−443.5	—	—
P_4O_{10}(s)	−2984	228.86	−2697.7
H_3PO_4(s)	−1279	110.5	−1119.1
Potassium			
K(s)	0	64.18	0
KF(s)	−567.27	66.57	−537.75

Species	ΔH_f° (298.15 K) (kJ/mol)	S° (298.15 K) (J K^{-1} mol^{-1})	ΔG_f° (298.15 K) (kJ/mol)
KCl(s)	−436.747	82.59	−409.14
KCl(aq)	−419.53	159.0	−414.49
KBr(s)	−393.798	95.90	−380.66
KI(s)	−327.900	106.32	−324.892
$KClO_3$(s)	−397.73	143.1	−296.25
KOH(s)	−424.764	78.9	−379.08
KOH(aq)	−482.37	91.6	−440.5
Silicon			
Si(s)	0	18.83	0
$SiBr_4$(ℓ)	−457.3	277.8	−443.8
SiC(s)	−65.3	16.61	−62.8
$SiCl_4$(g)	−657.01	330.73	−616.98
SiH_4(g)	34.3	204.62	56.9
SiF_4(g)	−1614.94	282.49	−1572.65
SiO_2(s, quartz)	−910.94	41.84	−856.64
Silver			
Ag(s)	0	42.55	0
Ag^+(aq)	105.579	72.68	77.107
Ag_2O(s)	−31.05	121.3	−11.2
AgCl(s)	−127.068	96.2	−109.789
AgI(s)	−61.84	115.5	−66.19
AgN_3(s)	620.60	99.22	591.0
$AgNO_3$(s)	−124.39	140.92	−33.41
$AgNO_3$(aq)	−101.8	219.2	−34.16
Sodium			
Na(s)	0	51.21	0
Na(g)	107.32	153.712	76.761
Na^+(g)	609.358	—	—
Na^+(aq)	−240.12	59.0	−261.905
NaF(s)	−573.647	51.46	−543.494
NaF(aq)	−572.75	45.2	−540.68
NaCl(s)	−411.153	72.13	−384.138
NaCl(g)	−176.65	229.81	−196.66
NaCl(aq)	−407.27	115.5	−393.133
NaBr(s)	−361.062	86.82	−348.983
NaBr(aq)	−361.665	141.4	−365.849
NaI(s)	−287.78	98.53	−286.06
NaI(aq)	−295.31	170.3	−313.47
NaOH(s)	−425.609	64.455	−379.484
NaOH(aq)	−470.114	48.1	−419.15
$NaClO_3$(s)	−365.774	123.4	−262.259
$NaHCO_3$(s)	−950.81	101.7	−851.0
Na_2CO_3(s)	−1130.68	134.98	−1044.44
Na_2SO_4(s)	−1387.08	149.58	−1270.16

Species	ΔH_f° (298.15 K) (kJ/mol)	S° (298.15 K) (J K^{-1} mol^{-1})	ΔG_f° (298.15 K) (kJ/mol)
Sulfur			
S(s, monoclinic)	0.33	—	—
S(s, rhombic)	0	31.80	0
S(g)	278.805	167.821	238.250
S^{2-}(aq)	33.1	−14.6	85.8
S_2Cl_2(g)	−18.4	331.5	−31.8
SF_6(g)	−1209.	291.82	−1105.3
SF_4(g)	−774.9	292.03	−731.3
H_2S(g)	−20.63	205.79	−33.56
H_2S(aq)	−39.7	121	−27.83
HS^-(aq)	−17.6	62.8	12.08
SO_2(g)	−296.830	248.22	−300.194
SO_3(g)	−395.72	256.76	−371.06
$SOCl_2$(g)	−212.5	309.77	−198.3
SO_4^{2-}(aq)	−909.27	20.1	−744.53
H_2SO_4(ℓ)	−813.989	156.904	−690.003
H_2SO_4(aq)	−909.27	20.1	−744.53
HSO_4^-(aq)	−887.34	131.8	−755.91
Tin			
Sn(s, white)	0	51.55	0
Sn(s, gray)	−2.09	44.14	0.13
$SnCl_2$(s)	−325.1	—	—
$SnCl_4$(ℓ)	−511.3	258.6	−440.1
$SnCl_4$(g)	−471.5	365.8	−432.2
SnO_2(s)	−580.7	52.3	−519.6
Titanium			
Ti(s)	0	30.63	0
$TiCl_4$(ℓ)	−804.2	252.34	−737.2
$TiCl_4$(g)	−763.2	354.9	−726.7
TiO_2(s)	−939.7	49.92	−884.5
Uranium			
U(s)	0	50.21	0
UO_2(s)	−1084.9	77.03	−1031.7
UO_3(s)	−1223.8	96.11	−1145.9
UF_4(s)	−1914.2	151.67	−1823.3
UF_6(g)	−2147.4	377.9	−2063.7
UF_6(s)	−2197.0	227.6	−2068.5
Zinc			
Zn(s)	0	41.63	0
$ZnCl_2$(s)	−415.05	111.46	−369.398
ZnO(s)	−348.28	43.64	−318.3
ZnS(s, sphalerite)	−205.98	57.7	−201.29

†Many hydrogen-containing and oxygen-containing compounds are listed only under other elements; for example, HNO_3 appears under nitrogen.

Answers to Problem-Solving Practice Problems

Chapter 1

1.1 (1) *Define the problem:* You are asked to find the volume of the sample, and you know the mass.
(2) *Develop a plan:* Density relates mass and volume and is the appropriate conversion factor, so look up the density in a table. Volume is proportional to mass, so the mass has to be either multiplied by the density or multiplied by the reciprocal of the density. Use the units to decide which.
(3) *Execute the plan:* According to Table 1.1, the density of benzene is 0.880 g/mL. Setting up the calculation so that the unit (grams) cancels gives

$$4.33\ \cancel{g} \times \frac{1\ \text{mL}}{0.880\ \cancel{g}} = 4.92\ \text{mL}$$

Notice that the result is expressed to three significant figures, because both the mass and the density had three significant figures.
(4) *Check your answer:* Because the density is a little less than 1.00 g/mL, the volume in milliliters should be a little larger than the mass in grams. The calculated answer, 4.92 mL, is a little larger than the mass, 4.33 g.

1.2 Substance A must be a mixture since some of it dissolves and some, substance B, does not.
Substance C is the soluble portion of substance A. Since all of substance C dissolves in water there is no way to determine how many components it has. Additionally, it is not possible to determine whether the one or more components themselves are elements or compounds. Therefore it is not possible to say whether C is an element, a compound, or a mixture.
The only thing we know about substance B is that it is insoluble in water. We do not know whether it is one insoluble substance, or more than one insoluble substance. Additionally, we do not know whether the substance or substances of B are elements or compounds. Therefore it is not possible to say whether B is an element, a compound, or a mixture.

1.3 Oxygen is O_2; ozone is O_3. Oxygen is a colorless, odorless gas; ozone is a pale blue gas with a pungent odor.

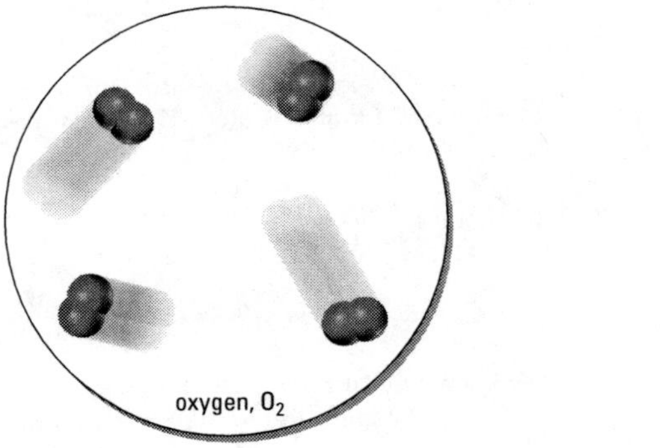

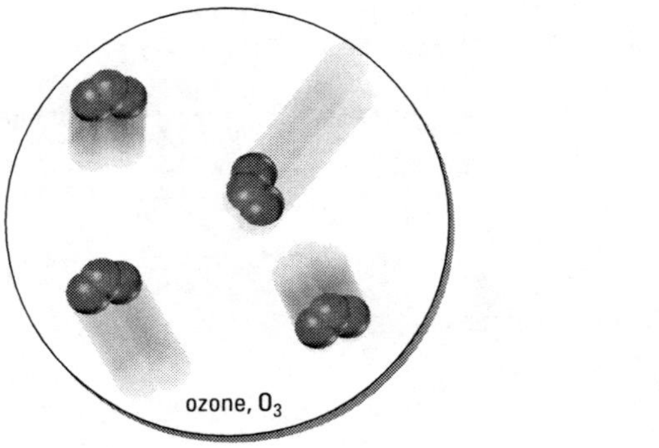

Chapter 2

2.1 (a) 10 gal = 40 qt. There are 1.0567 quarts per liter, so

$$40\ \text{qt} \times \frac{1\ \text{L}}{1.0567\ \text{qt}} = 37.9\ \text{L or } 38\ \text{L}$$

(b) $100\ \text{yds} \times \frac{3\ \text{ft}}{\text{yd}} \times \frac{12\ \text{in}}{\text{ft}} \times \frac{2.54\ \text{cm}}{\text{in}} \times \frac{1\ \text{m}}{100\ \text{cm}} = 91.46\ \text{m}$

2.2 (a) 1 lb = 453.59 g, so 5 lb = 2268. g
(b) $3\ \text{pt} \times \frac{1\ \text{qt}}{2\ \text{pt}} \times \frac{1\ \text{L}}{1.057\ \text{qt}} \times \frac{1000\ \text{ml}}{1\ \text{L}} = 1420\ \text{ml}$
(c) $\frac{1.420\ \text{L}}{5\ \text{L}} \times 100\% = 28\%$

2.3 Work with the numerator first: 165 mg is 0.165 g. Work with the denominator next: 1 dL = 0.1 L. Therefore, the concentration is

$$\frac{0.165\ \text{g}}{0.1\ \text{L}} = 1.65\ \text{g/L}.$$

2.4 (a) 0.00602 g — 3 sf
(b) 22.871 mg — 5 sf
(c) 344. °C — 3 sf
(d) 100.0 mL — 4 sf
(e) 0.00042 m — 2 sf
(f) 0.002001 L — 4 sf

2.5 (a) 244.2 + 0.1732 = 244.4
(b) 6.19 × 5.2222 = 32.3
(c) $\frac{7.2234 - 11.3851}{4.22} = -0.986$

2.6 (a) A phosphorus atom (Z = 15) with 16 neutrons has A = 31.
(b) A neon-22 atom has A = 22 and Z = 10, so the number of electrons must be 10 and the number of neutrons must be $A - Z = 22 - 10 = 12$ neutrons.
(c) The periodic table shows us that the element with 82 protons is lead. The atomic weight of this isotope of lead is 82 + 125 = 207, so the correct symbol is $^{207}_{82}Pb$.

2.7 The magnesium isotope with 12 neutrons has 12 protons, so Z = 12 and the notation is $^{24}_{12}Mg$; the isotope with 13 neutrons has Z = 12 and $^{25}_{12}Mg$; and the isotope with 14 neutrons has Z = 12 and $^{26}_{12}Mg$.

2.8 75 g wire × (fraction Ni) = g Ni, so 75 g Ni × 0.80 = 60 g Ni. For Cr we have 75 g Cr × 0.20 = 15 g Cr. Or, we could have solved for the mass of Cr from 75 g wire − 60 g Ni = 15 g Cr.

2.9 (a) 1 mg Mo = 1×10^{-3} g Mo

$$1 \times 10^{-3}\ \text{g Mo} \times \frac{1\ \text{mol Mo}}{95.94\ \text{g Mo}} = 1.04 \times 10^{-5}\ \text{mol Mo}$$

(b) $5.00 \times 10^{-3}\ \text{mol Au} \times \frac{196.97\ \text{g Au}}{1\ \text{mol Au}} = 0.985\ \text{g Au}$

Chapter 3

3.1 (a) $C_{10}H_{11}O_{13}N_5P_3$ (b) $C_{18}H_{27}O_3N$ (c) $C_2H_2O_4$

3.2 (a) Sulfur dioxide
(b) Boron trifluoride
(c) Carbon tetrachloride

3.3 Yes, a similar trend would be expected. The absolute values of the boiling points of the chlorine-containing compounds would be different from their alkane parents, but the differences between successive chlorine-containing compounds should follow a similar trend as for the alkanes themselves.

3.4 (a) A Ca^{4+} charge is unlikely because calcium is in Group 2A, the elements of which lose two electrons to form 2+ ions.
(b) Cr^{2+} is possible because chromium is a transition metal ion that forms 2+ and 3+ ions.
(c) Strontium is a Group 2A metal and forms 2+ ions; thus, a Sr^- ion is highly unlikely.

3.5 (a) CH_4 is formed from two nonmetals and is molecular.
(b) $CaBr_2$ is formed from a metal and a nonmetal, so it is ionic.
(c) $MgCl_2$ is formed from a metal and a nonmetal, so it is ionic.
(d) PCl_3 is formed from two nonmetals and is molecular.
(e) KCl is formed from a metal and a nonmetal and is ionic.

3.6 (a) $In_2(SO_3)_3$ contains two In^{3+} and three SO_3^{2-} ions. There are 14 atoms in this formula unit.
(b) $(NH_4)_3PO_4$ contains three ammonium ions, NH_4^+, and one phosphate ion, PO_4^{3-}, collectively containing 20 atoms.

3.7 (a) One Mg^{2+} ion and two Br^- ions
(b) Two Li^+ ions and one CO_3^{2-} ion
(c) One NH_4^+ ion and one Cl^- ion
(d) Two Fe^{3+} ions and three SO_4^{2-} ions
(e) CuCl and $CuCl_2$

3.8 (a) KNO_2 is potassium nitrite.
(b) $NaHSO_3$ is sodium hydrogen sulfite or sodium bisulfite.
(c) $Mn(OH)_2$ is manganese(II) hydroxide.
(d) $Mn_2(SO_4)_3$ is manganese(III) sulfate.
(e) Ba_3N_2 is barium nitride.
(f) LiH is lithium hydride.

3.9 (a) KH_2PO_4 (b) CuOH (c) NaClO
(d) NH_4ClO_4 (e) $CrCl_3$ (f) $FeSO_3$

3.10 (a) The molar mass of $K_2Cr_2O_7$ is 294.2 g/mol.

$$\frac{12.5\text{ g}}{294.2\text{ g/mol}} = 4.25 \times 10^{-2}\text{ mol}$$

(b) The molar mass of $KMnO_4$ is 158.0 g/mol.

$$\frac{12.5\text{ g}}{158.0\text{ g/mol}} = 7.91 \times 10^{-2}\text{ mol}$$

(c) The molar mass of $(NH_4)_2CO_3$ is 96.1 g/mol.

$$\frac{12.5\text{ g}}{96.1\text{ g/mol}} = 1.30 \times 10^{-1}\text{ mol}$$

3.11 (a) The molar mass of sucrose, $C_{12}H_{22}O_{11}$, is 342.3 g/mol.

$$5.0 \times 10^{-3}\text{ mol sucrose} \times \frac{342.3\text{ g sucrose}}{1\text{ mol sucrose}} = 1.7\text{ g sucrose}$$

(b) $$3.0 \times 10^{-6}\text{ mol ACTH} \times \frac{4600\text{ g ACTH}}{1\text{ mol ACTH}} = 1.4 \times 10^{-2}\text{ g ACTH}$$

$$1.4 \times 10^{-2}\text{ g} \times \frac{10^3\text{ mg}}{1\text{ g}} = 14.\text{ mg ACTH}$$

3.12 (a) The molar mass of cholesterol is 386.7 g/mol.

$$\frac{10.0\text{ g}}{386.7\text{ g/mol}} = 2.59 \times 10^{-2}\text{ mol}$$

The molar mass of $Mn_2(SO_4)_3$ is 398.1 g/mol.

$$\frac{10.0\text{ g}}{398.1\text{ g/mol}} = 2.51 \times 10^{-2}\text{ mol}$$

(b) The molar mass of K_2HPO_4 is 174.2 g/mol.

$$0.25\text{ mol} \times \frac{174.2\text{ g}}{1\text{ mol}} = 44.\text{ g}$$

The molar mass of caffeine is 194.2 g/mol.

$$0.25\text{ mol} \times \frac{194.2\text{ g}}{1\text{ mol}} = 49.\text{ g}$$

3.13 The mass of Si in 1 mol SiO_2 is 28.0855 g. The mass of O in 1 mol SiO_2 is 31.9988 g.

$$\%\text{ Si in SiO}_2 = \frac{28.0855\text{ g}}{60.08\text{ g}} \times 100\% = 46.7\%\text{ Si}$$

$$\%\text{ O in SiO}_2 = \frac{31.9988\text{ g}}{60.08\text{ g}} \times 100\% = 53.3\%\text{ O}$$

3.14 The molar mass of hydrated nickel chloride is

$$58.69\text{ g/mol} + 2(35.45\text{ g/mol}) + 12(1.008\text{ g/mol}) + 6(16.00\text{ g/mol}) = 237.69\text{ g/mol.}$$

The percentages by weight for each element are found from the ratios of the mass of each element in 1 mole of hydrated nickel chloride to the molar mass of hydrated nickel chloride:

$$\frac{58.69\text{ g Ni}}{237.69\text{ g hydrated nickel chloride}} \times 100\% = 24.7\%\text{ Ni}$$

$$\frac{70.90\text{ g Cl}}{237.69\text{ g hydrated nickel chloride}} \times 100\% = 29.8\%\text{ Cl}$$

$$\frac{12.096\text{ g H}}{237.69\text{ g hydrated nickel chloride}} \times 100\% = 5.09\%\text{ H}$$

$$\frac{96.00\text{ g O}}{237.69\text{ g hydrated nickel chloride}} \times 100\% = 40.4\%\text{ O}$$

3.15 A 100-g sample of the phosphorus oxide contains 43.64 g P and 56.36 g O.

$$43.64\text{ g P} \times \frac{1\text{ mol P}}{30.9738\text{ g P}} = 1.41\text{ mol P}$$

$$56.36\text{ g O} \times \frac{1\text{ mol O}}{15.9994\text{ g O}} = 3.52\text{ mol O}$$

The mole ratio is

$$\frac{3.52\text{ mol O}}{1.41\text{ mol P}} = \frac{2.50\text{ mol O}}{1.00\text{ mol P}}$$

There are 2.5 oxygen atoms for every phosphorus atom. Thus, the empirical formula is P_2O_5. The molar mass corresponding to this empirical formula is

$$\left(2\text{ mol P} \times \frac{30.9738\text{ g P}}{1\text{ mol P}}\right) + \left(5\text{ mol O} \times \frac{15.994\text{ g O}}{1\text{ mol O}}\right) = 141.9\text{ g/mol}$$

The known molar mass is 283.89 g/mol. The molar mass is twice as large as the empirical formula mass, so the molecular formula of the oxide is P_4O_{10}.

3.16 Find the number of moles of each element in 100.0 g of vitamin C.

$$40.9\text{ g C} \times \frac{1\text{ mol C}}{12.011\text{ g C}} = 3.405\text{ mol C}$$

$$4.58\text{ g H} \times \frac{1\text{ mol H}}{1.0079\text{ g H}} = 4.544\text{ mol H}$$

$$54.5\text{ g O} \times \frac{1\text{ mol O}}{15.9994\text{ g O}} = 3.406\text{ mol O}$$

Find the mole ratios.

$$\frac{4.544 \text{ mol H}}{3.406 \text{ mol O}} = \frac{1.334 \text{ mol H}}{1.000 \text{ mol O}}$$

The same ratio holds for H to C. Using whole numbers, we have $C_3H_4O_3$ for the empirical formula. The empirical formula weight is (3)(12.011) + (4)(1.0079) + (3)(15.9994) = 88.06 g. The molar mass, however, is 176.13 g/mol, so the molecular formula must be twice the empirical formula: $C_6H_8O_6$.

Chapter 4

4.1 (a) N_2; combination (b) O_2; combination
(c) N_2; decomposition

4.2 (a) Decomposition reaction:

$$2\ Al(OH)_3(s) \longrightarrow Al_2O_3(s) + 3\ H_2O(g)$$

(b) Combination reaction:

$$Na_2O(s) + H_2O(\ell) \longrightarrow 2\ NaOH(aq)$$

(c) Combination reaction: $S_8(s) + 24\ F_2(g) \rightarrow 8\ SF_6(g)$
(d) Exchange reaction:

$$3\ NaOH(aq) + H_3PO_4(aq) \longrightarrow Na_3PO_4(aq) + 3\ H_2O(\ell)$$

(e) Displacement:

$$3\ C(s) + Fe_2O_3(s) \longrightarrow 3\ CO(g) + 2\ Fe(\ell)$$

4.3 (a) $2\ Cr(s) + 3\ Cl_2 \rightarrow 2\ CrCl_3(s)$
(b) $As_2O_3(s) + 3\ H_2(g) \rightarrow 2\ As(s) + 3\ H_2O(\ell)$

4.4 (a) $C_2H_5OH + 3\ O_2 \rightarrow 2\ CO_2 + 3\ H_2O$
(b) $C_2H_5OH + 2\ O_2 \rightarrow 2\ CO + 3\ H_2O$

4.5 0.433 mol hematite needs 0.433 × 3 = 1.30 mol CO. Molar mass of CO is 28.01, so 1.30 × 28.01 = 36.4 g CO.

4.6 (a) $0.300 \text{ mol cassiterite} \times \frac{1 \text{ mol Sn}}{1 \text{ mol cassiterite}} \times \frac{118.7 \text{ g Sn}}{1 \text{ mol Sn}} = 35.6 \text{ g Sn}$

(b) $35.6 \text{ g Sn} \times \frac{1 \text{ mol Sn}}{118.7 \text{ g Sn}} \times \frac{2 \text{ mol C}}{1 \text{ mol Sn}} \times \frac{12.01 \text{ g C}}{1 \text{ mol C}} = 7.20 \text{ g C}$

4.7 (a) $57.\text{ g C} \times \frac{1 \text{ mol C}}{12.01 \text{ g C}} \times \frac{1 \text{ mol } O_2}{2 \text{ mol C}} \times \frac{32.0 \text{ g } O_2}{1 \text{ mol } O_2} = 76.\text{ g } O_2$

(b) $57.\text{ g C} \times \frac{1 \text{ mol C}}{12.01 \text{ g C}} \times \frac{2 \text{ mol CO}}{2 \text{ mol C}} \times \frac{28.0 \text{ g CO}}{1 \text{ mol CO}} = 1.3 \times 10^2 \text{ g CO}$

4.8 $6.46 \text{ g } MgCl_2 \times \frac{1 \text{ mol } MgCl_2}{95.2104 \text{ g } MgCl_2} = 6.78 \times 10^{-2} \text{ mol } MgCl_2$

The same number of moles of Mg as $MgCl_2$ are involved, so

$$6.78 \times 10^{-2} \text{ mol Mg} \times \frac{24.3050 \text{ g Mg}}{1 \text{ mol Mg}} = 1.65 \text{ g Mg}$$

$$\frac{1.65 \text{ g Mg}}{1.72\text{-g sample}} \times 100\% = 95.9\% \text{ Mg in sample}$$

4.9 $0.75 \text{ mol } CO_2 \times \frac{1 \text{ mol } (NH_2)_2CO}{1 \text{ mol } CO_2} = 0.75 \text{ mol } (NH_2)_2CO$

4.10 (a) $CS_2(\ell) + 3\ O_2(g) \rightarrow CO_2(g) + 2\ SO_2(g)$
(b) Determine the quantity of CO_2 produced by each reactant; the limiting reactant produces the lesser quantity.

$$3.5 \text{ g } CS_2 \times \frac{1 \text{ mol } CS_2}{76.0 \text{ g } CS_2} \times \frac{1 \text{ mol } CO_2}{1 \text{ mol } CS_2} \times \frac{44.01 \text{ g } CO_2}{1 \text{ mol } CO_2} = 2.0 \text{ g } CO_2$$

$$17.5 \text{ g } O_2 \times \frac{1 \text{ mol } O_2}{31.998 \text{ g } O_2} \times \frac{1 \text{ mol } CO_2}{3 \text{ mol } O_2} \times \frac{44.01 \text{ g } CO_2}{1 \text{ mol } CO_2} = 8.02 \text{ g } CO_2$$

Therefore, CS_2 is the limiting reagent.
(c) The yield of SO_2 must be calculated using the limiting reagent, CS_2.

$$3.5 \text{ g } CS_2 \times \frac{1 \text{ mol } CS_2}{76.0 \text{ g } CS_2} \times \frac{2 \text{ mol } SO_2}{1 \text{ mol } CS_2} \times \frac{64.1 \text{ g } SO_2}{1 \text{ mol } SO_2} = 5.9 \text{ g } SO_2$$

4.11 Find the number of moles of each reactant.

$$100.\text{ g } SiCl_4 \times \frac{1 \text{ mol } SiCl_4}{169.90 \text{ g } SiCl_4} = 0.589 \text{ mol } SiCl_4$$

$$100.\text{ g Mg} \times \frac{1 \text{ mol Mg}}{24.3050 \text{ g Mg}} = 4.11 \text{ mol Mg}$$

Find the mass of Si produced, based on the mass available of each reactant.

$$0.589 \text{ mol } SiCl_4 \times \frac{1 \text{ mol Si}}{1 \text{ mol } SiCl_4} \times \frac{28.0855 \text{ g Si}}{1 \text{ mol Si}} = 16.5 \text{ g Si}$$

$$4.11 \text{ mol Mg} \times \frac{1 \text{ mol Si}}{2 \text{ mol Mg}} \times \frac{28.0855 \text{ g Si}}{1 \text{ mol Si}} = 57.7 \text{ g Si}$$

Thus, $SiCl_4$ is the limiting reactant, and the mass of Si produced is 16.5 g.

4.12 To make 1.0 kg CH_3OH with 85% yield will require using enough reactant to produce 1000/0.85, or 1180 g CH_3OH.

$$1180 \text{ g } CH_3OH \times \frac{1 \text{ mol}}{32.042 \text{ g}} = 36.83 \text{ mol } CH_3OH$$

$$36.83 \text{ mol } CH_3OH \times \frac{2 \text{ mol } H_2}{1 \text{ mol } CH_3OH} = 73.65 \text{ mol } H_2$$

$$73.65 \text{ mol } H_2 \times \frac{2.0158 \text{ g } H_2}{1 \text{ mol } H_2} = 149 \text{ g } H_2$$

4.13 Calculate the mass of Cu_2S you should have produced and compare it with the amount actually produced.

$$2.50 \text{ g Cu} \times \frac{1 \text{ mol Cu}}{63.546 \text{ g Cu}} = 3.93 \times 10^{-2} \text{ mol Cu}$$

$$3.93 \times 10^{-2} \text{ mol Cu} \times \frac{8 \text{ mol } Cu_2S}{16 \text{ mol Cu}} = 1.97 \times 10^{-2} \text{ mol } Cu_2S$$

$$1.97 \times 10^{-2} \text{ mol } Cu_2S \times \frac{159.16 \text{ g } Cu_2S}{1 \text{ mol } Cu_2S} = 3.14 \text{ g } Cu_2S$$

$$\frac{2.53 \text{ g}}{3.14 \text{ g}} \times 100\% = 80.6\% \text{ yield was obtained}$$

Your synthesis met the standard.

4.14 (a) $491 \text{ mg } CO_2 \times \frac{1 \text{ g } CO_2}{10^3 \text{ mg } CO_2} \times \frac{1 \text{ mol } CO_2}{44.01 \text{ g } CO_2} \times \frac{1 \text{ mol C}}{1 \text{ mol } CO_2} = 1.116 \times 10^{-2} \text{ mol C}$

$$1.116 \times 10^{-2} \text{ mol C} \times \frac{12.01 \text{ g C}}{1 \text{ mol C}} = 0.1340 \text{ g C} = 134.0 \text{ mg C}$$

$$100\text{ mg }H_2O \times \frac{1\text{ g }H_2O}{10^3\text{ mg }H_2O} \times \frac{1\text{ mol }H_2O}{18.02\text{ g }H_2O} \times \frac{2\text{ mol H}}{1\text{ mol }H_2O} = 1.110 \times 10^{-2}\text{ mol H}$$

$$1.110 \times 10^{-2}\text{ mol H} \times \frac{1.008\text{ g H}}{1\text{ mol H}} = 1.119 \times 10^{-2}\text{ g H} = 11.2\text{ mg H}$$

The mass of oxygen in the compound

= total mass − (mass C + mass H)

= 175 mg − (134.0 mg C + 11.2 mg H) = 29.8 mg O

The moles of oxygen are

$$29.8\text{ mg O} \times \frac{1\text{ g O}}{10^3\text{ mg O}} \times \frac{1\text{ mol O}}{16.00\text{ g O}} = 1.862 \times 10^{-3}\text{ mol O}$$

The empirical formula can be derived from the mole ratios of the elements.

$$\frac{1.116 \times 10^{-2}\text{ mol C}}{1.862 \times 10^{-3}\text{ mol O}} = 5.993\text{ mol C/mol O}$$

$$\frac{1.110 \times 10^{-2}\text{ mol H}}{1.862 \times 10^{-3}\text{ mol O}} = 5.961\text{ mol H/mol O}$$

$$\frac{1.862 \times 10^{-3}\text{ mol O}}{1.862 \times 10^{-3}\text{ mol O}} = 1.000\text{ mol O}$$

The empirical formula of phenol is C_6H_6O.

(b) The molar mass is needed to determine the molecular formula.

4.15 $$0.569\text{ g Sn} \times \frac{1\text{ mol Sn}}{118.7\text{ g Sn}} = 4.794 \times 10^{-3}\text{ mol Sn}$$

$$2.434\text{ g }I_2 \times \frac{1\text{ mol }I_2}{253.81\text{ g }I_2} \times \frac{2\text{ mol I}}{1\text{ mol }I_2} = 1.918 \times 10^{-2}\text{ mol I}$$

$$\frac{1.918 \times 10^{-2}\text{ mol I}}{4.794 \times 10^{-3}\text{ mol Sn}} = \frac{4.001\text{ mol I}}{1.000\text{ mol Sn}}$$

Therefore, the empirical formula is SnI_4.

Chapter 5

5.1 (a) NaF is soluble.
(b) $Ca(CH_3COO)_2$ is soluble.
(c) $SrCl_2$ is soluble.
(d) MgO is not soluble.
(e) $PbCl_2$ is not soluble.
(f) HgS is not soluble.

5.2 (a) This exchange reaction forms insoluble nickel hydroxide and aqueous sodium chloride.

$$NiCl_2(aq) + 2\ NaOH(aq) \longrightarrow Ni(OH)_2(s) + 2\ NaCl(aq)$$

(b) This is an exchange reaction that forms aqueous potassium bromide and a precipitate of calcium carbonate.

$$K_2CO_3(aq) + CaBr_2(aq) \longrightarrow CaCO_3(s) + 2\ KBr(aq)$$

5.3 (a) $BaCl_2(aq) + Na_2SO_4(aq) \rightarrow BaSO_4(s) + 2\ NaCl(aq)$

$$Ba^{2+}(aq) + SO_4^{2-}(aq) \longrightarrow BaSO_4(s)$$

(b) $(NH_4)_2S(aq) + FeCl_2(aq) \rightarrow FeS(s) + 2\ NH_4Cl(aq)$

$$Fe^{2+}(aq) + S^{2-}(aq) \rightarrow FeS(s)$$

5.4 Any of the strong acids in Table 5.2 would also be strong electrolytes. Any of the weak acids or bases in Table 5.2 would be weak electrolytes. Any organic compound that yields no ions on dissolution would be a nonelectrolyte.

5.5 $H_3PO_4(aq) + 3\ NaOH(aq) \rightarrow Na_3PO_4(aq) + 3\ H_2O(\ell)$

5.6 (a) Sulfuric acid and magnesium hydroxide
(b) Carbonic acid and strontium hydroxide

5.7

$$2\ HCN(aq) + Ca(OH)_2(aq) \longrightarrow Ca(CN)_2(aq) + 2\ H_2O(\ell)$$

$$2\ HCN(aq) + Ca^{2+}(aq) + 2\ OH^-(aq) \longrightarrow Ca^{2+}(aq) + 2\ CN^-(aq) + 2\ H_2O(\ell)$$

$$HCN(aq) + OH^-(aq) \longrightarrow CN^-(aq) + H_2O(\ell)$$

5.8 The oxidation numbers of Fe and Sb are 0 (Rule 1). The oxidation numbers in Sb_2S_3 are +3 for Sb^{3+} and −2 for S^{2-} (Rules 2 and 4). The oxidation numbers in FeS are +2 for Fe^{2+} and −2 for S^{2-} (Rules 2 and 4).

5.9 In the reaction $PbO(s) + CO(g) \rightarrow Pb(s) + CO_2(g)$, Pb^{2+} is reduced to Pb; Pb^{2+} is the oxidizing agent. C^{2+} is oxidized to C^{4+}; C^{2+} is the reducing agent.

5.10 Reactions (a) and (b) will occur. Aluminum is above copper and chromium in Table 5.5; therefore, aluminum will be oxidized and acts as the reducing agent in reactions (a) and (b). In reaction (a), Cu^{2+} is reduced, and Cu^{2+} is the oxidizing agent. Cr^{3+} is the oxidizing agent in reaction (b) and is reduced to Cr metal. Reactions (c) and (d) do not occur because Pt cannot reduce H^+, and Au cannot reduce Ag^+.

5.11 $$36.0\text{ g }Na_2SO_4 \times \frac{1\text{ mol }Na_2SO_4}{142.0\text{ g }Na_2SO_4} = 0.254\text{ mol }Na_2SO_4$$

$$\text{Molarity} = \frac{0.254\text{ mol}}{0.750\text{ L}} = 0.339\text{ molar}$$

5.12 $$V(\text{conc}) = \frac{0.150\text{ molar} \times 0.050\text{ L}}{0.500\text{ molar}} = 0.015\text{ L} = 15\text{ mL}$$

5.13 (a) 1.00 L of 0.125 M Na_2CO_3 contains 0.125 mol Na_2CO_3.

$$0.125\text{ mol} \times \frac{105.99\text{ g}}{1\text{ mol}} = 13.2\text{ g }Na_2CO_3$$

Prepare the solution by adding 13.2 g Na_2CO_3 to a volumetric flask, dissolving it and mixing thoroughly, and adding sufficient water until the solution volume is 1.0 L.

(b) Use water to dilute a specific volume of the 0.125 M solution to 100 mL.

$$V(\text{conc}) = \frac{0.0500\text{ M} \times 0.100\text{ L}}{0.125\text{ M}} = 0.040\text{ L} = 40.\text{ mL of }0.125\text{ M solution}$$

Therefore, put 40. mL of the more concentrated solution into a container and add water until the solution volume equals 100 mL.

(c) 500 mL of 0.215 M $KMnO_4$ contains 1.70 g $KMnO_4$.

$$0.500\text{ L} \times \frac{0.0215\text{ mol }KMnO_4}{1\text{ L}} = 0.01075\text{ mol }KMnO_4$$

$$0.01075\text{ mol }KMnO_4 \times \frac{158.0\text{ g }KMnO_4}{1\text{ mol }KMnO_4} = 1.70\text{ g }KMnO_4$$

Put 1.70 g $KMnO_4$ into a container and add water until the solution volume is 500 mL.

(d) Dilute the more concentrated solution by adding sufficient water to 52.3 mL of 0.0215 M $KMnO_4$ until the solution volume is 250 mL.

$$V(\text{conc}) = \frac{0.00450\text{ M} \times 0.250\text{ L}}{0.0215\text{ M}} = 0.0523\text{ L} = 52.3\text{ mL}$$

5.14 $$1.2 \times 10^{10}\text{ kg NaOH} \times \frac{1\text{ mol NaOH}}{0.040\text{ kg NaOH}} \times \frac{2\text{ mol NaCl}}{2\text{ mol NaOH}} \times \frac{58.5\text{ g NaCl}}{1\text{ mol NaCl}} \times \frac{1\text{ L brine}}{360\text{ g NaCl}} = 4.9 \times 10^{10}\text{ L}$$

5.15 The net ionic equation is $AgBr(s) + 2\ S_2O_3^{2-}(aq) \rightarrow Ag(S_2O_3)_2^{3-}(aq) + Br^-(aq)$. Moles $Na_2S_2O_3$ = $(0.0200\ M)(0.125\ L) = 0.0025$ mol $Na_2S_2O_3$.
2 mol $Na_2S_2O_3$ dissolves 1 mol AgBr, so 0.0025 mol $Na_2S_2O_3$ dissolves 0.00125 mol AgBr. The molar mass of AgBr is 187.8 g/mol, so 0.00125 mol AgBr × 187.8 g/mol = 0.235 g AgBr or 235 mg AgBr.

5.16 $H_2SO_4(aq) + 2\ NaOH(aq) \rightarrow Na_2SO_4(aq) + 2\ H_2O(\ell)$

$$\text{Moles NaOH} = (0.0413\ \text{L})(0.100\ \text{M}) = 0.00413\ \text{mol NaOH}$$

$$\text{Moles } H_2SO_4 = \tfrac{1}{2} \times 0.00413 = 0.002065\ \text{mol } H_2SO_4$$

$$\text{Molarity} = \frac{0.002065\ \text{mol}}{0.020\ \text{L}} = 0.103\ \text{M } H_2SO_4$$

Chapter 6

6.1 (a) $160\ \text{Cal} \times \dfrac{1000\ \text{cal}}{\text{Cal}} \times \dfrac{4.184\ \text{J}}{\text{cal}} = 6.7 \times 10^5\ \text{J}$

(b) 75 W = 75 J/s;
$75\ \text{J/s} \times 3.0\ \text{h} \times 60\ \text{min/h} \times 60\ \text{s/min} = 8.1 \times 10^5\ \text{J}$

(c) $16\ \text{kJ} \times \dfrac{1\ \text{kcal}}{4.184\ \text{kJ}} = 3.8\ \text{kcal}$

6.2 $\Delta E = -2400\ \text{J} = q + w = -1.89\ \text{kJ} + w$
$w = -2400\ \text{J} + 1.89\ \text{kJ} = -2.4\ \text{kJ} + 1.89\ \text{kJ} = -0.5\ \text{kJ}$

6.3 $q = c \times m \times \Delta T = c \times m \times (T_{\text{final}} - T_{\text{initial}})$

$$T_{\text{final}} = T_{\text{initial}} + \frac{q}{c \times m} = 5\ °\text{C} + \frac{24{,}100\ \text{J}}{(0.902\ \text{J g}^{-1}\ °\text{C}^{-1})(250.\ \text{g})}$$
$$= 5\ °\text{C} + 106.8\ °\text{C} = 112\ °\text{C}$$

6.4 Since no work is done, $\Delta E = q$. Assume that the tea has a mass of 250. g and that its specific heat capacity is the same as that of water, namely $4.184\ \text{J g}^{-1}\ °\text{C}^{-1}$.
$\Delta E = q$ = (mass) × (specific heat capacity) × (change in temperature)
$\Delta E = q = (250.\ \text{g}) \times (4.184\ \text{J g}^{-1}\ °\text{C}^{-1}) \times [(65 - 37)\ °\text{C}]$
$= 2.9 \times 10^4\ \text{J} = 2.9 \times 10^1\ \text{kJ}$

6.5 $q_{\text{water}} = -q_{\text{iron}}$
$(4.184\ \text{J/g °C})(1000.\ \text{g})(32.8\ °\text{C} - 20.0\ °\text{C}) = -(0.451\ \text{J/g °C})(400.\ \text{g})(32.8\ °\text{C} - T_i)$
$T_i = (297 + 32.8)\ °\text{C} = 330.\ °\text{C}$

6.6 $1.00\ \text{g K(s)} \times \dfrac{1\ \text{mL}}{0.86\ \text{g}} = 1.16\ \text{mL};$
$1.00\ \text{g K}(\ell) \times \dfrac{1\ \text{mL}}{0.82\ \text{g}} = 1.22\ \text{mL}$

The change in volume is (1.22 − 1.16) mL = 0.06 mL.

$$w = 0.06\ \text{mL} \times \frac{0.10\ \text{J}}{1\ \text{mL}} = 6 \times 10^{-3}\ \text{J}$$
$$\Delta H = \frac{14.6\ \text{cal}}{1\ \text{g}} \times 1.00\ \text{g} \times \frac{4.184\ \text{J}}{1\ \text{cal}} = 61.1\ \text{J}$$
$$\Delta E = \Delta H + w = 61.1\ \text{J} + (6 \times 10^{-3}\ \text{J}) = 61.1\ \text{J}$$

6.7 (a) $10.0\ \text{g } I_2 \times \dfrac{1\ \text{mol } I_2}{253.8\ \text{g } I_2} \times \dfrac{62.4\ \text{kJ}}{1\ \text{mol } I_2} = 2.46\ \text{kJ}$

(b) $3.42\ \text{g } I_2 \times \dfrac{1\ \text{mol } I_2}{253.8\ \text{g } I_2} \times \dfrac{-62.4\ \text{kJ}}{1\ \text{mol } I_2} = -0.841\ \text{kJ} = -841\ \text{J}$

(c) This process is the reverse of the one in part (a), so $\Delta H°$ is negative. Thus the process is exothermic. The quantity of energy transferred is 841 J.

6.8 The equation as written involves CO_2 as a reactant, but the question asks for CO_2 as a product. Therefore we will have to change the sign of $\Delta H°$. In addition, since the question asks about production of 4 mol CO_2, we must multiply $\Delta H°$ for the endothermic decomposition by 4. So for the production of 4 mol CO_2,

$$\Delta H° = (4) \times (662.8\ \text{kJ}) = 2651\ \text{kJ}$$

6.9 According to the thermochemical expression, the reaction is endothermic, so 285.8 kJ of energy is transferred into the system per mole of $H_2O(\ell)$ decomposed. Thus,

$$12.6\ \text{g } H_2O \times \frac{1\ \text{mol } H_2O}{18.02\ \text{g } H_2O} \times \frac{285.8\ \text{kJ}}{1\ \text{mol } H_2O} = 200.\ \text{kJ}$$

6.10 $\Delta T = (25.43 - 20.64)\ °\text{C} = 4.79\ °\text{C}$

$$\Delta E_{\text{calorimeter}} = \frac{877\ \text{J}}{°\text{C}} \times 4.79\ °\text{C} = 4.200 \times 10^3\ \text{J} = 4.200\ \text{kJ}$$
$$\Delta E_{\text{water}} = 832\ \text{g} \times \frac{4.184\ \text{J}}{\text{g °C}} \times 4.79\ °\text{C} = 16.67\ \text{kJ}$$
$$\Delta E_{\text{reaction}} = -(q_{\text{calorimeter}} + q_{\text{water}}) = -(4.200 + 16.67)\ \text{kJ} = -20.87\ \text{kJ}$$
$$20.87\ \text{kJ} \times \frac{1\ \text{kcal}}{4.184\ \text{kJ}} \times \frac{1\ \text{Cal}}{1\ \text{kcal}} = 4.99\ \text{Cal}$$

Since metabolizing the Fritos chip corresponds to oxidizing it, the result of 4.99 Cal verifies the statement that one chip provides 5 Cal.

6.11 The total volume of the initial solutions is 200. mL, which corresponds to 200. g of solution. The quantities of reactants are 0.10 mol $H^+(aq)$ and 0.050 mol $OH^-(aq)$, so 0.050 mol H_2O is formed.

$$0.050\ \text{mol } H_2O \times \frac{-58.6\ \text{kJ}}{1\ \text{mol } H_2O} = -2.93\ \text{kJ}$$

Since $\Delta H°$ is negative, energy is transferred to the water, and its temperature will rise.

$$\Delta T = \frac{q}{c \times m} = \frac{2.93 \times 10^3\ \text{J}}{(4.184\ \text{J g}^{-1}\ °\text{C}^{-1})(200.\ \text{g})} = 3.5\ °\text{C}$$

The final temperature will be (20.4 + 3.5) °C = 23.9 °C.

6.12 The balanced chemical equation is

$$2\ Fe_3O_4(s) \rightarrow 6\ FeO(s) + O_2(g)$$

The equations given in the problem can be arranged so that when added they give this balanced equation:

$2 \times [Fe_3O_4(s) \rightarrow 3\ Fe(s) + 2\ O_2(g)]$ $\quad \Delta H° = 2(1118.4\ \text{kJ})$
$6 \times [Fe(s) + \tfrac{1}{2} O_2(g) \rightarrow FeO(s)]$ $\quad \Delta H° = 6(-272.0\ \text{kJ})$

So

$$\Delta H° = 2236.8\ \text{kJ} - 1632.0\ \text{kJ} = 604.8\ \text{kJ}$$

6.13 (a) $\tfrac{1}{2} N_2(g) + \tfrac{3}{2} H_2(g) \rightarrow NH_3(g)$ $\quad \Delta H_f° = -46.11$ kJ/mol
(b) $C(\text{graphite}) + \tfrac{1}{2} O_2(g) \rightarrow CO(g)$ $\quad \Delta H_f° = -110.525$ kJ/mol

6.14 For the reaction given,

$$\begin{aligned}\Delta H° = {} & \{6\ \text{mol } CO_2(g)\} \times \Delta H_f°\{CO_2(g)\} \\ & + \{5\ \text{mol } H_2O(g)\} \times \Delta H_f°\{H_2O(g)\} \\ & - (2\ \text{mol } \{C_3H_5(NO_3)_3(\ell)\} \times \Delta H_f°\{C_3H_5(NO_3)_3(\ell)\} \\ = {} & \{6(-393.509) + 5(-241.818) - 2(-364)\}\ \text{kJ} \\ = {} & -2.84 \times 10^3\ \text{kJ}\end{aligned}$$

For 10.0 g nitroglycerin (nitro),

$$q = 10.0\ \text{g} \times \frac{1\ \text{mol nitro}}{227.09\ \text{g}} \times \frac{-2.84 \times 10^3\ \text{kJ}}{2\ \text{mol nitro}} = -62.5\ \text{kJ}$$

(The 2 mol nitro in the last factor comes from the coefficient of 2 associated with nitroglycerin in the chemical equation.)

6.15 $SO_2(g) + \frac{1}{2}O_2(g) \rightarrow SO_3(g) \quad \Delta H° = ?$

$$\Delta H° = \Delta H_f°\{SO_3(g)\} - [\Delta H_f°\{SO_2(g)\} + \tfrac{1}{2}\Delta H_f°\{O_2(g)\}]$$

$$= -395.72 \text{ kJ} - (-296.830 + 0) \text{ kJ} = -98.89 \text{ kJ}$$

6.16 (a) $227 \text{ g milk} \times \frac{5.0 \text{ g carbohydrate}}{100 \text{ g milk}} \times \frac{17 \text{ kJ}}{1 \text{ g carbohydrate}} = 193 \text{ kJ}$

$$227 \text{ g milk} \times \frac{4.0 \text{ g fat}}{100 \text{ g milk}} \times \frac{38 \text{ kJ}}{1 \text{ g fat}} = 345 \text{ kJ}$$

$$227 \text{ g milk} \times \frac{3.3 \text{ g protein}}{100 \text{ g milk}} \times \frac{17 \text{ kJ}}{1 \text{ g protein}} = 127 \text{ kJ}$$

Total caloric intake = (193 + 345 + 127) kJ = 665 kJ

Reduce by 10% to digest, absorb, and metabolize, giving 665 kJ − 66.5 kJ = 598 kJ.

(b) Walking requires $2.5 \times \text{BMR} = 2.5 \times \frac{1750 \text{ Cal}}{1 \text{ day}}$

$$\times \frac{4.184 \text{ kJ}}{1 \text{ Cal}} \times \frac{1 \text{ day}}{24 \text{ h}} \times \frac{1 \text{ h}}{60 \text{ min}} = 12.7 \text{ kJ/min}$$

$$598 \text{ kJ} \times \frac{1 \text{ min}}{12.7 \text{ kJ}} = 47 \text{ min}$$

Chapter 7

7.1 $\nu = \frac{c}{\lambda} = \frac{2.998 \times 10^8 \text{ m/s}}{4.05 \times 10^{-7} \text{ m}} = 7.40 \times 10^{14} \text{ s}^{-1}$

or 7.40×10^{14} Hz

7.2 (a) One photon of ultraviolet radiation has more energy because ν is larger in the UV spectral region than in the microwave region.

(b) One photon of blue light has more energy because the blue portion of the visible spectrum has a higher frequency than the green portion of the visible spectrum.

7.3 Any from $n_{hi} > 8$ to $n_{lo} = 2$

7.4 (a) $\nu = \frac{2.179 \times 10^{-18} \text{ J}}{h}\left(\frac{1}{n_i^2} - \frac{1}{n_f^2}\right)$

$$= \left(\frac{2.179 \times 10^{-18} \text{ J}}{6.626 \times 10^{-34} \text{ J·s}}\right)\left(\frac{1}{6^2} - \frac{1}{4^2}\right)$$

$$= (3.289 \times 10^{15} \text{ s}^{-1})\left(\frac{1}{36} - \frac{1}{16}\right)$$

$$= (3.289 \times 10^{15} \text{ s}^{-1})(-3.47 \times 10^{-2})$$

$$= -1.14 \times 10^{14} \text{ s}^{-1}$$

The negative sign indicates that energy is emitted.

$$\lambda = 2.63 \times 10^{-6} \text{ m}$$

(b) Longer than that of the $n = 7$ to $n = 4$ transition.

7.5 $\lambda = \frac{h}{mv} = \frac{6.626 \times 10^{-34} \text{ J·s}}{1.67 \times 10^{-27} \text{ kg} \times 2.998 \times 10^7 \text{ m/s}}$

$$= 1.32 \times 10^{-14} \text{ m}$$

7.6 (a) 6d (b) 5 (c) 2, 1, 0, −1, −2

7.7 (a) [Ne]$3s^2 3p^2$ (b) [Ne] 3s [↑↓] 3p [↑] [↑] [ ]

7.8 The electron configurations for :S̤e: and :T̤e: are [Ar]$4s^2 3d^{10} 4p^4$ and [Kr]$5s^2 4d^{10} 5p^4$, respectively. Elements in the same main group have similar electron configurations.

7.9 (a) P^{3-} (b) Ca^{2+}

7.10 The ground state Cu atom has a configuration [Ar]$4s^1 3d^{10}$. When it loses one electron, it becomes the Cu^+ ion with configuration [Ar]$3d^{10}$. There is an added stability for the completely filled set of 3*d* orbitals.

7.11 B < Mg < Na < K

7.12 (a) Cs^+ (b) La^{3+}

7.13 F > N > P > Na

Chapter 8

8.1 (a) 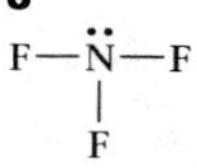 (b) 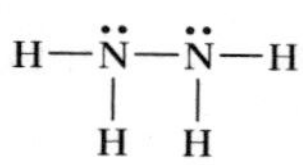

(c) 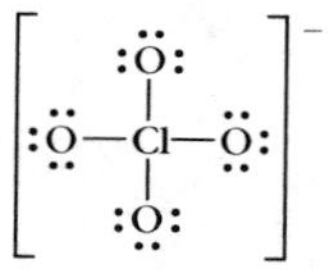

8.2 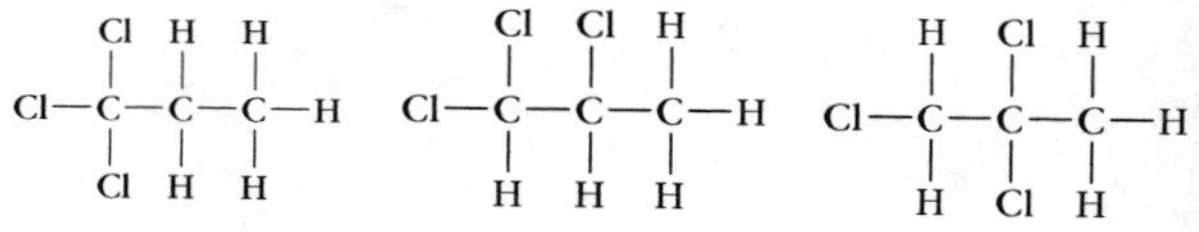

8.3 (a) $[:N{\equiv}O:]^+$ (b) 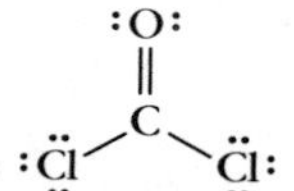

8.4 Only (c) can have geometric isomers. Molecules in (a) and (b) each have the same two groups on one of the double-bonded carbons.

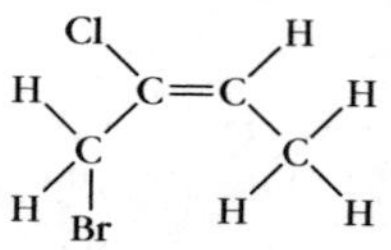

cis-1-bromo-2-chloro-2-butene

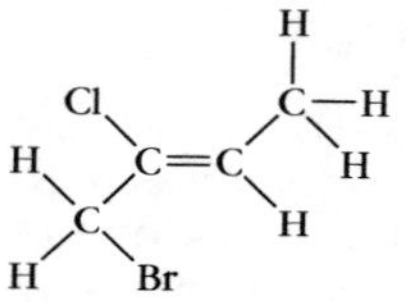

trans-1-bromo-2-chloro-2-butene

8.5 (a) Si is a larger atom than S. (b) Br is a larger atom than Cl.

(c) The greater electron density in the triple bond brings the N≡O atoms closer together than the smaller electron density in the N=O double bond does.

8.6

$$\Delta H = [(4 \text{ mol C—H})(416 \text{ kJ/mol}) + (2 \text{ mol O=O})(498 \text{ kJ/mol})]$$
$$- [(4 \text{ mol O—H})(467 \text{ kJ/mol}) + (2 \text{ mol C=O})(803 \text{ kJ/mol})]$$
$$= (2660 \text{ kJ}) - (3474 \text{ kJ}) = -814 \text{ kJ}$$

8.7 (a) B—Cl is more polar; $\overset{\delta+}{B}$—$\overset{\delta-}{Cl}$; O—H is more polar; $\overset{\delta-}{O}$—$\overset{\delta+}{H}$.

8.8 The other Lewis structure is :O≡N—N̤̈:

	O	N	N
Valence electrons	6	5	5
Lone pair electrons	2	0	6
$\frac{1}{2}$ shared electrons	3	4	1
Formal charge	+1	+1	−2

8.9 The N-to-O bond length in NO_2^- is 124 pm. From Table 8.1, N—O is 136 pm; N=O is 115 pm. Thus, the nature of the bond in NO_2^- is between that of a N—O single bond and a N=O double bond.

8.10 (a) :F̤̈—Be—F̤̈: (b) :Ö—C̤̈l—Ö:

(c) 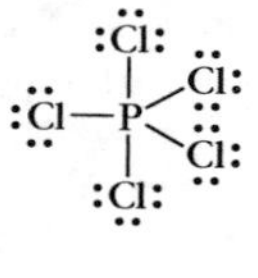 (d) $[H—B—H]^+$

(e) 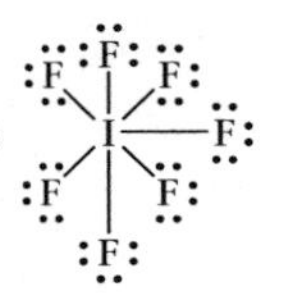

BeF_2—not an octet around the central Be atom; ClO_2—an odd number of electrons around Cl; PCl_5—more than four electron pairs around the central phosphorus atom; BH_2^+—only two electron pairs around the central B atom; IF_7—iodine has seven shared electron pairs.

8.11 Ten valence electrons. The bond order is (8 − 2)/2 = 3. No unpaired electrons. See Table 8.4.

8.12 Bond order = (8 − 5)/2 = 1.5. There is one unpaired electron.

Chapter 9

9.1 There are two Be—F bonds in BeF_2 and no lone pairs on beryllium. Therefore, the electron-pair and the molecular geometry are the same, linear, with 180° Be—F bond angles.

9.2

Central Atom (underlined)	Bond Pairs	Lone Pairs	Electron-Pair Geometry	Molecular Shape
BrO_3^-	3	1	Tetrahedral	Triangular pyramid
SeF_2	2	2	Tetrahedral	Angular
NO_2^-	3	1	Triangular planar	Angular

9.3 (a) ClF_2^-: triangular bipyramidal electron-pair geometry and linear molecular geometry

(b) XeO_3: tetrahedral electron-pair geometry and triangular pyramidal molecular geometry

9.4 (a) $BeCl_2$: *sp* hybridization (two bonding electron pairs around the central Be atom), linear geometry

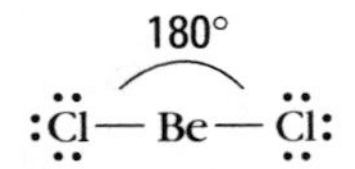

(b) The central N atom has four bonding pairs and no lone pairs in sp^3 hybridized orbitals on N giving tetrahedral electron-pair and molecular geometries.

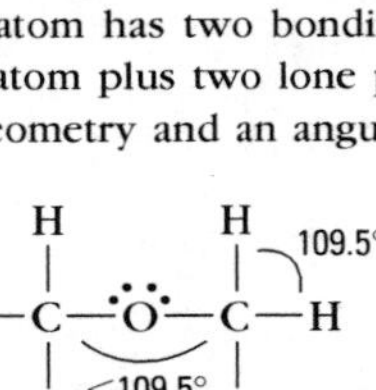

(c) Each carbon is sp^3 hybridized with no lone pairs, so the electron-pair and molecular geometries are both tetrahedral. The sp^3 hybridized oxygen atom has two bonding pairs, each in single bonds to a carbon atom plus two lone pairs giving it a tetrahedral electron-pair geometry and an angular molecular geometry.

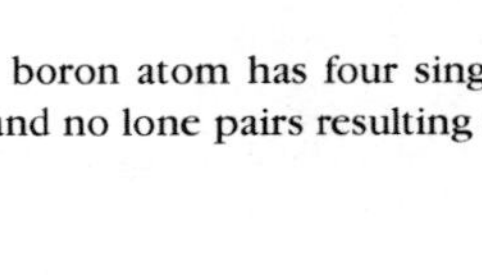

(d) The central boron atom has four single bonds, one to each fluorine atom, and no lone pairs resulting in tetrahedral electron-pair and molecular geometries. The boron is sp^3 hybridized to accommodate the four bonding pairs.

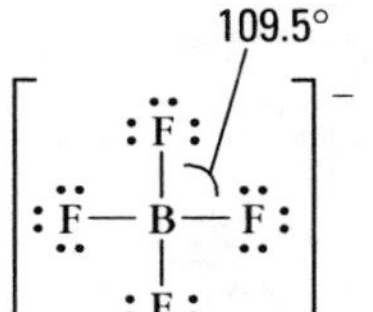

9.5 (a) The central P atom has six bonding pairs and no lone pairs, and is sp^3d^2 hybridized.

(b) The central I atom has three bonding pairs and two lone pairs; these five electron pairs are in sp^3d hybridized orbitals on I.

(c) In ICl_4^-, the central I has four bonding pairs, two lone pairs; these six pairs are in sp^3d^2 orbitals.

9.6 (a) In HCN, the *sp* hybridized carbon atom is sigma bonded to H and to N, as well as having two pi bonds to N. The sigma and two pi bonds form the C≡N triple bond. The nitrogen is *sp* hybridized with a sigma and two pi bonds to carbon; a lone pair is in the nonbonding *sp* hybrid orbital on N.

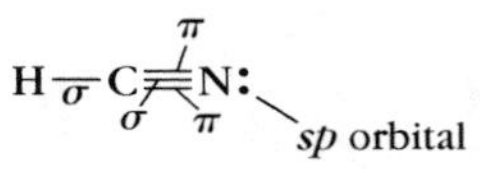

(b) The double-bonded carbon and nitrogen are both sp^2 hybridized. The sp^2 hybrid orbitals on C form sigma bonds to H and to N; the unhybridized *p* orbital on C forms a pi bond with the unhybridized *p* orbital on N. The sp^2 hybrid orbitals on N form sigma bonds to carbon and to H; the N lone pair is in the nonbonding sp^2 hybrid orbital.

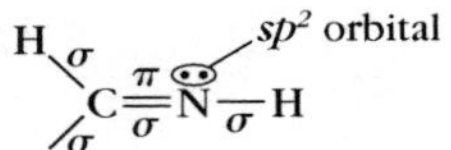

9.7 (a) $BFCl_2$ is a triangular planar molecule with polar B—F and B—Cl bonds. The molecule is polar because the B—F bond is more polar than the B—Cl bonds, resulting in a net dipole.

(b) NH_2Cl is a triangular pyramidal molecule with polar N—H bonds. (N—Cl is a nonpolar bond; N and Cl have the same electronegativity.) It is a polar molecule because the N—H dipoles do not cancel and produce a net dipole.

(c) SCl_2 is an angular polar molecule. The polar S—Cl bond dipoles do not cancel each other because they are not symmetrically arranged due to the two lone pairs on S.

9.8 (a) London forces between Kr atoms must be overcome for krypton to melt.

(b) The C—H covalent bonds in propane must be broken to form C and H atoms; the H atoms covalently bond to form H_2.

9.9 (a) London forces occur between N_2 molecules.

(b) CO_2 is nonpolar, and London forces occur between it and polar water molecules.

(c) London forces occur between the two molecules, but the principal intermolecular forces are the hydrogen bonds between the H on NH_3 with the lone pairs on the OH oxygen, and the hydrogen bonds between the H on the oxygen in CH_3OH and lone pair on nitrogen in NH_3.

Chapter 10

10.1 (a) Pressure in atm =

$$29.5 \text{ in Hg} \times \frac{1 \text{ atm}}{76.0 \text{ cm Hg}} \times \frac{2.54 \text{ cm}}{1 \text{ in}} = 0.986 \text{ atm}$$

(b) Pressure in mm Hg $= 29.5 \text{ in Hg} \times \frac{25.4 \text{ mm}}{1 \text{ in}} = 749 \text{ mm Hg}$

(c) Pressure in bar =

$$29.5 \text{ in Hg} \times \frac{1.013 \text{ bar}}{760 \text{ mm Hg}} \times \frac{25.4 \text{ mm}}{1 \text{ in}} = 0.999 \text{ bar}$$

(d) Pressure in kPa =

$$29.5 \text{ in Hg} \times \frac{101.3 \text{ kPa}}{760 \text{ mm Hg}} \times \frac{25.4 \text{ mm}}{1 \text{ in}} = 99.9 \text{ kPa}$$

10.2 The temperature remains constant, so the average energy of the gas molecules remains constant. If the volume is decreased, then the gas molecules must hit the walls more frequently, and the pressure is increased.

10.3 Volume of NO gas $= 1.0 \text{ L } O_2 \times \frac{2 \text{ L NO}}{1 \text{ L } O_2} = 2.0 \text{ L NO}$

10.4 $V = \frac{nRT}{P}$

$$= \frac{(2.64 \text{ mol})(0.0821 \text{ L atm mol}^{-1}\text{ K}^{-1})(304 \text{ K})}{0.640 \text{ atm}} = 103 \text{ L}$$

10.5 $V_2 = \frac{P_1V_1}{P_2} = \frac{(1.00 \text{ atm})(400. \text{ mL})}{0.750 \text{ atm}} = 533 \text{ mL}$

10.6 (a) $V_2 = \frac{P_1V_1T_2}{P_2T_1}$

$$= \frac{(710 \text{ mm Hg})(21 \text{ mL})(299.6 \text{ K})}{(740 \text{ mm Hg})(295.4 \text{ K})} = 20. \text{ mL}$$

(b) $V_2 = \frac{(21 \text{ mL})(299.6 \text{ K})}{(295.4 \text{ K})} = 21 \text{ mL}$

10.7 $\frac{10.0 \text{ g } NH_4NO_3}{80.043 \text{ g/mol}} = 0.1249 \text{ mol } NH_4NO_3$

$$0.1249 \text{ mol } NH_4NO_3 \times \frac{7 \text{ mol product gases}}{2 \text{ mol } NH_4NO_3}$$

$$= 0.437 \text{ mol produced}$$

$$V = \frac{(0.437 \text{ mol})(0.0821 \text{ L atm mol}^{-1}\text{ K}^{-1})(298 \text{ K})}{1 \text{ atm}} = 10.7 \text{ L}$$

10.8 $\frac{1.0 \text{ g LiOH}}{23.94 \text{ g/mol}} = 0.0418 \text{ mol LiOH}$

$$0.0418 \text{ mol LiOH} \times \frac{1 \text{ mol } CO_2}{2 \text{ mol LiOH}} = 0.0209 \text{ mol } CO_2$$

$$V = \frac{(0.0209 \text{ mol})(0.0821 \text{ L atm mol}^{-1}\text{ K}^{-1})(295 \text{ K})}{1 \text{ atm}}$$

$$= 0.51 \text{ L } CO_2$$

10.9 $V = \frac{4}{3}\pi r^3 = \frac{4}{3}\pi(10. \text{ cm})^3 = 4190 \text{ cm}^3 = 4.19 \text{ L}$

Amount of CO_2 gas, $n = \frac{PV}{RT}$

$$= \frac{(2.00 \text{ atm})(4.19 \text{ L})}{(0.0821 \text{ L atm mol}^{-1}\text{ K}^{-1})(293 \text{ K})} = 0.348 \text{ mol } CO_2$$

Mass of $NaHCO_3$ = 0.348 mol CO_2

$$\times \frac{1 \text{ mol } NaHCO_3}{1 \text{ mol } CO_2} \times \frac{84.00 \text{ g } NaHCO_3}{1 \text{ mol } NaHCO_3} = 29 \text{ g } NaHCO_3$$

10.10 Amount of gas, $n = \frac{PV}{RT}$

$$= \frac{(0.850 \text{ atm})(1.00 \text{ L})}{(0.0821 \text{ L atm mol}^{-1}\text{ K}^{-1})(293 \text{ K})} = 0.0353 \text{ mol}$$

Molar mass $= \frac{1.13 \text{ g}}{0.0353 \text{ mol}} = 32.0 \text{ g/mol}$

The gas is probably oxygen.

10.11 Amount of $N_2 = 7.0 \text{ g } N_2 \times \frac{1 \text{ mol } N_2}{28.10 \text{ g } N_2} = 0.25 \text{ mol } N_2$

Amount of $H_2 = 6.0 \text{ g } H_2 \times \frac{1 \text{ mol } H_2}{2.02 \text{ g } H_2} = 3.0 \text{ mol } H_2$

Total number of moles = 3.0 + 0.25 = 3.25 mol

$$X_{N_2} = \frac{0.25 \text{ mol}}{3.25 \text{ mol}} = 0.077 \qquad X_{H_2} = \frac{3.0 \text{ mol}}{3.25 \text{ mol}} = 0.92$$

$$P_{N_2} = \frac{(0.25 \text{ mol})(0.0821 \text{ L atm mol}^{-1}\text{ K}^{-1})(773 \text{ K})}{5.0 \text{ L}} = 3.2 \text{ atm}$$

$$P_{H_2} = \frac{(3.0 \text{ mol})(0.0821 \text{ L atm mol}^{-1}\text{ K}^{-1})(773 \text{ K})}{5.0 \text{ L}} = 38 \text{ atm}$$

10.12 For NO:

$$n = \frac{(1.0 \text{ atm})(4.0 \text{ L})}{(0.0821 \text{ L atm mol}^{-1}\text{ K}^{-1})(298 \text{ K})} = 0.163 \text{ mol NO}$$

For O_2:

$$n = \frac{(0.40 \text{ atm})(2.0 \text{ L})}{(0.0821 \text{ L atm mol}^{-1}\text{ K}^{-1})(298 \text{ K})} = 0.0327 \text{ mol } O_2$$

All the O_2 is used.

$$0.0327 \text{ mol } O_2 \times \frac{2 \text{ mol NO}}{1 \text{ mol } O_2} = 0.0654 \text{ mol NO used}$$

0.163 mol − 0.0654 mol = 0.0976 mol NO remains

$$0.0327 \text{ mol } O_2 \times \frac{2 \text{ mol } NO_2}{1 \text{ mol } O_2} = 0.0654 \text{ mol } NO_2 \text{ formed}$$

n_{total} = 0.0976 + 0.0654 = 0.163 mol of gas

$$P_{total} = \frac{nRT}{V} = \frac{(0.163 \text{ mol})(0.0821 \text{ L atm mol}^{-1}\text{ K}^{-1})(298 \text{ K})}{6.0 \text{ L}}$$

$$= 0.665 \text{ atm}$$

10.13 $P_{HCl} = P_{total} - P_{water} = 740 \text{ mm Hg} - 21 \text{ mm Hg} = 719 \text{ mm Hg}$

$$n = \frac{PV}{RT} = \frac{(719/760 \text{ atm})(0.260 \text{ L})}{(0.0821 \text{ L atm mol}^{-1}\text{ K}^{-1})(296 \text{ K})}$$

$$= 0.0101 \text{ mol } H_2$$

$$0.0101 \text{ mol} \times 2.0158 \text{ g/mol} = 0.0204 \text{ g} = 20.4 \text{ mg } H_2$$

10.14 $P = \frac{nRT}{V} = \frac{(5.00 \text{ mol})(0.0821 \text{ L atm mol}^{-1}\text{ K}^{-1})(273 \text{ K})}{20.0 \text{ L}}$

$$= 5.60 \text{ atm}$$

$$P = \left(\frac{nRT}{V - nb}\right) - \left(\frac{n^2a}{V^2}\right)$$

$$P = \left(\frac{(5.00 \text{ mol})(0.0821 \text{ L atm mol}^{-1}\text{ K}^{-1})(273 \text{ K})}{(20.0 \text{ L}) - (5.00 \text{ mol})(0.0428 \text{ L/mol})}\right)$$

$$- \left(\frac{(5.00 \text{ mol})^2(2.25 \text{ L}^2 \text{ atm/mol}^2)}{(20.0 \text{ L})^2}\right) = 5.523 \text{ atm}$$

Percentage difference in pressure $= \frac{5.60 \text{ atm} - 5.52 \text{ atm}}{5.60 \text{ atm}} \times 100\%$

$= 1.43\%$

Chapter 11

11.1 $\ln\left(\frac{P_2}{143.0 \text{ torr}}\right) = \frac{3.21 \times 10^4 \text{ J/mol}}{8.31 \text{ J mol}^{-1}\text{ K}^{-1}}\left[\frac{1}{303.15 \text{ K}} - \frac{1}{333.15 \text{ K}}\right]$

$$\ln\left(\frac{P_2}{143.0 \text{ torr}}\right) = 1.1473$$

$$\ln P_2 = -1.1473 - \ln(143.0)$$

$$P_2 = 450. \text{ torr}$$

11.2 From Table 11.2, $\Delta H_{vap}(Br_2)$ is 29.54 kJ/mol at its normal boiling point.

So 29.54 kJ/mol × 0.500 mol = 14.77 kJ.

11.3 Heat $= 2.5 \times 10^{10} \text{ kg } H_2O \times \frac{10^3 \text{ g}}{1 \text{ kg}} \times \frac{1 \text{ mol } H_2O}{18.02 \text{ g } H_2O}$

$$\times \frac{-44.0 \text{ kJ}}{\text{mol}} = -6.10 \times 10^{13} \text{ kJ}$$

This process is exothermic as water vapor condenses, forming rain.

11.4 (21.95)/2 = 10.98 kJ

11.5 The gas phase.

11.6 (a) Solid decane is a molecular solid.

(b) Solid $MgCl_2$ is composed of Mg^{2+} and Cl^- ions and is an ionic solid.

11.7 There are two atoms per bcc unit cell. The diagonal of the bcc unit cell is four times the radius of the atoms in the unit cell, so, solving for the edge,

$$\text{Edge} = \frac{4 \times 144 \text{ pm}}{\sqrt{3}} = 333 \text{ pm}$$

$$\text{Density} = \frac{\text{mass}}{\text{volume}}$$

$$= \frac{(2 \text{ Au atoms})(196.97 \text{ g Au}/6.022 \times 10^{23} \text{ Au atoms})}{[(333 \text{ pm})(1 \text{ m}/10^{12} \text{ pm})(10^2 \text{ cm/m})]^3}$$

$$= 17.7 \text{ g/cm}^3$$

11.8 The edge of the KCl unit cell would be 2 × 152 pm + 2 × 167 pm = 638 pm.
The unit cell of KCl is larger than that of NaCl.

$$\text{Volume of the unit cell} = (638 \text{ pm})^3$$

$$= 2.60 \times 10^{18} \text{ pm}^3 \times \left(\frac{10^{-10} \text{ cm}}{\text{pm}}\right)^3$$

$$= 2.60 \times 10^{-22} \text{ cm}^3$$

$$D = \frac{m}{V}$$

$$= \frac{(4 \text{ formula units KCl}) \times 74.55 \text{ g KCl}/6.022 \times 10^{23} \text{ formula units}}{2.60 \times 10^{-22} \text{ cm}^3}$$

$$D = 1.91 \text{ g/cm}^3$$

11.9 Energy transfer required

$$= 1.45 \text{ g Al} \times \frac{1 \text{ mol Al}}{26.98 \text{ g Al}} \times \frac{10.7 \text{ kJ}}{\text{mol}} = 0.575 \text{ kJ}$$

Chapter 12

12.1 The balanced combustion reaction for methanol vapor is

$$CH_3OH(g) + \tfrac{3}{2} O_2(g) \longrightarrow CO_2(g) + 2 H_2O(g)$$

Using Hess's law, we see that the heat of combustion of methanol vapor is

$$\Delta H_{comb} = [\Delta H_f^\circ CO_2(g)] + 2[\Delta H_f^\circ H_2O(g)] - 1[\Delta H_f^\circ CH_3OH(g)]$$

$$= -393.509 \text{ kJ/mol} + 2(-241.818 \text{ kJ/mol}) - (-200.66 \text{ kJ/mol})$$

$$= -676.49 \text{ kJ/mol}$$

For methanol,

$$-676.49 \text{ kJ/mol}\left(\frac{1 \text{ mol}}{32.04 \text{ g}}\right)\left(\frac{0.791 \text{ g}}{1 \text{ mL}}\right)\left(\frac{1000 \text{ mL}}{\text{L}}\right)$$

$$= -1.67 \times 10^4 \text{ kJ/L}$$

Methanol yields less energy per liter than ethanol.

12.2 (a) $C_8H_{18}(\ell) + \frac{25}{2} O_2(g) \rightarrow 8 CO_2(g) + 9 H_2O(g)$

$$\Delta H^\circ = [8(-393.509) + 9(-241.818) - (-249.952)] \text{ kJ}$$

$$= -5074.48 \text{ kJ}$$

$$\frac{5074.48 \text{ kJ}}{1 \text{ mol } C_8H_{18}} \times \frac{1 \text{ mol}}{114.23 \text{ g}} = 44.423 \text{ kJ/g } C_8H_{18}$$

$$44.423 \text{ kJ/g } C_7H_{18} \times 0.699 \text{ g/mL} \times \frac{10^3 \text{ mL}}{\text{L}}$$

$$= 3.11 \times 10^4 \text{ kJ/L } C_8H_{18}$$

(b) $N_2H_4(\ell) + O_2(g) \rightarrow N_2(g) + 2 H_2O(g)$

$$\Delta H^\circ = [2(-241.818) - 50.63] \text{ kJ} = -534.26 \text{ kJ}$$

$$\frac{534.26 \text{ kJ}}{1 \text{ mol } N_2H_4} \times \frac{1 \text{ mol}}{32.045 \text{ g}} = 16.672 \text{ kJ/g } N_2H_4$$

$$16.672 \text{ kJ/g } N_2H_4 \times 1004 \text{ g/L} = 1.67 \times 10^4 \text{ kJ/L } N_2H_4$$

(c) $C_6H_{12}O_6(g) + 6 O_2(g) \rightarrow 6 CO_2(g) + 6 H_2O(g)$

$$\Delta H^\circ = [6(-393.509) + 6(-241.818) - (-1274.4)] \text{ kJ}$$

$$= -2537.56 \text{ kJ}$$

$$\frac{2537.56 \text{ kJ}}{\text{mol } C_6H_{12}O_6} \times \frac{1 \text{ mol}}{180.158 \text{ g}} = 14.085 \text{ kJ/g}$$

$$14.085 \text{ kJ/g} \times 1560 \text{ g/L} = 2.20 \times 10^4 \text{ kJ/L}$$

12.3 $\text{Energy} = 4.2 \times 10^9 \text{ t coal} \times \frac{26.4 \times 10^9 \text{ J}}{1 \text{ t coal}} = 1.1 \times 10^{20} \text{ J}$

$$\text{ft}^3 \text{ natural gas} = 1.1 \times 10^{20} \text{ J} \times \frac{1 \text{ ft}^3 \text{ natural gas}}{1.055 \times 10^6 \text{ J}}$$

$$= 1.0 \times 10^{14} \text{ ft}^3 \text{ natural gas}$$

12.4 The chiral centers are identified by an asterisk in the structural formula. Each of those carbon atoms has four different groups or atoms attached to it.

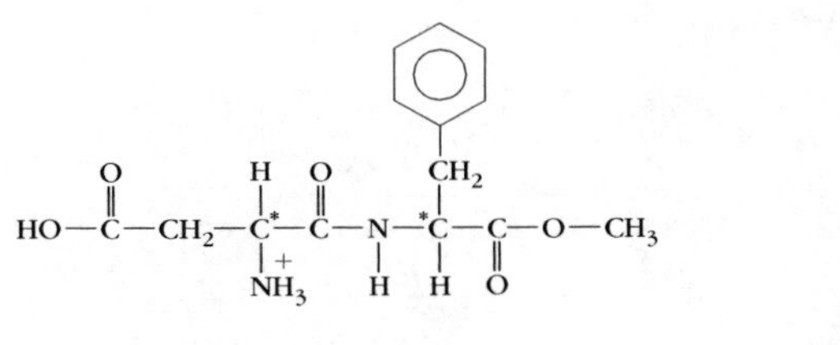

12.5 $CO(g) + 2 H_2(g) \rightarrow CH_3OH(g)$

$$\Delta H^\circ = [(1 \text{ mol C}\equiv\text{O})(1073 \text{ kJ/mol}) + (2 \text{ mol H—H})(436 \text{ kJ/mol})] - [(3 \text{ mol C—H})(416 \text{ kJ/mol})] + (1 \text{ mol C—O})(336 \text{ kJ/mol}) + (1 \text{ mol O—H})(467 \text{ kJ/mol})$$

$$= (1945 \text{ kJ}) - (2051 \text{ kJ}) = -106 \text{ kJ}$$

12.6 (a) The first oxidation product of $CH_3CH_2CH_2OH$ is the aldehyde.

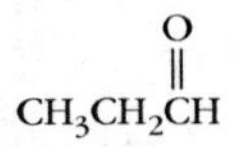

The second oxidation product of $CH_3CH_2CH_2OH$ is the acid.

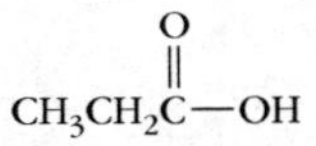

(b) The oxidation product of this secondary alcohol is the ketone.

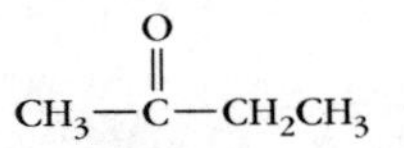

12.7 In this case, stearic acid would be on carbon 2 of glycerol where it would be flanked by oleic acids at carbons 1 and 3 of glycerol. See Problem-Solving Example 12.7 (p. 572) for the structural formulas of stearic and oleic acids.

12.8
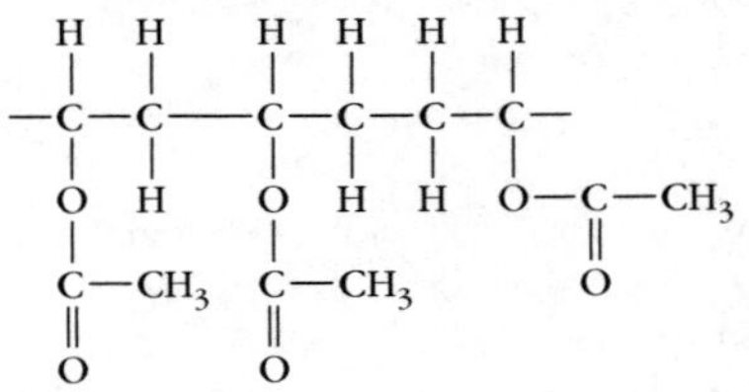

12.9 (a)
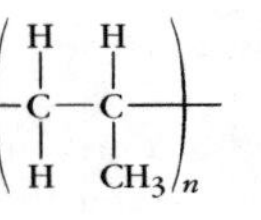

(b)
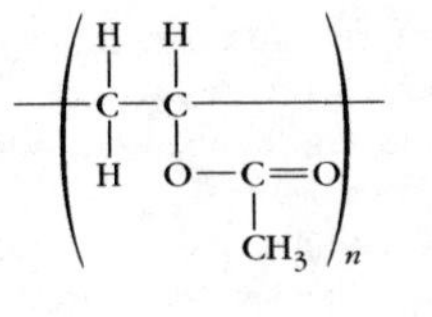

(c)
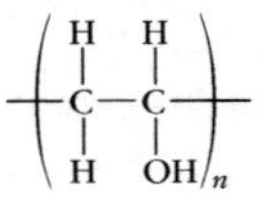

12.10 MM vinylchloride, C_2H_3Cl, is 62.5 g/mol.

$$\text{Degree of polymerization} = 1.50 \times 10^5 \text{ g} \times \frac{1 \text{ monomer unit}}{62.5 \text{ g}}$$
$$= 2.40 \times 10^3 \text{ monomer units}$$

12.11 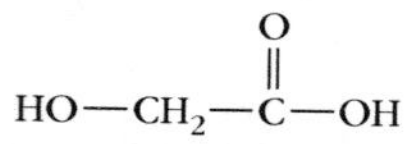

12.12 Twelve moles of water

12.13 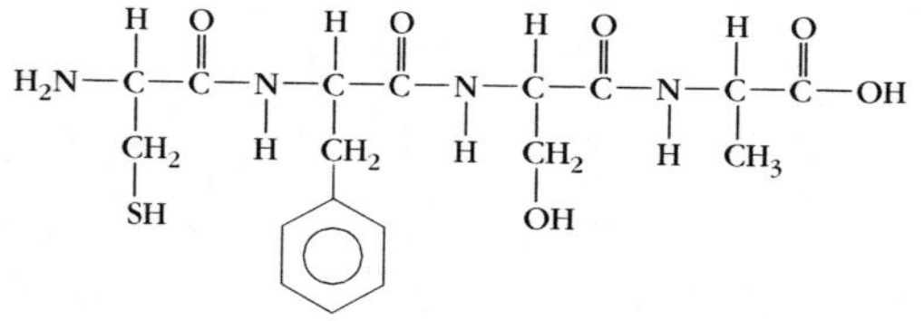

Chapter 13

13.1 (a) $\text{Rate} = \frac{-\Delta[\text{Cv}^+]}{\Delta t} = 1.27 \times 10^{-6} \text{ mol L}^{-1} \text{ s}^{-1}$

$$\Delta t = \frac{-\Delta[\text{Cv}^+]}{1.27 \times 10^{-6} \text{ mol L}^{-1} \text{ s}^{-1}}$$
$$= \frac{(4.30 \times 10^{-5} - 3.96 \times 10^{-5}) \text{ mol/L}}{1.27 \times 10^{-6} \text{ mol L}^{-1} \text{ s}^{-1}}$$
$$= 2.7 \text{ s}$$

(b) No. The rate of reaction depends on the concentration of Cv^+ and, therefore, becomes slower as the reaction progresses. Therefore, the method used in part (a) works only over a small range of concentrations.

13.2 (a) The balanced chemical equation shows that for every mole of O_2 consumed two moles of N_2O_5 are produced. Therefore, the rate of formation of N_2O_5 is twice the rate of disappearance of O_2.
(b) Four moles of NO_2 are consumed for every mole of O_2 consumed. Therefore, if O_2 is consumed at the rate of 0.0037 mol $\text{L}^{-1} \text{ s}^{-1}$ the rate of disappearance of NO_2 is four times this rate.

$$4 \times (0.0037 \text{ mol L}^{-1} \text{ s}^{-1}) = 0.015 \text{ mol L}^{-1} \text{ s}^{-1}$$

13.3 (a) The effect of $[\text{OH}^-]$ on the rate of reaction cannot be determined, because the $[\text{OH}^-]$ is the same in all three experiments.

(b) $\text{Rate} = k[\text{Cv}^+]$

(c) $k_1 = \frac{\text{rate}}{[\text{Cv}^+]} = \frac{1.3 \times 10^{-6} \text{ mol L}^{-1} \text{ s}^{-1}}{4.3 \times 10^{-5} \text{ mol/L}}$
$= 3.0 \times 10^{-2} \text{ s}^{-1}$
$k_2 = 3.0 \times 10^{-2} \text{ s}^{-1}$
$k_3 = 3.0 \times 10^{-2} \text{ s}^{-1}$
$k = \frac{k_1 + k_2 + k_3}{3} = 3.0 \times 10^{-2} \text{ s}^{-1}$

(d) $\text{Rate} = k[\text{Cv}^+]$
$= (3.0 \times 10^{-2} \text{ s}^{-1})(0.00045 \text{ mol/L})$
$= 1.4 \times 10^{-5} \text{ mol L}^{-1} \text{ s}^{-1}$

(e) $\text{Rate} = (3.0 \times 10^{-2} \text{ s}^{-1})(0.5 \times 0.00045 \text{ mol/L})$
$= 6.8 \times 10^{-6} \text{ mol L}^{-1} \text{ s}^{-1}$

13.4 (a) The order of the reaction with respect to each chemical is the exponent associated with the concentration of that chemical. So the reaction is second-order with respect to NO and it is first-order with respect to Cl_2.
(b) Tripling the concentration of NO will make the reaction go $3^2 = 9$ times faster but decreasing the concentration of Cl_2 by a factor of 8 will make the reaction go at 1/8 the initial rate. If these two changes are made simultaneously the relevant factor will be 9/8 = 1.13, so the reaction will occur 13% faster than it did under the initial conditions.

13.5 Make three plots of the data.

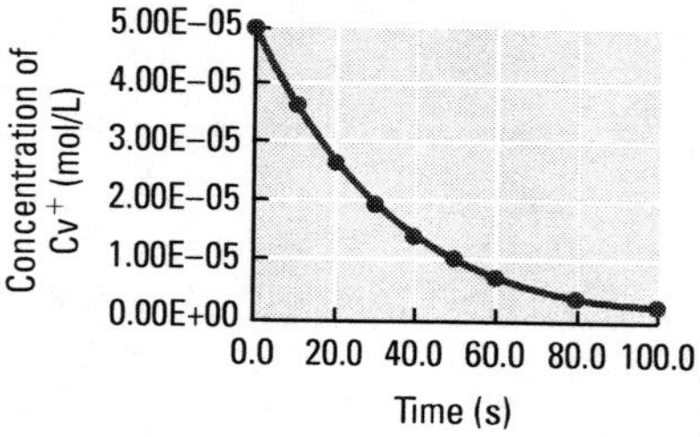

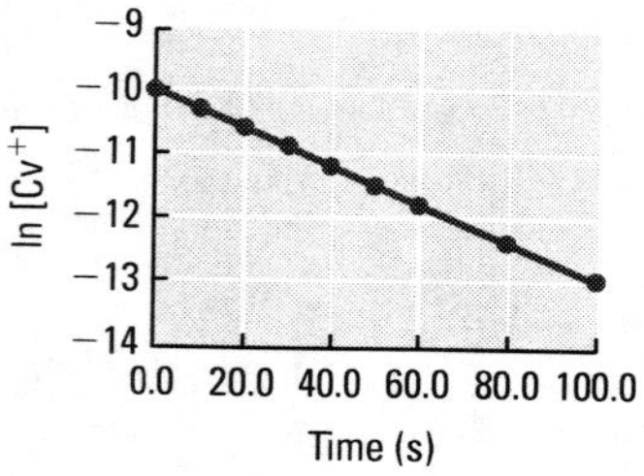

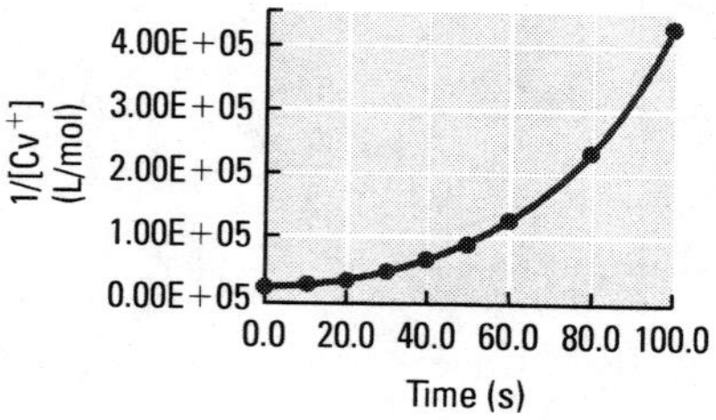

The first-order plot is a straight line and the other plots are curved, so the reaction is first-order. The slope of the first-order plot is -0.0307 s^{-1}, so $k = -\text{slope} = 0.031 \text{ s}^{-1}$.

13.6 Use the integrated first-order rate law from Table 13.2.
$\ln[\text{A}]_t = -kt + \ln[\text{A}]_0$
$\ln\frac{[\text{A}]_t}{[\text{A}]_0} = -kt$
$t = -\frac{1}{k}\ln\frac{[\text{A}]_t}{[\text{A}]_0} = -\left(\frac{1}{3.43 \times 10^{-2} \text{ d}^{-1}}\right)\ln\left(\frac{0.1}{1.0}\right)$
$= -(29.15 \text{ d})(-2.303) = 67.1 \text{ d}$

13.7 In Figure 13.3 the $[\text{Cv}^+]$ falls from 5.00×10^{-5} M to 2.5×10^{-5} M in 23 s. The $[\text{Cv}^+]$ falls from 2.5×10^{-5} M to 1.25×10^{-5} M between 23 s and 46 s. The two times are equal, so $t_{1/2} = 23$ s.

$$k = \frac{0.693}{t_{1/2}} = \frac{0.693}{23 \text{ s}} = 3.0 \times 10^{-2} \text{ s}^{-1}$$

13.8 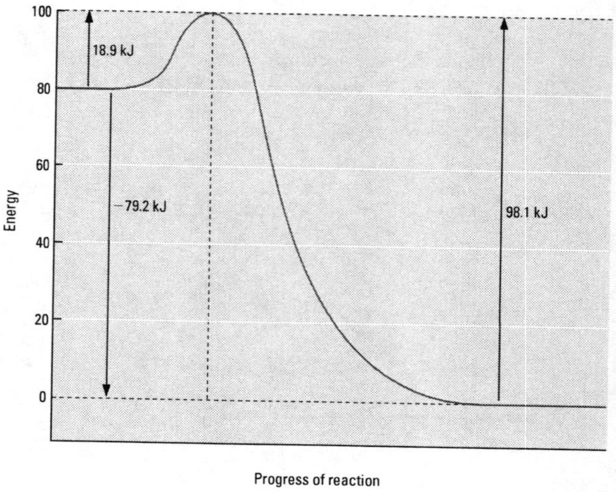

$$Cl_2(g) + 2\,NO(g) \rightarrow 2\,NOCl(g)$$

Since the energy of the products is less than that of reactants, the reaction is exothermic.

13.9 Obtain the value $E_a = 76.3$ kJ/mol from the discussion and analysis of the data in Figure 13.10 and the value $k = 4.18 \times 10^{-5}$ L mol^{-1} s^{-1} at 273 K from Table 13.3.

$$\frac{k_1}{k_2} = e^{\left[\frac{E_a}{R}\left(\frac{1}{T_2} - \frac{1}{T_1}\right)\right]} = e^{\left[\frac{76{,}300\ \text{J/mol}}{8.314\ \text{J K}^{-1}\ \text{mol}^{-1}}\left(\frac{1}{348\ \text{K}} - \frac{1}{273\ \text{K}}\right)\right]}$$

$$= e^{-7.245} = 7.138 \times 10^{-4}$$

$$k_2 = \frac{k_1}{7.138 \times 10^{-4}} = \frac{4.18 \times 10^{-5}\ \text{L mol}^{-1}\ \text{s}^{-1}}{7.138 \times 10^{-4}}$$

$$= 5.86 \times 10^{-2}\ \text{L mol}^{-1}\ \text{s}^{-1}$$

13.10 (a) $2\,NH_3(aq) + OCl^-(aq) \rightarrow N_2H_4(aq) + Cl^-(aq) + H_2O(\ell)$

(b) Step 1

(c) NH_2Cl, OH^-, $N_2H_5^+$

(d) Rate = rate of step 1 = $k\,[NH_3][OCl^-]$

13.11 Choose the structure that is most similar to the structure of *p*-aminobenzoic acid. An enzyme might be inhibited by this molecule, which could fit the active site but not be converted to a product similar to folic acid. Or, the molecule might react in an enzyme-catalyzed process, producing a product whose biological function was different from folic acid. The best choice is

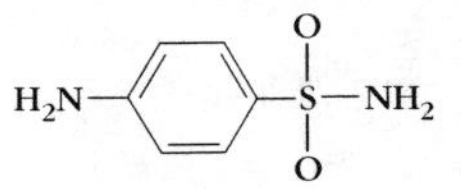

Chapter 14

14.1 (a) $K_c = [CO_2(g)]$ (b) $K_c = \frac{[H_2]}{[HCl]}$

(c) $K_c = \frac{[CO][H_2]^3}{[CH_4][H_2O]}$ (d) $K_c = \frac{[HCN][OH^-]}{[CN^-]}$

14.2 $K_c = K_{c_1} \times K_{c_2} = (4.2 \times 10^{-7})(4.8 \times 10^{-11})$

$= 2.0 \times 10^{-17}$

14.3 $[CH_3COO^-] = \frac{2.96}{100} \times 0.0200\ \text{mol/L} = 5.92 \times 10^{-4}$ M

$[H_3O^+] = 5.92 \times 10^{-4}$ M

$[CH_3\,COOH] = \frac{100 - 2.96}{100} \times 0.0200$ mol/L

$= 1.94 \times 10^{-2}$ M

$$K_c = \frac{[H_3O^+][CH_3COO^-]}{[CH_3COOH]} = \frac{(5.92 \times 10^{-4})(5.92 \times 10^{-4})}{1.94 \times 10^{-2}}$$

$= 1.81 \times 10^{-5}$

The result agrees with the value in Table 14.1.

14.4 (a) $K_c(\text{AgCl}) = 1.8 \times 10^{-10}$; $K_c(\text{AgI}) = 1.5 \times 10^{-16}$. Because $K_c(\text{AgI}) < K_c(\text{AgCl})$, the concentration of silver ions is larger in the beaker of AgCl.

(b) Unless all of the solid AgCl or AgI dissolves (which would mean that there was no equilibrium reaction), the concentrations at equilibrium are independent of the volume.

14.5 $$Q = \frac{(\text{conc. } SO_3)^2}{(\text{conc. } SO_2)^2(\text{conc. } O_2)}$$

$$= \frac{(0.184)^2}{(0.102 \times 2)^2(0.0132)} = 61.6$$

Since $Q < K_c$, the forward reaction should occur.

14.6

	$AuI(s) \rightleftharpoons$	$Au^+(aq)$ +	$I^-(aq)$
Initial concentration (mol/L)		0	0
Change as reaction occurs (mol/L)		$+x$	$+x$
Equilibrium concentration (mol/L)		x	x

$K_c = 1.6 \times 10^{-23} = [Au^+][I^-] = x^2$

$x = \sqrt{1.6 \times 10^{-23}} = 4.0 \times 10^{-12} = [Au^+] = [I^-]$

14.7 The reaction is the reverse of the one in Table 14.1, so

$$K_c = \frac{1}{1.7 \times 10^2} = 5.9 \times 10^{-3}$$

$$Q = \frac{(\text{conc. } NO_2)^2}{(\text{conc. } N_2O_4)} = \frac{\left(\frac{0.500\ \text{mol}}{4.00\ \text{L}}\right)^2}{\left(\frac{1.00\ \text{mol}}{4.00\ \text{L}}\right)} = 6.25 \times 10^{-2}$$

Because $Q > K_c$, the reaction should go in the reverse direction. Therefore, let x be the change in concentration of N_2O_4, giving the ICE table:

	N_2O_4 $\rightleftharpoons$	$2\,NO_2$
Initial concentration (mol/L)	$\frac{1.00}{4.00} = 0.250$	$\frac{0.500}{4.00} = 0.125$
Change as reaction occurs (mol/L)	x	$-2x$
Equilibrium concentration (mol/L)	$0.250 + x$	$0.125 - 2x$

$$K_c = 5.9 \times 10^{-3} = \frac{(0.125 - 2x)^2}{0.250 + x}$$

$$= \frac{(1.56 \times 10^{-2}) - 0.500x + 4x^2}{0.250 - x}$$

$(1.48 \times 10^{-3}) + (5.9 \times 10^{-3})x$

$= (1.56 \times 10^{-2}) - 0.500x + 4x^2$

$4x^2 - 0.5059x + (1.412 \times 10^{-2}) = 0$

$$x = \frac{-(-0.5059) \pm \sqrt{(-0.5059)^2 - 4 \times 4 \times 1.412 \times 10^{-2}}}{2 \times 4}$$

$$= \frac{0.5059 \pm \sqrt{3.001 \times 10^{-2}}}{8}$$

$$= \frac{0.5059 \pm 0.1732}{8}$$

$x = 8.49 \times 10^{-2}$ or $x = 4.16 \times 10^{-2}$

If $x = 8.49 \times 10^{-2}$, then $[N_2O_4] = 0.250 + x = 0.335$ and $[NO_2] = 0.125 - 2x = 0.125 - (2 \times 7.86 \times 10^{-2}) = -0.0448$. A negative concentration is impossible, so x must be 4.16×10^{-2}. Then

$[N_2O_4] = 0.250 + 0.0416 = 0.292$

$[NO_2] = 0.125 - (2 \times 0.0416) = 0.0418$

As predicted by Q, the reverse reaction has occurred, and the concentration of N_2O_4 has increased.

14.8 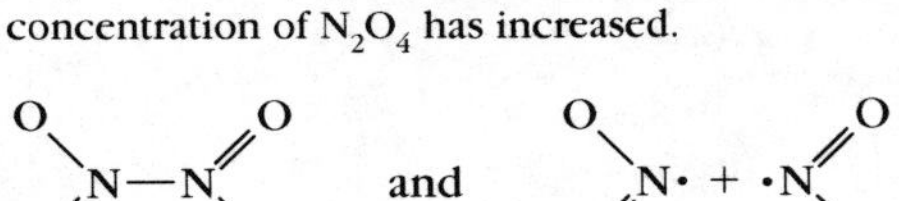

Because a bond is broken and because bond breaking is always endothermic (← **p. 241**), the reaction must be endothermic. Increasing temperature shifts the equilibrium in the endothermic direction. Figure 14.3 shows that at a higher temperature there is a greater concentration of brown NO_2.

14.9 (a) There are more moles of gas phase reactants than products, so entropy favors the reactants.

(b) Data from Appendix J show that $\Delta H° = -168.66$ kJ. The reaction is exothermic, so the energy effect favors the products.

(c) As T increases the reaction shifts in the endothermic direction, which is toward reactants. The entropy effect also becomes more important at high T, and it favors reactants. There is a greater concentration of SO_2 at low temperature.

Chapter 15

15.1 (a) Ethylene glycol molecules are polar and attracted to each other by dipole-dipole attractions and hydrogen bonding. They will not dissolve in gasoline, a nonpolar substance.
(b) Molecular iodine and carbon tetrachloride are nonpolar; therefore iodine should dissolve readily in carbon tetrachloride.
(c) Motor oil contains a mixture of nonpolar hydrocarbons that will dissolve in carbon tetrachloride, a nonpolar solvent.

15.2 The —OH groups attached to the ring and to the side chain of vitamin C hydrogen bond to water molecules. The oxygen atoms in the ring also form hydrogen bonds to water.

15.3 Use Henry's law, the Henry's law constant, and the fact that air is only 21 mol percent oxygen, a 0.21 mole fraction of oxygen.

$$\text{Pressure of } O_2 = (1.0\text{ atm})\left(\frac{760\text{ mm Hg}}{1\text{ atm}}\right)(0.21)$$
$$= 160.\text{ mm Hg}$$
$$S_g = k_H P_g = \left(1.66 \times 10^{-6}\,\frac{\text{mol/L}}{\text{mm Hg}}\right)(160.\text{ mm Hg})$$
$$= 2.66 \times 10^{-4}\text{ mol/L}$$
$$(2.66 \times 10^{-4}\text{ mol/L})\left(\frac{32.00\text{ g } O_2}{1\text{ mol } O_2}\right) = 0.0085\text{ g/L or } 8.5\text{ mg/L}$$

15.4 Total mass is 750 + 21.5 = 771.5 g.

$$\text{Weight percent glucose} = \frac{21.5\text{ g}}{771.5\text{ g}} \times 100\% = 2.79\%$$

15.5 $$\left(\frac{30\text{ g Se}}{10^9\text{ g } H_2O}\right)\left(\frac{1\text{ g } H_2O}{1\text{ mL } H_2O}\right)\left(\frac{10^6\,\mu\text{g Se}}{1\text{ g Se}}\right)$$
$$= 3.0 \times 10^{-2}\,\mu\text{g Se/mL } H_2O$$

Se in 100 mL of water

$$= \left(\frac{3.0 \times 10^{-2}\mu\text{g Se}}{1\text{ mL } H_2O}\right)(100\text{ mL } H_2O) = 3.0\,\mu\text{g Se}$$

15.6 (a) $$(0.250\text{ L})\left(\frac{0.0750\text{ mol NaBr}}{1\text{ L}}\right)\left(\frac{102.9\text{ g NaBr}}{1\text{ mol NaBr}}\right) = 1.93\text{ g NaBr}$$

(b) $$V_c = \frac{M_d \times V_d}{M_c} = \frac{(0.00150\text{ M})(0.500\text{ L})}{0.0750\text{ M}}$$
$$= 0.0100\text{ L} = 10.0\text{ mL}$$

15.7 (a) $$\left(\frac{0.0556\text{ mol Mg}^{2+}}{1\text{ L}}\right)\left(\frac{24.3\text{ g Mg}^{2+}}{1\text{ mol Mg}^{2+}}\right)$$
$$\times\left(\frac{1.35\text{ g Mg}^{2+}}{1.03 \times 10^{-3}\text{ g solution}}\right) = 0.00131\,\frac{\text{g Mg}^{2+}}{\text{g solution}}$$

(b) $0.00131 \times 10^6\text{ ppm} = 1310\text{ ppm}$

15.8 $$\text{Molarity } H_2O_2 = \frac{\text{moles } H_2O_2}{\text{L solution}}$$
$$= \frac{30.0\text{ g } H_2O_2}{100.\text{ g solution}} \times \frac{1.11\text{ g solution}}{1\text{ mL solution}}$$
$$\times \frac{10^3\text{ mL solution}}{1\text{ L solution}} \times \frac{1\text{ mol } H_2O_2}{34.0\text{ g } H_2O_2}$$
$$= \frac{3.33 \times 10^4\text{ mol } H_2O_2}{3.40 \times 10^3\text{ L}} = 9.79\text{ M}$$

15.9 $$\text{Molarity, M} = \left(\frac{20\text{ g NaCl}}{100\text{ g solution}}\right)\left(\frac{1.148\text{ g solution}}{1\text{ mL solution}}\right)$$
$$\times\left(\frac{1\text{ mol NaCl}}{58.5\text{ g NaCl}}\right)\left(\frac{10^3\text{ mL}}{1\text{ L}}\right)$$
$$= 3.9\text{ mol NaCl/L}$$
$$\text{Molality, } m = \left(\frac{20\text{ g NaCl}}{0.0080\text{ kg } H_2O}\right)\left(\frac{1\text{ mol NaCl}}{58.5\text{ g NaCl}}\right)$$
$$= 4.3\text{ mol NaCl/kg } H_2O$$

15.10 $$P_{\text{water}} = (X_{\text{water}})(P^\circ_{\text{water}})$$
$$291.2\text{ mm Hg} = (X_{\text{water}})(355.1\text{ mm Hg})$$
$$X_{\text{water}} = \frac{291.2\text{ mm Hg}}{355.1\text{ mm Hg}} = 0.8201$$
$$X_{\text{urea}} = 1.000 - X_{\text{water}} = 1.000 - 0.8201 = 0.1799$$

15.11 $$\text{Molality of solution} = \left(\frac{1.20\text{ kg ethylene glycol}}{6.50\text{ kg } H_2O}\right)$$
$$\left(\frac{1000\text{ g}}{\text{kg}}\right)\left(\frac{1\text{ mol ethylene glycol}}{62.068\text{ g ethylene glycol}}\right) = 2.97\text{ mol/kg}$$

Next, calculate the freezing point depression of a 2.97 mol/kg solution.

$$\Delta T_f = (1.86\text{ °C kg mol}^{-1})(2.97\text{ mol/kg}) = 5.52\text{ °C}$$

This solution will freeze at −5.52 °C, so this quantity of ethylene glycol will not protect the 6.5 kg water in the tank if the temperature drops to −25 °C.

15.12 F.P. benzene = 5.50 °C; ΔT_f = 5.50 °C − 5.15 °C = 0.35 °C.

$$\text{Molality} = \frac{\Delta T_f}{K_f} = \frac{0.35\text{ °C}}{5.10\text{ °C kg mol}^{-1}} = 0.0686\text{ mol/kg}$$
$$\frac{0.0686\text{ mol solute}}{1\text{ kg benzene}} \times 0.0500\text{ kg benzene} = 0.00343\text{ mol solute}$$
$$\frac{0.180\text{ g solute}}{0.00343\text{ mol solute}} = 52.5\text{ g/mol}$$

15.13 Hemoglobin is a molecular substance so the factor *i* is 1.

$$c = \frac{\Pi}{RTi} = \frac{1.8 \times 10^{-3}\text{ atm}}{(0.0821\text{ L atm mol}^{-1}\text{ K}^{-1})(298\text{ K})(1)}$$
$$= 7.36 \times 10^{-5}\text{ mol/L}$$
$$\text{MM} = \frac{5.0\text{ g}}{7.36 \times 10^{-5}\text{ mol}} = 6.8 \times 10^4\text{ g/mol}$$

Chapter 16

16.1

Acid	Its Conjugate Base	Base	Its Conjugate Acid
$H_2PO_4^-$	HPO_4^{2-}	PO_4^{3-}	HPO_4^{2-}
H_2	H^-	NH_2^-	NH_3
HSO_3^-	SO_3^{2-}	ClO_4^-	$HClO_4$
HF	F^-	Br^-	HBr

16.2 $[OH^-] = 3.0 \times 10^{-8}$ M;

$$[H_3O^+] = \frac{1.0 \times 10^{-14}}{3.0 \times 10^{-8}} = 3.3 \times 10^{-7}\text{ M}$$

Therefore, the solution whose $[H_3O^+]$ is 5.0×10^{-4} M is more acidic.

16.3 The 2.0×10^{-5} M H^+ solution is more acidic.

16.4 In a 0.040 M solution of NaOH, the $[OH^-]$ is 0.040 because the NaOH is 100% dissociated; pH = 12.60.

16.5 (a) $[H_3O^+] = 10^{-7.90} = 1.3 \times 10^{-8}$ M
(b) A pH of 7.90 is basic.

16.6 (a) $HN_3(aq) \rightleftharpoons H^+(aq) + N_3^-(aq)$ $$K_a = \frac{[H^+][N_3^-]}{[HN_3]}$$

(b) $HCOOH(aq) \rightleftharpoons H^+(aq) + HCOO^-(aq)$ $$K_a = \frac{[H^+][HCOO^-]}{[HCOOH]}$$

(c) $HClO_2(aq) \rightleftharpoons H^+(aq) + ClO_2^-(aq)$ $$K_a = \frac{[H^+][ClO_2^-]}{[HClO_2]}$$

16.7 (a) $CH_3NH_2(aq) + H_2O(\ell) \rightleftharpoons CH_3NH_3^+(aq) + OH^-(aq)$

$$K_b = \frac{[CH_3NH_3^+][OH^-]}{[CH_3NH_2]}$$

(b) $PH_3(aq) + H_2O(\ell) \rightleftharpoons PH_4^+(aq) + OH^-(aq)$

$$K_b = \frac{[PH_4^+][OH^-]}{[PH_3]}$$

(c) $NO_2^-(aq) + H_2O(\ell) \rightleftharpoons HNO_2(aq) + OH^-(aq)$

$$K_b = \frac{[HNO_2][OH^-]}{[NO_2^-]}$$

16.8 Setting up a small table for lactic acid, HLa:

	$HLa + H_2O \rightleftharpoons$	H_3O^+	$+ La^-$
Initial concentration (mol/L)	0.10	10^{-7}	0
Concentration change due to reaction (mol/L)	$-x$	$+x$	$+x$
Equilibrium concentration (mol/L)	$0.10 - x$	x	x

But $x = 10^{-2.43} = 3.7 \times 10^{-3}$ because $x = [H_3O^+]$. Substituting in the K_a expression,

$$K_a = \frac{[H_3O^+][La^-]}{[HLa]} = \frac{(3.7 \times 10^{-3})^2}{0.10 - (3.7 \times 10^{-3})}$$

$$= \frac{1.4 \times 10^{-5}}{0.1} = 1.4 \times 10^{-4}$$

Lactic acid is a stronger acid than propionic acid, with a K_a of 1.4×10^{-5}.

16.9 (a) Using the same methods as shown in the example,

$$\frac{x^2}{0.015} = 1.9 \times 10^{-5}$$

Solving for x, which is $[H_3O^+]$, we get

$$x = \sqrt{(1.9 \times 10^{-5})(0.015)} = 5.3 \times 10^{-4} = [H_3O^+].$$

So the pH of this solution is $-\log(5.3 \times 10^{-4}) = 3.28$.

(b) $$\% \text{ ionization} = \frac{[H_3O^+]}{[HN_3]_{initial}} \times 100\% = \frac{5.4 \times 10^{-4}}{0.015} \times 100\% = 3.6\%$$

16.10 In such cases use the K_b expression and value to calculate $[OH^-]$ and then pOH from $[OH^-]$. Calculate pH from 14 − pOH.

$$C_6H_{11}NH_2(aq) + H_2O(\ell) \rightleftharpoons C_6H_{11}NH_3^+(aq) + OH^-(aq)$$

$$K_b = \frac{[C_6H_{11}NH_3^+][OH^-]}{[C_6H_{11}NH_2]} = 4.6 \times 10^{-4}$$

$$K_b = \frac{[C_6H_{11}NH_3^+][OH^-]}{[C_6H_{11}NH_2]} = \frac{x^2}{0.015 - x} = 4.6 \times 10^{-4}$$

$$x^2 = (0.015 - x)(4.6 \times 10^{-4}) = (6.9 \times 10^{-6}) - (4.6 \times 10^{-4} x)$$

Solve the quadratic equation for x.

$$x = \frac{4.8 \times 10^{-3}}{2} = 2.4 \times 10^{-3} = [OH^-]$$

$$pOH = -\log(2.4 \times 10^{-3}) = 2.62; \quad pH = 14.00 - 2.62 = 11.38$$

16.11 Using the same methods as those used in the example, letting $x = [OH^-]$ and $[HCO_3^-]$, and using the value of 2.1×10^{-4} for K_b for CO_3^{2-}, we get

$$\frac{x^2}{1.0} = 2.1 \times 10^{-4} \qquad x = \sqrt{2.1 \times 10^{-4}} = 1.45 \times 10^{-2}$$

pOH = 1.84 and pH = 12.16

16.12 NH_4Cl dissolves by dissociating into NH_4^+ and Cl^- ions. The ammonium ions react with water to produce an acidic solution.

$$NH_4^+(aq) - H_2O(\ell) \rightleftharpoons H_3O^-(aq) + NH_3(aq)$$

The K_a of $NH_4^+ = \dfrac{1.0 \times 10^{-14}}{1.8 \times 10^{-5}} = \dfrac{K_w}{K_b}$;

$$K_a = 5.6 \times 10^{-10} = \frac{[H_3O^+][NH_3]}{[NH_4^+]}$$

NH_4^+	H_2O	H_3O^+	NH_3
Initial	0.10	0	0
Change	$-x$	$+x$	$+x$
Equilibrium	$0.10 - x$	x	x

$$5.6 \times 10^{-10} = \frac{(x)(x)}{(0.10 - x)}$$

Assume $0.10 - x \approx 0.10$ because K_a is so small. Thus,
$(5.6 \times 10^{-10})(0.10) = x^2$; $x = [H_3O^+] = 7.48 \times 10^{-6}$ M.
$pH = -\log[H_3O^+] = -\log(7.48 \times 10^{-6}) = 5.16$

$$NH_4Cl(s) \rightleftharpoons NH_4^+(aq) + Cl^-(aq)$$

16.13 The formula weights and moles of acid per gram for the five antacids are as follows:

	Formula Weight	Mol Acid/Gram
$Mg(OH)_2$	58.32	1 mol acid/29.16 g antacid
$CaCO_3$	100.10	1 mol acid/50.05 g antacid
$NaHCO_3$	84.00	1 mol acid/84.00 g antacid
$Al(OH)_3$	78.0034	1 mol acid/26.00 g antacid
$NaAl(OH)_2CO_3$	143.99	1 mol acid/36.00 g antacid

Of these antacids, $Al(OH)_3$ neutralizes the most stomach acid per gram.

Chapter 17

17.1 $$K_a = \frac{[H^+][HCO_3^-]}{[H_2CO_3]} = \frac{H^+(0.025)}{(0.0020)} = [H^+] \times 12.5$$

$$= 4.2 \times 10^{-7}$$

$$[H^+] = \frac{4.2 \times 10^{-7}}{12.5} = 3.4 \times 10^{-8}$$

$$pH = -\log(3.4 \times 10^{-8}) = 7.47$$

17.2 $$7.40 = 7.21 + \log(\text{ratio}) = 7.21 + \log\frac{[HPO_4^{2-}]}{[H_2PO_4^-]}$$

$$\log\frac{[HPO_4^{2-}]}{[H_2PO_4^-]} = 7.40 - 7.21 = 0.19$$

$$\frac{[HPO_4^{2-}]}{[H_2PO_4^-]} = 10^{0.19} = 1.5$$

Therefore, $[HPO_4^{2-}] = 1.5 \times [H_2PO_4^-]$.

17.3 (a) Lactic acid-lactate (b) Acetic acid-acetate
(c) Hypochlorous acid-hypochlorite or $H_2PO_4^-$-HPO_4^{2-}
(d) CO_3^{2-}-HCO_3^-

17.4 The buffer capacity will be exceeded when just over 0.25 mol KOH is added, which will have reacted with the 0.25 mol $H_2PO_4^-$.

$$0.25 \text{ mol } OH^- = 0.25 \text{ mol KOH} \times \frac{56 \text{ g KOH}}{1 \text{ mol KOH}} = 14 \text{ g.}$$ Thus, slightly more than 14 g KOH will exceed the buffer capacity.

17.5 (a) 0.075 mol HCl converts 0.075 mol of lactate to lactic acid (0.075 mol).

$$pH = 3.85 + \log\frac{(0.20 - 0.075)}{(0.15 + 0.075)} = 3.85 + \log\frac{(0.125)}{(0.225)}$$

$$= 3.85 + \log(0.556) = 3.85 + (-0.25) = 3.60$$

(b) 0.025 mol NaOH converts 0.025 mol of lactic acid to 0.025 mol of lactate.

$$pH = 3.85 + \log\frac{(0.20 + 0.025)}{(0.15 - 0.025)} = 3.85 + \log\frac{(0.225)}{(0.125)}$$

$$= 3.85 + \log(1.8) = 3.85 + (0.26) = 4.11$$

17.6 (a) $$[H_3O^+] = \frac{(5.00 \times 10^{-3}) - (1.00 \times 10^{-3})}{0.0500 + 0.0100}$$

$$= \frac{4.00 \times 10^{-3}}{0.0600} = 6.67 \times 10^{-2}\ M$$

$$pH = 1.176 = 1.18$$

(b) $$[H_3O^+] = \frac{(5.00 \times 10^{-3}) - 0.00250}{0.0500 + 0.0250}$$

$$= \frac{2.50 \times 10^{-3}}{0.0750} = 3.33 \times 10^{-2}\ M$$

$$pH = -\log(3.33 \times 10^{-2}) = 1.48$$

(c) $$[H_3O^+] = \frac{(5.00 \times 10^{-3}) - 0.00450}{0.0500 + 0.0450}$$

$$= \frac{5.00 \times 10^{-4}}{0.0950} = 5.26 \times 10^{-3}$$

$$pH = -\log(5.26 \times 10^{-3}) = 2.28$$

(d) $$[OH^-] = \frac{0.05 \times 10^{-3}\ mol}{0.0500\ L + 0.0505\ L}$$

$$= 5.0 \times 10^{-4}\ mol/L$$

$$pOH = -\log(5.0 \times 10^{-4}) = 3.30$$

$$pH = 14.00 - 3.30 = 10.70$$

17.7 (a) Adding 10.0 mL of 0.100 M NaOH is adding (0.100 mol/L)(0.0100 L) = 0.00100 mol OH^-, which neutralizes 0.00100 mol acetic acid, converting it to 0.00100 mol acetate ion.

$$pH = pH + \log\frac{[acetate]}{[acetic\ acid]}$$

$$= 4.74 + \log\frac{(0.00100/0.0600)}{(0.00400/0.0600)}$$

$$= 4.74 + \log(0.25) = 4.74 + (-0.602) = 4.14$$

(b) $$pH = 4.74 + \log\frac{(0.00250/0.0750)}{(0.00250/0.0750)}$$

$$= 4.74 + \log(1) = 4.74$$

(c) $$pH = 4.74 + \log\frac{(0.00450/0.0950)}{(0.00050/0.0950)}$$

$$= 4.74 + \log(9) = 4.74 + 0.95 = 5.70$$

(d) $$[OH^-] = \frac{0.10 \times 10^{-3}\ mol}{0.0500\ L + 0.0510\ L}$$

$$= 9.9 \times 10^{-4}\ mol/L$$

$$pOH = -\log(9.9 \times 10^{-4})$$

$$= 3.00$$

$$pH = 14.00 - 3.00 = 11.00$$

17.8 (a) $K_{sp} = [Cu^+][Br^-]$ (b) $K_{sp} = [Hg^{2+}][I^-]^2$

(c) $K_{sp} = [Sr^{2+}][SO_4^{2-}]$

17.9 $AgBr(s) \rightleftharpoons Ag^+(aq) + Br^-(aq)$

$K_{sp} = [Ag^+][Br^-] = 5 \times 10^{-10} = x^2$; x = solubility

$x = \sqrt{5 \times 10^{-10}} \cong 2 \times 10^{-5}$

17.10 $Ag_2C_2O_4(s) \rightleftharpoons 2\ Ag^+(aq) + C_2O_4^{2-}(aq)$

$K_{sp} = [Ag^+]^2[C_2O_4^{2-}]$

$K_{sp} = [Ag^+]^2[C_2O_4^{2-}] = (1.4 \times 10^{-4})^2\ (6.9 \times 10^{-5})$

$= 1.4 \times 10^{-12}$

17.11

	$PbCl_2 \rightleftharpoons Pb^{2+}$	$+ 2\ Cl^-$
Initially (mol/L)	0	0.5
Change due to dissolving (mol/L)	$+S$	$0.5 + 2S$
At equilibrium (mol/L) because S will be small)	S	0.5 (ignore $2S$)

$$K_{sp} = (S)(0.5)^2 = 1.7 \times 10^{-5}$$

$$S = \frac{1.7 \times 10^{-5}}{(0.5)^2} = 6.8 \times 10^{-5}\ mol/L = Pb^{2+}\ conc$$

17.12 (a) $PbCl_2\ (s) \rightleftharpoons Pb^{2+}(aq) + 2\ Cl^-(aq)$

$K_{sp} = [Pb^{2+}][Cl^-]^2 = 1.7 \times 10^{-5}$. Let S equal the solubility of lead chloride, which equals $[Pb^{2+}]$

$$K_{sp} = 1.7 \times 10^{-5} = (S)(2S)^2 = 4S^3;\ S = \sqrt[3]{\frac{1.7 \times 10^{-5}}{4}}$$

$$= (4.25 \times 10^{-6})^{1/3} = 1.6 \times 10^{-2}\ mol/L$$

(b) Let solubility of $PbCl_2 = [Pb^{2+}] = S = [Cl^-] = 0.20\ M$

$[Pb^{2+}] = S = \frac{1.7 \times 10^{-5}}{(0.20)^2} = 4.3 \times 10^{-4}\ mol/L$ This is less than that in pure water due to the common ion effect of the presence of chloride ion.

17.13 $AgCl(s) \rightleftharpoons Ag^+(aq) + Cl^-(aq)$ $K_{sp} = 1.8 \times 10^{-10}$

$Ag^+(aq) + 2\ S_2O_3^{2-}(aq) \rightleftharpoons Ag(S_2O_3)_2^{3-}(aq)$ $K_f = 2.0 \times 10^{13}$

Net reaction:

$AgCl(s) + 2\ S_2O_3^{2-}(aq) \rightleftharpoons Ag(S_2O_3)_2^{3-}(aq) + Cl^-(aq)$

Therefore, the equilibrium constant for the net reaction is the product of $K_{sp} \times K_f$: $K_{net} = K_{sp} \times K_f = (1.8 \times 10^{-10})(2.0 \times 10^{13}) = 3.6 \times 10^3$. Because K_{net} is much greater than 1, the net reaction is product-favored, and AgCl is much more soluble in a Na_2SO_4 solution than it is in water.

17.14 (a) $Q = (1.0 \times 10^{-5})(1.0 \times 10^{-5}) = 1.0 \times 10^{-10} < K_{sp}$; no precipitation.

(b) For precipitation to occur, $Q \geq K_{sp}$; Q = conc Ag^+ × conc Cl^-; $K_{sp} = [Ag^+][Cl^-]$; $1.8 \times 10^{-10} = [Ag^+][Cl^-]$;

$$[Cl^-] = \frac{1.8 \times 10^{-10}}{1.0 \times 10^{-5}} = 1.8 \times 10^{-5}\ M$$

the minimum for AgCl precipitation.

17.15 AgCl will precipitate first. $[Cl^-]$ needed to precipitate AgCl:

$$[Cl^-] = \frac{1.8 \times 10^{-10}}{1.0 \times 10^{-2}} = 1.8 \times 10^{-8}\ M$$

$[Cl^-]$ needed to precipitate $PbCl_2$:

$$[Cl^-] = \sqrt{\frac{1.7 \times 10^{-5}}{1.0 \times 10^{-1}}} = 1.3 \times 10^{-2}\ M$$

Chapter 18

18.1 $\Delta S = q_{rev}/T = (30.8 \times 10^3\ J)/(273.15 + 45.3)\ K$

$= (30.8 \times 10^3\ J)/(318.45\ K)$

$\Delta S = 96.7\ J/K$

18.2 (a) C(g) has higher $S°$, 158.096 J K^{-1} mol^{-1}, versus 5.740 J K^{-1} mol^{-1} for C (graphite).

(b) Ar(g) has higher $S°$, 154.7 J K^{-1} mol^{-1}, versus 41.42 J K^{-1} mol^{-1} for Ca(s).

(c) KOH(aq) has higher $S°$, 91.6 J K^{-1} mol^{-1}, versus 78.9 J K^{-1} mol^{-1} for KOH(s).

18.3 (a) $\Delta S° = 2\ \text{mol CO(g)} \times S°(\text{CO(g)}) + 1\ \text{mol } O_2(g) \times S°(O_2(g)) - 2\ \text{mol } CO_2(g) \times S°(CO_2(g))$
$= \{2 \times (197.674) + (205.138) - 2 \times (213.74)\}$ J/K
$= 173.01$ J/K

(b) $\Delta S° = 1\ \text{mol NaCl(aq)} \times S°(\text{NaCl(aq)}) - 1\ \text{mol NaCl(s)} \times S°(\text{NaCl(s)})$
$= (115.5 - 72.13)\ \text{J/K} = 43.4\ \text{J/K}$

(c) $\Delta S° = 1\ \text{mol MgO(s)} \times S°(\text{MgO(s)}) + 1\ \text{mol } CO_2(g) \times S°(CO_2(g)) - 1\ \text{mol } MgCO_3(s) \times S°(MgCO_3(s))$
$= (26.94 + 213.74 - 65.7)$ J/K
$= 175.0$ J/K

18.4 $N_2(g) + 3\ H_2(g) \rightarrow 2\ NH_3(g)$

$$\Delta H° = 2\ \text{mol } NH_3 \times \Delta H_f°(NH_3(g)) = 2(-46.11)\ \text{kJ} = -92.22\ \text{kJ}$$

$$\Delta S° = 2\ \text{mol } NH_3 \times S°(NH_3(g)) - 1\ \text{mol } N_2(g) \times S°(N_2(g)) - 3\ \text{mol } H_2 \times S°(H_2(g))$$

$$= 2(192.45)\ \text{J/K} - (191.61)\ \text{J/K} - 3(130.684)\ \text{J/K}$$

$$= -198.76\ \text{J/K}$$

$$\Delta S°_{\text{universe}} = \frac{-\Delta H°}{T} + \Delta S° = \frac{92.2\ \text{kJ}}{298.15\ \text{K}} + (-198.76\ \text{J/K})$$

$$= \frac{92{,}200\ \text{J}}{298.15\ \text{K}} - 198.76\ \text{J/K} = 110.5\ \text{J/K}$$

The process is product-favored.

18.5 (a) $\Delta H° = \{(-238.66) - (-110.525)\}\ \text{kJ} = -128.14\ \text{kJ}$
$\Delta S° = \{(126.8) - 197.674 - 2 \times 130.684\}$ J/K
$= -332.2$ J/K
$\Delta G° = \Delta H° = T\Delta S°$
$= -128.14 \times 10^3\ \text{J} - 298.15\ \text{K} \times (-332.2\ \text{J/K})$
$= -29.09 \times 10^3\ \text{J} = -29.09\ \text{kJ}$

(b) $\Delta G° = [-166.27 - (-137.168)]\ \text{kJ} = -29.10\ \text{kJ}$. The two results agree.

(c) $\Delta G°$ is negative. The reaction is product-favored at 298.15 K. Because $\Delta S°$ is negative, at very high temperatures the reaction will become reactant-favored.

18.6 (a) $T = \Delta H°/\Delta S° = (-565{,}968\ \text{J})/(-173.01\ \text{J/K}) = 3271\ \text{K}$

(b) The reaction is exothermic and therefore is product-favored at temperatures lower than 3271 K.

18.7 (a) $\Delta G° = \{-553.04 - 527.81 - (-1128.79)\}\ \text{kJ}$
$= 47.94$ kJ
$K° = e^{-\Delta G°/RT} = e^{-(47.94\ \text{kJ/mol})/(8.314\ \text{J K}^{-1}\ \text{mol}^{-1})(298\ \text{K})}$
$= e^{-(47{,}940\ \text{J/mol})/(8.314\ \text{J K}^{-1}\ \text{mol}^{-1})(298\ \text{K})}$
$= e^{-19.35} = 3.9 \times 10^{-9}$ (close to K_c)

(b) $K° = e^{-14.68} = 4.2 \times 10^{-7}$ (agrees with K_c)

(c) $K° = e^{-(-1.909)} = 6.75$ (agrees with K_P)

For reactions (a) and (b), $K_c = K°$.

18.8 (a) At 298 K,
$\Delta G° = 2 \times (-16.45)\ \text{kJ} = -32.9\ \text{kJ}$
$K° = e^{-(-32{,}900\ \text{J})/(8.314\ \text{J K}^{-1}\ \text{mol}^{-1})(298\ \text{K})} = e^{13.28} = 5.8 \times 10^5$

(b) At 450. K,
$\Delta G° = \Delta H° - T\Delta S° = -92.22\ \text{kJ} - (450.)(-0.19876)\ \text{kJ}$
$= -2.78$ kJ
$K° = e^{-(-2780\ \text{J})/(8.314\ \text{J K}^{-1})(450.\ \text{K})} = 2.10$

(c) At 800. K,
$\Delta G° = -92.22\ \text{kJ} - (800.)(-0.19876)\ \text{kJ} = 66.79\ \text{kJ}$
$K° = e^{-(66{,}790\ \text{J})/(8.314\ \text{J K}^{-1}\ \text{mol}^{-1})(800.\ \text{K})} = 4.3 \times 10^{-5}$

18.9 $\Delta G = \Delta G° + RT \ln Q$
$\Delta G°$ was calculated in Problem-Solving Practice 18.7 to be 47.94 kJ for the reverse of this reaction. Therefore,
$\Delta G° = -47.94$ kJ
$$\Delta G = -47.94\ \text{kJ/mol} + (8.314\ \text{J K}^{-1}\ \text{mol}^{-1})(298\ \text{K}) \ln\left(\frac{1}{(0.023)(0.13)}\right)$$
$$= -47.94\ \text{kJ/mol} + 1.44 \times 10^4\ \text{J/mol}$$
$$= -47.94\ \text{kJ/mol} + 14.4\ \text{kJ/mol} = -33.5\ \text{kJ/mol}$$

18.10 (a) $\Delta G° = 2(-137.168)\ \text{kJ} - 2(-394.359)\ \text{kJ} = 514.382\ \text{kJ}$. The reaction is reactant-favored, and at least 514.382 kJ of work must be done to make it occur.

(b) $\Delta G° = 2(-742.2)\ \text{kJ} = -1484.4\ \text{kJ}$. The reaction is product-favored and could do up to 1484.4 kJ of useful work.

18.11 $\Delta G°' = \Delta G°$ for this reaction because none of the reactants or products requires a standard state different from 1 bar or 1 mol/L.

18.12 (a) The strongest phosphate donor has the most negative $\Delta G°$ for its reaction with water to produce dihydrogen phosphate. The $\Delta G°'$ values are given in Problem-Solving Example 18.12. Creatine phosphate, at -43.1 kJ, has the most negative value and is the strongest phosphate donor.

(b) Glycerol 3-phosphate has the least negative $\Delta G°'$ at -9.7 kJ and therefore is the weakest phosphate donor.

(c) See parts (a) and (b) for explanation.

18.13 (a) $\Delta G_f°(\text{MgO(s)}) = -569.43$ kJ, so formation of MgO(s) is product-favored and MgO(s) is thermodynamically stable.

(b) $\Delta G_f°(N_2H_4(\ell)) = 149.34$ kJ; kinetically stable.

(c) $\Delta G_f°(C_2H_6(g)) = -32.82$ kJ; thermodynamically stable.

(d) $\Delta G_f°(N_2O(g)) = 104.20$ kJ; kinetically stable.

Chapter 19

19.1 Reducing agents are indicated by "red" and oxidizing agents are indicated by "ox." Oxidation numbers are shown above the symbols for the elements.

(a) $2\ \underset{\text{red}}{\overset{0}{\text{Fe}}}(s) + 3\ \underset{\text{ox}}{\overset{0}{\text{Cl}_2}}(g) \rightarrow 2\ \overset{+3}{\text{Fe}}\overset{-1}{\text{Cl}_3}(s)$

(b) $2\underset{\text{red}}{\overset{0}{\text{H}_2}}(g) + \underset{\text{ox}}{\overset{0}{\text{O}_2}}(g) \rightarrow 2\ \overset{+1}{\text{H}_2}\overset{-2}{\text{O}}(\ell)$

(c) $\underset{\text{red}}{\overset{0}{\text{Cu}}}(S) + 2\ \underset{\text{ox}}{\overset{+5}{\text{N}}\overset{-2}{\text{O}_3^-}}(aq) + 4\ \overset{+1}{\text{H}_3}\overset{-2}{\text{O}^+}(aq) \rightarrow \overset{+2}{\text{Cu}^{2+}}(aq) + 2\ \overset{+4}{\text{N}}\overset{-2}{\text{O}_2}(g) + 6\ \overset{+1}{\text{H}_2}\overset{-2}{\text{O}}(\ell)$

(d) $\underset{\text{red}}{\overset{0}{\text{C}}}(s) + \underset{\text{ox}}{\overset{0}{\text{O}_2}}(g) \rightarrow \overset{+4}{\text{C}}\overset{-2}{\text{O}_2}(g)$

(e) $6\ \underset{\text{red}}{\overset{+2}{\text{Fe}^{2+}}}(aq) + \underset{\text{ox}}{\overset{+6}{\text{Cr}_2}\overset{-2}{\text{O}_7^{2-}}}(aq) + 14\ \overset{+1}{\text{H}_3}\overset{-2}{\text{O}^+}(aq) \rightarrow 6\ \overset{+3}{\text{Fe}^{3+}}(aq) + 2\ \overset{+3}{\text{Cr}^{3+}}(aq) + 21\ \overset{+1}{\text{H}_2}\overset{-2}{\text{O}}(\ell)$

19.2 (a)
Ox: $Cd(s) \rightarrow Cd^{2+}(aq) + 2\ e^-$
Red: $Cu^{2+}(aq) + 2\ e^- \rightarrow Cu(s)$
Net: $Cd(s) + Cu^{2+}(aq) \rightarrow Cd^{2+}(aq) + Cu(s)$

(b)
Ox: $Zn(s) \rightarrow Zn^{2+}(aq) + 2\ e^-$
Red: $2\ H_3O^+(aq) + 2\ e^- \rightarrow H_2(g) + 2\ H_2O(\ell)$
Net: $Zn(s) + 2\ H_3O^+(aq) \rightarrow Zn^{2+}(aq) + H_2(g) + 2\ H_2O(\ell)$

(c)
Ox: $2\ Al(s) \rightarrow 2\ Al^{3+}(aq) + 6\ e^-$
Red: $3\ Zn^{2+}(aq) + 6\ e^- \rightarrow 3\ Zn(s)$
Net: $2\ Al(s) + 3\ Zn^{2+}(aq) \rightarrow 2\ Al^{3+}(aq) + 3\ Zn(s)$

19.3 ***Step 1.*** This is an oxidation-reduction reaction. It is obvious that Zn is oxidized by its change in oxidation state.
Step 2. The half-reactions are

$Zn(s) \longrightarrow Zn^{2+}(aq)$ (This is the oxidation reaction.)

$Cr_2O_7^{2-}(aq) \longrightarrow 2\,Cr^{3+}(aq)$ (This is the reduction reaction.)

Step 3. Balance the atoms in the half-reactions. The atoms are balanced in the Zn half-reaction. We need to add water and H in the $Cr_2O_7^{2-}$ half-reaction. Fourteen H^+ ions are required on the right to combine with the seven O atoms.

$$Cr_2O_7^{2-}(aq) + 14\,H^+(aq) \longrightarrow 2\,Cr^{3+}(aq) + 7\,H_2O(\ell)$$

Step 4. Balance the half-reactions for charge. Write the Zn half-reaction as

$$Zn(s) \longrightarrow Zn^{2+}(aq) + 2\,e^-$$

and write the $Cr_2O_7^{2-}$ half-reaction as

$$Cr_2O_7^{2-}(aq) + 14\,H^+(aq) + 6\,e^- \longrightarrow 2\,Cr^{3+}(aq) + 7\,H_2O(\ell)$$

Step 5. Multiply the half-reactions by factors to make the number of electrons gained equal to the number lost.

$$3\,[Zn(s) \longrightarrow Zn^{2+}(aq) + 2\,e^-]$$

$$1\,[Cr_2O_7^{2-}(aq) + 14\,H^+(aq) + 6\,e^- \longrightarrow 2\,Cr^{3+}(aq) + 7\,H_2O(\ell)]$$

Step 6. Add the two half-reactions, canceling the electrons.

$$3\,Zn(s) \longrightarrow 3\,Zn^{2+}(aq) + 6\,e^-$$

$$Cr_2O_7^{2-}(aq) + 14\,H^+(aq) + 6\,e^- \longrightarrow 2\,Cr^{3+}(aq) + 7\,H_2O(\ell)$$

$$Cr_2O_7^{2-}(aq) + 3\,Zn(s) + 14\,H^+(aq) \longrightarrow 2\,Cr^{3+}(aq) + 3\,Zn^{2+}(aq) + 7\,H_2O(\ell)$$

Step 7. Everything checks.
Step 8. Water was added in Step 3. The balanced equation is

$$Cr_2O_7^{2-}(aq) + 3\,Zn(s) + 14\,H_3O^+(aq) \longrightarrow 2\,Cr^{3+}(aq) + 3\,Zn^{2+}(aq) + 21\,H_2O(\ell)$$

19.4 ***Step 1.*** This is an oxidation-reduction reaction. The wording of the question says Al reduces NO_3^- ion. Al is oxidized.
Step 2. The half-reactions are:

$Al(s) \longrightarrow Al(OH)_4^-(aq)$ (This is the oxidation reaction.)

$NO_3^-(aq) \longrightarrow NH_3(aq)$ (This is the reduction reaction.)

Step 3. Balance the atoms in the half-reactions. For the Al half-reaction, add four H^+ ions on the right and four water molecules on the left.

$$Al(s) + 4\,H_2O(\ell) \longrightarrow Al(OH)_4^- + 4\,H^+(aq)$$

For the NO_3^- half-reaction,

$$NO_3^-(aq) + 9\,H^+(aq) \longrightarrow NH_3(aq) + 3\,H_2O(\ell)$$

Step 4. Balance the half-reactions for charge. Put $3\,e^-$ on the right in the Al half-reaction

$$Al(s) + 4\,H_2O(\ell) \longrightarrow Al(OH)_4^- + 4\,H^+(aq) + 3\,e^-$$

and put $8\,e^-$ on the left side of the NO_3^- half-reaction.

$$NO_3^-(aq) + 9\,H^+(aq) + 8\,e^- \longrightarrow NH_3(aq) + 3\,H_2O(\ell)$$

Step 5. Multiply the half-reactions by factors to make the electrons gained equal to those lost.

$$8[Al(s) + 4\,H_2O(\ell) \longrightarrow Al(OH)_4^- + 4\,H^+(aq) + 3\,e^-]$$

$$3[NO_3^-(aq) + 9\,H^+(aq) + 8\,e^- \longrightarrow NH_3(aq) + 3\,H_2O(\ell)]$$

Step 6. Remove $H^+(aq)$ ions by adding an appropriate amount of OH^-. For the Al half-reaction, add 32 OH^- ions to get

$$8\,Al(s) + 32\,OH^-(aq) + 32\,H_2O(\ell) \longrightarrow 8\,Al(OH)_4^- + 32\,H_2O + 24\,e^-$$

For the NO_3^- half-reactions, add 27 OH^- ions to get

$$3\,NO_3^-(aq) + 27\,H_2O + 24\,e^- \longrightarrow 3\,NH_3(aq) + 9\,H_2O(\ell) + 27\,OH^-(aq)$$

Step 7. Add both half-reactions and cancel the electrons.

$$8\,Al(s) + 32\,OH^-(aq) + 32\,H_2O(\ell) \longrightarrow 8\,Al(OH)_4^- + 32\,H_2O + 24\,e^-$$

$$3\,NO_3^-(aq) + 27\,H_2O + 24\,e^- \longrightarrow 3\,NH_3(aq) + 9\,H_2O(\ell) + 27\,OH^-(aq)$$

$$3\,NO_3^-(aq) + 8\,Al(s) + 59\,H_2O(\ell) + 32\,OH^-(aq) \longrightarrow 8\,Al(OH)_4^-(aq) + 3\,NH_3(aq) + 27\,OH^-(aq) + 41\,H_2O(\ell)$$

Step 8. Make a final check. Since there are OH^- ions and water molecules on both sides of the equation, cancel them out. This gives the final balanced equation.

$$3\,NO_3^-(aq) + 8\,Al(s) + 18\,H_2O(\ell) + 5\,OH^-(aq) \longrightarrow 8\,Al(OH)_4^-(aq) + 3\,NH_3(aq)$$

(This is a fairly complicated equation to balance. If you balanced this one with a minimum of effort, your understanding of balancing redox equations is rather good. If you had to struggle with one or more of the steps, go back and repeat them.)

19.5 (a) $Ni(s) \rightarrow Ni^{2+}(aq) + 2\,e^-$ (This is the oxidation half-reaction.)

$2\,Ag^+(aq) + 2\,e^- \rightarrow 2\,Ag(s)$ (This is the reduction half-reaction.)

(b) The oxidation of Ni takes place at the anode and the reduction of Ag^+ takes place at the cathode.
(c) Electrons would flow through an external circuit from the anode (where Ni is oxidized) to the cathode (where Ag^+ ions are reduced).
(d) Nitrate ions would flow through the salt bridge to the anode compartment. Potassium ions would flow into the cathode compartment.

19.6 Oxidation half-reaction: $Fe(s) \rightarrow Fe^{2+}(aq, 1\,M) + 2\,e^-$ (anode)

Reduction half-reaction: $Cu^{2+}(aq, 1\,M) + 2\,e^- \rightarrow Cu(s)$ (cathode)

$$E^\circ_{cell} = +0.78\text{ V} = E^\circ_{cathode} - E^\circ_{anode}$$

Since $E^\circ_{cathode} = +0.34$ V, E°_{anode} must be -0.44 V.

19.7 $F_2(g) + 2\,e^- \longrightarrow 2\,F^-(aq)$ $E^\circ_{cathode} = +2.87$ V

$2\,Li(s) \longrightarrow 2\,Li^+(aq) + 2\,e^-$ $E^\circ_{anode} = -3.045$ V

$2\,Li(s) + F_2(g) \longrightarrow 2\,Li^+(aq) + 2\,F^-(aq)$ $E^\circ_{cell} = +5.91$ V

$$E^\circ_{cell} = E^\circ_{cathode} - E^\circ_{anode} = +2.87 - (-3.045) = +5.91\text{ V}$$

19.8 The two half-reactions are

$Hg^{2+}(aq) + 2\,e^- \longrightarrow 2\,Hg(\ell)$ $E^\circ_{cathode} = +0.855$ V

$2\,I^-(aq) \longrightarrow I_2(s) + 2\,e^-$ $E^\circ_{anode} = +0.535$ V

$$E^\circ_{cell} = E^\circ_{cathode} - E^\circ_{anode} = +0.855 - 0.535 = +0.320\text{ V}$$

The reaction is product-favored as written.

19.9 We first need to calculate E°_{cell}, and to do this we break the reaction into two half-reactions.

$$\text{Ox: } Sn^{2+}(aq) \longrightarrow Sn^{4+}(aq) + 2\,e^- \qquad E^\circ_{anode} = +0.15\text{ V}$$

$$\text{Red: } I_2(s) + 2\,e^- \longrightarrow 2\,I^-(aq) \qquad E^\circ_{cathode} = +0.535\text{ V}$$

$$I_2(s) + Sn^{2+}(aq) \longrightarrow 2\,I^-(aq) + Sn^{4+}(aq) \qquad E^\circ_{cell} = +0.385\text{ V}$$

$$E^\circ_{cell} = E^\circ_{cathode} - E^\circ_{anode} = +0.535 - 0.15 = +0.385\text{ V}$$

E°_{cell} is 0.385 V, and 2 mol of electrons are transferred.

$$\log K = \frac{nE^\circ\text{ V}}{0.0592\text{ V}} = \frac{2 \times 0.385\text{ V}}{0.0592\text{ V}}$$

$$= 13.00 \text{ and } K = 1 \times 10^{13}$$

The large value of K indicates that the reaction is strongly product-favored as written.

19.10 $$E_{cell} = 0.51\text{ V} - \left(\frac{0.0592\text{ V}}{2} \times \log\frac{3}{0.010}\right)$$

$$= 0.51\text{ V} - (0.0296\text{ V} \times \log(300))$$

$$= 0.51\text{ V} - 0.073\text{ V} = +0.44\text{ V}$$

19.11 If the pH = 3.66, then the E_{cell} = 0.217 V.

19.12 (a) The net cell reaction would be

$$2\,Na^+ + 2\,Br^- \longrightarrow 2\,Na + Br_2$$

Sodium ions would be reduced at the cathode and bromide ions would be oxidized at the anode.

(b) H_2 would be produced at the cathode for the same reasons given in Problem-Solving Example 19.8. That reaction is

$$2\,H_2O(\ell) + 2\,e^- \longrightarrow H_2(g) + 2\,OH^-(aq)$$

At the anode, two reactions are possible: the oxidation of water and the oxidation of Br^- ions.

$$6\,H_2O(\ell) \longrightarrow O_2(g) + 4\,H_3O^+(aq) + 4\,e^- \qquad E^\circ = 1.229\text{ V}$$

$$2\,Br^-(aq) \longrightarrow Br_2(\ell) + 2\,e^- \qquad E^\circ = 1.08\text{ V}$$

Bromide ions will be oxidized to Br_2 because that potential is smaller. The net cell reaction is

$$2\,H_2O(\ell) + 2\,Br^-(aq) \longrightarrow Br_2(\ell) + H_2(g) + 2\,OH^-(aq)$$

(c) Sn metal will be formed at the cathode because its reduction potential (−0.14 V) is less negative than the potential for the reduction of water. O_2 will form at the anode because the E° value for the oxidation of water is smaller than the E° value for the oxidation of Cl^-. The net cell reaction is

$$2\,Sn^{2+}(aq) + 6\,H_2O(\ell) \longrightarrow 2\,Sn(s) + O_2(g) + 4\,H_3O^+(aq)$$

19.13 First, calculate the quantity of charge:

$$\text{Charge} = (25 \times 10^3\text{ A})(1\text{ h})\left(\frac{60\text{ s}}{1\text{ min}}\right)\left(\frac{60\text{ min}}{1\text{ h}}\right)$$

$$= 9.0 \times 10^7\text{ A·s} = 9.0 \times 10^7\text{ C}$$

Then calculate the mass of Na:

$$\text{Mass of Na} = (9.0 \times 10^7\text{ C}) \times \left(\frac{1\text{ mol e}^-}{96{,}500\text{ C}}\right)\left(\frac{1\text{ mol Na}}{1\text{ mol e}^-}\right)\left(\frac{22.99\text{ g Na}}{1\text{ mol Na}}\right)$$

$$= 2.1 \times 10^4\text{ g Na}$$

Chapter 20

20.1 (a) $^{237}_{93}Np \rightarrow {}^{4}_{2}He + {}^{233}_{91}Pa$ (b) $^{35}_{16}S \rightarrow {}^{0}_{-1}e + {}^{35}_{17}Cl$

20.2 (a) $^{11}_{6}C \rightarrow {}^{11}_{5}B + {}^{0}_{1}e$ (b) $^{35}_{16}S \rightarrow {}^{35}_{17}Cl + {}^{0}_{-1}e$

(c) $^{30}_{15}P \rightarrow {}^{0}_{+1}e + {}^{30}_{14}Si$ (d) $^{22}_{11}Na \rightarrow {}^{0}_{-1}e + {}^{22}_{12}Mg$

20.3 (a) $^{42}_{19}K \rightarrow {}^{0}_{-1}e + {}^{41}_{20}Ca$ (b) $^{234}_{92}U \rightarrow {}^{4}_{2}He + {}^{230}_{90}Th$

(c) $^{20}_{9}F \rightarrow {}^{0}_{-1}e + {}^{20}_{10}Ne$

20.4 (a) $^{90}_{38}Sr \rightarrow {}^{0}_{-1}e + {}^{90}_{39}Y$

(b) It takes 4 half-lives (4 × 29 y = 116 y) for the activity to decrease to 125 beta particles emitted per minute:

Number of Half-lives	Change of Activity	Total Elapsed Time (y)
1	2000 to 1000	29
2	1000 to 500	58
3	500 to 250	87
4	250 to 125	116

20.5 (a) $$t_{1/2} = \frac{0.693}{9.3 \times 10^{-3}\text{ d}^{-1}} = 75\text{ d}$$

(b) ln(fraction remaining) = $-k \times t = -(9.3 \times 10^{-3}\text{ d}^{-1}) \times (100\text{ d}) = -0.930$

Fraction of iridium-192 remaining = $e^{-0.930}$ = 0.39. Therefore, 39% of the original iridium-192 remains.

20.6 $$k = \frac{0.693}{1.60 \times 10^3\text{ y}} = 4.33 \times 10^{-4}\text{ y}^{-1}$$

As of 2004: ln(fraction remaining) = $-k \times t = -(4.33 \times 10^{-4}\text{ y}^{-1}) \times 83\text{ y} = -3.39 \times 10^{-2}$

Fraction of radium-226 remaining = $e^{-0.0339}$ = 0.965. Therefore, 96.5% of the original radium-226 remains; 0.965 × 1.00 g = 0.965 g.

20.7 $\ln(0.60) = -0.510 = -k \times t$

$$k = \frac{0.693}{t_{1/2}} = \frac{0.693}{12.3\text{ y}} = 0.0563\text{ y}^{-1}$$

$$t = \frac{-0.510}{-0.0563\text{ y}^{-1}} = 9.1\text{ y}$$

Chapter 21

21.1 $$1.5 \times 10^9\text{ mol Na} \times \frac{4\text{ mol NaCl}}{4\text{ mol Na}} \times \frac{58.5\text{ g NaCl}}{1\text{ mol NaCl}} \times \frac{1\text{ lb NaCl}}{454\text{ g NaCl}} \times \frac{1\text{ ton NaCl}}{2000\text{ lb NaCl}} = 9.7 \times 10^4\text{ ton NaCl}$$

21.2 $$\text{mol of Al} = 1.00\text{ ton Al} \times \frac{2000\text{ lb Al}}{1\text{ ton Al}} \times \frac{454\text{ g Al}}{1\text{ ton Al}} \times \frac{1\text{ mol Al}}{26.98\text{ g Al}} = 3.37 \times 10^4\text{ mol Al}$$

$Al^{3+} + 3\,e^- \rightarrow Al$; therefore, 3 mol electrons are needed to produce 1 mol Al.

Number of moles of electrons

$$= 3.37 \times 10^4\text{ mol Al} \times \frac{3\text{ mol e}^-}{1\text{ mol Al}}$$

$$= 1.01 \times 10^5\text{ mol e}^-$$

$$\text{Charge} = 1.01 \times 10^5\text{ mol e}^- \times \frac{9.65 \times 10^4\text{ C}}{1\text{ mol e}^-}$$

$$= 9.75 \times 10^9\text{ C}$$

$$\text{Time} = 9.75 \times 10^9\text{ C} \times \frac{1\text{ s}}{1.00 \times 10^5\text{ C}} = 9.75 \times 10^4\text{ s}$$

$$= 1.63 \times 10^3\text{ min} = 27.0\text{ h}$$

21.3 I^- is oxidized to I_2; IO_3 is reduced to I_2. IO_3^- is the oxidizing agent and I^- is the reducing agent.

21.4 (a)

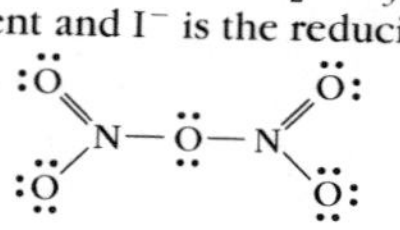

(b) $N_2O_5 + H_2O \rightarrow 2\ HNO_3$

21.5 (a) The formation of NO_2 from NO is exothermic. Thus, lowering the temperature favors the forward reaction (NO_2 formation).

(b) By reacting with water, NO_2 is converted to HNO_3 thereby removing NO_2 from the reaction mixture.

21.6

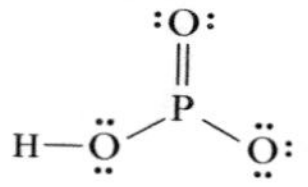

21.7 $S_8(s) + 12\ O_2(g) \longrightarrow 8\ SO_3(g)$

$$1.3 \times 10^{10}\ \text{kg}\ S_8 \times \frac{1\ \text{mol}\ S_8}{0.256\ \text{kg}\ S_8} \times \frac{8\ \text{mol}\ SO_3}{1\ \text{mol}\ S_8} \times \frac{0.080\ \text{kg}\ SO_3}{1\ \text{mol}\ SO_3} = 3.3 \times 10^{10}\ \text{kg}\ SO_3$$

21.8 (a) Non-redox reaction; no change in oxidation numbers

(b) Redox reaction; F_2 is the oxidizing agent; S_8 is the reducing agent.

Chapter 22

22.1 (a) Mn [Ar] $3d^5 4s^2$

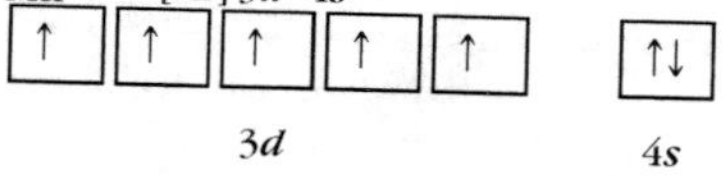

Mn^{2+} [Ar] $3d^5 4s^0$

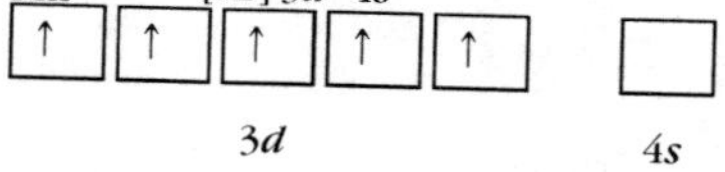

(b) Cr [Ar] $3d^5 4s^1$

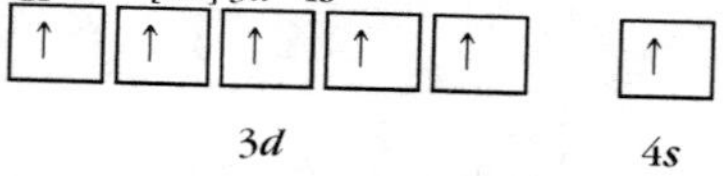

Cr^{3+} [Ar] $3d^3 4s^0$

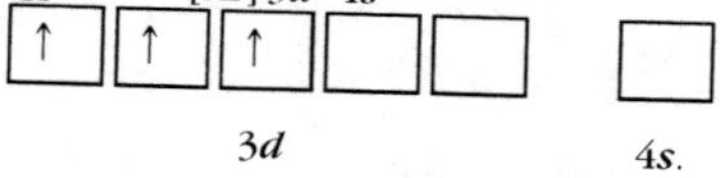

22.2 Cooling the iron slowly would shift the equilibrium to favor the reverse reaction, the conversion of cementite to iron and carbon (graphite).

22.3 Assume that 50% of the iron comes from each ore.

$$Fe_2O_3\text{: } 5.00 \times 10^2\ \text{kg Fe} \times \frac{159.7\ \text{kg}\ Fe_2O_3}{111.7\ \text{kg Fe}} = 7.15 \times 10^2\ \text{kg}\ Fe_2O_3$$

$$Fe_3O_4\text{: } 5.00 \times 10^2\ \text{kg Fe} \times \frac{231.6\ \text{kg}\ Fe_3O_4}{167.6\ \text{kg Fe}} = 6.91 \times 10^2\ \text{kg}\ Fe_3O_4$$

Total $= 7.15 \times 10^2$ kg $+ 6.91 \times 10^2$ kg $= 1.41 \times 10^3$ kg

22.4 By controlling the voltage, the zinc could be removed and then the lead.

22.5 $E_{cell} = 0.00\ \text{V} = +0.795\ \text{V} - 0.00985 \log\left(\frac{1}{[H^+]^{14}}\right)$

$$-0.795 = -0.00985 \log \frac{1}{[H^+]^{14}}$$

$$\log \frac{1}{[H^+]^{14}} = \frac{-0.795}{-0.00985} = 80.7$$

$$\frac{1}{[H^+]^{14}} = 10^{80.7} = 5.01 \times 10^{80}$$

$$1 = (5.01 \times 10^{80})[H^+]^{14}$$

$$[H^+]^{14} = \frac{1}{5.01 \times 10^{80}} = 2.00 \times 10^{-81}$$

$$14 \log[H^+] = \log 3.16 \times 10^{-81}$$

$$\log[H^+] = \frac{-80.7}{14} = -5.76$$

$$-\log[H^+] = \text{pH} = 5.76$$

22.6 (a) SO_4^{2-} (b) Cu^{2+} (c) NH_3 (d) $[Cu(NH_3)_4]^{2+}$

22.7 (a) Diamminesilver(I) nitrate

(b) $[Fe(H_2O)_5(NCS)]Cl_2$

22.8 (a) Two (b) Zero (c) Five

22.9 Two

22.10 High-spin: four unpaired electrons; low-spin: two unpaired electrons; both complexes are paramagnetic due to their unpaired electrons.

Answers to Exercises

Chapter 1

1.1 (a) These temperatures can be compared to the boiling point of water, 212 °F or 100 °C. So 110 °C is a higher temperature than 180 °F.
(b) These temperatures can be compared to normal body temperature, 98.6 °F or 37.0 °C. So 36 °C is a lower temperature than 100 °F.
(c) This temperature can be compared to normal body temperature, 37.0 °C. Since body temperature is above the melting point, gallium held in one's hand will melt.

1.2 Reference to the figure on page 10 indicates that kerosene is the top layer, vegetable oil is the middle layer, and water is the bottom layer.
(a) Since the least dense liquid will be the top layer and the densest liquid will be the bottom layer, the densities increase in the order kerosene, vegetable oil, water.
(b) If vegetable oil is added to the tube, the top and bottom layers will remain the same, but the middle layer will become larger.
(c) If kerosene is now added to the tube the top layer will grow, but the middle and bottom layers will remain the same. The order of levels will *not change*. Density does not depend on the quantity of material present. So no matter how much of each liquid is present, the densities increase in the order kerosene, vegetable oil, water.

1.3 (a) Properties: blue (qualitative), melts at 99 °C (quantitative)
Change: melting
(b) Properties: white, cubic (both qualitative)
Change: none
(c) Properties: mass of 0.123 g, melts at 327 °C (both quantitative)
Change: melting
(d) Properties: colorless, vaporizes easily (both qualitative), boils at 78 °C, density of 0.789 g/mL (both quantitative)
Changes: vaporizing, boiling

1.4 Physical change: boiling water
Chemical changes: combustion of propane, cooking the egg

1.5 (a) Homogeneous mixture (solution)
(b) Heterogeneous mixture (contains carbon dioxide gas bubbles in a solution of sugar and other substances in water)
(c) Heterogeneous mixture of dirt and oil
(d) Element; diamond is pure carbon.
(e) Modern quarters (since 1965) are composed of a pure copper core (that can be seen when they are viewed side-on) and an outer layer of 75% Cu, 25% Ni alloy, so they are heterogeneous matter. Pre-1965 quarters are fairly pure silver.
(f) Compound; contains carbon, hydrogen, and oxygen

1.6 (a) Energy from the sun warms the ice and the water molecules vibrate more; eventually they break away from their fixed positions in the solid and liquid water forms. As the temperature of the liquid increases, some of the molecules have enough energy to become widely separated from the other molecules, forming water vapor (gas).
(b) Some of the water molecules in the clothes have enough speed and energy to escape from the liquid state and become water vapor; these molecules are carried away from the clothes by breezes or air currents. Eventually nearly every water molecule in the clothes vaporizes, and the clothes become dry.
(c) Water molecules from the air come into contact with the cold glass, and their speeds are decreased, allowing them to become liquid. As more and more molecules enter the liquid state, droplets form on the glass.
(d) Some water molecules escape from the liquid state, forming water vapor. As more and more molecules escape, the ratio of sugar molecules to water molecules becomes larger and larger, and eventually some sugar molecules start to stick together. As more and more sugar molecules stick to each other, a visible crystal forms. Eventually all of the water molecules escape, leaving sugar crystals behind.

1.7 (a) Tellurium, Te, earth (Latin *tellus* means earth); uranium, U, for Uranus; neptunium, Np, for Neptune; and plutonium, Pu, for Pluto. (Mercury, like the planet Mercury, is named for a Roman god.)
(b) Californium, Cf
(c) Curium, Cm, for Marie Curie; and meitnerium, Mt, for Lise Meitner
(d) Scandium, Sc, for Scandinavia; gallium, Ga, for France (Latin *Gallia* means France); germanium, Ge, for Germany; ruthenium, Ru, for Russia; europium, Eu, for Europe; polonium, Po, for Poland; francium, Fr, for France; americium, Am, for America; californium, Cf, for California
(e) H, He, C, N, O, F, Ne, P, S, Cl, Ar, Se, Br, Kr, I, Xe, At, Rn

1.8 (a) Elements that consist of diatomic molecules are H, N, O, F, Cl, Br, and I; At is radioactive and there is probably less than 50 mg of naturally occurring At on earth, but it does form diatomic molecules; H, N, O, plus group 7A.
(b) Metalloids are B, Si, Ge, As, Sb, and Te; along a zig-zag line from B to Te.

1.9 Tin and lead are two different elements; allotropes are two different forms of the same element, so tin and lead are not allotropes.

Chapter 2

2.1 The movement of the comb though your hair removes some electrons, leaving slight charges on your hair and the comb. The charges must sum to zero; therefore, one must be slightly positive and one must be slightly negative, so they attract each other.

2.2 (a) A nucleus is about one ten-thousandth as large as an atom, so $100 \text{ m} \times (1 \times 10^{-4}) = 1 \times 10^{-2} \text{ m} = 1 \text{ cm}$. (b) Many everyday objects are about 1 cm in size—for example, a grape.

2.3 The statement is wrong because two atoms that are isotopes always have the same number of protons. It is the number of neutrons that varies from one isotope of an element to another.

2.4 Atomic weight of lithium
$= (0.07500)(6.015121 \text{ amu}) + (0.9250)(7.016003 \text{ amu})$
$= 0.451134 \text{ amu} + 6.489802 \text{ amu}$
$= 6.940936 \text{ amu, or } 6.941 \text{ amu}$

2.5 Because the most abundant isotope is magnesium-24 (78.70%), the atomic weight of magnesium is closer to 24 than to 25 or 26, the mass numbers of the other magnesium isotopes, which make up approximately 21% of the remaining mass. The simple arithmetic average is (24 + 25 + 26)/3 = 25, which is larger than the atomic weight. In the arithmetic average, the relative abundance of each magnesium isotope is 33%, far less than the actual percent abundance of magnesium-24, and much more than the natural percent abundances of magnesium-25 and magnesium-26.

2.6 There is no reasonable pair of values of the mass numbers for Ga that would have an average value of 69.72.

2.7 Start by calculating the number of moles in 10.00 g of each element.

$$10.00 \text{ g Li} \times \frac{1 \text{ mol Li}}{6.941 \text{ g Li}} = 1.441 \text{ mol Li}$$

$$10.00 \text{ g Ir} \times \frac{1 \text{ mol Ir}}{192.22 \text{ g Ir}} = 0.05202 \text{ mol Ir}$$

Multiply the number of moles of each element by Avogadro's number.

$1.441 \text{ mol Li} \times 6.022 \times 10^{23} \text{ atoms/mol} = 8.678 \times 10^{23} \text{ atoms Li}$

$0.05202 \text{ mol Ir} \times 6.022 \times 10^{23} \text{ atoms/mol} = 3.133 \times 10^{22} \text{ atoms Ir}$

Find the difference.

$(8.678 \times 10^{23}) - (0.3133 \times 10^{23})$
$= 8.365 \times 10^{23}$ more atoms of Li than Ir

2.8 1. (a) 13 metals: potassium (K), calcium (Ca), scandium (Sc), titanium (Ti), vanadium (V), chromium (Cr), manganese (Mn), iron (Fe), cobalt (Co), nickel (Ni), copper (Cu), zinc (Zn), and gallium (Ga)

(b) Three nonmetals: selenium (Se), bromine (Br), and krypton (Kr)

(c) Two metalloids: germanium (Ge) and arsenic (As)

2. (a) Groups 1A (except hydrogen), 2A, 1B, 2B, 3B, 4B, 5B, 6B, 7B, 8B

(b) Groups 7A and 8 (c) None

3. Period 6

2.9 The question should ask: Which of the following men does not have an *element* named after him? The correct answer to the question, after it is properly posed, is Isaac Newton.

Chapter 3

3.1 Propylene glycol structural formula:

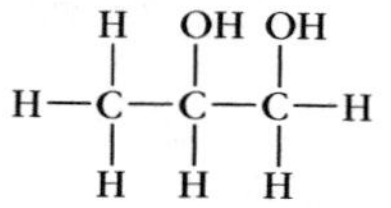

Condensed formula:

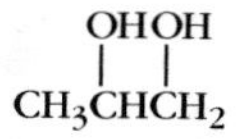

Molecular formula: $C_3H_8O_2$

3.2 (a) CS_2 (b) PCl_3 (c) SBr_2 (d) SeO_2 (e) OF_2 (f) XeO_3

3.3 (a) $C_{16}H_{34}$ and $C_{28}H_{58}$ (b) $C_{14}H_{30}$, 14 carbon atoms and 30 hydrogen atoms

3.4 The structural and condensed formulas for three constitutional isomers of five-carbon alkanes (pentanes) are

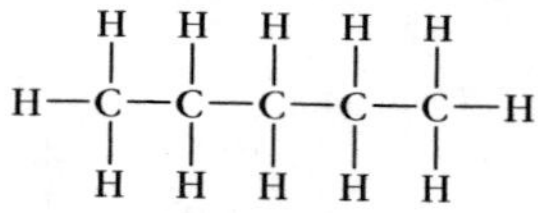

$CH_3CH_2CH_2CH_2CH_3$

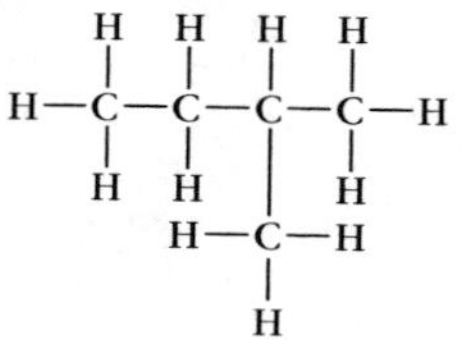

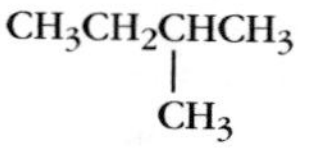

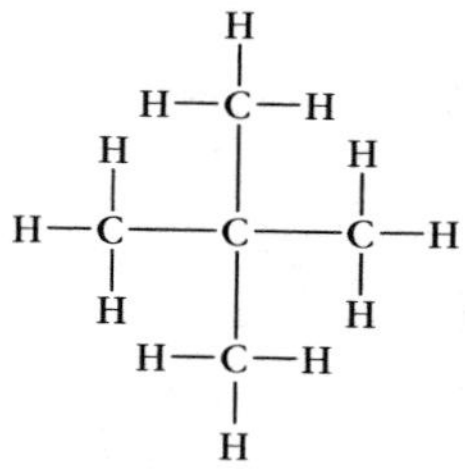

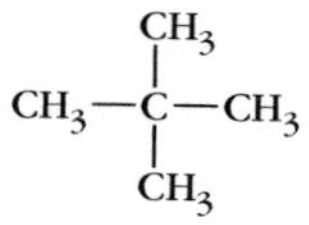

3.5 The compound is a solid at room temperature and is soluble in water, so it is likely to be an ionic compound.

3.6 (a) 174.18 g/mol (b) 386.66 g/mol (c) 398.07 g/mol (d) 194.19 g/mol

3.7 The statement is true. Because both compounds have the same formula, they have the same molar mass. Thus, 100 g of each compound contains the same number of moles.

3.8 Epsom salt is $MgSO_4 \cdot 7H_2O$, which has a molar mass of 246 g/mol.

$$20 \text{ g} \times \frac{1 \text{ mol}}{246 \text{ g}} = 8.1 \times 10^{-2} \text{ mol Epsom salt}$$

3.9 (a) SF_6 molar mass is 146.06 g/mol; 1.000 mol SF_6 contains 32.07 g S and $18.9984 \times 6 = 113.99$ g F. The mass percents are

$$\frac{32.07 \text{ g S}}{146.06 \text{ g } SF_6} \times 100\% = 21.96\% \text{ S}$$

$$100.0\% - 21.96\% = 78.04\% \text{ F}$$

(b) $C_{12}H_{22}O_{11}$ has a molar mass of 342.3 g/mol; 1.000 mol $C_{12}H_{22}O_{11}$ contains

$$12.011 \times 12 = 144.13 \text{ g C}$$

$$1.0079 \times 22 = 22.174 \text{ g H}$$

$$15.9994 \times 11 = 175.99 \text{ g O}$$

The mass percents of the three elements are

$$\frac{144.13 \text{ g C}}{342.3 \text{ g}} \times 100\% = 42.12\% \text{ C}$$

$$\frac{22.174 \text{ g H}}{342.3 \text{ g}} \times 100\% = 6.478\% \text{ H}$$

$$\frac{175.99 \text{ g O}}{342.3 \text{ g}} \times 100\% = 51.41\% \text{ O}$$

(c) $Al_2(SO_4)_3$ molar mass is 342.15 g/mol; 1.000 mol $Al_2(SO_4)_3$ contains

$$26.9815 \times 2 = 53.96 \text{ g Al}$$

$$32.066 \times 3 = 96.20 \text{ g S}$$

$$15.9994 \times 12 = 192.0 \text{ g O}$$

The mass percents of the three elements are

$$\frac{53.96 \text{ g Al}}{342.15 \text{ g}} \times 100\% = 15.77\% \text{ Al}$$

$$\frac{96.20 \text{ g S}}{342.15 \text{ g}} \times 100\% = 28.12\% \text{ S}$$

$$\frac{192.0 \text{ g O}}{342.15 \text{ g}} \times 100\% = 56.12\% \text{ O}$$

(d) $U(OTeF_5)_6$ molar mass is 1669.6 g/mol; 1.000 mol $U(OTeF_5)_6$ contains 238.0289 g of U and

$$15.9994 \times 6 = 96.00 \text{ g O}$$

$$127.60 \times 6 = 765.6 \text{ g Te}$$

$$18.9984 \times 30 = 570.0 \text{ g F}$$

The mass percents of the four elements are

$$\frac{238.0289 \text{ g U}}{1669.6 \text{ g}} \times 100\% = 14.26\% \text{ U}$$

$$\frac{96.00 \text{ g O}}{1669.6 \text{ g}} \times 100\% = 5.750\% \text{ O}$$

$$\frac{765.6 \text{ g Te}}{1669.6 \text{ g}} \times 100\% = 45.86\% \text{ Te}$$

$$\frac{570.0 \text{ g F}}{1669.6 \text{ g}} \times 100\% = 34.14\% \text{ F}$$

3.10 (a) Carbon, nitrogen, oxygen, phosphorus, hydrogen, selenium, sulfur, Cl, Br, I (b) Calcium and magnesium (c) Chloride, bromide, and iodide (d) Iron, copper, zinc, vanadium (also chromium, manganese, cobalt, nickel, molybdenum, and cadmium)

Chapter 4

4.1 One mol of methane reacts with 2 mol oxygen to produce 1 mol carbon dioxide and 2 mol water.

4.2 (a) The total mass of reactants {4 Fe(s) + 3 O_2(g)} must equal the total mass of products {2 Fe_2O_3(s)}, which is 2.50 g.
(b) The stoichiometric coefficients are 4, 3, and 2.
(c) $1.000 \times 10^4 \text{ O atoms} \times \frac{1 \text{ O}_2 \text{ molecule}}{2 \text{ O atoms}} \times \frac{4 \text{ Fe atoms}}{3 \text{ O}_2 \text{ molecules}} = 6.667 \times 10^3 \text{ Fe atoms}$

4.3 (a) Not balanced; the number of oxygen atoms do not match.
(b) Not balanced; the number of bromine atoms do not match.
(c) Not balanced; the number of sulfur atoms do not match.

4.4 (a) To predict the product of a combination reaction between two elements, we need to know the ion that will be formed by each element when combined. (b) For calcium, Ca^{2+} ions are formed, and for fluorine, F^- ions are formed. (c) The product is CaF_2.

4.5 (a) Magnesium chloride, $MgCl_2$
(b) Magnesium oxide, MgO, and carbon dioxide, CO_2

4.6 $\frac{2 \text{ mol Al}}{3 \text{ mol Br}_2}$, $\frac{2 \text{ mol Al}}{1 \text{ mol Al}_2\text{Br}_6}$, $\frac{3 \text{ mol Br}_2}{1 \text{ mol Al}_2\text{Br}_6}$, and their reciprocals

4.7 $0.300 \text{ mol CH}_4 \times \frac{2 \text{ mol H}_2\text{O}}{1 \text{ mol CH}_4} = 0.600 \text{ mol H}_2\text{O}$

$$0.600 \text{ mol H}_2\text{O} \times \frac{18.02 \text{ g H}_2\text{O}}{1 \text{ mol H}_2\text{O}} = 10.8 \text{ g H}_2\text{O}$$

4.8 (a) $300. \text{ g urea} \times \frac{1 \text{ mol urea}}{60.06 \text{ g urea}} \times \frac{2 \text{ mol NH}_3}{1 \text{ mol urea}} \times \frac{17.03 \text{ g NH}_3}{1 \text{ mol NH}_3} = 170. \text{ g urea}$

$$100. \text{ g H}_2\text{O} \times \frac{1 \text{ mol H}_2\text{O}}{18.02 \text{ g H}_2\text{O}} \times \frac{2 \text{ mol NH}_3}{1 \text{ mol H}_2\text{O}} \times \frac{17.03 \text{ g NH}_3}{1 \text{ mol NH}_3} = 189. \text{ g HN}_3$$

Therefore, urea is the limiting reactant.
(b) 176. g NH_3

$$300. \text{ g urea} \times \frac{1 \text{ mol urea}}{60.06 \text{ g urea}} \times \frac{1 \text{ mol H}_2\text{O}}{1 \text{ mol urea}} \times \frac{44.01 \text{ g CO}_2}{1 \text{ mol CO}_2} = 220. \text{ g CO}_2$$

(c) $300. \text{ g urea} \times \frac{1 \text{ mol urea}}{60.06 \text{ g urea}} \times \frac{1 \text{ mol H}_2\text{O}}{1 \text{ mol urea}} \times \frac{18.02 \text{ g H}_2\text{O}}{1 \text{ mol H}_2\text{O}} = 90.0 \text{ g H}_2\text{O}$

100. g − 90.0 g = 10.0 g H_2O remains

4.9 (1) Impure reactants; (2) Inaccurate weighing of reactants and products

4.10 Assuming that the nicotine is pure, weigh a sample of nicotine and burn the sample. Separately collect and weigh the carbon dioxide and water generated, and calculate the moles and grams of carbon and hydrogen collected. By mass difference, determine the mass of nitrogen in the original sample, then calculate the moles of nitrogen. Calculate the mole ratios of carbon, hydrogen, and nitrogen in nicotine to determine its empirical formula.

Chapter 5

5.1 It is possible for an exchange reaction to form two different precipitates—for example, the reaction between barium hydroxide and iron(II) sulfate:

$$Ba(OH)_2(aq) + FeSO_4(aq) \rightarrow BaSO_4(s) + Fe(OH)_2(s)$$

5.2 $H_3PO_4(aq) \rightleftharpoons H_2PO_4^-(aq) + H^+(aq)$
$H_2PO_4^-(aq) \rightleftharpoons HPO_4^{2-}(aq) + H^+(aq)$
$HPO_4^{2-}(aq) \rightleftharpoons PO_4^{3-}(aq) + H^+(aq)$

5.3 (a) Hydrogen ions and perchlorate ions:

$$HClO_4(aq) \rightarrow H^+(aq) + ClO_4^-(aq)$$

(b) $Ca(OH)_2(aq) \rightarrow Ca^{2+}(aq) + 2\,OH^-(aq)$

5.4 (a) $H^+(aq) + Cl^-(aq) + K^+(aq) + OH^-(aq) \rightarrow H_2O(\ell) + K^+(aq) + Cl^-(aq)$
$H^+(aq) + OH^-(aq) \rightarrow H_2O(\ell)$
(b) $2\,H^+(aq) + SO_4^{2-}(aq) + Ba^{2+}(aq) + 2\,OH^-(aq) \rightarrow 2\,H_2O(\ell) + BaSO_4(s)$
$H^+(aq) + OH^-(aq) \rightarrow H_2O(\ell)$
$Ba^{2+}(aq) + SO_4^{2-}(aq) \rightarrow BaSO_4(s)$
(c) $2\,CH_3\,COOH(aq) + Ca^{2+}(aq) + 2\,OH^-(aq) \rightarrow Ca^{2+}(aq) + 2\,CH_3COO^-(aq) + 2\,H_2O(\ell)$
$CH_3\,COOH(aq) + OH^-(aq) \rightarrow H_2O(\ell) + CH_3COO^-(aq)$

5.5 $Al(OH)_3(s) + 3\,H^+(aq) + 3\,Cl^-(aq) \rightarrow 3\,H_2O(\ell) + Al^{3+}(aq) + 3\,Cl^-(aq)$
$H^+(aq) + OH^-(aq) \rightarrow H_2O(\ell)$

5.6 (a) The products are aqueous sodium sulfate, water, and carbon dioxide gas.

$$Na_2CO_3(aq) + H_2SO_4(aq) \rightarrow Na_2SO_4(aq) + H_2O(\ell) + CO_2(g)$$
$$2\,H^+(aq) + CO_3^{2-}(aq) \rightarrow H_2O(\ell) + CO_2(g)$$

(b) The products are aqueous iron(II) chloride and hydrogen sulfide gas.

$$FeS(s) + 2\,HCl(aq) \rightarrow FeCl_2(aq) + H_2S(g)$$
$$2\,H^+(aq) + S^{2-}(aq) \rightarrow H_2S(g)$$

(c) The products are aqueous potassium chloride, water, and sulfur dioxide gas.

$$K_2SO_3(aq) + 2\,HCl(aq) \rightarrow 2\,KCl(aq) + H_2O(\ell) + SO_2(g)$$
$$2\,H^+(aq) + SO_3^{2-}(aq) \rightarrow H_2O(\ell) + SO_2(g)$$

5.7 (a) Gas-forming reaction; the products are aqueous nickel sulfate, water, and carbon dioxide gas.

$$NiCO_3(s) + H_2SO_4(aq) \rightarrow NiSO_4(aq) + H_2O(\ell) + CO_2(g)$$
$$NiCO_3(s) + 2\,H^+(aq) \rightarrow Ni^{2+}(aq) + H_2O(\ell) + CO_2(g)$$

(b) Acid-base reaction; nitric acid reacts with strontium hydroxide, a base, to produce water and strontium nitrate, a salt.

$$2\,HNO_3(aq) + Sr(OH)_2(s) \rightarrow Sr(NO_3)_2(aq) + 2\,H_2O(\ell)$$
$$Sr(OH)_2(s) + 2\,H^+(aq) \rightarrow Sr^{2+}(aq) + 2\,H_2O(\ell)$$

(c) Precipitation reaction; aqueous sodium chloride and insoluble barium oxalate are produced.

$$BaCl_2(aq) + Na_2C_2O_4(aq) \rightarrow BaC_2O_4(s) + 2\,NaCl(aq)$$
$$Ba^{2+}(aq) + C_2O_4^{2-}(aq) \rightarrow BaC_2O_4(s)$$

(d) Precipitation and gas-forming reaction; lead sulfate precipitates and carbon dioxide gas is released.

$PbCO_3(aq) + H_2SO_4(aq) \rightarrow PbSO_4(s) + H_2O(\ell) + CO_2(g)$

$Pb^{2+}(aq) + SO_4^{2-}(aq) \rightarrow PbSO_4(s)$

$2\,H^+(aq) + CO_3^{2-}(aq) \rightarrow H_2O(\ell) + CO_2(g)$

5.8 In the reaction $2\,Ca(s) + O_2(g) \rightarrow 2\,CaO(s)$, Ca loses electrons, is oxidized, and is the reducing agent; O gains electrons, is reduced, and is the oxidizing agent.

5.9 $Cl_2(g) + Ca(s) \rightarrow CaCl_2(s)$. $Cl_2(g)$ is the oxidizing agent.

5.10 (a) This is not a redox reaction. Nitric acid is a strong oxidizing agent, but here it serves as an acid.
(b) In this redox reaction, chromium metal (Cr) is oxidized (loses electrons) to form Cr^{3+} ions in Cr_2O_3; oxygen (O_2) is reduced (gains electrons) to form oxide ions, O^{2-}. Oxygen is the oxidizing agent, and chromium is the reducing agent.
(c) This is an acid-base reaction, but not a redox reaction; there are no strong oxidizing or reducing agents present.
(d) Copper is oxidized and chlorine is reduced in this redox reaction, in which copper is the reducing agent and chlorine is the oxidizing agent. The equations are $Cu \rightarrow Cu^{2+} + 2e^-$ and $Cl_2 + 2e^- \rightarrow 2\,Cl^-$.

5.11 (a) Carbon in oxalate ion, $C_2O_4^{2}$ (oxidation state = 13), is oxidized to oxidation state +4 in CO_2.
(b) Carbon is reduced from +4 in CCl_2F_2 to 0 in C(s).

5.12 (a) $CH_3CH_2OH(\ell) + 3\,O_2(g) \rightarrow 3\,H_2O(\ell) + 2\,CO_2(g)$; redox
(b) $2\,Fe(s) + 6\,HNO_3(aq) \rightarrow 2\,Fe(NO_3)_3(aq) + 3\,H_2(g)$; redox
(c) $AgNO_3(aq) + KBr(aq) \rightarrow AgBr(s) + KNO_3(aq)$; not redox

5.13 Molar mass of cholesterol = 386.7 g/mol

$$240\text{ mg} \times \frac{1\text{ g}}{10^3\text{ mg}} \times \frac{1\text{ mol}}{386.7\text{ g}} = 6.21 \times 10^{-4}\text{ mol cholesterol}$$

$$\frac{6.21 \times 10^{-4}\text{ mol}}{0.100\text{ L}} = 6.2 \times 10^{-3}\text{ M}$$

5.14 (a) $$6.37\text{ g Al(NO}_3)_3 \times \frac{1\text{ mol Al(NO}_3)_3}{213.0\text{ g Al(NO}_3)_3} = 0.0299\text{ mol Al(NO}_3)_3;$$

$$\frac{0.0299\text{ mol}}{0.250\text{ L}} = 0.120\text{ M Al(NO}_3)_3$$

(b) Molarity: Al^{3+} = 0.120; NO_3^- = 3(0.120) = 0.360

5.15 If the description of solution preparation is always worded in terms of adding enough solvent to make a specific volume of solution, then any possible expansion or contraction has no effect on the molarity of the solution. The denominator of the definition of molarity is liters of *solution.*

5.16 The moles of HCl in the concentrated solution are given by (6.0 mol/L)(0.100 L) = 0.6 mol HCl. The moles of HCl in the dilute solution are given by (1.20 mol/L)(0.500 L) = 0.6 mol HCl.

5.17 The molarity could be increased by evaporating some of the solvent.

5.18 $$0.0193\text{ L} \times \frac{0.200\text{ mol AgNO}_3}{1\text{ L}} \times \frac{1\text{ mol Ag}^+}{1\text{ mol AgNO}_3} \times \frac{1\text{ mol Cl}^-}{1\text{ mol Ag}^+} \times \frac{1\text{ mol NaCl}}{1\text{ mol Cl}^-} = 3.86 \times 10^{-3}\text{ mol NaCl}$$

$$\frac{3.86 \times 10^{-3}\text{ mol NaCl}}{0.0250\text{ L}} = 0.154\text{ M NaCl}$$

Chapter 6

6.1 You transfer some mechanical energy to the ball to accelerate it upward. The ball's potential energy increases the higher it gets, but its kinetic energy decreases by an equal quantity, and eventually it stops rising and begins to fall. As it falls, some of the ball's potential energy changes to kinetic energy, and the ball goes faster and faster until it hits the floor. When the ball hits the floor, some of its kinetic energy is transferred to the atoms, molecules, or ions that make up the floor, causing them to move faster. Eventually all of the ball's kinetic energy is transferred, and the ball stops moving. The nanoscale particles in the floor (and some in the air that the ball fell through) are moving faster on average, and the temperature of the floor (and the air) is slightly higher. The energy has spread out over a much larger number of particles.

6.2

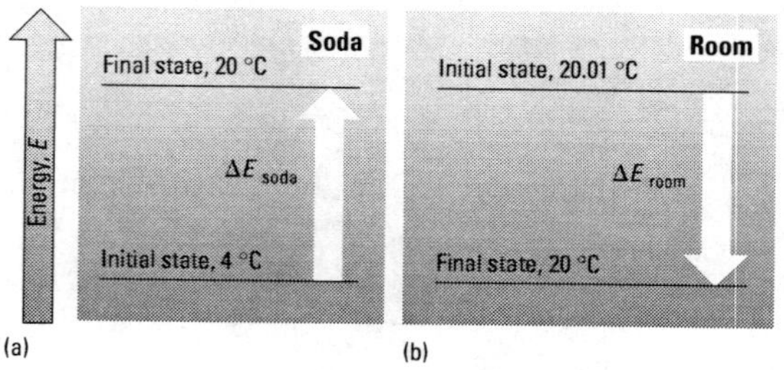

6.3 (a) Heat transfer $= (25.0\ °C - 1.0\ °C)\left(\frac{1.5\text{ kJ}}{1.0\ °C}\right) = 36\text{ kJ}$
(b) The system is the can and the liquid it contains.
(c) The surroundings includes the air and other materials in contact with the can, or close to the can.
(d) ΔE is negative because the system transferred energy to the surroundings as it cooled; $\Delta E = -36$ kJ.
(e)

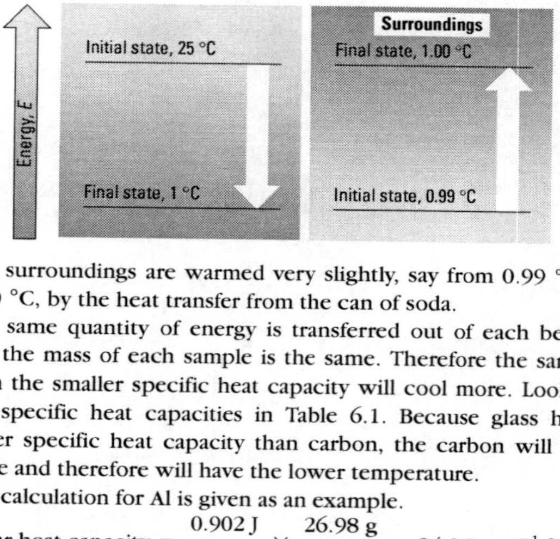

The surroundings are warmed very slightly, say from 0.99 °C to 1.00 °C, by the heat transfer from the can of soda.

6.4 The same quantity of energy is transferred out of each beaker and the mass of each sample is the same. Therefore the sample with the smaller specific heat capacity will cool more. Look up the specific heat capacities in Table 6.1. Because glass has a larger specific heat capacity than carbon, the carbon will cool more and therefore will have the lower temperature.

6.5 The calculation for Al is given as an example.

$$\text{Molar heat capacity} = \frac{0.902\text{ J}}{\text{g °C}} \times \frac{26.98\text{ g}}{1\text{ mol}} = 24.3\text{ J mol}^{-1}\text{ °C}^{-1}$$

Metal	Molar Heat Capacity (J mol^{-1} °C^{-1})	Metal	Molar Heat Capacity (J mol^{-1} °C^{-1})
Al	24.3	Cu	24.5
Fe	25.2	Au	25.2

The molar heat capacities of most metals are close to 25 J mol^{-1} °C^{-1}. This rule does not work for ethanol or other compounds listed in Table 6.2.

6.6 (a) Since the heat of vaporization is almost seven times larger than the heat of fusion, the temperature stays constant at 100 °C almost seven times longer than it stays constant at 0 °C. It stays constant at 0 °C for slightly less time than it takes to heat the water from 0 °C to 100 °C (see graph). Because the heating is at a constant rate, time is proportional to quantity of energy transferred.

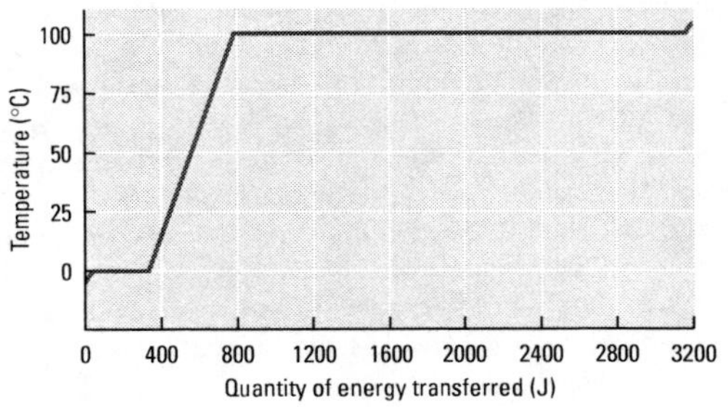

(b) The mass of water is half as great as in part (a), so each process takes half as long. A graph to the same scale as in part (a) begins at 105 °C and reaches −5 °C with half the quantity of energy transferred.

6.7 Heat of fusion: 237 g × 333 J/g = 78.9 kJ
Heating liquid: 237 g × 4.184 J g^{-1} $°C^{-1}$ × 100.0 °C = 99.2 kJ
Heat of vaporization: 237 g × 2260 J/g = 536 kJ
Total heating = (78.9 + 99.2 + 536) kJ = 714 kJ

6.8 The direction of energy transfer is indicated by the sign of the enthalpy change. Transfer to the system corresponds to a positive enthalpy change.

6.9 Because of heats of fusion and heats of vaporization, the enthalpy change is different when a reactant or product is in a different state.

6.10 When 1.0 mol of H_2 reacts (Equation 6.3), $\Delta H = -241.8$ kJ. When half that much H_2 reacts, ΔH is half as great; that is, $0.5 \times (-241.8) = -120.9$ kJ.

6.11 $\frac{-92.22\ \text{kJ}}{1\ \text{mol}\ N_2(g)}$ $\frac{-92.22\ \text{kJ}}{3\ \text{mol}\ H_2(g)}$ $\frac{-92.22\ \text{kJ}}{2\ \text{mol}\ NH_3(g)}$

$\frac{1\ \text{mol}\ N_2(g)}{-92.22\ \text{kJ}}$ $\frac{3\ \text{mol}\ H_2(g)}{-92.22\ \text{kJ}}$ $\frac{2\ \text{mol}\ NH_3(g)}{-92.22\ \text{kJ}}$

6.12 The reaction used must be exothermic. Because it can be started by opening the package, it probably involves oxygen from the air, and the sealed package prevents the reaction from occurring before it is needed. Many metals can be oxidized easily and exothermically. The reaction of iron with oxygen (as in the *Chemistry You Can Do* experiment) is a good candidate.

6.13 Yes, it would violate the first law of thermodynamics. According to the supposition, we could create energy by starting with 2 mol HCl, breaking all the molecules apart, recombining the atoms to form 1 mol H_2 and 1 mol Cl_2, and then reacting the H_2 and Cl_2 to give 2 HCl.

$$2\ HCl \longrightarrow \text{atoms} \longrightarrow H_2 + Cl_2 \qquad \Delta H° = +185\ \text{kJ}$$
$$H_2 + Cl_2 \longrightarrow 2\ HCl \qquad \Delta H° = -190\ \text{kJ}$$

The net effect of these two processes is that there is still 2 mol HCl, but 5 kJ of energy has been created. This is impossible according to the first law of thermodynamics.

6.14 (a) In the reaction 2 HF → $H_2 + F_2$ there are two bonds in the two reactant molecules and two bonds in the two product molecules. Since the reaction is endothermic, the bonds in the reactant molecules must be stronger than in the products.
(b) For the reaction 2 H_2O → 2 H_2 + O_2, there are four bonds in the two reactant molecules but only three bonds in the three product molecules. The reaction is endothermic because more bonds are broken than are formed.

6.15 $C_6H_{12}O_6(s) + 6\ O_2(g) \rightarrow 6\ CO_2(g) + 6\ H_2O(\ell)$
Because the volume of any ideal gas is proportional to the amount (moles) of gas, and because there are 6 mol of gaseous reactant and 6 mol of gaseous product, there will be very little change in volume. Almost no work will be done, and $\Delta H \cong \Delta E$.

6.16 In the Problem-Solving Example 6.11 the reaction produced 0.25 mol NaCl and the heat transfer associated with the reaction caused 500 mL of solution to warm by 7 °C.
(a) Here the reaction produces 0.20 mol NaCl by neutralizing 0.20 mol NaOH and the heat transfer warms 400. mL of water. So there is less heat transfer but it will be heating a smaller volume. The quantity of reaction is $\frac{0.20\ \text{mol}}{0.25\ \text{mol}} = 0.80$ as much, so the heat transfer is 0.80 as much. The quantity of water to be heated is $\frac{400.\ \text{mL}}{500.\ \text{mL}} = 0.800$ as much. Therefore the combined effect on temperature is the same as in Problem-Solving Example 6.11, and the temperature change associated with this process will also be 7 °C.
(b) Here the limiting reactant is 0.10 mol NaOH. (Only half of the H_2SO_4 is used up.) The heat transfer from the reaction warms 200. mL of water. So there is less heat transfer but it will heat a smaller volume. The quantity of reaction is $\frac{0.10\ \text{mol}}{0.25\ \text{mol}} = 0.40$ as much, so the heat transfer is 0.40 as much. The quantity of water is $\frac{200.}{400.} = 0.40$ as much. Therefore once again the combined effect on temperature is the same as in Problem-Solving Example 6.11, and the temperature change associated with this process will also be 7 °C.

6.17 $N_2(g) \rightarrow N_2(g)$
(a) The product is the same as the reactant, so there is no change—nothing happens.
(b) Since product and reactant are the same, $\Delta H = 0$.

6.18 (a) It takes 160 kJ to break 1 mol N—N bonds, 4 × 391 kJ to break 4 mol N—H bonds, and 498 kJ to break 1 mol of bonds in O_2.
(b) Forming 1 mol of bonds in N_2 releases 946 kJ, and forming 4 mol O—H bonds releases 4 × 467 kJ.
(c) Therefore, $\Delta H = \{160 + (4 \times 391) + 498\}$ kJ $- \{946 + (4 \times 467)\}$ kJ $= -592$ kJ
$$N_2H_4(g) + O_2(g) \rightarrow N_2(g) + 2\ H_2O(g) \qquad \Delta H° = -592\ \text{kJ}$$

6.19 (a) $CH_4(g) + 2\ O_2(g) \rightarrow CO_2(g) + 2\ H_2O(g)$
$\Delta H° = \{-393.509 + 2(-241.818) - (-74.81)\}$ kJ
$= -802.34$ kJ
$$\frac{802.34\ \text{kJ}}{1\ \text{mol}\ CH_4} \times \frac{1\ \text{mol}}{16.0426\ \text{g}} = 50.013\ \text{kJ/g}\ CH_4$$
(b) $C_8H_{18}(\ell) + \frac{25}{2}\ O_2(g) \rightarrow 8\ CO_2(g) + 9\ H_2O(g)$
$\Delta H° = \{8(-393.509) + 9(-241.818) - (-249.952)\}$ kJ
$= -5074.48$ kJ
$$\frac{5074.48\ \text{kJ}}{1\ \text{mol}\ C_8H_{18}} \times \frac{1\ \text{mol}}{114.23\ \text{g}} = 44.423\ \text{kJ/g}\ C_8H_{18}$$
(c) $C_2H_5OH(\ell) + 3\ O_2(g) \rightarrow 2\ CO_2 + 3\ H_2O(g)$
$\Delta H° = \{2(-393.509) + 3(-241.818) - (-277.69)\}$ kJ
$= -1234.782$ kJ
$$\frac{1234.782\ \text{kJ}}{1\ \text{mol}\ C_2H_5OH(\ell)} \times \frac{1\ \text{mol}}{46.068\ \text{g}} = 26.8\ \text{kJ/g}\ C_2H_5OH$$
(d) $N_2H_4(\ell) + O_2(g) \rightarrow N_2(g) + 2\ H_2O(g)$
$\Delta H° = \{2(-241.818) - 50.63\}$ kJ $= -534.27$ kJ
$$\frac{534.26\ \text{kJ}}{1\ \text{mol}\ N_2H_4} \times \frac{1\ \text{mol}}{32.045\ \text{g}} = 16.672\ \text{kJ/g}\ N_2H_4$$
(e) $H_2(g) + \frac{1}{2}\ O_2(g) \rightarrow H_2O(g) \qquad \Delta H° = -241.818$ kJ
$$\frac{241.818\ \text{kJ}}{1\ \text{mol}\ H_2} \times \frac{1\ \text{mol}}{2.0158\ \text{g}} = 119.96\ \text{kJ/g}\ H_2$$
(f) $C_6H_{12}O_6(s) + 6\ O_2(g) \rightarrow 6\ CO_2(g) + 6\ H_2O(g)$
$\Delta H° = \{6(-393.509) + 6(-241.818) - (-1274.4)\}$ kJ
$= -2537.6$ kJ
$$\frac{2537.6\ \text{kJ}}{1\ \text{mol}\ C_6H_{12}O_6(s)} \times \frac{1\ \text{mol}}{180.16\ \text{g}} = 14.085\ \text{kJ/g}\ C_6H_{12}O_6$$
(g) Biomass gives the same result as glucose.
Hydrogen has the greatest fuel value. Octane has the greatest energy density. Its fuel value is more than twice that of the other

liquids and solids, and its density is far greater than for $CH_4(g)$ and $H_2(g)$. Energy density values are

$$CH_4(g) \quad \frac{50.013\ \text{kJ}}{1\ \text{g}} \times \frac{6.9 \times 10^{-4}\ \text{g}}{1\ \text{mL}} = 3.4 \times 10^{-2}\ \text{kJ/mL}$$

$$C_8H_{18}(\ell) \quad \frac{44.423\ \text{kJ}}{1\ \text{g}} \times \frac{0.70\ \text{g}}{1\ \text{mL}} = 31\ \text{kJ/mL}$$

$$C_2H_5OH(\ell) \quad \frac{26.8\ \text{kJ}}{1\ \text{g}} \times \frac{0.80\ \text{g}}{1\ \text{mL}} = 21\ \text{kJ/mL}$$

$$N_2H_4(\ell) \quad \frac{16.672\ \text{kJ}}{1\ \text{g}} \times \frac{1.00\ \text{g}}{1\ \text{mL}} = 16.7\ \text{kJ/mL}$$

$$H_2(g) \quad \frac{119.96\ \text{kJ}}{1\ \text{g}} \times \frac{8.2 \times 10^{-5}\ \text{g}}{1\ \text{mL}} = 9.8 \times 10^{-3}\ \text{kJ/mL}$$

$$\text{Carbohydrate} \quad \frac{14.1\ \text{kJ}}{1\ \text{g}} \times \frac{1.56\ \text{g}}{1\ \text{mL}} = 22.0\ \text{kJ/mL}$$

6.20 According to the thermochemical equation, 2801.6 kJ is released per mole of glucose.

$$\frac{2801.6\ \text{kJ}}{1\ \text{mol}} \times \frac{1\ \text{mol}}{180.16\ \text{g}} \times \frac{1\ \text{kcal}}{4.184\ \text{kJ}} \times \frac{1\ \text{Cal}}{1\ \text{kcal}} = 3.717\ \text{Cal}$$

This rounds to 4 Cal.

6.21 (a) The average BMR is given in the text as 1750 Cal/day for a 70-kg male at rest. So the BMR is

$$\frac{1750\ \text{Cal}}{\text{d}} \times \frac{1000\ \text{cal}}{\text{Cal}} \times \frac{4.184\ \text{J}}{\text{cal}} = 7.32 \times 10^6\ \text{J/day}$$

$$(7.322 \times 10^6\ \text{J/day}) \times (1\ \text{day}/24\ \text{h}) \times (1\ \text{h}/60\ \text{min}) \times (1\ \text{min}/60\ \text{s}) = 84.75\ \text{W}$$

(b) The average BMR for a 70-kg male playing basketball is 7 times the above or 593.2 W. Typical incandescent light bulbs are in the range of 50–250 W.

Chapter 7

7.1 Wavelength and frequency are inversely related. Therefore, low-frequency radiation has long-wavelength radiation.

7.2 Cellular phones use higher frequency radio waves.

7.3 $E = h\nu; \quad \lambda = \dfrac{hc}{E}$

$$E = h\nu = (6.626 \times 10^{-34}\ \text{J}\cdot\text{s})(2.45 \times 10^9\ \text{s}^{-1})$$

$$= 1.62 \times 10^{-24}\ \text{J}$$

$$\lambda = \frac{(6.626 \times 10^{-34}\ \text{J}\cdot\text{s})(2.998 \times 10^8\ \text{m/s})}{1.62 \times 10^{-24}\ \text{J}} = 1.23 \times 10^{-1}\ \text{m}$$

7.4 In a sample of excited hydrogen gas there are many atoms, and each can exist in one of the excited states possible for hydrogen. The observed spectral lines are a result of all the possible transitions of all these hydrogen atoms.

7.5 (a) Emitted (b) Absorbed
(c) Emitted (d) Emitted

7.6 $(2.179 \times 10^{-18}\ \text{J/photon})$

$$\times \left(\frac{1\ \text{kJ}}{10^3\ \text{J}}\right)\left(\frac{6.022 \times 10^{23}\ \text{photons}}{1\ \text{mol}}\right)$$

$$= 1312\ \text{kJ/mol photons}$$

7.7 (a) $5d$ (b) $4f$ (c) $6p$

7.8 The $n = 3$ level can have only three types of sublevels—s, p, and d. The $n = 2$ level can have only s and p sublevels, not d sublevels ($l = 2$).

7.9 $3, 0, 0, +\frac{1}{2}$; $3, 0, 0\ -\frac{1}{2}$

7.10 (a) $3, 0, 0, +\frac{1}{2}$ (b) $3, 1, 1, +\frac{1}{2}$

7.11 Electron a is in the $3p_y$ orbital. Electron b is in the $3p_z$ orbital.

7.12 (a) The maximum number of electrons in the $n = 3$ level is 18 (2 electrons per orbital). The orbitals would be designated $3s$, $3p_x$, $3p_y$, $3p_z$, $3d_{z^2}$, $3d_{xy}$, $3d_{yz}$, $3d_{xz}$, and $3d_{x^2-y^2}$.
(b) The maximum number of electrons in the $n = 5$ level is 50. The orbitals would be designated $5s$, $5p_x$, $5p_y$, $5p_z$, $5d_{yz}$, $5d_{xz}$, $5dz^2$, $5d_{xy}$, and the seven $5f$ orbitals and the nine $5g$, which are not designated by name in the text.

7.13 The first shell that could contain g orbitals would be the $n = 5$ shell. There would be nine g orbitals.

7.14 For the chlorine atom, $n = 3$, and there are seven electrons in this highest energy level. The configuration is

3s: [↑↓] 3p: [↑↓][↑↓][↑]. For the selenium atom, the highest energy level is $n = 4$, and there are six electrons in the $n = 4$ level. The configuration is 4s: [↑↓] 4p: [↑↓][↑][↑].

7.15 The $[Ar]3d^44s^2$ configuration for chromium has four unpaired electrons, and the $[Ar]3d^54s^1$ configuration has six unpaired electrons.

7.16 The $Fe(acac)_2$ contains an Fe^{2+} ion with a $3d$ electron configuration of [↑↓][↑][↑][↑][↑]. This configuration has four unpaired electrons. The compound $Fe(acac)_3$ contains an Fe^{3+} ion, with a $3d$ electron configuration of [↑][↑][↑][↑][↑]. This configuration has five unpaired electrons. The $Fe(acac)_3$, with more unpaired electrons per molecule, would be attracted more strongly into a magnetic field.

Chapter 8

8.1 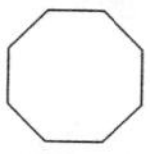 C_8H_{16}

8.2 N_2 has only 10 valence electrons. The Lewis structure shown has 14 valence electrons.

8.3 None of the structures are correct. (a) is incorrect because sulfur does not have an octet of electrons (it has only six); (b) is incorrect because, although it shows the correct number of valence electrons (26), there is a double bond between F and N rather than a single bond with a lone pair on N; (c) is incorrect because the left carbon has five bonds; (d) is incorrect because COCl should have 17 valence electrons, not 18 as shown.

8.4 (a) C_5H_{10} (b) Two

8.5 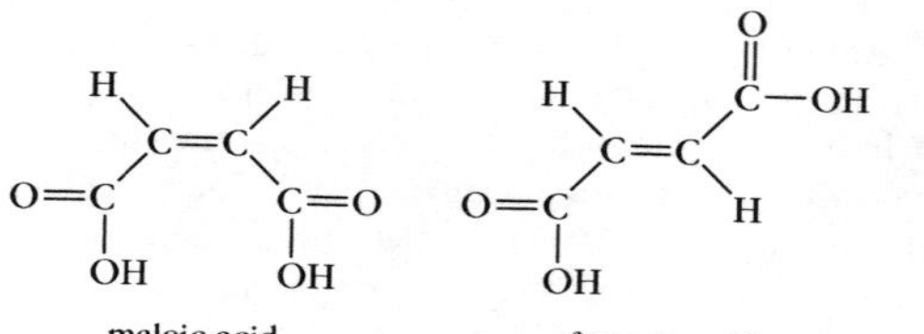

maleic acid (the *cis* isomer) fumaric acid (the *trans* isomer)

8.6 C—N > C=N > C≡N. The order of decreasing bond energy is the reverse order: C≡N > C=N > C—N. See Tables 8.1 and 8.2.

8.7 (a) The electronegativity difference between sodium and chlorine is 2.0, sufficient to cause electron transfer from sodium to chlorine to form Na^+ and Cl^- ions. Molten NaCl conducts an electric current, indicating the presence of ions.

(b) There is an electronegativity difference of 1.2 in BrF, which is sufficient to form a polar covalent bond, but not great enough to cause electron transfer leading to ion formation.

8.8 The Lewis structure of hydrazine is

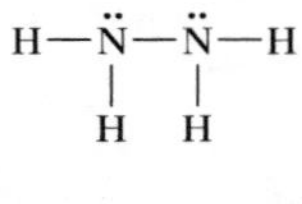

	H	H	N	N	H	H
Valence electrons	1	1	5	5	1	1
Lone pair electrons	0	0	2	2	0	0
$\frac{1}{2}$ shared electrons	1	1	3	3	1	1
Formal charge	0	0	0	0	0	0

8.9 Atoms cannot be rearranged to derive a resonance structure. There is no N-to-O bond in cyanate ion; therefore, such an arrangement cannot be a resonance structure of cyanate ion.

8.10

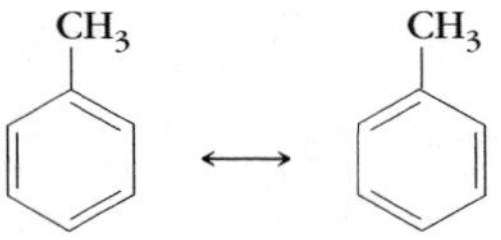

8.11

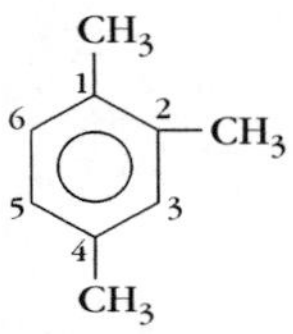

1,2,4-trimethylbenzene

The ring is numbered to give the lowest numbers for the substituents in 1, 2, 3-trimethylbenzene.

8.12 1. (a) 20 carbon atoms and 30 hydrogen atoms
(b) The carbon atom at the top of the six-membered ring
(c) Five C=C double bonds

2. (a) $C_{29}H_{50}O_2$ (b) No C=C double bonds
(c) The H—O bond

Chapter 9

9.1 When the central atom has no lone pairs

9.2 The triangular bipyramidal shape has three of the five pairs situated in equatorial positions 120° apart and the remaining two pairs in axial positions. The square pyramidal shape has four of the atoms bonded to the central atom in a square plane, with the other bonded atom directly above the central atom and equidistant from the other four.

9.3 (a) AX_2E_3 (b) AX_3E_1 (c) AX_2E_3

9.4 Pi bonding is not possible for a carbon atom with sp^3 hybridization because it has no unhybridized $2p$ orbitals. All of its $2p$ orbitals have been hybridized.

9.5 (a) Bromine is more electronegative than iodine, and the H—Br bond is more polar than the H—I bond.
(b) Chlorine is more electronegative than the other two halogens; therefore, the C—Cl bond is more polar than the C—Br and C—I bonds.

9.6

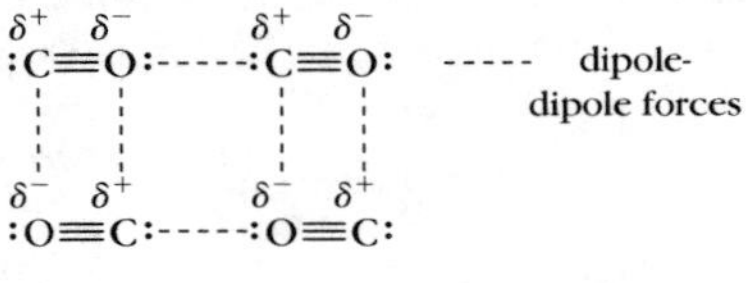

9.7 The F—H · · · F—H hydrogen bond is the strongest because the electronegativity difference between H and F produces a more polar F—H bond than does the lesser electronegativity difference between O and H or N and H in the O—H or N—H bonds.

9.8

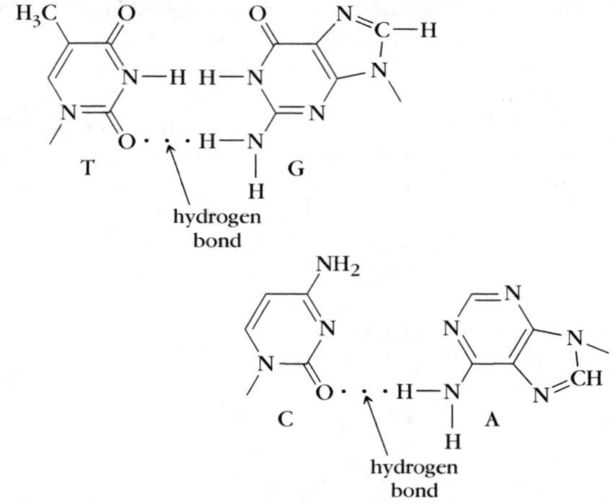

9.9 Replication would be very difficult because covalent bonds would have to be broken. DNA replicates easily because it is hydrogen bonds, not covalent bonds, that occur between the base pairs and hold the two DNA strands together.

Chapter 10

10.1 $(2.7 \times 10^{14} \text{ molecules}) \times \left(\dfrac{64.06 \text{ g } SO_2}{6.02 \times 10^{23} \text{ molecules}}\right) = 2.9 \times 10^{-8} \text{ g } SO_2$

10.2 First, gas molecules are far apart. This allows most light to pass through. Second, molecules are much smaller than the wavelengths of visible light. This means that the waves are not reflected or diffracted by the molecules.

10.3 As more gas molecules are added to a container of fixed volume, there will be more collisions of all of the gas molecules with the container walls. This causes the observed pressure to rise.

10.4 All have the same kinetic energy at the same temperature.

10.5 For a sample of helium, the plot would look like the curve marked He in Figure 10.7. When an equal number of argon molecules, which are heavier, are added to the helium, the distribution of molecular speeds would look like the sum of the curves marked He and O_2 in Figure 10.7, except that the curve for Ar would have its peak a little to the left of the O_2 curve.

10.6 (a) The balloon placed in the freezer will be smaller than the one kept at room temperature because its sample of helium is colder.
(b) Upon warming, the helium balloon that had been in the freezer will be either the same size as the balloon kept at room temperature or perhaps slightly larger because there is a greater chance that He atoms leaked out of the room temperature balloon during the time the other balloon was kept in the freezer. This would be caused by the faster-moving He atoms in the room temperature balloon having more chances to escape from tiny openings in the balloon's walls.

10.7 The gas in the shock absorbers will be more highly compressed. The gas molecules will be closer together. The gas molecules will collide with the walls of the shock absorber more often, and the pressure exerted will be larger.

10.8 Increasing the temperature of a gas causes the gas molecules to move faster, on average. This means that each collision with the container walls involves greater force, because on average, a molecule is moving faster and hits the wall harder. If the container remained the same (constant volume), there would also be more collisions with the container wall because faster-moving molecules would hit the walls more often. Increasing the volume of the container, on the other hand, requires that the faster-moving molecules must travel a greater distance before they strike the container walls. Increasing the volume enough would just balance the greater numbers of harder collisions caused by increased temperature. To maintain a constant volume requires that the pressure increases to match the greater pressure due to more and harder collisions of gas molecules with the walls.

10.9 Two moles of O_2 gas are required for the combustion of one mole of methane gas. If air were pure O_2, the oxygen delivery tube would need to be twice as large as the delivery tube for methane. Since air is only one-fifth O_2, the air delivery tube would need to be 10 times larger than the methane delivery tube to ensure complete combustion.

10.10 Using the ratio of 100 balloons/26.8 g He, calculate the number of balloons 41.8 g of He can fill.

$$\text{Balloons} = (41.8 \text{ g He})\left(\frac{100 \text{ balloons}}{26.8 \text{ g He}}\right) = 155 \text{ balloons}$$

This much He will fill more balloons than needed.

10.11 1. Increase the pressure.
2. Decrease the temperature.
3. Remove some of the gas by reaction to form a nongaseous product.

10.12 Density of Cl_2 at 25 °C and 0.750 atm $= \dfrac{PM}{RT}$

$$= \frac{(0.750 \text{ atm})(70.906 \text{ g/mol})}{(0.0821 \text{ L atm mol}^{-1}\text{ K}^{-1})(298 \text{ K})} = 2.17 \text{ g/L}$$

Density of SO_2 at 25 °C and 0.750 atm $= \dfrac{PM}{RT}$

$$= \frac{(0.750 \text{ atm})(64.06 \text{ g/mol})}{(0.0821 \text{ L atm mol}^{-1}\text{ K}^{-1})(298 \text{ K})} = 1.96 \text{ g/L}$$

Density of Cl_2 at 35 °C and 0.750 atm $= \dfrac{PM}{RT}$

$$= \frac{(0.750 \text{ atm})(70.906 \text{ g/mol})}{(0.0821 \text{ L atm mol}^{-1}\text{ K}^{-1})(308 \text{ K})} = 2.10 \text{ g/L}$$

Density of SO_2 at 25 °C and 2.60 atm $= \dfrac{PM}{RT}$

$$= \frac{(2.60 \text{ atm})(64.06 \text{ g/mol})}{(0.0821 \text{ L atm mol}^{-1}\text{ K}^{-1})(298 \text{ K})} = 6.81 \text{ g/L}$$

10.13 Density of He $= 1.23 \times 10^{-4}$ g/mL
Density of Li $= 0.53$ g/mL
Since the density of He is so much less than that of Li, the atoms in a sample of He must be much farther apart than the atoms in a sample of Li. This idea is in keeping with the general principle of the kinetic-molecular theory that the particles making up a gas are far from one another.

10.14 A 50-50 mixture of N_2 and O_2 would have less N_2 in it than does air. Since O_2 molecules have greater mass than N_2 molecules, this 50-50 mixture has greater density than air.

10.15 (a) If lowering the temperature causes the volume to decrease, by $PV = nRT$, the pressure can be assumed to be constant. The value of n is unchanged. Since both P and n remain unchanged, the partial pressures of the gases in the mixture remain unchanged.
(b) When the total pressure of a gas mixture increases, the partial pressure of each gas in the mixture increases because the partial pressure of each gas in the mixture is the product of the mole fraction for that gas and the total pressure.

10.16 We can calculate the total number of moles of gas in the flask from the given information.

$$n = \frac{PV}{RT} = \frac{\left(\frac{626}{760}\right) \text{atm } (0.355 \text{ L})}{(0.0821 \text{ L atm mol}^{-1}\text{ K}^{-1})(308 \text{ K})} = 0.01156 \text{ mol gas}$$

The number of moles of Ne is

$$0.146 \text{ g Ne} \times \frac{1 \text{ mol Ne}}{20.18 \text{ g/mol}} = 0.007235 \text{ mol Ne}$$

We find the number of moles of Ar by subtraction.

$$0.01156 \text{ mol gas} - 0.007235 \text{ mol Ne} = 0.004325 \text{ mol Ar}$$

$$0.004325 \text{ mol Ar} \times 39.948 \text{ g/mol} = 0.173 \text{ g Ar}$$

10.17 The value of n depends directly on the measured pressure, P. Intermolecular attractions in a real gas would cause the measured P to be slightly smaller than for an ideal gas. The lower value of P would cause the calculated number of moles to be somewhat smaller. Using this slightly smaller value of n in the denominator would cause the calculated molar mass to be a little larger than it should be.

10.18 Mass of S burned per hour $= (3.06 \times 10^6 \text{ kg})(0.04)$

$$= 1 \times 10^5 \text{ kg}$$

$$\text{Mass of } SO_2 \text{ per hour} = (1 \times 10^5 \text{ kg})\left(\frac{64.06 \text{ kg } SO_2}{32.07 \text{ kg S}}\right) 2 \times 10^5 \text{ kg}$$

$$\text{Mass of } SO_2 \text{ per year} = (2 \times 10^5 \text{ kg/hr})(8760 \text{ hr/yr}) = 2 \times 10^9 \text{ kg/yr}$$

10.19 Vol percent $SO_2 = (5 \text{ parts } SO_2/10^6 \text{ parts air}) \times 100\%$

$$= 5 \times 10^{-4} \text{ vol\%}$$

10.20 1 metric ton $= 1000$ kg $= 10^6$ g $= 1$ Mg

$$\text{Mass of } HNO_3 = (400 \text{ Mg } N_2)\left(\frac{2 \text{ Mg NO}}{\text{Mg } N_2}\right) \times \left(\frac{1 \text{ Mg } NO_2}{1 \text{ Mg NO}}\right)\left(\frac{1 \text{ Mg } HNO_3}{1 \text{ Mg } NO_2}\right) = 800 \text{ Mg } HNO_3$$

10.21 $\cdot NO_2 \xrightarrow{h\nu} NO\cdot + \cdot O\cdot$

$$O_3 \xrightarrow{h\nu} O_2 + \cdot O\cdot$$

$$\cdot O\cdot + O_2 \longrightarrow O_3$$

10.22 Among the many possible molecules would be: NO, which comes from automobile combustion; NO_2, which comes from reactions of NO and O_2 in the atmosphere; O_3, which comes from reactions of NO, NO_2, and O_2 in the atmosphere; and hydrocarbons, and oxidation products of hydrocarbon reactions with O_2 and other reactive species.

10.23 Natural sources: animal respiration, forest fires, decay of cellulose materials, partial digestion of carbohydrates, volcanoes. Human sources: burning fossil fuels, burning agricultural wastes and refined cellulose products such as paper, decay of carbon compounds in landfills.

10.24 (a) 4.7%; (b) 19.0%; (c) 4.2%; 1950–2001 showed the greatest percentage increase in CO_2.

10.25 The fluctuations occur because of the seasons. Photosynthesis, which uses CO_2, is greatest during the spring and summer, accounting for lower CO_2 levels.

10.26 For this calculation, we can use the figure of 450×10^9 passenger miles. Using the ratio of 2×10^3 kg CO_2/3000 passenger miles, we can calculate the CO_2 released.

$$\text{Quantity of } CO_2 = 450 \times 10^9 \text{ passenger mi} \times \frac{2 \times 10^3 \text{ kg } CO_2}{3 \times 10^3 \text{ passenger mi}} = 3 \times 10^{11} \text{ kg } CO_2$$

If a typical automobile gets 20 mi/gal of fuel and about 1.5 passengers are transported for every mile the automobile travels, then an automobile gets 30 passenger miles per gallon. The number of gallons used is

$$\text{Volume of gasoline} = 450 \times 10^9 \text{ passenger mi} \times \frac{1 \text{ gal gasoline}}{30 \text{ passenger mi}} = 2 \times 10^{10} \text{ gal gasoline}$$

Assume the gasoline produces about the same mass of CO_2 per gallon as does jet fuel, or 2×10^3 kg CO_2/200 gal.

$$\text{Quantity of } CO_2 \text{ from gasoline} = 2 \times 10^{10} \text{ gal gasoline} \times \frac{2 \times 10^3 \text{ kg } CO_2}{200 \text{ gal gasoline}} = 2 \times 10^{11} \text{ kg } CO_2$$

So the numbers are about the same for these two modes of transportation.

10.27 He meant the burning coal converted its carbon into carbon dioxide in the air, thus increasing atmospheric CO_2 concentration.

Chapter 11

11.1 The London forces are greater between bromoform molecules than between chloroform molecules because the bromoform molecules have more electrons. This stronger intermolecular attraction causes the $CHBr_3$ molecules to exhibit a greater surface tension. (The dipole in each molecule contributes less than the London forces to the intermolecular attractions.)

11.2 (a) Water and glycerol would have similar surface tensions because of extensive hydrogen bonding. (b) Octane and decane would have similar surface tensions because both are alkane hydrocarbons.

11.3 (a) 62 °C (b) 0 °C (c) 80 °C

11.4 Bubbles form within a boiling liquid when the vapor pressure of the liquid equals the pressure of the surroundings of the liquid sample. The bubbles are actually filled with vapor of the boiling liquid. One way to prove this would be to trap some of these bubbles and allow them to condense. They would condense to form the liquid that had boiled.

11.5 The evaporating water carries with it thermal energy from the water inside the pot. In addition, a large quantity of thermal energy is required to cause the water to evaporate. Much of this thermal energy comes from the water inside the pot.

11.6 Estimated ΔH°_{vap} for Kr ≈ 20 kJ/mol based on HBr, Cl_2, and C_4H_{10}, but based on Xe, the value is probably closer to 10 kJ/mol. Estimated ΔH°_{vap} for NO_2 ≈ 20 kJ/mol based on propane and HCl.

11.7 (a) Bromine molecules have more electrons than chlorine molecules. Therefore, bromine molecules are held together by stronger intermolecular attractions.
(b) Ammonia molecules are attracted to one another by hydrogen bonds. This causes ammonia to have a higher boiling point than that of methane, which has no hydrogen bonding.

11.8 Two moles of liquid bromine crystallizing liberates 21.59 kJ of energy. One mole of liquid water crystallizing liberates 6.02 kJ of energy.

11.9 High humidity conditions make the evaporation of water or the sublimation of ice less favorable. Under these conditions, the sublimation of ice required to make the frost-free refrigerator work is less favorable, so the defrost cycle is less effective.

11.10 The impurity molecules are less likely to be converted from the solid phase to the vapor phase. This causes them to be left behind as the molecules that sublime go into the gas phase and then condense at some other place. The molecules that condense are almost all of the same kind, so the sublimed sample is much purer than the original.

11.11 The curve is the vapor pressure curve. Upward: condensation. Downward: vaporization. Left to right: vaporization. Right to left: condensation.

11.12 (a) If liquid CO_2 is slowly released from a cylinder of CO_2, gaseous CO_2 is formed. The temperature remains constant (at room temperature) because there is time for energy to be transferred from the surroundings to separate the CO_2 molecules from their intermolecular attractions. This can be seen from the phase diagram as the phase changes from liquid to vapor as the pressure decreases.
(b) If the pressure is suddenly released, the attractive forces between a large number of CO_2 molecules must be overcome, which requires energy. This energy comes from the surroundings as well as from the CO_2 molecules themselves, causing the temperature of both the surroundings and the CO_2 molecules to decrease. On the phase diagram for CO_2, a decrease in both temperature and pressure moves into a region where only solid CO_2 exists.

11.13 It is predicted that a small concentration of gold will be found in the lead and that a small concentration of lead will be found in the gold. This will occur because of the movement of the metal atoms with time, as predicted by the kinetic molecular theory.

11.14 One Po atom belongs to its unit cell. Two Li atoms belong to its unit cell. Four Ca atoms belong to its unit cell.

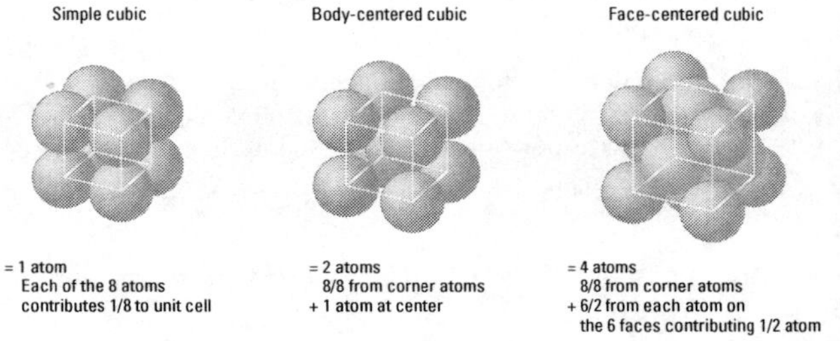

11.15 Each Cs^+ ion at the center of the cube has eight Cl^- ions as its neighbors. One eighth of each Cl^- ion belongs to that Cs^+ ion. So the formula for this salt must be a 1 : 1 ratio of Cs^+ ions to Cl^- ions, or CsCl.

11.16 Cooling a liquid above its freezing point causes the temperature to decrease. When the liquid begins to solidify, energy is released as atoms, molecules, or ions move closer together to form in the solid crystal lattice. This causes the temperature to remain constant until all the molecules in the liquid have positioned themselves in the lattice. Further cooling then causes the temperature to decrease. The shape of this curve is common to all substances that can exist as liquids.

11.17 Increasing strength of metallic bonding is related to increasing numbers of valence electrons. In the transition metals, the presence of *d*-orbital electrons causes stronger metallic bonding. Beyond a half-filled set of *d*-orbitals, however, extra electrons have the effect of decreasing the strength of metallic bonding.

Chapter 12

12.1 (a) $4\ H_2$
(b) $C_7H_{16} \rightarrow C_7H_8 + 4\ H_2$
(c) Toluene has a much higher octane number and can be used as an octane enhancer.

12.2 $$\%\text{ oxygen} = \left(\frac{16.0}{46.0}\right) \times 100\% = 34.8\%$$

Ethanol is more highly oxygenated than the hydrocarbons in gasoline.

12.3 (a) $C_2H_6O + 2\ O_2 \rightarrow 2\ CO + 3\ H_2O$

$$\frac{\text{g CO}}{\text{g ethanol}} = \frac{2(28.0\text{ g})}{46.0\text{ g}} = 1.22 \text{ g CO/g ethanol}$$

(b) $C_7H_8 + \frac{11}{2} O_2 \rightarrow 7\ CO + 4\ H_2O$

$$\frac{\text{g CO}}{\text{g toluene}} = \frac{7(28.0\ \text{g})}{92.0\ \text{g}} = 2.13\ \text{g CO/g toluene}$$

(c) Ethanol produces less CO per gram than does toluene.

12.4 $CH_4(g) + \frac{3}{2} O_2(g) \rightarrow CO(g) + 2\ H_2O(g)$

Thus, 28.0 g CO is produced per 16.0 g CH_4;

$$\frac{28.0\ \text{g CO}}{16.0\ \text{g CH}_4} = 1.75\ \text{g CO/g CH}_4$$

$C_8H_{18}(\ell) + \frac{17}{2} O_2(g) \rightarrow 8\ CO(g) + 9\ H_2O(g)$

114.0 g octane produces 224.0 g CO;

$$\frac{224\ \text{g CO}}{114.0\ \text{g octane}} = 1.96\ \text{g CO/g C}_8\text{H}_{18}$$

$\frac{1.96}{1.75} = 1.12$, which indicates 12% more CO is produced per gram of octane than per gram of methane.

12.5 Thermal energy $= 1.5 \times 10^6\ \text{bbl oil} \times \frac{5.9 \times 10^9\ \text{J}}{1\ \text{bbl oil}} = 8.9 \times 10^{15}\ \text{J}$

Electricity delivered $= 1.5 \times 10^6\ \text{bbl} \times \frac{1628\ \text{kWh}}{1\ \text{bbl}} \times 0.33 = 8.1 \times 10^8\ \text{kWh}$

12.6 Carbon dioxide cannot be burned.

12.7 Ten or so carbon atoms in an alcohol molecule will make it much less water-soluble than alcohols with fewer numbers of carbon atoms.

12.8

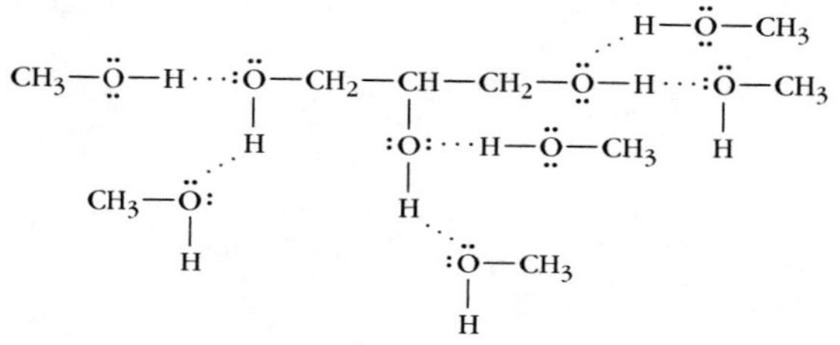

12.9 The acetaldehyde molecule has two fewer hydrogen atoms compared with the ethanol molecule. Loss of hydrogen is oxidation. The acetaldehyde molecule is more oxidized than the ethanol molecule. Comparing the formulas for acetaldehyde and acetic acid, the hydrogen atoms are the same, but the acetic acid molecule has one additional oxygen atom. Gain of oxygen is oxidation. So the acetic acid molecule is more oxidized than the acetaldehyde molecule.

12.10

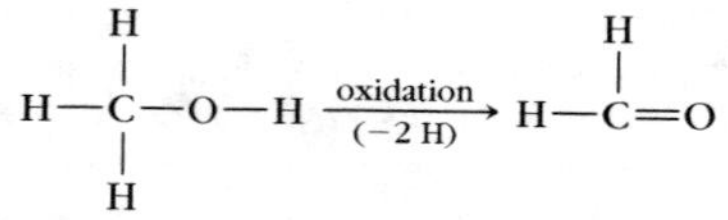

12.11 $CH_3CH_2CH_2OH$, 1-propanol

12.12 (a) Estradiol contains two alcohol groups (—OH).

(b) Secondary alcohol

(c) Oxidation (removal of two hydrogens)

(d) Estradiol: Two alcohol groups, aromatic ring, one $—CH_3$ group

Testosterone: One alcohol group; one ketone group; C=C double bond in ring; two $—CH_3$ groups

12.13 Conversion of a ketone on the five-membered ring to a secondary alcohol by reduction (addition of 2 H atoms)

12.14

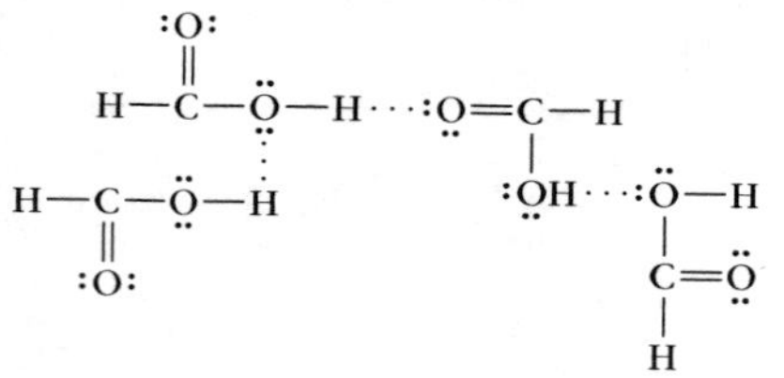

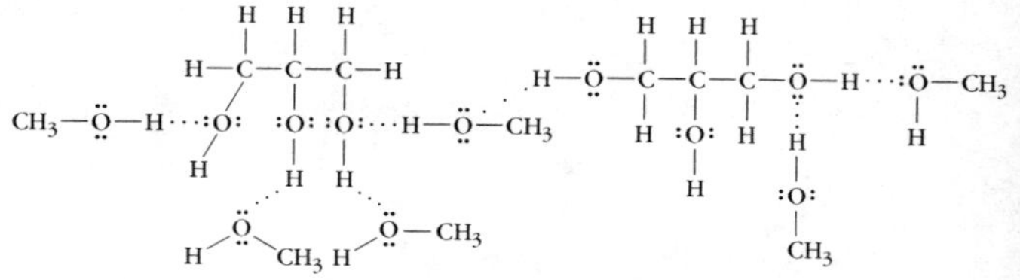

12.15 (a)

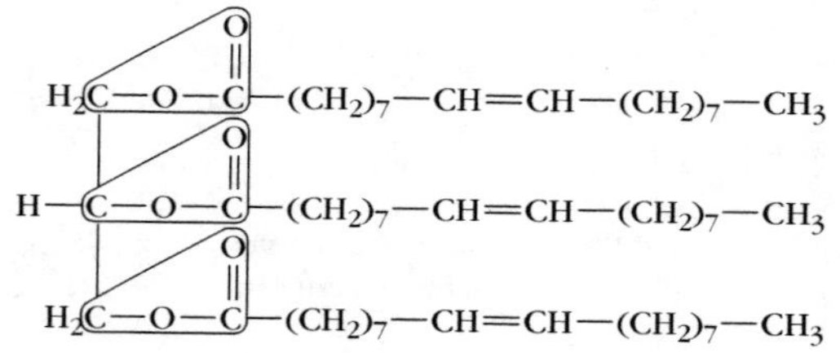

(b)

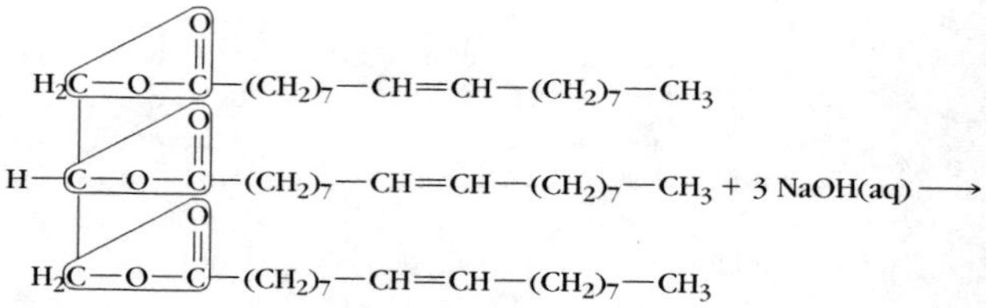

(c)

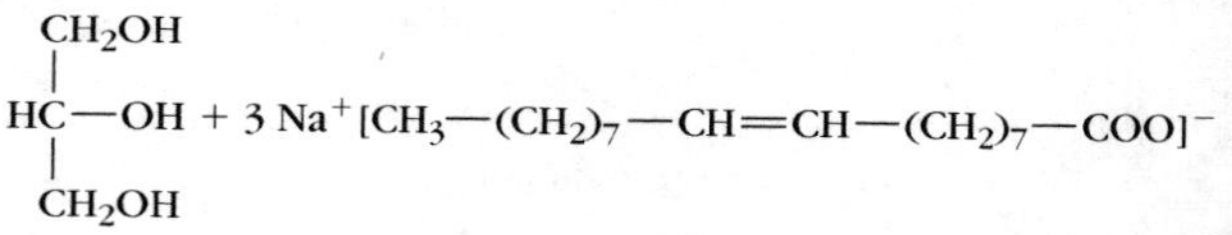

12.16 The ends of the chains are possibly occupied by the OR groups from the initiator molecules.

12.17

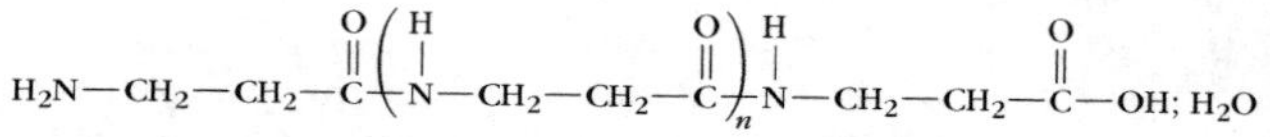

12.18 (1) Amine (2) Carboxylic acid (3) Amide (4) Ester

12.19 Serine and glutamine could hydrogen-bond to one another if they were close in two adjacent protein chains because they have polar groups containing H atoms in their R groups. Glycine and valine would not because they have no additional polar groups in their R groups.

12.20

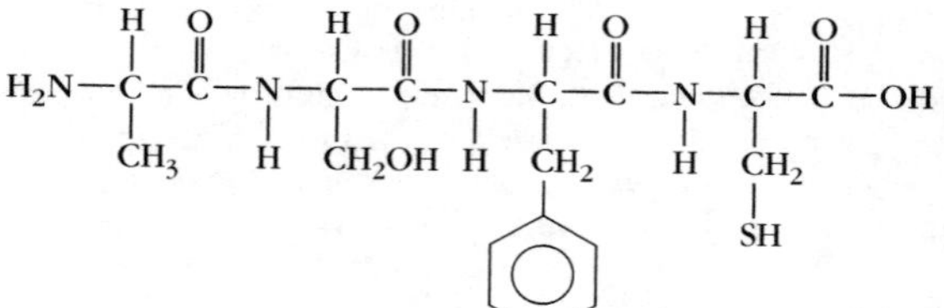

12.21 The OH groups in this molecule allow it to be extensively hydrogen-bonded with solvent water molecules.

12.22 Cellulose contains glucose molecules linked together by *trans* 1,4 linkages. Ruminant animals have large colonies of bacteria and protozoa that live in the forestomach and digest cellulose.

12.23 If humans could digest cellulose, then common plants that are easy to grow could become food. There might be less reliance upon cultivation of plants for food. In addition, the entire plant could be used for food rather than just certain parts eaten and the other parts wasted. On the other hand, in times of famine, there might not be enough cellulose to go around. Destroying trees and other plants for food might cause enlargements of desert regions and the disappearance of entire species of plants.

Chapter 13

13.1 (a)

i. $\text{Rate} = -\dfrac{\Delta[\text{Cv}^+]}{\Delta t}$

$= -\dfrac{(0.793 \times 10^{-5} - 1.46 \times 10^{-5})\ \text{mol/L}}{(60.0 - 40.0)\ \text{s}}$

$= \dfrac{6.67 \times 10^{-6}\ \text{mol/L}}{20.0\ \text{s}} = 3.3 \times 10^{-7}\ \text{mol L}^{-1}\ \text{s}^{-1}$

ii. $\text{Rate} = -\dfrac{(0.429 \times 10^{-5} - 2.71 \times 10^{-5})\ \text{mol/L}}{(80.0 - 20.0)\ \text{s}}$

$= 3.8 \times 10^{-7}\ \text{mol L}^{-1}\ \text{s}^{-1}$

iii. $\text{Rate} = -\dfrac{(0.232 \times 10^{-5} - 5.00 \times 10^{-5})\ \text{mol/L}}{(100.0 - 0.0)\ \text{s}}$

$= 4.8 \times 10^{-7}\ \text{mol L}^{-1}\ \text{s}^{-1}$

(b)

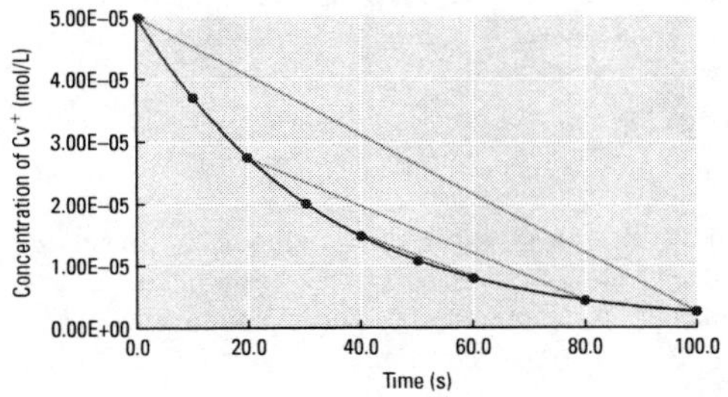

(c) The rate is faster when the concentration of Cv^+ is larger. As the reaction takes place, the rate gets slower. There is a much larger change in concentration from 0 s to 50 s than from 50 s to 100 s. Therefore, the $\Delta\ [\text{Cv}^+]$ is more than three times bigger for the time range from 20 s to 80 s than it is for the time range from 40 s to 60 s, even though Δt is exactly three times larger.

13.2 (a) Rate (1) is twice rate (3); rate (2) is twice rate (4); rate (3) is twice rate (5).
(b) In each case, the $[\text{Cv}^+]$ is twice as great when the rate is twice as great.
(c) Yes, the rate doubles when $[\text{Cv}^+]$ doubles.

13.3

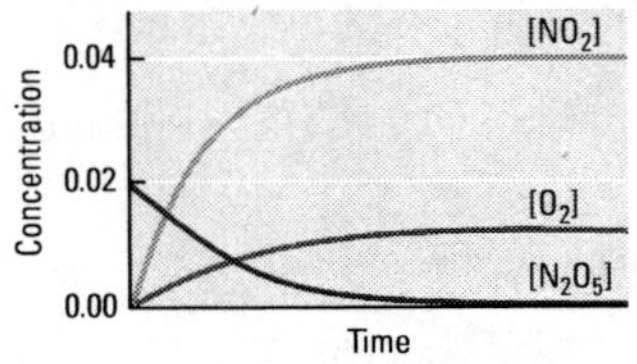

13.4 $\text{Rate}_1 = k[\text{CH}_3\text{COOCH}_3][\text{OH}^-]$
$\text{Rate}_2 = k(2[\text{CH}_3\text{COOCH}_3])(\tfrac{1}{2}[\text{OH}^-] = k[\text{CH}_3\text{COOCH}_3][\text{OH}^-]$
The rate is unchanged.

13.5

$$\text{Rate} = k[\text{NO}]^x[\text{Cl}_2]^y$$

Taking the log of both sides and applying to experiments 4 and 2 gives

$$\log(\text{Rate}_4) = \log(k) + x\log[\text{NO}]_4 + y\log[\text{Cl}_2]_4$$

$$\log(\text{Rate}_2) = \log(k) + x\log[\text{NO}]_2 + y\log[\text{Cl}_2]_2$$

Recognizing that $[\text{Cl}_2]_4 = [\text{Cl}_2]_2$ and then subtracting the second equation from the first gives

$$\log(\text{Rate}_4) - \log(\text{Rate}_2) = x\log[\text{NO}]_4 - x\log[\text{NO}]_2$$

Using the properties of logarithms gives

$$\log\{\text{Rate}_4/\text{Rate}_2\} = x\{\log[\text{NO}]_4/[\text{NO}]_2\}$$

So

$$x = \log\{\text{Rate}_4/\text{Rate}_2\}/\{\log[\text{NO}]_4/[\text{NO}]_2\} \quad \text{QED}$$

Now we can insert the actual numbers from experiments 4 and 2:

$$x = [\log(6.60 \times 10^{-4}/1.65 \times 10^{-4})]/\log(0.04/0.02)$$

$$x = \log 4/\log 2 = 0.602/0.301 = 2$$

13.6 (a) $\text{CH}_3\text{NC} \rightarrow \text{CH}_3\text{CN}$ unimolecular
(b) $2\ \text{HI} \rightarrow \text{H}_2 + \text{I}_2$ bimolecular
(c) $\text{NO}_2\text{Cl} \rightarrow \text{NO}_2 + \text{Cl}$ unimolecular
(d) $\text{C}_4\text{H}_8 \rightarrow \text{C}_4\text{H}_8$ unimolecular
(e) $\text{NO}_2\text{Cl} + \text{Cl} \rightarrow \text{NO}_2 + \text{Cl}_2$ bimolecular

13.7

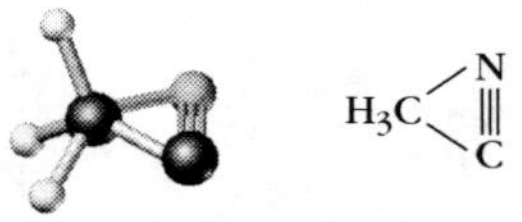

The Lewis structure has five pairs of electrons around one C atom, which would not be stable. However, this is a transition state, which is, by definition, unstable.

13.8 (1) (2) (3) (4)

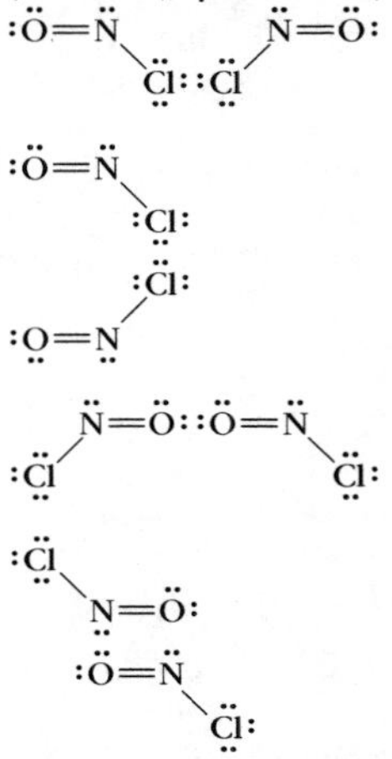

(1) and (2) are much more likely to result in a reaction than are (3) and (4).

(1) and (2) are much more likely to result in a reaction than are (3) and (4).

13.9 (a) $k = Ae^{-E_a/RT}$

$$= (6.31 \times 10^8\ \text{L mol}^{-1}\ \text{s}^{-1})\, e^{\frac{-10{,}000\ \text{J/mol}}{(8.314\ \text{J K}^{-1}\ \text{mol}^{-1})(370\ \text{K})}}$$

$$k = 2.4 \times 10^7\ \text{L mol}^{-1}\ \text{S}^{-1}$$

(b) $\text{Rate} = k[\text{NO}][\text{O}_3]$

$$= (2.4 \times 10^7\ \text{L mol}^{-1}\ \text{s}^{-1})(1.0 \times 10^{-3}\ \text{mol/L}) \times (5.0 \times 10^{-4}\ \text{mol/L})$$

$$= 12\ \text{mol L}^{-1}\ \text{s}^{-1}$$

13.10 The reaction does not occur in a single step. If it did, the rate law would be $\text{Rate} = k[\text{NO}_2][\text{CO}]$.

13.11 $\text{Rate} = k[\text{HOI}][\text{I}^-]$

13.12 (a) $2\ \text{ICl(g)} + \text{H}_2\text{(g)} \rightarrow 2\ \text{HCl(g)} + \text{I}_2\text{(g)}$
(b) $\text{Rate} = k_2[\text{HI}][\text{ICl}]$
However, HI is an intermediate. Assume that the concentration of HI reaches a steady state.

Rate of step +1 = rate of step −1 + rate of step 2

Also assume that step 2 is much slower than step +1 and step −1. Then

$$k_1[\text{ICl}][\text{H}_2] = k_{-1}[\text{HI}][\text{HCl}]$$

$$[\text{HI}] = \frac{k_1[\text{ICl}][\text{H}_2]}{k_{-1}[\text{HCl}]}$$

$$\text{Rate} = k_2[\text{ICl}][\text{HI}] = k_2[\text{ICl}] \times \frac{k_1[\text{ICl}][\text{H}_2]}{k_{-1}[\text{HCl}]}$$
$$= \frac{k_1k_2}{k_{-1}}[\text{ICl}]^2[\text{H}_2][\text{HCl}]^{-1}$$

(c) The rate is inversely proportional to the concentration of the product, HCl.
(d) Because [HCl] increases as the reaction proceeds, the rate of reaction will decrease more quickly over time than it would if $[\text{HCl}]^{-1}$ were not in the rate law. However, the rate constant will not change.

13.13 (a) $Ce^{4+} + Mn^{2+} \rightarrow Ce^{3+} + Mn^{3+}$
$Ce^{4+} + Mn^{3+} \rightarrow Ce^{3+} + Mn^{4+}$
$Mn^{4+} + Tl^{+} \rightarrow Mn^{2+} + Tl^{3+}$
$2\,Ce^{4+} + Tl^{+} \rightarrow 2\,Ce^{3+} + Tl^{3+}$
(b) Intermediates are Mn^{3+} and Mn^{4+}.
(c) The catalyst is Mn^{2+}.
(d) Rate = $k[Ce^{4+}][Mn^{2+}]$
(e) Rate = $k[Ce^{4+}]^2[Mn^{2+}][Ce^{3+}]^{-1}$

13.14 (a) The concentration of a homogeneous catalyst *must* appear in the rate law.
(b) A catalyst does not appear in the equation for an overall reaction.
(c) A *homogeneous* catalyst must always be in the same phase as the reactants.

Chapter 14

14.1 (a) $(\text{conc. Al}) = \frac{2.70\text{ g}}{\text{mL}} \times \frac{1000\text{ mL}}{1\text{ L}} \times \frac{1\text{ mol}}{26.98\text{ g}}$
$= 100.\text{ mol/L}$

(b) $(\text{conc. benzene}) = \frac{0.880\text{ g}}{\text{mL}} \times \frac{1000\text{ mL}}{1\text{ L}} \times \frac{1\text{ mol}}{78.11\text{ g}}$
$= 11.3\text{ mol/L}$

(c) $(\text{conc. water}) = \frac{0.998\text{ g}}{\text{mL}} \times \frac{1000\text{ mL}}{1\text{ L}} \times \frac{1\text{ mol}}{18.02\text{ g}}$
$= 55.4\text{ mol/L}$

(d) $(\text{conc. Au}) = \frac{19.32\text{ g}}{\text{mL}} \times \frac{1000\text{ mL}}{1\text{ L}} \times \frac{1\text{ mol}}{196.97\text{ g}}$
$= 98.1\text{ mol/L}$

14.2 The mixture is not at equilibrium, but the reaction is so slow that there is no change in concentrations. You could show that the system was not at equilibrium by providing a catalyst or by raising the temperature to speed up the reaction.

14.3 (a) The new mixture is not at equilibrium because the quotient (conc. *trans*)/(conc. *cis*) no longer equals the equilibrium constant. Because (conc. *cis*) was halved, the quotient is twice K_c.
(b) The rate *trans* → *cis* remains the same as before, because (conc. *trans*) did not change. The rate *cis* → *trans* is only half as great, because (conc. *cis*) is half as great as at equilibrium.
(c) At 600 K, K_c is 1.47. Thus, [*trans*] = 1.47[*cis*].
(d) 0.15 mol/L

14.4 (a) If the coefficients of an equation are halved, the numerical value for the new equilibrium constant is the square root of the previous equilibrium constant. So the new equilibrium constant is $(6.25 \times 10^{-58})^{1/2} = 2.50 \times 10^{-29}$.
(b) If a chemical equation is reversed, the value for the new equilibrium constant is the reciprocal of the previous equilibrium constant. So the new equilibrium constant is $1/(6.25 \times 10^{-58}) = 1.60 \times 10^{57}$.

14.5 (a) $K_P = K_c \times (RT)^{\Delta n} = (3.5 \times 10^8\text{ L}^2\text{ mol}^{-2})$
$\times \{(0.082057\text{ L atm K}^{-1}\text{ mol}^{-1})(298)\}^{-2}$
$= 5.8 \times 10^5\text{ atm}^{-2}$
(b) $K_P = (3.2 \times 10^{81}\text{ L mol}^{-1})$
$\times \{(0.082057\text{ L atm mol}^{-1}\text{ K}^{-1})(298\text{ K})\}^{-1}$
$= 1.3 \times 10^{80}\text{ atm}^{-1}$
(c) $K_P = K_c = 1.7 \times 10^{-3}$
(d) $K_P = (1.7 \times 10^2\text{ L mol}^{-1})$
$\times \{(0.082057\text{ L atm mol}^{-1}\text{ K}^{-1})(298\text{ K})\}^{-1}$
$= 6.9\text{ atm}^{-1}$

14.6 (a) Because K_c for the forward reaction is small, K_c' for the reverse reaction is large.
(b) $K_c' = \frac{1}{K_c} = \frac{1}{1.8 \times 10^{-5}} = 5.6 \times 10^4$
(c) Ammonium ions and hydroxide ions should react, using up nearly all of whichever is the limiting reactant.
(d) $NH_4^+(aq) + OH^-(aq) \rightleftharpoons NH_3(aq) + H_2O(\ell)$
$NH_3(aq) \rightleftharpoons NH_3(g)$
You might detect the odor of $NH_3(g)$ above the solution. A piece of moist red litmus paper above the solution would turn blue.

14.7 Q should have the same mathematical form as K_P, so for the general Equation 14.1

$$Q_P = \frac{P_C^c \times P_D^d}{P_A^a \times P_B^b}$$

The rules for Q_P and K_P are analogous to those for Q and K_c:
If $Q_P > K_P$, then the reverse reaction occurs.
If $Q_P = K_P$, then the system is at equilibrium.
If $Q_P < K_P$, the forward reaction occurs.

14.8 $PCl_5(s) \rightleftharpoons PCl_3(g) + Cl_2(g)$
(a) Adding Cl_2 shifts the equilibrium to the left.
(b) Adding PCl_3 to the container shifts the equilibrium to the left.
(c) Because $PCl_5(s)$ does not appear in the K_c expression, adding some will not affect the equilibrium.

14.9 $Q = \frac{(\text{conc. H}_2)(\text{conc. I}_2)}{(\text{conc. HI})^2} = \frac{(0.102 \times 3)(0.0018 \times 3)}{(0.096 \times 3)^2}$
$= \frac{(0.102)(0.0018)(9)}{(0.096)^2(9)} = 0.020 = K_c$
Since $Q = K_c$, the system is at equilibrium under the new conditions. No shift is needed and none occurs.

14.10 From Problem-Solving Practice 14.7, $[NO_2] = 0.0418$ mol/L and $[N_2O_4] = 0.292$ mol/L.
Decreasing the volume from 4.00 to 1.33 L increases the concentrations as

$$(\text{conc. NO}_2) = 0.0418 \times \frac{4.00}{1.33} = 0.1257\text{ mol/L}$$

$$(\text{conc. N}_2\text{O}_4) = 0.292 \times \frac{4.00}{1.33} = 0.8782\text{ mol/L}$$

$$Q = \frac{(\text{conc. NO}_2)^2}{(\text{conc. N}_2\text{O}_4)} = \frac{(0.1257)^2}{0.8782} = 1.80 \times 10^{-2}$$

which is greater than K_c. Therefore, the equilibrium should shift to the left. Let x be the change in concentration of NO_2, (which should be negative).

	N_2O_4	⇌	$2\,NO_2$
Initial concentration (mol/L)	0.8782		0.1257
Change as reaction occurs (mol/L)	$-\frac{1}{2}x$		x
New equilibrium concentration (mol/L)	$0.8782 - \frac{1}{2}x$		$0.1257 + x$

$$K_c = 5.9 \times 10^{-3} = \frac{(0.1257 + x)^2}{0.8782 - 0.500x}$$

$$= \frac{(1.580 \times 10^{-2}) + (2.514 \times 10^{-1})x + x^2}{0.8782 - 0.500x}$$

$$5.18 \times 10^{-3} - (2.95 \times 10^{-3})x$$

$$= (1.580 \times 10^{-2}) + (2.514 \times 10^{-1})x + x^2$$

$$x^2 + 0.2544x + (1.062 \times 10^{-2}) = 0$$

$$x = \frac{-0.2544 \pm \sqrt{6.472 \times 10^{-2} - (4 \times 1 \times 1.062 \times 10^{-2})}}{2}$$

$$x = \frac{-0.2544 \pm 0.1491}{2}$$

$$x = -0.0526 \quad \text{or} \quad x = -0.2018$$

The second root is mathematically reasonable, but results in a negative value for the $[NO_2]$. The new equilibrium concentrations are

$$[NO_2] = 0.1257 - 0.0526 = 0.0730 \text{ mol/L}$$

$$[N_2O_4] = 0.8782 - \tfrac{1}{2}(-0.0526) = 0.9045 \text{ mol/L}$$

Compared to the initial equilibrium, the concentrations have changed by

$$NO_2: \frac{0.0730}{0.0418} = 1.75 \qquad N_2O_4: \frac{0.945}{0.292} = 3.10$$

The concentration of N_2O_4 did increase by more than a factor of 3. The concentration of NO_2 increased by 1.75, which is less than a factor of 3 increase.

14.11

	How Reaction System Changes	Equilibrium Shifts	Change in K_c?
(a) Add reactant	Some reactants consumed	To right	No
(b) Remove reactant	More reactants formed	To left	No
(c) Add product	More reactants formed	To left	No
(d) Remove product	More products formed	To right	No
(e) Increase *P* by decreasing *V*	Total pressure decreases	Toward fewer gas molecules	No
(f) Decrease *P* by increasing *V*	Total pressure increases	Toward more gas molecules	No
(g) Increase *T*	Heat transfer into system	In endothermic direction	Yes
(h) Decrease *T*	Heat transfer out of system	In exothermic direction	Yes

If a substance is added or removed, the equilibrium is affected only if the substance's concentration appears in the equilibrium constant expression, or if its addition or removal changes concentrations that appear in the equilibrium constant expression. Changing pressure by changing volume affects an equilibrium only for gas phase reactions in which there is a difference in the number of moles of gaseous reactants and products.

14.12 (a) The reaction is exothermic. $\Delta H^\circ = -46.11$ kJ.
(b) The reaction is not favored by entropy.
(c) The reaction produces more products at low temperatures.
(d) If you increase *T* the reaction will go faster, but a smaller amount of products will be produced.

Chapter 15

15.1 The data in Table 15.2 indicate that the solubility of alcohols decrease as the hydrocarbon chain lengthens. Thus, 1-octanol is less soluble in water than 1-heptanol and 1-decanol should be even less soluble than 1-octanol.

15.2 Methanol is more water soluble than is octanol, but octanol is more soluble in gasoline. The octanol molecule is more hydrocarbon-like and this explains its solubility in gasoline. The methanol molecule is more water-like and this explains its greater solubility in water.

15.3 34 g NH_4Cl would crystallize from solution at 20 °C.

15.4 (a) Unsaturated (b) Supersaturated (c) Saturated

15.5 The solubility of CO_2 decreases with increasing temperature, and the beverage loses its carbonation, causing it to go "flat."

15.6 Putting back water that is too warm would decrease the solubility of oxygen in the lake or river, thereby decreasing the oxygen concentration. This could cause a fish kill if the oxygen concentration dropped sufficiently.

15.7 Hot solvent would cause more of the solute to dissolve because Le Chatelier's principle states that at higher temperature an equilibrium will shift in the endothermic direction.

15.8 (a) Mass fraction of $NaHCO_3$

$$= \frac{0.20}{1000 + 6.5 + 0.20 + 0.1 + 0.10} = 2.0 \times 10^{-4}$$

$$\text{Wt. fraction} = 2.0 \times 10^{-4} \times 100\% = 2.0 \times 10^{-2}$$

(b) KCl and $CaCl_2$ each have the lowest mass fraction, 0.015.

15.9 (a) The 20-ppb sample has the higher lead concentration. (The other sample is 3 ppb lead.)
(b) 0.015 mg/L is equivalent to 0.015 ppm, which is 15 ppb. The 20-ppb sample exceeds the EPA limit; the 3-ppb sample does not.

15.10 $\frac{280 \text{ mg}}{1 \text{ d}} \times \frac{0.500 \text{ L}}{12 \text{ mg}} = \frac{12 \text{ L}}{\text{d}} = 12$ bottles per day

15.11 $3.5 \times 10^{20} \text{ gal} \times \frac{3.785 \text{ L}}{\text{gal}} \times \frac{1 \times 10^{-3} \text{ mg Au}}{1 \text{ L}}$

$$= 1 \times 10^{18} \text{ mg Au} = 1 \times 10^{15} \text{ g Au}$$

$$1 \times 10^{15} \text{ g Au} \times \frac{1 \text{ lb Au}}{454 \text{ g Au}} = 2 \times 10^{12} \text{ lb Au}$$

15.12 90 proof = 45 mL ethanol/100 mL beverage

$$\frac{45 \text{ mL ethanol}}{100 \text{ mL BVG}} \times \frac{1 \text{ mL BVG}}{0.861 \text{ g BVG}} \times \frac{0.79 \text{ g ethanol}}{1 \text{ mL ethanol}} = \frac{0.414 \text{ g ethanol}}{\text{g BVG}}$$

Mass of BVG: $1 \text{ qt} \times \frac{1 \text{ L}}{1.057 \text{ qt}} \times \frac{861 \text{ g}}{1 \text{ L}} = 814.5$ g BVG.

Moles of ethanol: $814.5 \text{ g BVG} \times \frac{0.414 \text{ g ethanol}}{\text{g BVG}} \times \frac{1 \text{ mol ethanol}}{46.0 \text{ g ethanol}} = 7.32$ mol ethanol

Mass of ethanol: $814.5 \text{ g BVG} \times \frac{0.414 \text{ g ethanol}}{\text{g BVG}} = 336.8$ g ethanol

Mass of solvent: 814.5 g BVG − 336.8 g ethanol = 477.7 g solvent = 0.4777 kg solvent

$$m_{\text{ethanol}} = \frac{7.32 \text{ mol ethanol}}{0.4777 \text{ kg solvent}} = 15.3 \text{ mol/kg}$$

15.13 (a) Moles of solute and kilograms of solvent
(b) Molar mass of the solute and the density of the solution

15.14 $50.0 \text{ g sucrose} \times \left(\frac{1 \text{ mol sucrose}}{342 \text{ g sucrose}}\right) = 0.146 \text{ mol sucrose}$

$$100.0 \text{ g water} \times \left(\frac{1 \text{ mol water}}{18.0 \text{ g water}}\right) = 5.56 \text{ mol water}$$

$$X_{H_2O} = \frac{5.56}{5.56 + 0.146} = \frac{5.56}{5.706} = 0.974$$

Applying Raoult's law:

$$P_{water} = (X_{water})(P^0_{water}) = (0.974)(71.88 \text{ mm Hg}) = 70.0 \text{ mm Hg}$$

15.15 $\Delta T_b = (2.53 \text{ °C kg mol}^{-1})(0.10 \text{ mol/kg}) = 0.25 \text{ °C}$. The boiling point of the solution is 80.10 °C + 0.25 °C = 80.35 °C.

15.16 First, calculate the required molality of the solution that would have a freezing point of −30 °C.

$$\Delta T_f = -30 \text{ °C} = (-1.86 \text{ °C·kg mol}^{-1}) \times m$$

$$m = \frac{-30 \text{ °C}}{-1.86 \text{ °C kg mol}^{-1}} = 16.1 \text{ mol/kg}$$

To protect 4 kg of water from this freezing temperature, you would need 4 × 16.1 mol of ethylene glycol, or 65 mol.

$$65 \text{ mol}\left(\frac{62.1 \text{ g}}{\text{mol}}\right)\left(\frac{1 \text{ mL}}{1.113 \text{ g}}\right)\left(\frac{1 \text{ L}}{1000 \text{ mL}}\right) = 3.6 \text{ L}$$

15.17 $\Delta T_f = K_f \times m \times i$;

$$4.78 \text{ °C} = (1.86 \text{ °C kg mol}^{-1})(2.0 \text{ mol/kg})(i)$$

$$i = \frac{4.78 \text{ °C}}{(2.0 \text{ mol/kg})(1.86 \text{ °C kg mol}^{-1})} = 1.28$$

Degree of dissociation: If completely dissociated, 1 mol $CaCl_2$ should yield 3 mol ions

$$CaCl_2 \longrightarrow Ca^{2+} + 2\,Cl^-$$

and i should be 3. The degree of dissociation in this solution is $\frac{1.28}{3} = 0.427 \approx 43\%$.

15.18 The 0.02 mol/kg solution of ordinary soap would contain more particles since a soap is a salt of a fatty acid while sucrose is a nonelectrolyte.

15.19 $\frac{3 \text{ qt}}{\text{d}} \times \frac{1 \text{ L}}{1.06 \text{ qt}} \times \frac{0.050 \text{ mg Se}}{\text{L}} \times \frac{10^3 \text{ mg}}{1 \text{ mg}} = \frac{142 \text{ mg Se}}{\text{d}}$

15.20 0.025 ppm Pb means that for every liter (1 kg) of water, there is 0.025 mg, or 25 μg of Pb. Using this factor

$$\text{Volume of water} = 100.0 \text{ μg Pb}\left(\frac{1 \text{ L}}{25 \text{ μg Pb}}\right) = 4.0 \text{ L}$$

Chapter 16

16.1 (a) Acid (b) Base
(c) Acid (d) Base

16.2 More water molecules are available per NH_3 molecule in a very dilute solution of NH_3.

16.3 (a) $H_3O^+(aq) + CN^-(aq)$
(b) $H_3O^+ (aq) + Br^- (aq)$
(c) $CH_3NH_3^+(aq) + OH^-(aq)$
(d) $(CH_3)_2NH_2^+(aq) + OH^-(aq)$

16.4 (a) $HSO_4^-(aq) + H_2O(\ell) \rightarrow H_2SO_4(aq) + OH^-(aq)$
(b) H_2SO_4 is the conjugate acid of HSO_4^-; water is the conjugate acid of OH^-.
(c) Yes; it can be an H^+ donor or acceptor.

16.5 The reverse reaction is favored because HSO_4^- is a stronger acid than CH_3COOH.

16.6 (a)

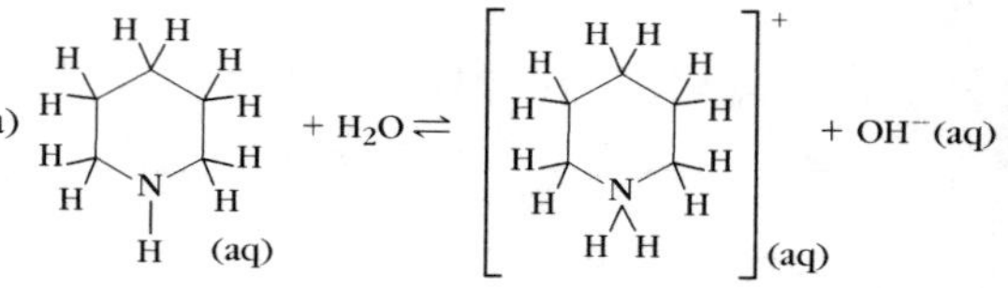

(b)

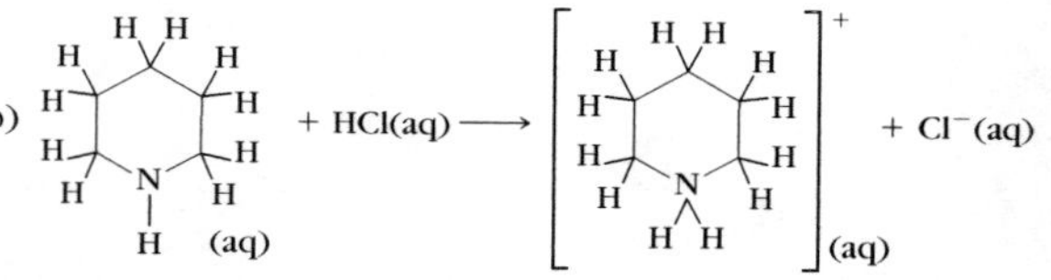

16.7 (a) Amine (b) Neither
(c) Acid (d) Amine
(e) Amine and acid

16.8 The pH values of 0.1 M solutions of these two strong acids would be essentially the same since they both are 100% ionized, resulting in $[H_3O^+]$ values that are the same.

16.9 $[H^+] = 10^{-pH} = 10^{-(-3.6)} = 10^{3.6} = 4 \times 10^3$ M

16.10 Because pH + pOH = 14.0, both solutions have a pOH of 8.5. The $[H_3O^+] = 10^{-pH} = 10^{-5.5} = 3.16 \times 10^{-6}$ M.

16.11 Pyruvic acid is the stronger acid, as indicated by its larger K_a value. Lactic acid's ionization reaction is more reactant-favored (less acid ionizes).

16.12 Being negatively charged, the HSO_4^- ion has a lower tendency to lose a positively charged proton because of the electrostatic attractions of opposite charges.

16.13 (a) Step 1: $HOOC{-}COOH(aq) + H_2O(\ell) \rightleftharpoons H_3O^+(aq) + HOOC{-}COO^-(aq)$

Step 2: $HOOC{-}COO^-(aq) + H_2O(\ell) \rightleftharpoons H_3O^+(aq) + {}^-OOC{-}COO^-(aq)$

(b) Step 1: $C_3H_5(COOH)_3(aq) + H_2O \rightleftharpoons H_3O^+(aq) + C_3H_5(COOH)_2COO^-(aq)$

Step 2: $C_3H_5(COOH)_2COO^-(aq) + H_2O \rightleftharpoons H_3O^+(aq) + C_3H_5(COOH)(COO)_2^{2-}(aq)$

Step 3: $C_3H_5(COOH)(COO)_2^{2-}(aq) + H_2O \rightleftharpoons H_3O^+(aq) + C_3H_5(COO)_3^{3-}(aq)$

16.14 (a) Fluorobenzoic acid (b) Chloroacetic acid
In both cases, the more electronegative halogen atom increases electron withdrawal from the acidic hydrogen, thereby increasing its partial positive charge.

16.15 Oxalic acid is the stronger acid because it has a greater number of oxygens.

16.16 (a)

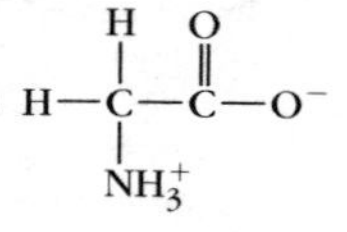

(b)

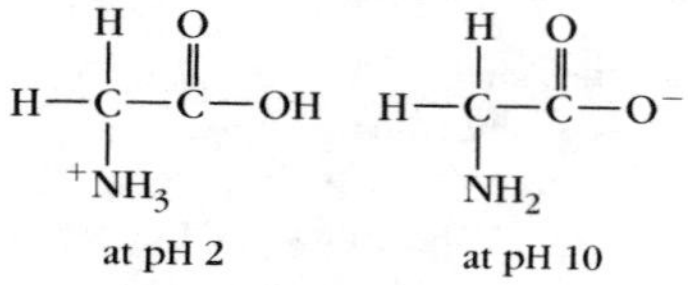

16.17

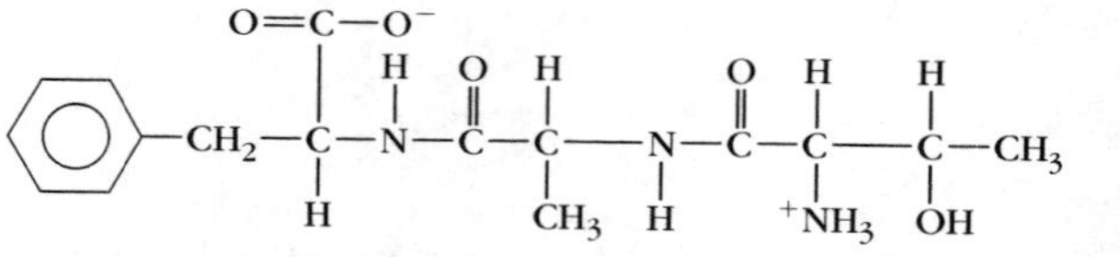

16.18 A reaction had these conditions:

	$Ni(H_2O)_6^{2+}(aq) + H_2O(\ell) \rightleftharpoons$	$Ni(H_2O)_5(OH)^+(aq) +$	$H_3O^+(aq)$
Initial concentration (mol/L)	0.15	0	10^{-7}
Change in concentration on reaction (mol/L)	$-x$	$+x$	$+x$
Concentration at equilibrium (mol/L)	$0.15 - x$	x	x

Substituting these values in the equilibrium constant expression, and simplifying $0.15 - x$ to be 0.15 because the value of K_a is so small

$$K_a = \frac{[Ni(H_2O)_5(OH)^+][H_3O^+]}{[Ni(H_2O)_6^{2+}]}$$

$$= \frac{(x)(x)}{(0.15 - x)} \approx \frac{x^2}{0.15} = 2.5 \times 10^{-11}$$

Solving for x, which is the $[H_3O^+]$

$$x = \sqrt{(0.15)(2.5 \times 10^{-11})} = 1.9 \times 10^{-6}$$

So, the pH of this solution is $\log(1.9 \times 10^{-6}) = 5.72$.

16.19 $K_b = \dfrac{1.0 \times 10^{-14}}{K_a} = \dfrac{1.0 \times 10^{-14}}{1.3 \times 10^{-10}} = 7.7 \times 10^{-5}$; carbonate or pentaaquairon(II) ion; by comparing K_b values.

16.20 The pH of soaps is >7 due to the reaction with water of the conjugate base in the soap to form a basic solution.

16.21 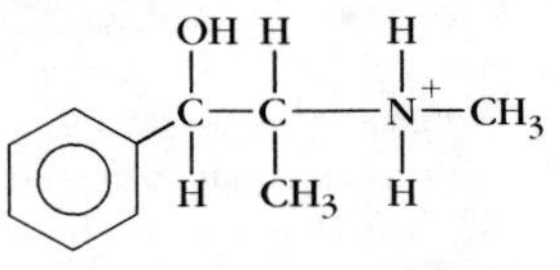

Cl^-

16.22 Ammonium acetate. The pH of a solution of this salt will be 7.

16.23 (a) Lewis base (b) Lewis acid
(c) Lewis acid and base (d) Lewis acid
(e) Lewis acid (f) Lewis base

16.24 Strong bases would cause damage to tissue.

16.25 Baking powder and baking soda are sources of bicarbonate; buttermilk and baking powder are sources of acid.

16.26 Set up a small table for the hydrolysis reaction.

	CO_3^{2-} + H_2O ⇌	HCO_3^- +	OH^-
Initial concentration (mol/L)	5.2	0	10^{-7}
Concentration change due to reaction (mol/L)	$-x$	$+x$	$+x$
Concentration at equilibrium (mol/L)	$5.2 - x$	x	x

Using the K_b expression and substituting the values from the table

$$K_b = \frac{K_w}{K_a(HCO_3^-)} = \frac{[HCO_3^-][OH^-]}{[CO_3^{2-}]} = \frac{x^2}{5.2 - x}$$

$$\approx \frac{x^2}{5.2} = 2.1 \times 10^{-4}.$$

$$x = [OH^-] = \sqrt{(5.2)(2.1 \times 10^{-4})} = 3.3 \times 10^{-2}$$

$$pOH = -\log(3.3 \times 10^{-2}) = 1.48$$

$$pH = 14.00 - 1.48 = 12.52$$

Chapter 17

17.1 HCl and NaCl: no; has no significant H^+ acceptor (Cl^- is a very poor base).
KOH and KCl: no; has no H^+ donor.

17.2 $pH = 7.21 + \log\dfrac{(0.0025)}{(0.00015)} = 7.21 + \log(1.67)$

$= 7.21 + 0.22 = 7.43$

17.3 $pH = pK_a + \log\dfrac{[\text{acetate}]}{[\text{acetic acid}]}$

$4.68 = 4.74 + \log\dfrac{[\text{acetate}]}{[\text{acetic acid}]}$

$\log\dfrac{[\text{acetate}]}{[\text{acetic acid}]} = 4.68 - 4.74 = -0.06;$

$\dfrac{[\text{acetate}]}{[\text{acetic acid}]} = 10^{-0.06} = 0.86$

Therefore, $[\text{acetate}] = 0.86 \times [\text{acetic acid}]$.

17.4 (a) $pH = 6.38 + \log\dfrac{[0.25]}{[0.10]} = 6.38 + 0.398 = 6.78$

(b) $pH = 7.21 + \log\dfrac{[HPO_4^{2-}]}{[H_2PO_4^-]}$

$= 7.21 + \log\dfrac{(0.25)}{(0.10)} = 7.21 + 0.398 = 7.61$

17.5 Since CO_2 reacts to form an acid, H_2CO_3, the phosphate ion that is the stronger base, HPO_4^{2-}, will be used to counteract its presence.

17.6 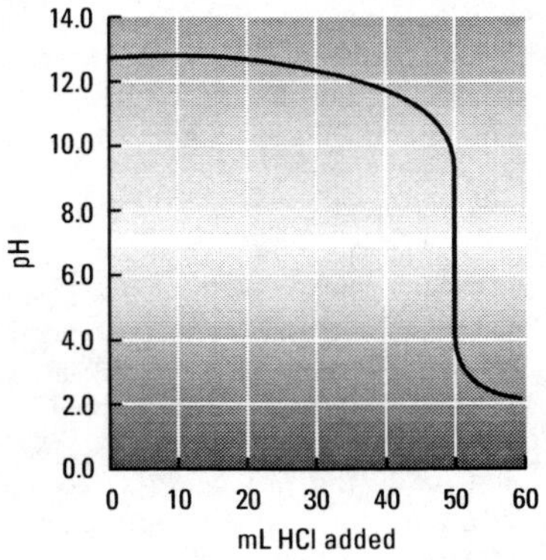

17.7 The addition of 30.0 mL of 0.100 M NaOH neutralizes 30.0 mL of 0.100 M acetic acid, forming 0.0030 mol of acetate ions, which is in 80.0 mL of solution. There is (0.0200 L)(0.100 M) = 0.00200 mol of acetic acid that is unreacted.

$$K_a = 1.8 \times 10^{-5} = \frac{[H^+][C_2H_3O_2^-]}{[HC_2H_3O_2]}$$

$$= \frac{[H^+] \times \left(\dfrac{0.00300 \text{ mol}}{0.0800 \text{ L}}\right)}{\left(\dfrac{0.00200 \text{ mol}}{0.0800 \text{ L}}\right)}$$

$$1.8 \times 10^{-5} = \frac{[H^+] \times (0.0375)}{(0.025)} = [H^+] \times 1.5$$

$$[H^+] = \frac{1.8 \times 10^{-5}}{1.5} = 1.2 \times 10^{-5}$$

$$pH = -\log(1.2 \times 10^{-5}) = 4.92$$

17.8 As NaOH is added, it reacts with acetic acid to form sodium acetate. After 20.0 mL NaOH has been added, just less than half of the acetic acid has been converted to sodium acetate; when 30.0 mL NaOH has been added, just over half of the acetic acid has been neutralized. Thus, after 20.0 mL and 30.0 mL base have been added, the solution contains approximately equal amounts of acetic acid and acetate ion, its conjugate base, which acts as a buffer.

17.9 Because Reaction (b) occurs to an appreciable extent, CO_3^{2-} is used as it forms by Reaction (a), causing additional $CaCO_3(s)$ to dissolve.

17.10 (a) The excess iodide would create a stress on the equilibrium and shift it to the left; some AgI and some PbI_2 would precipitate from solution.
(b) The added SO_4^{2-} would cause the precipitation of $BaSO_4$.

Chapter 18

18.1 (a) $H_2O(\ell) \rightarrow H_2O(g)$ Product-favored
(b) $SiO_2(s) \rightarrow Si(s) + O_2(g)$ Reactant-favored
(c) $(C_6H_{10}O_5)_n(s) + 6n\ O_2(g) \rightarrow$
$6n\ CO_2(g) + 5n\ H_2O(g)$ Product-favored
(d) $C_{12}H_{22}O_{11}(s) \rightarrow C_{12}H_{22}O_{11}(aq)$ Product-favored

18.2 A*** A**B* A*B** B***

If C, D, and E are added, there are many more arrangements in addition to these:

A*B*C*	A*B*D*	A*B*E*	A*C*D*	A*C*E*
A*D*E*	B*C*D*	B*C*E*	B*D*E*	C*D*E*
A**C*	A**D*	A**E*	B**C*	B**D*
B**E*	C**A*	C**B*	C**D*	C**E*
D**A*	D**B*	D**C*	D**E*	E**A*
E**B*	E**C*	E**D*	C***	D***
E***				

There are 35 possible arrangements, but only 4 of them have the energy confined to atoms A and B. The probability that all energy remains with A and B is thus 4/35 = 0.114, or a little more than 11%.

18.3 Using Celsius temperature and $\Delta S = q_{rev}/T$, if the temperature were −10 °C, the value of ΔS would be negative, in disagreement with the fact that transfer of energy to a sample should increase molecular motion and, hence, entropy.

18.4 (a) The reactant is a gas. The products are also gases, but the number of molecules has increased, so entropy is greater for products. (Entropy increases.)
(b) The reactant is a solid. The product is a solution. Mixing sodium and chloride ions among water molecules results in greater entropy for the product. (Entropy increases.)
(c) The reactant is a solid. The products are a solid and a gas. The much larger entropy of the gas results in greater entropy for the products. (Entropy increases.)

18.5 (a) Because $\Delta S_{surroundings} = -\Delta H/T$ at a given temperature, the larger the value of T, the smaller the value of $\Delta S_{surroundings}$.
(b) If ΔS_{system} does not change much with temperature, then $S_{universe}$ must also get smaller. In this case, because ΔS_{system} is negative, $\Delta S_{universe}$ would become negative at a high enough temperature.

18.6 (a) The reaction would have gaseous water as a product.
(b) Both $\Delta H°$ and $\Delta S°$ would change. $\Delta H° = -10{,}232.197$ kJ and $\Delta S° = 756.57$ J/K.
(c) If any of the reactants or products change to a different phase (s, ℓ, or g) over the range of temperature, $\Delta H°$ and $\Delta S°$ will change significantly at the temperature of the phase transition.

18.7

Reaction	$\Delta H°$, 298 K (kJ)	$\Delta S°$, 298 K (J/K)
(a)	−1410.94	−267.67
(b)	467.87	560.32
(c)	−393.509	2.862
(d)	1241.2	−461.50

Reaction (a) is product-favored at low T (room temperature) and reactant-favored at high T.
Reaction (b) is reactant-favored at low T, product-favored at high T.
Reaction (c) is product-favored at all values of T.
Reaction (d) is reactant-favored at all values of T.

18.8 (a)
$$\Delta S°_{system} = 2\text{ mol HCl(g)} \times S°(\text{HCl[g]}) - 1\text{ mol H}_2\text{[g]} \times S°(\text{H}_2\text{[g]}) - 1\text{ mol Cl}_2\text{[g]} \times S°(\text{Cl}_2\text{[g]})$$
$$= (2 \times 186.908 - 130.684 - 223.066)\text{ J/K}$$
$$= 20.055\text{ J/K}$$
$$\Delta S°_{surroundings} = -\Delta H°/T = -\Delta H°/T$$
$$= -[2\text{ mol HCl(g)} \times (-92.307\text{ kJ/mol})]/298.15\text{ K}$$
$$= 619.20\text{ J/K}$$

(b) $\Delta S°_{universe} = (619.20 + 20.066)\text{ J/K} = 639.27\text{ J/K}$ (Product-favored)

18.9

Sign of $\Delta H°$	Sign of $\Delta S°$	Sign of $\Delta G°$	Product-favored?
Negative (exothermic)	Positive	Negative	Yes
Negative (exothermic)	Negative	Depends on T	Yes at low T; no at high T
Positive (endothermic)	Positive	Depends on T	No at low T; yes at high T
Positive (endothermic)	Negative	Positive	No

18.10 (a) At 400 °C the equation is

$$2\text{ HgO(s)} \longrightarrow 2\text{ Hg(g)} + \text{O}_2\text{(g)}$$

Because Hg(g) is a product, instead of Hg(ℓ), both $\Delta H°$ and $\Delta S°$ will have significantly different values above 356 °C from their values below 356 °C. Therefore, the method of estimating $\Delta G°$ would not work above 356 °C.
(b) At 400 °C the entropy change should be more positive, which would make the reaction more product-favored. Because $\Delta H°$ and $\Delta S°$ are both positive, the reaction is product-favored at high temperatures.

18.11 (a) If the extent of reaction is 0.10, then 0.10 mol of NaOH has reacted with 0.10 mol of CO_2 to produce 0.10 mol of $NaHCO_3$.

$$\Delta G°(0.10\text{ extent}) = 0.10\text{ mol} \times \Delta G_f°(\text{NaHCO}_3\text{[s]}) - 0.10\text{ mol} \times \Delta G_f°(\text{NaOH[s]}) - 0.10\text{ mol} \times \Delta G_f°(\text{CO}_2\text{[g]})$$
$$= -0.10 \times 851.0\text{ kJ} + 0.10 \times 379.484\text{ kJ} + 0.10 \times 394.359\text{ kJ}$$
$$= -7.72\text{ kJ}$$

Similarly,

$$\Delta G°(0.40\text{ extent}) = -30.9\text{ kJ } (= 0.40[-72.2\text{ kJ}])$$
$$\Delta G°(0.80\text{ extent}) = -61.8\text{ kJ } (= 0.80[-72.2\text{ kJ}])$$

(b) In each case, $\Delta G°(x\text{ extent}) = x\Delta G°(\text{full extent})$, which verifies the statement.
(c) Since $\Delta G°(x\text{ extent}) = x\Delta G°(\text{full extent})$,

$$y = xm + b$$

where b = 0 and m = $\Delta G°$(full extent) = slope.

18.12 (a)
$$\Delta S°(\text{i}) = \{2 \times (27.78) + \tfrac{3}{2} \times (205.138) - (87.40)\}\text{ J/K} = 275.86\text{ kJ}$$
$$\Delta H°(\text{i}) = -\Delta H_f°(\text{Fe}_2\text{O}_3\text{[s]}) = 824.2\text{ kJ}$$
$$\Delta G°(\text{i}) = -\Delta G_f°(\text{Fe}_2\text{O}_3\text{[s]}) = 742.2\text{ kJ}$$
$$\Delta S°(\text{ii}) = \{50.92 - 2 \times (28.3) - \tfrac{3}{2} \times (205.138)\}\text{ J/K} = -313.4\text{ kJ}$$
$$\Delta H°(\text{ii}) = \Delta H_f°(\text{Al}_2\text{O}_3\text{[s]}) = -1675.7\text{ kJ}$$
$$\Delta G°(\text{ii}) = \Delta G_f°(\text{Al}_2\text{O}_3\text{[s]}) = -1582.3\text{ kJ}$$

Step (i) is reactant-favored. Step (ii) is product-favored.
(b) Net reaction
$Fe_2O_3(s) + 2\ Al(s) \rightarrow 2\ Fe(s) + Al_2O_3(s)$
$\Delta S° = 275.86\text{ J/K} + (-313.4\text{ J/K}) = -37.5\text{ J/K}$
$\Delta H° = 824.2\text{ kJ} + (-1675.7\text{ kJ}) = -851.5\text{ kJ}$
$\Delta G° = 742.2\text{ kJ} + (-1582.3\text{ kJ}) = -840.1\text{ kJ}$

The net reaction has negative $\Delta G°$ and is therefore product-favored. For the *net* reaction, $\Delta S°$, $\Delta H°$, and $\Delta G°$ are all negative.
(c) If the two reactions are coupled, it is possible to obtain iron from iron(III) oxide even though that reaction is not product-favored by itself. The large negative $\Delta G°$ for formation of $Al_2O_3(s)$ makes the overall $\Delta G°$ negative for the coupled reactions.
(d) $Mg(s) + \frac{1}{2}O_2(g) \rightarrow MgO(s)$

$$\Delta G° = \Delta G_f°(MgO[s]) = -569.43 \text{ kJ}$$

Coupling the reactions, we have

$$Fe_2O_3(s) \longrightarrow 2\,Fe(s) + \tfrac{3}{2}O_2(g) \qquad \Delta G_1° = 742.2 \text{ kJ}$$

$$3 \times (Mg[s] + \tfrac{1}{2}O_2[g] \longrightarrow MgO[s])$$

$$\Delta G_2° = 3(-569.43) \text{ kJ} = -1708.29 \text{ kJ}$$

$$Fe_2O_3(s) + 3\,Mg(s) \longrightarrow 2\,Fe(s) + 3\,MgO(s)$$

$$\Delta G_3° = -966.1 \text{ kJ}$$

18.13 $\Delta G° = -2870$ kJ + 32 × (30.5 kJ) = −1894 kJ. The 1894 kJ of Gibbs free energy is transformed into thermal energy.

18.14 64,500 g ATP/50 g ATP = 1290 times each ADP must be recycled to ATP on average each day.

Chapter 19

19.1 This is an application of the law of conservation of matter. If the number of electrons gained were different from the number of electrons lost, some electrons must have been created or destroyed.

19.2 Removal of the salt bridge would effectively switch off the flow of electricity from the battery.

19.3 Avogadro's number of electrons is 96,500 coulombs of charge, so it is 96,500 times as large as one coulomb of charge.

19.4 The zinc anode could be weighed before the battery was put into use. After a period of time, the zinc anode could be dried and reweighed. A loss in weight would be interpreted as being caused by the loss of Zn atoms from the surface through oxidation.

19.5 No, because Hg^{2+} ions can oxidize Al metal to Al^{3+} ions. The net cell reaction is

$$2\,Al(s) + 3\,Hg^{2+}(aq) \longrightarrow 2\,Al^{3+}(aq) + 3\,Hg(\ell)$$

$$E_{cell} = +2.51 \text{ V}$$

19.6 For this table,
(a) V^{2+} ion is the weakest oxidizing agent.
(b) Cl_2 is the strongest oxidizing agent.
(c) V is the strongest reducing agent.
(d) Cl^- is the weakest reducing agent.
(e) No, E_{cell} for that reaction would be <0.
(f) No, E_{cell} for that reaction would be <0.
(g) Pb can reduce I_2 and Cl_2.

19.7 In Table 19.1, Sb would be above H_2 and Pb would be below H_2. For Sb, the reduction potential would be between 0.00 and +0.337 V, and for Pb the value would be between 0.00 and −0.14 V.

19.8 For Na^+: $E_{ion} = 61.5 \log\left(\frac{150}{18}\right) = 61.5 \log(8.33)$

$$= 61.5 \times 0.921 = 57 \text{ mV}$$

19.9 During charging, the reactions at each electrode are reversed. At the electrode that is normally the anode, the charging reaction is

$$Cd(OH)_2(s) + 2\,e^- \longrightarrow Cd(s) + 2\,OH^-(aq)$$

This is reduction, so this electrode is now a cathode.
At the electrode that is normally the cathode, the charging reaction is

$$Ni(OH)_2 + OH^-(aq) \longrightarrow NiO(OH)(s) + H_2O(\ell) + e^-$$

This is oxidation, so this electrode is now an anode.

19.10 Remove the lead cathodes and as much sulfuric acid as you can from the discharged battery. Find some steel and construct a battery with Cl_2 gas flowing across a piece of steel. The two half-reactions would be

$$Cl_2(g) + 2\,e^- \longrightarrow 2\,Cl^-(aq) \qquad +1.36 \text{ V}$$

$$Pb(s) + SO_4^{2-}(aq) \longrightarrow PbSO_4(s) + 2\,e^- \qquad +0.356 \text{ V}$$

$$E_{cell} = 1.36 + 0.356 = 1.71 \text{ V}$$

19.11 Potassium metal was produced at the cathode.
Oxidation reaction: $2\,F^-(\text{molten}) \rightarrow F_2(g) + 2\,e^-$
Reduction reaction: $2(K^+[\text{molten}] + e^- \rightarrow K[\ell])$
Net cell reaction:
$2\,K^+(\text{molten}) + 2F^-(\text{molten}) \rightarrow 2\,K(\ell) + F_2(g)$

19.12 Reaction (c) making 2 mol of Cu from Cu^{2+} would require 4 Faradays of electricity. Two F are required for part (b), and 3 F are required for part (a).

19.13 First, calculate how many coulombs of electricity are required to make this much aluminum.

$$(2000.\text{ ton Al})\left(\frac{2000 \text{ lb Al}}{1 \text{ ton Al}}\right)\left(\frac{454.6 \text{ g Al}}{1 \text{ lb Al}}\right)\left(\frac{1 \text{ mol Al}}{26.982 \text{ g Al}}\right)$$

$$\times \left(\frac{3 \text{ mol } e^-}{1 \text{ mol Al}}\right)\left(\frac{96{,}500 \text{ C}}{1 \text{ mol } e^-}\right) = 1.950 \times 10^{13} \text{ C}$$

Next, using the product of charge and voltage, calculate how many joules are required; then convert to kilowatt-hours.

$$\text{Energy} = (1.950 \times 10^{13} \text{ C})(4.0 \text{ V})\left(\frac{1 \text{ J}}{1 \text{ C} - \times 1 \text{ V}}\right)$$

$$\times \left(\frac{1 \text{ kWh}}{3.60 \times 10^6 \text{ J}}\right) = 2.2 \times 10^7 \text{ kWh}$$

19.14 To calculate how much energy is stored in a battery, you need the voltage and the number of coulombs of charge the battery can provide. The voltage is generally given on the battery label. To determine the number of coulombs available, you would have to disassemble the battery and determine the masses of the chemicals at the cathode and anode.

19.15 $(0.50 \text{ A})(20.\text{ min})\left(\frac{60 \text{ s}}{1 \text{ min}}\right)\left(\frac{1 \text{ C}}{1 \text{ A s}}\right)\left(\frac{1 \text{ mol } e^-}{96{,}500 \text{ C}}\right)$

$$\times \left(\frac{1 \text{ mol Ag}}{1 \text{ mol } e^-}\right)\left(\frac{107.9 \text{ g Ag}}{1 \text{ mol Ag}}\right) = 0.67 \text{ g Ag}$$

19.16 No, not all metals corrode as easily. Three metals that would corrode about as readily as Fe and Al are Zn, Mg, and Cd. Three metals that do not corrode as readily as Fe and Al are Cu, Ag, and Au. These three metals are used in making coins and jewelry. Metals fall into these two broad groups because of their relative ease of oxidation compared with the oxidation of H_2. In Table 19.1, you can see this breakdown easily.

19.17 (b) > (a) > (d) > (c)
Sand by the seashore, (b), would contain both moisture and salts, which would aid corrosion. Moist clay, (a), would contain water but less dissolved salts. If an iron object were embedded within the clay, its impervious nature might prevent oxygen from getting to the iron, which would also lower the rate of corrosion. Desert sand in Arizona, (d), would be quite dry, and this low-moisture environment would not lead to a rapid rate of corrosion. On the moon, (c), there would be a lack of moisture and oxygen. This would lead to a very low rate of corrosion.

Chapter 20

20.1 $^{235}_{92}U \rightarrow {}^{4}_{2}He + {}^{231}_{90}Th$
$^{231}_{90}Th \rightarrow {}^{0}_{-1}e + {}^{231}_{91}Pa$
$^{231}_{91}Pa \rightarrow {}^{4}_{2}He + {}^{227}_{89}Ac$
$^{227}_{89}Ac \rightarrow {}^{4}_{2}He + {}^{223}_{87}Fr$
$^{223}_{87}Fr \rightarrow {}^{0}_{-1}e + {}^{223}_{88}Ra$

20.2 $^{26}_{13}Al \rightarrow {}^{0}_{+1}e + {}^{26}_{12}Mg$
$^{26}_{13}Al + {}^{0}_{-1}e \rightarrow {}^{26}_{12}Mg$

20.3 Mass difference = $\Delta m = -0.03438$ g/mol
$\Delta E = (-3.438 \times 10^{-5}$ kg/mol$)(2.998 \times 10^{8}$ m/s$)^2$
$= -3.090 \times 10^{12}$ J/mol $= -3.090 \times 10^{8}$ kJ/mol
E_b per nucleon = 5.150×10^{8} kJ/nucleon
E_b for ^{6}Li is smaller than E_b for ^{4}He; therefore, helium-4 is more stable than lithium-6.

20.4 From the graph it can be seen that the binding energy per nucleon increases more sharply for the fusion of lighter elements than it does for heavy elements undergoing fission. Therefore, fusion is more exothermic per gram than fission.

20.5 $(\frac{1}{2})^{10} = 9.8 \times 10^{-4}$; this is equivalent to 0.098% of the radioisotope remaining.

20.6 All the lead came from the decay of ^{238}U; therefore, at the time the rock was dated, $N = 100$ and $N_0 = 109$. The decay constant, k, can be determined:

$$k = \frac{0.693}{4.51 \times 10^{9}\ y} = 1.54 \times 10^{-10}\ y^{-1}$$

The age of the rock (t) can be calculated using Equation 20.3:

$$\ln \frac{100}{209} = -(1.54 \times 10^{-10}\ y^{-1}) \times t$$
$$t = 4.80 \times 10^{9} y$$

20.7 Ethylene is derived from petroleum, which was formed millennia ago. The half-life of ^{14}C is 5730 y, and thus much of ethylene's ^{14}C would have decayed and would be much less than that of the ^{14}C alcohol produced by fermentation.

20.8 (a) $^{13}_{6}C + {}^{1}_{0}n \rightarrow {}^{4}_{2}He + {}^{10}_{4}Be$
(b) $^{14}_{7}N + {}^{4}_{2}He \rightarrow {}^{1}_{0}n + {}^{17}_{9}F$
(c) $^{253}_{99}Es + {}^{4}_{2}He \rightarrow {}^{1}_{0}n + {}^{256}_{101}Md$

20.9 $^{208}_{82}Pb + {}^{70}_{30}Zn \rightarrow {}^{277}_{112}E + {}^{1}_{0}n$

20.10 Burning a metric ton of coal produces 2.8×10^{7} kJ of energy.

$$\left(\frac{2.8 \times 10^{4}\ kJ}{1.0\ kg}\right)\left(\frac{10^{3}\ kg}{metric\ ton}\right) = 2.8 \times 10^{7}\ kJ\ of\ energy$$

The fission of 1.0 kg of ^{235}U produces

$$\frac{2.1 \times 10^{10}\ kJ}{0.235\ kg\ ^{235}U} = 8.93 \times 10^{10}\ kJ$$

It would require burning 3.2×10^{3} metric tons of coal to equal the amount of energy from 1.0 kg of ^{235}U:

$$8.93 \times 10^{10}\ kJ\ from\ ^{235}U \times \frac{1\ metric\ ton\ coal}{2.9 \times 10^{7}\ kJ}$$
$$= 3.2 \times 10^{3} metric\ tons$$

20.11 $k = \dfrac{0.693}{29.1\ y} = 2.38 \times 10^{-2}\ y^{-1}$

ln(fraction) $= -(2.38 \times 10^{-2}\ y^{-1})$ (18 y, as of 2004) $= -0.4284$
fraction $= e^{-0.4284} = 0.652 = 65.2\%$

20.12 $k = \dfrac{0.693}{30.2\ y} = 2.29 \times 10^{-2}\ y^{-1}$

(a) 60% drop in activity; 40% activity remaining
$\ln(0.40) = -0.916 = -(2.29 \times 10^{-2}\ y^{-1}) \times t$

$$t = \frac{-0.916}{-2.29 \times 10^{-2}\ y^{-1}} = 40\ y$$

(b) 90% drop in activity, 10% remains
$\ln(0.10) = -2.30 = -(2.29 \times 10^{-2}\ y^{-1}) \times t$

$$t = \frac{-2.30}{-2.29 \times 10^{-2}\ y^{-1}} = 100\ y$$

20.13 (a) $^{7}_{3}Li + {}^{1}_{1}H \rightarrow {}^{1}_{0}n + {}^{7}_{4}Be$
(b) $^{2}_{1}H + {}^{3}_{2}He \rightarrow {}^{4}_{2}He + {}^{1}_{1}H$

20.14 $k = \dfrac{0.693}{3.82\ d} = 0.181\ d^{-1}$

(a) The drop from 8 to 4 pCi represents one half-life, 3.82 days.
(b) $\ln\left(\dfrac{1.5}{8}\right) = -1.67 = -(0.181\ d^{-1}) \times t$

$$t = \frac{-1.67}{-0.181\ d^{-1}} = 9.25\ d$$

20.15 $k = \dfrac{0.693}{78.2\ h} = 8.86 \times 10^{-3}\ h^{-1}$

$$\ln(0.10) = -2.30 = -(8.86 \times 10^{-3}\ h^{-1}) \times t$$
$$t = 260\ h$$

20.16 Iron-59 $k = \dfrac{0.693}{44.5\ d} = 1.557 \times 10^{-2}\ d^{-1}$

Chromium-51 $k = \dfrac{0.693}{27.7\ d} = 0.0250\ d^{-1}$

Fractions remaining:

^{59}Fe: ln(fraction) $= -(1.557 \times 10^{-2}\ d^{-1}) \times 90$ d
fraction $= e^{-1.40} = 0.246$; 80 mg $\times$ 0.246 = 19.7 mg left
^{51}Cr: ln(fraction) $= -(0.0250\ d^{-1}) \times 90$ d; 10.5 mg left

Alternatively, consider the fact that 90 days is approximately two half-lives of ^{59}Fe. Therefore, approximately $\frac{3}{4}$ of it (about 60 mg) has decayed after 90 days, and about 20 mg remains. In that same time, ^{51}Cr has undergone more than three half-lives, so that less than $\frac{1}{8}$ remains (less than 12.5 mg).

Chapter 21

21.1 $^{12}_{6}C + {}^{4}_{2}He \rightarrow {}^{16}_{8}O$
$^{16}_{8}O + {}^{4}_{2}He \rightarrow {}^{20}_{10}Ne$
$^{20}_{10}Ne + {}^{4}_{2}He \rightarrow {}^{24}_{12}Mg$

21.2
$^{130}_{48}Cd \rightarrow {}^{0}_{-1}e + {}^{130}_{49}In$
$^{130}_{49}In \rightarrow {}^{0}_{-1}e + {}^{130}_{50}Sn$
$^{130}_{50}Sn \rightarrow {}^{0}_{-1}e + {}^{130}_{51}Sb$
$^{130}_{51}Sb \rightarrow {}^{0}_{-1}e + {}^{130}_{52}Te$

21.3 Two of the four oxygens in an SiO_4 unit are shared with other SiO_4 tetrahedra. Therefore, for each SiO_4 unit,

1 Si + two oxygen not shared + 2 oxygen shared $= SiO_{2+1}$
$= SiO_3^{2-}$

21.4 $5.0\ L \times \dfrac{1.4\ g}{mL} \times \dfrac{10^{3}\ mL}{1\ L} = 7.0 \times 10^{3}\ g\ O_2$

$$7.0 \times 10^3\ g \times \frac{1\ mol}{32.0\ g} = 2.2 \times 10^2\ mol;\ PV = nRT$$

$$V = \frac{(2.2 \times 10^2\ mol)(0.0821\ L\cdot atm\cdot mol^{-1}\cdot K^{-1})(273\ K)}{1\ atm}$$

$$= 4.9 \times 10^3\ L$$

21.5 $2\ NaCl(\ell) \rightarrow 2\ Na(\ell) + Cl_2(g)$
Coulombs (C) = (A)(s)

$$= 2.0 \times 10^4\ A \times 24\ h \times \frac{3600\ s}{h} = 1.7 \times 10^9\ C$$

$$1.7 \times 10^9\ C \times \frac{1\ mol\ e^-}{9.65 \times 10^4\ C} = 1.8 \times 10^4\ mol\ e^-$$

$$1.8 \times 10^4\ mol\ e^- \times \frac{1\ mol\ Na}{1\ mol\ e^-} \times \frac{23.0\ g\ Na}{1\ mol\ Na} \times \frac{1\ lb}{454\ g} \times \frac{1\ ton}{2000\ lb} = 0.46\ tons\ Na$$

$$1.8 \times 10^4\ mol\ e^- \times \frac{1\ mol\ Cl_2}{2\ mol\ e^-} \times \frac{70.9\ g\ Cl_2}{1\ mol\ Cl_2} \times \frac{1\ lb}{454\ g} \times \frac{1\ ton}{2000\ lb} = 0.70\ tons\ Cl_2$$

21.6 $C = 2.00 \times 10^4\ A \times 100.\ h \times \frac{3600\ s}{h} = 7.20 \times 10^9\ C$

$$7.20 \times 10^9\ C \times \frac{1\ mol\ e^-}{9.65 \times 10^4\ C} \times \frac{1\ mol\ NaOH}{1\ mol\ e^-} \times \frac{40.00\ g\ NaOH}{1\ mol\ NaOH} \times \frac{1\ lb}{454\ g} \times \frac{1\ ton}{2000\ lb}$$
$$= 3.29\ tons\ NaOH$$

21.7 Phosphorus in $Ca_3(PO_4)_2$ has an oxidation state of +5; it is reduced to zero in P_4. Carbon is oxidized to CO (oxidation state changes from zero to −2).

21.8 $\frac{93\ g}{502\ g} \times 100\% = 19\%\ P$

21.9 Br^- (reducing agent) is oxidized to Br_2; Cl_2 (oxidizing agent) is reduced to Cl^-.

21.10 $I_2(s) + 2\ e^- \rightarrow 2\ I^-(aq)\quad E° = +0.535\ V$
$Br_2(\ell) + 2\ e^- \rightarrow 2\ Br^-(aq)\quad E° = +1.08\ V$
$I_2(s)$ is below $Br^-(aq)$ so iodine will not oxidize bromide ion to bromine, as seen by the negative cell voltage. Rather, bromine will oxidize iodide to iodine.

$$I_2(s) + 2\ e^- \rightarrow 2\ I^-(aq)\quad E°_{cathode} = +0.535\ V$$
$$2\ Br^-(aq) \rightarrow Br_2\ (\ell) + 2\ e^- +\quad E°_{anode} = -1.08\ V$$
$$I_2(s) + 2\ Br^-(aq) \rightarrow 2\ I^-(aq) + Br_2(\ell)\quad E°_{cell} = -0.545\ V$$

21.11 Oxide, O^{2-}, $[:\ddot{O}:]^{2+}$; peroxide, O_2^{2-}, $[:\ddot{O}:\ddot{O}:]^{2-}$; superperoxide, O_2^-, $[:\ddot{O}:\ddot{O}\cdot]^-$

21.12 (a) CaO (b) BaO_z (c) Sr_3N_2
(d) CaC_2

21.13 (a) Mg_3N_2 (b) $3\ Mg(s) + N_2(g) \rightarrow Mg_3N_2(s)$

21.14 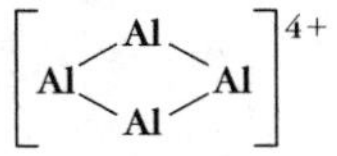

21.15 NO_3^-; oxidation number of oxygen is −2; oxidation number of N is +5.
NH_4^+; oxidation number of hydrogen is +1; oxidation number of nitrogen is −3.

21.16 $150.\ g\ NaN_3 \times \frac{1\ mol\ NaN_3}{65.0\ g\ NaN_3} \times \frac{3\ mol\ N_2}{2\ mol\ NaN_3} = 3.46\ mol\ N_2$

$$V = \frac{nRT}{P} = \frac{(3.46)(0.0821)(273)}{(1)} = 77.6\ L$$

Chapter 22

22.1 (a) V^{+5} (b) Ag^{+3} (c) Co^{+2} (d) Mn^{+2}

22.2 Cu^{+2}

22.3 (a) $500\ g \times \frac{18\ g\ W}{100\ g} = 90\ g\ W$

$$500\ g \times \frac{6.0\ g\ Co}{100\ g} = 30\ g\ Co$$

(b) Iron is present in the greatest mole percent.

$$500\ g \times \frac{68.9\ g\ Fe}{100\ g} = 344\ g\ Fe = 6.2\ mol$$

$$\frac{6.2}{8.0} \times 100\% = 77.5\%\ Fe$$

22.4 $Cu^{2+}(aq) + 2\ e^- \rightarrow Cu(s)$

$$12.0\ h\left(\frac{3600\ s}{h}\right)\left(\frac{250\ C}{s}\right)\left(\frac{1\ mol\ e^-}{9.65 \times 10^4\ C}\right) \times \left(\frac{1\ mol\ Cu}{2\ mol\ e^-}\right)\left(\frac{63.55\ g\ Cu}{1\ mol\ Cu}\right) = 3.56 \times 10^3\ g\ Cu$$

22.5 (a) NO_3^- is the oxidizing agent; silver metal is the reducing agent.
(b) NO_3^- is the oxidizing agent; gold is the reducing agent.

22.6 $2\ Al(s) + Cr_2O_3(s) \rightarrow Al_2O_3(s) + 2\ Cr(s)$

$$\Delta H_f^\circ = \Delta H^\circ_{f_{Al_2O_3(s)}} - \Delta H^\circ_{f_{Cr_2O_3(s)}}$$
$$= (-1675.7\ kJ) - (-1139.7\ kJ)$$
$$= -536.0\ kJ/mol\ Cr_2O_3$$

$$\Delta G° = \Delta G^\circ_{f_{Al_2O_3(s)}} - \Delta G^\circ_{f_{Cr_2O_3(s)}}$$
$$= (-1582.3\ kJ) - (-1058.1\ kJ)$$
$$-524.2\ kJ/mol\ Cr_2O_3$$

22.7 The addition of acid shifts the equilibrium to the right, converting CrO_4^{2-} to $Cr_2O_7^{2-}$. Added base reacts with H^+ to form water, causing the equilibrium to shift to the left, converting $Cr_2O_7^{2-}$ to CrO_4^{2-}.

22.8 $[Cr(H_2O)_2(NH_3)_2(OH)_2]^+$

22.9 Should be $M_2^+X^{2-}$; such as K_2SO_4

22.10 (a) Three (b) 4− (c) Five

22.11 (a) Fe^2 (b) Fe^{3+}

22.12 Two isomers

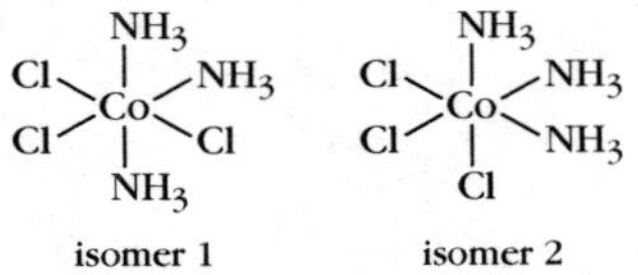

isomer 1 isomer 2

22.13 Ni^{2+} ions have a $3d^8$ configuration, which has three pairs of electrons in the t_2 orbitals and an unpaired electron in each of the two e orbitals. No other electron configuration is possible, so high- and low-spin Ni^{2+} complex ions are not formed.

22.14 Water is a weaker-field ligand (spectrochemical series), as indicated by the blue color of the complex ion due to absorption of longer-wavelength light. Therefore, the *d* orbital electrons would have the maximum number of unpaired electrons and the complex ion would be high-spin.

Answers to Selected Questions for Review and Thought

Chapter 1

11. (a) Quantitative (b) Qualitative (c) Qualitative
(d) Quantitative and qualitative (e) Qualitative
13. (a) Qualitative (b) Quantitative
(c) Quantitative and qualitative (d) Qualitative
15. Sulfur is a pale yellow, powdery solid. Bromine is a dark, red-brown liquid and a red-brown gas that fills the upper part of the flask. Both the melting point and the boiling point of sulfur must be above room temperature. The boiling point, but not the melting point, of bromine must be above room temperature. Both substances are colored. Most of their other properties appear to be different.
17. The liquid will boil because your body temperature of 37 °C is above the boiling point of 20 °C.
19. (a) 20 °C (b) 100 °C
(c) 60 °C (d) 20 °F
21. Copper
23. Aluminum
25. 3.9×10^3 g
27. (a) Physical (b) Chemical
(c) Chemical (d) Physical
29. (a) Chemical (b) Chemical (c) Physical
31. (a) An outside source of energy is forcing a chemical reaction to occur.
(b) A chemical reaction is releasing energy and causing work to be done.
(c) A chemical reaction is releasing energy and causing work to be done.
(d) An outside source of energy is forcing a chemical reaction to occur.
33. Heterogeneous; use a magnet.
35. (a) Homogeneous (b) Heterogeneous
(c) Heterogeneous (d) Heterogeneous
37. (a) A compound decomposed
(b) A compound decomposed
39. (a) Heterogeneous mixture (b) Pure compound
(c) Heterogeneous mixture (d) Homogeneous mixture
41. (a) Heterogeneous mixture (b) Pure compound
(c) Element (d) Homogeneous mixture
43. (a) No (b) Maybe
45. The macroscopic world; a parallelepiped shape; the atom crystal arrangement is a parallelepiped shape.
47. Microscale world
49. Carbon dioxide molecules are crowded in the unopened can. When opened, the molecules quickly escape through the hole.
51. When sucrose is heated, the motion of the atoms increases. Only when that motion is extreme enough, will the bonds in the sucrose break, allowing for the formation of new bonds to produce the "caramelization" products.
53. (a) 3.275×10^4 m (b) 3.42×10^4 nm (c) 1.21×10^{-3} μm
55. Because atoms in the starting materials must all be accounted for in the substances produced, and because the mass of each atom does not change, there would be no change in the mass.
57. (Remember, you are instructed to use your own words to answer this question.) Consider two compounds that both contain the same two elements. In each compound, the proportion of these two elements is a whole-number integer ratio. Because they are different compounds, these ratios must be different. If you pick a sample of each of these compounds such that both samples contain the same number of atoms of the first element, and then you count the number of atoms of the second type, you will find that a small integer relationship exists between the number of atoms of the second type in the first compound and the number of atoms of the second type in the second compound.
59. If two compounds contain the same elements and samples of those two compounds both contain the same mass of one element, then the ratio of the masses of the other elements will be small whole numbers.
61. Many responses are equally valid here. Common examples given here: (a) iron, Fe; gold, Au (b) carbon, C; hydrogen, H
(c) boron, B; silicon, Si (d) nitrogen, N_2; oxygen, O_2.
63.

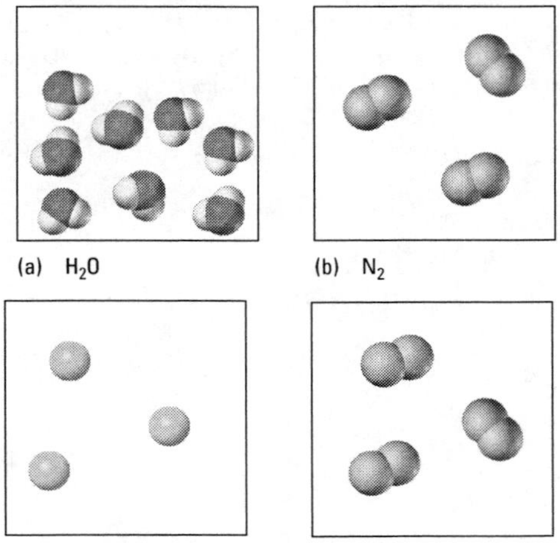

(a) H_2O (b) N_2
(c) Ne (d) Cl_2

65. $2\,H_2(g) + O_2(g) \longrightarrow 2\,H_2O(g)$

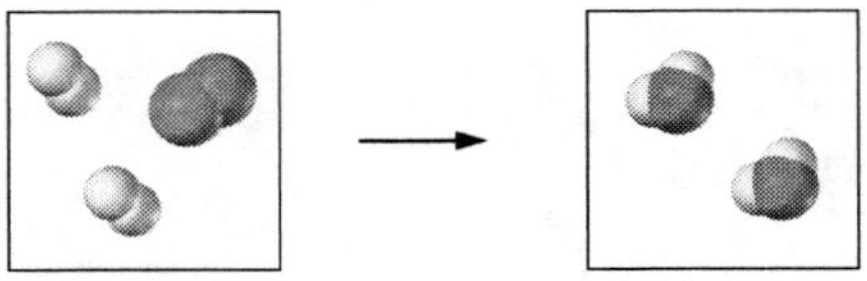

Hydrogen and Water vapor

67. $I_2(s) \longrightarrow I_2(g)$

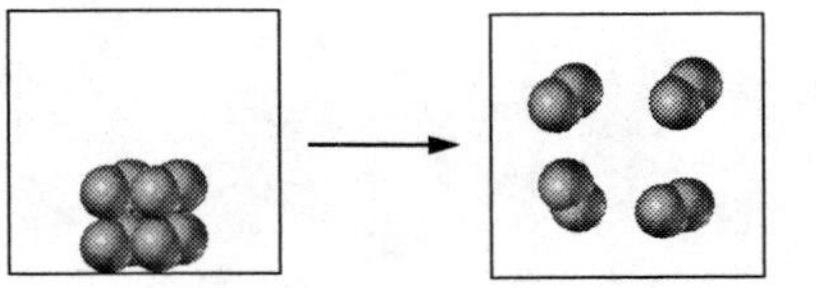

Solid iodine Iodine gas

69. (a) Mass is quantitative and related to a physical property. Colors are qualitative and related to physical properties. Reaction is qualitative and related to a chemical property.
(b) Mass is quantitative and related to a physical property. The fact that a chemical reaction occurs between substances is qualitative information and related to a chemical property.
71. In solid calcium, smaller radius atoms are more closely packed, making a smaller volume. In solid potassium, larger radius atoms are less closely packed, making a larger volume.
73. They are different by how the atoms are organized and bonded together.
75. (a) Bromobenzene (b) Gold (c) Lead
77. (a) 2.7×10^2 mL ice
(b) Bulging, cracking, deformed, or broken
79. Gold
81. (a) Water layer on top of bromobenzene layer.
(b) If it is poured slowly and carefully, ethanol will float on top of the water and slowly dissolve in the water. Both ethanol and water will float on the bromobenzene.
(c) Stirring will speed up dissolving of ethanol and water in each other. After stirring only two layers will remain.

83. Drawing (b)
85. 6.02×10^{-29} m^3
87. (a) Gray and blue (b) Lavender (c) Orange
89. It is difficult to prove that something cannot be broken down (see Section 1.3).
91. (a) Nickel, lead, and magnesium (b) Titanium
93. Obtain four or more lemons. Keep one unaltered to be the "control" case. Perform designated tasks to others, including applying both tasks to the same lemon; then juice all of them, recording results, such as juice volume and ease of task. Repeat with more lemons to achieve better reliability. Hypothesis: Disrupting the "juice sacks" inside the pulp helps to release the juice more easily.

Chapter 2

7. 40,000 cm
9. 614 cm, 242 cm, 20.1 ft
11. 76.2 kg
13. 2.0×10^3 cm^3, 2.0 L
15. 1550 in^2
17. 2.8×10^9 m^3
22. (a) 4 (b) 3 (c) 4 (d) 4 (e) 3
24. (a) 4.33×10^{-4} (b) 4.47×10^1 (c) 2.25×10^1 (d) 8.84×10^{-3}
26. (a) 1.9 g/mL (b) 218.4 cm^3 (c) 0.0217 (d) 5.21×10^{-5}
28. 80.1% silver, 19.9% copper
30. 245 g sulfuric acid
32. 0.9% Na
37. Number of neutrons
39. 27 protons, 27 electrons, and 33 neutrons
41. 78.92 amu/atom
43. (a) 9 (b) 48 (c) 70
45. (a) ${}^{23}_{11}Na$ (b) ${}^{39}_{18}Ar$ (c) ${}^{69}_{31}Ga$
47. (a) 20 e^-, 20 p^+, 20 n^0 (b) 50 e^-, 50 p^+, 69 n^0 (c) 94 e^-, 94 p^+, 150 n^0
49.

Z	*A*	Number of Neutrons	Element
35	81	46	Br
46	108	62	Pd
77	192	115	Ir
63	151	88	Eu

51. ${}^{18}_{9}X$, ${}^{20}_{9}X$ and ${}^{15}_{9}X$
53. Ions
55. Using a magnetic field
57. 6.941 amu/atom
59. 60.12% ^{69}Ga, 39.87% ^{71}Ga
61. ^{7}Li
63. Pair (2), dozen (12), gross (144), million (1,000,000) (Other answers are possible.)
66. (a) 27 g B (b) 0.48 g O_2 (c) 6.98×10^{-2} g Fe (d) 2.61×10^3 g H
68. (a) 1.9998 mol Cu (b) 0.499 mol Ca (c) 0.6208 mol Al (d) 3.1×10^{-4} mol K (e) 2.1×10^{-5} mol Am
70. 2.19 mol Na
72. 9.42×10^{-5} mol Kr
74. 4.131×10^{23} Cr atoms
76. 1.055×10^{-22} g Cu
78. In a group, elements share the same vertical column. In a period, elements share the same horizontal row.
83. Transition elements: iron, copper, chromium
Halogens: fluorine and chlorine
Alkali metal: sodium
(Other answers are possible.)
85. Five; nonmetal: carbon (C), metalloids: silicon (Si) and germanium (Ge), and metals: tin (Sn) and lead (Pb).
87. (a) I (b) In (c) Ir (d) Fe
89. Sixth period
91. (a) Mg (b) Na (c) C (d) S (e) I (f) Mg (g) Kr (h) S (i) Ge [Other answers are possible for (a), (b), and (i).]
93. (a) Iron or magnesium (b) Hydrogen (c) Silicon (d) Iron (e) Chlorine
97. (a) 0.197 nm (b) 197 pm
99. (a) 0.178 nm^3 (b) 1.78×10^{-22} cm^3
102. 89 tons/yr
104. ^{39}K
107. (a) Ti; 22; 47.88 (b) Group 4B; Period 4; zirconium, hafnium, rutherfordium (c) light-weight and strong (d) strong, low-density, highly corrosion resistant, occurs widely, light weight, high-temperature stability (Other answers are possible.)
109. 0.038 mol
111. $3,800
113. 3.4 mol, 2.0×10^{24} atoms
114. (a) Not possible (b) Possible (c) Not possible (d) Not possible (e) Possible (f) Not possible
116. (a) Same (b) Second (c) Same (d) Same (e) Same (f) Second (g) Same (h) First (i) Second (j) First
118. (a) 270 mL (b) No
121. (a) ^{79}Br—^{79}Br, ^{79}Br—^{81}Br, ^{81}Br—^{81}Br (b) 78.918 g/mol, 80.196 g/mol (c) 79.90 g/mol (d) 51.1% ^{79}Br, 48.9% ^{81}Br
123. (a) K (b) Ar (c) Cu (d) Ge (e) H (f) Al (g) O (h) Ca (i) Br (j) P
125. (a) Se (b) ^{39}K (c) ^{79}Br (d) ^{20}Ne

Chapter 3

9. (a) BrF_3 (b) XeF_2 (c) P_2F_4 (d) $C_{15}H_{32}$ (e) N_2H_4
11. Butanol, $C_4H_{10}O$, $CH_3CH_2CH_2CH_2OH$

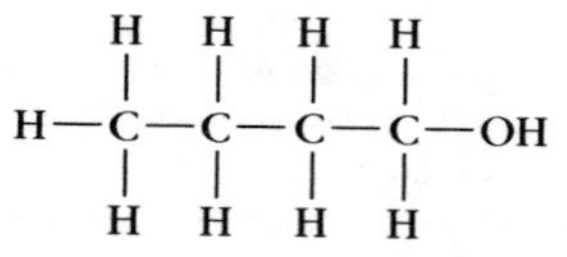

Pentanol, $C_5H_{12}O$, $CH_3CH_2CH_2CH_2CH_2OH$

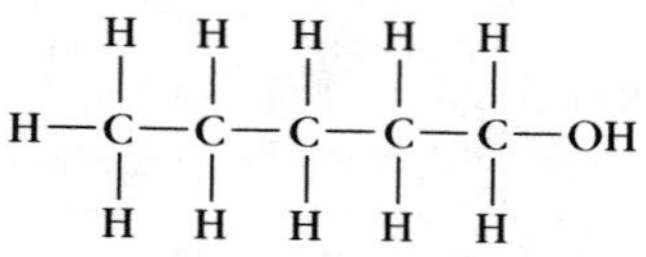

14. (a) C_6H_6 (b) $C_6H_8O_6$
16. (a) 1 calcium atom, 2 carbon atoms, and 4 oxygen atoms
(b) 8 carbon atoms and 8 hydrogen atoms
(c) 2 nitrogen atoms, 8 hydrogen atoms, 1 sulfur atom, and 4 oxygen atoms
(d) 1 platinum atom, 2 nitrogen atoms, 6 hydrogen atoms, and 2 chlorine atoms
(e) 4 potassium atoms, 1 iron atom, 6 carbon atoms, and 6 nitrogen atoms

18. (a) Same number of atoms of each kind
(b) Different bonding arrangements
20. (a) Li^+ (b) Sr^{2+} (c) Al^{3+} (d) Ca^{2+}
(e) Zn^{2+}
22. Ba: 2+, Br: −1
24. (a) +2 (b) +2 (c) +2 or +3 (d) +3
26. CoO, Co_2O_3
28. (c) and (d) are correct formulas. (a) $AlCl_3$ (b) NaF
30. Mn
32. (a) 1 Pb^{2+} and 2 NO_3^- (b) 1 Ni^{2+} and 1 CO_3^{2-}
(c) 3 NH_4^+ and 1 PO_4^{3-} (d) 2 K^+ and 1 SO_4^{2-}
34. $BaSO_4$, barium ion, 2+, sulfate, 2−; $Mg(NO_3)_2$, magnesium ion, 2+, nitrate, 1−; $NaCH_3CO_2$, sodium ion, 1+, acetate, 1−
36. (a) $Ni(NO_3)_2$ (b) $NaHCO_3$ (c) LiClO
(d) $Mg(ClO_3)_2$ (e) $CaSO_3$
38. (b), (c), and (e) are ionic.
40. Only (e) is ionic, with metal and nonmetal combined. (a)-(d) are composed of only nonmetals.
42. (a) $(NH_4)_2CO_3$ (b) CaI_2 (c) $CuBr_2$ (d) $AlPO_4$
44. (a) Potassium sulfide (b) Nickel(II) sulfate (c) Ammonium phosphate (d) Aluminum hydroxide (e) Cobalt(III) sulfate
46. MgO; MgO has higher ionic charges and smaller ion sizes than NaCl.
48. Conducts electricity in water; check electrical conductivity; examples: NaCl and $C_{12}H_{22}O_{11}$. (Other answers are possible.)
50. Molecular compounds are generally not ionic compounds and, therefore, would not ionize in water.
52. (a) K^+ and OH^- (b) K^+ and SO_4^{2-}
(c) Na^+ and NO_3^- (d) NH_4^+ and Cl^-
54. (a) and (d)
56.

	CH_3OH	Carbon
No. of moles	One	One
No. of molecules or atoms	6.022×10^{23} molecules	6.022×10^{23} atoms
Molar mass	32.0417 g/mol	12.0107 g/mol

	Hydrogen	Oxygen
No. of moles	Four	One
No. of molecules or atoms	2.409×10^{24} atoms	6.022×10^{23} atoms
Molar mass	4.0316 g/mol	15.9994 g/mol

58. (a) 159.688 g/mol (b) 67.806 g/mol (c) 44.0128 g/mol
(d) 197.905 g/mol (e) 176.1238 g/mol
60. (a) 0.0312 mol (b) 0.0101 mol (c) 0.0125 mol
(d) 0.00406 mol (e) 0.00599 mol
62. (a) 179.855 g/mol (b) 36.0 g (c) 0.0259 mol
64. (a) 151.1622 g/mol (b) 0.0352 mol (c) 25.1 g
66. (a) 0.400 mol (b) 0.250 mol (c) 0.628 mol
68. 2.7×10^{23} atoms
70. 1.2×10^{24} molecules
72. (a) 0.250 mol CF_3CH_2F
(b) 6.02×10^{23} F atoms
75. (a) 239.3 g/mol PbS, 86.60% Pb, 13.40% S
(b) 30.0688 g/mol C_2H_6, 79.8881% C, 20.1119% H
(c) 60.0518 g/mol CH_3CO_2H, 40.0011% C, 6.7135% H, 53.2854% O
(d) 80.0432 g/mol NH_4NO_3, 34.9979% C, 5.0368% H, 59.9654% O
77. 58.0% M in MO
79. 245.745 g/mol, 25.858% Cu, 22.7992% N, 5.74197% H, 13.048% S, 32.5528% O
81. One
83. (a) −2 (b) Al_2X_3 (c) Se
86. An empirical formula shows the simplest whole-number ratio of the elements, e.g., CH_3; a molecular formula shows the actual number of atoms of each element, e.g., C_2H_6.
88. $C_4H_4O_4$
90. $C_2H_3OF_3$
92. KNO_3
94. B_5H_7
96. (a) C_3H_4 (b) C_9H_{12}
98. (a) C_5H_7N (b) $C_{10}H_{14}N_2$
100. $C_5H_{14}N_2$
102. $x = 7$
110. (a) $C_7H_5N_3O_6$ (b) $C_3H_7NO_3$
113. (a) (i) Chlorine tribromide (ii) Nitrogen trichloride
(iii) Calcium sulfate (iv) Heptane (v) Xenon tetrafluoride
(vi) Oxygen difluoride (vii) Sodium iodide
(viii) Aluminum sulfide (ix) Phosphorus pentachloride
(x) Potassium phosphate
(b) (iii), (vii), (viii), and (x)
115. (a) 2.39 mol (b) 21.7 cm^3
117. (a) CO_2F_2 (b) CO_2F_2
119. $MnC_9H_7O_3$
121. (a) 1.66×10^{-3} mol (b) 0.346 g
123. 2.14×10^5 g
126.

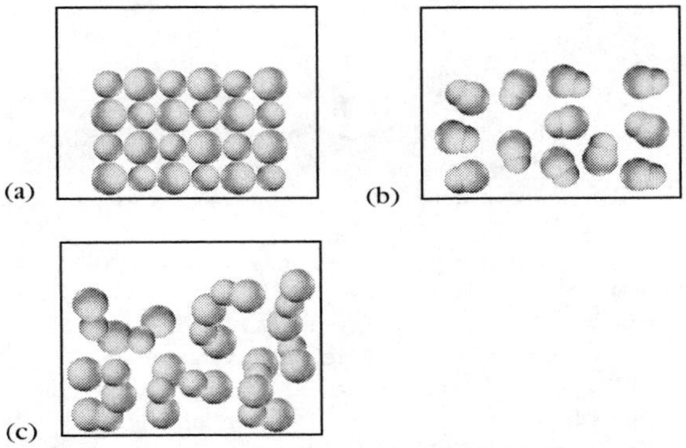

128. (a) Three (b) Three pairs are identical:

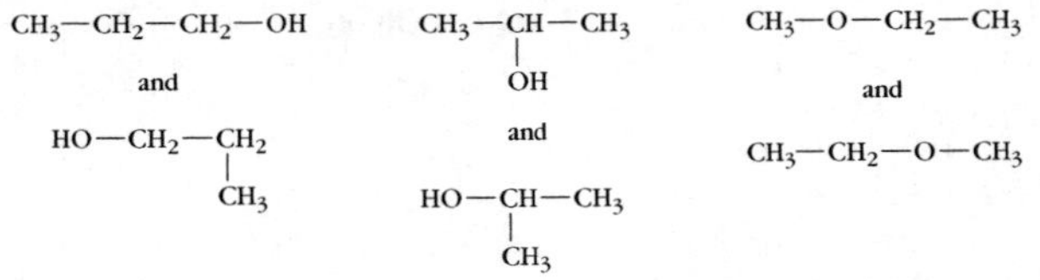

130. Tl_2CO_3, Tl_2SO_4
132. (a) Perbromate, bromate, bromite, hypobromite
(b) Selenate, selenite
135. (a) 0.0130 mol Ni (b) NiF_2
(c) Nickel(II) fluoride
137. CO_2
139. $MgSO_3$, magnesium sulfite
141. 5.0 lb N, 4.4 lb P, 4.2 lb K

Chapter 4

10.

	KOH	HCl
No. molecules	1	1
No. atoms	3	2
No. moles of molecules	1	1
Mass	56.1056 g	36.4609 g
Total mass of reactants	92.5665 g	
Total mass of products		

	KCl	H_2O
No. molecules	1	1
No. atoms	2	3
No. moles of molecules	1	1
Mass	74.5513 g	18.0152 g
Total mass of reactants		
Total mass of products	92.5665 g	

12. (a) 1.00 g (b) 2 for Mg, 1 for O_2, and 2 for MgO (c) 50 atoms of Mg
14. $4\ Fe(s) + 3\ O_2(g) \rightarrow 2\ Fe_2O_3(s)$
16. Equation (b)
18.

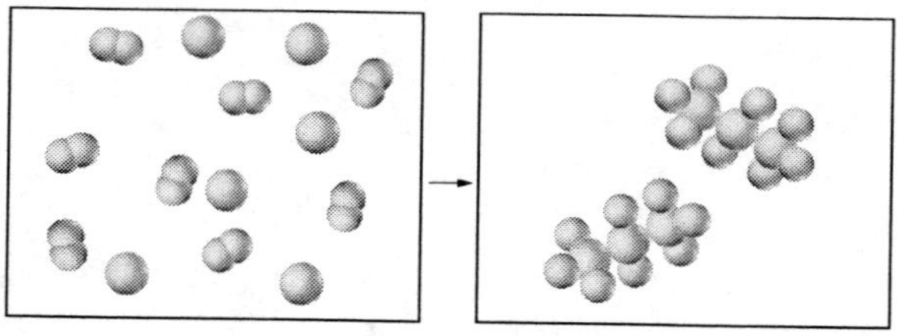

20. (a) Combination (b) Decomposition (c) Exchange (d) Displacement
22. (a) Decomposition (b) Displacement (c) Combination (d) Exchange
24. (a) $2\ C_4H_{10}(g) + 13\ O_2(g) \rightarrow 8\ CO_2(g) + 10\ H_2O(g)$
(b) $C_6H_{12}O_6(s) + 6\ O_2(g) \rightarrow 6\ CO_2(g) + 6\ H_2O(g)$
(c) $2\ C_4H_8O(\ell) + 11\ O_2(g) \rightarrow 8\ CO_2(g) + 8\ H_2O(g)$
26. (a) $2\ Mg(s) + O_2(g) \rightarrow 2\ MgO(s)$, magnesium oxide
(b) $2\ Ca(s) + O_2(g) \rightarrow 2\ CaO(s)$, calcium oxide
(c) $4\ In(s) + 3\ O_2(g) \rightarrow 2\ In_2O_3(s)$, indium oxide
28. (a) $2\ K(s) + Cl_2(g) \rightarrow 2\ KCl(s)$, potassium chloride
(b) $Mg(s) + Br_2(\ell) \rightarrow MgBr_2(s)$, magnesium bromide
(c) $2\ Al(s) + 3\ F_2(g) \rightarrow 2\ AlF_3(s)$, aluminum fluoride
30. (a) $4\ Al(s) + 3\ O_2(g) \rightarrow 2\ Al_2O_3(s)$
(b) $N_2(g) + 3\ H_2(g) \rightarrow 2\ NH_3(g)$
(c) $2\ C_6H_6(\ell) + 15\ O_2(g) \rightarrow 6\ H_2O(\ell) + 12\ CO_2(g)$
32. (a) $UO_2(s) + 4\ HF(\ell) \rightarrow UF_4(s) + 2\ H_2O(\ell)$
(b) $B_2O_3(s) + 6\ HF(\ell) \rightarrow 2\ BF_3(s) + 3\ H_2O(\ell)$
(c) $BF_3(g) + 3\ H_2O(\ell) \rightarrow 3\ HF(\ell) + H_3BO_3(s)$
34. (a) $H_2NCl(aq) + 2\ NH_3(g) \rightarrow NH_4Cl(aq) + N_2H_4(aq)$
(b) $(CH_3)_2N_2H_2(\ell) + 2\ N_2O_4(g) \rightarrow 3\ N_2(g) + 4\ H_2O(g) + 2\ CO_2(g)$
(c) $CaC_2(s) + 2\ H_2O(\ell) \rightarrow Ca(OH)_2(s) + C_2H_2(g)$
36. (a) $C_6H_{12}O_6 + 6\ O_2 \rightarrow 6\ CO_2 + 6\ H_2O$
(b) $C_5H_{12} + 8\ O_2 \rightarrow 5\ CO_2 + 6\ H_2O$
(c) $2\ C_7H_{14}O_2 + 19\ O_2 \rightarrow 14\ CO_2 + 14\ H_2O$
(d) $C_2H_4O_2 + 2\ O_2 \rightarrow 2\ CO_2 + 2\ H_2O$
38. 50.0 mol HCl
40. 12.8 g
42. 1.1 mol O_2, 35 g O_2, 1.0×10^2 g NO_2
44. 12.7 g Cl_2, 0.179 mol $FeCl_2$, 22.7 g $FeCl_2$ expected
46.

$(NH_4)_2PtCl_6$	Pt	HCl
12.35 g	5.428 g	5.410 g
0.02782 mol	0.02782 mol	0.1484 mol

48. (a) 0.148 mol H_2O (b) 5.89 g TiO_2, 10.8 g HCl
50. 2.0 mol, 36.0304 g
52. 0.699 g Ga and 0.751 g As
54. (a) $4\ Fe(s) + 3\ O_2(g) \rightarrow 2\ Fe_2O_3(s)$
(b) 7.98 g (c) 2.40 g
56. (a) $CCl_2F_2 + 2\ Na_2C_2O_4 \rightarrow C + 4\ CO_2 + 2\ NaCl + 2\ NaF$
(b) 170. g $Na_2C_2O_4$ (b) 112 g CO_2
58. (a) 699 g (b) 526 g
60. $BaCl_2$, 1.12081 g $BaSO_4$
62. (a) Cl_2 is limiting. (b) 5.08 g Al_2Cl_6
(c) 1.67 g Al unreacted
64. (a) CO (b) 1.3 g H_2 (c) 85.2 g
66. 0 mol CaO, 0.19 mol NH_4Cl, 2.00 mol H_2O, 4.00 mol NH_3, 2.00 mol $CaCl_2$
68. 1.40 kg Fe
71. 699 g, 93.5%
73. 56.0%
75. 8.8%
77. 5.3 g SCl_2
80. SO_3
82. CH
84. $C_3H_6O_2$
87. 21.6 g N_2
89. Element (b)
91. 12.5 g $Pt(NH_3)_2Cl_2$
93. SiH_4
95. KOH, KOH
97. Two butane molecules react with 13 diatomic oxygen molecules to produce 8 carbon dioxide molecules and 10 water molecules. Two moles of gaseous butane molecules react with 13 moles of gaseous diatomic oxygen molecules to produce 8 moles of gaseous carbon dioxide molecules and 10 moles of liquid water molecules.
99. A_3B
101. Ag^+, Cu^{2+}, and NO_3^-
104. Equation (b)
106. When the metal mass is less than 1.2 g, the metal is the limiting reactant. When the metal mass is greater than 1.2 g, the bromine is the limiting reactant.
108. $H_2(g) + 3\ Fe_2O_3(s) \rightarrow H_2O(\ell) + 2\ Fe_3O_4(s)$
110. 86.3 g
112. (a) CH_4 (b) 200 g (c) 700 g
114. 44.9 amu
116. 0 g $AgNO_3$, 9.82 g Na_2CO_3, 6.79 g Ag_2CO_3, 4.19 g $NaNO_3$
118. 99.7% CH_3OH, 0.3% C_2H_5OH
120. (a) $C_9H_{11}NO_4$ (b) $C_9H_{11}NO_4$

Chapter 5

11. All soluble (a) Fe^{2+} and ClO_4^- (b) Na^+ and SO_4^{2-} (c) K^+ and Br^- (d) Na^+ and CO_3^{2-}
13. All soluble (a) K^+ and HPO_4^{2-} (b) Na^+ and ClO^- (c) Mg^{2+} and Cl^- (d) Ca^{2+} and OH^- (e) Al^{3+} and Br^-
15. $2\ HNO_3(aq) + Ca(OH)_2(aq) \rightarrow 2\ H_2O(\ell) + Ca(NO_3)_2(aq)$
17. (a) $MnCl_2(aq) + Na_2S(aq) \rightarrow MnS(s) + 2\ NaCl(aq)$
(b) No precipitate
(c) No precipitate
(d) $Hg(NO_3)_2(aq) + Na_2S(aq) \rightarrow HgS(s) + 2\ NaNO_3(aq)$
(e) $Pb(NO_3)_2(aq) + 2\ HCl(aq) \rightarrow PbCl_2(s) + 2\ HNO_3(aq)$
(f) $BaCl_2(aq) + H_2SO_4(aq) \rightarrow BaSO_4(s) + 2\ HCl(aq)$

19. (a) CuS insoluble;
$Cu^{2+} + H_2S(aq) \rightarrow CuS(s) + 2\,H^+$;
spectator ion is Cl^-.
(b) $CaCO_3$ insoluble;
$Ca^{2+} + CO_3^{2-} \rightarrow CaCO_3(s)$; spectator ions are K^+ and Cl^-.
(c) AgI insoluble;
$Ag^+ + I^- \rightarrow AgI(s)$; spectator ions are Na^+ and NO_3^-.
21. Complete ionic equation:
$2\,K^+ + CO_3^{2-} + Cu^{2+} + 2\,NO_3^- \rightarrow CuCO_3(s) + 2\,K^+ + 2\,NO_3^-$
Net ionic equation:
$CO_3^{2-} + Cu^{2+} \rightarrow CuCO_3(s)$
Precipitate is copper(II) carbonate.
23. (a) $Zn(s) + 2\,HCl(aq) \rightarrow H_2(g) + ZnCl_2(aq)$
$Zn(s) + 2\,H^+(aq) + 2\,Cl^-(aq) \rightarrow H_2(g) + Zn^{2+}(aq) + 2\,Cl^-(aq)$
$Zn(s) + 2\,H^+(aq) \rightarrow H_2(g) + Zn^{2+}(aq)$
(b) $Mg(OH)_2(s) + 2\,HCl(aq) \rightarrow MgCl_2(aq) + 2\,H_2O(\ell)$
$Mg(OH)_2(s) + 2\,H^+(aq) + 2\,Cl^-(aq) \rightarrow Mg^{2+}(aq) + 2\,Cl^-(aq) + 2\,H_2O(\ell)$
$Mg(OH)_2(s) + 2\,H^+(aq) \rightarrow Mg^{2+}(aq) + 2\,H_2O(\ell)$
(c) $2\,HNO_3(aq) + CaCO_3(s) \rightarrow Ca(NO_3)_2(aq) + H_2O(\ell) + CO_2(g)$
$2\,H^+(aq) + 2\,NO_3^-(aq) + CaCO_3(s) \rightarrow Ca^{2+}(aq) + 2\,NO_3^-(aq) + H_2O(\ell) + CO_2(g)$
$2\,H^+(aq) + CaCO_3(s) \rightarrow Ca^{2+}(aq) + H_2O(\ell) + CO_2(g)$
(d) $4\,HCl(aq) + MnO_2(s) \rightarrow MnCl_2(aq) + Cl_2(g) + 2\,H_2O(\ell)$
$4\,H^+(aq) + 4\,Cl^-(aq) + MnO_2(s) \rightarrow Mn^{2+}(aq) + 2\,Cl^-(aq) + Cl_2(g) + 2\,H_2O(\ell)$
$4\,H^+(aq) + 2\,Cl^-(aq) + MnO_2(s) \rightarrow Mn^{2+}(aq) + Cl_2(g) + 2\,H_2O(\ell)$
25. (a) $Ca(OH)_2(s) + 2\,HNO_3(aq) \rightarrow Ca(NO_3)_2(aq) + 2\,H_2O(\ell)$
$Ca(OH)_2(s) + 2\,H^+(aq) + 2\,NO_3^-(aq) \rightarrow Ca^{2+}(aq) + 2\,NO_3^-(aq) + 2\,H_2O(\ell)$
$Ca(OH)_2(s) + 2\,H^+(aq) \rightarrow Ca^{2+}(aq) + 2\,H_2O(\ell)$
(b) $BaCl_2(aq) + Na_2CO_3(aq) \rightarrow BaCO_3(s) + 2\,NaCl(aq)$
$Ba^{2+}(aq) + 2\,Cl^-(aq) + 2\,Na^+(aq) + CO_3^{2-}(aq) \rightarrow BaCO_3(s) + 2\,Na^+(aq) + 2\,Cl^-(aq)$
$Ba^{2+}(aq) + CO_3^{2-}(aq) \rightarrow BaCO_3(s)$
(c) $2\,Na_3PO_4(aq) + 3\,Ni(NO_3)_2(aq) \rightarrow Ni_3(PO_4)_2(s) + 6\,NaNO_3(aq)$
$6\,Na^+(aq) + 2\,PO_4^{3-}(aq) + 3\,Ni^{2+}(aq) + 6\,NO_3^-(aq) \rightarrow Ni_3(PO_4)_2(s) + 6\,Na^+(aq) + 6\,NO_3^-(aq)$
$2\,PO_4^{3-}(aq) + 3\,Ni^{2+}(aq) \rightarrow Ni_3(PO_4)_2(s)$
27. $Ba(OH)_2(aq) + 2\,HNO_3(aq) \longrightarrow Ba(NO_3)_2(aq) + 2\,H_2O(\ell)$
29. $CdCl_2(aq) + 2\,NaOH(aq) \longrightarrow Cd(OH)_2(s) + 2\,NaCl(aq)$
$Cd^{2+}(aq) + 2\,Cl^-(aq) + 2\,Na^+(aq) + 2\,OH^-(aq) \longrightarrow Cd(OH)_2(s) + 2\,Na^+(aq) + 2\,Cl^-(aq)$
$Cd^{2+}(aq) + 2\,OH^-(aq) \longrightarrow Cd(OH)_2(s)$
31. $Pb(NO_3)_2(aq) + 2\,KCl(aq) \rightarrow PbCl_2(s) + 2\,KNO_3(aq)$
Reactants: lead(II) nitrate and potassium chloride
Products: lead(II) chloride and potassium nitrate
34. (a) Base strong, K^+ and OH^-
(b) Base strong, Mg^{2+} and OH^-
(c) Acid weak, small amounts of H^+ and ClO^-
(d) Acid strong, H^+ and Br^-
(e) Base strong, Li^+ and OH^-
(f) Acid weak, small amounts of H^+, HSO_3^-, and SO_3^{2-}
36. (a) Acid: HNO_2, base: NaOH
complete ionic form:
$HNO_2(aq) + Na^+ + OH^- \longrightarrow H_2O(\ell) + Na^+ + NO_2^-$
net ionic form:
$HNO_2(aq) + OH^- \longrightarrow H_2O(\ell) + NO_2^-$
(b) Acid: H_2SO_4 base: $Ca(OH)_2$
complete ionic and net ionic forms:
$H^+ + HSO_4^- + Ca(OH)_2(s) \longrightarrow 2\,H_2O(\ell) + CaSO_4(s)$
(c) Acid: HI, base: NaOH
complete ionic form:
$H^+ + I^- + Na^+ + OH^- \longrightarrow H_2O(\ell) + Na^+ + I^-$
net ionic form: $H^+ + OH^- \longrightarrow H_2O(\ell)$
(d) Acid: H_3PO_4, base: $Mg(OH)_2$
complete ionic and net ionic forms:
$2\,H_3PO_4(aq) + 3\,Mg(OH)_2(s) \longrightarrow 6\,H_2O(\ell) + Mg_3(PO_4)_2(s)$
38. (a) Precipitation reaction; products are NaCl and MnS;
$MnCl_2(aq) + Na_2S(aq) \rightarrow 2\,NaCl(aq) + MnS(s)$ (b) Precipitation reaction; products are NaCl and $ZnCO_3$;
$Na_2CO_3(aq) + ZnCl_2(aq) \rightarrow 2\,NaCl(aq) + ZnCO_3(s)$
(c) Gas-forming reaction; products are $KClO_4$, H_2O, and CO_2;
$K_2CO_3(aq) + 2\,HClO_4(aq) \rightarrow 2\,KClO_4(aq) + H_2O(\ell) + CO_2(g)$
40. (a) Ox. # O = −2, Ox. # S = +6
(b) Ox. # O = −2, Ox. # H = +1, Ox. # N = +5
(c) Ox. # K = +1, Ox. # O = −2, Ox. # Mn = +7
(d) Ox. # O = −2, Ox. # H = +1
(e) Ox. # Li = +1, Ox. # O = −2, Ox. # H = +1
(f) Ox. # Cl = −1, Ox. # H = +1, Ox. # C = 0
42. (a) S: +6, O: −2 (b) N: +5, O: −2
(c) Mn: +7, O: −2 (d) Cr: +3, O: −2, H: +1
(e) P: +5, O: −2, H: +1 (f) S: +2, O: −2
44. (a) −1 (b) +1 (c) +3 (d) +5
(e) +7
46. (a) −2 (b) 0 (c) +2 (d) +4
(e) +6
48. Only reaction (b) is an oxidation-reduction reaction; oxidation numbers change. Reaction (a) is precipitation and reaction; (c) is acid-base neutralization.
51. Substances (b), (c), and (d)
53. (a) $CO_2(g)$ or $CO(g)$ (b) $PCl_3(g)$ or $PCl_5(g)$
(c) $TiCl_2(s)$ or $TiCl_4(s)$ (d) $Mg_3N_2(s)$
(e) $Fe_2O_3(s)$ (f) $NO_2(g)$
55. F_2 is the best oxidizing agent; I^- anion is the best reducing agent.
57. (b) Br_2 is reduced. NaI is oxidized. Br_2 is oxidizing agent. NaI is reducing agent.
(c) F_2 is reduced. NaCl is oxidized. F_2 is oxidizing agent. NaCl is reducing agent.
(d) Cl_2 is reduced. NaBr is oxidized. Cl_2 is oxidizing agent. NaBr is reducing agent.
59. This is just an example:
$Fe(s) + 2\,HCl(aq) \longrightarrow FeCl_2(aq) + H_2(g)$
(a) Fe is oxidized. (b) HCl is reduced.
(c) The reducing agent is Fe(s).
(d) The oxidizing agent is HCl(aq).
(Other answers are possible.)
61. (a) N.R. (b) N.R. (c) N.R.
(d) $Au^{3+}(aq) + 3\,Ag(s) \longrightarrow 3\,Ag^+(aq) + Au(s)$
63. 0.12 M Ba^{2+}, 0.24 M Cl^-
65. (a) 0.254 M Na_2CO_3 (b) 0.508 M Na^+, 0.254 M CO_3^{2-}
67. 0.494 g $KMnO_4$
69. 5.08×10^3 mL
71. 0.0150 M $CuSO_4$
73. Method (b)
75. 39.4 g $NiSO_4 \cdot 6H_2O$
77. 0.205 g Na_2CO_3
79. 121 mL HNO_3 solution
81. 22.9 mL NaOH solution
83. 0.18 g AgCl, NaCl, 0.0080 M NaCl
85. (a) Step (ii) is wrong. Steps (iii) and (iv) are wrong because Step (ii) is wrong.
(b) 0.00394 g citric acid
87. 1.192 M HCl
89. 96.8% pure

91. Chloride is the spectator ion.
$CaCO_3(s) + 2\,H^+(aq) \longrightarrow CO_2(g) + Ca^{2+}(aq) + H_2O(\ell)$
gas-forming exchange reaction

93. (a) $(NH_4)_2S(aq) + Hg(NO_3)_2(aq) \rightarrow HgS(s) + 2\,NH_4NO_3(aq)$
(b) Reactants: ammonium sulfide, mercury(II) nitrate; products: mercury(II) sulfide, ammonium nitrate
(c) $S^{2-}(aq) + Hg^{2+}(aq) \longrightarrow HgS(s)$
(d) Precipitation reaction

95. (a) Combination reaction; product: $H_2SO_4(aq)$
(b) Combination reaction; product: $SrH_2(s)$
(c) Displacement reaction; products: $MgSO_4(aq)$ and $H_2(g)$
(d) Exchange (precipitation) reaction; products: $Ag_3PO_4(s)$ and $NaNO_3(aq)$
(e) Decomposition and gas-forming reaction; products: $CaO(s)$, $H_2O(\ell)$, and $CO_2(g)$
(f) Oxidation-reduction reaction; products: $Fe^{2+}(aq)$ and $Sn^{4+}(aq)$

97. (a) $NH_3(aq)$, H_2O (b) $CH_3CO_2H(aq)$, H_2O
(c) Na^+, OH^-, H_2O (d) H^+, Br^-, H_2O

99. (c) is a redox reaction. The oxidizing agent is Ti. The reducing agent is Mg.

101. Case 1 (a) Before: clear colorless solution; after: solid at the bottom of beaker with colorless solution above it
(b)

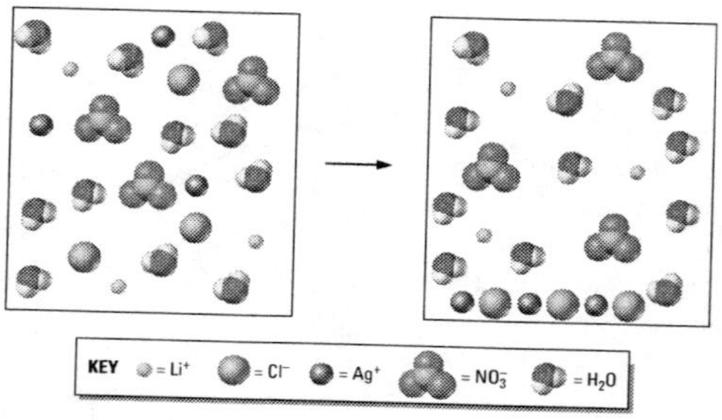

(c) $Li^+ + Cl^- + Ag^+ + NO_3^- \rightarrow Li^+ + AgCl(s) + NO_3^-$
Case 2 (a) Before and after: clear colorless solutions
(b)

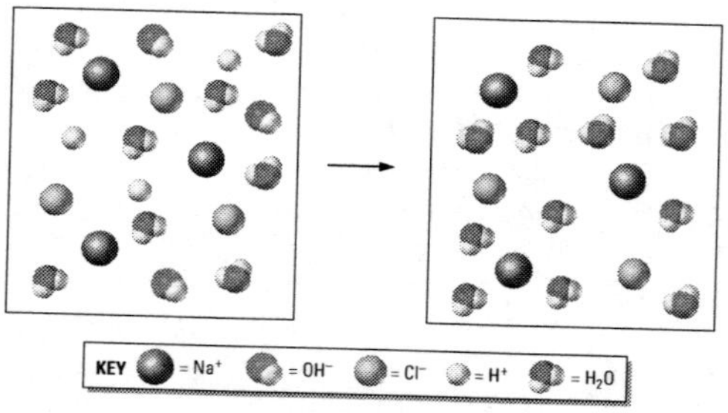

(c) $Na^+ + OH^- + H^+ + Cl^- \rightarrow Na^+ + H_2O(\ell) + Cl^-$

103. (a) Combine $Ba(OH)_2(aq)$ and $H_2SO_4(aq)$
(b) Combine $Na_2SO_4(aq)$ and $Ba(NO_3)_2(aq)$
(c) Combine $BaCO_3(s)$ and $H_2SO_4(aq)$

105. HCl(aq); insoluble lead(II) chloride would precipitate if Pb^{2+} was present, but no precipitate would be seen if only Ba^{2+} was present.

107. The products are the result of something being oxidized and something being reduced. Only the reactants are oxidized and reduced.

109. (d)

111. (a) and (d) are correct.

113. (a) $MgBr_2$, magnesium bromide; $CaBr_2$, calcium bromide; $SrBr_2$, strontium bromide
(b) $Mg(s) + Br_2(\ell) \rightarrow MgBr_2(s)$
$Ca(s) + Br_2(\ell) \rightarrow CaBr_2(s)$
$Sr(s) + Br_2(\ell) \rightarrow SrBr_2(s)$
(c) Oxidation-reduction
(d) The point where increase stops gives: $\frac{\text{g metal}}{\text{g product}}$. The different metals have different molar masses, so the ratios will be different. Use grams to find moles and then set up a ratio.

115. (a) Groups C and D: $Ag^+ + Cl^- \rightarrow AgCl(s)$, Groups A and B: $Ag^+ + Br^- \rightarrow AgBr(s)$
(b) Different silver halide produced in Group C and D than in Groups A and B
(c) Bromide is heavier than chloride.

117. 104 g/mol

119. (a) $CaF_2(s) + H_2SO_4(aq) \rightarrow 2\,HF(g) + CaSO_4(s)$
Reactant: calcium fluoride and sulfuric acid
Products: hydrogen fluoride and calcium sulfate
(b) Precipitation reaction.
(c) Carbon tetrachloride, antimony(V) chloride, hydrogen chloride
(d) CCl_3F

121. 2.26 g, 1.45 g

123. 0.0154 M $CaSO_4$; 0.341 g $CaSO_4$ undissolved

125. 2.6×10^{-3} M

127. 184 mL

129. 6.28% impurity

Chapter 6

11. (a) 399 Cal (b) 5.0×10^6 J/day

13. 1.12×10^4 J

14. 3×10^8 J

15. 3.60×10^6 J, \$0.03

17. (a) The chemical potential energy of the atoms in the match, fuse, and fuel are converted to thermal energy (due to the combustion reaction), potential energy (as the rocket's altitude increases), and light energy (colorful sparkles). (b) The chemical potential energy of the atoms in the fuel is converted to thermal energy (due to the combustion reaction), some of which is converted to kinetic energy (for the movement of the vehicle).

19. (a) The system: the plant (stem, leaves, roots, etc.); the surroundings: anything not the plant (air, soil, water, sun, etc.) (b) To study the plant growing, we must isolate it and see how it interacts with its surroundings. (c) Light energy and carbon dioxide are absorbed by the leaves and are converted to other molecules storing the energy as chemical energy that is used to increase the size of the plant. Minerals and water are absorbed through the soil. CO_2 is absorbed from the air. The plant expels oxygen and other waste materials into the surroundings.

21. (a) The system: NH_4 Cl; the surroundings: anything not NH_4Cl, including the water. (b) To study the release of energy during the phase change of this chemical, we must isolate it and see how it interacts with the surroundings. (c) The system's interaction with the surroundings causes heat to be transferred into the system and from the surroundings. There is no material transfer in this process, but there is a change in the specific interaction between the water and system. (d) Endothermic

23. $\Delta E = +32$ J

25.

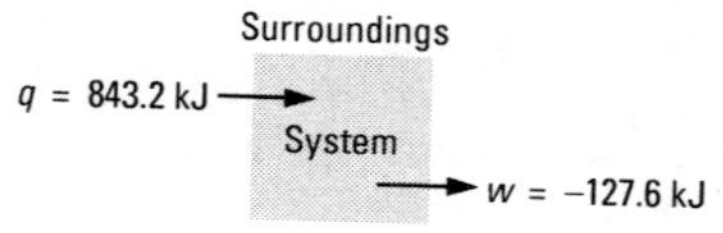

$\Delta E = 715.6$ J

27. Process (a) requires greater transfer of energy than (b).

29. It takes less time to raise the Cu sample to body temperature.
31. 1.0×10^2 kJ
33. More energy (1.48×10^6 J) is absorbed by the water than by the ethylene glycol (9.56×10^5 J).
35. 330. °C
37. (a) 0.45 J g^{-1} °C^{-1}, 25 J mol^{-1} °C^{-1}
39. Gold
41. 160 °C
43. Positive; Negative
45. 4.13×10^5 J
47. 5.00×10^5 J
49. 270 J
51.

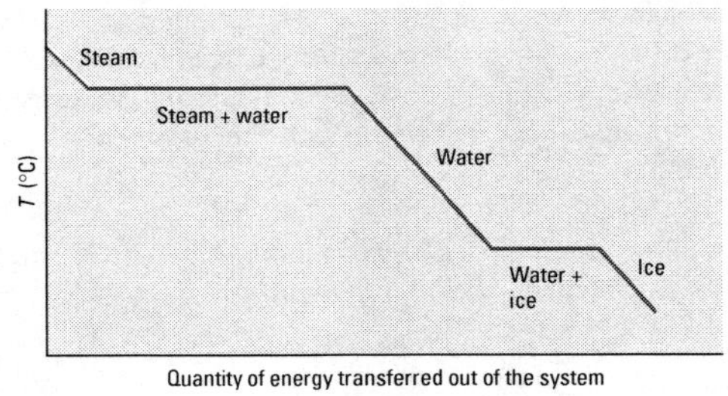

53. (a) X(ℓ) (b) Heat of fusion
(c) Enthalpy of vaporization is positive.
55. Endothermic
57. Endothermic
59. 6.0 kJ of energy is used to convert one mole of ice into liquid water.
61. (a) −210 kJ (b) −33 kJ
63. (a) $\frac{1}{2}\,C_8H_{18}(\ell) + \frac{25}{4}\,O_2(g) \rightarrow 4\,CO_2(g) + \frac{9}{2}\,H_2O(\ell)$
$\Delta H° = -2748.0$ kJ
(b) $100\,C_8H_{18}(\ell) + 1250\,O_2(g) \rightarrow 800\,CO_2(g) + 900\,H_2O(\ell)$
$\Delta H° = -5.4960 \times 10^5$ kJ
(c) $C_8H_{18}(\ell) + \frac{25}{2}\,O_2(g) \rightarrow 8\,CO_2(g) + 9\,H_2O(\ell)$
$\Delta H° = -5496.0$ kJ
65. $\frac{464.8\text{ kJ}}{1\text{ mol CaO}}, \frac{464.8\text{ kJ}}{3\text{ mol C}}, \frac{464.8\text{ kJ}}{1\text{ mol CaC}_2}, \frac{464.8\text{ kJ}}{1\text{ mol CO}}, \frac{1\text{ mol CaO}}{464.8\text{ kJ}}, \frac{3\text{ mol C}}{464.8\text{ kJ}}, \frac{1\text{ mol CaC}_2}{464.8\text{ kJ}}, \frac{1\text{ mol CO}}{464.8\text{ kJ}}$
67. (a) 2.83×10^5 kJ into system (b) 3.63×10^4 kJ into system
(c) 139 kJ out of system
69. $\Delta H = -1450$ kJ/mol
71. 35.5 kJ
73. 6×10^4 kJ released
75. HF
77. For $H_2 + F_2 \longrightarrow 2$ HF reaction: (a) 594 kJ (b) −1132 kJ
(c) −538 kJ
For $H_2 + Cl_2 \longrightarrow 2$ HCl reaction: (a) 678 kJ (b) −862 kJ
(c) −184 kJ (d) ΔH of HF is most exothermic.
79. 18 °C
81. (a) 1.4×10^4 J (b) −42 kJ
83. 6.6 kJ
85. 394 kJ/mol evolved
87. $\Delta H_f^\circ(SrCO_3) = -1220.$ kJ/mol
89. $\Delta H_f^\circ(PbO) = -217.3$ kJ/mol, 2.6×10^2 kJ evolved
91. $Ag(s) + \frac{1}{2}\,Cl_2(g) \rightarrow AgCl(s)$ $\Delta H° = -127.1$ kJ
93. (a) $2\,Al(s) + \frac{3}{2}\,O_2(g) \rightarrow Al_2O_3(s)$ $\Delta H° = -1675.7$ kJ
(b) $Ti(s) + 2\,Cl_2(g) \rightarrow TiCl_4(\ell)$ $\Delta H° = -804.2$ kJ
(c) $N_2(g) + 2\,H_2(g) + \frac{3}{2}\,O_2(g) \rightarrow NH_4NO_3(s)$
$\Delta H° = -365.56$ kJ
95. $\Delta H° = -98.89$ kJ
97. (a) $\Delta H° = 1372.5$ kJ (b) Endothermic
99. $\Delta H° = -228$ kJ
101. 41.2 kJ evolved
103. 0.78 g propane
105. 44.422 kJ/g octane > 19.927 kJ/g methanol
107. 720 kJ
109. 2.2 hours walking
111. Gold reaches 100 °C first.
113. 75.4 g ice melted
115. $\Delta H_f^\circ(B_2H_6) = 36$ kJ/mol
117. 2.19×10^7 kJ
119. $\Delta H_f^\circ(C_2H_4Cl_2(\ell)) = -165.2$ kJ/mol
121. $\Delta H_f^\circ(CH_3OH) = -200.660$ kJ/mol
123. (a) 36.03 kJ evolved (b) 1.18×10^4 kJ evolved
125. Step 1: −106.32 kJ, Step 2: 275.341 kJ, Step 3: 72.80 kJ
$H_2O\,(g) \longrightarrow H_2(g) + \frac{1}{2}\,O_2(g)$
$\Delta H° = 241.82$ kJ, endothermic.
127. Melting is endothermic. Freezing is exothermic.
129. Substance A
131. Greater; a larger mass of water will contain a larger quantity of thermal energy at a given temperature.
133. The given reaction produces 2 mol SO_3. Formation enthalpy from Table 6.2 is for the production of 1 mol SO_3.
135. $\Delta E = 310$ J, $w = 0$ J
137. $\Delta H_f^\circ(OF_2) = 18$ kJ/mol
139. CH_4, 50.014 kJ/g; C_2H_6, 47.484 kJ/g; C_3H_8, 46.354 kJ/g; C_4H_{10}, 45.7140 kJ/g; $CH_4 > C_2H_6 > C_3H_8 > C_4H_{10}$
141. (a) 26.6 °C (Above $C_6H_8O_6$ masses of 8.81 g, NaOH is the limiting reactant.)
(b) $C_6H_8O_6$ limits in Experiments 1–3 and NaOH limits in Experiments 4 and 5.
(c) Ascorbic acid has one hydrogen ion; equal quantities of reactant in Exp. 3 at stoichiometric equivalence point.
143. Note: Great variability in answers may result from specific assumptions made.
(a) Approx. 1.0×10^{10} kJ
(b) Approx. 2.1 metric kilotons TNT
(c) 15 kilotons for Hiroshima bomb, 20 kilotons for Nagasaki; max ever = 50,000 kilotons; approx. 14% Hiroshima bomb or 10% Nagasaki bomb
(d) Approx. 20 hours of continuous hurricane damage

Chapter 7

10. Short wavelength and high frequency
12. (a) Radio waves have less energy than infrared.
(b) Microwaves are higher frequency than radio waves.
14. (a) 3.00×10^{-3} m (b) 6.63×10^{-23} J/photon
(c) 39.9 J/mol
16. (d) < (c) < (a) < (b)
18. 6.06×10^{14} Hz
20. 4.4×10^{-19} J/photon
22. Many types of electromagnetic radiation, including visible, ultraviolet, infrared, microwaves
24. 1.1×10^{15} Hz, 7.4×10^{-19} J/photon
26. X-ray (8.42×10^{-17} J/photon) energy is larger than that of orange light (3.18×10^{-19} J/photon).
28. 1.20×10^8 J/mol
30. Photons of this light are too low in energy. Increasing the intensity only increases the number of photons, not their individual energy.
32. No
34. Line emission spectra are mostly dark, with discrete bands of light. Sunlight is a continuous rainbow of colors.
36. The higher-energy state to the lower-energy state; difference
38. (a) Absorbed (b) Emitted (c) Absorbed
(d) Emitted

40. (a), (b), (d)
42. $\Delta E = -6.19 \times 10^{-19}$ J; $\lambda = 321$ nm; ultraviolet
44. $\Delta E = -1.84 \times 10^{-17}$ J; 10.8 nm; ultraviolet
46. 4.576×10^{-19} J absorbed, 434.0 nm
48. 0.05 nm
50. (a) First electron: $n = 1$, $\ell = 0$, $m_\ell = 0$, $m_s = +\frac{1}{2}$; second electron: $n = 1$, $\ell = 0$, $m_\ell = 0$, $m_s = -\frac{1}{2}$; third electron: $n = 2$, $\ell = 0$, $m_\ell = 0$, $m_s = +\frac{1}{2}$; fourth electron: $n = 2$, $\ell = 0$, $m_\ell = 0$, $m_s = -\frac{1}{2}$; fifth electron: $n = 2$, $\ell = 1$, $m_\ell = 1$, $m_s = +\frac{1}{2}$ (The fifth electron could have different m_ℓ and m_s values.)
(b) $n = 3$, $\ell = 0$, $m_\ell = 0$, $m_s = +\frac{1}{2}$ and $n = 3$, $\ell = 0$, $m_\ell = 0$, $m_s = -\frac{1}{2}$
(c) $n = 3$, $\ell = 2$, $m_\ell = 2$, $m_s = +\frac{1}{2}$ (Different m_ℓ and m_s values are also possible.)
52. (a) Cannot occur, m_ℓ too large (b) Can occur
(c) Cannot occur, m_s cannot be 1, here.
(d) Cannot occur, ℓ must be less than n. (e) Can occur
54. (a) $n = 4$, $\ell = 0$, $m_\ell = 0$, $m_s = +\frac{1}{2}$
(b) $n = 3$, $\ell = 1$, $m_\ell = 1$, $m_s = -\frac{1}{2}$
(c) $n = 3$, $\ell = 2$, $m_\ell = 0$, $m_s = +\frac{1}{2}$
56. Four subshells
58. Electrons do not follow simple paths as planets do.
60. Orbits have predetermined paths—position and momentum are both exactly known at all times. Heisenberg's uncertainty principle says that we cannot know both simultaneously.
62. d, p, and s orbitals; nine orbitals total
64. $_{13}$Al: $1s^22s^22p^63s^23p^1$; $_{16}$S: $1s^22s^22p^63s^23p^4$
66. $_{32}$Ge: $1s^22s^22p^63s^23p^63d^{10}4s^24p^2$
68. Oxygen; Group 6A has 6 valence electrons with valence electron configuration of ns^2np^4.
70. (a) 4s orbital must be full.
(b) Orbital labels must be 3, not 2; electrons in 3p subshell should be in separate orbitals with parallel spin.
(c) 4d orbitals must be completely filled before 5p orbitals start filling.
72. (a) V

3d 4s
[Ar] [↑] [↑] [↑] [ ] [ ] [↑↓]

(b) V^{2+}

3d
[Ar] [↑] [↑] [↑] [ ] [ ]

(c) V^{4+}

3d
[Ar] [↑] [ ] [ ] [ ] [ ]

74. 18 elements, all possible orbital electron combinations are already used
76. Mn: $1s^22s^22p^63s^23p^63d^54s^2$; it has 5 unpaired electrons:

3d 4s
[Ar] [↑] [↑] [↑] [↑] [↑] [↑↓]

Mn^{2+}: $1s^22s^22p^63s^23p^63d^5$; it has 5 unpaired electrons:

3d
[Ar] [↑] [↑] [↑] [↑] [↑]

Mn^{3+}: $1s^22s^22p^63s^23p^63d^4$; it has 4 unpaired electrons:

3d
[Ar] [↑] [↑] [↑] [↑] [ ]

78. [Ne]$3s^23p^4$
80. (a) $_{63}$Eu: [Xe]$4f^76s^2$ (b) $_{70}$Eu: [Xe]$4f^{14}6s^2$
82. (a) ·Sr· (b) :B̈r· (c) ·Ġa· (d) ·S̈b·
84. (a) [Ar] (b) [Ar]
(c) [Ne]; Ca^{2+} and K^+ are isoelectronic.
86. $_{50}$Sn: [Kr]$4d^{10}5s^25p^2$
$_{50}Sn^{2+}$: [Kr]$4d^{10}5s^2$
$_{50}Sn^{4+}$: [Kr]$4d^{10}$
88. Ferromagnetism is a property of permanent magnets. It occurs when the spins of unpaired electrons in a cluster of atoms (called a domain) in the solid are all aligned in the same direction. Only metals in the Fe, Co, Ni subgroup (Group 8B) exhibit this property.
90. In both paramagnetic and ferromagnetic substances, atoms have unpaired spins and thus are attracted to magnets. Ferromagnetic substances retain their aligned spins after an external magnetic field has been removed, so they can function as magnets. Paramagnetic substances lose their aligned spins after a time and, therefore, cannot be used as permanent magnets.
92. Number
94. P < Ge < Ca < Sr < Rb
96. (a) Rb smaller (b) O smaller (c) Br smaller
(d) Ba^{2+} smaller (e) Ca^{2+} smaller
98. Al < Mg < P < F
100. (c)
102. Na; it must have one valence electron.
104. (a) Al (b) Al (c) Al < B < C
106. (a) H^- (b) N^{3-} (c) F^-
108. Adding a negative electron to a negatively charged ion requires additional energy to overcome the coulombic charge repulsion.
110. −862 kJ
112. Red < Yellow < Green < Violet
114. Seven pairs
116. (a) He (b) Sc (c) Na
118. (a) F < O < S (b) S
120. (a) Sulfur (b) Radium (c) Nitrogen
(d) Ruthenium (e) Copper
122. (a) Z (b) Z
124. In^{4+}, Fe^{6+}, and Sn^{5+}; very high successive ionization energies
126. (a) False; shorter, not longer (b) True
(c) True (d) False; inversely, not directly
128. (a) Directly related, not inversely related
(b) Inversely proportional to *the square of* the principle quantum number, not inversely proportional to the principle quantum number
(c) Before, not as soon as
(d) Wavelength, not frequency
130. Ultraviolet; 91 nm or shorter wavelength is needed to ionize hydrogen.
132. (a) [Rn]$5f^{14}6d^{10}7s^27p^68s^2$
(b) Magnesium (c) EtO, $EtCl_2$
134. $1s^22s^22p^4$
136. XCl
138. (a) Ground state (b) Could be ground state or excited state
(c) Excited state (d) Impossible
(e) Excited state (f) Excited state
140. [Rn]$5f^{14}5g^{18}6d^{10}6f^{14}7s^27p^67d^{10}8s^28p^2$, Group 4A
141. (a) Increase, decrease
(b) Helium
(c) 5 and 13
(d) He has only two electrons; there are no electrons left.
(e) The first electron is a valence electron, but the second electron is a core electron.
(f) $Mg^{2+}(g) \rightarrow Mg^{3+}(g) + e^-$
144. (a) 4.34×10^{-19} J (b) 6.54×10^{14} Hz
146. 2.18×10^{-18} J
148. To remove an electron from a N atom requires disrupting a half-filled subshell (p^3), which is relatively stable, so the ionization of O requires less energy than the ionization of N.

150. (a) Ir (b) $[Rn]7s^2 5f^{14} 6d^7$

152. (a) Transition elements (b) $[Rn]7s^2 5f^{14} 6d^{10}$

Chapter 8

14. (a) 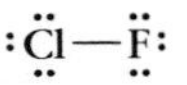 (b) 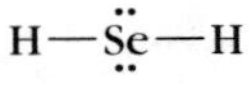

(c) 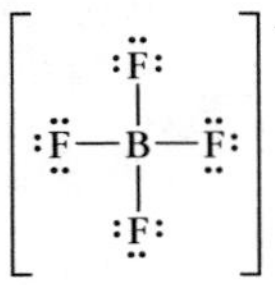 (d) 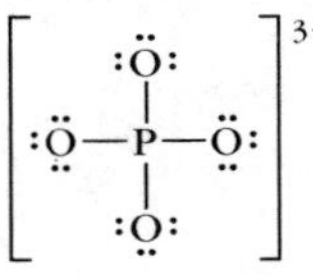

16. (a) 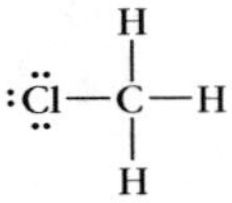 (b) 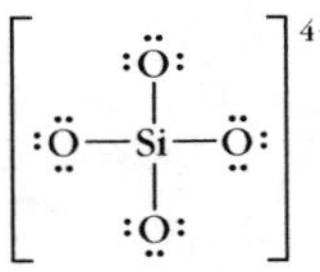

(c) 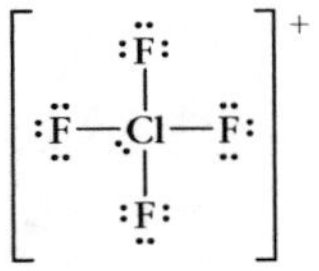 (d) 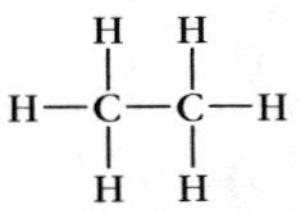

18. (a) 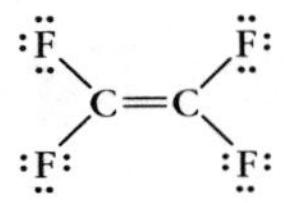 (b) 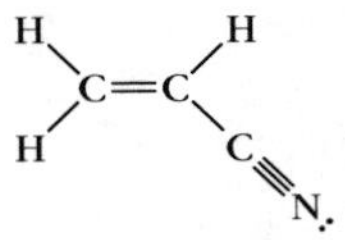

22. (a) Incorrect; the F atoms are missing electrons.
(b) Incorrect; the structure has 10 electrons, but needs 12 electrons.
(c) Incorrect. The structure has three too many electrons; Carbon has nine electrons. The single electron should be deleted. Oxygen has ten electrons; delete one pair of electrons.
(d) Incorrect; one hydrogen atom has more than two electrons. One hydrogen atom is completely missing.
(e) Incorrect; the structure has 16 electrons, but needs 18 electrons. The N atom doesn't follow the octet rule. It needs another pair of electrons in the form of a lone pair.

24. Four branched-chain compounds

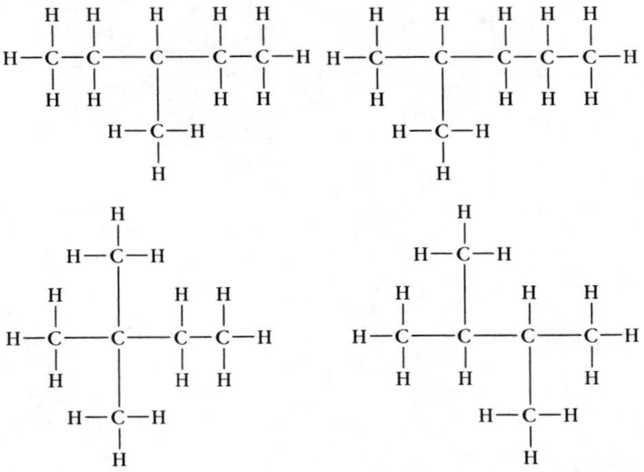

26. (a) Alkyne (b) Alkane (c) Alkene

28. *cis*-2-pentene *trans*-2-pentene

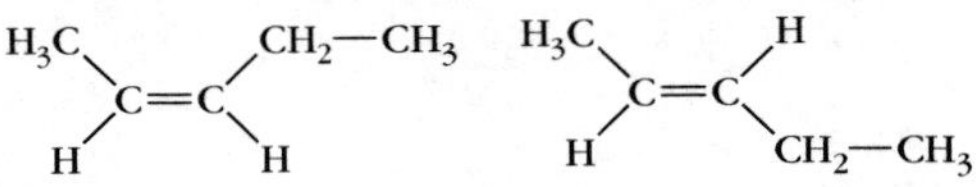

30. (a) No
(b) Yes *cis* *trans*

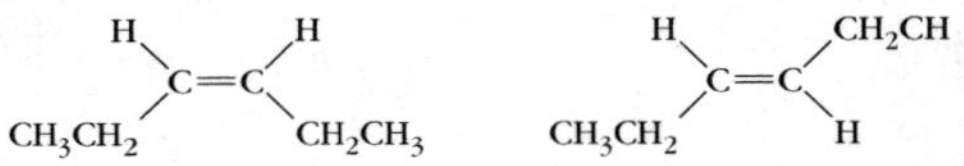

(c) Yes *cis* *trans*

(d) No

32. No; free rotation about the single C—C bond prevents it.

34. (a) B—Cl (b) C—O (c) P—O (d) C=O

36. (a)

38. CO

40. CO_3^{2-} has longer C—O bonds.

42. −92 kJ; the reaction is exothermic.

44. HF has the strongest bond; −538. kJ; −184 kJ; −103 kJ; −11 kJ. The reaction of H_2 with F_2 is most exothermic.

46. (a) N, C, Br, O
(b) S—O is the most polar.

48. (a) All the bonds in urea are somewhat polar.
(b) The most polar bond is C=O; the O end is partially negative.

50. The total formal charge on a molecule is always zero. The total formal charge on an ion is the ionic charge.

52. (a) 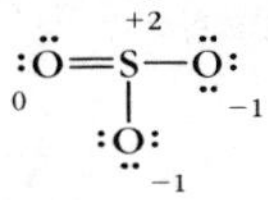 (b) 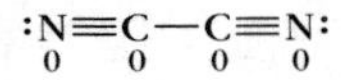

(c) 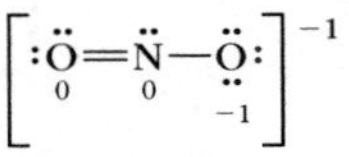

54. (a) 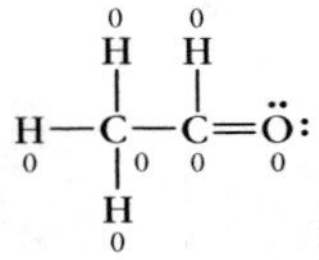 (b) 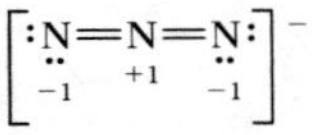

(c) 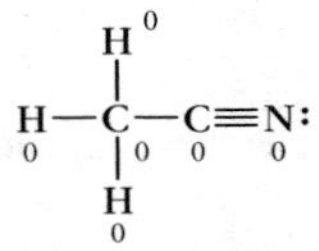

56. 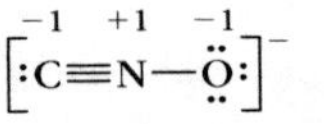

58. 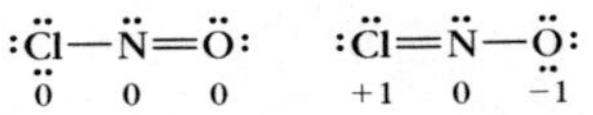

60. (a)

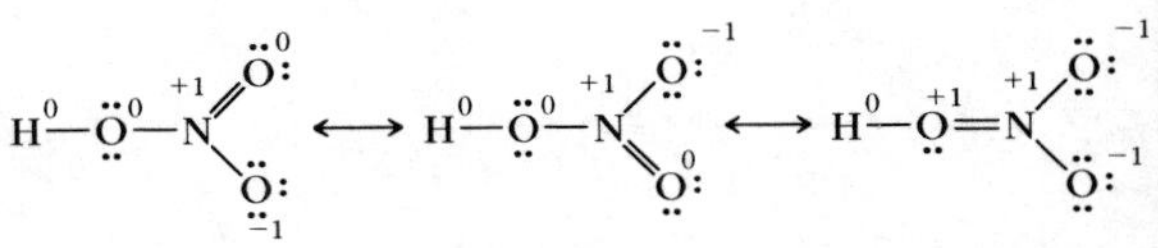

(b)

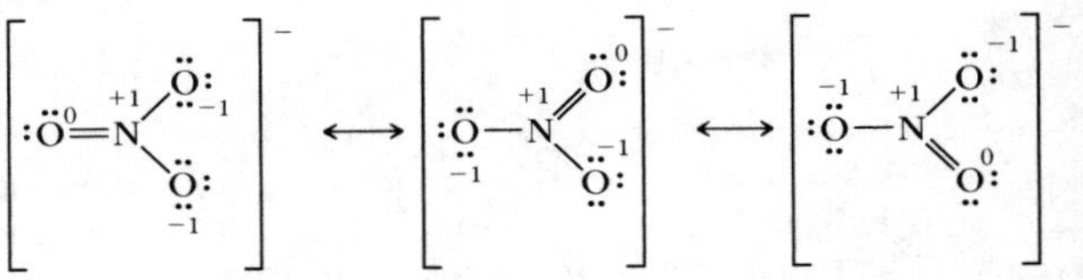

62. 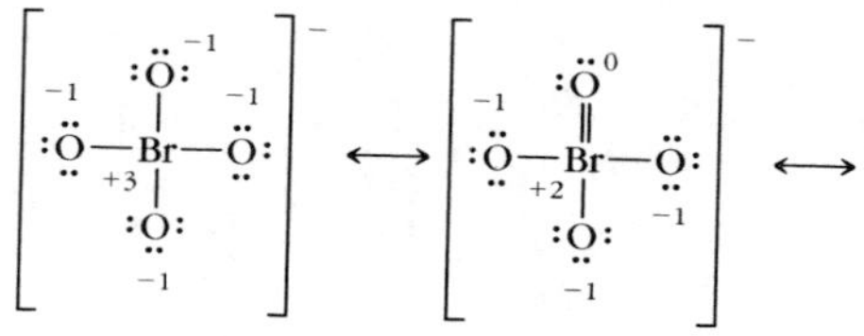

Most plausible 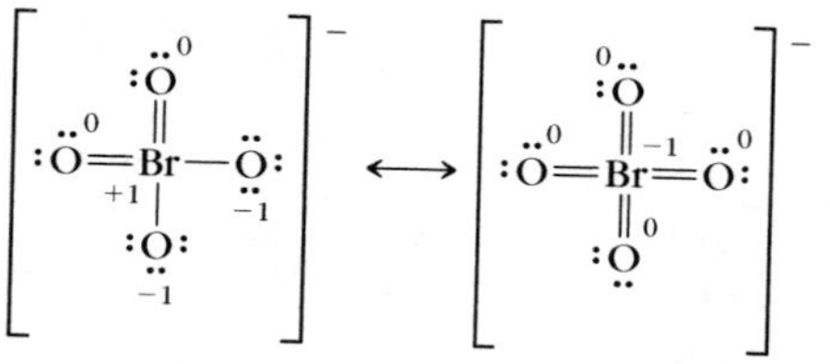

65. 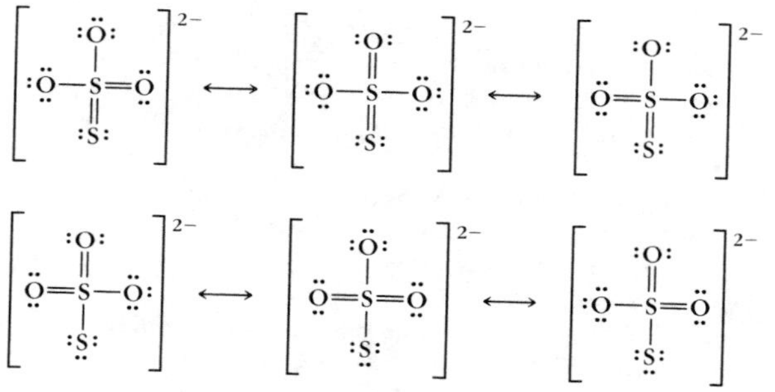

67. (a) 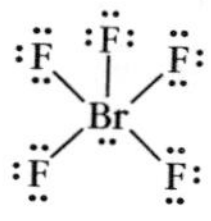 (b) 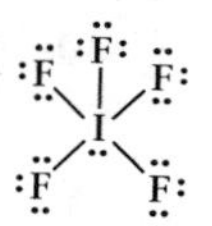 (c) 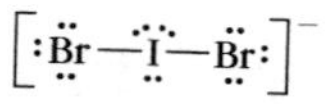

69. P, Cl, Se, Sn

71. Against; with C=C and C—C, the bond lengths would be different.

73. $C_{14}H_{10}$

75.

	σ_{2s}	σ^*_{2s}	π_{2p}	π_{2p}	σ_{2p}	π^*_{2p}	π^*_{2p}	σ^*_{2p}
NO^+	(↑↓)	(↑↓)	(↑↓)	(↑↓)	(↑↓)	( )	( )	( )

NO^+ has three bonds and no unpaired electrons.

78. Si—F; Si is in the third period and less electronegative than C, S, or O.

80. Yes; "close" means similar electronegativities, therefore covalent bonds. "Far apart" means different electronegativities, therefore ionic bonds.

82. (a) The C=C is shorter. (b) The C=C is stronger.
(c) C≡N (δ^+ δ^-)

84. (a) 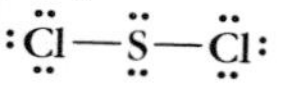
(b) 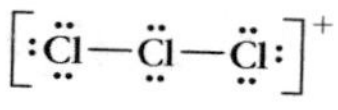
(c) 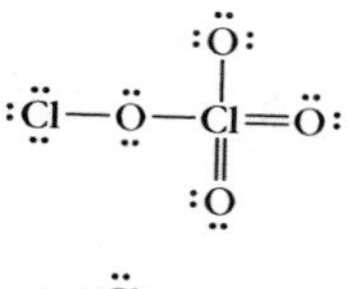
(d) 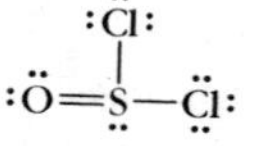

86. O—O < Cl—O < O—H < O=O < O=C

88. (a) Aromatic (b) Aromatic (c) Neither category
(d) Alkane (e) Alkane (f) Neither category

90. The student forgot to subtract one electron for the positive charge.

94. Atoms are not bonded to the same atoms.

96. (a) 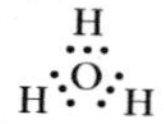 (b) 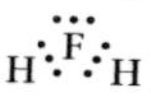

98. Cl: 3.0, S: 2.5, Br: 2.5, Se: 2.4, As: 2.1

100. NF_5; you cannot expand the octet of N.

102. 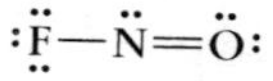
(a) N—F (b) N=O (c) F—N

104. (a) C—O (b) C≡N (c) C—O

106. (a) 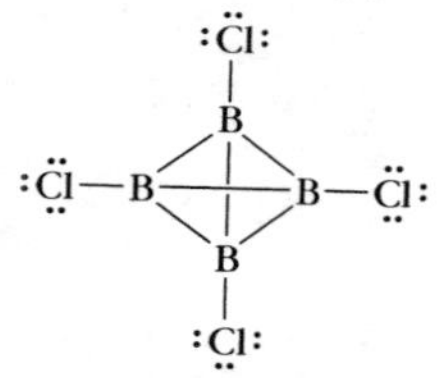
(b) 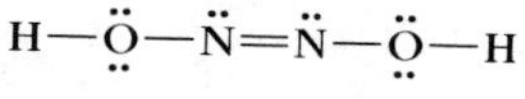

108. (a) 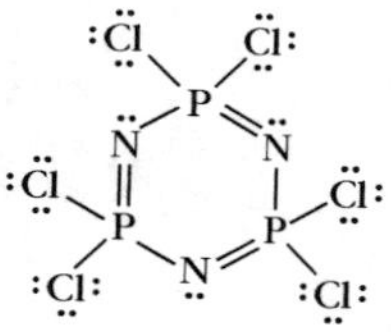 (b) 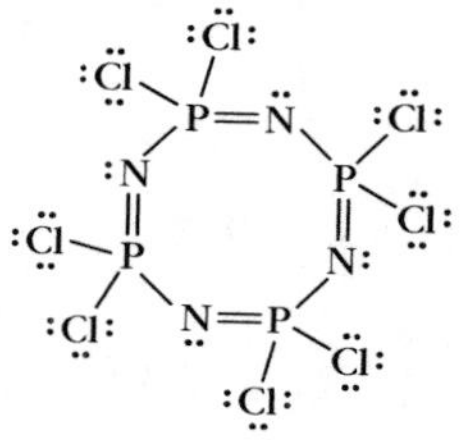

110. 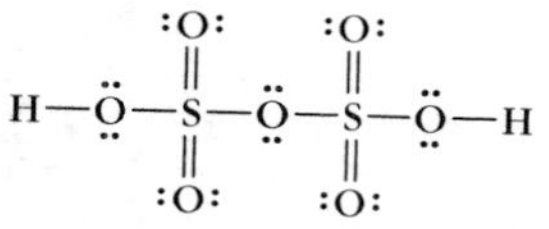

112. (a) 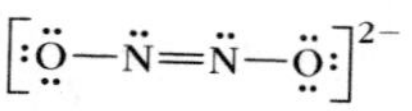 (b) 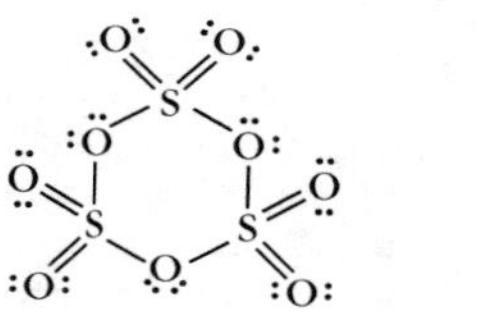

114. H—C≡C—C≡N:

116. 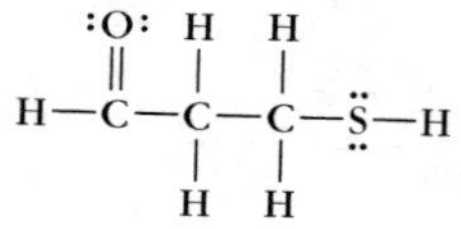

118. 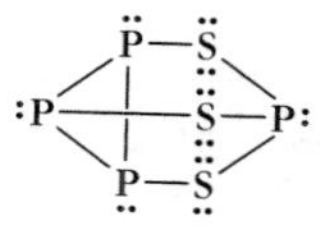

120. (a) 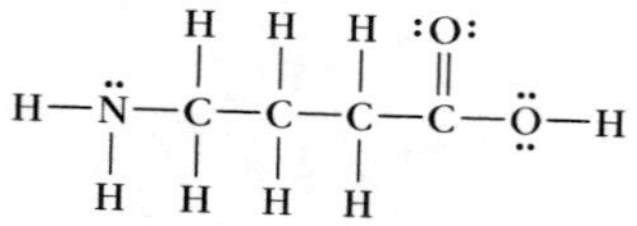
(b) C—C (c) C=O (d) C=O

Chapter 9

13. (a) H—Be—H
Linear
(b) 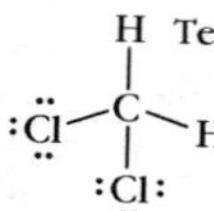 Tetrahedral

(c) 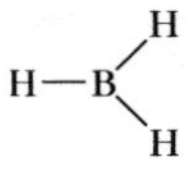 Triangular planar

(d) 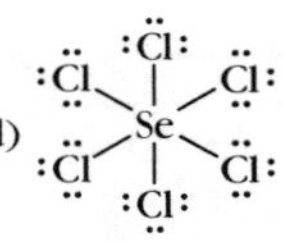 Octahedral

(e) 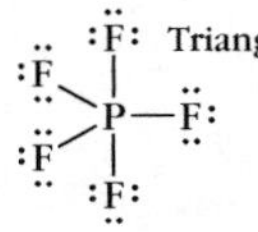 Triangular bipyramid

15. (a) Both tetrahedral (b) Tetrahedral, angular (109.5°)
 (c) Both triangular planar (d) Both triangular planar
17. (a) Both triangular planar (b) Both triangular planar
 (c) Tetrahedral, triangular pyramid
 (d) Tetrahedral, triangular pyramidal
 Three atoms bonded to the central atom gives triangular shape; however, structures with 26 electrons have the shape of a triangular pyramid and structures with 24 electrons have the shape of a triangular planar.
19. (a) Both octahedral
 (b) Triangular bipyramid and see-saw
 (c) Both triangular bipyramid
 (d) Octahedral and square planar
21. (a) 120° (b) 120°
 (c) H—C—H angle is 120°, C—C—N angle is 180°
 (d) H—O—N angle = 109.5°, O—N—O angle = 120°
23. (a) 90°, 120°, and 180° (b) 120° and 90° (c) 90° and 120°
25. The O—N—O angle in NO_2^+ is larger than in NO_2.
27. (a) sp^3 (b) sp^3d^2 (c) sp^2
29. Tetrahedral, sp^3 hybridized carbon atom
31. The central S atom in SF_4 has sp^3d hybridization; the central S atom in SF_6 has sp^3d^2 hybridization.
33. PCl_4^+ is tetrahedral; Ge is sp^3 hybridized. PCl_5 is triangular bipyramidal. P atom is sp^3d hybridized. PCl_6^- is isoctahedral. P atom is sp^3d^2 hybridized.
35. There are no d orbitals in the $n = 2$ shell and the student did not use all the valence p orbitals before including a d orbital.
38. The N atom is sp^3 hybridized with 109.5° angles. The first two carbons are sp^3 hybridized with 109.5° angles. The third carbon is sp^2 hybridized with 120° angles. The single-bonded oxygen is sp^3 hybridized with 109.5° angles. The double-bonded O is sp^2 hybridized with 120° angles.
40. (a) The first two carbon atoms are sp^3 hybridized with 109.5° angles. The third and fourth carbon atoms are sp hybridized with 180° angles.
 (b) C≡C (c) C≡C

42. (a) 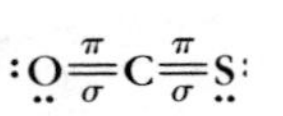 (b) 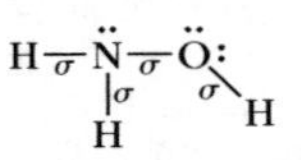

 (c) 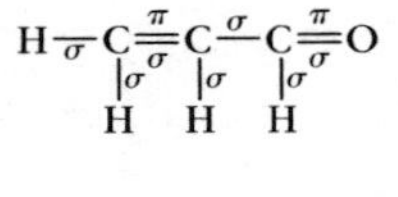 (d) 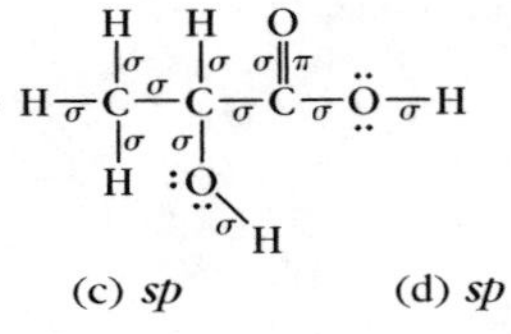

44. (a) Six (b) Three (c) sp (d) sp
 (e) Both sp^2
46. (a) H_2O (b) CO_2 and CCl_4 (c) F
48. (a) Nonpolar
 (b) Polar; the H-side of the molecule is more positive.
 (c) Polar; the H-side of the molecule is more positive.
 (d) Nonpolar
50. (a) The Br—F bond has a larger electronegativity difference.
 (b) The H—O bond has a larger electronegativity difference.

52. (a) 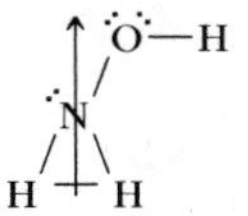 (b) 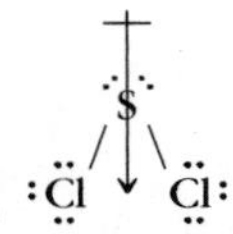

54.

Interaction	Distance	Example
Ion-ion	Longest range	Na^+ interaction with Cl^-
Ion-dipole	Long range	Na^+ ions in H_2O
Dipole-dipole	Medium range	H_2O interaction with H_2O
Dipole-induced dipole	Short range	H_2O interaction with Br_2
Induced dipole-induced dipole	Shortest range	Br_2 interaction with Br_2

56. Wax molecules interact using London forces. Water molecules interact using hydrogen bonding. The water molecules interact much more strongly with other water molecules; hence, beads form as the water tries to avoid contact with the surface of the wax.
58. (c), (d), and (e)
60. Vitamin C is capable of forming hydrogen bonds with water.
62. (a) London forces (b) London forces
 (c) Intramolecular (covalent) forces
 (d) Dipole-dipole force (e) Hydrogen bonding
65. (a) C—C stretch (b) O—H stretch
67. 427 nm, 483 nm; 427 nm is the more energetic transition.
69.

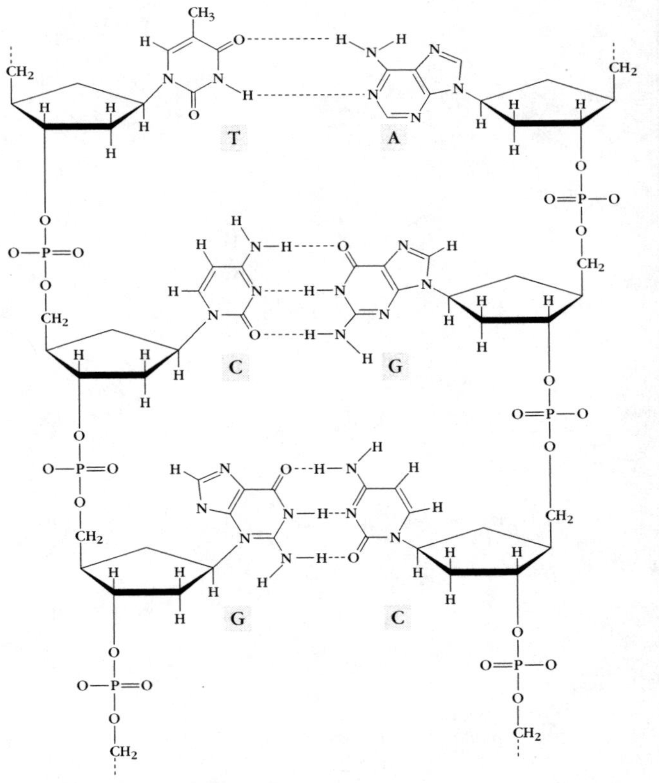

71. (a) (1) NCC = angle 180°, (2) HCH angle = 109.5°,
 (3) COC angle = 109.5°
 (b) C=O
 (c) C=O
73. (a) $\ddot{O}$=C=C=C=$\ddot{O}$ (b) 180° (c) 180°
75. It has an extended conjugated pi-system, so yes, it should absorb visible light.

77. (a)

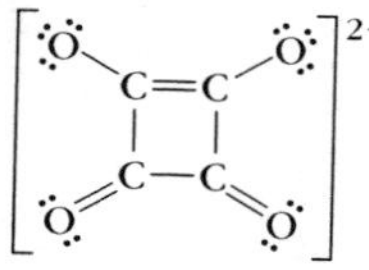

(b) Each C is sp^2 hybridized.

79. HCl has $\delta^+ = 2.69 \times 10^{-20}$ C and HF has $\delta^+ = 6.95 \times 10^{-20}$ C; therefore, F is more electronegative than Cl.

81. KF has $\delta^+ = 1.32 \times 10^{-19}$ C, which is 81.6% of the charge of the electron, so KF is not completely ionic.

83. If the polarity of the bonds exactly cancel each other, a molecule will be nonpolar.

87. (a) Nitrogen (b) Boron (c) Phosphorus
(d) Iodine (There are other right answers.)

89. Five

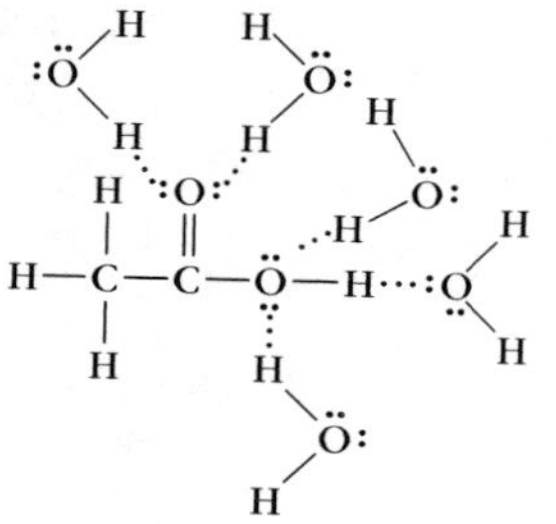

91. Diagram (d) is correct.

93.

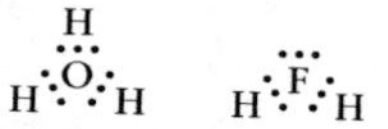

95. (a)

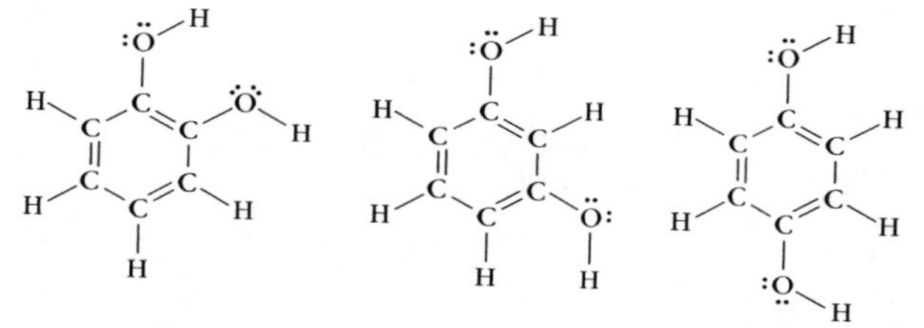

(i) (ii) (iii)

(b) (i) < (ii) < (iii)

97. (a)

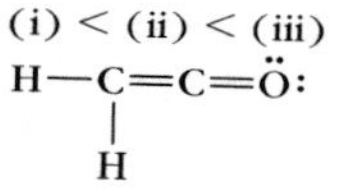

(b) Triangular planar, linear, H—C—C angle = 120°, C—C—O angle = 180°

(c) sp^2, sp, sp (d) Polar

99. (a)

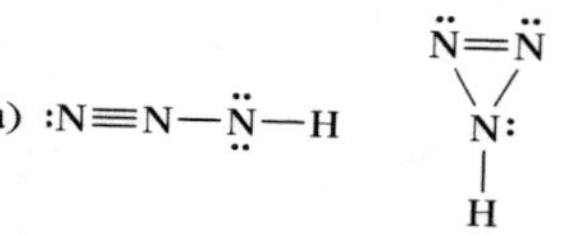

(b) sp, sp, sp^2 (c) sp^2, sp^2, sp^3
(d) 3, 4 (e) 2, 1
(f) molecule 1 120°, 180°; molecule 2 120°, 120°, 109.5°

101. (a) Angle 1: 120°, angle 2: 120°, angle 3: 109.5° (b) sp^3
(c) For O with two single bonds, sp^3; for O with one double bond, sp^2

Chapter 10

11. Nitrogen serves to moderate the reactiveness of oxygen by diluting it. Oxygen sustains animal life as a reactant in the conversion of food to energy. Oxygen is produced by plants in the process of photosynthesis.

13.

Molecule	ppm	ppb	
N_2	780,840	780,840,000	↑
O_2	209,480	209,480,000	
Ar	9,340	9,340,000	
CO_2	330	330,000	
Ne	18.2	18,200	>1 ppm
H_2	10.	10,000	
He	5.2	5,200	
CH_4	2	2,000	↓
Kr	1	1,000	↑
CO	0.1	100	between
Xe	0.08	80	1 ppm
O_3	0.02	20	and
NH_3	0.01	10	1 ppb
NO_2	0.001	1	↓
SO_2	0.0002	0.2	<1 ppb

15. 1.5×10^8 metric tons SO_2, 2×10^6 metric tons SO_2

16. (a) 0.947 atm (b) 950. mm Hg (c) 542 torr
(d) 98.7 kPa (e) 6.91 atm

18. 14 m

20. With a perfect vacuum at the top of the well, atmospheric pressure can only push water up to about 34 feet. So, the well cannot be deeper than that, not even using a high-quality vacuum pump.

22. I. A gas is composed of molecules whose size is much smaller than the distances between them.
II. Gas molecules move randomly at various speeds and in every possible direction.
III. Except when molecules collide, forces of attraction and repulsion between them are negligible.
IV. When collisions occur, they are elastic.
V. The average kinetic energy of gas molecules is proportional to the absolute temperature.
Postulate I will become false at very high pressures. Postulates III and IV will become false at very high pressures or very low temperatures. Postulate II is most likely to always be correct.

24. Slowest CH_2Cl_2 < Kr < N_2 < CH_4 fastest

26. Ne will arrive first.

29. 4.2×10^{-5} mol CO

30. 25.5 L

32. 62.5 mm Hg

35. 172 mm Hg

37. 26.5 mL

39. −96 °C

41. 4.00 atm

43. 501 mL

45. 0.507 atm

47. Largest number in (d); smallest number in (c)

49. 6.0 L H_2

51. 1.9 L CO_2; about half the loaf is CO_2.

53. 10.4 L O_2, 10.4 L H_2O

55. 21 mm Hg

57. 10.0 L Br_2

59. 1.44 g $Ni(CO)_4$

61. (a) $2\ CH_3OH(\ell) + 3\ O_2(g) \rightarrow 2\ CO_2(g) + 4\ H_2O(g)$
(b) 1.1×10^3 L CO_2

63. 130. g/mol

65. 2.7×10^3 mL

67. P_{He} is 7.000 times greater than P_{N_2}.

69. 3.7×10^{-4} g/L

71. $P_{tot} = 4.51$ atm

73. (a) 154 mm Hg
(b) $X_{N_2} = 0.777$, $X_{O_2} = 0.208$, $X_{Ar} = 0.0093$, $X_{H_2O} = 0.0053$, $X_{CO_2} = 0.0003$
(c) 77.7% N_2, 20.8% O_2, 0.93% Ar, 0.03% CO_2, 0.54% H_2O. This sample is wet. Table 1.3 gives percentages for dry air, so the percentages are slightly different due to the water in this sample.

75. (a) $P_{tot} = 1.98$ atm
(b) $P_{O_2} = 0.438$ atm, $P_{N_2} = 0.182$ atm, $P_{Ar} = 1.36$ atm

77. Membrane irritation: 1×10^{-4} atm; Fatal narcosis: 0.02 atm

79. 0.0041; 3.1 mm Hg; the mean partial pressure includes humid and dry air, summer and winter, worldwide.

82. 18. mL $H_2O(\ell)$, 22.4 L $H_2O(g)$; No, because the vapor pressure of water at 0 °C is 4.6 mm Hg; we cannot achieve 1 atm pressure for this gas at this temperature.

84. Molecular attractions become larger at higher pressures. Molecules hitting the walls hit them with somewhat less force due to the opposing attractions of other molecules.

86. N_2 is more like an ideal gas at high P than CO_2.

88. A free radical is an atom or group of atoms with one or more unpaired electrons; as a result, it is highly reactive. Example: $O_2 \rightarrow \cdot O \cdot + \cdot O \cdot$ (there are other possible examples.)

90. (a) NH_3; Ox. # N = −3 (b) NH_4^+; Ox. # N = −3
(c) N_2O; Ox. # N = +1 (d) N_2; Ox. # N = 0
(e) HNO_3; Ox. # N = +5 (f) HNO_2; Ox # N = +3
(g) NO_2; Ox. # N = +4

92. (a) $\cdot O \cdot + H_2O \rightarrow \cdot OH + \cdot OH$
(b) $\cdot NO_2 + \cdot OH \rightarrow HNO_3$
(c) $RH + \cdot OH \rightarrow \cdot R + H_2O$

94. These reactions can be found in Section 10.11.
(a) $CF_3Cl \xrightarrow{h\nu} \cdot CF_3 + \cdot Cl$ (b) $\cdot Cl + \cdot O \cdot \rightarrow ClO \cdot$
(c) $ClO \cdot + \cdot O \cdot \rightarrow \cdot Cl + O_2$

96. CH_3F has no C—Cl bonds, which in CH_3Cl are readily broken when exposed to UV light to produce ozone-depleting radical halogen, ·Cl.

98. CFCs are not toxic. Refrigerants used before CFCs were very dangerous. One example is NH_3, a strong-smelling, reactive chemical. Use the keywords "CFCs" or "refrigerants" and "toxicity" in any web browser.

101. Primary pollutants (e.g., particle pollutants, including aerosols and particulates, sulfur dioxide, nitrogen oxides, hydrocarbons); secondary pollutants (e.g., ozone); (see Section 10.12 for details).

103. Adsorption means firmly attaching to a surface. Absorption means drawing into the bulk of a solid or liquid.

105. 1.6×10^9 metric tons, 2.3×10^6 hours

107. $O_2 \xrightarrow{h\nu} \cdot O \cdot + \cdot O \cdot$, No, the reaction will not occur if the light is visible light.

109. SO_2, coal and oil, $2\ SO_2 + O_2 \longrightarrow 2\ SO_3$

111. $N_2 + O_2 \xrightarrow{heat} 2\ NO$; reaction takes elemental nitrogen and makes a compound of nitrogen.

113. (a) $P_i = 1.33 \times 10^{-4}$ mm Hg
(b) $X_{SO_2} = 1.75 \times 10^{-7}$
(c) 500. μg SO_2

114. Greenhouse effect = trapping of heat by atmospheric gases. Global warming = increase of the average global temperature. Global warming is caused by an increase in the amount of greenhouse gases in the atmosphere.

116. Examples of CO_2 sources: animal respiration, burning fossil fuels and other plant materials, decomposition of organic matter, etc. Examples of CO_2 removal: photosynthesis in plants, being dissolved in rain water, incorporation into carbonate and bicarbonate compounds in the oceans, etc. Currently, CO_2 production exceeds CO_2 removal.

118. (a) Before: $P_{H_2} = 3.7$ atm; $P_{Cl_2} = 4.9$ atm
(b) Before: $P_{tot} = 8.6$ atm (c) After: $P_{tot} = 8.6$ atm
(d) Cl_2; 0.5 moles remain (e) $P_{HCl} = 7.4$ atm; $P_{Cl_2} = 1.2$ atm
(f) $P = 8.9$ atm

120. Statements (a), (b), (c), and (d) are true.

122.

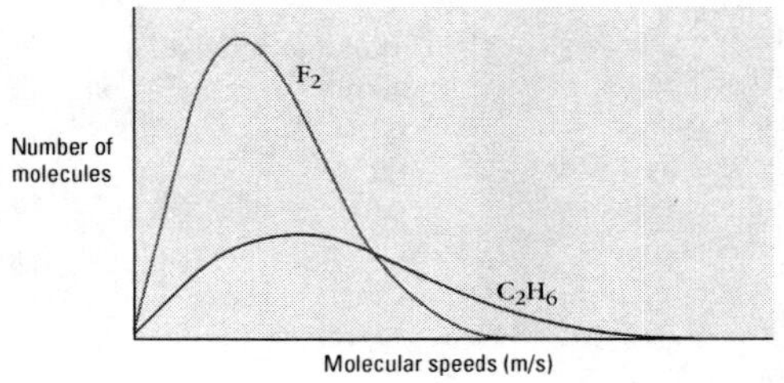

124. For reference, the initial state looks like this:

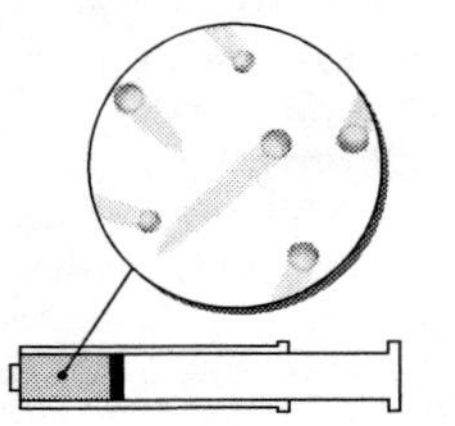

(a)

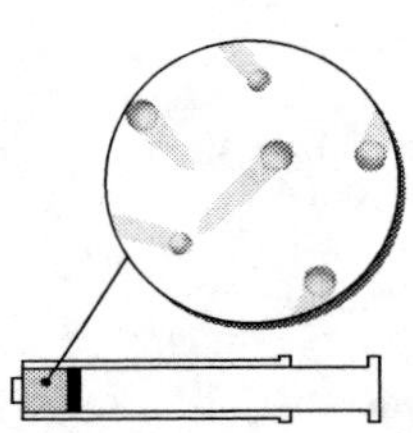

(b)

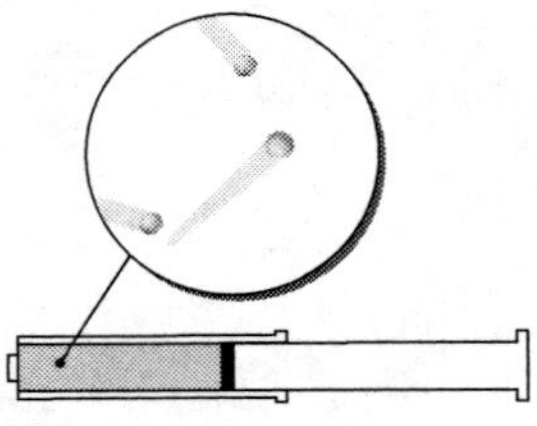

(c)

126. Box (b). The initial-to-final volume ratio is 2:1, so, for every two molecules of gas reactants, there must be one molecule of gas products. 6 reactant molecules must produce 3 product molecules.

128. (a) 64.1 g/mol
(b) Empirical formula = CHF; molecular formula = $C_2H_2F_2$
(c) If the F atoms are on different C atoms

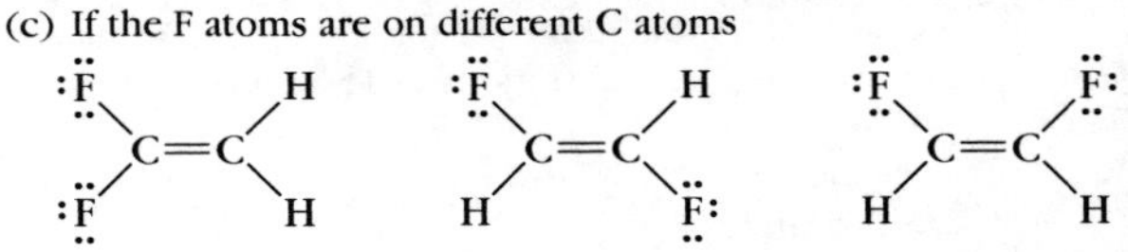

130. $P_{tot} = 0.88$ atm

132. $\frac{m_{Ne}}{m_{Ar}} = 0.2$

134. (a) 29.1 mol CO_2; 14.6 mol N_2; 2.43 mol O_2
(b) $1.1 = 10^3$ L
(c) $P_{N_2} = 0.317$ atm; $P_{CO_2} = 0.631$ atm; $P_{O_2} = 0.0527$ atm

136. 458 torr

138. 4.5 mm^3

140. (a) More significant, because of more collisions
(b) More significant, because of more collisions
(c) Less significant, because the molecules will move faster

Chapter 11

13. At higher temperatures, the molecules move around more. The increased random motion disrupts the intermolecular interactions responsible for surface tension.
15. Reduce the pressure
17. The molecules of water in your sweat have a wide distribution of molecular speeds. The fastest of these molecules are more likely to escape the liquid state into the gas phase. The low-speed molecules left behind will have a lower average speed and, therefore, a lower average kinetic energy that, according to kinetic molecular theory, implies that the temperature lowers.
19. 1.5×10^6 kJ
21. 233 kJ
23. 2.00 kJ required for Hg is more than 1.13 kJ required for H_2O sample. Hg has a much greater mass.
25. NH_3 has a relatively large boiling point because the molecules interact using relatively strong hydrogen-bonding intermolecular forces. The increase in the boiling points of the series PH_3, AsH_3, and SbH_3 is related to the increasing London dispersion intermolecular forces experienced, due to the larger central atom in the molecule. (Size: P < As < Sb)
27. Methanol molecules are capable of hydrogen bonding, whereas formaldehyde molecules use dipole-dipole forces to interact. Molecules experiencing stronger intermolecular forces (such as methanol here) will have higher boiling points and lower vapor pressures compared to molecules experiencing weaker intermolecular forces (such as formaldehyde here).
30. 0.21 atm, approximately 57 °C
32. 1600 mm Hg
34. ΔH_{vap} = 70. kJ/mol
36. The interparticle forces in the solid are very strong.
38. The intermolecular forces between the molecules of H_2O in the solid (hydrogen bonding) are stronger than the intermolecular forces between the molecules of H_2S (dipole-dipole).
40. 27 kJ
42. 51.9 g CCl_2F_2
44. LiF, because the ions are smaller, making the charges more localized and closer together, causing a higher coulombic interaction between the ions.
46. The highest melting point is (a). The extended network of covalent bonds in SiC are the strongest interparticle forces of the listed choices. The lowest melting point is (d). Both I_2 and $CH_3CH_2CH_2CH_3$ interact using the weakest intermolecular forces—London dispersion forces—but large I_2 has many more electrons, so its London forces are relatively stronger.
48. The freezer compartment of a frost-free refrigerator keeps the air so cold and dry that ice inside the freezer compartment sublimes [(s) → (g)]. The hail stones would eventually disappear.
51. (a) Gas phase
(b) Liquid phase
(c) Solid phase
54. (a) Molecular (b) Metallic
(c) Network (d) Ionic
56. (a) Amorphous; it decomposes before melting and does not conduct electricity. (b) Molecular; low melting point and nonconducting (c) Ionic; high melting point and only liquid (molten ions) conduct electricity. (d) Metallic; both solid and liquid conduct electricity.
58. (a) Molecular (b) Ionic
(c) Metallic or network (d) Amorphous
60. See Figure 11.21 and its description
62. 220 pm
65. Diagonal is 696 pm, side length is 401 pm.
67. No; the ratio of ions in the unit cell must reflect the empirical formula of the compound.
69. (a) 152 pm
(b) Radius of I^- = 212 pm and radius of Li^+ = 88.0 pm
(c) It is reasonable that the atom is larger than the cation. The assumption that anions touch anions seems unreasonable; there would be some repulsion and probably a small gap or distortion.
70. Carbon atoms in diamond are sp^3 hybridized and are tetrahedrally bonded to four other carbon atoms. Carbon atoms in pure graphite are sp^2 hybridized and bonded with a triangle planar shape to other carbon atoms. These bonds are partially double bonded so they are shorter than the single bonds in diamond. However, the planar sheets of sp^2 hybridized carbon atoms are only weakly attracted by intermolecular forces to adjacent layers, so these interplanar distances are much longer than the C—C single bonds. The net result is that graphite is less dense than diamond.
72. Diamond is an electrical insulator because all the electrons are in single bonds that are shared between two specific atoms and cannot move around. However, graphite is a good conductor of electricity because its electrons are delocalized in conjugated double bonds that allow the electrons to move easily through the graphite sheets.
74. $\nu = 5.30 \times 10^{17} s^{-1}$; (a) 3.51×10^{-16} J/photon
(b) 2.11×10^8 J/mol, X ray
76. 361 pm
79. In a conductor, the valence band is only partially filled, whereas, in an insulator, the valence band is completely full, the conduction band is empty, and there is a wide energy gap between the two. In a semiconductor, the gap between the valence band and the conduction band is very small so that electrons are easily excited into the conduction band.
81. Substance (c), Ag, has the greatest electrical conductivity because it is a metal. Substance (d), P_4, has the smallest electrical conductivity because it is a nonmetal. (The other two are metalloids.)
83. A superconductor is a substance that is able to conduct electricity with no resistance. Two examples are $YBa_2Cu_3O_7$ and $Hg_{0.8}Tl_{0.2}Ba_2Ca_2Cu_3O_{8.23}$.
85. $SiO_2(s) + 2\ C(s) \rightarrow Si(s) + 2\ CO(g)$; Si is being reduced and C is being oxidized. $SiCl_2(\ell) + 2\ Mg(s) \rightarrow Si(s) + 2\ MgCl_2(s)$; Si is being reduced and Mg is being oxidized.
87. Doping is the intentional addition of small amounts of specific impurities into very pure silicon. Group III elements are used because they have one less electron per atom than the Group IV silicon. Group V elements are used because they have one more electron per atom.
90. The amorphous solids known as glasses are different from NaCl because they lack symmetry or long-range order, whereas ionic solids such as NaCl are extremely symmetrical. NaCl must be heated to melting temperatures and then cooled very slowly to make a glass.
92. (a) Two examples of oxide ceramics: Al_2O_3 and MgO
(b) Two examples of nonoxide ceramics: Si_3N_2 and SiC.
(other answers are possible)
94. 780 kJ, 1.6×10^4 kJ
96. (a) Dipole-dipole forces and London forces
(b) $CH_4 < NH_3 < SO_2 < H_2O$
97. (a) Approx. 80 mm Hg (b) Approx. 18 °C
(c) Approx. 640 mm Hg (d) Diethyl ether and ethanol
(e) Diethyl ether evaporates immediately. Ethanol and water remain liquid.
(f) Water
99. The butane in the lighter is under great enough pressure so that the vapor pressure of butane at room temperature is less than the pressure inside the light. Hence, it exists as a liquid.
101. 1 and C, 2 and E, 3 and B, 4 and F, 5 and G, 6 and H, 7 and A
103. Each has the same fraction of filled space. The fraction of spaces filled by the closest packed, equal-sized spheres is the same, no matter what the size of the spheres.

104. Vapor-phase water condenses on contact with the skin and the condensation is exothermic, which imparts more energy to the skin.

107. (a) Condensation, freezing (b) Triple point
(c) Melting point curve

109. (a) Approx. 560 mm Hg (b) Benzene
(c) 73 °C
(d) Methyl ethyl ether, approx. 7 °C; carbon disulfide, approx. 47 °C; benzene, approx. 81 °C

111. 22.2 °C

113. 0.533 g/cm^3

Chapter 12

22. (a) 20–200 °C
(b) The octane rating of the straight-run gasoline fraction is 55.
(c) No; because the octane rating is far lower than regular gasoline we buy at the pump (86–94), that means it would cause far more pre-ignition than we expect from the gasoline. It would need to be reformulated to make it an acceptable motor fuel.

24. Gasolines contain molecules in the liquid phase that, at ambient temperatures, can easily overcome their intermolecular forces and escape into the vapor phase. That means all gasolines evaporate easily.

26. (a) 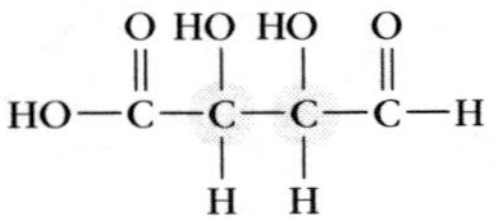 (b) No chiral centers

(c) 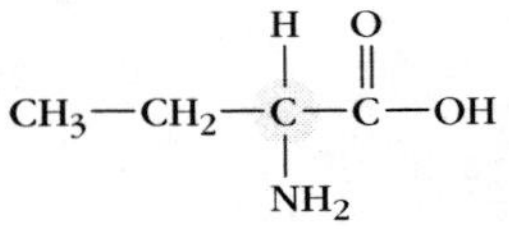

28. (a) No chiral centers (b) No chiral centers

(c) 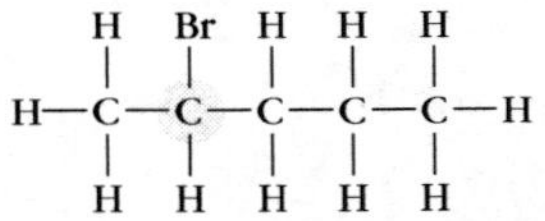 (d) No chiral centers

30. If four different things are bonded to one atom in the structural formula, then the compound can exist as a pair of enantiomers.

32. (b), (c), (e), (g), (h), and (j)

33. (a) $CH_3—CH_2—CH_2—OH$

(b) 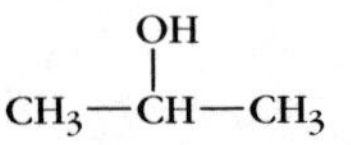 (c) 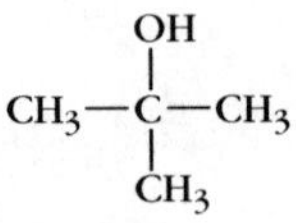

(There are other correct answers)

35. (a) Tertiary (b) Primary (c) Secondary
(d) Secondary (e) Tertiary (f) Secondary

37. 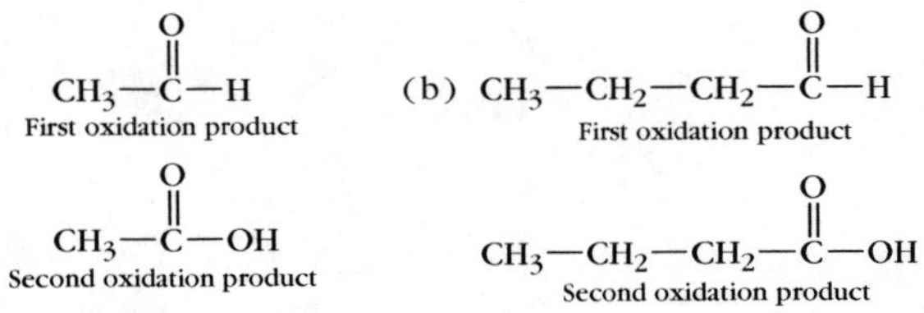

39. (a) 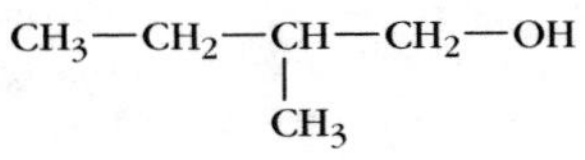

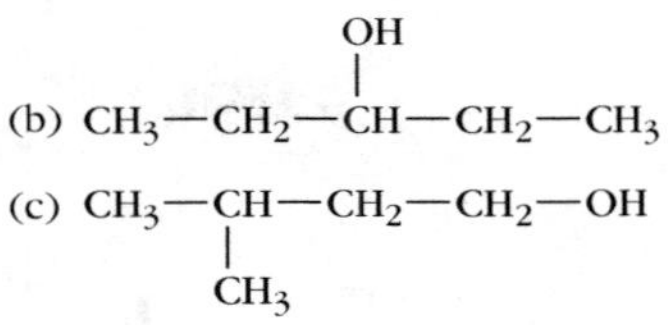

41. Wood alcohol (methanol) is made by heating hardwoods such as beech, hickory, maple, or birch. Grain alcohol (ethanol) is made from the fermentation of plant materials such as grains.

43. —OH groups are a common site of hydrogen-bonding intermolecular forces. Their presence would increase the solubility of the biological molecule in water and create specific interactions with other biological molecules.

45. (a) $CH_3COOCH_2CH_3$ (b) $CH_3CH_2COOCH_2CH_2CH_3$
(c) $CH_3CH_2COOCH_3$

47. (a) $CH_3CH_2COOH + CH_3OH$
(b) $HCOOH + CH_3CH_2OH$
(c) $CH_3COOH + CH_3CH_2OH$

49. Examples of thermoplastics are milk jugs (polyethylene), sunglasses and toys (polystyrene), and CD audio discs (polycarbonates). Thermoplastics soften and flow when heated.

51. 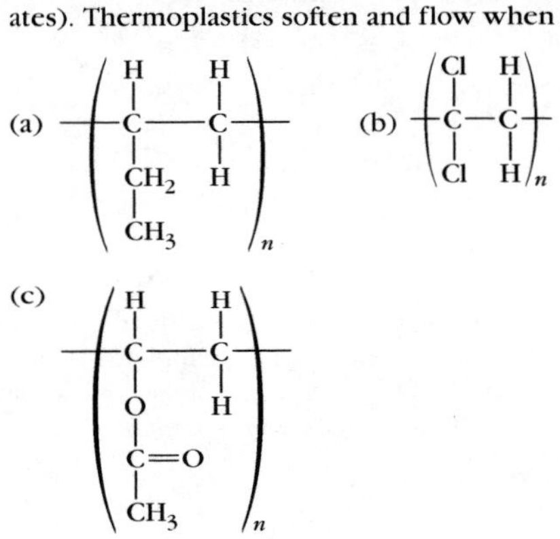

53. (a) 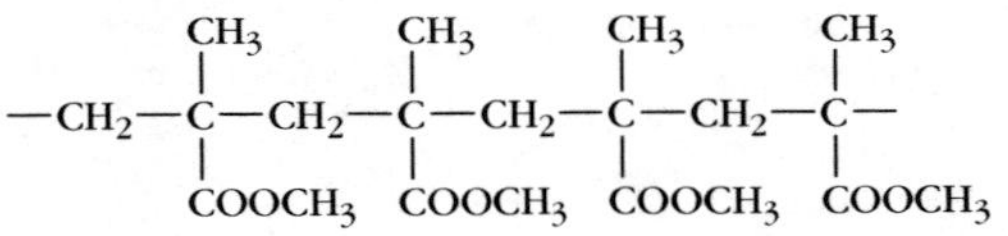

(b) 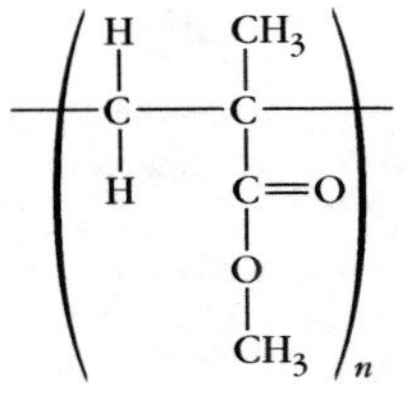

55. (a) $5\ F_2C{=}CF_2 + 2\ \bullet OR \longrightarrow$

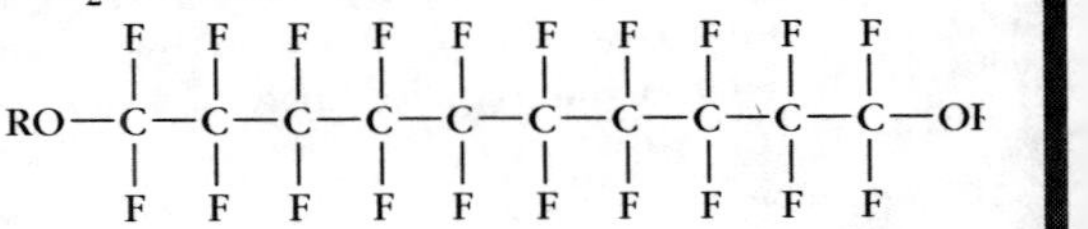

(b) $5\ H_2C{=}CCl_2 + 2\ \bullet OR \longrightarrow$

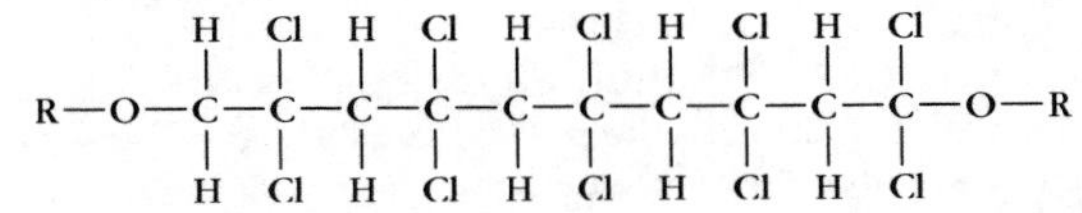

57. Isoprene, 2-methyl-1,3-butadiene; *cis*-isomer

59.

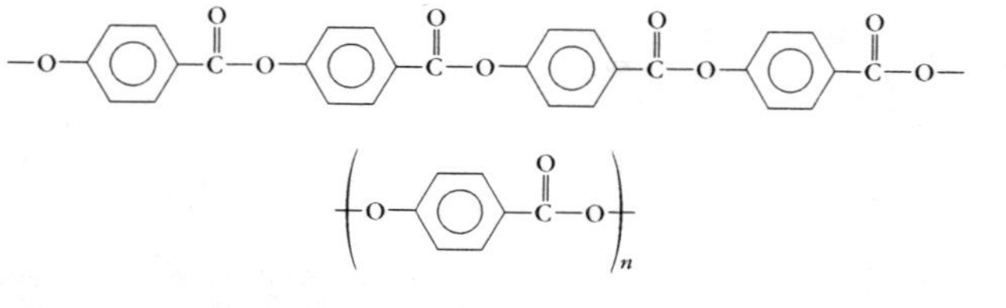

61. Carboxylic acid and alcohol
63. Carboxylic acid and amine; nylon
65. One major difference is that the protein polymer's monomers are not all alike. Different side chains change the properties of the protein.
67. $CH_2{=}CHCN$
69. 16,000 monomer units

71. (a)

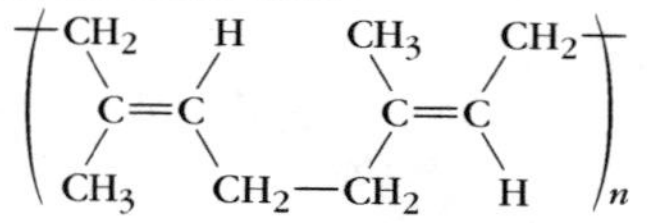

(b)

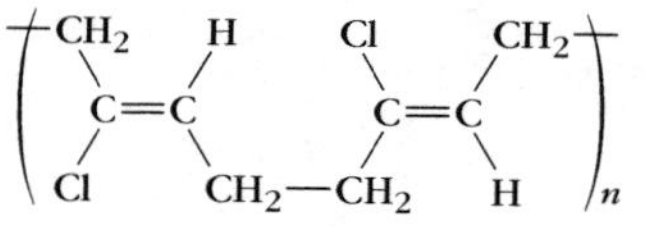

(c)

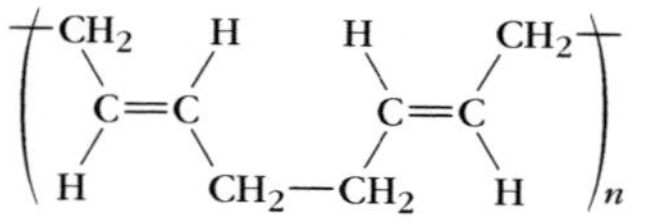

72. Major end uses for recycled PET include fiberfill for ski jackets and sleeping bags, carpet fibers, and tennis balls. HDPE is converted into a fiber used for sportswear, insulating wrap for new buildings, and very durable shipping containers.
74. Proteins, DNA, RNA
76.

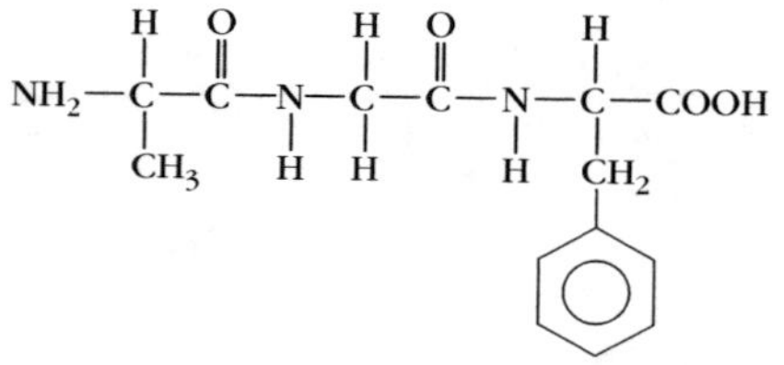

78. (a) A monosaccharide is a molecule composed of one simple sugar molecule, while disaccharides are molecules composed of two simple sugar molecules.
(b) Disaccharides have only two simple sugar molecules whereas polysaccharides have many.
80. Starch and cellulose
82. (a) Glycogen contains glucose linked together with the glycosidic linkages in "*cis*-positions," and cellulose contains glucose with the glycosidic linkages in "*trans*-positions." Humans do not have the enzyme required to break the *trans*-linkage in cellulose.
(b) Cows have the enzymes for breaking the *trans*-linkage of cellulose.
84. It will show up earlier on the chromatograph. Polar molecules would not be attracted to the stationary phase, so they would exit the chamber more quickly.
86. $CH_3CH_2CH_2CH_2CH_2CH_2CH_2CH_2CH_2CH_2OH$ is a larger molecule than CH_3CH_2OH. The polar alcohol group will interact well with the water; however, the nonpolar end of the molecule will not. The longer nonpolar end of the decanol will not be miscible in water, lowering the solubility compared to smaller, more polar ethanol.
88. Vulcanized rubber has short chains of sulfur atoms that bond together the polymer chains of natural rubber.

90.

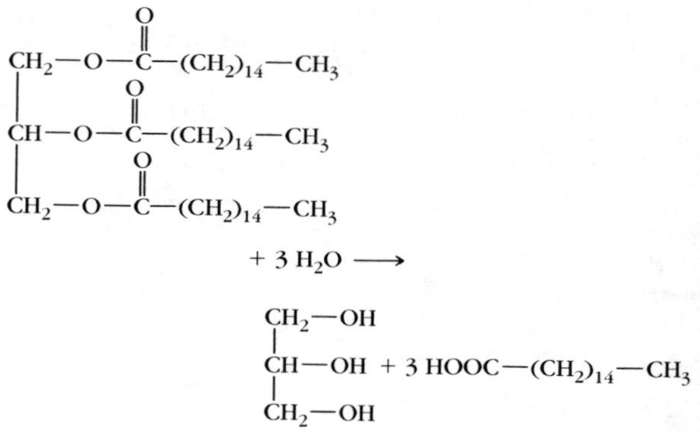

92. (a) $2\,C_8H_{18}(\ell) + 25\,O_2(g) \rightarrow 16\,CO_2(g) + 18\,H_2O(g)$
(b) 1.4×10^3 L CO_2
94. Glycogen has the glycosidic linkages in "*cis*-positions" whereas cellulose has glycosidic linkages in "*trans*-positions."

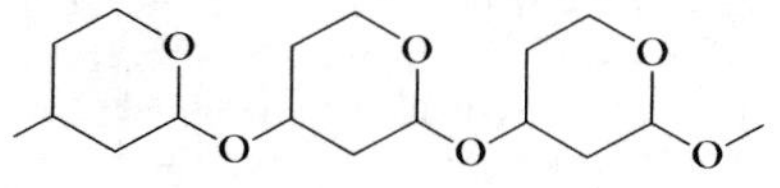

Glycogen

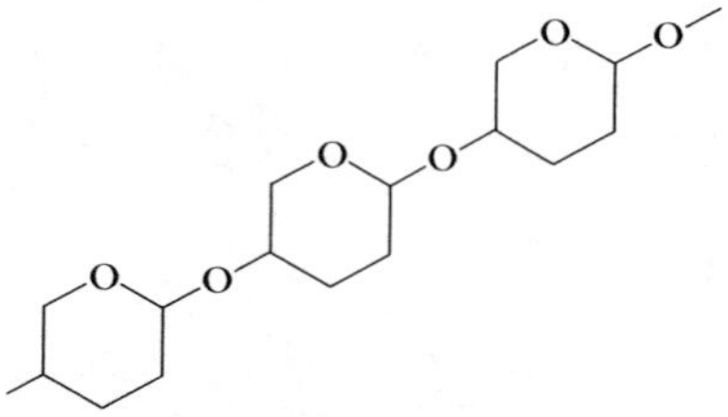

Cellulose

96.

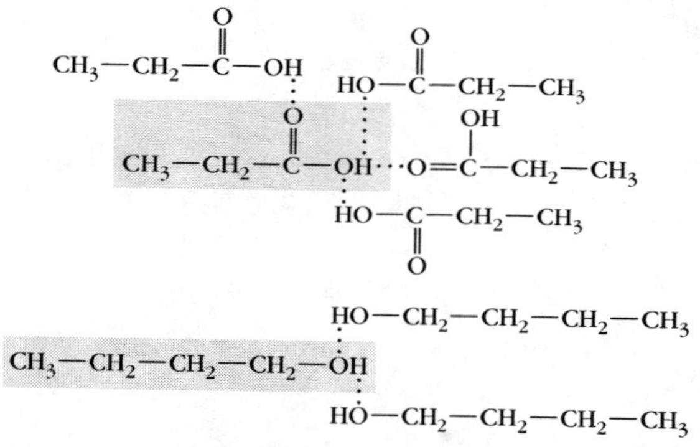

Propanoic acid boils at higher *T*, due to more H-bonding.

98. $CH_3-C\equiv C-H$
100.

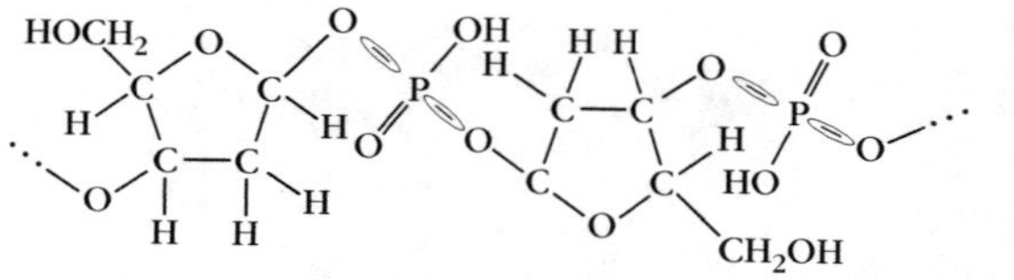

102. Some data that you would need to know are: sources and amounts of CO_2 generated over time to determine additional CO_2; photosynthesis rate of depletion per tree per year; average number of trees per acre; the number of acres of land in Australia that could support trees; and the allowable tree density. Other data besides these may need to be contemplated, so consider it a challenge to think of other things you would need to know.

103. (a) 3×10^8 light bulbs (b) 2×10^3 toasters

105. Less energy; single bonds are easier to stretch.

107. (a) CH_2 (b) Alkene

(c) 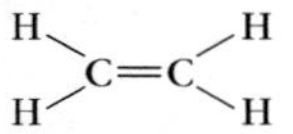

(Other structures also work.)

109.

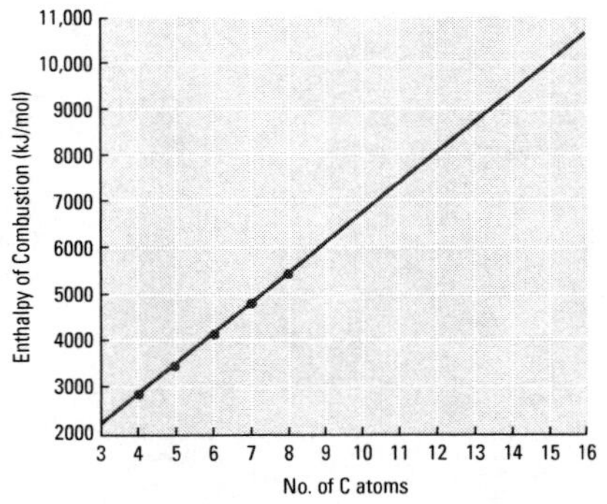

Estimate: C_3, 2200 kJ/mol; C_9, 6100 kJ/mol; C_{16}, 10,700 kJ/mol

111.

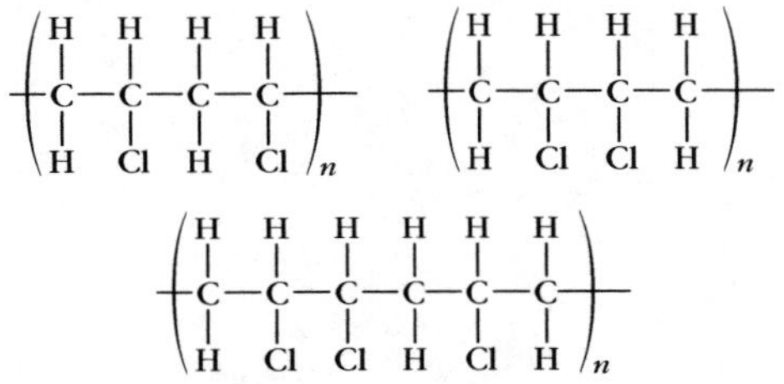

113. (a) 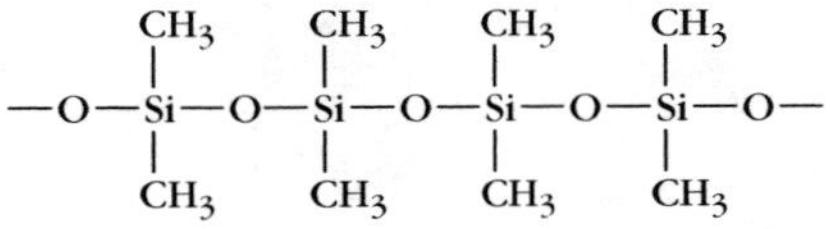

(b) Condensation polymerization

115.

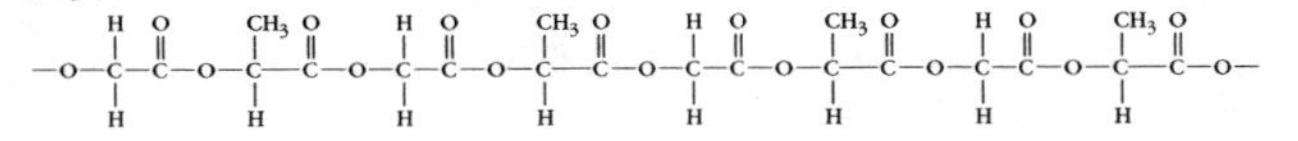

Chapter 13

9. (d) dissolves fastest; (a) dissolves slowest. Rate of dissolving is larger when the grains of sugar are smaller, because there is more surface contact with the solvent.

11. (a)

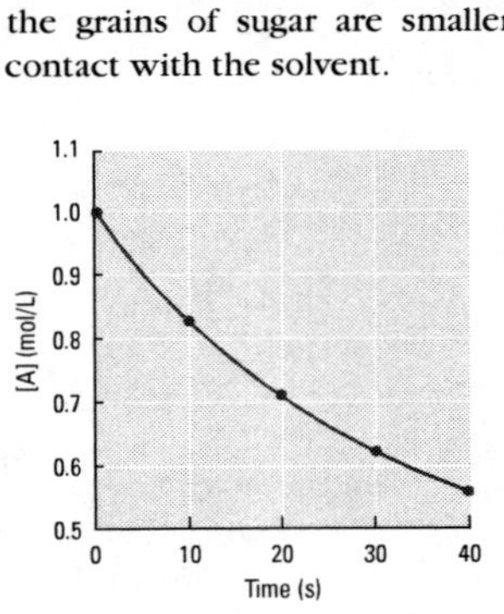

0.0167 M/s, 0.0119 M/s, 0.0089 M/s, 0.0070 M/s

The concentration of the reactant is decreasing.

(b) The rate of change of [B] is twice as fast as the rate of change of [A].

(c) 0.0238 M/s

13. (a) 0.23 mol/L·h (b) 0.20 mol/L·h (c) 0.161 mol/L·h (d) 0.12 mol/L·h (e) 0.090 mol/L·h (f) 0.066 mol/L·h

15. (a) Calculate the average concentration for each time interval and plot average concentration vs. average rate:

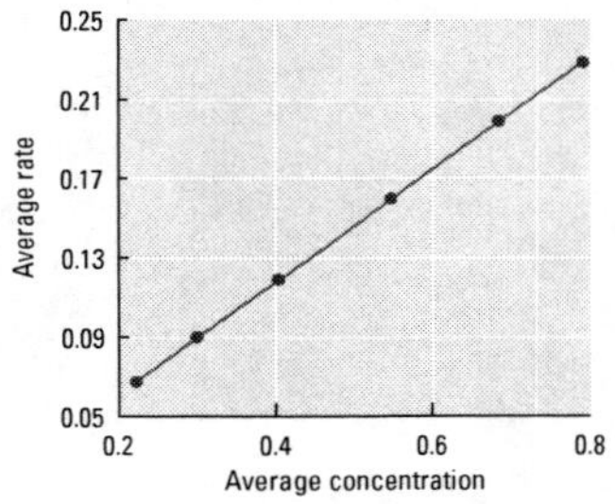

The linear relationship shows: Rate = $k[N_2O_5]$.

(b) $k = 0.29\ h^{-1}$

17.

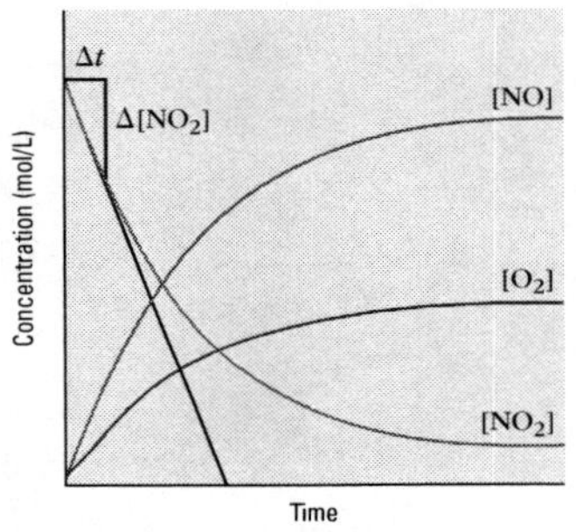

(a) To calculate initial rate, obtain values for Δt and Δ(concentration) near initial time, where the curve can still be approximated by a straight line (the dashed line, above) then divide Δ(concentration) by Δt and change the sign to make it positive, e.g.,

$$\text{Initial rate} = \frac{-\Delta\,[NO_2]}{\Delta t}$$

(b) The curves on the graph become horizontal after a very long time, so the final rate will be zero.

19. (a) The rate increases by a factor of nine.

(b) The rate will be one fourth as fast.

21. (a) Rate = $k[NO_2]^2$

(b) The rate will be one fourth as fast.

(c) The rate is unchanged.

23. (a) (i) 9.0×10^{-4} M/h, (ii) 1.8×10^{-3} M/h, (iii) 3.6×10^{-3} M/h

(b) If the initial concentration of $Pt(NH_3)_2Cl_2$ is high, the rate of disappearance of $Pt(NH_3)_2Cl_2$ is high. If the initial concentration of $Pt(NH_3)_2Cl_2$ is low, the rate of disappearance of $Pt(NH_3)_2Cl_2$ is low. The rate of disappearance of $Pt(NH_3)_2Cl_2$ is directly proportional to $[Pt(NH_3)_2Cl_2]$.

(c) The rate law shows direct proportionality between rate and $[Pt(NH_3)_2Cl_2]$.

(d) When the initial $[Pt(NH_3)_2Cl_2]$ is high, the rate of appearance of Cl^- is high. When the initial concentration is low, the rate of appearance of Cl^- is low. The rate of appearance of Cl^- is directly proportional to $[Pt(NH_3)_2Cl_2]$.

25. (a) Rate = k[I][II]

(b) $k = 1.04\ \dfrac{L}{mol \cdot s}$

27. (a) The order with respect to NO is one and with respect to H_2 is one.

(b) The reaction is second-order.

(c) Rate $= k[NO][H_2]$
(d) $k = 2.4 \times 10^2$ L mol^{-1} s^{-1}
(e) Initial rate $= 1.5 \times 10^{-2}$ mol L^{-1} s^{-1}

29. (a) First-order in A and third-order in B, fourth-order overall
(b) First-order in A and first-order in B, second-order overall
(c) First-order in A and zero-order in B, first-order overall
(d) Third-order in A and first-order in B, fourth-order overall

31. Equation (a) cannot be right

33. (a) Rate $= k$[phenyl acetate]
(b) First-order in phenyl acetate
(c) $k = 1.259$ s^{-1} (d) $0.13 \frac{\text{mol}}{\text{L}\cdot\text{s}}$

35. (a) Rate $= k[NO_2][CO]$
(b) First-order in both NO_2 and CO
(c) $4.2 \times 10^8 \frac{\text{L}}{\text{mol}\cdot\text{h}}$

37. (a) Rate $= k[CH_3COCH_3][H_3O^+]$; first-order in both H_3O^+ and CH_3COCH_3, and zero-order in Br_2
(b) $4 \times 10^{-3} \frac{\text{L}}{\text{mol}\cdot\text{s}}$ (c) $2 \times 10^{-5} \frac{\text{mol}}{\text{L}\cdot\text{s}}$

39.

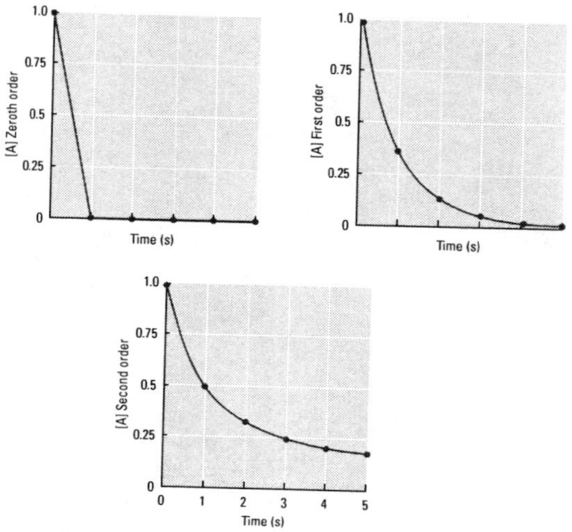

Only the first graph constructed here can be compared directly with one of the graphs in Figure 13.5—in particular, Figure 13.5(c). They both show a downward linear functional dependence of [A] versus time, which is characteristic of zero-order reactions.

41. (a) 0.16 mol/L (b) 90. s (c) 120 s

43. $t = 5.49 \times 10^4$ s

45. (a) Not elementary (b) Bimolecular and elementary
(c) Not elementary (d) Unimolecular and elementary

47. NO + O_3, NO is an asymmetric molecule and Cl is a symmetric atom.

49. $E_a = 19$ kJ/mol, Ratio = 1.8

51. 10.7 times faster.

53. (a) $E_a = 120.$ kJ/mol, $A = 1.22 \times 10^{14}$ s^{-1}
(b) $k = 1.7 \times 10^{-3}$ s^{-1}

55. (a) $E_a = 22.2$ kJ/mol, $A = 6.66 \times 10^7 \frac{\text{L}^2}{\text{mol}^2\cdot\text{s}}$
(b) $k = 8.39 \times 10^4 \frac{\text{L}^2}{\text{mol}^2\cdot\text{s}}$

57. (a) 3×10^{-20} (b) 4×10^{-16}
(c) 4×10^{-10} (d) 1.9×10^{-6}

59. (a) $8 \times 10^{-4} \frac{\text{mol}}{\text{L}\cdot\text{s}}$ (b) $3 \times 10^{1} \frac{\text{mol}}{\text{L}\cdot\text{s}}$

61. 3×10^2 kJ/mol

63. Exothermic

65. (a)

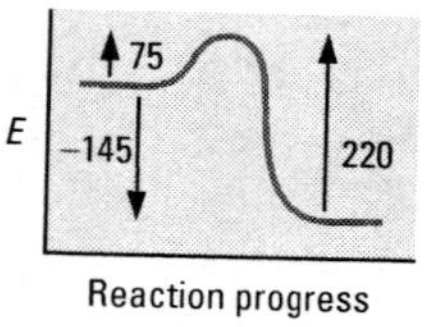

(b)

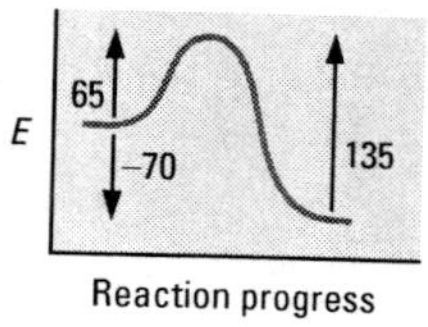

(c)

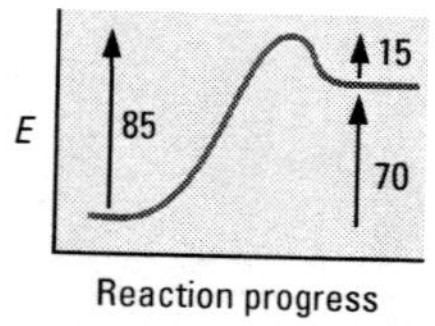

66. (a)

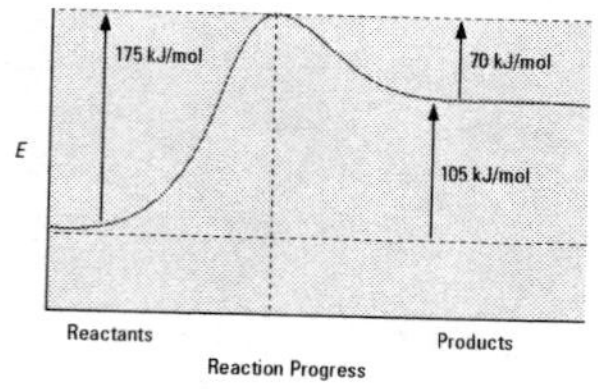

(b)

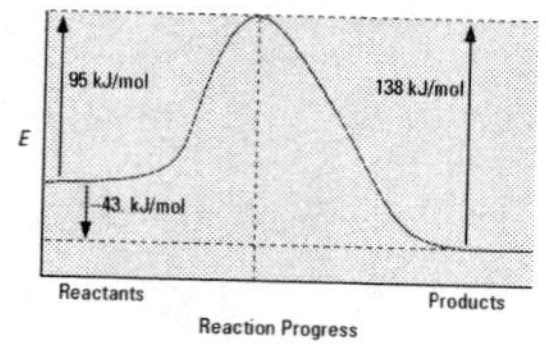

(c)

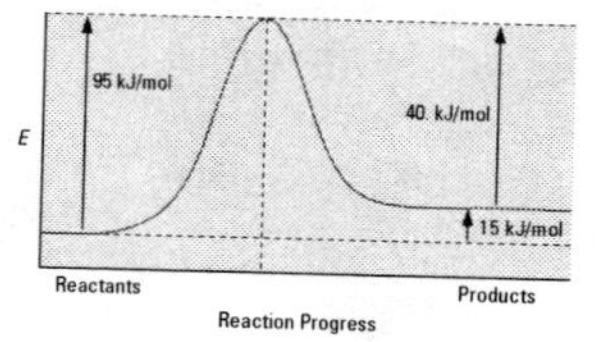

67. (a) Reaction (b) (b) Reaction (c)

69. (a) Reaction (c) (b) Reaction (a)

71. (a) Rate $= k[NO][NO_3]$ (b) Rate $= k[O][O_3]$
(c) Rate $= k[(CH_3)_3CBr]$ (d) Rate $= k[HI]^2$

73. (a)
$$NO_2 + F_2 \longrightarrow FNO_2 + \not{F}$$
$$+\ NO_2 + \not{F} \longrightarrow FNO_2$$
$$\overline{2\ NO_2 + F_2 \longrightarrow 2\ FNO_2}$$
(b) The first step is rate-determining.

75. (a) Rate $= k'[NO]^2[Cl_2]$
(b) $NO + NO \rightleftharpoons N_2O_2$ fast
$N_2O_2 + Cl_2 \rightarrow 2\ NOCl$ slow
(c) $NO + Cl_2 \rightarrow NOCl + Cl$ slow
$NO + Cl \rightarrow NOCl$ fast
There can be other answers for (b) and (c).

77. (a) $CH_3COOH + H_2O \rightleftharpoons CH_3COOH + CH_3OH$
(b) rate $= k'[CH_3COOH][H_3O^+]$
(c) Catalyst: H_3O^+
(d) Intermediates: $H_3C(OH)OCH_3^+$, $H_3C(H_2O)(OH)OCH_3^+$, $H_3C(OH)_2OHCH_3^+$, and H_2O.

79. Only mechanism (a) is compatible with the observed rate law.

81. (a) is true.

83. (a) and (c); (a) homogeneous (c) heterogeneous

85. Enzyme: A protein that catalyzes a biological reaction.
Cofactor: A small molecule that interacts with an enzyme to allow it to catalyze a biological reaction.
Polypeptides: Molecules made by polymerizing several amino acids.
Monomer: The small molecule reactant in the formation of a polymer.

Polysaccharide: An ether-linked chain of monomer sugars.
Lysozyme: An enzyme that speeds the hydrolysis of certain polysaccharides.
Substrate: The reactant of a reaction catalyzed by an enzyme.
Active site: That part of an enzyme where the substrate binds to the enzyme in preparation for conversion into products.
Proteins: Large polypeptide molecules that serve as structural and functional molecules in living organisms.
Inhibition: When a molecule that is not the substrate enters and occupies the active site of an enzyme preventing substrate binding and reaction.

87. 30. times faster
89. The active site on the enzyme (where the substrate binds to form an intermediate complex) is designed to accommodate the substrate's four terminal O atoms. Malonate and oxalate also have four terminal O atoms. When either of these two ions occupy the active site of an enzyme, they prevent the substrate from binding. With a smaller number of active sites free for reaction, the rate of the succinate dehydrogenation reaction decreases.
91. Catalysts make possible the production of vital products. Without them, many necessities and luxuries could not be made efficiently, if at all.
93. (a) To maximize the surface area and increase contact with the heterogeneous catalyst
(b) Catalysis happens only at the surface of the metal; strips or rods with less surface area would be less efficient and more costly.
95.

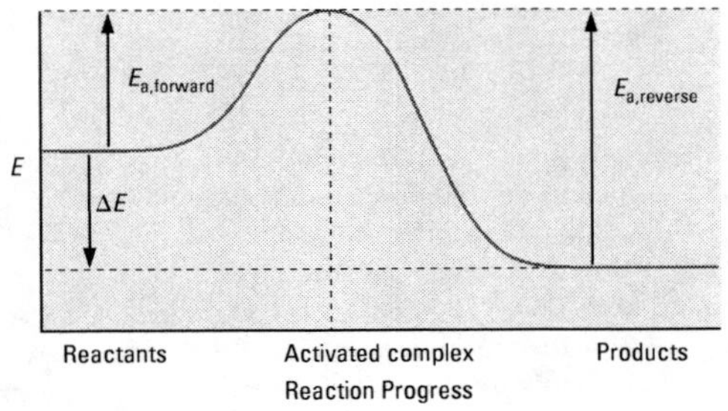

$\Delta E = E_{a,\ forward} - E_{a,\ reverse}$

97. (a) True
(b) False. "The reaction rate decreases as a first-order reaction proceeds at a constant temperature."
(c) True
(d) False. "As a second-order reaction proceeds at a constant temperature, the rate constant does not change."
(Other corrections for (b) and (d) are also possible.)
99. Rate $= k[H_2][NO]^2$
101. (a) NO is second-order, O_2 is first-order.
(b) Rate $= k[NO]^2[O_2]$ (c) $25 \dfrac{L^2}{mol^2 \cdot s}$
(d) $7.8 \times 10^{-4} \dfrac{mol}{L \cdot s}$ (e) $-\dfrac{\Delta[NO]}{\Delta t} = 2.0 \times 10^{-4} \dfrac{mol}{L \cdot s}$,

$$+\frac{\Delta[NO_2]}{\Delta t} = 2.0 \times 10^{-4} \frac{mol}{L \cdot s}$$

103. (a) First-order in $HCrO_4^-$, first-order in H_2O_2, and first-order in H_3O^+
(b) Cancel intermediates, H_2CrO_4 and $H_2CrO(O_2)_2$, and add the three reactions.
(c) Second step
105. The catalytic role of the chlorine atom (produced from the light decomposition of chlorofluorocarbons) in the mechanism for the destruction of ozone indicates that even small amounts of CFCs released into the atmosphere pose a serious risk.
107. Curve A represents $[H_2O(g)]$ increase with time, Curve B represents $[O_2(g)]$ increase with time, and Curve C represents $[H_2O_2(g)]$ decrease with time.
109. Snapshot (b)
111. Rate $= k[A]^3[B][C]^2$
113. E_a is very, very small—approximately zero.
115. The Pb must permanently bind with the Pt atoms on the surface of the metal occupying the active sites of the catalyst.
117. (a) Rate $= 2.4 \times 10^{-7}$ mol L^{-1} s^{-1} $+ k[BSC][F^-]$
(b) 0.3 L mol^{-1} s^{-1}
119. (a) 2.8×10^3 s (b) 1.4×10^4 s (c) 2.0×10^4 s
121. (a) $E_a = 3 \times 10^2$ kJ (b) $t = 2 \times 10^3$ s
123. Note: there are other correct answers to this question; the following are examples:

(a)	$CH_3CO_2CH_3 + H_3O^+ \longrightarrow CH_3COHOCH_3 + H_2O$	slow
	$CH_3COHOCH_3 + H_2O \longrightarrow CH_3COH(OH_2)OCH_3$	fast
	$CH_3COH(OH_2)OCH_3 \longrightarrow CH_3C(OH)_2 + CH_3OH$	fast
	$CH_3C(OH)_2 + H_2O \longrightarrow CH_3COOH + H_3O^+$	fast
(b)	$H_2 + I_2 \longrightarrow 2\ HI$	slow
(c)	$H_2 + Pt(s) \longrightarrow PtH_2$	fast
	$PtH_2 + I_2 \longrightarrow PtH_2I_2$	slow
	$PtH_2I_2 + O_2 \longrightarrow PtI_2O + H_2O$	fast
	$PtI_2O + H_2 \longrightarrow Pt(s) + I_2 + H_2O$	fast
(d)	$H_2 \longrightarrow 2\ H$	fast
	$H + CO \longrightarrow HCO$	slow
	$HCO + H \longrightarrow H_2CO$	fast

125. Approximately 26 times faster
127. Estimated $E_a = 402 \times 10^{-21}$ J/molecule; it is the same to one significant figure as the E_a given in Figure 13.7.
131. (i) Define the reaction rate in terms of [A]: Rate $= -\dfrac{\Delta[A]}{\Delta t}$

(ii) Write the rate law using [A], k and t: $-\dfrac{\Delta[A]}{\Delta t} = k[A]$.

Calculus uses "d" instead of "Δ": $-\dfrac{d[A]}{dt} = k[A]$.

(iii) Separate the variables: $\dfrac{d[A]}{[A]} = -kdt$

(iv) Do a separate definite integral on each side of the equation:

$$\int_0^t \frac{d[A]}{[A]} = -k\int_0^t dt$$

$$\ln[A]_t - \ln[A]_0 = -k(t_t - t_0)$$

(v) With $t = t_t - t_0$:

$$\ln[A]_t - \ln[A]_0 = -kt$$
$$\ln[A]_t = -kt + \ln[A]_0$$

The above equation is in the proper form, with $y = \ln[A]_t$, $m = -k$, $x = t$, and $b = \ln[A]_0$.

(vi) $t = t_{1/2}$, when $[A]_t = \frac{1}{2}[A]_0$

$$\ln\frac{1}{2}[A]_0 - \ln[A]_0 = -kt_{1/2}$$
$$\ln[A]_0 - \ln 2 - \ln[A]_0 = -kt_{1/2}$$
$$-\ln 2 = -kt_{1/2}$$
$$t_{1/2} = \frac{-\ln 2}{-k} = \frac{\ln 2}{k}$$

Chapter 14

7. There are many answers to this question; this is an example: Prepare a sample of N_2O_4 in which the N atoms are the heavier isotopes ^{15}N. Introduce the heavy isotope of N_2O_4 into an equilibrium mixture of N_2O_4 and NO_2. Use spectroscopic methods,

such as infrared spectroscopy to observe the distribution of the radioisotope among the reactants and products.

9. (a) 0 °C (b) Dynamic equilibrium; Molecules at the interface between the water and the ice may detach from the ice and enter the liquid phase or may attach to the solid phase leaving the liquid phase.

11.

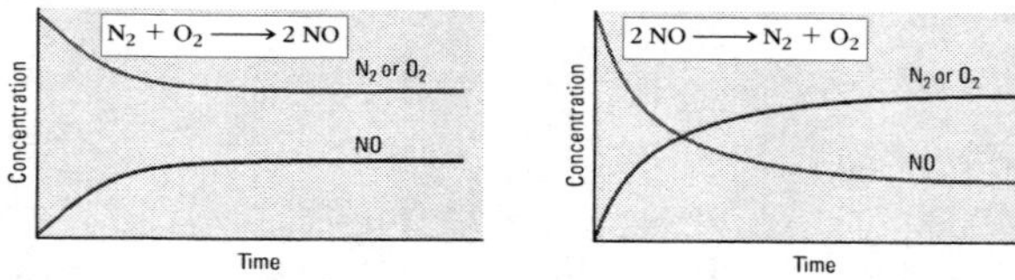

13. (a) $K_c = \frac{[H_2O]^2[O_2]}{[H_2O_2]^2}$ (b) $K_c = \frac{[PCl_5]}{[PCl_3][Cl_2]}$

(c) $K_c = [CO]^2$ (d) $K_c = \frac{[H_2S]}{[H_2]}$

15. (a) $K_c = [Cl_2]$ (b) $K_c = \frac{[Cu^{2+}][Cl^-]^4}{[CuCl_4^{2-}]}$

(c) $K_c = \frac{[CO_2][H_2]}{[CO][H_2O]}$ (d) $K_c = \frac{[Mn^{2+}][Cl_2]}{[H_3O^+]^4[Cl^-]^2}$

17. (a) $K_c = [H_2O]^2$ (b) $K_c = \frac{[HF]^4}{[SiF_4][H_2O]^2}$

(c) $K_c = \frac{[HCl]^2}{[H_2O]}$

19. Equation (e)

21. $K_c = 1.1 \times 10^{47}$

23. (a) $K_P = \frac{P_{H_2O}^2 P_{O_2}}{P_{H_2O_2}^2}$ (b) $K_P = \frac{P_{PCl_5}}{P_{PCl_3}P_{Cl_2}}$

(c) $K_P = P_{CO}^2$ (d) $K_P = \frac{P_{H_2S}}{P_{H_2}}$

25. $K_p = 0.0161$

27. (a) $K_c = 1.0$ (b) $K_c = 1.0$ (c) $K_c = 1$

29. $K_c = 67$

31. $K_p = 1.6$

33. $K_c = 0.075$

35. $K_c = 75$

37. Reactions (b) and (c) are product-favored. Most reactant-favored is (a), then (b), and then (c).

39. (a) $Ag_2SO_4(s) \rightleftharpoons 2\,Ag^+(aq) + SO_4^{2-}(aq)$
$K = [Ag^+]^2[SO_4^{2-}] = 1.7 \times 10^{-5}$
$Ag_2S(s) \rightleftharpoons 2\,Ag^+(aq) + S^{2-}(aq)$
$K = [Ag^+]^2[S^{2-}] = 6 \times 10^{-30}$
(b) $Ag_2SO_4(s)$ (c) $Ag_2S(s)$

41. (a)

	butane $\rightleftharpoons$	**2-methylpropane**
Conc. initial	0.100 mol/L	0.100 mol/L
Change conc.	$-x$	$+x$
Equilibrium conc.	$0.100 - x$	$0.100 + x$

(b) $K_c = \frac{[\text{2-methylpropane}]}{[\text{butane}]} = 2.5 = \frac{0.100 + x}{0.100 - x}$ $x = 0.043$

(c) [2-methylpropane] = 0.024 mol/L, [butane] = 0.010 mol/L

43. 3.39 g $C_6H_{12}(g)$

45. [HI] = 4×10^{-2} M; $[H_2] = [I_2] = 5 \times 10^{-3}$ M

47. (a) 1.94 mol HI (b) 1.92 mol HI (c) 1.98 mol HI

49. (a) $[CO] = [H_2O] = 0.33$ mol/L, $[CO_2] = [H_2] = 0.667$ mol/L
(b) $[CO] = [H_2O] = 1.33$ mol/L, $[CO_2] = [H_2] = 0.67$ mol/L

51. 1.15%

53. (a) No (b) Proceed toward products

55. (a) No (b) Proceed toward reactants
(c) $[N_2] = [O_2] = 0.002$ M; [NO] = 0.061 M

57. Choice (b); because heat is a reactant, increasing the temperature drives the reaction toward the products.

59.

Change	**[Br_2]**	**[HBr]**	**K_c**	**K_p**
Some H_2 is added to the container.	Decrease	Increase	No change	No change
Temperature of the gases in the container is increased.	Increase	Decrease	Decrease	Decrease
The pressure of HBr is increased.	Increase	Increase	No change	No change

61. (a) No change (b) Left (c) Left

63. (a) Right (b) Left (c) Right

65. (a) Decrease
(b)

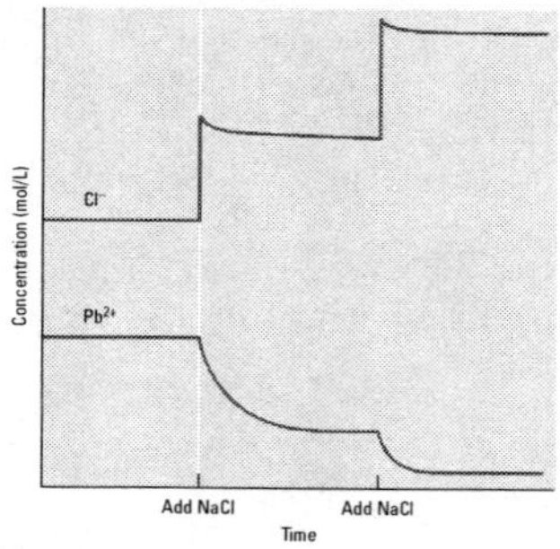

67. (a) Energy effect (b) Entropy effect (c) Neither

69. (a) Insufficient information is available.
(b) Greater than 1, products favored
(c) Less than 1, reactants favored

71. A reaction will only go significantly toward products if it is product-favored. If a reaction is accompanied by an increase in entropy (a favorable entropy effect) and the products are lower in energy (a favorable enthalpy effect), then products are favored. However, if the reaction is favored only by an entropy effect, then it needs high temperatures to assist the endothermic process. If the reaction is favored only by an enthalpy effect, then it needs low temperatures to keep randomness at a minimum.

73. (a) First reaction: $\Delta H = -296.830$ kJ, second reaction: $\Delta H = -197.78$ kJ, third reaction: $\Delta H = -132.44$ kJ
(b) All three are exothermic, none are endothermic.
(c) None of the reactions have entropy increase, the second and third reaction have entropy decrease, and the first reaction entropy is about the same.
(d) Low temperature favors all three reactions.

75. $K_c = [H^+][OH^-]$, $K_c = \frac{[CH_3COO^-][H^+]}{[CH_3COOH]}$,

$K_c = \frac{[NH_3]^2}{[N_2][H_2]^3}$, $K_c = \frac{[CO_2][H_2]}{[CO][H_2O]}$

First reaction
(a) $(1.0 + x)(1.0 + x) = 1.0 \times 10^{-14}$
(b) Quadratic (c) N/A
Second reaction
(a) $\frac{(1.0 + x)(1.0 + x)}{(1.0 - x)} = 1.8 \times 10^{-5}$
(b) Quadratic (c) N/A
Third reaction
(a) $\frac{(1.0 + 2x)^2}{(1.0 - x)(1.0 - 3x)^3} = 3.5 \times 10^8$

(b) Not quadratic
(c) Use approximation techniques
Fourth reaction

(a) $\dfrac{(1.0 + x)(1.0 + x)}{(1.00 - x)(1.00 - x)} = 4.00$

(b) This equation is quadratic.
(c) Not applicable

77. (a)

Species	Br_2	Cl_2	F_2	H_2	N_2	O_2
[*E*] (mol/L)	0.28	0.057	1.44	1.76×10^{-5}	4×10^{-14}	4.0×10^{-6}

(b) F_2; (At this temperature, the lowest bond energy is predicted from the reaction that gives the most products.) Compared to Table 8.2, the product production decreases as the bond energy increases: 156 kJ F_2, 193 kJ Br_2, 242 kJ Cl_2, 436 kJ H_2, 498 kJ O_2, 946 kJ N_2. Lewis structures of F_2, Br_2, Cl_2, H_2 have a single bond and more products are produced than O_2 with double bond and N_2 with triple bonds.

79. (a) $K_c = 0.67$ (b) Same result

81. Cases a and b will have decreased [HI] at equilibrium, and Cases c and d will have increased [HI].

83. It is at equilibrium at 600. K. No more experiments are needed.

85. LeChatlier's Principle says the equilibrium will shift to compensate for changes made. The pressure causes the H_2O molecules to be pushed together. Because water is more dense than ice, some of the ice will melt to the liquid state, reducing the pressure.

87. (a) (iii) (b) (i)

89. In the warmer sample, the molecules would be moving faster and more NO_2 molecules would be seen. In the cooler sample, the molecules would be moving somewhat slower and fewer NO_2 molecules would be seen. In both samples, the molecules are moving very fast. The average speed of gas molecules is commonly hundreds of miles per hour. In both samples, one would see a dynamic equilibrium with some N_2O_4 molecules decomposing and some NO_2 molecules reacting with each other, at equal rates.

91. Diagrams (b), (c), and (d)

93. The following is an example of a diagram. (Other answers are possible.)

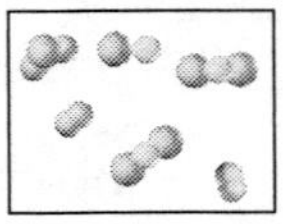

95. Dynamic equilibria with small values of K introduce a small amount of D^+ ions in place of H^+ ions in the place of the acidic hydrogen.

97. Dynamic equilibria representing the decomposition of the dimer $N_2O_4(g)$ produce $NO_2(g)$ and $^*NO_2(g)$, which will occasionally recombine into the mixed dimer, $O_2N^*{-}NO_2(g)$

$O_2N{-}NO_2(g) \rightleftharpoons 2\,NO_2(g)$

$O_2N^*{-}^*NO_2(g) \rightleftharpoons 2\,^*NO_2(g)$

$O_2N^*{-}NO_2(g) \rightleftharpoons {}^*NO_2(g) + NO_2(g)$

99. (a) $K_c = 0.168$ (b) 0.661 atm (c) 0.514

101. (a) $[PCl_3] = [Cl_2] = 0.14$ mol/L, $[PCl_5] = 0.005$ mol/L
(b) $[PCl_3] = 0.29$ mol/L, $[Cl_2] = 0.14$ mol/L, $[PCl_5] = 0.01$ mol/L

103. (a) (i) Right (ii) Right (iii) Left
(b) (i) Left (ii) No shift (iii) Right
(c) (i) Right (ii) Right (iii) No shift
(d) (i) Right (ii) Right (iii) Left

105. $K_c = \dfrac{A_f e^{(-E_{a,f}/RT)}}{A_r e^{(-E_{a,r}/RT)}} = \dfrac{A_f}{A_r} e^{[(E_{a,r}-E_{a,f})/RT]}$

When a catalyst is added, the activation energies of both the forward and reverse reactions get smaller:

$$K_{c,\,cat} = \frac{A_{f,cat}}{A_{r,cat}} e^{[(E_{a,r,cat}-E_{a,f,cat})/RT]}$$

The frequency factors did not change and, because the reaction has to conserve energy, the E_a values must each be reduced by the same amount of energy X:

$A_{f,cat} = A_f$ $\quad E_{a,f,cat} = E_{a,f} - X$

$A_{r,cat} = A_r$ $\quad E_{a,r,cat} = E_{a,r} - X$

Notice that

$E_{a,f,cat} - E_{a,r,cat} = (E_{a,f} - X) - (E_{a,r} - X)$
$= E_{a,f} - X - E_{a,r} + X = E_{a,f} - E_{a,r}$

Substituting into the $K_{c,cat}$ equation gives

$$K_{c,cat} = \frac{A_f}{A_r} e^{[(E_{a,r}-E_{a,f})/RT]} = K_c$$

Therefore, the equilibrium state, as described quantitatively by the equilibrium constant, does not change with the addition of a catalyst.

107. (a) $H_2(g) + Br_2(g) \rightleftharpoons 2\,HBr\,(g)$ (b) −103 kJ
(c) Energy effect (d) To the left (e) No effect
(f) The reactants must achieve activation energy. Bromine is a liquid at room temperature.

109. (a) $K_p = 0.03126$; $K_c = 0.0128$
(b) $K_p = 1$
(c) $K_c = 1/(RT_{bp})$

Chapter 15

25. If the solid interacts with the solvent using similar (or stronger) intermolecular forces, it will dissolve readily. If the solute interacts with the solvent using different intermolecular forces than those experienced in the solvent, it will be almost insoluble. For example, consider dissolving an ionic solid in water and oil. The interactions between the ions in the solid and water are very strong, since ions would be attracted to the highly polar water molecule; hence, the solid would have a high solubility. However, the ions in the solid interact with each other much more strongly than the London dispersion forces experienced between the nonpolar hydrocarbons in the oil; hence, the solid would have a low solubility. (Other examples exist.)

27. The dissolving process was endothermic, so the temperature dropped as more solute was added. The solubility of the solid at the lower temperature is lower, so some of the solid did not dissolve. As the solution warmed up, however, the solubility increased again. What remained of the solid dissolved. The solution was saturated at the lower temperature, but is no longer saturated at the current temperature.

29. When an organic acid has a large (non-polar) piece, it interacts primarily using London dispersion intermolecular forces. Since water interacts via hydrogen-bonding intermolecular forces, it would rather interact with itself than with the acid. Hence, the solubility of the large organic acids drops, and some are completely insoluble.

31. The positive H end of the very polar water molecule interacts with the negative ions. The negative O end of the very polar water molecule interacts with the positive ions.

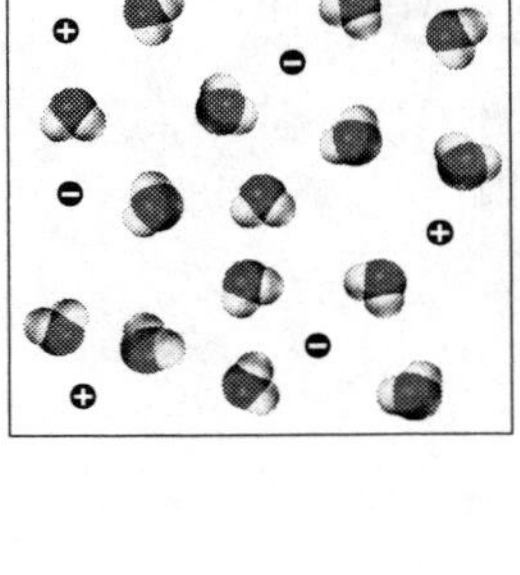

33. 1×10^{-3} M

36. 0.00732% by weight

38. $1 \text{ ppb} = \dfrac{1 \text{ g part}}{10^9 \text{ g whole}} \times \dfrac{1 \ \mu\text{g part}}{10^{-6} \text{ g part}} \times \dfrac{1000 \text{ g whole}}{1 \text{ kg whole}}$

$= \dfrac{1 \ \mu\text{g part}}{1 \text{ kg whole}}$

40. 90. g ethanol

43. 1.6×10^{-6} g Pb

45. (a) 160. g NH_4Cl (b) 83.9 g KCl (c) 7.46 g Na_2SO_4

46. (a) 0.762 M (b) 0.174 M
(c) 0.0126 M (d) 0.167 M

47. (a) 0.180 M (b) 0.683 M
(c) 0.0260 M (d) 0.0416 M

49. 96% H_2SO_4

51. 0.1 M NaCl

53. 59 g

55. 1.2×10^{-7} M

59. 100.26 °C

61. (a) < (d) < (b) < (c)

63. $T_f = -1.65$ °C, $T_b = 100.46$ °C

65. $X_{H2O} = 0.79999$, 712 g sucrose

67. 1.9×10^2 g/mol

69. 3.6×10^2 g/mol; $C_{20}H_{16}Fe_2$

71. 1.8×10^2 g/mol, $C_{14}H_{10}$

73. (a) 2.5 kg (b) 104.2 °C

75. 29 atm

78. 5×10^{-4} g As

80. No

82. The lime-soda process relies on the precipitation of insoluble compounds to remove the "hard water" ions. The ion-exchange process relies on the high charge of the "hard water" ions to attract them to an ion-exchange resin, thereby removing them from the water.

84. Water is sprayed into the air to oxidize organic substances dissolved in it.

86. Fish take in oxygen by extracting it from the water, while plants take in carbon dioxide by extracting it from the water. The concentrations of these gases in calm water drop unless they are replenished. The concentration of dissolved gases in the water is replenished by bubbling air through the water in the aquarium.

88. 4%

90. Water in the cells of the wood leaked out, since the osmotic pressure inside the cells was less than that of the seawater in which the wood was sitting.

92. 28% NH_3

94. 0.982 *m*, 10.2%

96. (a) = (c) < (d) < (b)

98. 1.77 g

100. (a) $Na_2SO_4(aq) + Ba(NO_3)_2(aq) \rightarrow 2 \ NaNO_3(aq) + BaSO_4(s)$
(b) 15.0 mL (c) 12.0 mL

102. (a)

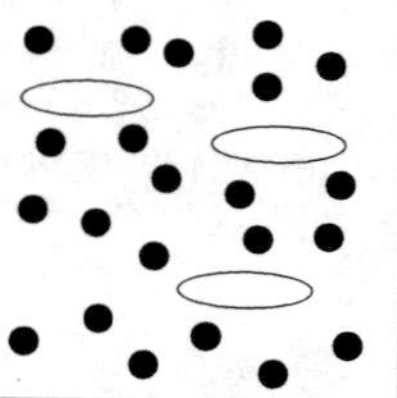

(b)

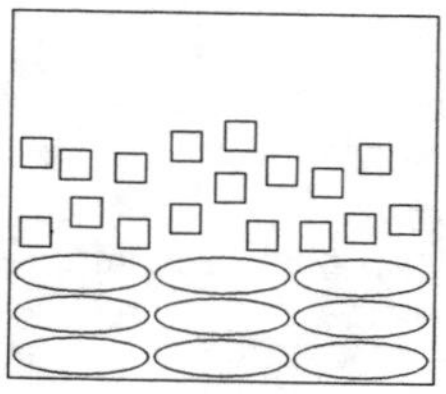

104. (a) Unsaturated (b) Supersaturated
(c) Supersaturated (d) Unsaturated

106.

Compound	Mass of Compound	Mass of Water	Mass Fraction of Solute	Weight Percent of Solute	Conc of Solute
Lye	**75.0 g**	125 g	0.375	**37.5%**	**3.75×10^5 ppm**
Glycerol	33 g	200. g	**0.14**	**14%**	**1.4×10^5 ppm**
Acetylene	0.0015	**2×10^2 g**	**0.000009**	0.0009%	**9 ppm**

108. Molecules slow down. The reduced motion prevents them from randomly translocating as they had in the liquid state. As a result, the intermolecular forces between one molecule and the next begin to organize them into a crystal form. The presence of a nonvolatile solute disrupts the formation of the crystal. Its size and shape will be different from that of the solute. Intermolecular forces between the solute and solvent are also different from those of solvent molecules with each other. To form the crystalline solid, the solute has to be excluded. If the ice in an iceberg is in regular crystalline form, the water will be pure. Only if the ice is crushed or dirty will other particles be included. So, melting an iceberg will produce relatively pure water.

110. (a) Seawater contains more dissolved solutes than fresh water. The presence of a solute lowers the freezing point. That means a lower temperature is required to freeze the seawater than to freeze fresh water.
(b) Salt added to a mixture of ice and water will lower the freezing point of the water. If the ice cream is mixed at a lower temperature, its temperature will drop faster; hence, it will freeze faster.

112. The empirical and molecular formulas are both $C_{18}H_{24}Cr$.

114. (a) No (b) 108.9°

116. 28 m

118. 0.30 M

120. (a)

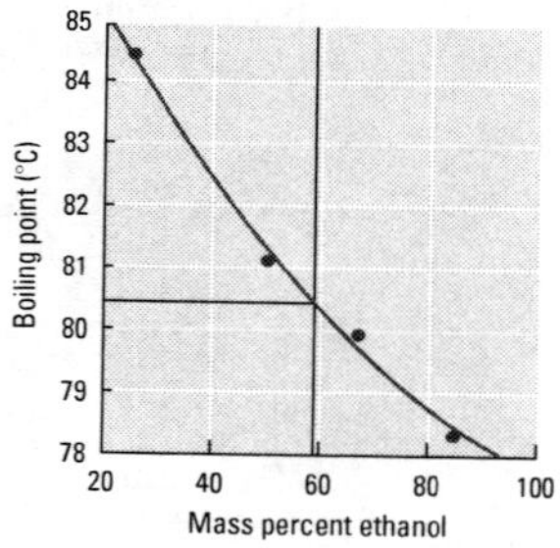

Approx. 80.4 °C
(b) 12.3 M; 44.1 mol/kg

122. (a) Freezes at −3.36°, when the solute concentration is 0.50 *m*.

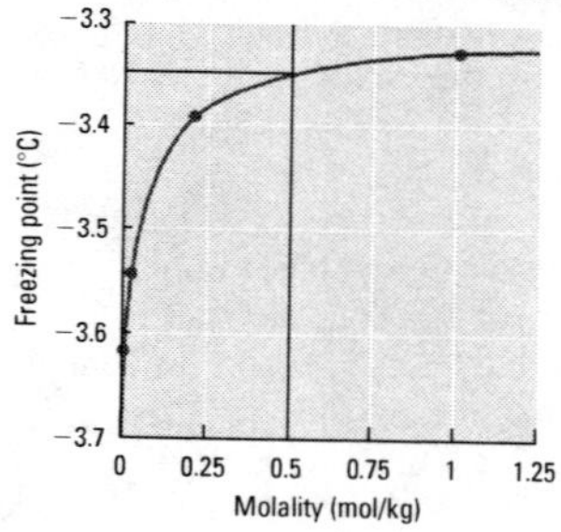

(b) 39,000%, 9,400%, 810%, 80%

124. (a) 6300 ppm, 6300000 ppb
(b) 0.040 M (c) 4.99×10^5 bottles

Chapter 16

12. (a) $HCO_3^- + H_2O \rightleftharpoons CO_3^{2-} + H_3O^+$
(b) $HCl + H_2O \rightleftharpoons Cl^- + H_3O^+$
(c) $CH_3COOH + H_2O \rightleftharpoons CH_3COO^- + H_3O^+$
(d) $HCN + H_2O \rightleftharpoons CN^- + H_3O^+$

14. (a) $HIO + H_2O \rightleftharpoons IO^- + H_3O^+$
(b) $CH_3(CH_2)_4COOH + H_2O \rightleftharpoons CH_3(CH_2)_4COO^- + H_3O^+$
(c) $HOOCCOOH + H_2O \rightleftharpoons HOOCCOO^- + H_3O^+$
$HOOCCOO^- + H_2O \rightleftharpoons {}^-OOCCOO^- + H_3O^+$
(d) $CH_3NH_3^+ + H_2O \rightleftharpoons CH_3NH_2 + H_3O^+$

16. (a) $HSO_4^- + H_2O \leftrightharpoons H_2SO_4 + OH^-$
(b) $CH_3NH_2 + H_2O \rightleftharpoons CH_3NH_3^+ + OH^-$
(c) $I^- + H_2O \leftrightharpoons HI + OH^-$
(d) $H_2PO_4^- + H_2O \rightleftharpoons H_3PO_4 + OH^-$

20. (a) H_2SO_4 (b) HNO_3 (c) $HClO_4$
(d) $HClO_3$ (e) H_2SO_4

22. (a) I^-, iodide, conjugate base
(b) HNO_3, nitric acid, conjugate acid
(c) HCO_3^-, hydrogen carbonate ion, conjugate acid
(d) HCO_3^-, hydrogen carbonate ion, conjugate base
(e) SO_4^{2-}, sulfate ion, conjugate base, H_2SO_4, sulfuric acid, conjugate acid
(f) HSO_3^-, hydrogen sulfite ion, conjugate acid

24. Pairs (b), (c), and (d)

26. (a) Reactant acid = H_2O, reactant base = HS^-, product conjugate acid = H_2S, product conjugate base = OH^-
(b) Reactant acid = NH_4^+, reactant base = S^{2-}, product conjugate acid = HS^-, product conjugate base = NH_3
(c) Reactant acid = HSO_4^-, reactant base = HCO_3^-, product conjugate acid = H_2CO_3, product conjugate base = SO_4^{2-}
(d) Reactant acid = NH_3, reactant base = NH_2^-, product conjugate base = NH_2^-, product conjugate acid = NH_3

28. (a) Reactant acid = CH_3COOH, reactant base = CN^-, product conjugate acid = HCN, product conjugate base = CH_3COO^-
(b) Reactant acid = H_2O, reactant base = O^{2-}, product conjugate acid = OH^-, product conjugate base = OH^-
(c) Reactant acid = H_2O, reactant base = HCO_2^-, product conjugate acid = HCOOH, product conjugate base = OH^-

31. (a) $CO_3^{2-} + H_2O \rightleftharpoons HCO_3^- + OH^-$
$HCO_3^- + H_2O \rightleftharpoons H_2CO_3 + OH^-$
(b) $H_3AsO_4 + H_2O \rightleftharpoons H_2AsO_4^- + H_3O^+$
$H_2AsO_4^- + H_2O \rightleftharpoons HAsO_4^{2-} + H_3O^+$
$HAsO_4^{2-} + H_2O \rightleftharpoons AsO_4^{3-} + H_3O^+$
(c) $NH_2CH_2COO^- + H_2O \rightleftharpoons {}^+NH_3CH_2COO^- + OH^-$
${}^+NH_3CH_2COO^- + H_2O \rightleftharpoons {}^+NH_3CH_2COOH + OH^-$

33. 3×10^{-11} M, basic
35. 3.6×10^{-3} M, acidic
37. pH = 12.40, pOH = 1.60
39. pOH = 12.51
41. 5×10^{-2} M, 2 g HCl
43.

pH	$[H_3O^+]$ (M)	$[OH^-]$ (M)	Acidic or Basic
(a) 6.21	6.1×10^{-7}	1.6×10^{-8}	Acidic
(b) 5.34	4.5×10^{-6}	2.2×10^{-9}	Acidic
(c) 4.67	2.1×10^{-5}	4.7×10^{-10}	Acidic
(d) 1.60	2.5×10^{-2}	4.0×10^{-13}	Acidic
(e) 9.12	7.6×10^{-10}	1.3×10^{-5}	Basic

45. (a) 100 times more acidic (b) 10^4 times more basic
(c) 16 times more basic (d) 2×10^4 times more acidic

47. (a) 5.0×10^{-9} M (b) Basic

49. (a) $F^-(aq) + H_2O(\ell) \rightleftharpoons HF(aq) + OH^-(aq)$ $K = \frac{[HF][OH^-]}{[F^-]}$
(b) $NH_3(aq) + H_2O(\ell) \rightleftharpoons NH_4^+(aq) + OH^-(aq)$
$K = \frac{[NH_4^+][OH^-]}{[NH_3]}$
(c) $H_2CO_3(aq) + H_2O(\ell) \rightleftharpoons HCO_3^-(aq) + H_3O^+(aq)$
$K = \frac{[HCO_3^-][H_3O^+]}{[H_2CO_3]}$
(d) $H_3PO_4(aq) + H_2O(\ell) \rightleftharpoons H_2PO_4^-(aq) + H_3O^+(aq)$
$K = \frac{[H_2PO_4^-][H_3O^+]}{[H_3PO_4]}$
(e) $CH_3COO^-(aq) + H_2O(\ell) \rightleftharpoons CH_3COOH(aq) + OH^-(aq)$
$K = \frac{[CH_3COOH][OH^-]}{[CH_3COO^-]}$
(f) $S^{2-}(aq) + H_2O(\ell) \rightleftharpoons HS^-(aq) + OH^-(aq)$
$K = \frac{[HS^-][OH^-]}{[S^{2-}]}$

51. (a) NH_3 (b) K_2S (c) $NaCH_3COO$ (d) KCN
54. (a) 2.19 (b) 5.13 (c) 8.07 (d) 9.02
(e) 13.30 (f) 1.54 (g) 9.69 (h) 7.00
56. $K_a = 1.6 \times 10^{-5}$
58. $[H_3O^+] = [A^-] = 1.3 \times 10^{-5}$ M, [HA] = 0.040 M
60. $K_a = 1.4 \times 10^{-5}$
62. 8.85
64. $K_b = 1.3 \times 10^{-3}$
66. (a) $C_{10}H_{15}NH_2 + H_2O \rightleftharpoons C_{10}H_{15}NH_3^+ + OH^-$
(b) 10.55
68. 3.28
72. (a) CN^-, product-favored (b) HS^-, reactant-favored
(c) $H_2(g)$, reactant-favored
74. (a) $NH_4^+ + HPO_4^{2-} \rightarrow NH_3 + H_2PO_4^-$, reactant-favored
(b) $CH_3COOH + OH^- \rightarrow CH_3COO^- + H_2O$, product-favored
(c) $HSO_4^- + H_2PO_4^- \rightarrow H_3PO_4 + SO_4^{2-}$, product-favored
(d) $CH_3COOH + F^- \rightarrow CH_3COO^- + HF$, reactant-favored
76. (a) pH < 7 (b) pH > 7 (c) pH = 7
78. (a) pH > 7 (b) pH > 7 (c) pH > 7
80. $[Zn(H_2O)_4]^{2+}$
82. All of them
84. $Na_2CO_3 + 2\ CH_3(CH_2)_{16}COOH \rightarrow$
$2\ CH_3(CH_2)_{16}COONa + H_2O + CO_2$
86. Dishwasher detergent is very basic and should not be used to wash anything by hand, including a car. If it gets into the engine area, it can also dissolve automobile grease and oil, which could prevent the engine from running correctly.
88. Lemon juice is acidic and neutralizes the basic amines. The acid formed from the neutralized base is an ion and not volatile.
90. All three are Lewis bases; CO_2 is a Lewis acid.
92. Cr^{3+} and SO_3 are Lewis acids. CH_3NH_2 is a Lewis base.
94. (a) I_2 is a Lewis acid and I^- is a Lewis base.
(b) BF_3 is a Lewis acid and SO_2 is a Lewis base.
(c) Au^+ is a Lewis acid and CN^- is a Lewis base.
(d) CO_2 is a Lewis acid and H_2O is a Lewis base.
96.

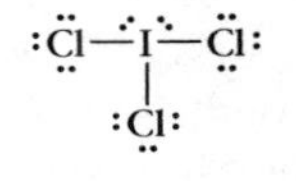

T-shaped

It functions as a Lewis acid.

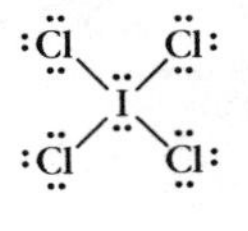

Square planar

98. (a) Weak acid (b) Strong base (c) Strong acid
(d) Weak base (e) Strong base (f) Amphiprotic
100. (a) Less than 7 (b) Equal to 7 (c) Greater than 7
102. 2.85
104. (a) Increase (b) Stays the same (c) Stays the same
106. 9.73
108. At 10 °C, pH = 7.27; at 25 °C, pH = 6.998; and at 50 °C, pH = 6.631. At 10 °C, at 25 °C, and at 50 °C the solutions are neutral, since $[H_3O^+] = [OH^-]$.
110. (a) $H_2O > Cl^- = H_3O^+ \gg OH^-$
(b) $H_2O > Na^+ = ClO_4^- \gg H_3O^+ = OH^-$
(c) $H_2O > HNO_2 > H_3O^+ = NO_2^- \gg OH^-$
(d) $H_2O > Na^+ \cong ClO^- > OH^- = HClO \gg H_3O^+$
(e) $H_2O > NH_4^+ \cong Cl^- > H_3O^+ = NH_3 \gg OH^-$
(f) $H_2O > Na^+ = OH^- \gg H_3O^+$
112. Conjugates must differ by just one H^+.
114. Arrhenius Theory: Electron pairs on the solvent water molecules (Lewis base) form a bond with the hydrogen ion (Lewis acid) producing aqueous H_3O^+ ions. Electron pairs on the OH^- ions (Lewis base) form a bond with the hydrogen ion (Lewis acid) in the solvent water molecule, producing aqueous OH^- ions.
Brønsted-Lowry Theory: The H^+ ion from the Brønsted-Lowry acid is bonded to a Brønsted-Lowry base using an electron pair on the base. The electron-pair acceptor, the H1 ion, is the Lewis acid and the electron-pair donor is the Lewis base.
116. (a) 2.01 (b) 23 times
119. Lactic acid sample
120. 0.76 L; No
121. Yes, higher pH
123. Br has a higher electronegativity than H. $ClNH_2$ is weaker, because Cl has a higher electronegativity than Br.
125. Strongest HM > HQ > HZ weakest; $K_{a,HZ} = 1 \times 10^{-5}$, $K_{a,HQ} = 1 \times 10^{-3}$, $K_{a,HM} = 1 \times 10^{-1}$ or larger
127. (a) Weak (b) Weak
(c) Acid/base conjugates (d) 6.26
129. Dilute solution is 9%, saturated solution is 2%.
131. (a) $NH_2CH_2CH_2CH_2CH_2CH_2NH_2$
(b) $NH_3CH_2CH_2CH_2CH_2CH_2NH_3^{2+}$ (c) 9.13
133. The carboxylic acid substituent is an acid (related to pK_a = 2.18). The two NH_2 groups are bases (related to pK_a = 8.95 and 10.53).

Chapter 17

16. (c)
18. (a) pH = 2.1 (b) pH = 7.21 (c) pH = 12.44
20. (a) Lactic acid and lactate ion
(b) Acetic acid and acetate ion
(c) HClO and ClO^-
(d) HCO_3^- and CO_3^{2-}
22. 4.8 g
24. pH = 8.62
26. pH = 9.55, pH = 9.51
28. Sample (b). Only (b) results in a solution containing a conjugate acid/base pair.
30. (a) ΔpH = 0.1 (b) Δ pH = 3.8 (c) Δ pH = 7.25
32. (a) pH = 5.02 (b) pH = 4.99 (c) pH = 4.06
34. At the equivalence point, the solution contains the conjugate base of the weak acid. Weaker acids have stronger conjugate bases. Stronger bases have a higher pH, so the titration of a weaker acid will have a more basic equivalence point.
36. (a) Bromothymol blue
(b) Phenolphthalein
(c) Methyl red
(d) Bromothymol blue. Suitable pH color changes
38. 0.0253 M HCl
40. 93.6%
42. (a) 29.2 mL (b) 600. mL (c) 1.20 L (d) 2.7 mL
44. (a) pH = 3.90 (b) pH = 8.45 (c) pH = 12.15
46. (a) pH = 0.824 (b) pH = 1.30 (c) pH = 3.8
(d) pH = 7.000 (e) pH = 10.2 (f) 12.48

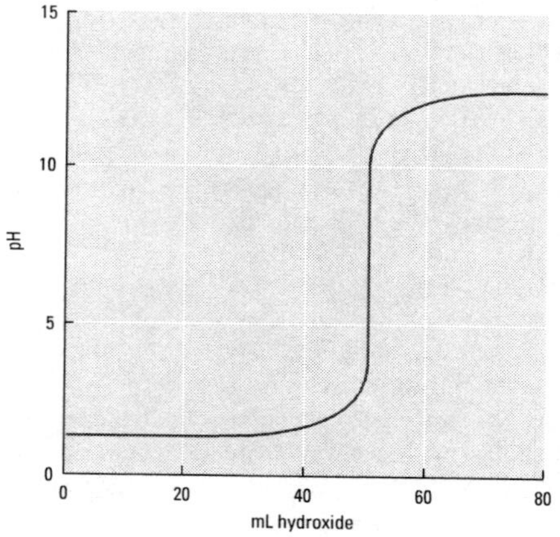

48. NO_2 reaction: $2\ NO_2(g) + H_2O(g) \rightarrow HNO_3(g) + HNO_2(g)$
SO_3 reactions: $2\ SO_2(g) + O_2(g) \rightarrow 2\ SO_3(g)$
$SO_3(g) + H_2O(g) \rightarrow H_2SO_4(g)$
50. $CaCO_3(s) + 2\ H^+(aq) \rightarrow Ca^{2+}(aq) + CO_2(g) + H_2O(\ell)$
54. (a) $FeCO_3(s) \rightleftharpoons Fe^{2+}(aq) + CO_3^{2-}(aq)$ $K_{sp} = [Fe^{2+}][CO_3^{2-}]$
(b) $Ag_2SO_4(s) \rightleftharpoons 2\ Ag^+(aq) + SO_4^{2-}(aq)$ $K_{sp} = [Ag^+]^2[SO_4^{2-}]$
(c) $Ca_3(PO_4)_2(s) \rightleftharpoons 3\ Ca^{2+}(aq) + 2\ PO_4^{3-}(aq)$
$K_{sp} = [Ca^{2+}]^3[PO_4^{3-}]^2$
(d) $Mn(OH)_2(s) \rightleftharpoons Mn^{2+}(aq) + 2\ OH^-(aq)$
$K_{sp} = [Mn^{2+}][OH^-]^2$
55. $K_{sp} = 3.0 \times 10^{-18}$
56. $K_{sp} = 2.22 \times 10^{-4}$
58. $K_{sp} = 2.2 \times 10^{-12}$
60. $K_{sp} = 1.7 \times 10^{-5}$
62. 6.2×10^{-11} M Zn^{2+}
64. 3.1×10^{-5} mol/L
66. (a) $K_{sp} = 1 \times 10^{-11}$ (b) $[OH^-]$ must be 0.008 M or higher.
68. 4.5×10^{-9} M
70. pH = 9.0
72. (a) $Ag^+(aq) + 2\ CN^-(aq) \rightleftharpoons [Ag(CN)_2]^-(aq)$
$$K_f = \frac{[[Ag(CN)_2]^-]}{[Ag^+][CN^-]^2}$$
(b) $Cd^{2+}(aq) + 4\ NH_3(aq) \rightleftharpoons [Cd(NH_3)_3]^{2+}(aq)$
$$K_f = \frac{[[Cd(NH_3)_4]^{2+}]}{[Cd^{2+}][NH_3]^4}$$
74. 0.0078 mol or more
76. (a) $Zn(OH)_2(s) + 2\ H_3O^+(aq) \rightarrow Zn^{2+}(aq) + 4\ H_2O(\ell)$
$Zn(OH)_2(s) + 2\ OH^-(aq) \rightarrow [Zn(OH)_4]^{2-}(aq)$
(b) $Sb(OH)_3(s) + 3\ H_3O^+(aq) \rightarrow Sb^{3+}(aq) + 6\ H_2O(\ell)$
$Sb(OH)_3(s) + OH^-(aq) \rightarrow [Sb(OH)_4]^-(aq)$
78. (a) H_2O, CH_3COO^-, Na^+, CH_3COOH, H_3O^+, OH^-
(b) pH = 4.95
(c) pH = 5.05
(d) $CH_3COOH(aq) + H_2O(\ell) \rightleftharpoons CH_3COO^-(aq) + H_3O^+(aq)$
80. Ratio = 1.6
82. 0.020 mol added to 1 L
84. (a) pH = 2.78 (b) pH = 5.39
86. $K_a = 3.5 \times 10^{-6}$
88. No change
90. $K_{sp} = 2.2 \times 10^{-12}$
92. The tiny amount of base (CH_3COO^-) present is insufficient to prevent the pH from changing dramatically if a strong acid is introduced into the solution.

94. $K_a = 2.3 \times 10^{-4}$
96. Blood pH decreases; acidosis
98. (a) Adding Ca^{2+} drives the reaction more toward reactants, making more apatite.
(b) Acid reacts with OH^-, removing a product and driving the reaction toward the products, causing apatite to decompose.
100. Acidosis; increase
102. Sample A: $NaHCO_3$; Sample B: NaOH; Sample C: Mixture of NaOH and Na_2CO_3 and/or $NaHCO_3$; Sample D: Na_2CO_3
104. 5.61
106. 3.22
108. 3.2 g

Chapter 18

15. (a) $2\,H_2O(\ell) \rightarrow 2\,H_2(g) + O_2(g)$, reactant-favored
(b) $C_8H_{18}(\ell) \rightarrow C_8H_{18}(g)$, product-favored
(c) $C_{12}H_{22}O_{11}(s) \rightarrow C_{12}H_{22}O_{11}(aq)$, product-favored
17. (a) $\frac{1}{2}$ (b) $\frac{1}{2}$ (c) 50 of each
19. (a) Probability of $\frac{1}{2}$ in Flask A; probability of $\frac{1}{2}$ in flask B
(b) 50 in flask A and 50 in flask B
21. (a) Negative (b) Positive (c) Positive
23. (a) Positive (b) Positive (c) Positive
25. (a) Item 2 (b) Item 2 (c) Item 2
27. (a) NaCl(s) (b) $P_4(g)$ (c) $NH_4NO_3(aq)$
29. (a) $Ga(\ell)$ (b) $AsH_3(g)$ (c) NaF(s)
31. (a) Negative (b) Positive
(c) Negative (d) Positive
33. (a) Negative (b) Negative (c) Positive
35. $112\ J\ K^{-1}\ mol^{-1}$
37. (a) 2.63 J/K (b) 1000 J/K (c) 2.45 J/K
39. (a) +113.0 J/K (b) +38.17 J/K
41. (a) −120.64 J/K (b) 156.9 J/K
(c) −198.76 J/K (d) 160.6 J/K
43. (a) $-173.01\ J\ K^{-1}$ (b) $-326.69\ J\ K^{-1}$ (c) $137.55\ J\ K^{-1}$
45. $\Delta S° = -247.7$ J/K; Cannot tell without $\Delta H°$ also, since that is needed to calculate $\Delta G°$. $\Delta H° = -88.13$ kJ and $\Delta G° = -14.3$ kJ, so it is product-favored.
47. Product-favored at low temperatures; the exothermicity is sufficient to favor products if the temperature is low enough to overcome the decrease in entropy.
49. Exothermic reactions with an increase in disorder, exhibited by a larger number of gas-phase products than gas-phase reactants, never need help from the surroundings to favor products.
51. (a) Enthalpy change (ΔH) is negative; entropy change (ΔS) is positive.
(b) Using enthalpy of formations and Hess's law: $\Delta H° = -184.28$ kJ; $\Delta S° = -7.7\ J\ K^{-1}$
The enthalpy change is negative, as predicted in (a). But the entropy change is negative, not as predicted in (a). The aqueous solute must have sufficient order to compensate for the high disorder of the gas. The value of $-7.7\ J\ K^{-1}$ is pretty small.
53. Entropy increase is insufficient to drive this highly endothermic reaction to form products without assistance from the surroundings at this temperature.
55. (a) $\Delta S° = -37.52$ J/K, $\Delta H° = -851.5$ kJ, product-favored at low temperature
(b) $\Delta S° = -21.77$ J/K, $\Delta H° = 66.36$ kJ, never product-favored
57. (a) $\Delta S_{univ} = 4.92 \times 10^3$ J/K (b) −1467.3 kJ
(c) Yes; ethane is used as a fuel; hence, we might expect that its combustion reaction is product-favored.

59.

Sign of $\Delta H°_{system}$	Sign of $\Delta S°_{system}$	Product-favored?	Sign of $\Delta G°_{system}$
Negative	Positive	Yes	Negative
Negative	Negative	Yes at low T; no at high T	—
Positive	Positive	No at low T; yes at high T	—
Positive	Negative	No	Positive

61. $\Delta G° = \Delta H° - T\Delta S°$ Here $\Delta H°$ is negative, and $\Delta S°$ is positive, so $\Delta G° = -|\Delta H°| - |T\Delta S°| = -(|\Delta H°| + |T\Delta S°|) < 0$.
63. $\Delta G° = 28.63$ kJ; reactant-favored
65. $\Delta G° = 462.28$ kJ; uncatalyzed; it would not be a good way to make Si.
67. (a) −141.05 kJ (b) 141.73 kJ (c) −959.43 kJ
Reactions (a) and (c) are product-favored.
69. (a) 385.7 K (b) 835.1 K
71. (a) 49.7 kJ (b) −178.2 kJ (c) −1267.5 kJ
73. (a) $\Delta H° = 178.32$ kJ, $\Delta S° = 160.6$ J/K, $\Delta G° = 130.5$ kJ
(b) Reactant-favored
(c) No; it is only product-favored at high temperatures.
(d) 1110. K
75. $\Delta G_f°(Ca(OH)_2) = 2867.8$ kJ
77. (a) $K = 4 \times 10^{-34}$ (b) $K = 5 \times 10^{-31}$
79. (a) $\Delta G° = -100.97$ kJ, product-favored
(b) $K = 5 \times 10^{17}$. When $\Delta G°$ is negative, K is larger than 1.
81. (a) $K°_{298} = 2 \times 10^{12}$, product-favored
$K°_{1000} = 2.0 \times 10^{-2}$, reactant-favored
(b) $K°_{298} = 10^{135}$, product-favored
$K°_{1000} = 3 \times 10^{33}$, product-favored
85. (a) $\Delta G° = -106$ kJ/mol (b) $\Delta G° = 8.55$ kJ/mol
(c) $\Delta G° = -33.8$ kJ/mol
87. (a) can be harnessed; (b) and (c) require work to be done.
89. Reaction 87(b), 5.068 g graphite oxidized; reaction 87(c), 26.94 g graphite oxidized
91. (a) $2\,C(s) + 2\,Cl_2(g) + TiO_2(s) \rightarrow TiCl_4(g) + 2\,CO(g)$
(b) $\Delta H°$ −44.6 kJ; $\Delta S° = 242.7\ J\ K^{-1}$; $\Delta G° = -116.5$ kJ
(c) Product-favored
93. CuO, Ag_2O, HgO, and PbO
95. (a) Five O—H bonds, seven C—O bonds, seven C—H bonds, five C—C bonds, and six O═O bonds are broken. Twelve C═O bonds and 12 O—H bonds are formed. $\Delta H° \cong -2873$ kJ.
(b) Interactive forces in condensed phases (solid glucose and liquid water) are neglected in this calculation.
97. (a) 6.46 mol ATP per mol of glucose
(b) $\Delta G° = -106$ kJ (c) Product-favored
99. The combustion of coal, petroleum, and natural gas are the most common sources used to supply free energy. We also use solar and nuclear energy as well as the kinetic energy of wind and water. (There may be other answers.)
101. (a) $\Delta G° = -86.5$ kJ, product-favored
(b) $\Delta G° = -873.1$ kJ (c) No (d) Yes
103. For $CH_4(g)$, $\Delta G° = -817.90$ kJ
For $C_6H_6(\ell)$, $\Delta G° = -3202.0$ kJ
For $CH_3OH(\ell)$, $\Delta G° = -702.34$ kJ
Organic compounds are complex molecular systems that require significant rearrangement of atoms and bonds to undergo combustion. This makes them likely candidates for being kinetically stable.
105. (a) 5.5×10^{18} J/yr
(b) 1.5×10^{16} J/day
(c) 1.7×10^{11} J/s
(d) 1.7×10^{11} W
(e) 6×10^2 W/person

107. (a) Reaction 2 (b) Reactions 1 and 5
(c) Reaction 2 (d) Reactions 2 and 3
(e) None of them

109. (a) $\Delta G° = 141.73$ kJ (b) No (c) Yes
(d) $K_p = 1 \times 10^4$ (e) $K_c = 7 \times 10^1$

111. (a) $\Delta G° = 31.8$ kJ (b) $K_p = P_{Hg(g)}$
(c) $K° = 2.7 \times 10^{-6}$ (d) $P_{Hg(g)} = 2.7 \times 10^{-6}$ atm
(e) $T = 450$ K

113. Scrambled is a very disordered state for an egg. The second law of thermodynamics says that the more disordered state is the more probable state. Putting the delicate tissues and fluids back where they were before the scrambling occurred would take a great deal of energy. Humpty Dumpty is a fictional character who was also an egg. He fell off a wall. A very probable result of that fall is for an egg to become scrambled. The story goes on to tell that all the energy of the king's horses and men was not sufficient to put Humpty together again.

114. Absolute entropies can be determined because the minimum value of $S°$ is zero at $T = 0$ K. It is not possible to define conditions for a specific minimum value for internal energy, enthalpy, or Gibbs free energy of a substance, so relative quantities must be used.

116. Many of the oxides have negative enthalpies of reaction, which means their oxidations are exothermic. These are probably product-favored reactions.

117. NaCl, in an orderly crystal structure, and pure water, with only O—H hydrogen bonding interactions in the liquid state, are far more ordered than the dispersed hydrated sodium and chloride ions interacting with the water molecules.

119. (a) False (b) False (c) True
(d) True (e) True

121. The energy obtained from nutrients is stored as ATP. The source of the energy needed to synthesize the sugars was sunlight used by plants to produce the sugars and other carbohydrates.

123. $\Delta G = 0$ means products are favored; however, the equilibrium state will always have some reactants present, too. To get all the reactants to go away requires the removal of the products from the reactants, so the reaction continues forward.

125. (a) 58.78 J/K (b) −53.29 J/K (c) −173.93 J/K
Adding more hydrogen makes the $\Delta S°$ more negative.

127. Product favored; $\Delta H°$ is negative. Assuming the $S°$ of C_8H_{16} and C_8H_{18} are approximately the same value, $\Delta S°$ is negative, but not large enough to give $\Delta G°$ a different sign; hence, $\Delta G°$ is negative, also.

129. (a) 331.51 K (b) 371. K

131. (a) $K_p = 1.5 \times 10^7$ (b) Product-favored (c) $K_c = 3.7 \times 10^8$

133. (a) $7\ C(s) + 6\ H_2O(g) \rightarrow 2\ C_2H_6(g) + 3\ CO_2(g)$
$5\ C(s) + 4\ H_2O(g) \rightarrow C_3H_8(g) + 2\ CO_2(g)$
$3\ C(s) + 4\ H_2O(g) \rightarrow 2\ CH_3OH(\ell) + CO_2(g)$
(b) For C_2H_6, $\Delta H° = 101.02$ kJ, $\Delta G° = 122.72$ kJ, $\Delta S° = -72.71$ J/K
For C_3H_8, $\Delta H° = 76.5$ kJ, $\Delta G° = 102.08$ kJ, $\Delta S° = -86.6$ J/K
For CH_3OH, $\Delta H° = 96.44$ kJ, $\Delta G° = 187.39$ kJ, $\Delta S° = -305.2$ J/K
None of these are feasible. $\Delta G°$ is positive. In addition, $\Delta H°$ is positive and $\Delta S°$ is negative, suggesting that there is no temperature at which the products would be favored.

135. $\Delta G° = -RT \ln K = \Delta H° - T\Delta S°$

$$\ln K = -\frac{\Delta H°}{RT} + \frac{\Delta S°}{R}$$

If ln K is plotted against $1/T$, the slope would be $-\Delta H°/R$, and the y-intercept would be $\Delta S°/R$. The linear graph shows that $\Delta S°$ and $\Delta H°$ are independent of temperature.

137. (a) (ii) (b) (i) (c) (ii)

Chapter 19

10. (a) $Zn(s) \rightarrow Zn^{2+}(aq) + 2\ e^-$
(b) $2\ H_3O^+(aq) + 2\ e^- \rightarrow 2\ H_2O(\ell) + H_2(g)$
(c) $Sn^{4+}(aq) + 2\ e^- \rightarrow Sn^{2+}(aq)$
(d) $Cl_2(g) + 2\ e^- \rightarrow 2\ Cl^-(aq)$
(e) $6\ H_2O(\ell) + SO_2(g) \rightarrow SO_4^{2-}(aq) + 4\ H_3O^+(aq) + 2\ e^-$

12. (a) $Al(s) \rightarrow Al^{3+}(aq) + 3\ e^-$
$Cl_2(g) + 2\ e^- \rightarrow 2\ Cl^-(aq)$
(b) $Fe^{2+}(aq) \rightarrow Fe^{3+}(aq) + e^-$
$MnO_4^-(aq) + 8\ H_3O^+(aq) + 5\ e^- \rightarrow Mn^{2+}(aq) + 12\ H_2O(\ell)$
(c) $FeS(s) + 12\ H_2O(\ell) \rightarrow Fe^{3+}(aq) + SO_4^{2-}(aq) + 8\ H_3O^+(aq) + 9\ e^-$
$NO_3^-(aq) + 4\ H_3O^+(aq) + 3\ e^- \rightarrow NO(g) + 6\ H_2O(\ell)$

14. $4\ Zn(s) + 7\ OH^-(aq) + NO_3^-(aq) + 6\ H_2O(\ell) \rightarrow 4\ Zn(OH)_4^{2-} + NH_3(aq)$

16. (a) $3\ CO(g) + O_3(g) \rightarrow 3\ CO_2(g)$
O_3 is the oxidizing agent; CO is the reducing agent.
(b) $H_2(g) + Cl_2(g) \rightarrow 2\ HCl(g)$
Cl_2 is the oxidizing agent; H_2 is the reducing agent.
(c) $H_2O_2(aq) + Ti^{2+}(aq) + 2\ H_3O^+(aq) \rightarrow 4\ H_2O(\ell) + Ti^{4+}(aq)$
H_2O_2 is the oxidizing agent; Ti^{2+} is the reducing agent.
(d) $2\ MnO_4^-(aq) + 6\ Cl^-(aq) + 8\ H_3O^+(aq) \rightarrow 2\ MnO_2(s) + 3\ Cl_2(g) + 12\ H_2O(\ell)$
MnO_4^- is the oxidizing agent; Cl^- is the reducing agent.
(e) $4\ FeS_2(s) + 11\ O_2(g) \rightarrow 2\ Fe_2O_3(s) + 8\ SO_2(g)$
O_2 is the oxidizing agent; FeS_2 is the reducing agent.
(f) $O_3(g) + NO(g) \rightarrow O_2(g) + NO_2(g)$
O_3 is the oxidizing agent; NO is the reducing agent.
(g) $Zn(Hg)(amalgam) + HgO(s) \rightarrow ZnO(s) + 2\ Hg(\ell)$
HgO is the oxidizing agent; Zn(Hg) is the reducing agent.

18. The generation of electricity occurs when electrons are transmitted through a wire from the metal to the cation. Here, the transfer of electrons would occur directly from the metal to the cation and the electrons would not flow through any wire.

20. In chemistry, they are conventionally written as reduction reactions.

22. (a) $Zn(s) + Pb^{2+}(aq) \rightarrow Zn^{2+}(aq) + Pb(s)$
(b) Oxidation of zinc occurs at the anode. The reduction of lead occurs at the cathode. The anode is metallic zinc. The cathode is metallic lead.
(c)

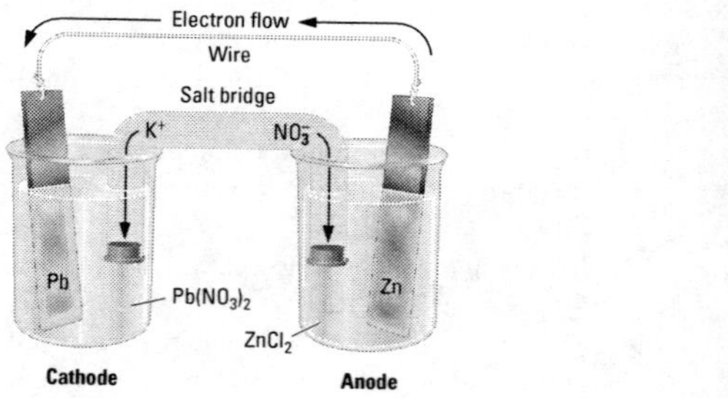

24. 7.5×10^3 C

26. (a) $Cu(s) \rightarrow Cu^{2+}(aq) + 2\ e^-$
$Ag^+(aq) + e^- \rightarrow Ag(s)$
(b) The copper half-reaction is oxidation and it occurs in the anode compartment. The silver half-reaction is reduction and it occurs in the cathode compartment.

28. Li is the strongest reducing agent and Li^+ is the weakest oxidizing agent. F_2 is the strongest oxidizing agent and F^- is the weakest reducing agent.

30. Worst oxidizing agent (d) < (c) < (a) < (b) best oxidizing agent

32. (a) 2.91 V (b) −0.028 V
(c) 0.65 V (d) 1.16 V
Reactions (a), (c), and (d) are product-favored.

34. (a) Al^{3+} (b) Ce^{4+} (c) Al
(d) Ce^{3+} (e) Yes (f) No
(g) Mercury(I) ion, silver ion, and cerium(IV) ion
(h) Hg, Sn, Ni, Al
36. Greater; less
38. (a) 1.55 V (b) −1196 kJ, 1.55 V
40. −409 kJ
42. 1×10^{-18}, 102 kJ
46. $K° = 4 \times 10^{1}$
48. (a) 1.20 V (b) 1.16 V (c) 3 M
50. −0.378 V
52. (conc. Pb^{2+})/(conc. Sn^{2+}) = 0.3
54. (a) $Ni^{2+}(aq) + Cd(s) \rightarrow Ni(s) + Cd^{2+}(aq)$
(b) Cd is oxidized, Ni^{2+} is reduced, Ni^{2+} is the oxidizing agent, and Cd is the reducing agent.
(c) Metallic Cd is the anode and metallic Ni is the cathode.
(d) 0.15 V
(e) Electrons flow from the Cd electrode to the Ni electrode.
(f) Toward the anode compartment
56. A fuel cell has a continuous supply of reactants and will be useable for as long as the reactants are supplied. A battery contains all the reactants of the reaction. Once the reactants are gone, the battery is no longer useable.
58. (a) The N_2H_4 half-reaction occurs at the anode and the O_2 half-reaction occurs at the cathode.
(b) $N_2H_4(g) + O_2(g) \rightarrow N_2(g) + 2\,H_2O(\ell)$
(c) 7.5 g N_2H_4 (d) 7.5 g O_2
59. $O_2(g)$ produced at anode; $H_2(g)$ produced at cathode; 2 mol H_2 per mol O_2
61. Au^{3+}, Hg^{2+}, Ag^{+}, Hg_2^{2+}, Fe^{3+}, Cu^{2+}, Sn^{4+}, Sn^{2+}, Ni^{2+}, Cd^{2+}, Fe^{2+}, Zn^{2+}
63. H_2, Br_2, and OH^- are produced. After the reaction is complete, the solution contains Na^+, OH^-, a small amount of dissolved Br_2 (though it has low solubility in water), and a very small amount of H_3O^+. H_2 is formed at the cathode. Br_2 is formed at the anode.
65. 0.16 g Ag
67. 5.93 g Cu
69. 2.7×10^{5} g Al
71. 1.9×10^{2} g Pb
73. 0.10 g Zn
75. 0.043 g Li; 0.64 g Pb
77. 6.85 min
80. Ions increase the electrolytic capacity of the solution.
82. Chromium is highly resistant to corrosion and protects iron in steel from oxidizing.
85. 0.00689 g Cu, 0.00195 g Al
87. Worst reducing agent B < D < A < C best reducing agent
89. (a) B is oxidized and A^{2+} is reduced.
(b) A^{2+} is the oxidizing agent and B is the reducing agent.
(c) B is the anode and A is the cathode.
(d) $A^{2+} + 2e^- \rightarrow A$
$B \rightarrow B^{2+} + 2e^-$
(e) A gains mass.
(f) Electrons flow from B to A.
(g) K^+ ions will migrate toward the A^{2+} solution.
91. (a) The reaction with water is spontaneous:
$$4\,Co^{3+}(aq) + 6\,H_2O(\ell) \rightarrow 4\,Co^{2+}(aq) + O_2(aq) + 4\,H_3O^+(aq) \quad E°_{cell} = 0.591\text{ V}$$
(b) The reaction with oxygen in air is spontaneous:
$$4\,Fe^{2+}(aq) + O_2(aq) + 4\,H_3O^+(aq) \rightarrow 4\,Fe^{3+}(aq) + 6\,H_2O(\ell) \quad E°_{cell} = 0.458\text{ V}$$
93. $E_{cell} = 0.379$ V
95. (a) 9.5×10^{6} g HF (b) 1.7×10^{3} kWh
97. $Cl_2(g) + 2\,Br^-(aq) \rightarrow Br_2(\ell) + 2\,Cl^-(aq)$
99. 4+
101. 75 s
103. 5×10^{-6} M Cu^{2+}

Chapter 20

11. (a) α emission (b) β emission (c) Electron capture or positron emission (d) β emission
13. (a) ${}^{238}_{92}U$ (b) ${}^{32}_{15}P$ (c) ${}^{10}_{5}B$ (d) ${}^{0}_{-1}e$
(e) ${}^{15}_{7}N$
15. (a) ${}^{28}_{12}Mg \rightarrow {}^{28}_{13}Al + {}^{0}_{-1}e$
(b) ${}^{238}_{92}U + {}^{12}_{6}C \rightarrow 4\,{}^{1}_{0}n + {}^{246}_{98}Cf$
(c) ${}^{2}_{1}H + {}^{3}_{2}He \rightarrow {}^{4}_{2}He + {}^{1}_{1}H$
(d) ${}^{38}_{19}K \rightarrow {}^{38}_{18}Ar + {}^{0}_{+1}e$
(e) ${}^{175}_{78}Pt \rightarrow {}^{4}_{2}He + {}^{171}_{76}Os$
17. ${}^{231}_{90}Th$, ${}^{231}_{91}Pa$, ${}^{227}_{89}Ac$, ${}^{227}_{90}Th$, ${}^{223}_{88}Ra$
19. ${}^{222}_{86}Rn \rightarrow {}^{4}_{2}He + {}^{218}_{84}Po$
${}^{218}_{84}Po \rightarrow {}^{4}_{2}He + {}^{214}_{82}Pb$
${}^{214}_{82}Pb \rightarrow {}^{0}_{-1}e + {}^{214}_{83}Bi$
${}^{214}_{83}Bi \rightarrow {}^{0}_{-1}e + {}^{214}_{84}Po$
${}^{214}_{84}Po \rightarrow {}^{4}_{2}He + {}^{210}_{82}Pb$
${}^{210}_{82}Pb \rightarrow {}^{0}_{-1}e + {}^{210}_{83}Bi$
${}^{210}_{83}Bi \rightarrow {}^{0}_{-1}e + {}^{210}_{84}Po$
${}^{210}_{84}Po \rightarrow {}^{4}_{2}He + {}^{206}_{82}Pb$
20. (a) ${}^{19}_{10}Ne \rightarrow {}^{19}_{9}F + {}^{0}_{+1}e$ (b) ${}^{230}_{90}Th \rightarrow {}^{0}_{-1}e + {}^{230}_{91}Pa$
(c) ${}^{82}_{35}Br \rightarrow {}^{0}_{-1}e + {}^{82}_{36}Kr$ (d) ${}^{212}_{84}Po \rightarrow {}^{4}_{2}He + {}^{208}_{82}Pb$
22. The binding energy per nucleon of ${}^{10}B$ is 6.252×10^{8} kJ/mol nucleon. The binding energy per nucleon of ${}^{11}B$ is 6.688×10^{8} kJ/mol nucleon. ${}^{11}B$ is more stable than ${}^{10}B$ because its binding energy is larger.
24. -1.7394×10^{11} kJ/mol ${}^{238}U$; 7.3086×10^{8} kJ/mol nucleon
27. 5 mg
29. (a) ${}^{131}_{53}I \rightarrow {}^{131}_{54}Xe + {}^{0}_{-1}e$ (b) 1.56 mg
31. 4.0 y
33. 34.8 d
35. 2.72×10^{3} y; Approx. 710 B.C.
37. 1.6×10^{5} y
39. ${}^{239}_{94}Pu + 2\,{}^{1}_{0}n \rightarrow {}^{0}_{-1}e + {}^{241}_{95}Am$
41. ${}^{12}_{6}C$
43. Cadmium rods (a neutron absorber to control the rate of the fission reaction), uranium rods (a source of fuel, since uranium is a reactant in the nuclear equation), and water (used for cooling by removing excess heat and used in steam/water cycle for the production of turning torque for the generator)
45. (a) ${}^{140}_{54}Xe$ (b) ${}^{101}_{41}Nb$ (c) ${}^{92}_{36}Kr$
47. 6.9×10^{3} barrels
49. A rad is a measure of the amount of radiation absorbed. A rem includes a quality factor that better describes the biological impact of a radiation dose. The unit rem would be more appropriate when talking about the effects of an atomic bomb on humans. The unit gray (Gy) is 100 rad.
51. Since most elements have some proportion of unstable isotopes that decay and we are composed of these elements (e.g., ${}^{14}C$), our bodies emit radiation particles.
53. The gamma ray is a high-energy photon. Its interaction with matter is most likely just to impart large quantities of energy. The alpha and beta particles are charged particles of matter, which could interact, and possibly react, with the matter composing the food.
55. 0.13 L

57. (a) ${}^{0}_{-1}e$ (b) ${}^{4}_{2}He$ (c) ${}^{87}_{35}Br$ (d) ${}^{216}_{284}Po$
(e) ${}^{68}_{31}Ga$
59. 2 mg
61. 3.6×10^9 y
63. (a) ${}^{247}_{299}Es$ (b) ${}^{16}_{8}O$ (c) ${}^{4}_{2}He$ (d) ${}^{12}_{6}C$
(e) ${}^{10}_{15}B$
65. Alpha and beta radiation decay particles are charged (${}^{4}_{2}He^{21}$ and ${}^{0}_{-1}e^{-}$), so they are better able to interact with and ionize tissues, disrupting the function of the cancer cells. Gamma radiation, like X rays, goes through soft tissue without much of it being absorbed. This is less likely to interfere with the cancerous cells.
67. ${}^{20}Ne$ is stable. The ${}^{17}Ne$ is likely to decay by positron emission, increasing the ratio of neutrons to protons. The ${}^{23}Ne$ is likely to decay by beta emission, decreasing the ratio of neutrons to protons.
69. A nuclear reaction occurred, making products. Therefore, some of the lost mass is found in the decay particles, if the decay is alpha or beta decay, and almost all of the rest is found in the element produced by the reaction.
71. They are spontaneous reactions due to the nature of the nucleus. No other species are involved.
73. 2.8×10^4 kg
75. 75.1 y
77. 3.92×10^3 y

Chapter 21

20. (a) Cathode (b) Chlorine gas (c) 2.027×10^9 C
(d) 1.6×10^3 kJ/mol
22. 7×10^3 kWh
24. 67.1 g Al
26. Answers are in **bold**.

Formula	Name	Oxidation State of Phosphorus
P_4	Phosphorus	0
$(NH_4)_2HPO_4$	**Ammonium hydrogen phosphate**	+5
$\mathbf{H_3PO_4}$	Phosphoric acid	+5
$\mathbf{P_4O_{10}}$	Tetraphosphorus decaoxide	+5
$Ca_3(PO_4)_2$	**Calcium phosphate**	+5
$\mathbf{Ca(H_2PO_4)_2}$	Calcium dihydrogen phosphate	+5

28. 1.7×10^7 tons
30.

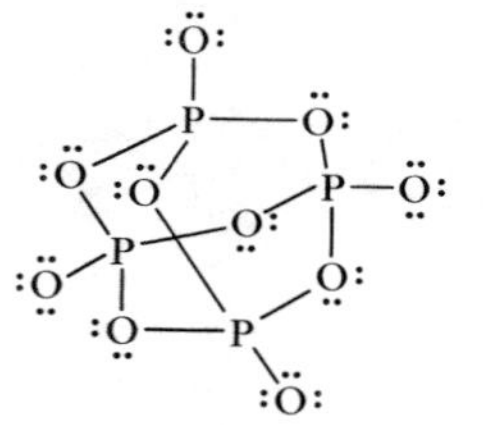

32. 962 K
34. Raw materials: sulfur, water, oxygen, and catalyst (Pt or VO_5)
$S_8(s) + 8\,O_2\,(g) \rightarrow 8\,SO_2\,(g)$
$2\,SO_2\,(g) + O_2\,(g) \rightarrow 2\,SO_3\,(g)$
$SO_3\,(g) + H_2SO_4(\ell) \rightarrow H_2S_2O_7(\ell)$
$H_2S_2O_7\,(\ell) + H_2O(\ell) \rightarrow 2\,H_2SO_4\,(aq)$
36.

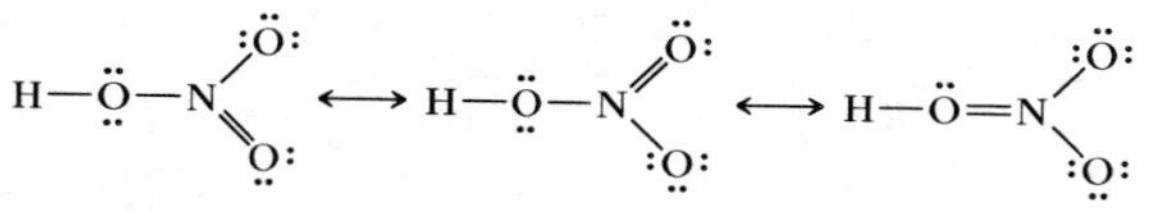

38. $K_c = 2.7$
40. 3 L
42. $K = 5.3 \times 10^5$
Putting seawater in the presence of $Ca(OH)_2$ will cause a precipitate of $Mg(OH)_2$ to form. The solid can be isolated after it settles.
44. N̈=N=N̈—N̈=Ö (Other structures are possible.)
46. (a) H—N̈=N̈=N̈ ↔ H—N̈—N≡N:
(b) +140. kJ with single and triple bond; +410. kJ with two double bonds
48. (a) $NO_2(g) + NO(g) \rightarrow N_2O_3(g)$
(b)

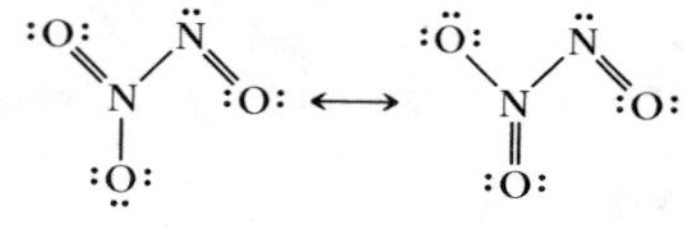

(c) The O—N—O angle is 120° and the N—N—O angle is slightly less than 120°.
51. (a) 7×10^2 kJ (b) 3 V must be used to overcome the cell potential.
53. (a) One; 120 °C, 1×10^{-4} atm (b) (i) Solid rhombic (ii) Liquid (iii) Solid monoclinic (iv) Vapor
55. (a) $4\,H_3O^+\,(aq) + MnO(s) + 2\,Br^-(aq) \rightarrow Mn^{2+}(aq) + 6\,H_2O(\ell) + Br_2(\ell)$
(b) 0.0813 mol Br^- (c) 3.54 g MnO_2
63. 6.3×10^5 J/mol
66. (a) $P_4(s) + 5\,O_2(g) \rightarrow P_4O_{10}(s)$ (b) pH = 1.18
(c) 25.0 g $Ca_3(PO_4)_2$ (d) 5.42 L
68. (a) Cl is reduced; Al and N are oxidized. (b) −2674 kJ
70. −2708. kJ/mol
72. $K_p = 1.985$
74. 2961 kJ, Mg^{2+} is a much smaller ion with higher charge density than Sr^{2+}, so the $Mg^{2+} + F^-$ ions are closer together and the ionic bond is much stronger.
76. B_6H_{12}

Chapter 22

14. (a) Ag [Kr] $4d^{10}5s^1$; Ag^+ [Kr] $4d^{10}$
(b) Au [Xe] $4f^{14}5d^{10}6s^1$; Au^+ [Xe]$4f^{14}\,5d^{10}$; Au^{3+} [Xe] $4f^{14}\,5d^8$
16. Cr^{2+} and Cr^{3+}
18. $Cr_2O_7^{2-}$ (in acid) > Cr^{3+} > Cr^{2+}; the species with a more positive oxidation state of Cr has greater tendency to be reduced. E°_{red}, respectively, is +1.33 V > −0.74 V > −0.91 V, so the more positive the oxidation state, the better the oxidizing agent.
20. (a) $Fe_2O_3(s) + 3\,CO(g) \rightarrow 2\,Fe(s) + 3\,CO_2(g)$
(b) $Fe(s) + 2\,H_3O^+(aq) \rightarrow Fe^{2+}\,(aq) + 2\,H_2O(\ell) + H_2(g)$ or $2\,Fe(s) + 6\,H_3O^+\,(aq) \rightarrow 2\,Fe^{3+}(aq) + 6\,H_2O(\ell) + 3\,H_2(g)$
22. $6\,H_3O^+(aq) + 3\,NO_3^-(aq) + Fe(s) \rightarrow Fe^{3+}(aq) + 3\,NO_2(g) + 9\,H_2O(\ell)$
26. (a) $[Cr(NH_3)_2(H_2O)_3(OH)]^{2+}$; +2
(b) The counter ion would be an anion, such as Cl^-.
28. (a) $C_2O_4^{2-}$ with 2− charge and Cl− with 1− charge
(b) 3+ charge
(c) $[Co(NH_3)_4Cl_2]^+$, with 1+ charge
30. For $Na_3[IrCl_6]$: (a) Six Cl^- (b) Ir with 3+ charge
(c) $[IrCl_6]^{3-}$ with 3− charge (d) Na^+
For $[Mo(CO)_4Br_2]$: (a) Four CO (b) Mo with 2+ charge
(c) $[Mo(CO)_4]^{2+}$ with 2+ charge (d) Br^-
32. (a) Four (b) Four
34. (a) $[Pt(NH_3)_2Br_2]$ (b) $[Pt(en)(NO_2)_2]$
(c) $[Pt(NH_3)_2BrCl]$

36. (a) Four (b) Four
(c) Six (d) Six
38. (a) Monodentate (b) Tetradentate
(c) Tridentate (d) Monodentate
40. For example, $FeCl_3$ (Other answers are possible.)
42. (a) Tetrachloromanganate (II)
(b) Potassium trioxalatoferrate (III)
(c) Diamminedicyanoplatinum (II)
(d) Pentaquahydroxoiron (III)
(e) Diethylenediaminedichloromanganese (II)

44. (a) 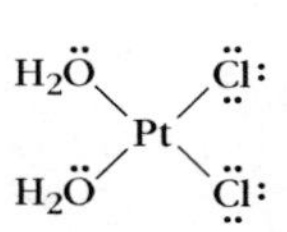 (b) 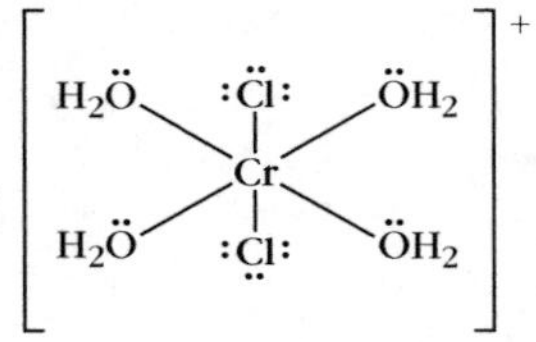

46. 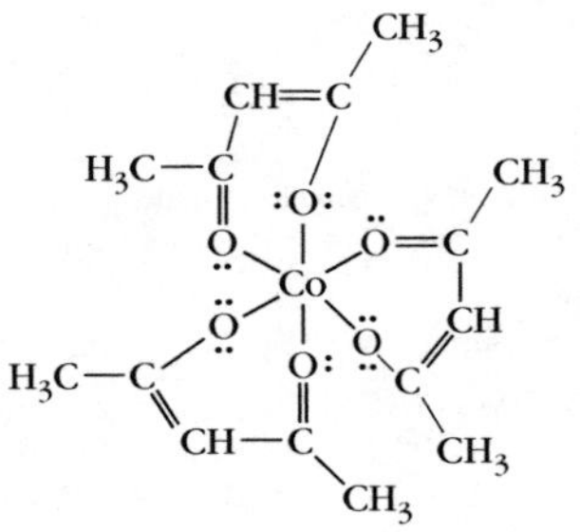

48. (a) and (b)
50. (a), (c), and (d)
52. (a) 4 (b) 5 (c) 5 (d) 3
54. Cr^{2+} has four electrons. Cr^{3+} has three electrons. Since there are three low-energy t_2 orbitals, the first three electrons can fill one into each t_2 orbital. The fourth electron (only found in Cr^{2+}) is required to pair up with one of the other electrons (low spin) or to span the Δ_o gap to go into an e orbital (high spin).
56. If Δ_o is large, electrons fill the t_2 orbitals and end up all paired. If Δ_o is small, all five orbitals are half-filled before any pairing begins, resulting in four unpaired electrons. So, high-spin Co^{3+} complexes are paramagnetic and low-spin Co^{3+} complexes are diamagnetic.
58. Cu^{2+} has nine *d*-electrons. All t_2 orbitals are filled, so high- and low-spin complexes do not form.
60. violet light; Approximately 400 nm
62. With CN^-: Δ_o increases and the observed color shifts closer to yellow-orange.
With Cl^-: Δ_o decreases and the observed color shifts closer to blue.
65. (a) [Ar] $3d^4$ (b) [Ar] $3d^{10}$ (c) [Ar] $3d^7$ (d) [Ar] $3d^3$

67.
(a) 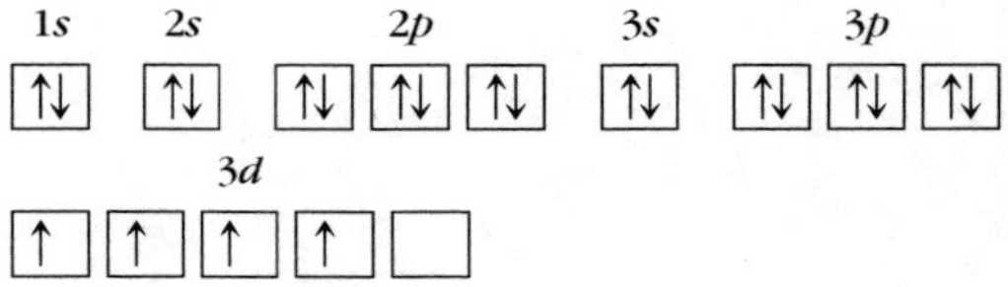

Four unpaired electrons

(b) 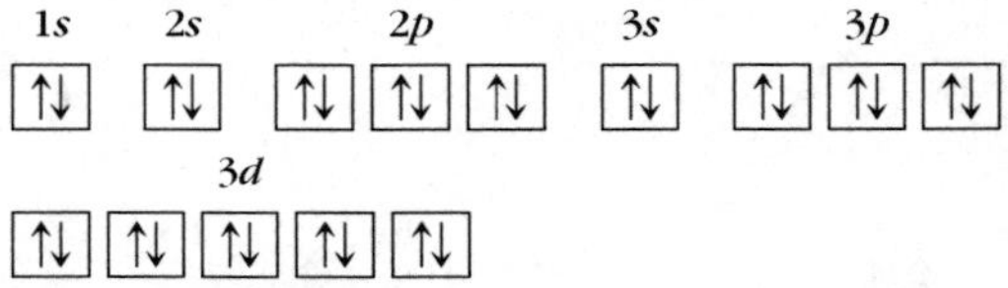

Zero unpaired electrons

(c) 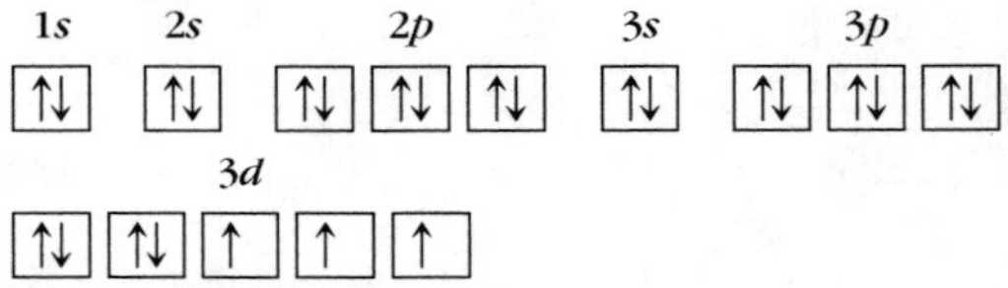

Three unpaired electrons

(d) 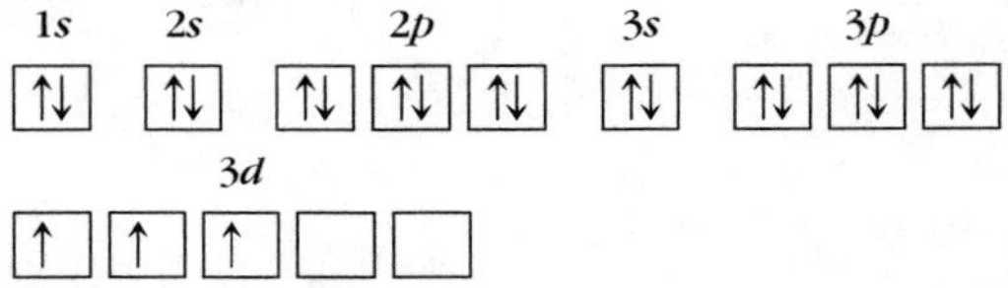

Three unpaired electrons

69. 14.8 g Cu
71. 0.40 ton SO_2
73. (a) Four (b) Six (c) Four (d) Six
75. 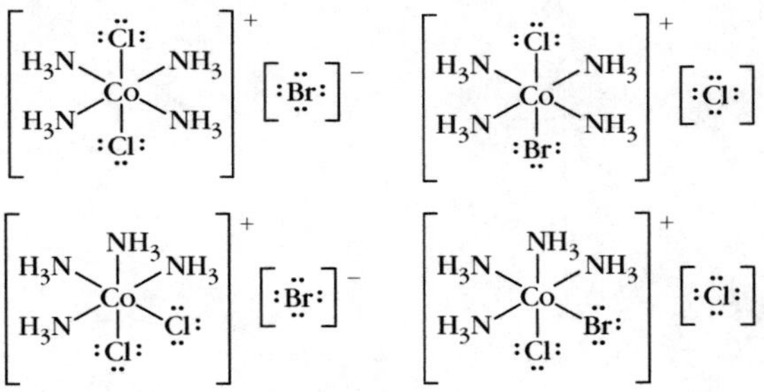

77. (a) False; the coordination number is six.
(b) False; Cu^+ has no unpaired electrons.
(c) False; the net charge is 3+.
78. (a) False; "In$[Pt(NH_3)_4]Cl_4$ the Pt has a 4+ charge and a coordination number of four."
(b) True
79. (a) +2
(b) 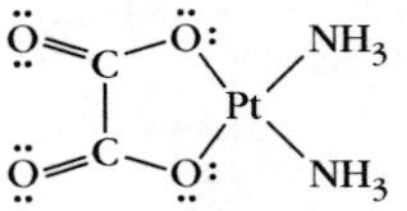

81. $Fe(s) + 2\,Fe^{3+}(aq) \rightarrow 3\,Fe^{2+}(aq)$
83. Four

85.

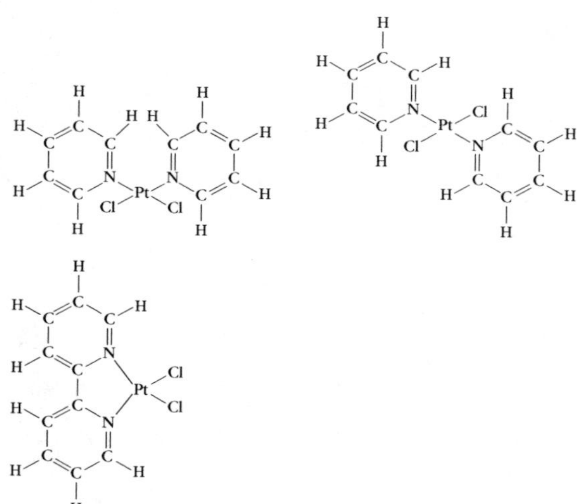

The bidentate ortho-phenanthroline is not able to form the *trans*-isomer.

87. (a) $2\ Ag^+ + Ni \rightarrow Ni^{2+} + 2\ Ag$
(b) +1.05V

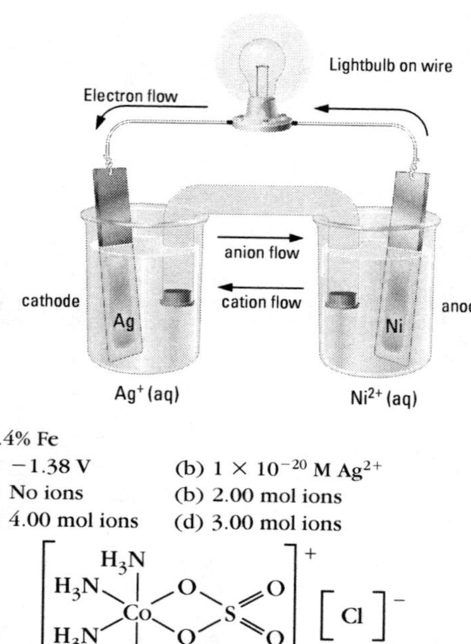

89. 17.4% Fe

91. (a) −1.38 V (b) 1×10^{-20} M Ag^{2+}

93. (a) No ions (b) 2.00 mol ions
(c) 4.00 mol ions (d) 3.00 mol ions

96.

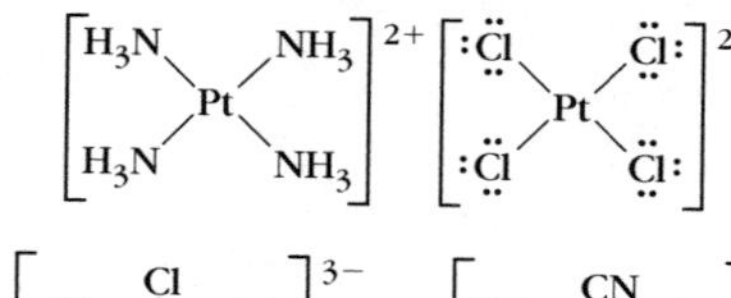

98. (a) $[Co(NH_3)_6]Cl_3$
(b) $[Co(NH_3)_6]Cl_3 \rightarrow [Co(NH_3)_6]^{3+}(aq) + 3\ Cl^-(aq)$

100.

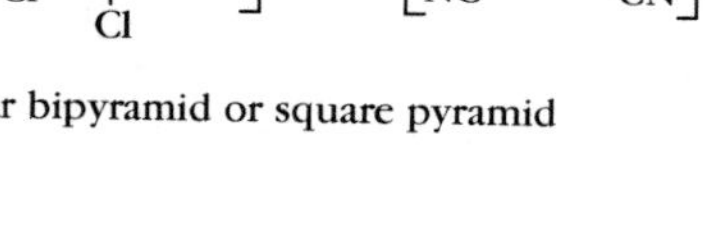

102.

Triangular bipyramid or square pyramid

104. A mixture of high spin and low spin complexes, in which the high spin species is favored by a 2:1 ratio, would give the observed 2.67 unpaired electrons per iron ion. High spin iron(II) has four unpaired electrons, while low spin iron(II) has zero unpaired electrons. This translates to 8 unpaired electrons for every three iron ions or 8/3 = 2.67 unpaired electrons per iron ion.

106.

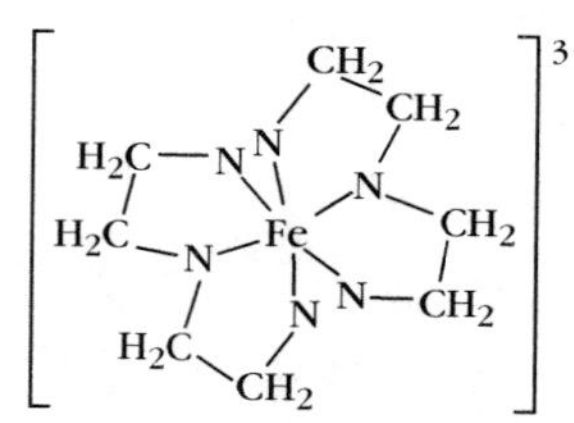

(One other structure is possible, too.)

Appendix A

4. The calculation is incomplete or incorrect. Check for incomplete unit conversions (e.g., cm^3 to L, g to kg, mm Hg to atm, etc.) and check to see that the numerator and denominator of unit factors are placed such that the unwanted units can cancel (e.g., $\frac{g}{mL}$ or $\frac{mL}{g}$).

6. Answer (c) gives the properly reported observation. Answers (a) and (b) do not have the proper units. Answer (d) is incomplete, with no units. Answer (e) shows the conversion of the observed measurement to new units, making (e) the result of a calculation, not the observed measurement.

8. (a) The units should not be squared. To do this correctly, add values with common units (g) and give the answer the same units (g). The result is 9.95 g.
(b) The unit factor is not set up to cancel unwanted units (g); the units reported (g) are not the units resulting from this calculation ($\frac{g^2}{mL}$). To do this correctly, $5.23\ g \times \frac{1.00\ mL}{4.87\ g} = 1.07$ mL.
(c) The unit factor must be cubed to cancel all unwanted units; the units reported (m^3) are not the units resulting from this calculation ($m \cdot cm^2$). To do this correctly, $3.57\ cm^3 \times (\frac{1\ m}{100\ cm})^3 = 3.57 \times 10^{-6}\ m^3$

10. (a) 7.994 ft ± 0.043 ft
(b) Three, because uncertainty is in the hundredths place
(c) The result is accurate (i.e., the true answer, 8.000 ft, is within the range of the uncertainty described by these values, 7.951 ft- 8.037 ft), though not very precise.

12. (a) 4 (b) 2 (c) 2 (d) 4

14. (a) 43.32 (b) 43.32 (c) 43.32
(d) 43.32 (e) 43.32 (f) 43.33

16. (a) 13.7 (b) 0.247 (c) 12.0

18. (a) 7.6003×10^4 (b) 3.7×10^{-4} (c) 3.4000×10^4

20. (a) 2.415×10^{-3} (b) 2.70×10^8 (c) 3.236

22. (a) −0.1351 (b) 3.541 (c) 23.7797
(d) 54.7549 (e) −7.455

24. (a) 5.404 (b) 9×10^{14}
(c) 110. (d) 3.75

26. (a) 0.708, −1.80 (b) 3.66, 1.38

28. 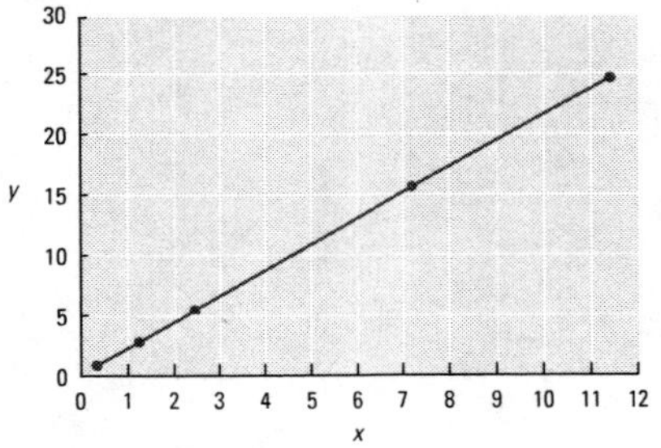

Yes, y is proportional to x.

Appendix B

1. (a) Meter, mega-; Mm (b) Kilogram, no additional prefix; kg (c) Square meter, deci-; dm^2
3. SI base (fundamental) units are set by convention; derived units are based on the fundamental units.
5. (a) 4.75×10^{-10} m (b) 5.6×10^{7} kg (c) 4.28×10^{-6} A
7. (a) 8.7×10^{-18} m^2 (b) 2.73×10^{-17} $kg \cdot m^2 \cdot s^{-2}$ (c) 2.73×10^{-5} $kg \cdot m/s^2$
9. (a) 2.20 lb (b) 2.22×10^{3} kg (c) 60 in^3 (d) 1×10^{5} Pa and 1 bar
11. (a) 99 °F (b) −10.5 °F (c) −40.0 °F

Glossary

absolute temperature scale (Kelvin temperature scale) A temperature scale on which the zero is the lowest possible temperature and the degree is the same size as the Celsius degree.

absolute zero Lowest possible temperature, 0 K.

absorb To draw a substance into the bulk of a liquid or a solid (compare with adsorb).

acid (Arrhenius) A substance that increases the concentration of hydronium ions, H_3O^+, in aqueous solution. (See also **Brønsted-Lowry acid, Lewis acid.**)

acid ionization constant (K_a) The equilibrium constant for the reaction of a weak acid with water to produce hydronium ions and the conjugate base of the weak acid.

acid ionization constant expression Mathematical expression in which the product of the equilibrium concentrations of hydronium ion and conjugate base is divided by the equilibrium concentration of the un-ionized conjugate acid.

acid rain Rain (or other precipitation) with a pH below about 5.6 (the pH of unpolluted rain water).

acidic solution An aqueous solution in which the concentration of hydronium ion exceeds the concentration of hydroxide ion.

actinides The elements after actinium in the seventh period; in actinides the 5*f* subshell is being filled.

activated complex A molecular structure corresponding to the maximum of a plot of energy versus reaction progress; also known as the transition state.

activation energy (E_a) The potential energy difference between reactants and activated complex; the minimum energy that reactant molecules must have to be converted to product molecules.

active site The part of an enzyme molecule that binds the substrate to help it to react.

activity (*A*) A measure of the rate of nuclear decay, given as disintegrations per unit time.

actual yield The quantity of a reaction product obtained experimentally; less than the theoretical yield.

addition polymer A polymer made when monomer molecules join directly with one another, with no other products formed in the reaction.

adsorb To attract and hold a substance on a surface (compare with absorb).

aerosols Small particles (1 nm to about 10,000 nm in diameter) that remain suspended indefinitely in air.

air pollutant A substance that degrades air quality.

alcohol An organic compound containing a hydroxyl group (—OH) covalently bonded to a saturated carbon atom.

aldehyde An organic compound characterized by a carbonyl group in which the carbon atom is bonded to a hydrogen atom; a molecule containing the —CHO functional group.

alkali metals The Group 1A elements in the periodic table (except hydrogen).

alkaline earth metals The elements in Group 2A of the periodic table.

alkane Any of a class of hydrocarbons characterized by the presence of only single carbon-carbon bonds.

alkene Any of a class of hydrocarbons characterized by the presence of a carbon-carbon double bond.

alkyl group A fragment of an alkane structure that results from the removal of a hydrogen atom from the alkane.

alkyne Any of a class of hydrocarbons characterized by the presence of a carbon-carbon triple bond.

allotropes Different forms of the same element that exist in the same physical state under the same conditions of temperature and pressure.

alpha carbon The carbon adjacent to the acid group (—COOH) in an amino acid.

alpha (α) particles Positively charged (2+) particles ejected at high speeds from certain radioactive nuclei; the nuclei of helium atoms.

alpha radiation Radiation composed of alpha particles (helium nuclei).

amide An organic compound characterized by the presence of a carbonyl group in which the carbon atom is bonded to a nitrogen atom ($—CONH_2$, —CONHR, $—CONR_2$); the product of the reaction of an amine with a carboxylic acid.

amide linkage A linkage consisting of a carbonyl group bonded to a nitrogen atom that connects monomers in a polymer.

amine An organic compound containing an $—NH_2$, —NHR, or $—NR_2$ functional group.

amino acids Organic molecules containing a carboxyl group with an R group and an amine group on the alpha carbon; building block monomers of proteins.

amorphous solid A solid whose constituent nanoscale particles have no long-range repeating structure.

amount A measure of the number of elementary entities (such as atoms, ions, molecules) in a sample of matter compared with the number of elementary entities in exactly 0.012 kg pure ^{12}C. Also called molar amount.

ampere The SI unit of electrical current; involves the flow of one coulomb of charge per second.

amphoteric Refers to a substance that can act as either an acid or a base.

anion An ion with a negative electrical charge.

anode The electrode of an electrochemical cell at which oxidation occurs.

anodic inhibition The prevention of oxidation of an active metal by painting it, coating it with grease or oil, or allowing a thin film of metal oxide to form.

antibonding molecular orbital A higher-energy molecular orbital that, if occupied by electrons, does not result in attraction between the atoms.

antioxidant Reducing agent that converts free radicals and other reactive oxygen species into less reactive substances.

aqueous solution A solution in which water is the solvent.

aromatic compound Any of a class of organic compounds characterized by the presence of one or more benzene rings or benzene-like rings.

Arrhenius equation Mathematical relation that gives the temperature dependence of the reaction rate constant; $k = Ae^{-E_a/RT}$.

asymmetric Describes a molecule or object that is not symmetrical.

atom The smallest particle of an element that can be involved in chemical combination with another element.

atom economy The fraction of atoms of starting materials incorporated into the desired final product in a chemical reaction.

atomic mass units (amu) The unit of a scale of relative atomic masses of the elements; 1 amu = 1/12 the mass of a six-proton, six-neutron carbon atom.

atomic number The number of protons in the nucleus of an atom of an element.

atomic radius One-half the distance between the nuclei centers of two like atoms in a molecule.

atomic structure The identity and arrangement of subatomic particles in an atom.

atomic weight The average mass of an atom in a representative sample of atoms of an element.

autoionization The equilibrium reaction in which water molecules react with each other to form hydronium ions and hydroxide ions.

average reaction rate A reaction rate calculated from a change in concentration divided by a change in time.

Avogadro's law The volume of a gas, at a given temperature and pressure, is directly proportional to the amount of gas.

Avogadro's number The number of particles in a mole of any substance (6.022×10^{23}).

axial position(s) Positions above and below the equatorial plane in a triangular bipyramidal structure.

background radiation Radiation from natural and synthetic radioactive sources to which all members of a population are exposed.

balanced chemical equation A chemical equation that shows equal numbers of atoms of each kind in the products and the reactants.

bar A pressure unit equal to 100,000 Pa.

barometer A device for measuring atmospheric pressure.

basal metabolic rate The energy required to maintain an organism that is awake, at rest, and not digesting or metabolizing food.

base (Arrhenius) Substance that increases concentration of hydroxide ions, OH^-, in aqueous solution. (See also **Brønsted–Lowry base, Lewis base.**)

base ionization constant (K_b) The equilibrium constant for the reaction of a weak base with water to produce hydroxide ions and the conjugate acid of the weak base.

base ionization constant expression Mathematical expression in which the product of the equilibrium concentrations of hydroxide ion and conjugate acid is divided by the equilibrium concentration of the conjugate base.

basic solution An aqueous solution in which the concentration of hydroxide ion is greater than the concentration of hydronium ion.

battery (voltaic cell) An electrochemical cell (or group of cells) in which a product-favored oxidation-reduction reaction is used to produce an electric current.

becquerel A unit of radioactivity equal to 1 nuclear disintegration per second.

beta particles Electrons ejected from certain radioactive nuclei.

beta radiation Radiation composed of electrons.

bidentate ligand A ligand that has two atoms with lone pairs that can form coordinate covalent bonds to the same metal ion.

bimolecular reaction An elementary reaction in which two particles must collide for products to be formed.

binary molecular compound A molecular compound whose molecules contain atoms of only two elements.

binding energy The energy required to separate all nucleons in an atomic nucleus.

binding energy per nucleon The energy per nucleon required to separate all nucleons in an atomic nucleus.

biodegradable Capable of being decomposed by biological means, especially by bacterial action.

boiling The process whereby a liquid vaporizes throughout when its vapor pressure equals atmospheric pressure.

boiling point The temperature at which the equilibrium vapor pressure of a liquid equals the external pressure on the liquid.

boiling-point elevation A colligative property; the difference between the normal boiling point of a pure solvent and the higher boiling point of a solution in which a nonvolatile nonelectrolyte solute is dissolved in that solvent.

bond Attractive force between two atoms holding them together, for example, as part of a molecule.

bond angle The angle between the bonds to two atoms that are bonded to the same third atom.

bond enthalpy (bond energy) The change in enthalpy when a mole of chemical bonds of a given type is broken, separating the bonded atoms; the atoms and molecules must be in the gas phase.

bond length The distance between the centers of the nuclei of two bonded atoms.

bonding electrons Electron pairs shared in covalent bonds.

bonding molecular orbital A lower-energy molecular orbital that can be occupied by bonding electrons.

bonding pair A pair of valence electrons that are shared between two atoms.

Born-Haber cycle A stepwise thermochemical cycle in which the constituent elements are converted to ions and combined to form an ionic compound.

boundary surface A surface within which there is a specified probability (often 90%) that an electron will be found.

Boyle's law The volume of a confined ideal gas varies inversely with the applied pressure, at constant temperature and amount of gas.

Brønsted-Lowry acid A hydrogen ion donor.

Brønsted-Lowry acid-base reaction A reaction in which an acid donates a hydrogen ion and a base accepts the hydrogen ion.

Brønsted-Lowry base A hydrogen ion acceptor.

buckyball Buckminsterfullerene; an allotrope of carbon consisting of molecules in which 60 carbon atoms are arranged in a cage-like structure consisting of five-membered rings sharing edges with six-membered rings.

buffer See **buffer solution.**

buffer capacity The quantity of acid or base a buffer can accommodate without a significant pH change (more than one pH unit).

buffer solution A solution that resists changes in pH when limited amounts of acids or bases are added; it contains a weak acid and its conjugate base, or a weak base and its conjugate acid.

caloric value The energy of complete combustion of a stated size sample of a food, usually reported in Calories (kilocalories).

calorie (cal) A unit of energy equal to 4.184 J. Approximately 1 cal is required to raise the temperature of 1 g of liquid water by 1 °C.

Calorie (Cal) A unit of energy equal to 4.184 kJ = 1 kcal. (See also **kilocalorie.**)

calorimeter A device for measuring the quantity of thermal energy transferred during a chemical reaction or some other process.

capillary action The process whereby a liquid rises in a small-diameter tube due to noncovalent interactions between the liquid and the tube's material.

carbohydrates Biochemical compounds with the general formula $C_x(H_2O)_y$, in which x and y are whole numbers.

carbonyl group An organic functional group consisting of carbon bonded to two other atoms and double bonded to oxygen; $>C{=}O$.

carboxylic acid An organic compound characterized by the presence of the carboxyl group (—COOH).

catalyst A substance that increases the rate of a reaction but is not consumed in the overall reaction.

catalytic cracking A petroleum refining process using a catalyst, heat, and pressure to break long-chain hydrocarbons into shorter-chain hydrocarbons, including both alkanes and alkenes suitable for gasoline.

catalytic reforming A petroleum refining process in which straight-chain hydrocarbons are converted to branched-chain hydrocarbons and aromatics for use in gasoline and the manufacture of other organic compounds.

catenation Formation of chains and rings by bonds between atoms of the same element.

cathode The electrode of an electrochemical cell at which reduction occurs.

cathodic protection A process of protecting a metal from corrosion whereby it is made the cathode by connecting it electrically to a more reactive metal.

cation An ion with a positive electrical charge.

cell voltage The electromotive force of an electrochemical cell; the quantity of work a cell can produce per coulomb of charge that the chemical reaction produces.

Celsius temperature scale A scale defined by the freezing (0 °C) and boiling (100 °C) points of pure water, at 1 atm.

cement A solid consisting of microscopic particles containing compounds of calcium, iron, aluminum, silicon, and oxygen in varying proportions and tightly bound to one another.

ceramics Materials fashioned from clay or other natural materials at room temperature and then hardened by heat.

CFCs See **chlorofluorocarbons.**

change of state A physical process in which one state of matter is changed into another (such as melting a solid to form a liquid).

Charles's law The volume of an ideal gas at constant pressure and amount of gas varies directly with its absolute temperature.

chelating ligand A ligand that uses more than one atom to bind to the same metal ion in a complex ion.

chemical change (chemical reaction) A process in which substances (reactants) change into other substances (products) by rearrangement, combination, or separation of atoms.

chemical compound (compound) A pure substance (e.g., sucrose or water) that can be decomposed into two or more different pure substances; homogeneous, constant-composition matter that consists of two or more chemically combined elements.

chemical element (element) A substance (e.g., carbon, hydrogen, or oxygen) that cannot be decomposed into two or more new substances by chemical or physical means.

chemical equilibrium A state in which the concentrations of reactants and products remain constant because the rates of forward and reverse reactions are equal.

chemical formula (formula) A notation combining element symbols and numerical subscripts that shows the relative numbers of each kind of atom in a molecule or formula unit of a substance.

chemical fuel A substance that reacts exothermically with atmospheric oxygen and is available at reasonable cost and in reasonable quantity.

chemical kinetics The study of the speeds of chemical reactions and the nanoscale pathways or rearrangements by which atoms, ions, and molecules are converted from reactants to products.

chemical periodicity, law of Law stating that the properties of the elements are periodic functions of atomic number.

chemical property Describes the kinds of chemical reactions that chemical elements or compounds can undergo.

chemical reaction (chemical change) A process in which substances (reactants) change into other substances (products) by rearrangements, combination, or separation of atoms.

chemistry The study of matter and the changes it can undergo.

chemotrophs (See also **phototrophs.**) Organisms that must depend on phototrophs to create the chemical substances from which they obtain Gibbs free energy.

chiral Describes a molecule or object that is not superimposable on its mirror image.

chlor-alkali process Electrolysis process for producing chlorine and sodium hydroxide from aqueous sodium chloride.

chlorination Addition of chlorine or a chlorine compound to kill bacteria in municipal water supplies; HOCl formed in water is the antibacterial agent.

chlorofluorocarbons (CFCs) Compounds of carbon, fluorine, and chlorine. CFCs have been implicated in stratospheric ozone depletion.

***cis* isomer** The isomer in which two like substituents are on the same side of a carbon-carbon double bond, the same side of a ring of carbon atoms, or the same side of a complex ion.

***cis-trans* isomerism** A form of stereoisomerism in which the isomers have the same molecular formula and the same atom-to-atom bonding sequence, but the atoms differ in the location of pairs of substituents on the same side or on opposite sides of a molecule.

Clausius-Clapeyron equation Equation that gives the relationship between vapor pressure and temperature.

closest packing Arranging atoms so that they are packed into the minimum volume.

coagulation The process in which the protective charge layer on colloidal particles is overcome, causing them to aggregate into a soft, semisolid, or solid mass.

coefficients (stoichiometric coefficients) The multiplying numbers assigned to the formulas in a chemical equation in order to balance the equation.

cofactor An inorganic or organic molecule or ion required by an enzyme to carry out its catalytic function.

colligative properties Properties of solutions that depend only on the concentration of solute particles in the solution, not on the nature of the solute particles.

colloid A state intermediate between a solution and a suspension, in which solute particles are large enough to scatter light, but too small to settle out; found in gas, liquid, and solid states.

combination reaction A reaction in which two reactants combine to give a single product.

combined gas law A form of the ideal gas law that relates the *P, V, T* of a given amount of gas before and after a change: $P_1V_1/T_1 = P_2V_2/T_2$.

combining volumes, law of At constant temperature and pressure, the volumes of reacting gases are always in the ratios of small whole numbers.

combustion analysis A quantitative method to obtain percent composition data for compounds that can burn in oxygen.

combustion reaction A reaction in which an element or compound burns in air or oxygen.

common ion effect Shift in equilibrium position that results from addition of an ion identical to one in the equilibrium.

complementary base pair Bases, each in a different DNA strand, that hydrogen-bond to each other: guanine with cytosine and adenine with thymine.

complex ion An ion with several molecules or ions connected to a central metal ion by coordinate covalent bonds.

composites Materials with components that may be metals, polymers, and ceramics.

compound See **chemical compound.**

compressibility The property of a gas that allows it to be compacted into a smaller volume by application of pressure.

concentration The relative quantities of solute and solvent in a solution.

concentration cell An electrochemical cell in which the voltage is generated because of a difference in concentrations of the same chemical species.

concrete A mixture of cement, sand, and aggregate (crushed stone or pebbles) in varying proportions that reacts with water and carbon dioxide to form a rock-hard solid.

condensation Process whereby a molecule in the gas phase enters the liquid phase.

condensation polymer A polymer made from the condensation reaction of monomer molecules that contain two or more functional groups.

condensation reaction A chemical reaction in which two (or more) molecules combine to form a larger molecule, simultaneously producing a small molecule such as water.

condensed formula A chemical formula of an organic compound indicating how atoms are grouped together in a molecule.

conduction band In a solid, an energy band that contains electrons of higher energy than those in the valence band.

conductor A material that conducts electric current; has an overlapping valence band and conduction band.

conjugate acid-base pair A pair of molecules or ions related to one another by the loss and gain of a single hydrogen ion.

conjugated Refers to a system of alternating single and double bonds in a molecule.

conservation of energy, law of (first law of thermodynamics) Law stating that energy can be neither created nor destroyed—the total energy of the universe is constant.

conservation of mass, law of Law stating that there is no detectable change in mass during an ordinary chemical reaction.

constant composition, law of Law stating that a chemical compound always contains the same elements in the same proportions by mass.

constitutional isomers (structural isomers) Compounds with the same molecular formula that differ in the order in which their atoms are bonded together.

continuous phase The solvent-like dispersing medium in a colloid.

continuous spectrum A spectrum consisting of all possible wavelengths.

conversion factor (proportionality factor) A relationship between two measurement units derived from the proportionality of one quantity to another; e.g., density is the conversion factor between mass and volume.

coordinate covalent bond A chemical bond in which both of the two electrons forming the bond were originally associated with the same one of the two bonded atoms.

coordination compound A compound in which complex ions are combined with oppositely charged ions to form a neutral compound.

coordination number The number of coordinate covalent bonds between ligands and a central metal ion in a complex ion.

copolymer A polymer formed by combining two different types of monomers.

core electrons The electrons in the filled inner shells of an atom.

corrosion Oxidation of a metal exposed to the environment.

coulomb The unit of electrical charge equal to the quantity of charge that passes a fixed point in an electrical circuit when a current of one ampere flows for one second.

Coulomb's law Law that represents the force of attraction between two charged particles; $F = k(q_1q_2/d^2)$.

covalent bond Interatomic attraction resulting from the sharing of electrons between two atoms.

critical mass The minimum quantity of fissionable material needed to support a self-sustaining chain reaction.

critical pressure The vapor pressure of a liquid at its critical temperature.

critical temperature The temperature above which there is no distinction between liquid and vapor phases.

cryogens Liquefied gases that have temperatures below −150 °C.

crystal-field splitting energy Energy difference between sets of *d* orbitals on the central metal ion in a coordination compound.

crystal-field theory Theory that predicts spectra and magnetism of coordination compounds based on electrostatic bonding between ligands and a metal ion.

crystal lattice The ordered, repeating arrangement of ions, molecules, or atoms in a crystalline solid.

crystalline solids Solids with an ordered arrangement of atoms, molecules, or ions that results in planar faces and sharp angles of the crystals.

crystallization The process in which mobile atoms, molecules, or ions in a liquid or solution convert into a crystalline solid.

cubic close packing The three-dimensional structure that results when atoms or ions are closest packed in the *abcabc* arrangement.

cubic unit cell A unit cell with equal-length edges that meet at 90° angles.

curie (Ci) A unit of radioactivity equal to 3.7×10^{10} disintegrations per second.

Dalton's law of partial pressures The total pressure exerted by a mixture of gases is the sum of the partial pressures of the individual gases in the mixture.

decomposition reaction A reaction in which a compound breaks down chemically to form two or more simpler substances.

degree of polymerization Number of repeating units in a polymer chain.

delocalized electrons Electrons, such as in benzene, that are spread over several atoms in a molecule or polyatomic ion.

denaturation Disruption in protein secondary and tertiary structure brought on by high temperature, heavy metals, and other substances.

density The ratio of the mass of an object to its volume.

deoxyribonucleic acid (DNA) A double-stranded polymer of nucleotides that stores genetic information.

deposition The process of a gas converting directly to a solid.

detergent(s) Molecules whose structure contains a long hydrocarbon portion that is hydrophobic and a polar end that is hydrophilic.

dew point Temperature at which the actual partial pressure of water vapor equals the equilibrium vapor pressure.

diamagnetic Describes atoms or ions in which all the electrons are paired in filled shells so their magnetic fields effectively cancel each other.

diatomic molecule A molecule that contains two atoms.

dietary minerals Essential elements that are not carbon, hydrogen, oxygen, or nitrogen.

diffusion Spread of gas molecules of one type through those of another type.

dimensional analysis A method of using units in calculations to check for correctness.

dimer A molecule made from two smaller units.

dipole moment The product of the magnitude of the partial charges ($\delta+$ and $\delta-$) of a molecule times the distance of separation between the charges.

dipole-dipole attraction The noncovalent force of attraction between any two polar molecules or polar regions in the same large molecule.

disaccharides Carbohydrates such as sucrose consisting of two monosaccharide units.

dispersed phase The larger-than-molecule-sized particles that are distributed uniformly throughout a colloid.

displacement reaction A reaction in which one element reacts with a compound to form a new compound and release a different element.

doping Adding a tiny concentration of one substance (a *dopant*) to improve the semiconducting properties of another.

double bond A bond formed by sharing two pairs of electrons between the same two atoms.

dynamic equilibrium A balance between opposing reactions occurring at equal rates.

effective nuclear charge The nuclear positive charge experienced by outer-shell electrons in a many-electron atom.

effusion Escape of gas molecules from a container through a tiny hole into a vacuum.

electrochemical cell A combination of anode, cathode, and other materials arranged so that a product-favored oxidation-reduction reaction can cause a current to flow or an electric current can cause a reactant-favored redox reaction to occur.

electrochemistry The study of the relationship between electron flow and oxidation-reduction reactions.

electrode A device such as a metal plate or wire that conducts electrons into and out of a system.

electrolysis The use of electrical energy to produce a chemical change.

electrolyte A substance that ionizes or dissociates when dissolved in water to form an electrically conducting solution.

electromagnetic radiation Radiation that consists of oscillating electric and magnetic fields that travel through space at the same rate (the speed of light: 186,000 miles/s or 10^8 m/s in a vacuum).

electromotive force (emf) The difference in electrical potential energy between the two electrodes in an electrochemical cell, measured in volts.

electron A negatively charged subatomic particle that occupies most of the volume of an atom.

electron affinity The energy change when a mole of electrons is added to a mole of atoms in the gas phase.

electron capture A radioactive decay process in which one of an atom's inner-shell electrons is captured by the nucleus, which decreases the atomic number by 1.

electron configuration The complete description of the orbitals occupied by all the electrons in an atom or ion.

electron density The probability of finding an electron within a tiny volume in an atom; determined by the square of the wave function.

electron-pair geometry The geometry around a central atom including the spatial positions of bonding and lone electron pairs.

electronegativity A measure of the ability of an atom in a molecule to attract bonding electrons to itself.

electronically excited molecule A molecule whose potential energy is greater than the minimum (ground-state) energy because of a change in its electronic structure.

element (chemical element) A substance (e.g., carbon, hydrogen, and oxygen) that cannot be decomposed into two or more new substances by chemical or physical means.

elementary reaction A nanoscale reaction whose equation indicates exactly which atoms, ions, or molecules collide or change as the reaction occurs.

empirical formula A formula showing the simplest possible ratio of atoms of elements in a compound.

emulsion A colloid consisting of a liquid dispersed in a second liquid; formed by the presence of an *emulsifier* that coats and stabilizes dispersed-phase particles.

enantiomers A pair of molecules consisting of a chiral molecule and its mirror-image isomer.

end point The point at which the indicator changes color during a titration.

endergonic Refers to a reaction that requires input of Gibbs free energy; applies to biochemical reactions that are reactant-favored at body temperature.

endothermic (process) A process in which thermal energy must be transferred into a thermodynamic system in order to maintain constant temperature.

energy The capacity to do work.

energy band In a solid, a large group of orbitals whose energies are closely spaced; in an atomic solid the average energy of a band equals the energy of the corresponding orbital in an individual atom.

energy conservation The conservation of useful energy, that is, of Gibbs free energy.

energy density The quantity of energy released per unit volume of a fuel.

enthalpy change (ΔH) The quantity of thermal energy transferred when a process takes place at constant temperature and pressure.

enthalpy of fusion The enthalpy change when a substance melts; the quantity of energy that must be transferred when a substance melts at constant temperature and pressure.

enthalpy of solution The quantity of thermal energy transferred when a solution is formed at constant T and P.

enthalpy of sublimation The enthalpy change when a solid sublimes; the quantity of energy, at constant pressure, that must be transferred to cause a solid to vaporize.

enthalpy of vaporization The enthalpy change when a substance vaporizes: the quantity of energy that must be transferred when a liquid vaporizes at constant temperature and pressure.

entropy A measure of the number of ways energy can be distributed in a system; a measure of the dispersal of energy in a system.

enzyme A highly efficient biochemical catalyst for one or more reactions in a living system.

enzyme-substrate complex The combination formed by the binding of an enzyme with a substrate through noncovalent forces.

equatorial position Position lying on the equator of an imaginary sphere around a triangular bipyramidal molecular or ionic structure.

equilibrium concentration The concentration of a substance (usually expressed as molarity) in a system that has reached the equilibrium state.

equilibrium constant (K) A quotient of equilibrium concentrations of product and reactant substances that has a constant value for a given reaction at a given temperature.

equilibrium constant expression The mathematical expression associated with an equilibrium constant.

equilibrium vapor pressure Pressure of the vapor of a substance in equilibrium with its liquid or solid in a closed container.

equivalence point The point in a titration at which a stoichiometrically equivalent amount of one substance has been added to another substance.

ester An organic compound formed by the reaction of an alcohol and a carboxylic acid.

evaporation The process of conversion of a liquid to a gas.

exchange reaction A reaction in which cations and anions that were partners in the reactants are interchanged in the products.

excited state The unstable state of an atom or molecule in which at least one electron does not have its lowest possible energy.

exergonic Refers to a reaction that releases Gibbs free energy; applies to biochemical reactions that are product-favored at body temperature.

exothermic Refers to a process in which thermal energy must be transferred out of a thermodynamic system in order to maintain constant temperature.

extent of reaction The fraction of reactants that has been converted to products.

Faraday constant (F) The quantity of electric charge on one mole of electrons, 9.6485×10^4 C/mol.

fat A solid triester of fatty acids with glycerol.

ferromagnetic A substance that contains clusters of atoms with unpaired electrons whose magnetic spins become aligned, causing permanent magnetism.

first law of thermodynamics (law of conservation of energy) Energy can neither be created nor destroyed—the total energy of the universe is constant.

formal charge The charge a bonded atom would have if its electrons were shared equally.

formation constant (K_f) The equilibrium constant for the formation of a complex ion.

formula (chemical formula) A notation combining element symbols and numerical subscripts that shows the relative numbers of each kind of atom in a molecule or formula unit of a substance.

formula unit The simplest cation-anion grouping represented by the formula of an ionic compound; also the collection of atoms represented by any formula.

formula weight The sum of the atomic weights in amu of all the atoms in a compound's formula.

fractional distillation The process of refining petroleum (or another mixture) by distillation to separate it into groups (fractions) of compounds having distinctive boiling point ranges.

Frasch process Process for recovering sulfur from underground deposits by melting the sulfur with superheated water.

free radical An atom, ion, or molecule that contains one or more unpaired electrons; usually highly reactive.

freezing-point lowering A colligative property; the difference between the freezing point of a pure solvent and the freezing point of a solution in which a nonvolatile nonelectrolyte solute is dissolved in the solvent.

frequency The number of complete traveling waves passing a point in a given period of time (cycles per second).

frequency factor The factor (A) in the Arrhenius equation that depends on how often molecules collide when all concentrations are 1 mol/L and on whether the molecules are properly oriented to react when they collide.

fuel cell An electrochemical cell that converts the chemical energy of fuels directly into electricity.

fuel value The quantity of energy released when 1 g of a fuel is burned.

fullerenes Allotropic forms of carbon that consist of many five- and six-membered rings of carbon atoms sharing edges.

functional group An atom or group of atoms that imparts characteristic properties and defines a given class of organic compounds (e.g., the —OH group is present in all alcohols).

galvanized Has a thin coating of zinc metal that forms an oxide coating impervious to oxygen, thereby protecting a less active metal, such as iron, from corrosion.

gamma radiation Radiation composed of highly energetic photons.

gas A phase or state of matter in which a substance has no definite shape and has a volume determined by the volume of its container.

gasohol A blended motor fuel consisting of 90% gasoline and 10% ethanol.

gene The unique sequence of nitrogen bases in DNA that codes for the synthesis of a specific protein; carrier of a genetic trait.

Gibbs free energy A thermodynamic function that decreases for any product-favored system. For a process at constant temperature and pressure, $\Delta G = \Delta H - T\Delta S$.

glass Amorphous, clear solids formed from silicates and other oxides.

global warming Increase in temperature at earth's surface as a result of the greenhouse effect amplified by increasing concentrations of carbon dioxide and other greenhouse gases.

glycogen A highly branched, high-molar-mass polymer of glucose found in animals.

glycosidic linkage The C—O—C bond that connects monosaccharides in disaccharides and polysaccharides; forms between carbons 1 and 4 or 1 and 6 of linked monosaccharides.

gram(s) The basic unit of mass in the metric system; equal to 1×10^{-3} kg.

gray The SI unit of absorbed radiation dose equal to the absorption of 1 joule per kilogram of material.

greenhouse effect Atmospheric warming caused when atmospheric carbon dioxide, water vapor, methane, ozone, and other greenhouse gases absorb infrared radiation reradiated from earth.

ground state The state of an atom or molecule in which all of the electrons are in their lowest possible energy levels.

groups The vertical columns of the periodic table of the elements.

Haber-Bosch process The process developed by Fritz Haber and Carl Bosch for the direct synthesis of ammonia from its elements.

half-cell One half of an electrochemical cell in which only the anode or cathode is located.

half-life, $t_{1/2}$ The time required for the concentration of one reactant to reach half its original value; radioactivity—the time required for the activity of a radioactive sample to reach half of its original value.

half-reaction A reaction that represents either an oxidation or a reduction process.

halide ion A monatomic ion (1−) of a halogen.

halogens The elements in Group 7A of the periodic table.

heat (heating) The energy-transfer process between two samples of matter at different temperatures.

heat capacity The quantity of energy that must be transferred to an object to raise its temperature by 1 °C.

heat of See **enthalpy of.**

heating curve A plot of the temperature of a substance versus the quantity of energy transferred to it by heating.

helium burning The fusion of helium nuclei to form beryllium-8, as it occurs in stars.

Henderson-Hasselbalch equation The equation describing the relationships among the pH of a buffer solution, the pK_a of the acid, and the concentrations of the acid and its conjugate base.

Henry's law A mathematical expression for the relationship of gas pressure and solubility; $S_g = k_H P_g$.

Hess's law If two or more chemical equations can be combined to give another equation, the enthalpy change for that equation will be the sum of the enthalpy changes for the equations that were combined.

heterogeneous catalyst A catalyst that is in a different phase from that of the reaction mixture.

heterogeneous mixture A mixture in which components remain separate and can be observed as individual substances or phases.

heterogeneous reaction A reaction that takes place at an interface between two phases, solid and gas for example.

hexadentate A ligand in which each of six different atoms donates an electron pair to a coordinated central metal ion.

hexagonal close packing The three-dimensional structure that results when layers of atoms in a solid are closest packed in the *ababab* arrangement.

high-spin complex A complex ion that has the maximum possible number of unpaired electrons.

homogeneous catalyst A catalyst that is in the same phase as that of the reaction mixture.

homogeneous mixture A mixture of two or more substances in a single phase that is uniform throughout.

homogeneous reaction A reaction in which the reactants and products are all in the same phase.

Hund's rule Electrons pair only after each orbital in a subshell is occupied by a single electron.

hybrid orbitals Orbitals formed by combining atomic orbitals of appropriate energy and orientation.

hybridized Refers to atomic orbitals of proper energy and orientation that have combined to form hybrid orbitals.

hydrate A solid compound that has a stoichiometric amount of water molecules bonded to metal ions or trapped within its crystal lattice.

hydration The binding of one or more water molecules to an ion or molecule within a solution or within a crystal lattice.

hydrocarbon An organic compound composed only of carbon and hydrogen.

hydrogen bond Noncovalent interaction between a hydrogen atom and a very electronegative atom to produce an unusually strong dipole-dipole force.

hydrogen burning The fusion of hydrogen nuclei (protons) to form helium, as it occurs in stars.

hydrogenation An addition reaction in which hydrogen adds to the double bond of an alkene; the catalyzed reaction of H_2 with a liquid triglyceride to produce saturated fatty acid chains, which convert the triglyceride into a semisolid or solid.

hydrolysis A reaction in which a bond is broken by reaction with a water molecule and the —H and —OH of the water add to the atoms of the broken bond.

hydronium ion H_3O^+; the simplest proton-water complex; responsible for acidity.

hydrophilic "Water-loving," a term describing a polar molecule or part of a molecule that is strongly attracted to water molecules.

hydrophobic "Water-fearing," a term describing a nonpolar molecule or part of a molecule that is not attracted to water molecules.

hydroxide ion OH^- ion; bases increase the concentration of hydroxide ions in solution.

hypertonic Refers to a solution having a higher concentration of nanoscale particles and therefore a higher osmotic pressure than another solution.

hypothesis A tentative explanation for an observation and a basis for experimentation.

hypotonic Refers to a solution having a lower solute concentration of nanoscale particles and therefore a lower osmotic pressure than another solution.

ideal gas A gas that behaves exactly as described by the ideal gas law, and by Boyle's, Charles's, and Avogadro's laws.

ideal gas constant The proportionality constant, *R*, in the equation $PV = nRT$; $R = 0.0821\ \text{L atm mol}^{-1}\ \text{K}^{-1} = 8.314\ \text{J K}^{-1}\ \text{mol}^{-1}$.

ideal gas law A law that relates pressure, volume, amount (moles), and temperature for an ideal gas; the relationship expressed by the equation $PV = nRT$.

immiscible Describes two liquids that form two separate phases when mixed because each is only slightly soluble in the other.

induced dipole A temporary dipole created by a momentary uneven distribution of electrons in a molecule or atom.

induced fit The change in the shape of an enzyme, its substrate, or both when they bind.

inhibitor A molecule or ion other than the substrate that causes a decrease in catalytic activity of an enzyme.

initial rate The instantaneous rate of a reaction determined at the very beginning of the reaction.

initiation The breaking of a carbon-carbon double bond in a polymerization reaction to produce a molecule with highly reactive sites that react with other molecules to produce a polymer; first step in a chain reaction.

inorganic compound A chemical compound that is not an organic compound; usually of mineral or nonbiological origin.

insoluble Describes a solute, almost none of which dissolves in a solvent.

instantaneous reaction rate The rate at a particular time after a reaction has begun.

insulator A material that has a large energy gap between fully occupied and empty energy bands, and does not conduct electricity.

intermolecular forces Noncovalent attractions between separate molecules.

internal energy The sum of the individual energies (kinetic and potential) of all of the nanoscale particles (atoms, molecules, or ions) in a sample of matter.

ion An atom or group of atoms that has lost or gained one or more electrons so that it is no longer electrically neutral.

ion product (*Q*) A value found from an expression with the same mathematical form as the solubility product expression (K_{sp}) but using the actual concentrations rather than equilibrium concentrations of the species involved. (See **reaction quotient.**)

ionic compound A compound that consists of positive and negative ions (cations and anions).

ionic hydrate Ionic compounds that incorporate water molecules in the ionic crystal lattice.

ionic radius Radius of an anion or cation in an ionic compound.

ionization constant for water (K_w) The equilibrium constant that is the mathematical product of the hydronium ion concentration and the concentration of hydroxide ion in any aqueous solution; $K_w = 1 \times 10^{-14}$ at 25 °C.

ionization energy The energy needed to remove a mole of electrons from a mole of atoms in the gas phase.

isoelectronic Refers to atoms and ions that have identical electron configurations.

isomers Compounds that have the same molecular formula but different arrangements of atoms.

isotonic Refers to a solution having the same concentration of nanoscale particles and therefore the same osmotic pressure as another solution.

isotopes Forms of an element composed of atoms with the same atomic number but different mass numbers owing to a difference in the number of neutrons.

joule (J) A unit of energy equal to 1 kg m^2/s^2. The kinetic energy of a 2-kg object traveling at a speed of 1 m/s.

Kelvin temperature scale (See also **absolute temperature scale.**) A temperature scale on which the zero is the lowest possible temperature and the degree is the same size as a Celsius degree.

ketone An organic compound characterized by the presence of a carbonyl group in which the carbon atom is bonded to two other carbon atoms ($R_2C{=}O$).

kilocalorie (kcal or Cal) (See also **calorie.**) A unit of energy equal to 4.184 kJ. Approximately 1 kcal (1 Cal) is required to raise the temperature of 1 kg of liquid water by 1 °C. The food Calorie.

kinetic energy Energy that an object has because of its motion. Equal to $\frac{1}{2}mv^2$, where m is the object's mass and v is its velocity.

kinetic-molecular theory The theory that matter consists of nanoscale particles that are in constant, random motion.

lanthanide contraction The decrease in atomic radii across the fourth-period and the fifth-period *f*-block elements (lanthanides and actinides) due to the lack of electron screening by electrons in the 4*f* and 5*f* orbitals.

lanthanides The elements after lanthanum in the sixth period in which the 4*f* subshell is being filled.

lattice energy Enthalpy of formation of 1 mol of an ionic solid from its separated gaseous ions.

law A statement that summarizes a wide range of experimental results and has not been contradicted by experiments.

law of chemical periodicity Law stating that the properties of the elements are periodic functions of atomic number.

law of combining volumes At constant temperature and pressure, the volumes of reacting gases are always in the ratios of small whole numbers.

law of conservation of energy (first law of thermodynamics) Law stating that energy can be neither created nor destroyed—the total energy of the universe is constant.

law of conservation of mass Law stating that there is no detectable change in mass in an ordinary chemical reaction.

law of constant composition Law stating that a chemical compound always contains the same elements in the same proportions by mass.

law of multiple proportions When two elements A and B can combine in two or more ways, the mass ratio A : B in one compound is a small-whole-number multiple of the mass ratio A : B in the other compound.

Le Chatelier's principle If a system is at equilibrium and the conditions are changed so that it is no longer at equilibrium, the system will react to give a new equilibrium in a way that partially counteracts the change.

Lewis acid A molecule or ion that can accept an electron pair from another atom, molecule, or ion to form a new bond.

Lewis base A molecule or ion that can donate an electron pair to another atom, molecule, or ion to form a new bond.

Lewis structure Structural formula for a molecule that shows all valence electrons as dots or as lines that represent covalent bonds.

Lewis dot symbol An atomic symbol with dots representing valence electrons.

ligands Atoms, molecules, or ions bonded to a central atom, such as the central metal ion in a coordination complex.

limiting reactant The reactant present in limited supply that controls the amount of product formed in a reaction.

line emission spectrum A spectrum produced by excited atoms and consisting of discrete wavelengths of light.

linear Molecular geometry in which there is a angle between bonded atoms.

lipid bilayer The structure of cell membranes that are composed of two aligned layers of phospholipids with their hydrophobic regions within the bilayer.

liquid A phase of matter in which a substance has no definite shape but a definite volume.

London forces Forces resulting from the attraction between positive and negative regions of momentary (induced) dipoles in neighboring molecules.

lone-pair electrons Paired valence electrons unused in bond formation; also called nonbonding pairs.

low-spin complex A complex ion that has the minimum possible number of unpaired electrons.

major minerals Dietary minerals present in humans in quantities greater than 100 mg per kg of body weight.

macromolecule A very large polymer molecule made by chemically joining many small molecules (monomers).

macroscale Refers to samples of matter that can be observed by the unaided human senses; samples of matter large enough to be seen, measured, and handled.

main-group elements Elements in the eight A groups to the left and right of the transition elements in the periodic table; the *s*- and *p*-block elements.

mass A measure of an object's resistance to acceleration.

mass fraction The ratio of the mass of one component to the total mass of a sample.

mass number The number of protons plus neutrons in the nucleus of an atom of an element.

mass percent The mass fraction multiplied by 100%.

mass spectrometer An analytical instrument used to measure atomic and molecular masses directly.

mass spectrum A plot of ion abundance versus the mass of the ions; produced by a mass spectrometer.

materials science The science of the relationships between the structure and the chemical and physical properties of materials.

matter Anything that has mass and occupies space.

melting point The temperature at which the structure of a solid collapses and the solid changes to a liquid.

meniscus A concave or convex surface that forms on a liquid as a result of the balance of noncovalent forces in a narrow container.

metabolism All of the chemical reactions that occur as an organism converts food nutrients into constituents of living cells, to stored Gibbs free energy, or to thermal energy.

metal An element that is malleable, ductile, forms alloys, and conducts an electric current.

metal activity series A ranking of relative reactivity of metals in displacement and other kinds of reactions.

metallic bonding In solid metals, the nondirectional attraction between positive metal ions and the surrounding sea of negatively charged electrons.

metalloid An element that has some typically metallic properties and other properties that are more characteristic of nonmetals.

methyl group A $-CH_3$ group.

metric system A decimalized measurement system.

micelles Colloid-sized particles built up from many surfactant molecules; micelles can transport various materials within them.

microscale Refers to samples of matter so small that they have to be viewed with a microscope.

millimeters of mercury (mm Hg) A unit of pressure related to the height of a column of mercury in a mercury barometer (760 mm Hg = 1 atm = 101.3 kPa).

mineral A naturally occurring inorganic compound with a characteristic composition and crystal structure.

miscible Describes two liquids that will dissolve in each other in any proportion.

model A mechanical or mathematical way to make a theory more concrete, such as a molecular model.

molality (*m*) A concentration term equal to the molar amount of solute per kilogram of solvent.

molar amount See **amount.**

molar enthalpy of fusion The energy transfer required to melt 1 mol of a pure solid.

molar heat capacity The quantity of energy that must be transferred to 1 mol of a substance to increase its temperature by 1 °C.

molar mass The mass in grams of 1 mol of atoms, molecules, or formula units of one kind, numerically equal to the atomic or molecular weight in amu.

molar solubility The solubility of a solute in a solvent, expressed in moles per liter.

molarity Solute concentration expressed as the molar amount of solute per liter of solution.

mole (mol) The amount of substance that contains as many elementary particles as there are atoms in exactly 0.012 kg of carbon-12 isotope.

mole fraction (X) The ratio of number of moles of one component to the total number of moles in a mixture of substances.

mole ratio (stoichiometric factor) A mole-to-mole ratio relating the molar amount of a reactant or product to the molar amount of another reactant or product.

molecular compound A compound composed of atoms of two or more elements chemically combined in molecules.

molecular formula A formula that expresses the number of atoms of each type within one molecule of a substance.

molecular geometry The three-dimensional arrangement of atoms in a molecule.

molecular orbitals Orbitals extending over an entire molecule generated by combining atomic orbitals.

molecular weight The sum of the atomic weights of all the atoms in a substance's formula.

molecule The smallest particle of an element or compound that exists independently, and retains the chemical properties of that element or compound.

momentum The product of the mass (m) times the velocity (v) of an object in motion.

monatomic ion An ion consisting of one atom bearing an electrical charge.

monodentate ligand A ligand that donates one electron pair to a coordinated metal ion.

monomer The small repeating unit from which a polymer is formed.

monoprotic acid An acid that can donate a single hydrogen ion per molecule.

monosaccharides The simplest carbohydrates, composed of one saccharide unit.

monounsaturated fatty acid Refers to fatty acids, such as oleic acid, that contain only one carbon-carbon double bond.

mortar A mixture of cement, sand, and lime that reacts with water and carbon dioxide to form a rock-hard solid.

multiple covalent bonds Double or triple covalent bonds.

multiple proportions, law of When two elements A and B can combine in two or more ways, the mass ratio A : B in one compound is a small-whole-number multiple of the mass ratio A : B in the other compound.

***n*-type semiconductor** A material made by doping a semiconductor with an impurity that leaves extra valence electrons.

nanoscale Refers to samples of matter (e.g., atoms and molecules) whose normal dimensions are in the 1–100 nanometer range.

nanotubes Members of the family of fullerenes in which graphite-like layers of carbon atoms form cylindrical shapes.

Nernst equation The equation relating the potential of an electrochemical cell to the concentrations of the chemical species involved in the oxidation-reduction reactions occurring in the cell.

net ionic equation A chemical equation in which only those molecules or ions undergoing chemical changes in the course of the reaction are represented.

network solid A solid consisting of one huge molecule in which all atoms are connected via a network of covalent bonds.

neurons Specialized cells that are part of animals' nervous systems and that function according to electrochemical principles.

neutral solution A solution containing equal concentrations of H_3O^+ and OH^-; a solution that is neither acidic nor basic.

neutron An electrically neutral subatomic particle found in the nucleus.

newton (N) The SI unit of force; equal to 1 kg times an acceleration of 1 m/s^2; 1 kg m/s^2.

nitrogen cycle The natural cycle of chemical transformations involving nitrogen and its compounds.

nitrogen fixation The conversion of atmospheric nitrogen (N_2) to nitrogen compounds utilizable by plants or industry.

noble gas notation An abbreviated electron configuration of an element in which filled inner shells are represented by the symbol of the preceding noble gas in brackets. For Al, this would be [Ne]$3s^23p^1$.

noble gases Gaseous elements in Group 8A; the least reactive elements.

nonbiodegradable Not capable of being decomposed by microorganisms.

noncovalent interactions All forces of attraction other than covalent, ionic, or metallic bonding.

nonelectrolyte A substance that dissolves in water to form a solution that does not conduct electricity.

nonmetal Element that does not have the chemical and physical properties of a metal.

nonpolar covalent bond A bond in which the electron pair is shared equally by the bonded atoms.

nonpolar molecule A molecule that is not polar either because it has no polar bonds or because its polar bonds are oriented symmetrically so that they cancel each other.

NO_x Oxides of nitrogen.

normal boiling point The temperature at which the vapor pressure of a liquid equals 1 atm.

nuclear burning The nuclear fusion reactions by which elements are formed in stars.

nuclear decay Spontaneous emission of radioactivity by an unstable nucleus that is converted into a more stable nucleus.

nuclear fission The highly exothermic process by which very heavy fissionable nuclei split to form lighter nuclei.

nuclear fusion The highly exothermic process by which very light nuclei combine to form heavier nuclei.

nuclear magnetic resonance The process in which the nuclear spins of atoms align in a magnetic field and absorb radio frequency photons to become excited. These excited atoms then return to a lower energy state when they emit the absorbed radio frequency photons.

nuclear medicine The use of radioisotopes in medical diagnosis and therapy.

nuclear reaction A process in which one or more atomic nuclei change into one or more different nuclei.

nuclear (atomic) reactor A container in which a controlled nuclear reaction takes place.

nucleon A nuclear particle, either a neutron or a proton.

nucleotide Repeating unit in DNA, composed of one sugar unit, one phosphate group, and one cyclic nitrogen base.

nucleus (atomic) The tiny central core of an atom; contains protons and neutrons. (There are no neutrons in hydrogen-1.)

nutrients The chemical raw materials, eaten as food, that are needed for survival of an organism.

octahedral Molecular geometry of six groups around a central atom in which all groups are at angles of 90° to other groups.

octane number A measure of the ability of a gasoline to burn smoothly in an internal-combustion engine.

octet rule In forming bonds, many main group elements gain, lose, or share electrons to achieve a stable electron configuration characterized by eight valence electrons.

optical fiber A fiber made of glass constructed so that light can pass through it with little loss of intensity; used for transmission of information.

orbital A region of an atom or molecule within which there is a significant probability that an electron will be found.

orbital shape The shape of an electron density distribution determined by an orbital.

order of reaction The reaction rate dependency on the concentration of a reactant or product, expressed as an exponent of a concentration term in the rate equation.

ores Minerals containing a sufficiently high concentration of an element to make its extraction profitable.

organic compound A compound of carbon with hydrogen, possibly also oxygen, nitrogen, sulfur, phosphorus, or other elements.

osmosis The movement of a solvent (water) through a semipermeable membrane from a region of lower solute concentration to a region of higher solute concentration.

osmotic pressure (Π) The pressure that must be applied to a solution to stop osmosis from a sample of pure solvent.

overall reaction order The sum of the exponents for all concentration terms in the rate equation.

oxidation The loss of electrons by an atom, ion, or molecule, leading to an increase in oxidation number.

oxidation number (oxidation state) The hypothetical charge an atom would have if all bonds to that atom were completely ionic.
oxidation-reduction reaction (redox reaction) A reaction involving the transfer of one or more electrons from one species to another so that oxidation numbers change.
oxides Compounds of oxygen combined with another element.
oxidized The result when an atom, molecule, or ion loses one or more electrons.
oxidizing agent The substance that accepts electron(s) and is reduced in an oxidation-reduction reaction.
oxoacids Acids in which the acidic hydrogen is bonded directly to an oxygen atom.
oxoanion A polyatomic anion that contains oxygen.
oxygenated gasolines Blends of gasoline with oxygen-containing organic compounds such as methanol, ethanol, and *tertiary*-butyl alcohol.
ozone hole Regions of ozone depletion in the stratosphere centered on the earth's poles, most significantly the South Pole.
ozone layer Region of maximum ozone concentration in the stratosphere.

***p*-block elements** Main-group elements in Groups 3A through 8A whose valence electrons consist of outermost *s* and *p* electrons.
***p-n* junction** An interface between *p*-type and *n*-type semiconductors that produces a rectifier that allows current to flow in only one direction.
***p*-type semiconductor** A material made by doping a semiconductor with an impurity that leaves a deficiency of valence electrons.
paramagnetic Refers to atoms, molecules, or ions that are attracted to a magnetic field because they have unpaired electrons in incompletely filled electron subshells.
partial hydrogenation Addition of hydrogen to some of the carbon-carbon double bonds in a triglyceride (a fat or oil).
partial pressure The pressure that one gas in a mixture of gases would exert if it occupied the same volume at the same temperature as the mixture.
particulate Atmospheric solid particles, generally larger than 10,000 nm in diameter.
parts per billion (ppb) One part in one billion (10^9) parts.
parts per million (ppm) One part in one million (10^6) parts.
parts per trillion (ppt) One part in one trillion (10^{12}) parts.
pascal (Pa) The SI unit of pressure; 1 Pa = 1 N/m^2.
Pauli exclusion principle An atomic principle that states that, at most, two electrons can be assigned to the same orbital in the same atom or molecule, and these two electrons must have opposite spins.
peptide linkage The amide linkage between two amino acid molecules; found in proteins.
percent abundance The percentage of atoms of a particular isotope in a natural sample of a pure element.
percent composition by mass The percentage of the mass of a compound represented by each of its constituent elements.
percent yield The ratio of actual yield to theoretical yield, multiplied by 100%.
periodic table A table of elements arranged in order of increasing atomic number so that those with similar chemical and physical properties fall in the same vertical groups.
periods The horizontal rows of the periodic table of the elements.
petroleum fractions The mixtures of hundreds of hydrocarbons in the same boiling point range obtained from the fractional distillation of petroleum.
pH The negative logarithm of the hydronium ion concentration ($-\log [H_3O^+]$).
pH meter An instrument for measuring pH of solutions using electrochemical principles.
phase Any of the three states of matter: gas, liquid, solid. Also, one of two or more solid-state structures of the same substance, such as iron in a body-centered cubic or face-centered cubic structure.
phase change A physical process in which one state or phase of matter is changed into another (such as melting a solid to form a liquid).
phase diagram A diagram showing the relationships among the phases of a substance (solid, liquid, and gas), at different temperatures and pressures.
phospholipid Glycerol derivative with two long, nonpolar fatty-acid chains and a polar phosphate group; present in cell membranes.
photochemical reactions Chemical reactions that take place as a result of absorption of photons by reactant molecules.
photochemical smog Smog produced by strong oxidizing agents, such as ozone and oxides of nitrogen, NO_x, that undergo light-initiated reactions with hydrocarbons.
photodissociation Splitting of a molecule into two free radicals by absorption of an ultraviolet photon.
photoelectric effect The emission of electrons by some metals when illuminated by light of certain wavelengths.
photon A massless particle of light whose energy is given by $h\nu$, where ν is the frequency of the light and h is Planck's constant.
photosynthesis A series of reactions in a green plant that combines carbon dioxide with water to form carbohydrate and oxygen.
phototrophs (See also **chemotrophs.**) Organisms that can carry out photosynthesis and therefore can use sunlight to supply their Gibbs free energy needs.
physical changes Changes in the physical properties of a substance, such as the transformation of a solid to a liquid.
physical properties Properties (e.g., melting point or density) that can be observed and measured without changing the composition of a substance.
pi (π) bond A bond formed by the sideways overlap of parallel *p* orbitals.
Planck's constant The proportionality constant, h, that relates energy of a photon to its frequency. The value of h is 6.626×10^{-34} J · s.
plasma A state of matter consisting of unbound nuclei and electrons.
plastic A polymeric material that has a soft or liquid state in which it can be molded or otherwise shaped. See also **thermoplastic** and **thermosetting plastic.**
polar covalent bond A covalent bond between atoms with different electronegativities; bonding electrons are shared unequally between the atoms.
polar molecule A molecule that is polar because it has polar bonds arranged so that electron density is concentrated at one end of the molecule.
polarization The induction of a temporary dipole in a molecule or atom by shifting of electron distribution.
polluted water Water that is unsuitable for an intended use, such as drinking, washing, irrigation, or industrial use.
polyamides Polymers in which the monomer units are connected by amide bonds.
polyatomic ion An ion consisting of more than one atom.
polydentate ligand Refers to ligands that can form two or more coordinate covalent bonds to the same metal ion.
polyester A polymer in which the monomer units are connected by ester bonds.
polymer A large molecule composed of many smaller repeating units, usually arranged in a chain-like structure.
polypeptide A polymer composed of 20–50 amino acid residues joined by peptide linkages (amide linkages).
polyprotic acids Acids that can donate more than one hydrogen ion per molecule.
polysaccharides Carbohydrates that consist of many monosaccharide units.
polyunsaturated acid A carboxylic acid containing two or more carbon-carbon double bonds; commonly refers to a fatty acid.
positron A nuclear particle having the same mass as an electron, but a positive charge.
potential energy Energy that an object has because of its position.
precipitate An insoluble product of an exchange reaction in aqueous solution.
pressure The force exerted on an object divided by the area over which the force is exerted.
primary battery A voltaic cell (or battery of cells) in which the oxidation and reduction half-reactions cannot easily be reversed to restore the cell to its original state.
primary pollutants Pollutants that enter the environment directly from their sources.

primary structure of proteins The sequence of amino acids along the polymer chain in a protein molecule.

principal energy level An energy level containing orbitals with the same quantum number ($n = 1, 2, 3 \ldots$).

principal quantum number An integer assigned to each of the allowed main electron energy levels in an atom.

product A substance formed as a result of a chemical reaction.

product-favored system A system in which, when a reaction appears to be over, products predominate over reactants.

proportionality factor (conversion factor) A relationship between two measurement units derived from the proportionality of one quantity to another; e.g., density is the conversion factor between mass and volume.

proton A positively charged subatomic particle found in the nucleus.

pyrometallurgy The extraction of a metal from its ore using chemical reactions carried out at high temperatures.

qualitative In observations, nonnumerical experimental information, such as a description of color or texture.

quantitative Numerical information, such as the mass or volume of a substance, expressed in appropriate units.

quantum The smallest possible unit of a distinct quantity; for example, the smallest possible unit of energy for electromagnetic radiation of a given frequency.

quantum theory The theory that energy comes in very small packets (quanta); this is analogous to matter occurring in very small particles—atoms.

racemic mixture A mixture of equal amounts of enantiomers of a chiral compound.

rad A unit of radioactivity; a measure of the energy of radiation absorbed by a substance, 1.00×10^{-2} J per kilogram.

radial distribution plot A graph showing the probability of finding an electron as a function of distance from the nucleus of an atom.

radioactive series A series of nuclear reactions in which a radioactive isotope undergoes successive nuclear transformations resulting ultimately in a stable, nonradioactive isotope.

radioactivity The spontaneous emission of energy and/or subatomic particles by unstable atomic nuclei; the energy or particles so emitted.

Raoult's law A mathematical expression for the vapor pressure of the solvent in a solution; $P_1 = X_1P_1^0$.

rate The change in some measurable quantity per unit time.

rate constant (*k*) A proportionality constant relating reaction rate and concentrations of reactants and other species that affect the rate of a specific reaction.

rate law (rate equation) A mathematical equation that summarizes the relationship between concentrations and reaction rate.

rate-limiting step The slowest step in a reaction mechanism.

reactant A substance that is initially present and undergoes change in a chemical reaction.

reactant-favored system A system in which, when a reaction appears to be over, reactants predominate over products.

reaction intermediate An atom, molecule, or ion produced in one step and used in a later step in a reaction mechanism; does not appear in the equation for the overall reaction.

reaction mechanism A sequence of unimolecular and bimolecular elementary reactions by which an overall reaction may occur.

reaction quotient (*Q*) A value found from an expression with the same mathematical form as the equilibrium constant expression but with the actual concentrations in a mixture not at equilibrium.

reaction rate The change in concentration of a reactant or product per unit time.

redox reaction (oxidation-reduction reaction) A reaction involving the transfer of one or more electrons from one species to another so that oxidation numbers change.

reduced The result when an atom, molecule, or ion gains one or more electrons.

reducing agent The atom, molecule, or ion that donates electron(s) and is oxidized in an oxidation-reduction reaction.

reduction The gain of electrons by an atom, ion, or molecule, leading to a decrease in its oxidation number.

reformulated gasolines Oxygenated gasolines with lower volatility and containing a lower percentage of aromatic hydrocarbons than regular gasoline.

relative humidity In the atmosphere, the ratio of actual partial pressure to equilibrium vapor pressure of water at the prevailing temperature.

rem A unit of radioactivity; 1 rem has the physiological effect of 1 roentgen of radiation.

replication The copying of DNA during regular cell division.

resonance hybrid The actual structure of a molecule that can be represented by more than one Lewis structure.

resonance structures The possible structures of a molecule for which more than one Lewis structure can be written, differing by the arrangement of electrons but having the same arrangement of atomic nuclei.

reverse osmosis Application of pressure greater than the osmotic pressure to cause solvent to flow through a semipermeable membrane from a concentrated solution to a solution of lower solute concentration.

reversible process A process for which a very small change in conditions will cause a reversal in direction.

roentgen (R) A unit of radioactivity; 1 R corresponds to deposition of 93.3×10^{-7} J per gram of tissue.

***s*-block elements** Main-group elements in Groups 1A and 2A whose valence electrons are *s* electrons.

salt An ionic compound whose cation comes from a base and whose anion comes from an acid.

salt bridge A device for maintaining balance of ion charges in the compartments of an electrochemical cell.

saponification The hydrolysis of a triglyceride (a fat or oil) by reaction with NaOH to give sodium salts that are soaps.

saturated fats Fats (or oils) that contain only carbon-carbon single bonds in their hydrocarbon chains.

saturated hydrocarbon Hydrocarbon in which carbon atoms are bonded to the maximum number of hydrogen atoms.

saturated solution A solution in which the concentration of solute is the concentration that would be in equilibrium with undissolved solute at a given temperature.

scanning tunneling microscope An analytical instrument that produces images of individual atoms or molecules on a surface.

screening effect Reduction of the effective attraction between nucleus and valence electrons as a result of repulsion of the outer valence electrons by electrons in inner shells.

second law of thermodynamics The total entropy of the universe (the system and surroundings) is continually increasing. In any product-favored system, the entropy of the universe is greater after a reaction than it was before.

secondary battery A voltaic cell (or battery of cells) in which the oxidation and reduction half-reactions can be reversed to restore the cell to its original state after discharge.

secondary pollutants Pollutants that are formed by chemical reactions of primary pollutants.

secondary structure of proteins Regular repeating patterns of molecular structure in proteins, such as α-helix, β-sheet.

semiconductor Material with a narrow energy gap between the valence band and the conduction band; a conductor when an electric field or a higher temperature is applied.

semipermeable membrane A thin layer of material through which only certain kinds of molecules can pass.

shell A collection of orbitals with the same value of the principal quantum number, *n*.

shifting an equilibrium Changing the conditions of an equilibrium system so that the system is no longer at equilibrium and there is a net reaction in either the forward or reverse direction until equilibrium is reestablished.

sievert The SI unit of effective dose of absorbed radiation, 1 Sv = 100 rem.

sigma (σ) bond A bond formed by head-to-head orbital overlap along the bond axis.

simple sugars Monosaccharides and disaccharides.

single covalent bond A bond formed by sharing one pair of electrons between the same two atoms.

smog A mixture of smoke (particulate matter), fog (an aerosol), and other substances that degrade air quality.

solar cell A device that converts solar photons into electricity; based on doped silicon.

solid A state of matter in which a substance has a definite shape and volume.

solubility The maximum amount of solute that will dissolve in a given volume of solvent at a given temperature when pure solute is in equilibrium with the solution.

solubility product constant (K_{sp}) An equilibrium constant that is the product of concentrations of ions in a solution in equilibrium with a solid ionic compound.

solubility product expression Molar concentrations of a cation and anion, each raised to a power equal to its coefficient in the balanced chemical equation for the solubility equilibrium.

solute The material dissolved in a solution.

solution A homogeneous mixture of two or more substances in a single phase.

solvent The medium in which a solute is dissolved to form a solution.

***sp* hybrid orbitals** Orbitals of the same atom formed by the combination of one *s* orbital and one *p* orbital.

sp^2 hybrid orbitals Orbitals of the same atom formed by the combination of one *s* orbital and two *p* orbitals.

sp^3 hybrid orbitals Orbitals of the same atom formed by the combination of one *s* orbital and three *p* orbitals.

sp^3d hybrid orbitals Orbitals of the same atom formed by the combination of one *s* orbital, three *p* orbitals, and one *d* orbital.

sp^3d^2 hybrid orbitals Orbitals of the same atom formed by the combination of one *s* orbital, three *p* orbitals, and two *d* orbitals.

specific heat capacity The quantity of energy that must be transferred to 1 g of a substance to increase its temperature by 1 °C.

spectator ion An ion that is present in a solution in which a reaction takes place, but is not involved in the net process.

spectrochemical series A list of ligands in the order of their crystal-field splitting energy.

spectroscopy Use of electromagnetic radiation to study the nature of matter.

spectrum A plot of the intensity of light (photons per unit time) as a function of the wavelength or frequency of light.

standard atmosphere (atm) A unit of pressure; 1 atm = 101.325 kPa = 1.01325 bar = 760 mm Hg exactly.

standard-state conditions These are 1 bar pressure for all gases, 1 M concentration for all solutes, at a specified temperature.

standard enthalpy change The enthalpy change when a process occurs with reactants and products all in their standard states.

standard equilibrium constant ($K°$) An equilibrium constant in which each concentration (or pressure) is divided by the standard-state concentration (or pressure); if concentrations are expressed in moles per liter (or pressures in bars) then the concentration (or pressure) equilibrium constant equals the standard equilibrium constant $\Delta G° = -RT \ln K°$.

standard hydrogen electrode The electrode against which standard reduction potentials are measured, consisting of a platinum electrode at which 1 M hydronium ion is reduced to hydrogen gas at 1 bar.

standard molar enthalpy of formation The standard enthalpy change for forming 1 mol of a compound from its elements, with all substances in their standard states.

standard molar volume The volume occupied by exactly 1 mol of an ideal gas at standard temperature (0 °C) and pressure (1 atm), equal to 22.414 L.

standard reduction potential ($E°$) The potential of an electrochemical cell when a given electrode is paired with a standard hydrogen electrode under standard conditions.

standard state The most stable form of a substance in the physical state in which it exists at 1 bar and a specified temperature.

standard solution A solution whose concentration is known accurately.

standard temperature and pressure (STP) A temperature of 0 °C and a pressure of 1 atm.

standard voltages Electrochemical cell voltages measured under standard conditions.

state function A property whose value is invariably the same if a system is in the same state.

steel A material made from iron with most P, S, and Si impurities removed, a low carbon content, and possibly other alloying metals.

steric factor A factor in the expression for rate of reaction that reflects the fact that some three-dimensional orientations of colliding molecules are more likely to result in reaction than others.

stoichiometric coefficients The multiplying numbers assigned to the species in a chemical equation in order to balance the equation.

stoichiometric factor (mole ratio) A factor relating number of moles of a reactant or product to number of moles of another reactant or product.

stoichiometry The study of the quantitative relations between amounts of reactants and products in chemical reactions.

stratosphere The region of the atmosphere approximately 12 to 50 km above sea level.

strong acid An acid that ionizes completely in aqueous solution.

strong base A base that ionizes completely in aqueous solution.

strong electrolyte An electrolyte that consists solely of ions in aqueous solution.

structural formulas Formulas written to show how atoms in a molecule or polyatomic ion are connected to each other.

structural isomers (constitutional isomers) Compounds with the same molecular formula that differ in the order in which their atoms are bonded together.

sublimation Conversion of a solid directly to a gas with no formation of liquid.

subshell A group of atomic orbitals with the same n and ℓ quantum numbers.

substance Matter of a particular kind; each substance, when pure, has a well-defined composition and a set of characteristic properties that differ from the properties of any other substance.

substrate A molecule or molecules whose reaction is catalyzed by an enzyme.

superconductor A substance that, below some temperature, offers no resistance to the flow of electric current.

supercritical fluid A substance above its critical temperature and pressure; has density characteristic of a liquid, but flow properties of a gas.

supersaturated solution A solution that temporarily contains more solute per unit volume than a saturated solution at a given temperature.

surface tension The energy required to overcome the attractive forces between molecules at the surface of a liquid.

surfactant(s) Compounds consisting of molecules that have both a hydrophobic part and a hydrophilic part.

surroundings Everything that can exchange energy with a thermodynamic system.

system In thermodynamics, that part of the universe that is singled out for observation and analysis. The region of primary concern.

temperature The physical property of matter that determines whether one object can heat another.

tertiary structure of proteins The overall three-dimensional folding of protein molecules.

tetrahedral Molecular geometry of four atoms or groups of atoms around a central atom with bond angles of 109.5°.

theoretical yield The maximum quantity of product theoretically obtainable from a given quantity of reactant in a chemical reaction.

theory A unifying principle that explains a body of facts and the laws based on them.

thermal equilibrium The condition of equal temperatures achieved between two samples of matter that are in contact.

thermochemical expression A balanced chemical equation, including specification of the states of matter of reactants and products, together with the corresponding value of the enthalpy change.

thermodynamics The science of heat, work, and the transformations of each into the other.

thermoplastic A plastic that can be repeatedly softened by heating and hardened by cooling.
thermosetting plastic A polymer that melts upon initial heating and forms cross-links so that it cannot be melted again without decomposition.
third law of thermodynamics A perfect crystal of any substance at 0 K has the lowest possible entropy.
titrant The solution being added from a buret to another solution during a titration.
titration A procedure whereby a substance in a standard solution reacts with a known stoichiometry with a substance whose concentration is to be determined.
titration curve A plot of the progress of a titration as a function of the volume of titrant added.
torr A unit of pressure equivalent to 1 mm Hg.
trace elements (See also **major minerals.**) The dietary minerals that are present in smaller concentrations than the major minerals, sometimes far smaller concentrations.
tracer A radioisotope used to track the pathway of a chemical reaction, industrial process, or medical procedure.
***trans* isomer** The isomer in which two like substituents are on opposite sides of a carbon-carbon double bond, a ring of carbon atoms, or a coordination complex.
transition elements Elements that lie in rows 4 through 7 of the periodic table in which *d* or *f* subshells are being filled; comprising scandium through zinc, yttrium through cadmium, lanthanum through mercury, and actinium and elements of higher atomic number.
transition state A molecular structure corresponding to the maximum of a plot of energy versus reaction progress; also known as the activated complex.
triangular bipyramidal Molecular geometry of five groups around a central atom in which three groups are in equatorial positions and two are in axial positions.
triangular planar Molecular geometry of three groups at the corners of an equilateral triangle around a central atom at the center of the triangle.
triglycerides Esters in which a glycerol molecule is joined with three fatty acid molecules.
triple bond A bond formed by sharing three pairs of electrons between two atoms.
triple point The point on a temperature/pressure phase diagram of a substance where solid, liquid, and gas phases are all in equilibrium.
troposphere The lowest region of the atmosphere, extending from the Earth's surface to an altitude of about 12 km.
Tyndall effect Scattering of visible light by a colloid.

uncertainty principle The statement that it is impossible to determine simultaneously the exact position and the exact momentum of an electron.
unimolecular reaction A reaction in which the rearrangement of the structure of a single molecule produces the product molecule or molecules.
unit cell A small portion of a crystal lattice that can be replicated in each of three directions to generate the entire lattice.
unsaturated fats Fats (or oils) that contain one or more carbon-carbon double bonds in their hydrocarbon chains.
unsaturated hydrocarbon A hydrocarbon containing double or triple carbon-carbon bonds.
unsaturated solution A solution that contains a smaller concentration of solute than the concentration of a saturated solution at a given temperature.

valence band In a solid, an energy band (group of closely spaced orbitals) that contains valence electrons.
valence bond model A theoretical model that describes a covalent bond as resulting from an overlap of one orbital on each of the bonded atoms.
valence electrons Electrons in an atom's highest occupied principal shell and in partially filled subshells of lower principal shells; electrons available to participate in bonding.
valence-shell electron-pair repulsion model (VSEPR) A simple model used to predict the shapes of molecules and polyatomic ions based on repulsions between bonding pairs and lone pairs around a central atom.
van der Waals equation An equation of state for gases that takes into account the volume occupied by molecules and noncovalent attractions between molecules:

$$\left[P + a\left(\frac{n}{V}\right)^2\right][V - bn] = nRT.$$

vaporization The change of a substance from the liquid to the gas phase.
vapor pressure The pressure of the vapor of a substance in equilibrium with its liquid or solid in a sealed container.
viscosity The resistance of a liquid to flow.
volatility The tendency of a liquid to vaporize.
volt (V) Electrical potential energy difference defined so that 1 joule (work) is performed when 1 coulomb (charge) moves through 1 volt (potential difference).
voltaic cell An electrochemical cell in which a product-favored oxidation-reduction reaction is used to produce an electric current.

water of hydration The water molecules trapped within the crystal lattice of an ionic hydrate or coordinated to a metal ion in a crystal lattice or in solution.
wave functions Solutions to the Schrödinger wave equation that describe the behavior of an electron in an atom.
wavelength The distance between adjacent crests (or troughs) in a wave.
weak acid An acid that is only partially ionized in aqueous solution.
weak base A base that is only partially ionized in aqueous solution.
weak electrolyte An electrolyte that is only partially ionized in aqueous solution.
weight percent A mass fraction expressed as a percent by multiplying by 100%; used for elemental composition of a compound, composition of a solute in solution.
work (working) A mechanical process that transfers energy to or from an object.

X-ray crystallography The science of determining nanoscale crystal structure by measuring the diffraction of X rays by a crystal.

zone refining A purification process in which a molten zone is moved through a solid sample, causing the impurities to concentrate in the liquefied portion.
zwitterion A structure containing both a positive charge and a negative charge, commonly due to loss and gain of a hydrogen ion within the same molecule.

Index

Page numbers in **bold face** refer to key term definitions
Page numbers in *italics* refer to images or diagrams
Page numbers followed by a "t" indicate a table.

D

E